METHODS IN DEVELOPMENTAL BIOLOGY

Under the general editorship of

JOHN P. TRINKAUS,

Yale University

METHODS IN DEVELOPMENTAL BIOLOGY

Edited by

FRED H. WILT
University of California, Berkeley

NORMAN K. WESSELLS
Stanford University

THOMAS Y. CROWELL COMPANY
New York / Established 1834

Library of Congress Catalog Card Number: 67–11561

Manufactured in the United States of America

Preface

The study of development has long occupied a central position in biology. Only thirty years ago, one might have said that the major problems of development had been clearly stated and that the powerful tools of transplantation and tissue culture would surely resolve some of the issues. The application of these methods, coupled with the biochemistry of the day, did indeed reveal many interesting phenomena that in large measure are the source of the problems being explored at present. But it seems that we are entering a phase of rapid expansion in developmental biology as the impact of advances in other areas of science comes to be felt. Problems are being restated, the array of organisms suitable for testing certain questions is becoming broader, and new biological and biochemical techniques are being introduced. Furthermore, scientists whose interests have lain primarily outside embryology and developmental biology are now becoming more aware than ever of the fascination of the study of development.

These considerations stimulated the editors to select, solicit, and prepare for publication a collection of articles on some methods used in developmental biology. This collection does not represent an attempt, nor perhaps would it be appropriate in such a rapidly growing area, to present a compendium. The topics chosen cover a selection of organisms and techniques that hopefully will contribute to the experimental analysis of development. The basis of selection is ultimately personal, and the editors must take full responsibility for it. We were influenced by our estimation of the usefulness, both actual and potential, of different biological and chemical techniques. We also wished to avoid excessive duplication of currently available sources. There is a plethora of good handbooks on embryology, cell physiology, and biochemistry. Techniques that have recently received extensive treatment are omitted (e.g., Kabat and Mayer, *Experimental Immunochemistry,* Charles C. Thomas, 1961; D. S. Prescott, ed., *Methods in Cell Physiology,* Academic Press, 1964; S. P. Colowick and N. D. Kaplan, eds., *Methods in Enzymology,* Academic Press, 1955).

The articles emphasize practical aspects of experimental problems. Much of the discussion centers on the organisms themselves and on the "tricks of the trade" in procuring, maintaining, and carrying out experimental manipulations with them. The discussions should be meaningful to both professional biologists and graduate students; and in some instances, the information may also be of use to the undergraduate or the advanced high school biology class. Essentially, it is hoped that the book will be used by: (1) developmental biologists, both pre- and postdoctoral, interested in new organisms and techniques for research purposes; (2) scientists not working directly in developmental biology who may wish to begin exploration of some of the problems of development; and (3) teachers looking for new materials for laboratory courses.

In some of the articles, original techniques, never before published, are described. The names of the originators of the techniques—not necessarily the authors themselves—are found in the index as well as in the text. It would be useful if researchers cited the originators of the new techniques in standard reference lists whenever possible.

The editors have had the valuable assistance of many people. We are especially indebted to Watson Laetsch and J. P. Trinkaus for stimulating discussions. Sally Wilt, Lynne Dixon, Jean Salomon, Julia Cohen, Jean Evans, and Lois Wessells were all particularly helpful in the preparation of the book.

April, 1966

Fred H. Wilt
Berkeley, California

Norman K. Wessells
Stanford, California

Contents

Contributors

Ursula K. Abbott
Department of Poultry Science
University of California
Davis, California 95616

W. A. Bailey
School of Agriculture and Life Sciences
North Carolina State College of
Agriculture and Engineering
P.O. Box 5847
Raleigh, North Carolina 27607

W. E. Berg
Department of Zoology
University of California
Berkeley, California 94720

C. W. Birky, Jr.
Department of Zoology
University of California
Berkeley, California 94720

Donald D. Brown
Department of Embryology
Carnegie Institution of Washington
110 West University Parkway
Baltimore, Maryland 21210

Martha B. Cahn
Department of Zoology
University of Washington
Seattle, Washingon 98105

Robert D. Cahn
Department of Zoology
University of Washington
Seattle, Washingon 98105

Mary E. Clutter
Department of Biology
Yale University
New Haven, Connecticut 06520

Hayden G. Coon
Department of Embryology
Carnegie Institution of Washington
110 West University Parkway
Baltimore, Maryland 21210

Alfred J. Coulombre
National Institutes of Health
Bethesda, Maryland 20014

Sears Crowell
Department of Zoology
Indiana University
Bloomington, Indiana 47401

Bruce G. Cumming
Department of Botany
The University of Western Ontario
London, Ontario, Canada

Elizabeth G. Cutter
Department of Botany
University of California
Davis, California 95616

Robert L. DeHaan
Department of Embryology
Carnegie Institution of Washington
110 West University Parkway
Baltimore, Maryland 21210

Marie A. DiBerardino
The Institute for Cancer Research
7701 Burholme Avenue
Fox Chase
Philadelphia, Pennsylvania 19111

Winifred W. Doane
Department of Biology
Kline Biology Tower
Yale University
New Haven, Connecticut 06520

R. J. Downs
School of Agriculture and Life Sciences
Phytotron, Director
North Carolina State College of Agriculture and Engineering
P.O. Box 5847
Raleigh, North Carolina 27607

William T. Doyle
Cowell College
University of California
Santa Cruz, California 95060

E. J. DuPraw
Department of Biochemistry
Stanford University School of Medicine
Stanford, California 94304

G. Fankhauser
Department of Biology
Princeton University
Princeton, New Jersey 08540

Paul E. Fell
Department of Biological Sciences
Stanford University
Stanford, California 94305

Meredith C. Gould
Department of Biological Sciences
Stanford University
Stanford, California 94305

James H. Gregg
Department of Zoology
University of Florida
Gainesville, Florida 32603

J. B. Gurdon
Department of Zoology
Oxford University
Oxford, England

Ralph T. Hinegardner
Department of Zoology
Columbia University
New York, New York 10027

Antone G. Jacobson
Department of Zoology
University of Texas
Austin, Texas 78712

M. M. Johri
MSU/AEC Plant Research Laboratory
Michigan State University
East Lansing, Michigan 48823

Robert F. Kallman
Department of Radiology
Stanford University School of Medicine
Stanford, California 94304

Joe L. Key
Department of Botany and Plant Pathology
Purdue University
Lafayette, Indiana 47907

Thomas J. King
The Institute for Cancer Research
7701 Burholme Avenue
Fox Chase
Philadelphia, Pennsylvania 19111

W. M. Laetsch
Department of Botany
University of California
Berkeley, California 94720

James S. Lovett
Department of Biology
Purdue University
Lafayette, Indiana 47907

T. Makinodan
Biology Division
Oak Ridge National Laboratory
Post Office Box Y
Oak Ridge, Tennessee 37830

Carlos O. Miller
Department of Botany
Indiana University
Bloomington, Indiana 47401

Beatrice Mintz
The Institute for Cancer Research
7701 Burholme Avenue
Fox Chase
Philadelphia, Pennsylvania 19111

D. James Morré
Department of Botany and Plant Pathology
Purdue University
Lafayette, Indiana 47907

Paul Nettesheim
Biology Division
NIH-AEC Carcinogenesis Program
Oak Ridge National Laboratory
Post Office Box Y
Oak Ridge, Tennessee 37830

Herbert B. Posner
Department of Biology
State University of New York at Binghamton
Binghamton, New York 13901

V. Raghavan
Department of Botany
The University of Malaya
Kuala Lumpur, Malaya

William J. Rutter
Departments of Biochemistry and Genetics
University of Washington
Seattle, Washington 98105

Imogene Schneider
Department of Entomology
Walter Reed Army Institute of Research
Washington, D. C. 20012

Howard A. Schneiderman
Developmental Biology Centre and Department of Biology
Western Reserve University
Cleveland, Ohio 44106

Donald Spencer
Division of Plant Industry
CSIRO
Canberra, Australia

Malcolm S. Steinberg
Department of Biology
Princeton University
Princeton, New Jersey 08540

H. E. Street
Department of Botany
University College of Swansea
Swansea, Wales, U. K.

Ian M. Sussex
Department of Biology
Osborn Memorial Laboratories
Yale University
New Haven, Connecticut 06520

Daniel Szollosi
Department of Biological Structure
School of Medicine
University of Washington
Seattle, Washington 98105

William H. Telfer
Leidy Laboratories of Biology
University of Pennsylvania
Philadelphia, Pennsylvania 19104

J. P. Trinkaus
Department of Biology
Yale University
New Haven, Connecticut 06520

Heinrich Ursprung
Mergenthaler Laboratory for Biology
The Johns Hopkins University
Baltimore, Maryland 21218

J. E. Varner
MSU/AEC Plant Research Laboratory
Michigan State University
East Lansing, Michigan 48823

Norman K. Wessells
Department of Biological Sciences
Stanford University
Stanford, California 94305

James A. Weston
Department of Biology
Western Reserve University
Cleveland, Ohio 44106

Philip R. White
The Jackson Laboratory
Bar Harbor, Maine 04609

Fred H. Wilt
Department of Zoology
University of California
Berkeley, California 94720

John E. Winesdorfer
Department of Zoology
University of Washington
Seattle, Washington 98105

John P. Wourms
Department of Biological Sciences
Stanford University
Stanford, California 94305

Toki-o Yamamoto
Biological Institute
Faculty of Science
Nagoya University
Chikusa-ku, Nagoya, Japan

METHODS IN DEVELOPMENTAL BIOLOGY

Part I

SYSTEMS: PROCUREMENT, MAINTENANCE, AND USE

The Mouse

By Robert F. Kallman

INTRODUCTION

As the literature pertaining to the care, maintenance, production, and biology of the laboratory mouse is exhaustive, this section will provide only a few selected guidelines on these and related topics. For a selective bibliography on this subject, the reader is referred to the *Guide for Laboratory Animal Facilities and Care* (1963). Other references which are particularly useful include the volume edited by Snell (1956) and the recent anatomy by Cook (1965), both of which provide information about some features of the biology of this organism. In addition to the now classic volume of Grüneberg (1952), a more recent coverage of many genetic aspects is to be found in the volume edited by Burdette (1963). The *UFAW Handbook* (Worden and Lane-Petter, 1957) is a general source of useful information on this and other mammalian species, as well as other vertebrates and invertebrates. Lane-Petter (1961 and 1963) provides a wealth of information relating to husbandry, hygiene, and several related subjects. Some elements in the design and organization of animal quarters and facilities are presented in the symposium *Laboratory Animals: Their Care and Their Facilities* (1960) and by Thorp (1961). The *Handbook on Genetically Standardized JAX Mice* (1962) is informative; and additional useful miscellaneous facts are to be gleaned from publications prepared by several of the commercial animal and feed suppliers (Charles River Digest, Carworth Farms, Rockland Farms, Ralston Purina, etc.). The *Mouse News Letter* is a publication which is primarily concerned with mouse genetics and is distributed free of charge to interested persons; periodic separate compilations are also distributed with the *Mouse News Letter*, namely, *Inbred Strains of Mice* and semiannual reference lists. In addition to the latter publications, the periodically published standardized nomenclature for inbred strains of mice (Staats, 1964) appears in the open literature and provides definitive information on genetically pure mouse strains, their sources, derivations, and related data. In general, numerous useful articles are to be found in *Laboratory Animal Care* and the *Journal of the Animal Technicians Association*, the primary journals which publish papers on practical aspects of animal maintenance, housing, etc.

MOUSE PROCUREMENT

The need has practically disappeared for any mouse user to continue to produce his own animals because of difficulties in obtaining healthy stocks from commercial dealers. Perhaps as recently as a decade ago, it was difficult to find many commercial sources that could be relied upon to supply vigorous, clean, and generally healthy animals that might be used in the laboratory with a minimum of acclimatization or quarantine. Furthermore, until the advent of relatively inexpensive and convenient air freight, it was necessary to purchase animals from dealers in one's immediate neighborhood. This is no longer the case; excellent commercial sources are to be found throughout the United States and elsewhere in the world. Also, until recently virtually the only mice that could be purchased from reliable dealers were not inbred, so that animals used in a given project over the course of several years were likely to be a rather inhomogeneous lot. Many dealers are now able to supply mice of several inbred strains on a routine basis. For example, one typical source presently supplies mice of the following inbred strains (and various of their hybrids): A/He, AKR, BALB/c, CBA, C3H/An, C57BL, C57L, DBA/2, RF, and 101.

Perhaps the principal justifications for maintaining one's own producing mouse colony are to be found in (1) investigations requiring the use of inbred mouse strains which are not commercially available; (2) the need for large numbers of animals at regular intervals, say, in excess of several hundred per week—a condition which makes it difficult to justify purchasing all such animals purely on economic considerations; and (3) the requirement for ready availability of gravid females from which embryos can be removed at precisely known ages. As the latter condition is the one which prompts the inclusion of this chapter in this volume, much of the material to follow is intended for the benefit of this segment of the readership.

An entirely feasible course to be followed by anyone desiring to provide himself with a few, say, 5–10, litters per week to be taken from gravid females in various stages of pregnancy would be to acquire from outside sources only that number of fertile females which must be reentered periodically into a breeding pool to replace those which must be sacrificed so that their litters may be removed for experimental use. The replacement requirements for males which must be mated with the fertile females is minimal, as a healthy fertile male may be bred continuously until at least about a year of age. Alternative plans that might be followed include: (1) produce all one's own mice; (2) purchase all mice including gravid females; (3) purchase a sufficiently large number of breeders so that enough pregnant females will be made available within, say, 1–2 months, and then allow enough gravid females to bear young which can, in turn, be bred as replacements for females that had to be sacrificed to provide embryos for experimentation. Should this supply of breeders fall behind experimental needs, fresh breeding stock can again be purchased.

One problem frequently encountered by prospective users who are not immediately concerned with genetic studies is the choice of a suitable mouse strain. Should one use random-bred or inbred mice? In the past, this kind of decision was usually dictated by convenience owing to the difficulties in procuring suitable inbred mice. Although these same difficulties no longer prevail, it must not be assumed that the inbred mouse *per se* automatically offers the most uniform, controlled experimental animal to be regarded as constant in its physiological properties from time to time or from place to place. Rather, as discussed by Biggers *et al.* (1958 and 1961) and Chai (1960 and 1961), suitably inbred animals which are by definition homozygous are highly sensitive to environmental changes. Thus, such an animal might be characterized by a set of physiological, behavioral, and even anatomical features which would differ from laboratory to laboratory if any of a large number of environmental variables are not kept absolutely constant. It must be appreciated, however, that the inbred homozygote can be more desirable, depending upon the purpose for which it is to be used: bio-assay data show it to be more variable or less responsive to some treatments and less variable or more responsive to others. The outbred animal may be thought of as being able to buffer small environmental variables, owing to its heterozygous condition. But, as pointed out by Dinsley (1963), it is not a simple matter to set up or maintain a truly outbred mouse colony. For this and other reasons and provided that there is no prior requirement for any given inbred strain, perhaps the most reliable animal to be employed for general experimental use is the F_1 hybrid. Of course, there is no single hybrid genotype which will satisfy the requirement of all users, and it is suggested that strains be chosen to serve as parents on the basis of expedient factors such as coat color, fertility, tumor incidence, maternal behavior, etc. Readily distinguishable coat colors of the two parental strains eliminate one common source of error in the handling of these animals for breeding; any strain characterized by a high incidence of, say, mammary tumors owing to the transmission of mammary tumor virus via the mother's milk would have obvious disadvantages as the female half of the breeding pair, but no such disadvantages if used as the male half of the pair; and the other properties are of obvious relevance. One particular strain combination found by the present author to be convenient, useful, and productive is the cross of C57BL with BALB/c. In this case, one parent is black, the other white, and the offspring brown in color (entirely independent of whether the female is C57BL and the male BALB/c, or vice versa).

HOUSING REQUIREMENTS

The variety of types of mouse cages employed in different laboratories is, to say the least, bewildering. Although the preferences expressed in these paragraphs admittedly reflect the author's personal prejudices, certain generalizations can be based upon popularity between laboratories. Thus, while it certainly offers some uniquely attractive features, the mesh-bottom cage is inferior for general experimental use and is particularly unsuitable when used for routine breeding. Solid-bottom cages of the "shoe box" type are commercially available in a wide range of materials including plastics, wood, and metals. For many years, wooden breeder pens were widely used, but they have been largely replaced by the overwhelmingly superior metal or plastic varieties. The choice of caging material is usually motivated by economic considerations, but, more often than most investigators care to admit, aesthetic features have some influence. Probably the most durable material is stainless steel but this is also the most expensive, particularly in the case of the deep-drawn seamless cage bottom. The cost can be reduced significantly by using aluminum cages which are available in a wide variety of sizes and weights, and this material has become very popular. In addition to its ruggedness, metal is advantageous in that it is unaffected by routine heat sterilization. The necessity of practicing routine sterilization is highly debatable, however, and unless experimentation with known infected animals is clearly anticipated, autoclavability need not be taken into consideration. The ability to withstand repeated heat sterilization disqualifies most, but not all, plastics, as a variety of cages are now being manufactured from polycarbonate resins which are claimed to be completely autoclavable and as impact-resistant as most metals in the gauges most often employed for cages. Because of the high cost of this material (approaching that of stainless steel), most of the plastics used in cages are of the heat-labile kind. Though it is less convenient and more expensive, chemical or gas sterilization can be used routinely with these materials. It is sometimes claimed that mice breed less well in a clear, transparent cage, but this has not been found to be the case in most laboratories, including the author's. On the contrary, cage transparency is one property which most have found to contribute to the usefulness of plastic cages. The wide variety of lids manufactured for this type of cage requires no discussion other than to remark that the most convenient types incorporate, all in the same piece, troughs to contain pelleted feed and space for holding an inverted water bottle. A survey of basic equipment is provided by Lane-Petter (1957) and a description of the system used by the author has been published (Kallman, 1961).

More important than the kind of cage is the space provided per animal. As stated in the *Guide for Laboratory Animal Facilities and Care* (1963), the numbers of animals to be housed in different sized cages is a matter of professional and scientific judgment and the recommendations given are arbitrary. They specify that a "small group cage" of 8 × 12 × 5 inches deep should be used for 1–6 mice providing an area of 0.1–0.7 square feet per mouse. A cage to house a breeding pair and a nursing litter need not be so large; a floor area of 30–35 square inches is entirely adequate (Cohen and Bond, 1952; Brent, 1964).

Day-to-day details of housing maintenance will vary from place to place and will depend upon density of mouse population per cage, availability and kind of bedding material, kind of food, watering system, etc. As an example, in a breeding cage containing, say, two male and five female mice, water and laboratory chow are present continually, and bedding consists of about one "handful" of pine shavings mixed with one and one-half "handfuls" of cedar shavings. For continued high pregnancy rates, some strains require supplemented diets (e.g., C3H may require spinach or kale once a week). Any colony should routinely be insulated from radical temperature changes; if constant temperature facilities are available, a setting near 80°F usually is satisfactory. For dependable pregnancy production as well as standard experimental needs, the mouse room should be placed on a controlled light-dark cycle, with a dark period lasting between 10 and 12 hours. Steps must be taken to ensure that lights are never left on at night for long periods by mistake. Minimum standards are specified in the *Guide for Laboratory Animal Facilities and Care* and the other references suggested. In general, diligent effort should be devoted to providing clean bedding, water, and cages at the optimal frequency of twice a week.

BREEDING SYSTEMS

Excellent descriptions of breeding systems are provided by Falconer (1957), Carter (1957), Lyon (1963), Dinsley (1963), and Green and Doolittle (1963). Choice of a breeding system will be determined primarily by genetic factors, i.e., whether the mice are to be inbred strains, linkage stocks, or random-bred. Perhaps the most common situations to be encountered when mice are to be used for studies not directed to genetic problems are those mentioned above and which require only the perpetuation of a given inbred strain or strains. Examples of the manner in which genetic principles are applied toward the maintenance of inbred strains and the simultaneous production of sufficient mice for experimentation are provided in the *Handbook on Genetically Standardized JAX Mice* (1962), Lane-Petter (1961), and Kallman (1966). The latter paper, plus that of Fritz *et al.* (1967), will illustrate ways in which digital computers may be used as an aid in selection and colony control.

Among the problems faced in maintaining an inbred strain are: (1) insuring a state of homozygosity over a long succession of generations comparable to that which characterized the strain when it entered one's laboratory; (2) insuring sufficient homogeneity within a large stock of animals such that the probability of isogenicity is always maximal, i.e., that any two or more mice taken at random from any generations will have essentially the same genotype; and (3) providing sufficient breeding stock to supply one's needs while still complying with the preceding two constraints.

Assuming that all inbreeding will be accomplished by sibling matings (brother × sister, or *b* × *s*), it remains that one must follow either a *parallel line* system, a *single line* system, or a combination of the two, as explained by Falconer (1957). Whatever system is followed, it is always necessary to practice selection; new mutant genes must be selected out, insofar as such mutations are phenotypically visible, and the influence of invisible mutations must be minimized so as to preserve maximal isogenicity across sublines. As the selection which can be practiced is almost invariably arbitrary, owing to the overwhelming preponderance of invisible mutations, one can readily appreciate the necessity of maintaining accurate breeding protocols and pedigrees. It is most frequently these pedigree records or charts which are the raw material for decisions that must be made in the selection process. A typical strain pedigree, as visualized by Lane-Petter (1961), is illustrated in Fig. 1. Here, each horizontal row represents a generation, and each circle a breeding pair. This pedigree records only those pairs that are used for breeding. All the young born to any of them, but not retained for breeding and therefore not shown in the pedigree, represent the output of the strain available for other purposes.

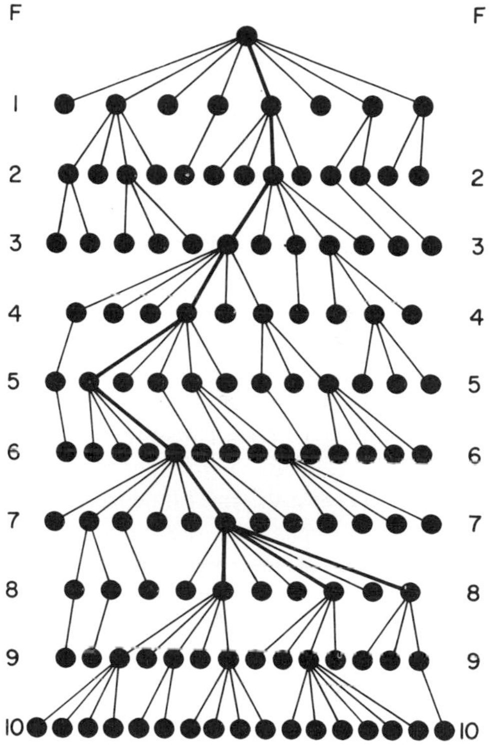

FIG. 1. A typical family tree for an individual inbred strain. The thick lines represent the single line of inheritance contributing to posterity, and the thin lines, the short branches that do not contribute. At the eighth generation there are three possible choices; one of these will be confirmed by selection based on the record of the tenth generation, and the other two abandoned. SOURCE: W. Lane-Petter, *Provision of Laboratory Animals for Research: A Practical Guide,* Elsevier Publishing Co., Amsterdam, 1961, p. 46. Reprinted by permission of publisher and author.

The field of selection at any stage in the history of the strain is thus much larger than might be estimated by examining the pedigree chart, for the chart shows only potential breeders; i.e., the short list from which the final choice is to be made. Actual selection of which potential line is to be chosen to perpetuate the strain, the route to be followed by the heavy line in Fig. 1, must usually be made by comparing the performance of the several candidate lines. The principal criterion will usually be productivity—the fertility and vigor of the animals in the generation (*Fs*) in which selection is to be made, plus the same characters in the next generation (*Fs* + 1) offspring and, insofar as possible, the same characters in the *Fs* + 2 offspring. Basing selection on offspring further removed than *Fs* + 2 would be desirable but is economically unfeasible. It must be kept in mind that when one selects the most productive lines to perpetuate a strain, he is in effect selecting against homozygosity since it is well established that all manifestations of vigor are reduced with increasing inbreeding. However, the influence of such *inbreeding decline* can be negligible in many proper strains which have already adjusted to numerous generations of $b \times s$ inbreeding.

A typical prototype situation that might be encountered in initiating a new colony of inbred mice from a nucleus of one $b \times s$ breeding pair may be illustrated as follows. Assume that a fertile female will bear her first litter at 100 days of age, an average of five subsequent litters will be born 50 days apart, an average of five mice will be weaned from each litter born, and approximately 80 percent of the weaned mice can be paired $b \times s$ for breeding. (These figures are based on the author's experience with one representative strain; Kallman, 1966.) Furthermore, let all breeding be by the pair-mating method (forced breeding) where a $b \times s$ pair is caged together from weaning until death and litters are removed periodically as they reach weaning age. Applying simple arithmetic to the figures assumed shows that approximately twelve breeding pairs will have been derived from the starting (P_1) pair by the time they have reached approximately 1 year of age, a convenient age for retiring all breeders from production. If all of the twelve F_1 pairs are bred uninterruptedly to produce an F_2 generation, this should result in the production of 12^2, or 144, F_2 pairs. Owing to the spacing between litters, the theoretical 144 pairs will not, of course, be attained at any given time, and it is probable that small numbers of mice can confidently be removed from the expansion stock without materially affecting the rate of expansion, at some 8 to 13 months after breeding of the original pair has been started. From that time on, the primary purpose of inbreeding will be strain perpetuation, and it should be possible to depart from strict sib mating in order to provide sufficient animals for experimentation. Several simple schemes have been described which provide means of achieving significantly greater output of suitably homozygous mice than can be gotten by rigid adherence to $b \times s$ mating protocols (*cf.* Lane-Petter, 1961, pp. 116–18; *Handbook on Genetically Standardized JAX Mice*, 1962, pp. 63–65; and Kallman, 1966). The rule of thumb in all of these systems is that mice may be regarded as adequately isogenic, that is to say, genetically homogeneous, if they are within three generations from a true inbred strain (established by at least twenty generations of $b \times s$ matings).

THE PRODUCTION OF PREGNANCIES FOR EXPERIMENTAL USE

Whether a monogamous or a polygamous mating scheme will be adopted in any laboratory will to some extent be determined by uniquely local requirements. Either approach has advantages and disadvantages. The monogamous system, of course, requires a greater number of mating cages and equal numbers of males and females. Polygamous matings employing, say, up to five females per male necessitate perhaps one-third the number of cages and one-fifth the number of males. In the case of those laboratories in which mice are being bred for strain perpetuation and colony expansion and which therefore are already following monogamous breeding protocols, it is probably far more convenient and less confusing to breed all mice in pairs. If polygamous mating cages are set up and some females are allowed to bear their litters, intentionally or otherwise, it is necessary to house the nursing mother and her litter separately. Because it is most convenient to isolate the mother before the litter is born, this precludes taking advantage of the brief postpartum estrus which in monogamous matings allows a female to carry one litter *in utero* while another litter is nursing. If, however, most or all breeding mice are to be purchased from outside the laboratory, polygamous matings offer distinct advantages: males need be replaced at a far lower rate than females, and caging space can be conserved as it will rarely be necessary to allow any pregnant female to give birth to her litter.

Whatever the mating scheme to be employed, it is important that it be decided whether mating is to be continuous or interrupted. It may not be assumed that males and females which have been caged apart will mate immediately or even shortly after they are placed together in the same cage. For example, it would be a great convenience if one could avoid pregnancy tests by the simple practice of introducing a single male to a cage of many females for a finite short time of, say, 12 hours (overnight); any females found by gross inspection to be pregnant during the subsequent 1–2 weeks could be assumed with confidence to have conceived during the known 12-hour mating period. Unfortunately, distressingly few timed pregnancies can be produced in this way, because of the random distribution of estrous cycles in any population of mature females and, perhaps more important, because of social factors which have been shown to influence estrus. As reviewed by Parkes and Bruce (1961), olfactory stimuli are of primary and profound importance in initiating the chain of events which can determine the onset of estrus and related phenomena. It appears that the grouping together of female mice leads to mutual disturbance of estrous cycles, by the intervention of pseudopregnancies if the groups are small (approximately 4 per cage) or of anestrus if the groups are large (approximately 30 per cage). These disturbances are reversible, as normal estrous cycles and pregnancies ensue if such mice are subsequently mated. When males are introduced to females that were housed in groups before being paired, mating does not take place with the same frequency on the first 4 nights after pairing as it does with females that have been housed individually before the introduction of the male (the Whitten effect). And if a male is kept together with 30 females, the estrous cycle is shorter and more regular than it is in his absence and the incidence of abnormal cycles is reduced. In addition, if a newly mated female is removed from a stud male and exposed to other males of the same or a different strain during the first 4 days of pregnancy, pregnancy and pseudopregnancy are both blocked to a large extent; the female returns to normal within 3–4 days of exposure and fertile matings can again take place (the Bruce effect).

In view of these factors, it remains that if accurate knowledge of embryo ages is required some kind of pregnancy test must be employed. The simplest and most universal is a test of coitus rather than actual pregnancy, namely, the examination for the presence of a vaginal plug. At the time of copulation in the mouse, secretions of the seminal vesicles and coagulating glands form a plug which can fill the vagina from the cervical canal to the vaginal orifice. This plug remains for less than about 12–24 hours, and may readily be detected if mated females are examined routinely every morning. This is easily done by placing the mouse on a table surface and covering it with the left hand (with the mouse facing the lateral edge of the palm) so that the tail can be grasped lightly between thumb and index finger. The hind end of the mouse is then raised by lifting the tail so that the forelegs remain touching the table. Then the vaginal orifice is carefully examined, first externally and then internally by gently probing with a sterile (alcohol dipped) round-tipped glass probe. Practice with this simple technique results in greatly improved speed and accuracy.

Because vaginal plugs are sometimes lost before examination can be made, an alternative procedure is to examine the vagina for the presence of spermatozoa. This is conveniently done by instilling a drop of distilled water into the vagina with a smooth-tipped (fire-polished) pipette or medicine dropper, sucking the vaginal washing back into the tube, smearing one drop on a slide, allowing it to air dry, and staining with a simple stain such as toluidine blue. Copulation during the preceding night is invariably detected by the presence of spermatozoa on the slide.

So that some estimate may be made of the size of the colony required for a given experimental program, the following figures represent the experience of one colony operated the year round for embryo production. It cannot be overemphasized that this is a specific case—innumerable factors contribute to variation from one colony to another. (1) The total number of breeding cages is 13, each containing two C3H litter-mate males (used for breeding from 5 months of age for an 8-week period, assuming performance is acceptable) with five strain C females (used first at 85–90 days of age and bred for a maximum of three pregnancies). (2) The yield averages 35–40 pregnancies per week, each litter having from 4 to 14 embryos; on any day, however, the number of females with vaginal plugs ranges from 0 (very rare) to 10. (3) The breeding colony for timed pregnancies is supplied continuously from 40 cages of C mice (includes breeding cages, young of varying ages, etc.), and 24 cages of C3H mice (breeders, etc.). (4) The colony is maintained at 82°F, with a daily light period of 14 hours followed by 10 hours of dark. Interruption of the dark period (by janitors, etc.) often leads to decreased pregnancy rates. (5) The colony requires about 30 hours a week of conscientious care.

CONCLUDING REMARKS

The mouse is the animal of choice for a wide variety of experimental applications, including developmental biology in a typical viviparous mammal. Many approaches have been described to facilitate the use of this animal and there is an abundant literature which can be consulted for detailed information.

REFERENCES

ANIMAL FACILITIES STANDARDS COMMITTEE, 1963: *Guide for Laboratory Animal Facilities and Care.* 33 pp. U.S. Dept. of Health, Education, and Welfare, P.H.S. U.S. Govt. Printing Office, Washington, D.C.

BIGGERS, J. D., A. MCLAREN, and D. MICHIE, 1958: Variance control in the animal house. *Nature*, 182: 77.

———, A. MCLAREN, and D. MICHIE, 1961: Choice of animals for bio-assay. *Nature*, 190: 891.

BRENT, R. L., 1964: An individual-unit small animal cage for radiation lethality and longevity studies. *Laboratory Animal Care*, 14: 207.

BURDETTE, W. J. (ed.), 1963: *Methodology in Mammalian Genetics*. 646 pp. Holden-Day, Inc., San Francisco, Calif.

CARTER, T. C., 1957: Breeding methods, II: Economic considerations. In A. N. Worden and W. Lane-Petter (eds.), *The UFAW Handbook on the Care and Management of Laboratory Animals*, 2nd ed., The Universities Federation for Animal Welfare, London, Eng., p. 108.

CHAI, C. K., 1960: Response of inbred and F_1 hybrid mice to hormone. *Nature*, 185: 514.

———, 1961: Comment on "Choice of animals for bio-assay." (Biggers *et al.*, 1961, *Nature*, 190: 891.)

COHEN, B. J., and F. BOND, 1952: Cage equipment for laboratory rats and mice. *Proc. Animal Care Panel*, 3rd Annual Meeting, p. 107.

COOK, M. J., 1965: *The Anatomy of the Laboratory Mouse*. 143 pp. Academic Press, New York.

DINSLEY, M., 1963: Inbreeding and selection. In W. Lane-Petter (ed.), *Animals for Research: Principles of Breeding and Management*, Academic Press, New York, p. 235.

FALCONER, D. S., 1957: Breeding methods, I: Genetic considerations. In A. N. Worden and W. Lane-Petter (eds.), *The UFAW Handbook on the Care and Management of Laboratory Animals*, 2nd ed., The Universities Federation for Animal Welfare, London, Eng., p. 85.

FRITZ, T. E., M. H. DIPERT, and R. J. FLYNN, 1967: The utilization of a digital computer for analysis and management of rodent breeding data. *Laboratory Animal Care*, 17: 114.

GREEN, E. L., and D. P. DOOLITTLE, 1963: Systems of mating used in mammalian genetics. In W. J. Burdette (ed.), *Methodology in Mammalian Genetics*, Holden-Day, Inc., San Francisco, Calif., p. 3.

GRÜNEBERG, H., 1952: *The Genetics of the Mouse*, 2nd ed. 650 pp. M. Nijhoff, The Hague, Netherlands.

Handbook on Genetically Standardized JAX Mice, 1962. 83 pp. Roscoe B. Jackson Memorial Laboratory, Bar Harbor, Maine.

KALLMAN, R. F., 1961: The maintenance of an experimental mouse colony in a university medical school department. *Proc. Animal Care Panel*, 11: 73.

———, 1966: A system for large-scale inbred mouse production, and a computer method to aid in subline selection. *Laboratory Animal Care*, 16: 345.

Laboratory animals: Their care and their facilities (Symposium; 1960). *J. Med. Education*, 35: 1.

LANE-PETTER, W., 1957: Animal house equipment. In A. N. Worden and W. Lane-Petter (eds.), *The UFAW Handbook on the Care and Management of Laboratory Animals*, 2nd ed., The Universities Federation for Animal Welfare, London, Eng., p. 23.

———, 1961: *Provision of Laboratory Animals for Research: A Practical Guide*. 147 pp. Elsevier Publishing Co., New York.

——— (ed.), 1963: *Animals for Research: Principles of Breeding and Management*. 531 pp. Academic Press, New York.

LYON, M. F., 1963: Genetics of the mouse. In W. Lane-Petter (ed.), *Animals for Research: Principles of Breeding and Management*, Academic Press, New York, p. 199.

Mouse News Letter. Collated by: M. F. Lyon, M.R.C. Radiobiological Research Unit, Harwell, Didcot, Berks., Eng. Distributed by: Internat. Committee on Lab. Animals & Lab. Animals Centre, M.R.C. Laboratories, Carshalton, Surrey, Eng.

PARKES, A. S., and H. M. BRUCE, 1961: Olfactory stimuli in mammalian reproduction. *Science*, 134: 1049.

SNELL, G. D. (ed.), 1966: *Biology of the Laboratory Mouse*. 706 pp. McGraw-Hill Book Co., New York.

STAATS, J. (prepared by), 1964: Standardized nomenclature for inbred strains of mice. 3rd listing. *Cancer Res.*, 24: 147.

THORP, W. T. S., 1961: Space requirements in the design of facilities for the small animal species. *Federation Proc.*, 20: 919.

WORDEN, A. N., and W. LANE-PETTER (eds.), 1957: *The UFAW Handbook on the Care and Management of Laboratory Animals*, 2nd ed., 951 pp. The Universities Federation for Animal Welfare, London, Eng.

Avian Developmental Genetics*

By Ursula K. Abbott

SPECIAL USEFULNESS OF AVIAN MUTANTS TO DEVELOPMENTAL BIOLOGISTS

The investigation of control mechanisms in differentiating systems of complex organisms is one of the most fascinating areas in modern biology. A variety of types of experimental material are required for such studies. While a number of organisms can be used, few possess the combination of attributes required for detailed study of the embryonic period. These requirements are: (1) entire embryonic period amenable to analysis and experimental intervention, (2) existence of large numbers of experimental animals with a low per unit cost, and (3) existence of a variety of genes with effects on specific differentiating systems or organs. Forms amenable to study and best investigated in developmental terms lack mutants (e.g., amphibians). Those with the greatest variety of mutants are very simple organisms exhibiting little morphogenesis (e.g., bacteria, fungi), are difficult to study during the interesting periods of development as well as exhibiting patterns very dissimilar to vertebrates (e.g., insects), or are complicated by inaccessibility, maternal affects, and resorption of abnormal young (e.g., mammals).

Avian embryos satisfy the requirements. The avian embryo is easy to incubate and can be examined, analyzed, or surgically interfered with from mid-gastrulation (its stage at oviposition) until hatching (the seventeenth day in quail, the twenty-first day in chickens, the twenty-fourth day in pheasants, and the twenty-eighth day in turkeys). Avian eggs are available in large numbers, at a low cost per experimental unit. Fowl have a large and increasing number of mutations with effects on a variety of different developmental systems.

The majority of workers in developmental biology and associated fields have with a few exceptions made little use of avian mutant material; in many cases, because they are unaware of its existence. It is intended in this chapter to outline the range of experimental material available in fowl, to consider problems that can be approached with such materials, and to provide information on a variety of factors relevant to the use, handling, and interpretation of results obtained with avian experimental stocks.

* Some of the work reported was supported in part by NSF Grant No. GB 633 and NIH Grant No. HE-02566.

Sex-Linked Genes

In birds, mutant genes located on the sex chromosome are particularly useful. Here the male is the homogametic sex while the female, effectively, has only one functional sex chromosome. In viable mutants the effect of two genes versus one on expression can be compared in the two sexes. The inactive X hypothesis (Lyon, 1961) to explain dosage compensation in mammalian sex-linked genes has recently received considerable attention. It seems doubtful that dosage compensation occurs in birds. While studies of the relative effect of one or two doses have not been made for all sex-linked genes in fowl, it is clear that expression in several (e.g., barring, dilution) definitely differs between the two sexes (Cock, 1964). For studies of sex-linked lethal genes, the major advantage of a system in which the male carries the mutant gene and the female expresses it, is the opportunity to produce a very large number of progeny, which can be then studied at a variety of developmental stages. Accordingly, adequate material for organ culture or for biochemical and other analyses can be produced with ease. Additionally, mutant carrier males may be crossed with females of any breed or variety, permitting studies of the effect of the residual genotype on the expression of the lethal character.

Lethal Genes

In most of the known avian lethal mutant genes, the first expression of abnormality is widely separated in time from events leading to embryo death. Death usually occurs as the consequence of a variety of secondary effects of the primary gene defect. Accordingly, the abnormality can be the subject of study and analysis for a considerable period of time. For example, in most of the lethal forms of polydactyly known in birds, death results from difficulties in assuming the correct position for hatching, completing yolk sac transfer, and successfully emerging from the shell, presumably as a consequence of the defectively formed limbs and beak. In polydactyly, however, the first phenotypic manifestation of the genetic defect is seen at stage 21. [All references to developmental stages of the chicken embryo in this chapter are expressed in terms of the Hamburger and Hamilton (1951) embryo series. In the case of other avian species, the stages are translated into Hamburger and Hamilton equivalents (Table 7).] Although observable histological changes are deferred until this period, it can be shown by means of transplantation experiments that determination has occurred earlier, by stage 17. Accordingly, polydactyly can be studied when the defect is irreversibly determined although there is no histological or histochemical evidence of differentiation, at the onset of visible signs of differentiation and during the relatively long period following, when an increasingly complex series of consequences of the original defect become manifest.

Analysis of Control Mechanisms

Histological, histochemical, or electron micrograph studies of normal material which have been interpreted to indicate participation of a specific organelle or process in differentiation may be reinforced, or perhaps clearly proved incorrect, by comparative studies of a mutant which fails to accomplish the step in question. Similarly, conclusions regarding inductive interactions in a normal differentiation sequence by techniques such as microsurgery, X-irradiation, or ultrasonation may be validated by using mutants affecting the sequence. This general approach is well illustrated by the use of several polydactylous and hypodactylous mutants in studies of limb differentiation (Goetinck and Abbott, 1964; Zwilling, 1956; Zwilling and Hansborough, 1956). Perhaps the best evidence for the inductive role of the apical ectodermal ridge (AER) in stimulating distal differentiation and outgrowth of the limb is provided by studies with the double ridge mutant, eudiplopodia (Goetinck, 1964). Similarly, the use of several of these mutants has indicated that both the mesodermal and the ectodermal components of the early limb bud participate in this induction system: the mesoderm by stimulating growth of the AER and by maintaining it in an "active state," and the ectoderm by stimulating mitotic activity in the mesoderm with consequent further distal growth and differentiation (Zwilling, 1956, 1961). The finding that these two control mechanisms can be separated was achieved by uncovering mutations affecting each of the two separately. Further evidence of the nature of the developmental interaction was obtained by the production of various combinations of mutants affecting the mesodermal or ectodermal component (Abbott, 1964). The availability of mutant material may accordingly permit one to take an apparently rather complicated system apart, and may often reveal that the reciprocal interaction of two rather simply controlled processes can give rise to a highly specialized and complicated structure.

Recognition of Critical Periods in Morphogenesis

Development in many animals is characterized by one or more "critical periods." These may be associated with simultaneous changes in activity of a number of enzymes, in respiratory quotients, in RNA levels, and in protein synthesis. An example is the onset of several endocrine functions in the chick embryo on the eighth day of development. In some cases, the simultaneous study of a number of genes affecting a system may provide evidence for a critical period. Thus, the analysis of the polydactylous avian mutants has suggested that stage 21 is a critical period in limb morphogenesis.

Studies of enzyme activity in normal tissues during different periods are complicated by a variety of problems (Herrmann and Tootle, 1964). Investigations of the role of enzymes in morphogenesis in vertebrates might be assisted by using appropriate mutants for comparative assays of activity.

Avian Mutants as Pilot Animals or in Screening Studies

The similarity of certain avian mutant expressions to pathological conditions found in various mammalian species permits their use as pilot animals. Frequently the object is to analyze and, hopefully, control the condition in a mammalian form which is itself difficult or impossible to study. Investigations can include nutritional and biochemical analyses, responses to various treatments, or in some cases characterization of the disease. Many human diseases differ in their expression in different races or families and in some instances a single genetic entity has a dozen or more clinical names and descriptions. Analyses of such conditions require large numbers; similar avian forms can often be used to assist in the interpretation. A number of actual or potential applications of avian mutants as pilot animals can be offered: biochemical and genetic studies of muscular dystrophy in chickens (Asmundson *et al.*, 1966); achondroplasia in turkeys (Abbott *et al.*, 1965), a condition remarkably similar to that in man and in cattle; scaleless, in chickens, where effects of long term hypothermic stress on the cardiovascular system (Abbott *et al.*, 1964) can be studied; neurological mutants having potential for studies of balance and various aspects of cerebellar degeneration as well as for tests of therapeutic agents; and the dehydrated lethal (Taylor and Stinnett, 1957) in which up to 30 percent of total body weight is lost in the first 24–48 hours after emerging from the shell, a situation somewhat similar to a condition found in human infants.

Embryonated chicken and quail eggs are used in a variety of screening tests for new drugs (Karnofsky, 1965; Murphy, 1965), herbicides, and pesticides (Shellenberger *et al.*, 1966). Such studies require carefully standardized stocks. While mutants have not been much used in such analyses, some example of interactions between teratogenic compounds and single genes have been provided, suggesting both that the genetic background of normal embryos used in such tests is important and that some of the tested compounds themselves may assist in analysis of the action of certain of the mutant genes (Landauer, 1959, 1960, 1965a).

Pigment Biology

The wealth of colors and patterns available in the various breeds and varieties of chickens, and to a lesser degree in turkeys, pheasants, and quail, have made these birds especially useful for studies of melanogenesis and pattern formation. While an extensive literature is available on the genetics of color and pattern (see Hutt, 1949), on the use of mutants, and on certain developmental aspects, the possible uses of this material in a variety of studies far exceed the work thus far accomplished (Nickerson, 1944; DuShane, 1944; Rawles, 1948, 1955; Waddington, 1952; Wilde, 1961).

SOURCES OF GENETICALLY DIFFERENT STOCK

Availability of Mutant Stocks

A number of mutant carrier stocks and specialty breeds are maintained by poultry or animal science departments, usually associated with one of the U.S. Land Grant Universities. Some are available through the U.S. Department of Agriculture at Beltsville, Maryland. Others, especially the more unusual fancy breeds (illustrated in the American Standard of Perfection, 1947), are kept only by hobbyists interested in show poultry. While such fanciers used to be abundant, their number is decreasing rapidly, especially in the United States and Canada. As a result, many once common breeds are becoming rare or, in some cases, have disappeared in North America.

The several experiment stations generally have only a few mutant stocks at any one time. A few stations have, however, traditionally maintained fairly sizable collections. These have included California, Connecticut, Cornell, Minnesota, Washington State, Ohio State, Oregon, and Virginia among others. Many potentially valuable research stocks are often lost or discarded under this haphazard arrangement. Also, it has been difficult for the researcher to obtain organized collections of mutants affecting a particular developing organ or system. Accordingly, an Avian Mutant Center is being proposed for Davis, California. The Center will maintain a large number of avian mutant genes, special strains, and breeds with characteristics of special research interest. Investigators at other institutions can be supplied with mutant stock or, in case they desire to carry out special investigations with a group of related mutants, the Center will provide laboratory facilities and materials for such studies.

Mutants presently available at Davis occur in chickens, turkeys, pheasants, and Japanese quail and include groups affecting limb differentiation (polydactylous, hypodactylous, and micromelic), feather and scale differentiation, color and pattern, and the nervous system, and those causing muscular dystrophy and several types of dwarfing. This collection will eventually contain approximately 100 chicken mutants or specialty lines, 15–20 quail mutants, as well as a small number in turkeys and pheasants. In addition, stocks of inbred chickens and quail will be available as will lines selected for various traits or performance characteristics.

Classification

In this chapter, the use of avian mutant material in the analysis of different developmental systems or processes is emphasized. Accordingly, sets of mutants affecting a specific system or organ are grouped together irrespective of their inheritance or the breed or species in which they occur. It is important to point out, however, that a large proportion have multiple effects. Accordingly, some mutants may be useful in the analysis of more than one developing system. A general statement about the mutants in each category or subcategory is provided, including, for example, notes on time of effect, expression, death, whether or not it is a breed characteristic, its mode of inheritance, and suitability for various studies. In the tables included in this chapter, each mutant is listed along with additional notes in cases where exceptions to the general statement exist or additional clarification is required. A mutant listed by name only implies that all generalizations apply.

References for each of the six major categories are numbered sequentially and appear as part of each table. This reference list is intended only to provide entrance into the literature, and accordingly, the following practice is adopted: (1) Three major reference sources are given where applicable. If the mutant in question is discussed in any or all of these, no original references are provided. (2) On mutants not cited in these three publications, special papers, either the original work or a paper providing a special example of research application, are cited. (3) All mutants listed occur in chickens unless otherwise noted.

Avian Limb Mutants (Table 1)[1]

Mutant genes affecting limb morphogenesis are common in all avian species and have been used in a variety of developmental studies including investigation of inductive interactions and pattern formation (see page 15). Some can be used as pilot animals for studies of similar abnormalities in other vertebrates. In Table 1, the limb mutations are grouped in three categories: polydactylous, hypodactylous, and micromelic. In almost all cases, effects on the limbs are accompanied by beak and often other skeletal defects as well.

POLYDACTYLY—GENERAL CHARACTERISTICS

1. Autosomal recessive inheritance.
2. Morphologically and histologically normal at stages 18–19, but "determined."
3. Histological changes first seen at stages 21–22.
4. Easily identified by stage 24, usually lethal just prior to hatching.
5. By recombination transplant experiments, determination of polydactyly

[1] Tables 1–7 are on pages 37–49.

has been shown to be in the mesodermal rather than the ectodermal component in several cases.

6. Usually, both legs and wings are polydactylous, with the leg exhibiting the more extreme effect. Legs usually have normal digits II, III, and IV present.

7. All long bones are reduced in length and may be curved.

8. Pleiotropic, with reduced upper beak and effects on the vertebral column and over-all body size.

HYPODACTYLY—GENERAL CHARACTERISTICS

1. Autosomal recessive inheritance.

2. First evidence of histological anomaly seen during third day of incubation (stages 17–18).

3. Recognizable morphological anomaly by stage 21.

4. Frequently the defect is restricted to either the legs *or* the wings.

5. Beak and other head parts may be involved.

6. Lethality is usually in two periods; at sixth or seventh day of incubation, and during hatching.

CHONDRODYSTROPHY AND/OR MICROMELIA—GENERAL CHARACTERISTICS

1. Generally autosomal recessive inheritance, but heterozygous birds may show some dominant morphological effects.

2. Abnormality evident by sixth or seventh day of incubation.

3. Abnormalities in cartilage in investigated cases.

4. Lethal just prior to hatching.

5. Proximodistal sequence in extent of reduction of the long bones.

6. Usually associated with defects of the beak.

7. Phenocopied by a variety of deficiency diets and chemical treatments.

Avian Epidermal Mutants (Table 2)

Mutations affecting epidermal derivatives are considered in four categories:

1. Feather structure and rate of feather growth.

2. Feather and scale distribution.

3. Spurs.

4. Comb structure.

The mutants in these four categories constitute one of the largest and best known groups in avian species. Many of these mutants are very old, having been established as breed characteristics for hundreds of years. Some can be followed through various embryonic stages and then through successive posthatching and adult stages.

Most of the epidermal derivatives which have been investigated experimentally differentiate by means of a series of timed reciprocal inductive interactions between dermal and epidermal components (Sengel, 1958; Wessells, 1965; Rawles, 1955, 1963). This is true in the case of skin, scales, feathers, and spurs. Combs have not been studied in this respect. Several of the mutants have potential for studies of such interaction systems. Mutants affecting distribution of feathers and/or scales can also be employed in investigations of the role of end organs in nerve and capillary differentiation.

FEATHER STRUCTURE AND RATE OF FEATHER GROWTH

Birds homozygous for mutations affecting feather structure and rate of feather growth are usually viable. The genes concerned are predominantly autosomal and about equally divided between semidominant and recessive inheritance. Detailed studies of embryonic stages are generally not available. Feather follicles differentiate; in some cases, these give rise to a variety of improperly formed feathers. In others, normal feathers form but the gene alters feather growth rate or duration of feather growth, usually in specific areas only. Both Frizzle (Landauer and Aberle, 1935) and Hookless (Eastlick and Wortham, 1946) have been shown by grafting experiments to differentiate autonomously.

Chemical analyses of skin and feather protein in feather mutants, similar to those of Bell and collaborators (Bell, 1965) for normally developing feathers, have not been made. X-ray diffraction studies as well as immunological investigations of the feather proteins produced by these mutant genes might be most helpful in furthering our understanding of the differentiation of skin and its derivatives.

FEATHER AND SCALE DISTRIBUTION

A number of avian mutant genes interfere with feather follicle distribution. Follicles fail to differentiate in certain locations. The expression can range from small bare patches on the head in some mutants to virtual nakedness in others. Other epidermal derivatives, in particular, scales, footpads, and spurs, may be missing as well.

Mutant genes in this group tend to be autosomal and recessive. The phenotype can be scored easily by the eighth or ninth day of incubation, and while most have not been studied during early incubation, studies with scaleless may serve as an example of this class of defect. Thus, scaleless has been shown by grafting experiments to be determined by stages 17–18. Grafts of recombined limb buds composed either of scaleless dermis and normal epidermis or the reciprocal combination have indicated that the defect is in the epidermal rather than the dermal component (Goetinck and Abbott, 1963). Similar results have been obtained with recombined skin in organ culture (Sengel and Abbott, 1963). Scaleless can, accordingly, be used as an ectodermal marker in a variety of transplantation studies. Scaleless is fully viable during embryonic stages and when first studied was completely lethal under normal rearing conditions (Abbott and Asmundson, 1957). By means of selection, viable homozygous lines were developed (Abbott and Asmundson, 1962). Additionally, it has been possible to select for numbers of feather follicles (Abbott, 1965) and so alter the degree of nakedness in homozygous scaleless birds. Lines characterized by high and low feather number are now available; this selection has not, however, restored scales.

SPURS

Spurs are modified scale derivatives. They may vary in size, shape, and number depending on sex, age, several single genes, and, in view of the success enjoyed by those breeding fighting cocks, presumably on polygenes as well. Spurs in the adult male are elongated, conical, bony structures, surrounded by spongy tissue and an outer cornified layer (Hutt, 1949). Spur primordia are visible as small epidermal papillae on the tenth or eleventh day of incubation. During later development, a growth of bone inward from the epidermis meets a bony outgrowth from the tarsometatarsus. These two eventually fuse to form the mature spur. Removal of the epidermal papillae prevents the bony outgrowth from the tarsometatarsus. By contrast, outgrowth from the shank is not essential to the further development of the epidermal component, for spur papillae will develop in a variety of other body locations including the comb (Kozelka, 1929). Rawles (1963) has shown that dermis from the spur primordium is strongly inductive at 9 days incubation. To date, the several spur mutants have not been used in experimental studies of this induction system nor has the effect of the spur genes on other scale derivatives been studied. Experimental evidence of which component of the induction system is altered in these mutants is lacking. The spur mutants can be recognized by the twelfth day of development. They are autosomal and show variable penetrance and expressivity. Their expression is sex-influenced.

COMB STRUCTURE

Among the oldest and best known characteristics of domestic fowl are the several types of combs. Bateson (1902) used them to obtain the first evidence of the operation of Mendelian laws in animals. The single comb, typified by a single blade with five or six serrations, is recessive to most other types. Several comb types are due to the interaction of two mutants and possibly additional modifying genes. Comb and wattle anlage are visible at 10–11 days of incubation as small epidermal papillae. The comb mutants tend to be autosomal and dominant. They are viable, but there is some evidence of detrimental effects on fertility (Fox *et al.*, 1964). The embryological basis of comb formation has not been investigated in either normal or mutant genotypes. It is not known whether pattern is controlled in the mesodermal or the ectodermal component, or how comb components interact with tissues from other sites.

Avian Neurological Mutants (Table 3)

A variety of neurological mutants have been found in avian species. Some result in abnormal reactions at hatching time while others fail to show any sign for several weeks. Limited histological and anatomical studies made with some of these mutant phenotypes have implicated the cerebellum and Purkinje's cells. However, these studies have not been detailed and in the case of several mutants no description, other than behavioral, exists. The resemblance of certain of these to neurological disorders in man suggests that they might be used to advantage as pilot animals. The high proportion of sex-linked mutants represents a considerable advantage since the mating of a carrier male with any female will provide abundant material for study and experiment. Additionally, the fact that a number are viable after hatching suggests that they can be studied during onset of the disease and perhaps used to test potentially therapeutic drugs.

GENERAL CHARACTERISTICS

1. Most are recessive and a majority are sex-linked.
2. Viable during embryonic stages.
3. Majority are viable after hatching for at least a few weeks although, generally, more susceptible than normal chicks to a variety of adverse environmental conditions.
4. They exhibit a variety of symptoms including ataxia, tremors, spatial disequilibrium, retraction of the head, excitability, and epileptic-type convulsions.
5. Symptoms are usually present at hatching.
6. No data are available on embryonic stages.

Avian Color and Pattern Genes (Table 4)

Mutations affecting color and feather pattern are common in all avian species. A large proportion of the color genes are either fully or partially dominant. Many of the plumage patterns distinguishing poultry breeds and varieties depend upon the interaction of several genes while others are based on only one. In general, color mutants are not lethal save in the case of certain albinos although some have adverse effects on both viability and hatchability. Additionally, color mutants may affect the requirements for certain nutrients.

Pigments may be developed in dermal and/or epidermal sites and may be largely restricted to feathers or may occur in several skin layers, nails, scales, beak, and even internal organs. The melanin pigments are produced by melanocytes, migrating cells derived (save for retinal pigments) from the neural crest of the early embryo. The lipochromes (xanthophylls) are yellow pigments formed from carotenoids in the diet. Melanin and xanthophyll may be present in both the epidermal and dermal layers of the skin, in one or the other, or absent in both. In addition, the type of melanin pigment formed may range from a complete black through intermediate shades of red and buff (so called phaeomelanins). The possible combinations of melanins and lipochromes in the skin layers give rise to a variety of shades of skin and feather color. While the presence of melanin of a particular type is genetically controlled, the amount of yellow pigment is related to diet and to egg production. Thus, laying hens of yellow-skinned breeds deposit carotenoid pigments in their eggs preferentially leading eventually to a complete bleaching of their skin. A mutation present in the white-skinned breeds prevents the deposition of yellow pigment in the skin in males and in nonlaying females as well.

Individual mutants cause complete albinism (pink eyes and white plumage); others affect feather, shank, and beak color but have no effect on melanization in the eyes. Some dilution mutants also reduce eye pigmentation while others do not. Mutants also occur in which the eyes are pink or red although the plumage and shanks may be colored.

Pigment and pattern formation can be studied through most of the embryonic period and followed through a succession of juvenile and adult plumages. Mutant genes are known which interfere at all levels in this system. They may affect the structure, survival, migration, and numbers of melanocytes. In addition, mutations may alter the local environment in which the migrating melanocytes come to lie, permitting them to develop full or partial color or completely preventing its formation. Mutations affect the rate of feather growth, cause rhythmic patterns in the laying down of pigment or in the type of pigment produced, and interfere with normal hormonal effects on pigmentation and pattern and with the deposition of lipochrome pigments in the skin.

Aside from the solid colors and albinos, chick down patterns are usually quite different from those of adult birds. This is especially true of pattern genes, where rates of feather growth and hormonal and dietary factors influence the outcome. Many chick patterns overlap. The wild-type chick down pattern is striped and very similar in Bronze turkeys, pheasants, quail, and chickens to the Jungle fowl (black-red game) pattern. Chick downs, aside from those with striking differences (albinos, blacks, etc.), do not offer the developmental biologist the advantages of later feather generations. Descriptions of chick downs found in different breeds and varieties are available in the *American Standard of Perfection* (1947). The few mutants whose known effects are restricted to down are listed in Table 4D, while some others are included with the description of the adult form.

In Table 4, the pigment and pattern mutants are organized as follows:

A. Type of melanin pigment
   1. Form (complete black or one of the intermediate forms of buff, brown, red)
   2. Intensity (dilution genes)
   3. Absence of melanin (whites and albinos)

B. Distribution of melanin
   1. Primary pattern (regional)
   2. Secondary pattern (within feathers)
   3. Dermal and subdermal

C. Affecting lipochrome (xanthophyll) pigment

D. Affecting chick down color and pattern

Miscellaneous Avian Mutants (Table 5)

A number of avian mutants do not fit in any of the categories discussed above. A few of these which have been used in research studies or which appear to have potential for such use are included. Since these mutants do not have special features in common, any description available is incorporated in Table 5.

Species, Genus, and Family Crosses (Table 6)

Hybrids may be produced among Galliform birds (Gray, 1958). Although natural hybrids will occur in species crosses and in some family crosses, the majority of avian hybrids and particularly those involving different genera are obtained by means of artificial insemination. The outcome of such hybridization may be:

1. Complete infertility
2. Fertility
   a. Embryos die prior to hatching; usually most of the mortality is extremely early, prior to oviposition or during the first day.
   b. Some hatchability of fertile eggs, but progeny may be infertile (they may lack gonads or if gonads form, the bird is usually male, or male-like). Histological studies of the gonad usually show a lack of cortex. Germ cells may or may not be present.
3. Fertility and hatchability may be normal or close to normal (often additional terata are found). The hybrids themselves may be fertile (either *inter-se* or in backcrosses to either parent) but their progeny may fail to hatch or, if they do, may show poor viability.

The incubation time required by hybrid progeny is generally about midway between that of the parents, if these differ (Fig. 1). In general, these crosses are characterized by low fertility and excessive early embryo mortality. Many terata are found in these embryos surviving early incubation. Crosses involving families or genera with relatively close egg and embryo size have a greater chance of success. In reciprocal crosses, between those with large discrepancies in size, using as female parent the one with the larger egg size will usually give best results.

Recently a group at Davis has been successful in selecting for an increased incidence of hybrid offspring in crosses of male chickens with female Japanese quail. In the first crosses made, approximately 3–7 percent of the eggs showed any development. After 13 generations, this percentage has increased to 40–50 percent in some lines (Haley *et al.*, 1966; Haley, 1967) with individual hens producing 60–70 percent fertile eggs. The percentage of young hatched increased as well (9–10 percent hatch of fertile eggs). While control data show that part of this gain is due to improved insemination techniques, the balance reflects success in selection and probably the purging of the lines of

INCUBATION TIME IN SELECTED AVIAN SPECIES AND HYBRIDS

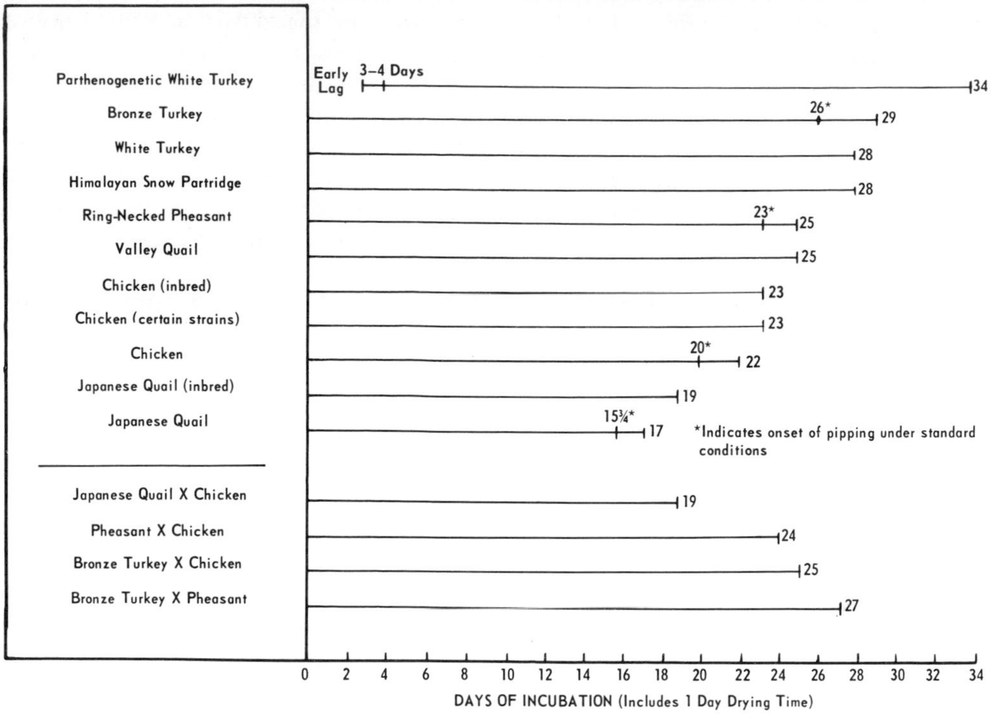

FIG. 1.

deleterious genes. Such results tend to cast doubt on ease of hybridization and level of fertility as reliable criteria for developing classification systems for birds.

Species hybrids are useful in a variety of genetic, immunological, and biochemical studies (Haley, 1965; Leone, 1964; Miller and Feeney, 1964). They can be used also in studies of the control of sex determination and differentiation and in comparative cytology (Stenius *et al.*, 1963).

HANDLING BIRD COLONIES AND EGGS

General Management of Stocks

CHICKENS

Most breeds of chickens can be kept successfully in floor pens, or in individual or colony cages. The complete diets now available permit their maintenance in closed rooms without access to natural sunlight, in which case, 14 hours of artificial light should be provided. They can be kept in controlled-temperature rooms or in exposed locations with considerable diurnal temperature change. During extremely hot dry weather, and especially if they are in exposed cages, artificial cooling (water misting lines) may be required. The combs and wattles of breeds such as the White Leghorn may need to be removed (Schwarte, 1965) if the birds are subjected to freezing temperatures, or to avoid injury from fighting. If cannibalism is a problem, which is frequently the case with birds kept in colony cages or in large groups, the upper beak may be cut back (Schwarte, 1965).

Either natural mating or artificial

insemination (Burrows and Quinn, 1939) can be used; usually a ratio of 1 male to 10–12 females for natural mating (fewer females in the heavy meat breeds). Artificial insemination at weekly intervals will maintain a high level of fertility. A break of at least 10 days should be allowed between matings when accurate parental records are required.

Chickens should not be brooded, reared, or maintained near other poultry or other birds including parakeets and game birds because of their susceptibility to a variety of diseases. Details of vaccination and antibiotic feed additives used as routine precautions and in specific disease outbreaks are to be found in *Diseases of Poultry* (1965).

TURKEYS

Turkeys are expensive to maintain as experimental animals and have several other disadvantages as well. Only one generation can be reared per year; their reproductive season is limited although it has been increased to about 5–6 months by selection and improved environmental control. They require a variety of special management techniques, e.g., if natural mating is used the females must wear canvas saddles to prevent damage. They require artificial lighting to bring them into breeding condition; the lighting schedules differ for the two sexes. Concentration by breeders on selection for body size has had adverse affects on fertility and hatchability in many turkey strains. With the largest turkeys, artificial insemination (Lorenz *et al.*, 1959; Ferebee *et al.*, 1966) is often the only way to obtain fertility. Only females of the smaller turkey breeds can be successfully kept in cages for prolonged periods.

After mating, fertility in turkeys persists for a considerable length of time. Occasional fertile eggs have been obtained 50 days after a single insemination. However, when males are used in sequence the majority of the offspring will always be from the most recent insemination. In the case of mutant-carrying lines, where accurate parental records are essential, this means that at least a 3-week interval should be permitted between mating with successive males. In view of the already limited reproduction season, this fact severely limits studies requiring matings of the same hen with several different males.

Turkeys are susceptible to an even wider variety of diseases than chickens and usually require a comprehensive disease-control program (*Diseases of Poultry*, 1965). Young poults are harder to raise than chickens since they possess a combination of stupidity and accident-proneness. Under adverse conditions, inadequate diet or crowding, turkeys may be cannibalistic. In view of these difficulties and the fact that development in turkeys is very similar to that in chickens and quail, differing largely only in rate and over-all time required, there is little justification for deliberately selecting turkey mutants for study. It seems reasonable to suggest that use of such material be restricted to studies in which comparisons of the several avian species are of interest (homologous mutants, species hybrids, comparative cytology) or to studies of conditions not available in chickens or quail. In this latter instance in order to produce sufficient material for study, it is essential that the gene be either viable (color and feather structure genes) or, if it is lethal, it should be sex-linked. A special advantage of turkeys, setting them apart from the other avian species, is the availability of parthenogens. Turkey stocks at Beltsville, Maryland, have been selected successfully for a high incidence of parthenogenesis (Olsen, 1965a). Although the majority of parthenogens die during the incubation period, a proportion will hatch and with special care can be reared to maturity. These have invariably been males. These parthenogens represent the only truly isogenic material available in avian species.

PHEASANTS

Pheasants are not usually kept for research purposes. Their limited seasonal reproduction period yields few eggs for study. Inbred lines are not available and few morphological mutants are known. Most of the information available on mutant genes in pheasants is restricted to viable color and pattern variants. Aside from analysis of these, their main research use has been in studies of hybridization.

JAPANESE QUAIL

This bird is a recent addition to the group important in biomedical research. For this reason, relatively few mutants are yet available. However, the rapid acceptance of Japanese quail, and their already widespread distribution in research institutions in several countries guarantees that this lack will not long exist. Already the development of inbred quail lines has led to the discovery of six mutants at the Davis, California station. Japanese quail have most of the attributes of chickens, and can, accordingly, be used as pilot animals for studies of this species. In addition, they possess a number of distinct advantages: (1) extremely rapid development and early sexual maturity; the incubation period for quail is 17 days, birds reach sexual maturity at 6 weeks and four or five generations can be raised each year; (2) high and continuous rate of egg production from sexual maturity until 24+ weeks (a quail hen lays her body weight in eggs every 2 weeks) and, (3) inexpensive maintenance in terms of space and feed. Ten quail may be kept in the space required for one chicken and 30 in that required for a turkey.

Considerable work has been done on methods of quail management since this species was suggested as a pilot animal for avian studies by Wilson *et al.* (1961). A manual is available (Woodard *et al.*, 1965) with detailed information on quail management. The "Quail Quarterly," a newsletter for biomedical research workers (Auburn University, Auburn, Alabama), distributes information on current research in laboratories using this bird.

Japanese quail can be kept in individual or colony wire-floor cages. A 6 × 10 × 6 inch cage can be used for individual birds or pair matings. A 12 × 12 × 12 inch colony cage is suitable for small group matings. Larger sizes can be adapted for other uses: rearing groups of young quail, holding, and mass matings.

Natural mating gives satisfactory results in either pair matings or with a 2♂:5♀ ratio. Artificial insemination is difficult and so far has not equaled natural mating because of the difficulty in obtaining adequate volumes of semen from coturnix males. Recently Marks and Lepore (1965) reported fertility levels between 45.3 and 72.9 percent with a modified artificial insemination technique. Semen from three or more males was required for each female; thus, this method is inefficient as well as unsuitable for pedigree studies.

Special care must be taken in collecting and handling quail eggs which are thin-shelled, more easily broken, and dehydrate more rapidly than chicken eggs. Quail eggs should be placed in the incubator within 5 days of laying because zygote viability declines with age more rapidly in quail than in either chicken or turkey eggs.

Inserts made of $\frac{1}{2} \times 1$ inch strips of welded wire convert a standard Jamesway incubator into one suitable for quail, permitting them to be set in a large-end-up position and turned at 2-hour intervals. The best fertility and hatchability is obtained with quail adults between 8 and 24 weeks of age. After 24 weeks, fertility

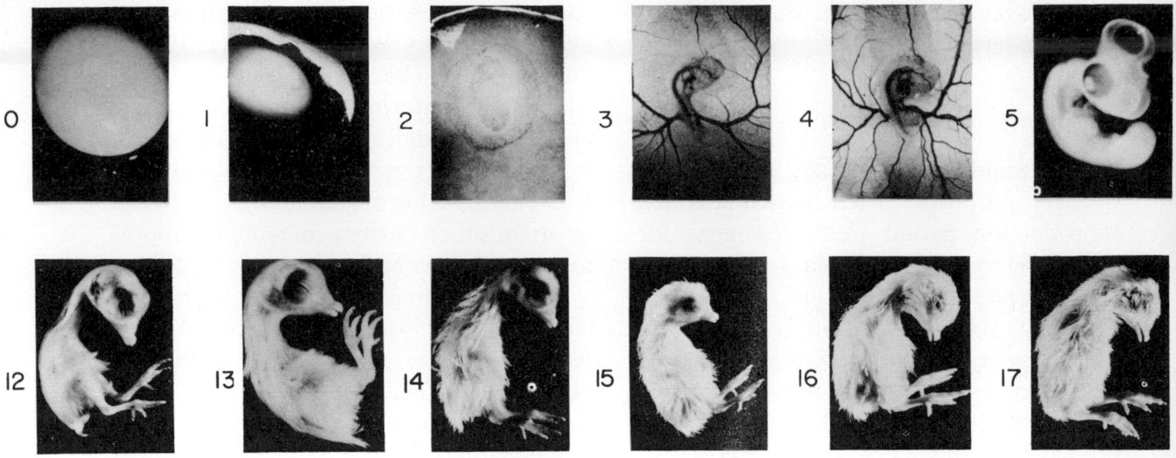

and hatchability as well as egg production decline. Quail chicks may be brooded on the floor or in several types of commercial chick or game-bird battery brooders. If chick brooders are used, the wire floor is covered with rough-surfaced paper during the first week and the sides and ends of each chick brooder are blocked with $\frac{1}{4}$ inch hardware cloth to prevent the chick's escape. For pedigree purposes, coturnix chicks can be banded at hatching with a game-bird size wing band.

Cannibalism in coturnix may result from overcrowding, inadequate diet, excessive disturbance or handling. At the first sign of this behavior, the birds should be debeaked using chicken debeaking equipment. Rooms containing quail should be predator-proof as they are defenseless against voracious rats.

The light requirement for optimum egg production is 14–18 hours per day. Coturnix, in contrast to chickens, lay most of their eggs in the late afternoon or early evening.

Coturnix require a high protein diet. A modified turkey starter ration containing 30 percent protein has proved satisfactory.

At oviposition, the coturnix egg is in an advanced stage of gastrulation. Table 7 indicates the average stage reached by chicken, turkey, and quail embryos after each successive 24-hour period of incubation. Figures 2 to 4 illustrate daily developmental stages in the three species.

MUTANT AND SPECIALTY STOCKS (SPECIAL PROBLEMS)

A number of avian mutant or specialty stocks may require special handling for one of a variety of reasons. The gene-controlled abnormality may affect the housing, diet, mating, or incubation requirements.

MUTANTS WITH ABNORMAL OR MISSING PLUMAGE. Additional heat may be required during all phases of rearing and reproduction to compensate for the excessive heat loss of birds with defective or missing plumage. All of the mutants in this class are to some degree lethal under normal rearing conditions. In general, survival of scaleless, naked, and homozygous frizzle chicks is satisfactory if brooder temperatures are maintained a few degrees above normal during the first 2 weeks. Either battery or floor brooders may be used. Chicks or poults should be watched closely for signs of discomfort: noise, huddling near the heat source, or

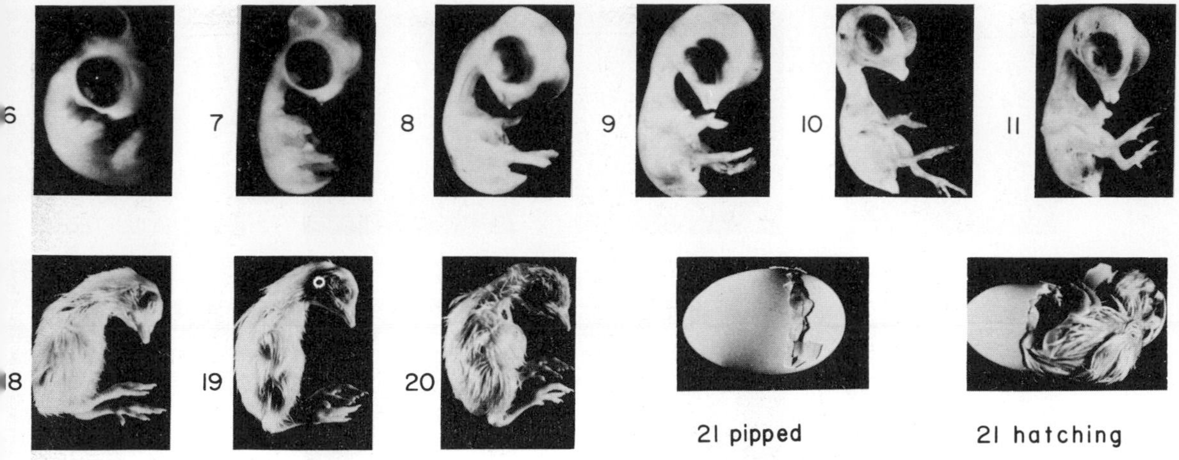

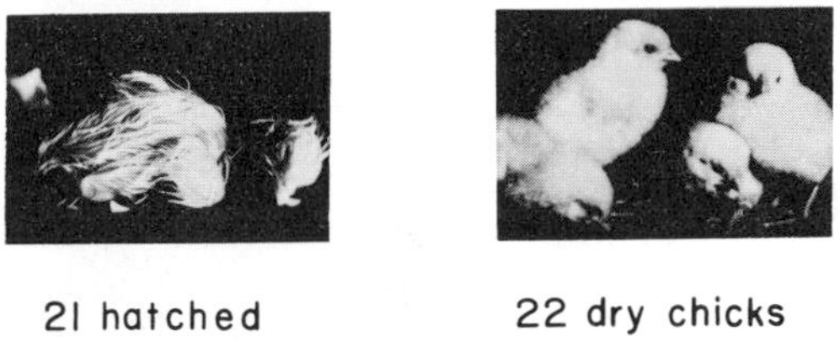

FIG. 2. Chicken development.

crowding away from it. They will not require supplementary heat after 6–8 weeks in mild climates or if kept in rooms with temperatures maintained above 70°F.

The skin of naked or seminaked birds is easily torn. The greater concentration of capillary nets near the skin surface makes them bleed easily. Accordingly, they should be housed and managed to minimize the risk of injury through fighting or natural mating. In practice, adults are best kept in 10–12 inch cages and mated by artificial insemination. However, even here, handling and removing birds from cages must be done carefully to avoid catching the wings on sharp surfaces. Naked birds are also susceptible to mosquito bites and will benefit from maintenance in a screened area if mosquitos are a problem.

Scaleless, frizzle fowl, and possibly the other naked mutants as well have higher total feed requirements than normally feathered birds, but may have a lower requirement for specific nutrients. Thus, scaleless chicks require less methionine and cysteine (Abbott *et al.*, 1962).

Scaleless lines resistant to cold stress have been developed by a crossing and selection program as have lines differing in feather number (Abbott, 1965). Similarly, heterozygous frizzle fowl are adapted to normal environments (Landauer, 1933).

Lines of homozygous scaleless with normal hatchability have been developed. In these, egg production tends to be from one-half to two-thirds that of normally feathered hens. Scaleless embryos need about 12 hours more incubation time than normally feathered embryos of similar breeding.

NEUROLOGICAL MUTANTS. Published information indicates that a number of the neurological mutants such as paroxysm are particularly sensitive to sudden noise, lights, etc. (Cole, 1961). The majority of birds with this genotype die by 15 or 16 weeks of age under normal maintenance. A quail mutant in this category does well when caged in a quiet light-controlled

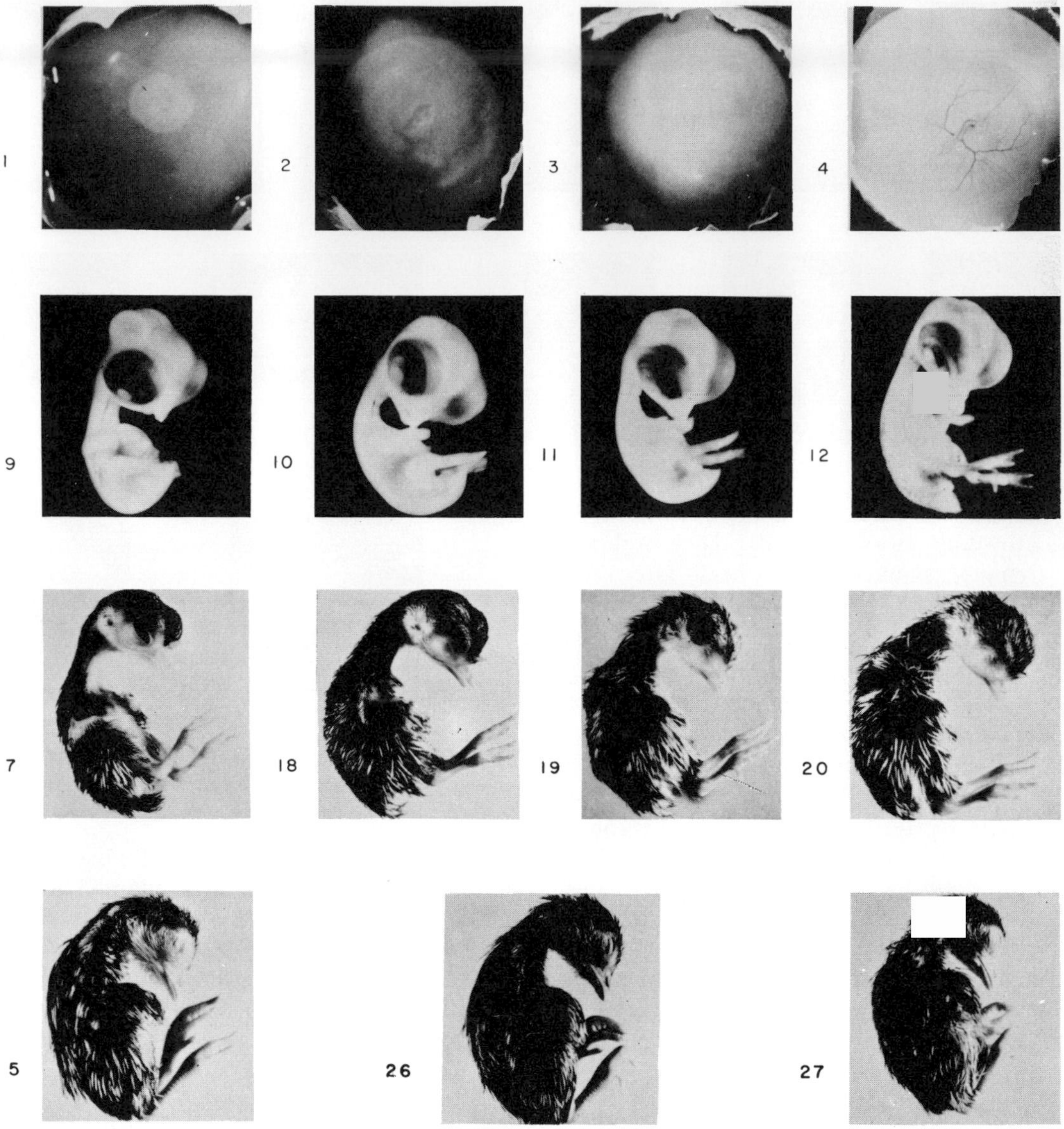

room. The use of tranquilizing or other drugs effective in man in preventing attacks of epilepsy does not appear to have been tried. This approach might be expected both to prolong life and to yield information on the mode of action of this class of semilethal mutants.

MUSCULAR DYSTROPHY. Chicks which are homozygous for muscular dystrophy (Asmundson *et al.*, 1966) may be raised either in battery brooders or under floor brooders. In either case, and particularly if reared on the floor, special supervision is essential. Numbers of chicks, especially

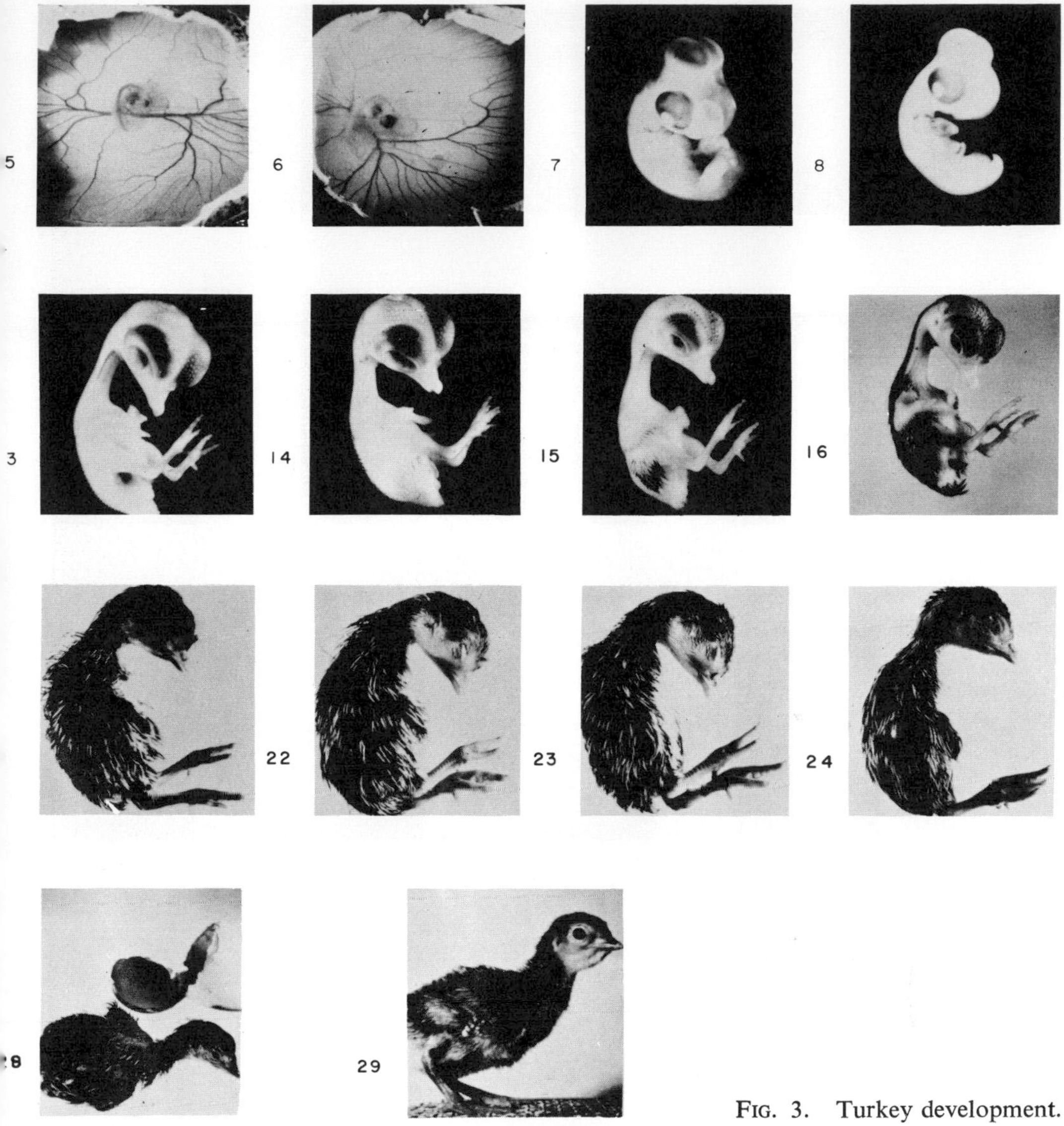

FIG. 3. Turkey development.

those in lines bred for early onset of the disease, will fall over on their backs and be unable to right themselves without assistance. Without extra attention, mortality in floor brooders may reach 18 percent as compared with an average of 3 percent for non-dystrophic birds of otherwise similar breeding. Rearing in smaller groups in wire-floored battery brooders has been satisfactory but, in this case too, the birds will need more than normal supervision. Some data are available which suggest that age of onset of dystrophic symptoms may be reduced

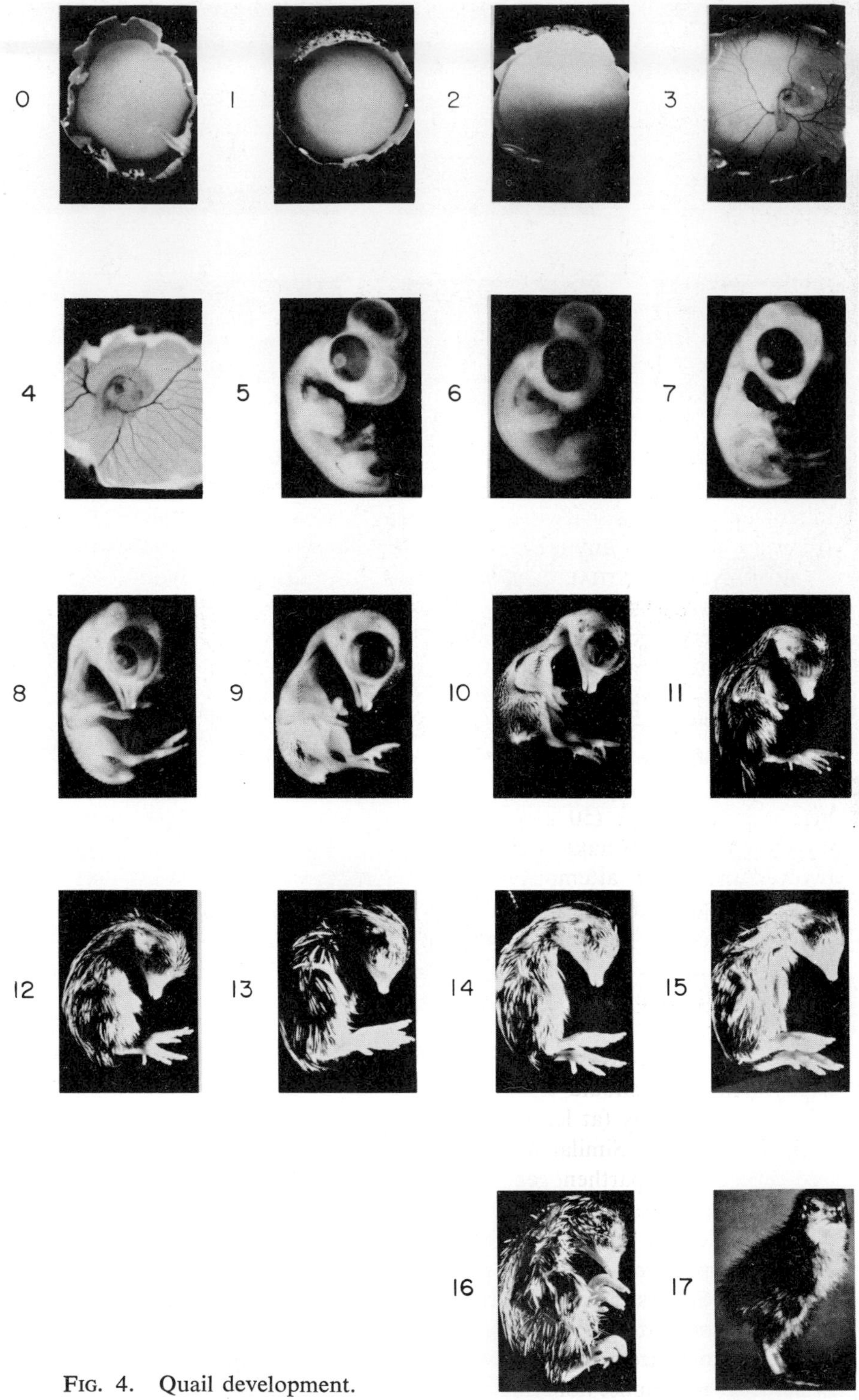

FIG. 4. Quail development.

in wire-floored battery brooders. This point should be kept in mind in experimental comparisons involving both rearing methods.

Adult dystrophic birds should be kept in individual cages (12 inch cages are satisfactory for birds of both sexes although females can be kept in 8 or 10 inch cages). Usually birds should be caged by 12 weeks of age; earlier, in exceptionally heavy birds of early onset lines. Adult dystrophic birds must not be kept in floor pens because of the difficulty they have in raising their wings; they cannot right themselves if they fall. They are unable to fly to roosts or elevated nest boxes. Artificial insemination must be used with dystrophic birds; with its use, fertility is equivalent to that of any other stock.

HOMOZYGOUS LETHAL MUTANTS, PARTHENOGENS, AND SPECIES HYBRIDS. Occasionally, chicks genetically homozygous for one of the lethal avian mutations will hatch. These may have an attenuated expression of the condition but are usually weak and infrequently able to survive to adulthood. However, the advantage of their use in matings (50 percent mutant progeny) will often make the extra work involved in rearing attempts worthwhile. For rearing such material a special nursery must be provided. The largest problem in such cases is to get the birds to commence eating and drinking. It may be necessary to hand feed them with an eyedropper, initially. Bright objects in the feed will help. Such birds should always be provided with company (at least one normal chick to emulate). Similar care has been used in rearing parthenogenetic turkey poults and to a lesser degree some species hybrids. It could be applied to some of the neurological mutants as well. In all these cases, the first 5 days are critical. If the chick is not eating by the time its yolk and water stores are exhausted, its chances for survival are almost nonexistent. None of these individuals will normally survive if raised in the company of large numbers of vigorous chicks. Throughout the rearing period, they will require extra warmth and careful supervision. The parthenogens and hybrids will be sterile but the mutant homozygotes will usually lay and be reasonably fertile. Artificial insemination will usually give better results than natural mating. The incubation period is frequently increased by about 24 hours in homozygous lethals. Parthenogenetic turkeys can require as much as 5 days (average 3 days) longer than the 28-day period normally required by turkeys (Olsen, 1965b). An initial delay appears to be responsible for the extended developmental period. The several kinds of species hybrids generally require an incubation period about midway between that of their parents (Fig. 1). Species hybrids require a high protein turkey ration.

SPECIALTY BREEDS. Many of these breeds are fairly highly inbred, have relatively poor vitality, and may require special protection. They are usually late maturing and have a reproductive period limited to the spring and early summer. They have a tendency to "go broody," the name given to the various manifestations of the maternal urge in poultry. Breeds in this category include Cochins (feathered shanks and toes), Silkies (hookless, feathered shanks and toes, black skin and bones), Japanese bantams (creeper gene), some of the excessively long-legged game birds and certain of the crested breeds (cerebral hernia). In some cases, e.g., Cochins, the selection for profuse feathering has resulted in a situation in which natural mating is largely unsuccessful unless the tail and vent feathers are trimmed. The long-tailed Japanese breeds (continuously growing tail feathers) are also extremely difficult to rear and house, especially if the 20–30 foot tail is to be maintained intact. Since fancy stocks are often displayed at poultry exhibitions and are freely exchanged between poultry fanciers who generally do not concern themselves with vaccination and disease-control programs, it is dangerous to introduce these stocks directly into facilities in which other birds are kept. If hatching eggs are to be obtained the parent stock should be blood tested for at least *Salmonella pullorum* (Van Roekel, 1965).

HANDLING EGGS FOR EXPERIMENTAL USE. Eggs for developmental studies should be of a uniform average size (avoid excessively large or small eggs) with clean sound shells. They should not be held for more than 7 days before being placed in the incubator. The room used to store these eggs before incubation should be maintained at 13°C (10°–15°C). Eggs for incubations should not be washed. If cleaning is required, it should be done with a clean abrasive (e.g., fine sanding paper). Eggs should be collected several times a day, especially in extreme climates. They should be obtained from healthy, disease-free stock, between 6 and 18 months of age in the case of chickens (see p. 25 for quail) receiving a breeder (high protein) diet. For normal embryos a constant, not selected, source is desirable. A four-way cross or incross is suitable.

Eggs from stocks carrying mutations or from other specialty lines usually can be handled in the same manner as normal eggs. However, there are certain problems which may require special handling techniques. Sometimes it may be necessary to hold eggs longer than the optimal time to obtain a sufficient number for a particular experiment. In this case, it is particularly important that holding conditions be optimal. If the eggs are to be held much longer than 10 days, they should be positioned large-end-up and turned through a 90° angle daily. It may also help if they are held in plastic bags (Gowe, 1965). To be effective these treatments must be initiated at the beginning of the holding period.

If older eggs are used they will require additional incubation time to reach developmental stages expected in fresh eggs. Add 2–3 hours of incubation per day of holding. Mutants are usually more susceptible to suboptimal holding conditions than normals. Thus, excessive aging or holding at high temperatures is likely to reduce the incidence of surviving mutants disproportionately in a segregating progeny.

Eggs for experimental purposes should be incubated in a clean disinfected incubator capable of maintaining a constant temperature of 37.5°C and a wet bulb reading of 29.5°C. This machine should have a fan to provide adequate air circulation and should be equipped to allow automatic turning of all eggs through an angle of 90° at least 4–6 times per 24 hours and preferably more. Turning is particularly critical during the earliest days of incubation. Lack of turning during the first 3 or 4 days will produce some malformed embryos as well as various minor defects. Some of these detrimental effects may not become evident until much later in incubation and will entirely escape the notice of the investigator who terminates an experiment before the hatching period.

Lack of turning is relatively less critical after 4 days and has no detrimental effects after the twelfth day in chickens and the sixteenth day in turkeys. Although commercial operators usually continue turning until the time of transfer of eggs to hatching trays or baskets, this practice is not necessary. If chicks are to be hatched, the eggs are removed to hatching conditions (horizontal position; lower temperature, 36.9°C; higher humidity, 31 to 32°C wet bulb) just prior to the onset of pipping. In some cases the rise in humidity is preceded by a short (12–24 hour) period of lowered humidity, 26.6°C called the dry down, during which time air intakes are opened to permit additional oxygen to enter the machine just prior to the onset of hatching activity. At high altitudes, additional oxygen will be required. For chickens this generally is not necessary below 5,000 feet. However, recent field studies with turkeys have indicated that additional oxygen may be beneficial at 3,000 feet. Incubation times required for chickens, turkeys, and quail are given in Fig. 4, together with that for some other avian species and certain species hybrids and parthenogens.

SOME SPECIAL PROBLEMS

There are a number of special factors to consider when using mutant gene material in developmental duties. Some are related to the handling of stocks or of embryonated eggs from segregating matings. Others are concerned with gene expression and, if not controlled, could affect the outcome of studies. Some might influence the choice of material for a given analysis.

Identifying the Mutant Embryos in Segregating Matings

In studies with recessive lethal mutants it is often desired to compare mutant and normal specimens at stages before the mutant can be distinguished from its normal sibs. Early stages may also be required for grafting or for biochemical analysis. Since only one-quarter of the fertile eggs will be expected to have the desired mutant genotype, it is necessary to use special methods to obtain the required material. Examples drawn from studies with limb mutants are given below.

1. One limb bud is removed for study or experiment. The donor embryo is returned to the incubator and permitted to develop until its phenotype is clearly expressed. This method is suitable for mutants characterized by a reasonably constant expression and, in particular, a high degree of bilateral concordance in limb expression.

2. One or more limb buds are removed and grown as coelomic, flank, or chorio-allantoic membrane grafts while the donor embryo is prepared for study. In this case the grafted limb bud is later used to diagnose the phenotype and the balance of the embryo is available for detailed analysis at a stage when its phenotype can not be identified. This method depends on the use of "determined" but non-differentiated limb buds and on their ability to differentiate in a new location.

In such studies the investigator frequently has prepared considerably more embryos than can be handled in any one experimental session. Thus he selects a certain proportion. It is common to choose the healthiest and most advanced embryos, especially if one is accustomed to working with normal material. In the case of many of the lethal mutants this is a mistake and in some cases practically guarantees that the group chosen will be found later to consist largely of normals rather than the desired mutants. Many mutants, although appearing morphologically normal, will be slightly retarded in development and possibly a bit anemic looking. Choosing, within limits, the worst looking embryos may yield the most mutants.

Identifying Lethal Mutant Carriers and Noncarriers among Adults

Studies of recessive lethal mutants are often complicated by the extensive progeny tests required to identify or otherwise classify the heterozygous carriers. With fully penetrant genes classification of males can be accomplished quickly; females will take more time, especially if the study requires that noncarriers be accurately identified as well, in which case at least 17 normal embryos must be obtained. Classification can be a real problem when one is dealing with genes of very low penetrance. Thus in a diplopod$_1$-carrier line selected for very low penetrance (Abbott, 1959; Taylor *et al.*, 1959) identification of carriers requires outcrossing to another high penetrance diplopod line, but even with this means of increasing the incidence of diplopod, progeny up to 50 offspring are required before a bird can be classified with certainty.

Background Effects on Mutant Gene Expression

Descriptions of mutant genes usually include notes on dominance, penetrance, and expressivity. Each of these properties depends upon the interaction of the gene in question and its developmental environment and is, accordingly, subject to modification by changes either in the genetic background of the gene or in other components of its developmental environment (nutritional, physical, etc.).

It is important to realize that a description of a particular gene in terms of these properties is probably exact only for the breed, variety, line, or family in which it was studied and at the particular point in time at which it was written. Individual genes vary with respect to their constancy in these characteristics in fluctuating developmental environments. Thus mutants affecting the limbs and beak are particularly subject to modification by both genetic and environmental means as are certain pigment and pattern genes. The same gene in one breed, line, or family may have a severe-form expression while in another its effects may be so mild as to render it undetectable. That certain breeds, strains, or varieties carry special constellations of modifier genes affecting the expression of particular mutants has been shown repeatedly by means of breed crossing. Second and third generation progeny of such crosses often show altered forms of the mutant or even mask its expression. Conversely, anomalies shown subsequently to be controlled by a single gene may appear in the progeny of such crosses, apparently having been effectively masked previously by modifier genes (Landauer, 1956, 1965c).

The genetic background of a gene can be changed by inbreeding, outcrossing, and selection. Either inbreeding of a mutant-carrying stock or outcrossing it to unrelated stocks can upset the balanced systems of modifying genes that act to control its expression and can result in changes either in its penetrance or in its expressivity. Inbreeding and outcrossing may have rather unpredictable effects on expression as may selection for a characteristic not related to the expression of the gene concerned (growth rate for example). However, expression also can be changed in a predictable and controlled manner by direct selection for increased or lowered dominance (Smith and Nordskog, 1963; Dunn and Landauer, 1936), for higher or lower penetrance (Taylor *et al.*, 1959; Abbott, 1959), and for severe or mild expressivity (Landauer, 1946, 1948, 1956, 1965b). Selection for either high or low penetrance usually changes expressivity as well and vice versa. Even the response of a mutant stock to a given environmental treatment can be selected for successfully (Landauer, 1948, 1965a).

Embryos homozygous for mutant genes are more likely to be affected by minor environmental fluctuations than normal embryos because of their lowered developmental stability (lack of canalization). Thus mutant embryos may show additional defects in systems not related to that of the gene (Abbott, 1959). Furthermore lines segregating for mutant genes may show an unexpectedly high incidence of sporadic developmental defects in normal embryos as well (Landauer, 1935, 1965c).

It is imperative that one recognize and control as many of the variables cited above as possible. It is also imperative that accurate information regarding breed, line, strain, and inbreeding be provided in research reports. Investigators attempting to replicate work accomplished at another institution may often obtain confusing or contradictory results with a given mutant because of these background effects.

Inbreeding and Inbred Lines

Inbreeding is of importance from two points of view: (1) the use and availability of highly inbred lines, and (2) the level of inbreeding frequently found in mutant-carrying stocks or in the various fancy breeds of fowl. These two points will be considered, then some of the consequences of inbreeding in general will be discussed.

Isogenic lines are not available in avian species although a few experiment stations as well as commercial enterprises maintain highly inbred lines (calculated inbreeding coefficients 0.6–0.8). Close inbreeding is difficult in birds. Thus if 100 inbred chicken lines are initiated and reproduced exclusively by brother-sister mating, at least 80 percent of these will have been eliminated after six to eight generations. The balance may be successful but will also have certain difficulties (discussed below). Japanese quail will tolerate even less inbreeding than chickens. Such lines are not truly isogenic and frequently exhibit heterozygosity in excess of expectation. If high inbreeding coefficients are approached more gradually, the rate of extinction will be reduced but the calculated inbreeding coefficient may depart more from the actual (Lerner, 1954).

Avian mutant-carrying lines are frequently highly inbred both because mutations are more likely to be discovered in inbred stocks and because the subsequent test matings needed to establish the inheritance of a new anomaly generally involve matings of close relatives. Many of the mutant descriptions available pertain only to a relatively inbred background. Similarly many fancy breeds and varieties are highly inbred. These have often been purged of deleterious lethal or semilethal genes and contain very specific sets of modifying genes. Accordingly outcrosses of these to unrelated stocks may often show enormous variability in a variety of characteristics.

Inbreeding affects the breeding stock as well as the offspring. Inbred males usually show poor fertility (often about 50 percent of normal) while inbred females lay poorly, producing small eggs of variable quality. Inbred embryos may be at a disadvantage both because of their own level of homozygosity and because of maternal effects—nutritional contents of egg and shell quality. Fertile eggs from inbred stocks will deteriorate more rapidly than those from non-inbred stocks under suboptimal holding conditions or with excessive aging (Abplanalp *et al.*, 1957). A group of highly inbred chicken embryos will show scattered mortality throughout incubation as well as accentuated mortality in the two normal peak periods, 2–3 days and 18–21 days. They will tend to be variable in rate of development, so that after 4 days incubation, embryos may range all the way from stage 15 to stage 22. A group of embryos from an inbred line will often require a longer than normal incubation period, with individuals hatching over a prolonged period. Inbred quail chicks may need up to 2 full days of additional incubation time. Inbred chicks tend to be weak and unthrifty, to vary in growth rate, and to be more susceptible than non-inbreds to disease and other adverse environmental effects. They may exhibit symptoms of nutritional deficiency on diets adequate for other stocks.

Inbreeding may have other rather unpredictable effects. Thus, phenotypic variability in the expression of a character may be *increased* with the result that inbred embryos may be less uniform than outbred embryos. The detrimental effect of inbreeding on early embryo viability may reduce the available period for study of a mutant phenotype. Additionally, since mutants are frequently more susceptible than their normal sibs to various detrimental effects, a highly inbred mutant-carrying line may show less than the expected proportion of mutant segregants. Inbreeding even affects the outcome of chicken × quail crosses; inbred quail hens yield fewer hybrids than non-inbreds when inseminated with semen from the same chicken males (Haley, 1967).

In general, sufficient numbers of birds from any mutant-carrying line or specialty stock should be maintained so that close inbreeding (brother-sister, half-sib, parent-offspring, or cousin matings) may be avoided. While excessive inbreeding can also be controlled by periodic outcrossing to a completely unrelated stock, this procedure may alter the expression of the character under study.

Highly inbred lines are useful in studies requiring homozygosity (i.e., grafting) or in screening potentially toxic compounds where their heightened "sensitivity" may be an advantage. In addition they are useful in studies of genetic background effects on gene expression. Some of the specialty stocks with specific modifier complexes can be compared under inbreeding and various outcrossing techniques as a means of studying the role of modifying gene complexes in evolution (Landauer, 1956). Neither the adults nor the embryos are suitable as control animals or for any other studies in which uniform material is required.

TABLE 1. AVIAN LIMB MUTANTS

NAME	EXCEPTIONS TO GENERAL DESCRIPTION	LITERATURE
	Polydactyly	
Polydactyly	Dominant, viable, breed characteristic (Dorkings, Silkies, Houdans) no effect on beak	1
Duplicate	Dominant allele of polydactyly, lethal soon after hatching, no effect on beak	1, 4
$Diplopodia_1$	..	1, 2, 3
$Diplopodia_2$	Mutant lost, no transplantation experiments	2, 3
$Diplopodia_3$	..	5
$Diplopodia_4$	Sex-linked	6
$Talpid_1$	Lethal (10–12 days incubation), digit *pattern* abnormal, mutant lost	1, 2, 3
$Talpid_2$	Lethal (13+ days incubation), digit *pattern* abnormal	2, 7
$Talpid_3$	Lethal (5–6 days incubation), digit *pattern* abnormal	8
Splitfoot	Duplication of third and fourth toes, wings normal, no transplantation experiments	9
Eudiplopodia	Two-plane duplication of normal digits, ectodermal defect, wings slightly affected in a few cases, beak normal	2, 10
Diplopodia	(Turkey) No transplantation experiments	11
Naked	(Turkey) Semiviable; 1 or 2 extra toes, polydactylism may be independent of naked (i.e., closely linked). No developmental studies	12
	Hypodactyly	
$Wingless_1$	Legs reduced, absence of lungs and other internal organs	1, 2
$Wingless_2$	Legs reduced	2, 3, 13
$Wingless_3$	Sex-linked, semiviable	14
Ectrodactyly	Reduced legs only in homozygous presence of scaleless gene; no early lethal period	15
Coloboma	Sex-linked, primary effect on beak and eyes, both sets of limbs reduced with greatest effect on wings	16
Stumpy	Lethal at $5\frac{1}{2}$–6 days incubation, wings normal	17
Stumpy (Hemimelia)	(Turkey) Semidominant, mild expression in some heterozygotes	18
	Chondrodystrophy and/or Micromelia	
Chondrodystrophy	..	1, 2, 3, 19, 20
Chondrodystrophy (called $Micromelia^H$)	..	2, 20
Cornish lethal	Semidominant, with heterozygotes viable, intermediate shortening of long bones	1, 2, 3
Creeper	Semidominant, with heterozygotes viable, inter-	1, 2, 3

TABLE 1 (*continued*)

NAME	EXCEPTIONS TO GENERAL DESCRIPTION	LITERATURE
	mediate shortening of long bones; most homozygotes die between 3–4 days incubation	
Micromelia	Two autosomal recessive genes	1, 2
Micromelia VII^{B}	..	2
Micromelia^{A}	Lethal between 15 and 18 days, hemorrhage and edema	20
Micromelia^{K}	..	2
Nanomelia	Slight shortening of long bones in heterozygotes	21
Short	(Turkey) Occasionally viable in homozygotes; heterozygotes viable with slight shortening of long bones	1
Achondroplasia	(Turkey) Sex-linked, bulging eyes and skull	22
Micromelia	(Turkey) Heterozygotes viable, with intermediate shortening of long bones	23
Micromelia	(Quail)	24

(1) F. B. Hutt, 1949: *Genetics of the Fowl.* McGraw-Hill Book Co., Inc., New York. (2) W. Landauer, 1961: *The Hatchability of Chicken Eggs as Influenced by Environment and Heredity.* Monograph 1, Univ. Conn. Agr. Exp. Sta., Storrs, Conn. (3) E. Hadorn, 1961: *Developmental Genetics and Lethal Factors* (translated by U. Mittwoch). John Wiley & Sons, Inc., New York. (4) E. Zwilling and L. A. Hansborough, 1956: Interaction between limb bud ectoderm and mesoderm in the chick embryo. III. Experiments with polydactylous limbs. *J. Exp. Zool.*, 132: 219–39. (5) L. W. Taylor, Unpublished studies. (6) M. Kieny and U. K. Abbott, 1962: Contribution à l'étude de la diplopodie liée au sexe et de l'achondroplasie Creeper chez l'embryon de poulet: culture *in vitro* des ébauches cartilagineuses du tibiotarse et du péroné. *Develop. Biol.*, 4: 473–88. (7) P. F. Goetinck and U. K. Abbott, 1964: Studies on limb morphogenesis. I. Experiments with the polydactylous mutant, talpid$_2$. *J. Exp. Zool.*, 155: 161–70. (8) D. A. Ede and W. A. Kelly, 1964: Developmental abnormalities in the trunk and limbs of the talpid$_3$ mutant of the fowl. *J. Embryol. Exp. Morphol.*, 12: 339–56. (9) U. K. Abbott and P. F. Goetinck, 1960: Splitfoot, a lethal mutation affecting the foot structure of the fowl. *J. Hered.*, 51: 161–66. (10) P. F. Goetinck, 1964: Studies on limb morphogenesis. II. Experiments with the polydactylous mutant eudiplopodia. *Develop. Biol.*, 10: 71–91. (11) U. K. Abbott, Unpublished studies. (12) H. K. Poole and S. J. Marsden, 1961: An autosomal naked mutation and associated polydactylism in Beltsville small white turkeys. *J. Hered.*, 52: 183–85. (13) E. Zwilling, 1956: Interaction between limb bud ectoderm and mesoderm in the chick embryo. IV. Experiments with a wingless mutant. *J. Exp. Zool.*, 132: 241–53. (14) M. S. Pease, 1962: Wingless poultry. *J. Hered.*, 53: 109–10. (15) U. K. Abbott and J. A. MacCabe, 1966: Ectrodactyly: A new embryonic lethal mutation in the chicken. *J. Hered.*, 57: 207–11. (16) U. K. Abbott, E. B. Bennett, and R. M. Craig, In prep. Facial coloboma, a sex-linked lethal defect in chick embryos. (17) U. K. Abbott, S. Calame-Bishop, and R. M. Craig, 1966: Teratology of stumpy chick embryos (Abstr. Papers, Sixth Ann. Meeting, Teratol. Soc.: p. 1. (18) U. K. Abbott and V. S. Asmundson, 1962: Hemimelia in turkeys. *Poultry Sci.*, 41: 1621 (Abstr.). (19) W. Landauer, 1965a: Chondrodystrophy of the fowl. Observations on penetrance and expressivity of Lamoreux's chondrodystrophy. *J. Hered.*, 56: 209–14. (20) W. Landauer, 1965b: Gene and phenocopy: Selection experiments and tests with 6-aminonicotinamide. *J. Exp. Zool.*, 160: 345–54. (21) W. Landauer, 1965c: Nanomelia, a lethal mutation of the fowl. *J. Hered.*, 56: 131–38. (22) U. K. Abbott, E. L. Iton, and P. Page, 1965: Achondroplasia in turkey embryos. Abstr. Papers, Fifth Ann. Meeting Teratol. Soc., p. 1. (23) U. K. Abbott. Unpublished studies. (24) W. G. Hill, G. L. Lloyd, and H. Abplanalp, 1963. Micromelia in Japanese quail. *J. Hered.*, 54: 188–90.

TABLE 2. AVIAN EPIDERMAL MUTANTS

NAME	EXCEPTIONS TO GENERAL DESCRIPTION	LITERATURE
	Feather Structure and Rate of Feather Growth	
Crest	Dominant; breed characteristic (Houdans), associated with cerebral hernia	1
Dehydrated	Oily feathers, rapid dehydration, and death immediately after hatching	4
Flightless	Dominant, semiviable, defects of beak and toenails	1, 2
Fray	Abnormal barbules	1
Frizzle	Semidominant. Curled feathers, homozygotes often lethal, heterozygous expression found in "Frizzle" breed	1, 3
Hen feathering	Dominant, sex-limited (♂ hormone), breed characteristic (Sebright bantams)	1
Hookless	Silky feathers, breed characteristic (Silkie bantams)	1
Muffs and beard	Dominant, breed characteristic (Houdans)	1
Naked	Sex-linked, 50% lethal between 18 days and hatching, feather follicles present but break at skin surface	1, 2, 3
Rapid feathering	Sex-linked	1, 5
Retarded (t^s), Tardy (t)	Alleles; bare back condition, recessive to normal allele (T) for normal feathering	1
Stringy	Barbules absent in wings and tail feathers, premaxilla and toenails overgrown	6
Sunsuit	Chick has wiry down, elongated beak and toenails, feathers confined in sheaths; reproduction subnormal	7
Vulture hocks	Feathers in region of tibia are large and stiff resembling wing feathers	1
Woolly	High mortality at hatching, poor viability, proximal barbules missing	8, 9
Hairy	(Turkey) Feather webs absent, barbules absent or reduced	10
Late feathering	(Turkey) Dominant, sex-linked, effect on over-all growth rate	11
	Feather and Scale Distribution	
Apterylosis	Dominant	1, 3
Naked neck	Dominant, breed characteristic (Transylvanian Naked neck)	1
Ptilopody	Semidominant, breed characteristic (Cochin) usually associated with brachydactyly, variable penetrance	1
Ragged wing	Recessive, condition develops after hatching, viable	1, 12
Scaleless	Recessive, absence of scales, spurs, footpads, most feathers, ectodermal defect; viable lines developed from originally lethal stock; feathering increased by selection	2, 13, 14,15

TABLE 2 (*continued*)

NAME	EXCEPTIONS TO GENERAL DESCRIPTION	LITERATURE
Congenital baldness	Low penetrance, blebs form at site of bald spots on 8th day incubation	1
Naked	(Turkeys) Similar to scaleless in chickens in appearance, associated (possibly linked) with polydactylism	16
Dactylosis	Scleroderma and foot lesions frequent—leading to missing toes. Symptoms resemble biotin or pantothenic acid deficiency. Variable penetrance, semiviable, detectable 7–10 days after hatching	1
	Spurs	
Double spurs	Variable penetrance, higher in females	1
Multiple spurs	Dominant (3–5 spurs present), breed characteristic (Sumatra)	1
Spurlessness	Partially sex-linked, some scales missing as well	1
Scaleless	See above. Also prevents spur growth; a small blunt protuberance is present in both sexes	1, 13
	Comb Structure	
Breda	Recessive, breed characteristic (Breda)	1
Duplex	Variable expression, breed characteristic (Houdans)	1
Rose	Dominant, detrimental effect on fertility, breed and varietal characteristic (Wyandotte)	1, 17
Spike blade	Incomplete recessive, sex influenced	1
Pea	Dominant, breed characteristic (Cornish)	1

(1) F. B. Hutt, 1949: *Genetics of the Fowl.* McGraw-Hill Book Co., Inc., New York. (2) W. Landauer, 1961: *The Hatchability of Chicken Eggs as Influenced by Environment and Heredity.* Monograph 1, Univ. Conn. Agr. Exp. Sta., Storrs, Conn. (3) E. Hadorn, 1961: *Developmental Genetics and Lethal Factors* (translated by U. Mittwoch). John Wiley & Sons, Inc., New York. (4) L. W. Taylor and V. M. Stinnett, 1957: Dehydrated, a new posthatching lethal mutation in the chicken. *Poultry Sci.*, 36: 1162–63. (Abstr.). (5) T. Ram and F. B. Hutt, 1956: The specificity of action of the K-k alleles affecting feathering in the fowl. *Poultry Sci.*, 35: 614–16. (6) E. G. Buss, B. B. Bohren, and D. C. Warren, 1950: The inheritance of "stringy," an abnormal feather condition in White Leghorn chickens. *J. Hered.*, 41: 143–44. (7) F. B. Hutt and J. Long, 1950: Sunsuit, a mutation reducing plumage in the fowl. *J. Hered.*, 41: 145–50. (8) D. G. Jones and W. Morgan, 1956: Woolly feathering in the fowl. *J. Hered.*, 45: 137–41. (9) W. Swanson and W. Morgan, 1956: Morphological effects of the woolly mutation on feather structure. *Proc. S.D. Acad. Sci.*, 35: 211–14. (10) J. R. Smyth, Jr., 1954: Hairy, a gene causing abnormal plumage in the turkey. *J. Hered.*, 45: 197–200. (11) V. S. Asmundson and U. K. Abbott, 1961: Dominant sex-linked late-feathering in the turkey. *J. Hered.*, 52: 99–104. (12) M. Juhn and C. S. Shaffner, 1962: Developmental dissociation of the feather tissues in ragged wing chicks. *J. Exp. Zool.*, 150: 155–63. (13) U. K. Abbott and V. S. Asmundson, 1957: Scaleless, an inherited ectodermal defect in the domestic fowl. *J. Hered.*, 48: 63–70. (14) P. F. Goetinck and U. K. Abbott, 1963: Tissue interaction in the scaleless mutant and the use of scaleless as an ectodermal marker in studies of normal limb differentiation. *J. Exp. Zool.*, 154: 7–19. (15) U. K. Abbott, 1965: Selection for feather number in scaleless chickens. *Poultry Sci.*, 44: 1347 (Abstr.). (16) H. K. Poole and S. J. Marsden, 1961: An autosomal naked mutation and associated polydactylism in Beltsville small white turkeys. *J. Hered.*, 52: 183–85. (17) T. W. Fox, Roy D. Crawford, and J. R. Smyth, Jr., 1964: Rose comb: an example of operational over-dominance in the domestic fowl. *Genet. Res.*, 5: 379–83.

TABLE 3. AVIAN NEUROLOGICAL MUTANTS

NAME	EXCEPTIONS TO GENERAL DESCRIPTION	LITERATURE
Jittery	..	2
Congenital tremor	Autosomal, lethal first week after hatching	1, 2
Congenital loco	Autosomal	1, 2
Shaker	..	2
xl Lethal	..	3, 4
Arched neck	Autosomal	5
Cerebellar hypoplasia	..	6
Cerebellar degeneration	..	7
Paroxysm	Lethal 14–15 weeks after hatching	4
Congenital loco	(Turkey) Autosomal, lethal first week after hatching	8
Vibrator	(Turkey)	9
Congenital loco	(Quail) Autosomal	10
Star gazer	(Quail) Inheritance not determined	11

(1) F. B. Hutt, 1949: *Genetics of the Fowl.* McGraw-Hill Book Co., Inc., New York. (2) E. Hadorn, 1961: *Developmental Genetics and Lethal Factors* (translated by U. Mittwoch). John Wiley & Sons, Inc., New York. (3) D. Goodwin, F. B. Hutt, and R. K. Cole, 1950: A sex-linked lethal gene in the fowl. *Science*, 112: 460–61. (4) R. K. Cole, 1961: Paroxysm—a sex-linked lethal of the fowl with a note on the xl lethal. *J. Hered.*, 52: 47–52. (5) M. H. Conner and C. S. Shaffner, 1953: An arched-neck character in chickens. *J. Hered.*, 44: 223–24. (6) R. W. Winterfield, 1953: Avian cerebellar hypoplasia and degeneration. *J. Am. Vet. Med. Assoc.*, 123: 136–38. (7) L. M. Markson, R. B. A. Carnaghan, and G. B. Young, 1959: Familial cerebellar degeneration and atrophy: a sex-linked disease affecting Light Sustex pullets. *J. Comp. Pathol.*, 69: 223–29. (8) R. K. Cole, 1957: Congenital loco in turkeys. *J. Hered.*, 48: 173–75. (9) T. H. Coleman, R. K. Ringer, W. J. Mathey, K. G. Rood, and C. W. Pope, 1960: Vibrator, a recessive sex-linked mutation in turkeys. *J. Hered.*, 51: 158–60. (10) K. Sittmann, W. P. C. Richards, and H. Abplanalp, 1965: Congenital loco in a third species of domestic fowl. *Can. J. Genet. Cytol.*, 7: 636–40. (11) K. Sittmann and H. Abplanalp, 1965: Japanese quail mutants. *Quail Quart.*, 2: 30–32.

TABLE 4. AVIAN COLOR AND PATTERN GENES

NAME	DESCRIPTION	LITERATURE
	A. *Type of Melanin Pigment*	
	1. FORM	
Black	See E locus (chickens), Table 4, B.1	1
Black	See B locus (turkeys), Table 4, B.1	2
Melanism (M)	(Pheasant) Incompletely dominant to wild type Permits full black coloration in MM	3
Bourbon red (r)	(Turkey) Jersey buff is (BBrr)	4
Brown (e)	(Turkey) Sex-linked	5, 2
Buff (pk)	(Quail) Pink eyes and buff down, reduced hatchability, fertility, and viability	6
Gold (s)	Recessive to silver (S), sex-linked, influences ground color upon which other pattern genes are expressed (ss is wild type)	1
	2. INTENSITY (DILUTION GENES)	
Blue (Bl)	Blue Andalusian breed (Blbl); homozygotes (BlBl) are white with a few blue feathers	1
Cream (ig)	Inhibitor of gold	1
Cream (ig)*	(Pheasant)	7
Dilute (sd)	(Pheasant) Sex-linked	7
Dilution (Sd)	Sex-linked; females and heterozygous males, blue and barred; homozygous males predominantly white	1
Faded bronze (f)	(Turkey) Affects post-hatching weight and vigor	8
Light buff (b)	(Pheasant) Heterozygous (Bb) are buff; male is buff and black or purplish above white neck ring, female completely brown or buff	9
N Locus	(Turkey) Sex-linked, three alleles in descending order of dominance, N (bronze) allows bronze coloration; n lightens typical bronze pattern to gray or light bronze as in the Narragansett breed; n^a (imperfect albino) permits very reduced pigmentation, is sublethal during incubation (all dead by 6 weeks of age), reduces plumage and causes blindness, eyes blue	1, 4, 5
Palm (p)	(Turkey) Royal Palm is (pp)	2
Slate (D)	(Turkey) Dominant; Blue Slate is BBDD	2, 4
Slate (sl)	(Turkey) Autosomal, recessive to nonslate interacts with Bourbon Red (r)	2
	3. ABSENCE OF MELANIN (WHITES AND ALBINOS)	
Albinism (a)	Autosomal, recessive, red eyes (iris and retina devoid of pigment)	1

* Symbols assigned here for consistency.

NAME	DESCRIPTION	LITERATURE
Albinism (al)	Sex-linked, recessive (imperfect pure white to chocolate chicks with pink eyes, short down). Faint barring in Barred Plymouth Rocks	1
Albinism (al)	(Quail) Sex-linked, recessive, pink eyes, faint pattern, poor viability after hatching	6, 10
Albino (al) or (n^a)	(Turkey) Sex-linked, recessive, see N locus, Table 4, A.2	1, 5
White (c)	Silkie, Plymouth Rocks	1, 11, 12
White (I)	Incompletely dominant in some genetic backgrounds (II) are white. (Ii) may show ticking, or salmon breast if (E) not present	1, 13, 14
White (c) also (w)	(Turkey) Autosomal, recessive (cc) suppresses any other color genes; breed characteristic (White Holland). White down results from interaction of (cc) with (B) or (b^1), Table 4, B.1	2, 4
White (c)	(Quail) Autosomal, recessive, white to creamy down, normal eyes, semilethal during incubation, 8% hatch but die by 2 days of age	16
White (c)	(Pheasant) Autosomal, recessive, blue eyes, pearl white legs and beak, heterozygotes may have some white feathers as well	17
White (w)	(Pheasant) Brown eyes, legs and feet buff	18, 19

B. *Distribution of Melanin*

1. PRIMARY PATTERN (REGIONAL)

B Locus	(Turkeys) Three alleles in descending order of dominance: (B) allows full black coloration (Black); (b) is wild type in turkeys (Bronze); and (b^1) restricts black to the wings (Black-Winged Bronze); wild type poults (b) have broad back and head stripes	2, 4
Columbian (Co)	Melanin restricted to hackles, wings, tail. More marked restriction in males; interacts with (e^b) (E locus), breed characteristic (Wyandotte)	20
E Locus	Seven alleles in descending order of dominance: (E, extended black) permits full black coloration, the others (dominant wheaten, e^{wh}), (partridge, e^p), (speckled head, e^s), (buttercup, e^{bc}), (recessive wheaten, e^y) act to limit melanin to specific areas. (e^+) is responsible for the wild type (red-black game pattern) in adults while chicks have broad back and head stripes. (Yellow-white e^y) shows up in chicks and in adult females, no effect in adult males. These alleles occur widely in most breeds	21, 22, 23, 24, 25, 26, 27
Red-splashed white (rs)	Restricts black and red pigments, adults predominantly white	1

TABLE 4 (*continued*)

NAME	DESCRIPTION	LITERATURE
	2. SECONDARY PATTERN (WITHIN FEATHERS)	
Barring (ab)	Pigment restricted within feather to regular black bars, breed characteristic (Campine)	1, 28
Barring (B)	Sex-linked, white bars on colored background, narrow in males, wide in females, breed characteristic (Plymouth Rock)	1, 29
Lacing (la)	Feathers have a black border, breed characteristic (Wyandotte)	1
Mottling (mo)	Pigment absent from tip of feathers	1
Pied (pi)	Some feathers black, some white, some black and white spotted	1
Pied (pi)*	(Pheasants) Autosomal, recessive	7
Spangling (S)	Feathers have black V-shaped tips; sex-influenced	1
Spotting (sp)	(Turkeys) Poults have brown head spots, otherwise white; adults have primarily white feathers with partially or completely black feathers scattered throughout. Breed characteristic (Nebraskan)	15
Spotting (sp)*	(Pheasants) Autosomal, recessive	30
	3. DERMAL AND SUBDERMAL	
Fibromelanosis (Fm)	Dominant but inhibited by (Id) (see below); melanin in dermis, nerve and muscle sheaths, tendons, mesenteries, brain, trachea, air sacs, periosteal and	1, 11, 31

* Symbols assigned here for consistency.

(1) F. B. Hutt, 1949: *Genetics of the Fowl.* McGraw-Hill Book Co., Inc., N.Y. (2) V. S. Asmundson, 1945: A triple-allele series and plumage color in turkeys. *Genetics*, 30: 305–22. (3) J. H. Bruckner, 1939: The inheritance of melanism in pheasants. *J. Hered.*, 30: 45–52. (4) W. R. B. Robertson, B. B. Bohren, and D. C. Warren, 1943: The inheritance of plumage color in the turkey. *J. Hered.*, 34: 246–56. (5) V. S. Asmundson, 1950: Sex-linkage in the turkey. *J. Hered.*, 41: 205–7. (6) K. Sittmann, W. O. Wilson, and L. Z. McFarland, 1966: Buff and albino Japanese Quail. Description, inheritance and fitness traits. *J. Hered.*, 57: 119–24. (7) J. H. Bruckner, 1941: Inheritance of plumage color in *Phasianus colchicus. Genetics*, 26: 142 (Abstr.). (8) C. E. Keeler, E. Hoffman, and R. K. Shearer, 1949: Faded bronze plumage: an autosomal mutant in the turkey. *Poultry Sci.*, 28: 633–35. (9) V. S. Asmundson, U. K. Abbott, and F. H. Lantz, 1964: Plumage color mutants in ring-neck pheasants. *J. Hered.*, 55: 150–53. (10) J. K. Lauber, 1964: Sex-linked albinism in the Japanese quail. *Science*, 146: 948–50. (11) R. F. White and H. L. Eastlick, 1953: The development of melanophores in the down feathers and skin of the silkie fowl. *Poultry Sci.*, 32: 235–47. (12) P. I. Prentice and H. L. Eastlick, 1954: The loss of melanin pigment from the epidermis of the White Plymouth Rock fowl. *Anat. Record*, 120: (Abstr.). (13) A. Cock and M. Pease, 1951: The genetics of the white pile pattern in the domestic fowl. *IXth World's Poultry Congr.* I: 49–53. (14) L. T. Smith and A. W. Nordskog, 1963: Studies on dominance and pleiotropy using segregating inbred lines of fowl. *Genetics*, 48: 1141–52. (15) V. S. Asmundson, 1955: Inheritance of spotting in the plumage of turkeys. *J. Hered.*, 46: 285–88. (16) K. Sittman and H. Abplanalp, 1965: White-feathered Japanese quail. *J. Hered.*, 56: 220–23. (17) J. H. Bruckner, 1941: Inheritance of white plumage in *Phasianus. Auk*, 58: 536–42. (18) W. Morgan, 1958: White pheasants among ring-necked pheasants in

NAME	DESCRIPTION	LITERATURE
	perichondral membranes, gonads. No effect on epidermal pigments, breed characteristics (Silkies)	
Inhibitor of dermal melanin (Id)	Sex-linked, incompletely dominant; independent of epidermal color but may affect iris color. It *may* also inhibit the subdermal melanin in Silkies (above); breed characteristic (Brahma and White Leghorn)	1
	C. *Affecting Lipochrome Pigment*	
Yellow head (g)	Autosomal, recessive, face and wattles remain yellow	1
White skin (W)	Autosomal, dominant, restricts xanthophyll to blood and body fat, breed characteristic (Orpington)	1
	D. *Chick Down Color and Pattern*	
Buff (pk)	(Quail) Pink eyes and buff plumage	6
Head streak (ko)	Sex-linked, dark head streak in gold spangled breeds	1
Light down (Li)	Sex-linked, reduces brown to yellowish color	1, 27
Marbling (ma)	Irregular striping in chick down (may be chick expression of spangling)	1
Snow white down (sw)	Removes color from down that would be yellow or cream; no effect on black or red down or on later plumage color (i.e., on melanin pigments)	32
Striped (St)	Wild type (see E locus)	1

South Dakota. *Wilson Bulletin*, 70: 281–84. (19) L. O. Shelley, 1935: Albinism among New Hampshire ring-necked pheasants. *Auk*, 52: 307 (note). (20) J. R. Smyth, Jr., and R. G. Somes, Jr., 1965: A new gene determining the Columbian feather pattern in the fowl. *J. Hered.*, 56: 151–56. (21) G. V. Morejohn, 1953: A gene for yellowish-white down in the Red Junglefowl. *J. Hered.*, 44: 47–52. (22) G. V. Morejohn, 1955: Plumage color allelism in the Red Jungle Fowl (*Gallus gallus*) and related domestic forms. *Genetics*, 40: 519–30. (23) J. R. Smyth, Jr., J. W. Porter, and B. B. Bohren, 1951: A study of pigments from red, brown, and buff feathers and hair. *Physiol. Zool.*, 24: 205–16. (24) J. R. Smyth, Jr., 1965: Allelic relationship of genes determining extended black, wild type and brown plumage patterns in the fowl. *Poultry Sci.*, 44: 89–98. (25) J. A. Brumbaugh and W. F. Hollander, 1963: A further study of the E pattern locus in the fowl. *Genetics*, 48: 884 (Abstr.). (26) R. G. Somes, Jr., and J. R. Smyth, Jr., 1965: Feather phaeomelanin intensity in Buff Orpington, New Hampshire and Rhode Island Red breeds of fowl. 2. Inheritance studies from whole feather extracts. *Poultry Sci.*, 44: 47–52. (27) M. Pease and A. Cock, 1951: Retarded pigmentation, a recessive gene affecting down color and pattern. *Rep. IXth World's Poultry Congr.*, I: 63–67. (28) M. E. Rawles, 1959: An experimental study on the development of regional variation in the plumage pattern of the Silver Campine fowl. *J. Morphol.*, 105: 33–48. (29) M. Nickerson, 1944: An experimental analysis of barred pattern formation in feathers. *J. Exp. Zool.*, 95: 361–97. (30) R. J. Greb, 1944: Occurrence of spotted pheasants. *J. Hered.*, 35: 362. (31) H. L. Eastlick and R. A. Wortham, 1946: An experimental study on the feather-pigmenting and subcutaneous melanophores in the Silkie fowl. *J. Exp. Zool.*, 103: 233–58. (32) F. B. Hutt, 1951: Snow-white down in the chick. *J. Hered.*, 42: 117–20.

TABLE 5. MISCELLANEOUS AVIAN MUTANTS

NAME	DESCRIPTION	LITERATURE
Rumplessness	Both dominant and recessive forms are known. Genes show variable penetrance and expressivity; their expression can be modified by selection and crossing, such stocks differ in insulin sensitivity. Rumpless birds are viable, but show poor fertility. Dominant rumplessness results from a degeneration of presumptive tail tissue during the 3rd day of incubation. Recessive rumplessness can first be detected histologically at $3\frac{1}{2}$ days. The tail forms (abnormally) and then degenerates, perhaps as late as the 5th day. Rumplessness is easily phenocopied by low temperature, shaking, and insulin injection	1, 2, 7
Dwarfing	In addition to disproportionate dwarfing (Table 1), several single genes acting to reduce body size in a proportionate way are known in both chickens and turkeys. Some Bantam breeds (e.g., Sebright) carry a dominant sex-linked gene. A second viable recessive sex-linked gene has been found in Leghorns. Both these genes have a disproportionate effect on the two sexes, with the male being more reduced than the female and thus closer in size to the female than are male and female full-size birds	1, 3
Muscular dystrophy	Autosomal, recessive, homozygous birds viable in suitable environment (see section on Handling Bird Colonies and Eggs). Used in a variety of biochemical, nutritional, genetic studies. Muscles of dystrophic chickens have a higher proportion of	4, 5, 6

(1) F. B. Hutt, 1949: *Genetics of the Fowl.* McGraw-Hill Book Co., Inc., New York. (2) W. Landauer, 1961: *The Hatchability of Chicken Eggs as Influenced by Environment and Heredity.* Monograph 1, Univ. Conn. Agr. Exp. Sta., Storrs, Conn. (3) F. B. Hutt, 1959: Sex-linked dwarfism in the fowl. *J. Hered.*, 50: 209–21. (4) V. S. Asmundson and L. M. Julian, 1956: Inherited muscle abnormality in the domestic fowl. *J. Hered.*, 47: 248–52. (5) V. S. Asmundson, F. H. Kratzer, and L. M. Julian, 1966: Hereditary myopathy in the chicken. *Ann. N.Y. Acad. Sci.*, 138: 49–58. (6) N. O. Kaplan and R. D. Cahn, 1962: Lactic dehydrogenases and muscular dystrophy in the chicken. *Proc. Nat. Acad. Sci.*, 48: 2123–30. (7) E. Zwilling, 1945: The embryogeny of a recessive rumpless condition of chickens. *J. Exp. Zool.*, 99: 79–91. (8) V. S. Asmundson, 1945: Crooked neck dwarf in the domestic fowl. *J. Hered.*, 36: 173–76. (9) V. S. Asmundson and C. F. Pun, 1956: Crooked neck dwarf in the turkey. *J. Exp. Zool.*, 131: 224–38. (10) C. F. Pun, 1954: The crooked neck dwarf lethal syndrome in the domestic fowl. *J. Exp. Zool.*, 126:

NAME	DESCRIPTION	LITERATURE
	H(heart) type LDH than muscles of normal chickens. Strains selected for high and low fat content of muscle and early and late onset of the disease available. No effect on embryo described	
Crooked neck dwarf	Autosomal, recessive in chickens, turkeys, and Japanese quail. Easily recognized by the 8th day in chickens and at comparable stages in other species. From developmental point of view, the failure of the esophagus to open (and so permit ingestion of the protein contents of the amnion) is of interest. Studies of the chicken form have demonstrated an increased sensitivity of heterozygotes to the teratogenic effects of nicotinamide, a phenocopying agent	8, 9, 10, 11
Riboflavin transfer	Autosomal, incomplete recessive; interferes with ability of hen to "transfer" riboflavin to egg, lethal to embryos from such hens if supplementary riboflavin is not injected into egg, but otherwise not detrimental to hen or embryo. Heterozygous hens produce eggs with intermediate levels of riboflavin. Mechanism of gene action is of considerable interest as is the fact that riboflavin-deficient embryos produced by rdrd hens do *not* show classical riboflavin-deficiency symptoms	12, 13, 14, 15
Gasper	Sex-linked, recessive; respiratory defect (bronchial rattle and gasping), semilethal	16

101–34. (11) K. Sittmann and R. M. Craig: Crooked neck dwarfs in Japanese quail. (In prep.). (12) A. J. G. Maw, 1954: Inherited riboflavin deficiency in chicken eggs. *Poultry Sci.*, 33: 216–17. (13) R. V. Boucher, E. G. Buss, and A. J. G. Maw, 1959: Physiological characteristics associated with a mutant gene in chickens that causes a deficiency of riboflavin. 2. Blood. *Poultry Sci.*, 38: 1190 (Abstr.). (14) R. V. Boucher, J. W. Cowan, and E. G. Buss, 1964: Riboflavin utilization by a mutant strain of single comb White Leghorn chickens. 1. Attempts to increase free riboflavin in the blood. *Poultry Sci.*, 43: 169–72. (15) J. R. Cowan, R. V. Boucher, and E. G. Buss, 1964: Riboflavin utilization by a mutant strain of single comb White Leghorn chickens. 2. Absorption of radioactive riboflavin from the digestive tract. *Poultry Sci.*, 43: 172–74. (16) D. J. Price, A. D. Smith, and R. B. Teskey, 1966: A sex-linked respiratory defect in chickens. *Poultry Sci.*, 45: 423–24.

TABLE 6. SPECIES, GENUS, AND FAMILY CROSSES

TYPE OF CROSS	DESCRIPTION	LITERATURE
Between Species		
Chicken	Fertile, backcross and F_2 progeny	1, 2, 3, 4
Turkey	Fertile, viable offspring	
Pheasant	May show "hybrid breakdown" later generations	
Between Genera		
Chicken × Pheasant	Fertile, viable offspring (predominantly male); hybrids sterile	1, 2, 3, 5
Between Families		
Chicken × Turkey	Fertile, viable offspring when female parent is turkey (selected for parthenogenesis); hybrids sterile	1, 2, 3, 5, 6
Chicken × Japanese quail	(Chicken ♂ × quail ♀) fertile, viable offspring (either male or lacking gonads); hybrids sterile	7
Pheasant × Turkey	Fertile, viable offspring (predominantly male); hybrids sterile	3, 5

(1) F. B. Hutt, 1949: *Genetics of the Fowl.* McGraw-Hill Book Co., Inc., New York. (2) W. Landauer, 1961: *The Hatchability of Chicken Eggs as Influenced by Environment and Heredity.* Monograph 1, Univ. Conn. Agr. Exp. Sta., Storrs, Conn. (3) A. P. Gray, 1958: *Bird Hybrids;* a Check-List with Bibliography. [Tech. Commun. No. 13, Commonwealth Bur. Animal Breeding Genet., Edinburgh.] Commonwealth Agr. Bur., Farnham Royal, Bucks, England. 390 pp. (4) F. W. Lorenz, V. S. Asmundson, and N. E. Wilson, 1956: Turkey hybrids. *J. Hered.*, 47: 143–46. (5) V. S. Asmundson and F. W. Lorenz, 1957: Hybrids of ring-necked pheasants, turkeys, and domestic fowl. *Poultry Sci.*, 36: 1323–34. (6) M. W. Olsen, 1960: Nine-year summary of parthenogenesis in turkeys. *Proc. Soc. Exp. Biol. Med.*, 105: 279–81. (7) L. E. Haley, H. Abplanalp, and K. Enya, 1966: Selection for increased fertility of female quail when mated to male chickens. *Evolution*, 20: 72–81.

TABLE 7. COMPARATIVE DEVELOPMENT IN TURKEY, CHICKEN, AND JAPANESE QUAIL EMBRYOS

DAYS OF INCUBATION	DEVELOPMENTAL STAGE*		
	TURKEY	CHICKEN	QUAIL
0	Early gastrulation	Mid-gastrulation	Late gastrulation
1	2+	4	6
2	8	11	14
3	11	17	20
4	18	21+	24+
5	21+	26	27+
6	24	28	29
7	26	30+	34
8	27	33	35+
9	30	34	37
10	32+	35+	38
11	34	36+	40
12	35	37+	41
13	35+	39	42
14	36	40	43
15	37	40+	44
16	38	41	45
17	38+	42	Hatched
18	39+	43+	
19	40	45	
20	41+	Pipping	
21	42	Hatched	
22	42+		
23	43+		
24	44		
25	44+		
26	45+		
27	Pipping		
28	Hatched		

* Stages are expressed in terms of Hamburger and Hamilton's (1951) chick embryo series but are based on actual incubation time in a commercial incubator. The stage given represents the average of from 6 to 10 embryos. Considerable variation is found between embryos in turkeys and Japanese quail especially.

REFERENCES

ABBOTT, U. K., 1959: Further studies on diplopodia. III. The relationship between expressivity and penetrance in selected lines and crosses. *J. Genet.*, 56: 197.

———, 1964: Limb development in several polydactylous mutants. *Int. Conf. Organogen.* (Abstr.). Baltimore, Md.

———, 1965: Selection for feather number in scaleless chickens. *Poultry Sci.*, 44: 1347 (Abstr.).

———, and V. S. ASMUNDSON, 1957: Scaleless, an inherited ectodermal defect in the domestic fowl. *J. Hered.*, 48: 63.

———, and ———, 1962: Responses to selection under severe environmental stress. In *Proc. XIIth World's Poultry Congr.*, Sydney, Australia, p. 30.

———, ———, and K. R. SHORTRIDGE, 1962: Nutritional studies with scaleless chickens. I. The sulfur-containing amino acids. *Genet. Res.*, 3: 181.

———, ———, and L. G. RAGGI, 1964: Effects of acute and prolonged hypothermic stress on the incidence of heart and other lesions in scaleless chickens. *Proc. Fed. Am. Soc. Exp. Biol.*, 23 (Part I): 311 (Abstr.).

———, E. L. ITON, and P. PAGE, 1965: Achondroplasia in turkey embryos. *Abstr. of Papers, Fifth Ann. Meeting Teratol. Soc.*, p. 1.

ABPLANALP, H., U. K. ABBOTT, and V. S. ASMUNDSON, 1957: Evolutionary significance of interruptions in the development of avian embryos of diverse origins. *Soc. Study Evol. Am. Inst. Biol. Soc.* (Unpublished paper).

American Standard of Perfection, 1947. 492 pp. Am. Poultry Assoc., Inc., Davenport, Iowa.

ASMUNDSON, V. S., F. H. KRATZER, and L. M. JULIAN, 1966: Hereditary myopathy in the chicken. *Ann. N.Y. Acad. Sci.*, 138: 49.

BATESON, W., 1902: Poultry. In *Experimental Studies in the Physiology of Heredity*, Rep. Evol. Comm. Roy. Soc. I, London, pp. 87–124.

BELL, E., 1965: The skin. In R. L. DeHaan and H. Ursprung (eds.), *Organogenesis*, Holt, Rinehart and Winston, New York, p. 361.

BURROWS, W. H., and J. P. QUINN, 1939: Artificial insemination of chickens and turkeys. U.S.D.A. Circ. No. 525, Supt. of Documents, Washington, D.C.

COCK, A. G., 1964: Dosage compensation and sex-chromatin in non-mammals. *Genet. Res. Camb.*, 5: 354.

COLE, R. K., 1961: Paroxysm—a sex-linked lethal of the fowl with a note on the xl lethal. *J. Hered.*, 52: 47.

Diseases of Poultry, 1965. 5th ed., 1382 pp. H. E. Biester and L. H. Schwarte (eds.), Iowa State Univ. Press, Ames, Iowa.

DUNN, L. C., and W. LANDAUER, 1936: Further data on genetic modification of rumplessness in the fowl. *J. Genet.*, 33: 401.

DU SHANE, G. P., 1944: The embryology of vertebrate pigment cells. II. Birds. *Quart. Rev. Biol.*, 19: 98.

EASTLICK, H. L., and R. A. WORTHAM, 1946: An experimental study on the feather-pigmenting and subcutaneous melanophores in the Silkie fowl. *J. Exp. Zool.*, 103: 233.

FEREBEE, D. C., F. X. OGASAWARA, and W. F. ROONEY, 1966: Plastic tube method of artificial insemination of turkeys. 16 pp. Univ. Calif. Agr. Ext. Serv., AXT 219.

FOX, T. W., R. D. CRAWFORD, and J. R. SMYTH, JR., 1964: Rose comb: an example of operational over-dominance in the domestic fowl. *Genet. Res.*, 5: 379.

GOETINCK, P. F., 1964: Studies on limb morphogenesis. II. Experiments with the polydactylous mutant eudiplopodia. *Develop. Biol.*, 10: 71.

———, and U. K. ABBOTT, 1963: Tissue interaction in the scaleless mutant and the use of scaleless as an ectodermal marker in studies of normal limb differentiation. *J. Exp. Zool.*, 154: 7.

———, and ———, 1964: Studies on limb morphogenesis. I. Experiments with the polydactylous mutant, talpid$_2$. *J. Exp.*

Zool., 155: 161.

GOWE, R. S., 1965: On the hatchability of chicken eggs stored in plastic bags flushed with nitrogen gas. *Poultry Sci.*, 44: 492.

GRAY, A. P., 1958: *Bird Hybrids, A Check-List with Bibliography.* 360 pp. (Tech. Commun. No. 13, Commonwealth Bur. Animal Breeding Genet., Edinburgh.) Commonwealth Agr. Bur., Farnham Royal, Bucks, Eng.

HALEY, L. E., 1965: Serum albumin polymorphism in quail and chicken-quail hybrids. *Genetics*, 51: 983.

———, 1967: Studies on the control of hybridization between chicks and Japanese quail. Unpublished Ph.D. thesis, Univ. of Calif., Davis, Calif.

———, H. ABPLANALP, and K. ENYA, 1966: Selection for increased fertility of female quail when mated to male chickens. *Evolution*, 20: 72.

HAMBURGER, V., and H. L. HAMILTON, 1951: A series of normal stages in the development of the chick embryo. *J. Morphol.*, 88: 49.

HERRMANN, H., and M. L. TOOTLE, 1964: Specific and general aspects of the development of enzymes and metabolic pathways. *Physiol. Revs.*, 44: 289.

HUTT, F. B., 1949: *Genetics of the Fowl.* McGraw-Hill Book Co., Inc., New York.

KARNOFSKY, D. A., 1965: Mechanisms of action of certain growth-inhibiting drugs. In J. G. Wilson and J. Warkany (eds.), *Teratology: Principles and Techniques*, University of Chicago Press, Chicago, Ill., p. 185.

KOZELKA, A. W., 1929: Integumental grafting in the domestic fowl. *J. Hered.*, 20: 2.

LANDAUER, W., 1933: A gene modifying frizzling in the fowl. *J. Hered.*, 24: 153.

———, 1935: Studies on the creeper fowl. IX. Malformations occurring in the creeper stock. *J. Genet.*, 30: 303.

———, 1946: The results of selection against expression of the "short upper beak" mutation in fowl. *Am. Nat.*, 80: 490.

———, 1948: The phenotypic modification of hereditary polydactylism of fowl by selection and by insulin. *Genetics*, 33: 133.

———, 1956: Cyclopia and related defects as a lethal mutation of fowl. *J. Genet.*, 54: 219.

———, 1957: Oxidative metabolism and seasonal variations in the incidence of perocephaly of chicken embryos. *J. Exp. Zool.*, 136: 171.

———, 1959: The phenocopy concept: Illusion or reality? *Experientia*, 25: 409.

———, 1960: Nicotine-induced malformations of chicken embryos and their bearing on the phenocopy problem. *J. Exp. Zool.*, 143: 107.

———, 1965a: Gene and phenocopy: Selection experiments and tests with 6-aminonicotinamide. *J. Exp. Zool.*, 160: 345.

———, 1965b: Chondrodystrophy of the fowl: Observations on penetrance and expressivity of Lamoreux's chondrodystrophy. *J. Hered.*, 56: 209.

———, 1965c: Nanomelia, a lethal mutation of the fowl. *J. Hered.*, 56: 131.

LANDAUER, W., and S. D. ABERLE, 1935: Studies on the endocrine glands of frizzle fowl. *Am. J. Anat.*, 57: 99.

LEONE, C. A. (ed.), 1964: Taxonomic serology of animals, Part VI. In *Taxonomic Biochemistry and Serology*, The Ronald Press Co., New York, p. 467.

LERNER, I. M., 1954: *Genetic Homeostasis.* 134 pp. Oliver and Boyd, Edinburgh, Scotland.

LORENZ, F. W., V. S. ASMUNDSON, H. E. ADLER, F. H. KRATZER, F. X. OGASAWARA, J. D. CARSON, 1959: *Turkey Fertility.* 28 pp. Univ. Calif. Agr. Ext. Serv. Circ. 472.

LYON, M. F., 1961: Gene action in the X-chromosome of the mouse (*Mus musculus* L.). *Nature*, 190: 372.

MARKS, H. L., and P. D. LEPORE, 1965: A procedure for artificial insemination of Japanese quail. *Poultry Sci.*, 44: 1001.

MILLER, H. T., and R. E. FEENEY, 1964: Immunochemical relationships of proteins of avian egg whites. *Arch. Biochem. Biophys.*, 108: 117.

MURPHY, M. L., 1965: Factors influencing teratogenic response to drugs. In J. G. Wilson and J. Warkany (eds.), *Teratology: Principles and Techniques*, The University of Chicago Press, Chicago, Ill., p. 145.

NICKERSON, M., 1944: An experimental analysis of barred pattern in feathers. *J. Exp. Zool.*, 95: 361.

OLSEN, M. W., 1965a: Twelve year summary of selection for parthenogenesis in Beltsville small white turkeys. *Brit. Poultry Sci.*, 6: 1.

———, 1965b: Delayed development and atypical cellular organization in blastodiscs of unfertilized turkey eggs. *Develop. Biol.*, 12: 1.

RAWLES, M. E., 1948: Origin of melanophores and their role in the development of color patterns in vertebrates. *Physiol. Revs.*, 28: 383.

———, 1955: Skin and its derivatives. In B. H. Willier, P. A. Weiss, and V. Hamburger (eds.), *Analysis of Development*, W. B. Saunders Co., Philadelphia, Pa., p. 499.

———, 1963: Tissue interactions in scale and feather development as studies in dermal-epidermal recombinations. *J. Embryol. Exp. Morphol.*, 11: 765.

SCHWARTE, L. H., 1965: Poultry surgery. In H. E. Biester and L. H. Schwarte (eds.), *Diseases of Poultry*, 5th ed., The Iowa State University Press, Ames, Iowa, p. 1149.

SENGEL, P., 1958: La différentiation de la peau et des germes plumaires de l'embryon de Poulet en culture *in vitro*. *Année Biol.*, 62: 29.

———, and U. K. ABBOTT, 1963: *In vitro* studies with the scaleless mutant: Interactions during feather and scale differentiation. *J. Hered.*, 54: 255.

SHELLENBERGER, T. E., G. W. NEWELL, R. F. ADAMS, and J. BARBACCIA, 1966: Cholinesterase inhibition and toxicologic evaluation of two organophosphate pesticides in Japanese quail. *Toxicol. Appl. Pharmacol.*, 8: 22.

SMITH, L. T., and A. W. NORDSKOG, 1963: Studies on dominance and pleiotropy using segregating inbred lines of fowl. *Genetics*, 48: 1141.

STENIUS, C., L. C. CHRISTIAN, and S. OHNO, 1963: Comparative cytological study of *Phasianus colchicus*, *Meleagris gallopavo*, and *Gallus domesticus*. *Chromosoma* (Berl.), 13: 515.

TAYLOR, L. W., and V. M. STINNETT, 1957: Dehydrated, a new posthatching lethal mutation in the chicken. *Poultry Sci.*, 36: 1162 (Abstr.).

———, U. K. ABBOTT, and C. A. GUNNS, 1959: Further studies on diplopodia. I. Modification on phenotypic segregation ratios by selection. *J. Genet.*, 56: 161.

VAN ROEKEL, H., 1965: Pullorum disease. In H. E. Biester and L. H. Schwarte (eds.), *Diseases of Poultry*, 5th ed., The Iowa State Univ. Press, Ames, Iowa, p. 220.

WADDINGTON, C. H., 1952: *The Epigenetics of Birds*. Cambridge University Press, Cambridge, Eng.

WESSELLS, N. K., 1965: Morphology and proliferation during early feather development. *Develop. Biol.*, 12: 131.

WILDE, C. E., JR., 1961: The differentiation of vertebrate pigment cells. In M. Abercrombie and J. Brachet (eds.), *Advances in Morphogenesis*, Vol. I, Academic Press, New York, p. 267.

WILSON, W. O., U. K. ABBOTT, and H. ABPLANALP, 1961: Evaluation of coturnix (Japanese quail) as pilot animal for poultry. *Poultry Sci.*, 40: 651.

WOODARD, A. E., H. ABPLANALP, and W. O. WILSON, 1965: Japanese quail husbandry in the laboratory. 35 pp. Dept. Poultry Husbandry, Univ. Calif., Davis, Calif.

ZWILLING, E., 1956: Interaction between limb bud ectoderm and mesoderm in the chick embryo. IV. Experiments with a wingless mutant. *J. Exp. Zool.*, 132: 241.

———, 1961: Limb morphogenesis. In M. Abercrombie and J. Brachet (eds.), *Advances in Morphogenesis*, Vol. I, Academic Press, New York, p. 301.

———, and L. A. HANSBOROUGH, 1956: Interaction between limb bud ectoderm and mesoderm in the chick embryo. III. Experiments with polydactylous limbs. *J. Exp. Zool.*, 132: 219.

Frogs*

By Marie A. DiBerardino

INTRODUCTION

The frog has served as a significant tool in the analysis of development. From the earliest days of experimental embryology, the developing frog embryo has been observed, dissected, and rearranged in order to unravel the complexity of development. To this end the quest for mechanisms of development has focused mainly on the phases of oogenesis, fertilization, cleavage, gastrulation, and organogenesis. It has long been recognized that the major components of the embryos are the nucleus and cytosome. Analysis of their function in embryogenesis along with the study of nucleocytoplasmic and intercellular interactions has contributed greatly to our understanding of development.

During the period of oogenesis, single cells destined to become mature ova grow to macroscopic size while forming cytoplasmic materials which later control the initial steps in organogenesis. In some yet unknown way the nonchromosomal constituents of the germinal vesicle are necessary for cytoplasmic maturation and subsequent cleavage. Fertilization, resulting in the fusion of the haploid gametes, also brings about a reshuffling of cytoplasmic materials. The most apparent cytoplasmic regional differentiation is the distinct gray crescent which in some anurans forms on one side of the equator approximately 1 hour after fertilization. Vital-staining experiments have shown that this area marks the future dorsal lip of the blastopore (see Holtfreter and Hamburger, 1955), the organizer of Spemann (1938). The next phase involves a rapid series of cell divisions leading to the formation of a blastula. All of the previous stages are preparatory to the dynamic period of gastrulation, when mass movements of cells bring the mesoderm into contact with the ectoderm, and this association results in the primary inductive-interaction system. From this stimulus, as well as secondary inductive-interaction systems, organogenesis proceeds in an epigenetic fashion. Through the use of mapping techniques the presumptive organ areas have been localized in the late blastula and early gastrula (Vogt, 1929;

* The author is indebted to Dr. Thomas J. King for permission to include some procedures in this manuscript which were previously developed in collaboration with him. The author is also grateful to Dr. Irene Corey Diller, Dr. Jerome J. Freed, and Dr. Thomas J. King for their critical reading of this manuscript. This investigation was supported by Public Health Service Research grants CA-05755 and CA-06927 from the National Cancer Institute.

see Hamburger, 1960). Explantation and transplantation experiments have demonstrated that these presumptive organ areas are at first labile and then become progressively determined via the inductive-competent interacting systems (see Holtfreter and Hamburger, 1955).

Various experimental approaches have been employed to determine whether nuclei exert any control over morphogenesis. Extensive reviews of this subject have been published (Barth, 1964; Briggs and King, 1959; and Fankhauser, 1955). Studies of the effect of quantitative and qualitative changes of chromosomes upon the development of the egg have shown that cleavage can occur without a balanced set of chromosomes and even without a nucleus if an active cleavage center is present. However, normal morphogenesis does not ensue without a normal set of chromosomes. From these studies we have learned that cleavage rate and pattern are inherent in the egg, but that beginning at gastrulation the nucleus plays a dominant role in the control of morphogenesis.

Central to the problem of development is the mechanism whereby the nucleus exerts control over morphogenesis. One approach to this problem has been first to determine whether nuclei undergo changes during embryogenesis. The constriction experiments of Spemann (1938) demonstrated that early cleavage nuclei of *Triton* were still identical and totipotent, and that nucleocytoplasmic relations existent in early development had not brought about nuclear specialization. Extension of this problem became feasible when Briggs and King (1952) devised in *Rana* a method of transplanting a nucleus from a given cell of the embryo into an unfertilized egg which was previously activated and enucleated (see King, this volume, pp. 737–751). An extensive series of nuclear transplantation tests in *Rana* and other forms of Anura and Urodela has shown that nuclei of cleavage and early morphogenetic stages are still capable of promoting the normal differentiation of the host egg. However, beyond this time most nuclei undergo changes which restrict their ability to promote normal development (Briggs and King, 1959; Gurdon, 1964; King, 1966).

Closely interwoven with the progressive developmental specialization of the embryo and its components are the biochemical changes that occur. For example, qualitative and quantitative changes in the classes of RNA arise during development (Brown and Caston, 1962a, b); new proteins involved in specific cell types are formed as well as those involved in the formation of antigens. The chemical changes and their significance in development have been critically reviewed in the textbooks of Brachet (1960) and Needham (1950).

The uses of the frog have by no means been limited to the embryonic period. Anatomical and physiological studies of organs and organ systems in the adult frog have contributed to our knowledge of vertebrate systemic mechanisms and functions (see Moore, 1964). For example, much of our knowledge of muscle and cardiac physiology has evolved from studies in the frog. In endocrinology the role of thyroxine in metamorphosis and the regulatory relationship existing between the hypophysis and other endocrine functions have been elucidated. Studies of reproductive endocrinology have explained sex differentiation in the embryo and larva as well as seasonal gametogenesis in the adult. Significant contributions to genetics and evolution have resulted from crossing the gametes of mutant and interspecific frogs (Merrell, 1965; Moore, 1955).

There occurs in *Rana pipiens* a spontaneous renal adenocarcinoma which was first described by Lucké (1934, 1952). Since the primary tumor develops frequently in some populations of *R. pipiens* and can be easily perpetuated in larval (Briggs, 1942) and adult hosts (Lucké and Schlumberger, 1939) as well as in tissue culture (Lucké, 1939), both the primary and transplanted tumors have been frequently employed to study problems of normal development and cancer. Some of the specific uses to which this neoplasm has been applied will be presented in subsequent sections of this paper.

Various characteristics of the frog and its embryos have been responsible for its use in developmental problems. The gametes of the adult are easily obtained and handled in the laboratory. Since development is external, innumerable studies are possible. The relatively large size of the eggs (about 2 mm in diameter) has made it useful in microsurgery. Since the female possesses approximately 2000 ripe ova, abundant material is available for various biochemical and genetic studies. In addition, any desired stage can be obtained from oogenesis to metamorphosis. Since this form is poikilothermic, the rate of development can be controlled conveniently within wide limits. The embryo develops in a closed system and no exogenous metabolites are required. These characteristics apply in general to all amphibian forms. It should be noted that although this chapter is concerned with the frog, the development of experimental animal embryology in the past has grown through the use of various vertebrate and invertebrate forms. Only through the selective use of the most advantageous form will we obtain our clearest answers to problems of development. In some cases this has necessitated employing relatively less complex forms, e.g., bacteria and unicellular animals. However, the stepwise unraveling of the complex nucleocytoplasmic and intercellular interactions of the developing metazoan embryo will have to be done in complex embryos.

The following account is intended to help the investigator obtain normal embryos for studying developmental problems, and information relative to procuring and maintaining adult frogs and embryos is provided. In addition, since the frog kidney adenocarcinoma has been a useful tool for analyzing developmental problems, information pertinent to procuring and propagating primary renal tumors is also included.

PROCUREMENT AND STORAGE OF ADULTS

Natural Source

The following brief account which describes the appearance, habitat, and geographic distribution of the most common *Rana* forms in the United States, together with two mutants of *R. pipiens*, is intended to aid the investigator who desires to collect his own frogs. Excellent handbooks, including maps of the geographic distribution of frogs, keys for identification, and general ecological information, have been published (Stebbins, 1951; Wright and Wright, 1949). For information concerning taxonomy see Schmidt (1953). Those interested in the general habits and behavior of frogs are referred to Holmes (1962), Noble (1954), and Oliver (1955). A field guide is also available (Conant, 1958).

1. *Rana catesbeiana* Shaw (bullfrog). SIZE: the largest of all U.S. frogs. Males, 85–180 mm; females, 89–184 mm, possibly greater. APPEARANCE: dorsum, greenish drab to almost black; venter, yellowish white, heavily mottled. Males have thickened thumbs and large tympana. HABITAT: strictly aquatic (lakes, ponds, brooks, marshy swamps, and streams). RANGE: from the Panhandle of Texas and Oklahoma, extreme western Kansas, Nebraska, extreme eastern South and North Dakotas

to the eastern coast, except for the southern third of Florida. Introduced into the west coast from the following areas: from southwestern Texas, New Mexico, Colorado, Wyoming, and Montana.

2. *Rana palustris* Le Conte (pickerel frog). SIZE: smaller than *R. pipiens*. Males, 46–64 mm; females, 49–79 mm. APPEARANCE: dorsum, usually pale brownish with dark spots which are oblong or square in shape and dark-bordered; they are more regularly arranged than in *R. pipiens*, namely, in two distinct rows. Venter: partly yellow, partly white. Males have thickened thumbs. HABITAT: springs, streams, ponds, sphagnum bogs, ravines, marshy places, meadowlands; hibernate in water. RANGE: from eastern Texas and Oklahoma, Missouri, eastern Iowa, Wisconsin to the east coast, except for southern Louisiana, eastern Mississippi, southern two-thirds of Alabama and Georgia, southern half of South Carolina and absent in Florida. Within the above range this species extends into Canada.

3. *Rana pipiens* Schreber (leopard frog). SIZE: males, 52–80 mm; females, 52–102 mm. APPEARANCE: dorsum, brown or green in general color with round or oval dark spots, usually irregularly spaced; venter, whitish or yellowish. Males have thickened thumbs. HABITAT: ponds, lakes, swampy marsh lands, grassy woodlands; hibernate in water. RANGE: all of the United States, except for the western edge of the Pacific coastal states; extends into Canada and Mexico.

4. [Mutant] *Rana pipiens burnsi* Weed (plain meadow frog). SIZE: maximal size is slightly smaller than *R. pipiens*. APPEARANCE: dorsum, apple green or wood brown with diminution or lack of spots; venter, whitish. RANGE: from western Wisconsin (a few counties) across central Minnesota to northeastern South Dakota, and from counties adjacent to the Mississippi River in southeastern Minnesota up into the northwestern part of the state (Merrell, 1965).

5. [Mutant] *Rana pipiens kandiyohi* Weed (mottled meadow frog). SIZE: about the same as *R. pipiens*. APPEARANCE: dorsum, a background of vermiculate mottlings in the interspaces between the dorsal pigment spots; venter, whitish. RANGE: restricted mainly to a few counties of southwestern Minnesota and western South Dakota (Merrell, 1965).

6. *Rana sylvatica sylvatica* Le Conte (wood frog). SIZE: males, 34–60 mm; females, 34–68 mm. Smaller than *R. palustris*. APPEARANCE: dorsum, reddish-brown; venter, whitish. Males have thickened thumbs. HABITAT: wooded areas, ponds, transient pools in wooded areas; hibernates on land in logs, stumps, under stones or boards in wooded ravines. RANGE: from southern Minnesota and Wisconsin, south to Arkansas, Tennessee, and northern South Carolina, through Appalachians to Maryland, north to Nova Scotia, then west through Quebec to Sault Sainte Marie.

Commercial Sources

An excellent index of suppliers of laboratory animals is periodically published by the National Academy of Sciences, National Research Council. The booklet is entitled "Laboratory Animals. II. Animals for Research." Suppliers of four *Rana* species have been extracted from the 1964 edition of this catalogue[1] and incorporated into Table 1. Known suppliers of *R. pipiens* mutants (*burnsi* and *kandiyohi*) are also included in the table.

Frogs can be purchased from dealers throughout most of the year. They will

[1] The current edition of "Laboratory Animals. II. Animals for Research" can be purchased from the National Academy of Sciences, National Research Council, 2101 Constitution Avenue, N.W., Washington, D.C.

TABLE 1. SOME COMMERCIAL SOURCES OF *Rana*

SUPPLIER	SPECIES		
	R. catesbeiana	*R. pipiens*	OTHERS
Canadian Breeding Laboratories St. Constant, Laprairie, Quebec, Canada	..	+	..
Carolina Biological Supply Co. Burlington, N.C.	+	+	..
Chase, Charles P. "Bill" 136 N.W. 57th Ave., Miami, Fla.	..	+	..
Connecticut Valley Biological Supply Co. Valley Road, Southampton, Mass.	+	+	..
Dahl, H. A., Co. 2017 Second Street, Berkeley 10, Calif.	+	..	..
General Biological Supply House, Inc. 8200 S. Hoyne Ave., Chicago, Ill.	..	+	..
Hazen, J. M., & Co. Alburg, Vt.	..	+	..
Hoffman, E. G., & Son Box 815, Oshkosh, Wis.	+	+	..
Jarvis, Earle J. Box 147, Alburg, Vt.	..	+	..
Lake Champlain Frog Farms Alburg, Vt.	+	+	*R. sylvatica*
Lemberger Co., The 1222 W. South Park Ave., Oshkosh, Wis.	+	+	*R. palustris; R. sylvatica*
National Biological Laboratories, Inc. P.O. Box 511, Vienna, Va.	+	..	..
Reptile Aquatic Supply Co., Inc. 75 Route 208, Wyckoff, N.J.	+	..	..
Rider Animal Co. Box 229, Warrenton, Va.	+	+	..
Schettle, J. R., Frog Farm, Inc. Box 184, Stillwater, Minn.	+	+ (*R. p. burnsi, R. p. kandiyohi*)*	..
Steinhilber, E. G., & Co., Inc. 102 Josslyn St., Oshkosh, Wis.	+	+ (*R. p. burnsi*)*	..
West Jersey Biological Supply S. Marion Ave., Wenonah, N.J.	+	+	..

* Mutants of *Rana pipiens*.

usually ship frogs from their stored stock, or if requested, they can send freshly caught frogs except during the hibernation period. However, if the gametes of the frogs are to be used for fertilization experiments, it is advisable to request the dealers to process the orders in the following way: the frogs should be collected immediately before or after hibernation; only large (mature) frogs should be sent; during the mating season males and females should be packed separately; the frogs should be shipped air freight where long distance shipping is involved. In the case of Vermont *R. pipiens*, a stock of frogs can be procured in late October and early April, which are the approximate times when these frogs enter and emerge from hibernation.

Storage

When the frogs arrive in the laboratory, they should be sorted and washed with water. Storage in small groups is advisable to prevent the spread of disease if it should occur; for example, place no more than 5 females or 6 males into individual 2-quart aquarium jars. Sufficient spring water should be added to almost cover the frogs (other sources of water can be used; see below). Cover the bowls with $\frac{1}{4}$ inch square wire mesh and press the four corners firmly around the lip of the bowl. Store the frogs at 4°C, and change the water three times weekly with previously chilled (4°C) spring water. No feeding is required when the frogs are maintained in cold storage.

Cleaning of Glassware

All glassware that houses embryos, larvae, or adult frogs should be thoroughly cleaned and rinsed. Ordinarily, the cleansing of glassware with detergents followed by thorough rinsing is sufficient. However, if glassware becomes contaminated with chemicals, which in small traces are lethal to living animals, it is necessary to clean the glassware in hot concentrated acid (95 parts of sulfuric acid and 5 parts of nitric acid). Subsequently, the glassware must be rinsed thoroughly to remove all traces of the acids. Assurance of this can be obtained by testing the glassware with an indicator dye, such as bromthymol blue.

Water

Water obtained from ponds, wells, and springs can be optimal media for frogs and their young. They can also be reared in tap water which has been filtered through charcoal or chemically dechlorinated. In all cases the water should be tested first on embryos and larvae to determine whether the water is optimal.

INDUCED OVULATION AND ARTIFICIAL INSEMINATION

The *Rana* forms have been a valuable tool for embryological studies, since their fertilization is external and the release of their gametes can be easily controlled in the laboratory. If adult females and males are captured just as they enter and emerge from hibernation and are stored immediately at 4°C, it is possible to obtain functional gametes throughout the year. However, Spring female frogs still in storage during August and September usually are not in optimal condition and the percentage of fertilization and normal development decreases. Rugh (1962) has devised the standard injection technique for induced ovulation and the procedure for artificial insemination; the following account is based mainly on his procedure. An abbreviated account is given in Hamburger's manual (1960).

Induced Ovulation

The anterior lobe of the pituitary gland contains the ovulation-inducing hormones. During the 1920's numerous investigators demonstrated in every major group of vertebrates that implantation of the anterior lobe of the pituitary gland induced ovulation. Subsequently, the procedure of injecting suspensions of anterior lobes of the pituitary glands into the coelomic cavities of frogs was devised (Rugh, 1934; the earlier references to induction of ovulation via implantation are also presented here).

The pituitaries of females are about twice as potent as those of males, and the dosage of pituitaries needed to induce ovulation varies with the season (Rugh, 1934). The suggested doses of female pituitaries for *R. pipiens*, listed below, were obtained from Rugh's manual (1962). The numbers in parentheses are the doses which we have found to be effective when injected frogs are kept at 18°C.

TIME OF INJECTION	NUMBER OF ♀ PITUITARIES	
September through December	5	(4–5)
January and February	4	(2–3)
March	3	(2)
April	2	(2)
May through August	. .	(1–2)

The size and potency of different anterior lobes of the pituitaries vary. The injected females likewise vary in response as well as in the quality of the eggs which they produce. Because of these facts it is advisable to inject two females for each experiment.

The ovulatory effect of pituitary factors can be augmented by injecting a female with a combination of progesterone and one female pituitary gland (Wright and Flathers, 1961). This procedure is particularly useful during seasons when large numbers of pituitary glands are needed to induce ovulation. Dosages of 0.5 to 5.0 mg of progesterone (aqueous suspension or dissolved in oil) are injected into the dorsal lymph sacs of females. A single pituitary gland in Ringer's solution is then injected into either the dorsal lymph sac or the coelomic cavity. Progesterone also reduces the time required for maximal response; for example, ova can be stripped in large numbers from the injected females within 12–16 hours (room temperature) following injection. When the females approach the season of their natural breeding time, progesterone should be eliminated, since at this time death can result from an injection of progesterone in combination with one pituitary gland (Freed, 1966). In the future, determination of the optimal dosage of progesterone during the breeding season could extend the usefulness of this procedure.

DISSECTION OF PITUITARY GLANDS

1. Select donors and recipients that are fully mature. It is inadvisable to use females under 75 mm and males under 70 mm in body length.

2. Sacrifice the frog by pithing the spinal cord from the hindbrain. This is accomplished by grasping the body of the frog in the left palm and deflecting the head with the left forefinger. Then with the right hand insert a thin-pointed steel needle into the spinal canal close to its juncture to the hindbrain. Immediately, turn the needle downward through the spinal canal for a distance of approximately 1 cm.

3. Insert the blunt blade of a strong pair of scissors into the mouth at the angle of the jaws and cut transversely just

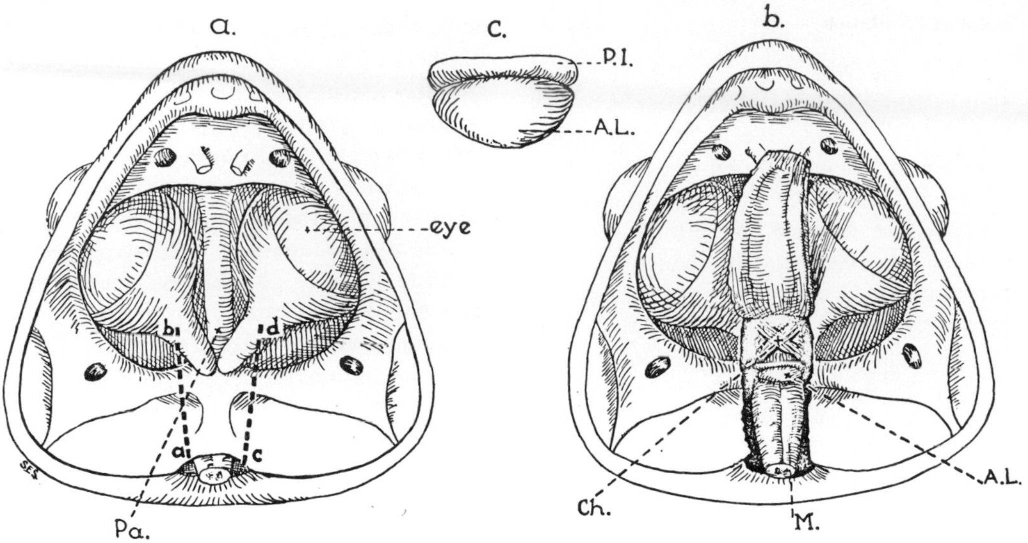

FIG. 1. Hypophysectomy. (a) head of a frog, ventral view. *Pa.* = parasphenoid bone. (b) ventral view; brain and hypophysis exposed. *A.L.* = anterior lobe; *Ch.* = optic chiasma; *M.* = medulla oblongata. (c) hypophysis isolated. *A.L.* = anterior lobe; *P.I.* = pars intermedia. SOURCE: *A Manual of Experimental Embryology* by Viktor Hamburger by permission of the author and The University of Chicago Press. Copyright 1942, 1960 by the University of Chicago.

posterior to the tympanic membrane. Repeat the same cut on the other side and decapitate the frog. If a more anterior cut is made, the pituitary gland will probably be dislodged or destroyed. Clean the severed head by rinsing with amphibian Ringer's solution.

4. Invert the severed head, so that the roof of the mouth is uppermost. Remove the skin of the oral cavity, and thus the cross formed by the parasphenoidal and transverse bones will be evident (Fig. 1a). Insert the pointed blade of a fine pair of scissors into the foramen magnum or the spinal canal, and make two oblique cuts directed toward the right and left eyeballs, respectively. Be sure to direct the cuts to the extreme right and left sides and sever the transverse bone.

5. The following dissections and observations should be done with a dissecting microscope. With practice the entire operation can be done without the aid of magnification. Grasp the triangular piece of bone firmly with coarse forceps and carefully deflect it forward without splintering the bone. The ventral side of the brain will now be exposed (Fig. 1b). Locate the hindbrain, the infundibulum, and the optic chiasma. The anterior lobe of the pituitary gland, surrounded to some extent by white endolymphatic tissue, can be identified by its pinkish color and kidney-like shape. It will either be in its normal position (attached to the infundibulum, posterior to the optic chiasma), or it may adhere to the deflected bone. Attached to its anterior straight edge is a slender whitish body, the pars intermedia and pars nervosa (Fig. 1c).

6. With a pair of watchmaker's forceps remove the entire gland by grasping the white endolymphatic tissue surrounding it. Place the gland into 2 ml of

amphibian Ringer's solution and remove the adhering endolymphatic tissue and the pars intermedia and pars nervosa. The anterior lobe can now be injected into a recipient female or stored in amphibian Ringer's solution in the frozen state for at least 6 months.

INJECTION AND TEST FOR OVULATION

1. Draw the glands with about $\frac{1}{2}$–1 ml of amphibian Ringer's solution into the barrel of a 2-ml glass syringe and then apply a hypodermic needle (#18–#23) to the syringe. Be sure the glands do not adhere to the wall of the syringe. With gentle tapping of the barrel one can center the glands over the opening of the syringe.

2. Insert the needle through the skin of the posterior ventral region. Move it forward under the skin about 1 cm and then through the body wall musculature and into the body cavity. Inject the glands and Ringer's solution slowly, remove the needle, and pinch the skin at the needle entrance to avoid leakage. To insure that no gland material has been retained in the barrel of the syringe or in the needle, draw about $\frac{1}{4}$–$\frac{1}{2}$ ml of Ringer's solution through the needle and reinject the frog.

3. Place the frog in a dry bowl for 15 minutes, then add water to a depth of about 2 cm. Keep the injected frog(s) in a cool place, preferably at 18–20°C for 38–48 hours. At this time most of the eggs should be in the uterus and fertilizable. If eggs are required sooner, the females can be kept at about 25°C; however, the chance of obtaining overripe eggs is greatly increased at warm temperatures.

4. The eggs can now be forced from the uterus through the cloaca by "stripping." Grasp the legs of the frog with the left hand. Place the palm of the right hand over the back of the frog and encircle the body just posterior to the forelimbs. Bend the body at the pelvic region and apply a gentle and steady pressure in the direction of the cloaca. In a few seconds the female will discharge her eggs which are encased in jelly. As soon as the stripping pressure is stopped the female will cease to release her eggs. Occasionally, some females will not discharge eggs at the first test of stripping, but will release only jelly or fluid. In this case the frog should be set aside and tested again after 12–24 hours. If no eggs are obtained, a second injection comprising about one-half the original pituitary dosage should be made.

5. The eggs of an ovulated female can be used adequately for approximately 5–7 days if she is stored at 4°C and is not exposed to laboratory temperature (18°C) for long intervals. A period of 45–60 minutes at 18°C is sufficient time for temperature equilibration following 4°C storage.

Artificial Insemination

PREPARATION OF SPERM SUSPENSION

1. Select a mature male (70 mm or > in body length) from 4°C storage and pith. Decapitate, remove and store the pituitary gland for future use.

2. Place the frog on its dorsal side and make a median incision into the abdominal cavity. The length of the cut should extend from the posterior abdominal region up to the thoracic area. Next, make four diagonal incisions, two from the center cut to each of the forelimb areas and two toward the hind-limb areas. Deflect the skin and musculature including the peritoneal lining and expose the abdominal cavity. Move the intestines aside and the pair of testes will be evident. They are yellow, oval bodies, located near the anterior borders of the kidneys.

3. Dissect the pair of testes and place them into 10 percent amphibian Ringer's

solution. [A 10 percent solution of either Holtfreter (1931), Niu-Twitty (1953), or Steinberg (1957) media can be substituted for 10 percent amphibian Ringer's; see Jacobson, this volume, p. 535, for formulae.] Remove any adhering tissue and blood. Transfer the testes to a small watch glass containing about 5 ml of fresh 10 percent Ringer's solution and macerate them thoroughly with fine forceps and scissors until a milky suspension is obtained. [Dilutions up to 10–15 ml still permit optimal fertilization (Rugh, 1934).] Allow the suspensions to stand for about 15 minutes during which time additional spermatozoa are released and become active. If there is any doubt concerning the potency of the sperm suspension, a drop of the suspension should be placed on a glass slide and viewed with the compound microscope. Check for the presence of numerous active and motile sperm.

4. Sperm suspensions prepared in the above manner and stored at 4°C can be successfully used for at least 34 hours, provided they are not kept at laboratory temperature (18°C) for long intervals. The suspension should be warmed at laboratory temperature for 15 minutes before use.

INSEMINATION

1. With a narrow mouth pipette (1–3 mm in diameter) agitate the sperm suspension and pipette a thin film of this suspension into a large watch glass or Syracuse dish.

2. Strip about 100 eggs and discard. Next, strip about 100–150 eggs directly into the sperm suspension. Usually, the eggs will ooze out in a single or double string and can be lined up in rows or concentric circles so that all the eggs are exposed to the sperm suspension. Occasionally, they will come out in clusters. When this happens pipette additional sperm suspension on top of the clustered eggs.

3. After 15 minutes flood the eggs with 10 percent amphibian Ringer's solution. Subsequently, the jelly membranes will swell.

4. At 1 hour after insemination, decant the solution and rinse twice with spring water. Loosen the eggs from the bottom of the dish with a section lifter. Cut the egg mass into small clusters of about 5–10 eggs per group. Transfer the eggs with a wide-mouth pipette (4–6 mm in diameter) into finger bowls (4 inches in diameter) filled with spring water. Place no more than 30–40 eggs in each finger bowl. Cover the bowl with a glass lid to reduce evaporation and to exclude dust. The embryos can be reared in this vessel until the feeding stage, and the spring water need not be changed during this interval.

MAINTENANCE OF EMBRYOS, LARVAE, AND ADULT FROGS

Embryos

Following insemination the eggs will cleave into two cells in approximately 2–3 hours, depending on the temperature. Since frogs are poikilothermic animals, the developmental rate of their progeny can be controlled within limits by the environmental temperature. Stage seriations of embryonic development in *Rana* were first published for *R. sylvatica* (Pollister and Moore, 1937). Subsequently, a similar seriation was prepared for *R. pipiens* (Shumway, 1940). In both cases the stage seriation was made on embryos reared at 18°C. In *R. pipiens*, during a developmental period of 12 days, 25 stages are clearly distinguished and tabulated on the basis of morphology, average body length, and age. This period starts with fertilization and includes the main embryonic events of cleavage, gastrulation, neurulation and concludes with the onset of feeding, when the operculum fold has just grown over the gills and all the main embryonic organ systems are completely developed. All of the aforementioned stages should be viewed with the stereomicroscope. The seriation for *R. sylvatica* covers 23 developmental stages, concluding with the onset of overgrowth of the opercular fold. Charts of these developmental stages have been reproduced in a number of publications (see Hamburger, 1960 and Rugh, 1962), and should be referred to, not only for temporal staging, but also to determine whether normal development is occurring. A stage seriation has also been outlined for *R. japonica* (Tahara, 1959), but no stage series is available for *R. catesbeiana* and *R. palustris*; however, reference to any one of the above charts, together with data presented below on developmental rates of the individual species, will be a sufficient guide.

The developmental rates of embryos reared at 18.5°–18.7°C from four species of *Rana* are listed in Table 2. In comparison with *R. pipiens*, *R. sylvatica* develops faster; whereas, *R. palustris* develops slightly slower and *R. catesbeiana*, considerably slower. Since it is often necessary for investigators to retard or hasten the development of embryos, the range of temperature tolerance of the individual

TABLE 2. DEVELOPMENTAL RATES OF *Rana* AT 18.5–18.7°C*

STAGE‡	TIME IN HOURS FROM FIRST CLEAVAGE TO STAGE 20†			
	R. pipiens	*R. palustris*	*R. sylvatica*	*R. catesbeiana*
	(18.6°)	(18.6°)	(18.5°)	(18.7°)
3	0	0	0	0
9	19–20.5	19–22	14–16	23
10	22–24	24–30	17–18	30.5
11	28–30	32	22–24	. .
12	32–41.5	36–45	26–30	. .
13	45.7	45–50	34	42.5
14	48–54	52–60	38	53.5
15	. .	. .	. .	68.0
16	60–65	65–68	49.5	77.5
17	68–73	73–78	52.5–54	. .
18	77–102	89–114	57–70	97–127.5
19	103–114	119–124	73	141–151.5
20	116	126	87	162.5
Temp. tolerance*	6–28°	7–30°	2.5–24°	15–32°

* Reproduced with permission from Moore (1939, 1942). *Rana* forms collected from New York State.
† When two figures are given they represent the earliest and latest hours at which embryos were observed in a particular stage.
‡ Stage series of Pollister and Moore (1937).

species is listed also in Table 2. Precaution should be taken when choosing the extreme temperatures, because occasionally some eggs of some females will develop abnormally (Moore, 1939); therefore, it is advisable not to select extreme temperatures. Additional information on the developmental rates of *Rana* forms at various temperatures can be found in the papers of Atlas (1935) and Moore (1939, 1942, 1949).

During the entire embryonic period, the frog embryos develop in a closed system and draw their nourishment chiefly from reserves stored in the form of yolk platelets. After hatching from their vitelline membranes and jelly capsules, they exhibit the primary features of young larvae—gill circulation and swimming. Approximately 6 days later (18°C) *R. pipiens* larvae have attained Shumway stage 25, the time at which the operculum fold has completely overgrown the external gills. The larvae now require food.

Larvae

The larval period and the completion of metamorphosis for *R. pipiens*, *R. palustris*, and *R. sylvatica* extend for about 2 to 4 months, depending on the environmental temperature and the species. In the case of *R. catesbeiana* this period covers about 2 years. Twenty-five larval and metamorphic stages of *R. pipiens* have been recorded photographically (Taylor and Kollros, 1946). The first eighteen stages are concerned with larval development, when definitive changes occur in the development of the hind limbs, and these changes serve to mark the stages distinctly. Thereafter, external changes relative to the metamorphic stages ensue: disappearance of the cloacal tail-piece, appearance of a distinct pigment pattern, emergence of the forelimbs, formation of the adult mouth, and resorption of the tail. During this period the body length of the tadpole has increased from approximately 11 mm to 25–28 mm. If hybrid or mutant studies are being conducted, the dorsal pigment pattern can be observed at this time to judge the contribution of the parents. Although the individual is merely a juvenile frog, the adult pigment pattern is essentially formed now and genetic information on the F_1 progeny of hybrid or mutant crosses can be obtained at this time. In addition, the sex of the newly metamorphosed frogs can be determined by laparotomy, except in some particular races of frogs which have not completed gonadal differentiation at this time (Witschi, 1929).

Place each larva in a finger bowl (4 inches in diameter) filled with spring water, and cover most of the bowl with a glass lid. Change the water three times weekly. When the larvae reach approximately 40 mm in total length, transfer each larva to an aquarium bowl (1-quart size, $4\frac{3}{4}$ inches top diameter), containing about 2 inches of spring water. Change the water a minimum of three times weekly. At the onset of metamorphosis when the forelimbs emerge, reduce the volume of water and tilt the bowl. Place a small amount of water sufficient to cover the tadpole in the lower level of the bowl.

A variety of food materials has been recommended for frog tadpoles: cooked lettuce and spinach, canned spinach, dry cereals (Pablum, oatmeal, corn meal), dried shrimp, liver, powdered egg yolk, and pellets of rabbit food. Although the larvae thrive well on a spinach diet, they develop calcium oxalate kidney stones (Briggs and Davidson, 1942), and this condition adversely affects the viability of metamorphosed frogs (Berns, 1965). We have raised tadpoles on cooked lettuce alone with considerable ease. Preferably, leafy lettuce such as romaine or escarole is washed thoroughly; the leafy areas are removed and autoclaved for 10 minutes in a small amount of water, sufficient to cover the lettuce. After cooling, the water is drained and the lettuce is stored in the refrigerator. Sufficient food for one day's feeding only should be provided. Excess food will deteriorate and foul the water and can thus cause death of the larvae. Once metamorphosis commences (emergence of the forelimbs) feeding should be discontinued. During this period metabolic and structural changes are occurring and the metamorphosing tadpole will not feed.

A temperature in the range of 15°–22°C can be chosen for convenience. Lower temperatures induce males of differentiated gonadal races to pass through a female phase, while higher temperatures cause females to transform into males (Witschi, 1929).

The rearing of tadpoles singly is time consuming, but allows optimal and uniform growth. However, if uniform growth is not a requirement and large numbers of tadpoles must be reared (e.g., for genetic studies), they can be raised in small or large groups in large vessels. In fact, Merrell (1963) has reared to metamorphosis more than 100 tadpoles per tank; the volume of water was kept constant but not changed; oxygen concentration was maintained by aeration, and the presence of scavengers (snails, guppies) prevented the water from becoming foul.

Adult Frogs

Adult frogs can be maintained in the laboratory (20°–25°C) singly, if isolation is desired, or they can be housed in groups. However, it is wise to restrict the size of the groups in order to prevent the spread of infectious diseases, if they should occur.

GROUPS

Individual frogs can be identified by their distinctive dorsal pigment pattern. A convenient method of recording this pattern is to photograph the dorsum on large cut film and subsequently use the developed negatives to identify the individual frogs (DiBerardino and King, 1965a).

Place 6 frogs into $3\frac{1}{2}$-gallon rectangular tanks constructed of glass sides and a slate floor. Provide each tank with 500 ml of dechlorinated tap water; change the water and wash the tank at least once a week. Dechlorination of the tap water is accomplished by adding 0.7–0.9 gm of sodium thiosulfate to 30 gallons of tap water; allow the tap water to stand a minimum of 24 hours before use (Humphrey, 1966). Tilt the tanks so that a dry area is available to the frogs. If long maintenance is planned, inject each frog with 3,000 units of penicillin intraperitoneally to prevent the possibility of deaths due to bacterial infections (Rafferty, 1962). Cover the tank with $\frac{1}{4}$ inch square mesh wire, held firmly in place so that the frogs cannot escape.

Frogs are carnivorous animals and are attracted by living, motile food. A variety of large insects and worms, such as earthworms, mealworms, grasshoppers, and crickets have been recommended. Feed the frogs twice weekly, alternating with worms and crickets. The worms should be dropped onto the dry part of the aquarium. Large insects, such as crickets, should be placed in a dry tank. This can be done conveniently when the tanks are drained and before the fresh water is added. One large worm and two or three large crickets per frog per week is a sufficient feeding schedule. If live food is not available, or if some frogs are refractory to eating voluntarily, mammalian liver can be forced into the mouth cavity with a pair of forceps (2 pieces approximately 10 × 10 × 5 mm are sufficient for a single feeding). Liver mixed with bone meal and cod liver oil provides a supplementary diet and a source of vitamin D (Rose, 1947). Adult frogs maintained under the above conditions have survived in a healthy state for 3 years (DiBerardino and King, 1965a).

ISOLATED

Individual frogs can be maintained conveniently in 1-quart aquarium bowls, covered by $\frac{1}{4}$ inch square mesh wire, held firmly in place. Add spring or dechlorinated tap water, sufficient to cover about one-half of the frog. Change a minimum of three times weekly. In most cases the frogs will not eat voluntarily in such a confined area; therefore, either force feed or transfer the frogs to larger vessels during feeding times.

PROCUREMENT AND PROPAGATION OF PRIMARY RENAL ADENOCARCINOMA

Natural Occurrence

The renal adenocarcinoma of *R. pipiens* is the most frequently occurring spontaneous tumor in *Rana*. Grossly the neoplasm appears as solitary or multiple ivory-white masses fairly well circumscribed by normal renal tissue. In previous years tumors have been found in 2.7 percent of these frogs from the Lake Champlain region of northern Vermont and contiguous areas of Canada (Lucké, 1952). Recently, wild-type *R. pipiens* and a mutant, *R. pipiens burnsi*, from the north central states have been surveyed for the presence of this tumor (McKinnell, 1965). Autopsy studies revealed that both the wild-type (8.9 percent) and the mutant (6.4 percent) possessed renal adenocarcinoma. In addition, Lunger, Darlington, and Granoff (1965) have reported that 1.6 percent of the frogs received from the Wisconsin-Minnesota area bore renal adenocarcinoma. Although a few isolated cases of renal tumors have been reported in frogs from Indiana, the Mississippi Valley, etc., only the two areas mentioned above provide a dependable source of renal tumors at this time. *Rana pipiens* from areas west of the Rocky Mountains were examined systematically for the presence of renal adenocarcinoma, but no such tumors were found (Mateyko, 1957).

Tumor-bearing frogs can sometimes be obtained through local dealers; however, these tumors are usually very large and necrotic. A more satisfactory method is either to palpate or to autopsy frogs collected in the field or those shipped to the laboratories.

"Induction"

PROMOTION OF RENAL TUMORS IN ADULT FROGS

In contrast to the low frequency of renal adenocarcinoma in nature (Lucké, 1952), frogs maintained in the laboratory for 8 months and longer develop renal tumors in 20–50 percent of the cases (Rafferty, 1964). Three factors responsible for promoting this high incidence of renal tumors are warm environmental temperatures, large body length of frogs (Rafferty, 1964), and crowding (DiBerardino and King, 1965a). The mechanism whereby these factors promote tumor development is unknown, but at present, maintenance of frogs in the laboratory under these conditions provides a dependable means of obtaining primary renal tumors.

The following maintenance schedule for promoting spontaneous renal adenocarcinoma in adult frogs is based mainly on the reports of Rafferty (1962) and DiBerardino and King (1965a).

1. Select males, 70 mm or more, and females, 75 mm or more, in body length.

2. Palpate for the presence of renal tumors.

3. Photograph the pigment pattern of the dorsum for identification purposes.

4. Place the frogs in 3½-gallon aquarium tanks and follow the maintenance schedule outlined above in the section on maintenance of adult frogs in groups. An alternate method, convenient for the maintenance of large numbers of frogs, has been used (Rafferty, 1962). Aquarium tanks, containing small holes, are stored in troughs, which are emptied daily and refilled.

5. Select a laboratory temperature in the range of 22° to 26.5°C.

6. Palpate the frogs monthly to detect the presence of renal tumors. When tumors do occur, utilize them before they become large enough to develop necrotic areas.

CHEMICAL INDUCTION OF RENAL TUMORS IN ADULT FROGS

Successful chemical induction of renal adenocarcinoma has been achieved in adult *R. pipiens* by injecting directly into the kidney 0.1 ml of olive oil containing 0.3–0.5 mg of either *p*-aminoazobenzene (AB) or 1,2,5,6-dibenzanthracene (DBA) (Strauss and Mateyko, 1964). Subsequent to injection, 35 percent mortality occurred. Of the remaining injected frogs, which were sacrificed at intervals between 3 weeks and 7 months, 26 percent of the DBA and 23 percent of the AB-injected frogs developed small renal adenocarcinomas. These growths were either solitary or multiple nodules ranging in size from 0.5 mm to about 6 mm (average diameter of nodules was 1.5 mm). By contrast, kidneys injected with olive oil alone did not develop renal adenocarcinomas and only 3 percent of the untreated frogs developed these tumors. Since the frogs were maintained at a temperature range between 14° and 16°C, it is not likely that high environmental temperature, known to be a factor in tumor promotion (Rafferty, 1962 and 1964), was responsible for this induction.

RENAL TUMOR TRANSMISSION IN FROG EMBRYOS BY SUBCELLULAR FRACTIONS

Recently, another means of obtaining primary renal adenocarcinoma in *R. pipiens* has been found (Tweedell, 1965). The success of this method appears quite promising; however, all of the details have not yet been published. Dilutions of large and small mitochondrial fractions, derived from inclusion-bearing renal tumors, were injected into embryos and larvae, and substantial tumor induction was obtained. For example, 57 to 87 percent (depending on dilution) of the tailbud embryos which survived the injection developed renal adenocarcinoma after metamorphosis.

Propagation of Primary Renal Adenocarcinoma

IN THE ANTERIOR EYE CHAMBERS OF ADULT FROGS

The suitability of the anterior eye chamber for tumor transplantation appears to have been recognized first by van Dooremaal, who in 1873 reported the results of his studies on intraocular implantation of various homologous tissues into dogs and rabbits. Although his studies involved the transplantation of normal tissue, he suggested that the same site might be useful for implanting tumor. During the subsequent years of the late nineteenth and early twentieth centuries, numerous investigators utilized this site for the transplantation of both normal and tumorous tissue of warm-blooded animals. This technique has proven to be extremely useful since at this site specific immunological resistance is weakly developed. In addition, the operation can be performed with ease and the development of the implant can be directly observed and followed under the stereomicroscope.

In 1939 Lucké and Schlumberger made the first successful intraocular tumor transplantations in cold-blooded animals (refer to this paper for a concise history of the early studies of intraocular transplantation). In this study fragments of spontaneous renal adenocarcinoma from Vermont *R. pipiens* were implanted into the anterior eye chambers of homologous hosts. Over 40 percent of the transplants from thirteen primary tumors grew successfully (range = 0 to 100 percent). Subsequent studies demonstrated that this tumor can be readily propagated in heterologous races and species of *Rana*, as well as in different species of *Bufo* (Lucké and Schlumberger, 1940a; Tweedell, 1955). Serial intraocular transplantation of the tumor in homologous and heterologous hosts affords another means of propagating the tumor (Lucké and Schlumberger, 1940a; Schlumberger and Lucké, 1949). Following Lucké and Schlumberger's original findings, numerous investigators have propagated spontaneous frog renal adenocarcinomas successfully in the anterior eye chambers of host frogs in order to study problems relative to development and cancer. Some of these studies have focused on the quest for the causative agent of the tumor (Mizell and Zambernard, 1965; Rose and Rose, 1952; Tweedell, 1955; Zambernard and Mizell, 1965). Others have involved nuclear differentiation problems (King and DiBerardino, 1965; King and McKinnell, 1960; McKinnell, 1962) and chromosome studies (DiBerardino and King, 1965b; DiBerardino, King, and McKinnell, 1963). Although in most cases the renal adenocarcinoma has been propagated in the frog intraocular cavity, a metastatic liver tumor (Schlumberger and Lucké, 1949) and a metastatic lung tumor (DiBerardino and King, unpublished) have also grown successfully in this site.

The following description of the technique of intraocular transplantation and tumor growth characteristics is based mainly on the report of Lucké and Schlumberger (1939).

1. Employ sterile instruments, glassware, and solutions.

2. Swab the tumor-bearing frog with 70 percent ethyl alcohol. Pith. Remove tumorous kidneys and place into amphibian Ringer's solution.

3. Select healthy portions of the renal adenocarcinoma, rinse twice in amphibian Ringer's solution, and cut into 1 to 2-mm fragments.

4. Anesthetize adult frogs with ether vapors; they can also be anesthetized by immersion in 0.5 percent solution of tricaine methanesulfonate-MS 222 (Zambernard and Mizell, 1965).[2]

5. With the aid of a thick pair of forceps open the frog's mouth and insert a wad of gauze, previously moistened with amphibian Ringer's solution. Position the gauze so that the eye to be operated on protrudes. The orbit of the frog is not separated from the oral cavity by a bony partition; therefore, the eye can be forced to protrude from the orbit by pressure from the mouth cavity. This greatly facilitates operative procedures; however, care must be taken not to exert excessive pressure upon the eyeball.

6. Wrap the frog in moistened gauze.

[2] MS 222, Tricaine Methanesulfonate, is an anesthetic recommended for cold-blooded animals and can be obtained from Sandoz Pharmaceuticals, Hanover, New Jersey.

Place it on its side on the stage of a stereomicroscope, and bathe the eye with sterile amphibian Ringer's solution. The operations and observations can be performed comfortably at magnifications around 9 to 18 ×.

7. For inoculation of the anterior eye chamber, retract the upper eyelid and make an incision, 2–3 mm in length, with a sharp corneal knife or a razor blade along the upper border of the sclerocorneal juncture. Precaution must be taken not to cut into the iris, because profuse hemorrhage will result and may prevent successful transplantation.

8. With delicate, long-pointed watchmaker's forceps insert a fragment of tumor through the wound. In order to prevent postoperative infection a pinch of sulfadiazine powder can be included with the transplant (Tweedell, 1955) or placed over the wound (Zambernard and Mizell, 1965).

9. The transplant can then be moved to any desired part of the chamber by gently stroking the surface of the cornea with a glass rod.

10. Remove the mouth plug and place the animal in a moistened glass bowl during recovery. Afterwards add water and maintain the animal according to the procedure described for isolated adult frogs in the section on Maintenance. If the frogs are kept at laboratory temperature (approximately 22°–25°C), earlier vascularization and faster growth of the tumor will occur than at lower temperatures; however, temperatures as low as 4°C produce no injury to the tumor, but merely arrest growth. When the animals are returned to higher temperatures, tumor growth ensues (Lucké and Schlumberger, 1940b). Thus, a temperature can be selected to fit the needs of the experimenter.

Immediately after the operation the surface of the tumor fragment appears ragged, but within 2 or 3 days the surface becomes regular in outline. This condition may persist for several days or as long as a month, depending on the environmental temperature and the growth rate of the particular tumor. Generally, the transplant becomes attached within a week to the iris, lens, or more rarely the cornea. Most tumor transplants exhibit a similar pattern of growth. Following an initial period of variable lag, there occurs a period of gradual tubular outgrowth, succeeded rather abruptly by a relatively short period of rapid growth, after which the increments gradually become smaller. Even before the growth becomes evident, there usually is a distinct difference between those transplants which will persist and those which will regress; the former are translucent; whereas, the latter become increasingly opaque. Usually sufficient growth will occur within 2–4 months at 22°–25°C to yield enough tumor material for various experimental purposes.

The form which the growing tumor assumes depends on its immediate physical environment. Unimpeded outgrowths into the aqueous humor characteristically assume a tubulo-papillary arrangement. Where the tumor grows in contact with firm, even surfaces, such as lens or cornea, broad membranes form; however, secondary outgrowths from these membranous forms are cylindrical or tubular. When the tumor attaches to loose tissue, like the iris, it invades this tissue and, supported by stroma, assumes an acinar pattern quite like that of the original adenocarcinoma of the kidney. After the tumor attains considerable size and occupies most of the chamber, growth declines and is followed by regression. Prior to regression the intraocular tumor can be removed from the host and further propagated through serial intraocular transplantations. Such serial tumor transplantations can consistently give rise to 100 percent successful takes in the subsequent generations (Schlumberger and Lucké, 1949; McKinnell, 1966), whereas first generation implants grow successfully in about 40 percent (mean value) of the cases (Lucké and Schlumberger, 1939).

IN THE LARVAL TAIL

The initial transplantations of kidney carcinoma from adult *R. pipiens* to the tails of young *R. pipiens* larvae were undertaken to study the effect of larval morphogenetic fields on the cancer cell (Briggs, 1942). These tumor implantations into the mesenchyme of the dorsal tail fin grew successfully in 48 percent of the cases (range = 20–60 percent), but regressed rapidly when the hosts reached premetamorphic stages of development. This regression was not associated with limitations of space or vascular supply, nor was it associated with the functions of the thyroid and pituitary glands in metamorphosis, because tumor implants into the tails of nonmetamorphosing (thyroidectomized or hypophysectomized) tadpoles followed the same growth-regression sequences as those implants in the tails of normal tadpoles (Briggs and Grant, 1943). Since carcinoma implants undergoing regression were usually surrounded by an accumulation of host mesenchyme cells, the authors have suggested that the regression phenomenon is probably due to the development of tissue specificity during later stages of larval development.

Despite the temporal limitations of larval hosts for tumor transplantation in those species with a short larval period, the tadpole tail still affords a convenient means of perpetuating primary renal adenocarcinoma for a period of approximately 6–7 weeks. Further propagation of the tumor can be accomplished by serial transplantation into the dorsal tail fins of young larvae of *R. pipiens* or *Bufo fowleri* (King, DiBerardino, and Evans, unpublished).

The following procedure for transplanting renal adenocarcinoma from adult frogs into the dorsal tail fins of tadpoles was obtained from the report of Briggs (1942).

1. Employ tadpoles 16–25 mm in total length as hosts.
2. Wash healthy portions of the tumor three or four times in sterile amphibian Ringer's solution and cut into small pieces about 1 mm in diameter. Place these pieces in fresh Ringer's in a covered dish, kept cool in ice water.
3. Anesthetize tadpoles in MS 222 (0.016 percent in amphibian Ringer's).
4. Place the host on absorbent cotton in amphibian Ringer's solution with the tail lying flat on its left side and extending straight out from the body.
5. The subsequent operations should be done under a stereomicroscope. With a small corneal knife pierce the epidermis of the proximal third of the dorsal fin in an area on its right lateral surface. Insert a small glass rod through the slit and into the mesenchyme, thus forming a small pocket.
6. With a pair of fine forceps place a small piece of tumorous tissue (0.3 to 0.5 mm in diameter) into the opening and then with the glass rod push the tumor fragment into the pocket formed in the mesenchyme.
7. Place the tadpoles in weaker MS 222 (0.005 percent in amphibian Ringer's) for 4–6 hours at a temperature of about 10°–15°C.
8. Transfer to 50 percent amphibian Ringer's solution (10°–15°C) for 1–2 days until healing is complete. Healing is usually completed within 1 day.
9. Transfer to spring water and resume feeding. Follow the maintenance schedule outlined for larvae in the section on Maintenance.

Since the tail fin in most tadpoles is transparent, the fate of the implant can be followed in the host. For a variable period following transplantation, usually 2 to 3 weeks, the tumor implants remain approximately constant in size. Subsequent to this latent period, successful implants begin to grow and continue for about 4 weeks. While the implants are small, they possess a semitranslucent whitish appearance; when they grow larger they acquire an opaque ivory-white hue. Following this growth period almost all of the tumors regress and exhibit the following changes: the sharp outline of the tumor is gradually replaced by a fuzzy, indistinct border which merges with the adjacent mesenchyme; the tumor itself loses its dense whitish appearance and becomes more transparent. In the final stage of regression the tumor cannot be distinguished from the mesenchyme; however, the site can be located by the greater density of the mesenchyme and the presence of melanophores.

IN VITRO

In vitro cultures of renal adenocarcinoma provide another means of perpetuating the tumor. Cultures can be initiated from either explants or isolated cells of the tumor. In the former case long-term cultures have been maintained for 6 months (Lucké, 1939) or over 8 months (Duryee, 1965). In the case of monolayer cultures initiated from dissociated tumor cells, variable success has resulted. Rafferty (1965; personal communication) has established a frog tumor cell culture line (LC-1), derived from an inclusion-free renal adenocarcinoma. LC-1 is, at the present time, 2½ years old and in the thirty-fifth subculture. Shah (1962) reported that primary cultures were kept as long as 3 months without any noticeable impairment of growth. However, Freed and Rosenfeld (1965) have found that within 1 to 4 weeks spontaneous cytopathy regularly occurs in cultures of cells from the frog renal adenocarcinoma. Since this phenomenon did not appear to result from infection and did not occur in cultures of cells from normal kidney, the authors have suggested that the cytopathy may result from the occurrence of viral replication in the tumor cells.

The variable procedures and different growth media employed in the above culture methods can be found in the individual papers.

REFERENCES

ATLAS, M., 1935: The effect of temperature on the development of *Rana pipiens*. *Physiol. Zool.*, 8: 290.

BARTH, L. J., 1964: The developmental physiology of Amphibia. In J. A. Moore (ed.), *Physiology of the Amphibia*, Academic Press, New York and London, p. 469.

BERNS, N. W., 1965: Mortality caused by kidney stones in spinach-fed frogs (*Rana pipiens*). *BioScience*, April issue: 297.

BRACHET, J., 1960: *The Biochemistry of Development*. 320 pp. Pergamon Press, New York, London, Paris.

BRIGGS, R., 1942: Transplantation of kidney carcinoma from adult frogs to tadpoles. *Cancer Research*, 2: 309.

———, and M. DAVIDSON, 1942: Some effects of spinach-feeding on *Rana pipiens* tadpoles. *J. Exptl. Zool.*, 90: 401.

———, and R. GRANT, 1943: Growth and regression of frog kidney carcinoma transplanted into the tails of permanent and normal tadpoles. *Cancer Research*, 3: 613.

———, and T. J. KING, 1952: Transplantation of living nuclei from blastula cells into enucleated frogs' eggs. *Proc. Natl. Acad. Sci. U.S.*, 38: 455.

———, and ———, 1959: Nucleocytoplasmic interactions in eggs and embryos. In J. Brachet and A. E. Mirsky (eds.), *The Cell*, 6 vols., Academic Press, New York and London, Vol. I, p. 537.

BROWN, D. D., and J. D. CASTON, 1962a: Biochemistry of amphibian development. I. Ribosome and protein synthesis in early development of *Rana pipiens*. *Develop. Biol.*, 5: 412.

———, and ———, 1962b: Biochemistry of amphibian development. II. High molecular weight RNA. *Develop. Biol.*, 5: 435.

CONANT, R., 1958: *A Field Guide to Reptiles and Amphibians of the United States and Canada East of the 100th Meridian.* The Peterson Field Guide Series. Houghton Mifflin Company, Boston, Mass.

DI BERARDINO, M. A., and T. J. KING, 1965a: Renal adenocarcinomas promoted by crowded conditions in laboratory frogs. *Cancer Research*, 25: 1910.

———, and ———, 1965b: Transplantation of nuclei from the frog renal adenocarcinoma. II. Chromosomal and histologic analysis of tumor nuclear-transplant embryos. *Develop. Biol.*, 11: 217.

———, and ———, 1967: Unpublished.

———, ———, and R. G. MC KINNELL, 1963: Chromosome studies of a frog renal adenocarcinoma line carried by serial intraocular transplantation. *J. Natl. Cancer Inst.*, 31: 769.

DURYEE, W. R., 1965: Factors influencing development of tumors in frogs. *Ann. N.Y. Acad. Sci.*, 126: 59.

FANKHAUSER, G., 1955: The role of the nucleus and cytoplasm. In B. H. Willier, P. A. Weiss, and V. Hamburger (eds.), *Analysis of Development*, W. B. Saunders Company, Philadelphia, Pa., and London, p. 126.

FREED, J. J., 1966: Personal communication. The Institute for Cancer Research, Philadelphia, Pa.

———, and S. J. ROSENFELD, 1965: Frog renal adenocarcinoma: Cytological studies *in situ* and *in vitro*. *Ann. N.Y. Acad. Sci.*, 126: 99.

GURDON, J. B., 1964: The transplantation of living cell nuclei. In M. Abercrombie and J. Brachet (eds.), *Advances in Morphogenesis*, Academic Press, New York and London, Vol. IV, p. 1.

HAMBURGER, V., 1960: *A Manual of Experimental Embryology*. 220 pp. The University of Chicago Press, Chicago, Ill.

HOLMES, S. J., 1962: *The Biology of the Frog*. 4th rev. ed. The Macmillan Company, New York.

HOLTFRETER, J., 1931: Über die Aufzucht isolierter Teile des Amphibienkeimes. *Arch. f. Entw'mech.*, 124: 404.

———, and V. HAMBURGER, 1955: Amphibians. In B. H. Willier, P. A. Weiss, and V. Hamburger (eds.), *Analysis of Development*, W. B. Saunders Company, Philadelphia, Pa., and London, p. 230.

HUMPHREY, R. R., 1966: Personal communication. Department of Zoology, Indiana University, Bloomington, Ind.

KING, T. J., 1966: Nuclear transplantation in Amphibia. In D. M. Prescott (ed.), *Methods in Cell Physiology*, Academic Press, New York and London, Vol. II, p. 1.

———, 1967: Amphibian nuclear transplantation. In this volume, pp. 737–751.

———, and M. A. DI BERARDINO, 1965: Transplantation of nuclei from the frog renal adenocarcinoma. I. Development of tumor nuclear-transplant embryos. *Ann. N.Y. Acad. Sci.*, 126: 115.

———, ———, and N. J. EVANS, 1967: Unpublished.

———, and R. G. MC KINNELL, 1960: An attempt to determine the developmental potentialities of the cancer cell nucleus by means of transplantation. In *Cell Physiology of Neoplasia*, The University of Texas Press, Austin, Texas, p. 591.

LUCKÉ, B., 1934: A neoplastic disease of the kidney of the frog, *Rana pipiens*. *Amer. J. Cancer*, 20: 352.

———, 1939: Characteristics of frog carcinoma in tissue culture. *J. Exptl. Med.*, 70: 269.

———, 1952: Kidney carcinoma in the leopard frog: A virus tumor. *Ann. N.Y. Acad. Sci.*, 54: 1093.

———, and H. SCHLUMBERGER, 1939: The manner of growth of frog carcinoma, studied by direct microscopic examination of living intraocular transplants. *J. Exptl. Med.*, 70: 257.

———, and ———, 1940a: Heterotransplantation of frog carcinoma; character of growth in the eyes of alien species. *J. Exptl. Med.*, 72: 311.

———, and ———, 1940b: The effect of temperature on the growth of frog carcinoma. I. Direct microscopic observations on living intraocular transplants. *J. Exptl. Med.*, 72: 321.

LUNGER, P. D., R. W. DARLINGTON, and A. GRANOFF, 1965: Cell-virus relationships in the Lucké renal adenocarcinoma: An ultrastructure study. *Ann. N.Y. Acad. Sci.*, 126: 289.

MATEYKO, G. M., 1957: Studies on renal neoplasms in western frogs. *Anat. Rec.*, 128: 587.

MC KINNELL, R. G., 1962: Development of *Rana pipiens* eggs transplanted with Lucké tumor cells. *Am. Zool.*, 2: 430.

———, 1965: Incidence and histology of renal tumors of leopard frogs from the north central states. *Ann. N.Y. Acad. Sci.*, 126: 85.

———, 1966: Personal communication. Department of Zoology, Newcomb College of Tulane University, New Orleans, La.

MERRELL, D. J., 1963: Rearing tadpoles of the leopard frog, *Rana pipiens*. *Turtox News*, 41: 263.

———, 1965: The distribution of the dominant *burnsi* gene in the leopard frog, *Rana pipiens*. *Evolution*, 19: 69.

MIZELL, M., and J. ZAMBERNARD, 1965: Viral particles of the frog renal adenocarcinoma: causative agent or passenger virus? II. A promising model system for the demonstration of a "lysogenic" state in a metazoan tumor. *Ann. N.Y. Acad. Sci.*, 126: 146.

MOORE, J. A., 1939: Temperature tolerance and rates of development in the eggs of Amphibia. *Ecology*, 20: 459.

———, 1942: Embryonic temperature tolerance and rate of development in *Rana catesbeiana*. *Biol. Bull.*, 83: 375.

———, 1949: Geographic variation of adaptive characters in *Rana pipiens* Schreber. *Evolution*, 3: 1.

———, 1955: Abnormal combinations of nuclear and cytoplasmic systems in frogs and toads. *Advan. Genet.*, 7: 139.

——— (ed.), 1964: *Physiology of the Amphibia*. 469 pp. Academic Press, New York and London.

NEEDHAM, J., 1950: *Biochemistry and Morphogenesis*. Cambridge University Press, London and New York.

NIU, M. C., and V. C. TWITTY, 1953: The differentiation of gastrula ectoderm in medium conditioned by axial mesoderm. *Proc. Natl. Acad. Sci. U.S.*, 39: 985.

NOBLE, G. K., 1954: *The Biology of the Amphibia*. Dover Publications, Inc., New York.

OLIVER, J. A., 1955: *The Natural History of North American Amphibians and Reptiles*. 359 pp. D. Van Nostrand Company, Inc., Princeton, N.J.

POLLISTER, A. W., and J. A. MOORE, 1937: Tables for the normal development of *Rana sylvatica*. *Anat. Rec.*, 68: 489.

RAFFERTY, K. A., JR., 1962: Age and environmental temperature as factors influencing development of kidney tumors in uninoculated frogs. *J. Natl. Cancer Inst.*, 29: 253.

———, 1964: Kidney tumors of the leopard frog: A review. *Cancer Research*, 24: 169.

———, 1965: The cultivation of inclusion-associated viruses from Lucké tumor frogs. *Ann. N.Y. Acad. Sci.*, 126: 3.

———, 1966: Personal communication. Department of Anatomy, Johns Hopkins Medical School, Baltimore, Md.

ROSE, S. M., 1947: Care of laboratory frogs. *Ward's Natural Sci. Bull.*, 20: 45.

———, and F. C. ROSE, 1952: Tumor agent transformations in Amphibia. *Cancer Research*, 12: 1.

RUGH, R., 1934: Induced ovulation and artificial fertilization in the frog. *Biol. Bull.*, 66: 22.

———, 1962: *Experimental Embryology: Techniques and Procedures*. 501 pp. Burgess Publishing Company, Minneapolis, Minn.

SCHLUMBERGER, H., and B. LUCKÉ, 1949: Serial intraocular transplantation of frog carcinoma for fourteen generations. *Cancer Research*, 9: 52.

SCHMIDT, K. P., 1953: *A Check List of North American Amphibians and Reptiles.* University of Chicago Press, Chicago, Ill.

SHAH, C. V., 1962: An improved technique of preparing primary cultures of isolated cells from adult frog kidney. *Experientia*, XVIII: 239.

SHUMWAY, W., 1940: Stages in the normal development of *Rana pipiens*. I. External form. *Anat. Rec.*, 78: 139.

SPEMANN, H., 1938: *Embryonic Development and Induction.* 401 pp. Yale University Press, New Haven, Conn.

STEBBINS, R. C., 1951: *Amphibians of Western North America.* 539 pp. University of California Press, Berkeley and Los Angeles, Calif.

STEINBERG, M., 1957: in *Carnegie Institution of Washington Yearbook* 56, p. 347. Report by J. D. Ebert.

STRAUSS, E., and G. M. MATEYKO, 1964: Chemical induction of neoplasms in the kidney of *Rana pipiens. Cancer Research*, 24: 1969.

TAHARA, Y., 1959: Table of the normal developmental stages of the frog, *Rana japonica*. I. Early development (stages 1–25). *Jap. J. Exptl. Morphol.*, 13: 49. (Japanese and English.)

TAYLOR, A. C., and J. J. KOLLROS, 1946: Stages in the normal development of *Rana pipiens* larvae. *Anat. Rec.*, 94: 7.

TWEEDELL, K. S., 1955: Adaptation of an amphibian renal carcinoma in kindred races. *Cancer Research*, 15: 410.

———, 1965: Renal tumor transmission in frog embryos by subcellular fractions. *Amer. Zool.*, 5: 711.

VAN DOOREMAAL, J. C., 1873: Die Entwicklung der in fremden Grund versetzten lebenden Gewebe. *Graefe's Archiv Ophthalmologie*, 19: 359.

VOGT, W., 1929: Gestaltungsanalyse am Amphibienkeim mit örtlicher Vitalfärbung. II. Gastrulation un mesodermbildung bei Urodelen und Anuren. *Arch. f. Entw'mech.*, 120: 384.

WITSCHI, E., 1929: Studies on sex differentiation and sex determination in amphibians. III. Rudimentary hermaphroditism and Y chromosome in *Rana temporaria. J. Exptl. Zool.*, 54: 157.

WRIGHT, P. A., and A. R. FLATHERS, 1961: Facilitation of pituitary-induced frog ovulation by progesterone in early fall. *Proc. Soc. Exptl. Biol. Med.*, 106: 346.

WRIGHT, A. H., and A. A. WRIGHT, 1949: *Handbook of Frogs and Toads of the United States and Canada.* 640 pp. Comstock Publishing Company, Inc., Ithaca, N.Y.

ZAMBERNARD, J., and M. MIZELL, 1965: Viral particles of the frog renal adenocarcinoma: Causative agent or passenger virus? I. Fine structure of primary tumors and subsequent intraocular transplants. *Ann. N.Y. Acad. Sci.*, 126: 127.

African Clawed Frogs*

By J. B. Gurdon

INTRODUCTION

The subfamily Xenopinae of the Anura includes three genera: *Xenopus*, *Hymenochirus*, and *Pseudhymenochirus*, all species of which are entirely aquatic and occur indigenously only in central and southern Africa. The use of *Xenopus laevis* for the medical identification of expectant mothers by the "pregnancy test" has been largely discontinued, but this species is now being used to an increasing extent for embryological research. For this purpose it offers the following advantages:

1. Fertile eggs can be obtained in large numbers at any time of year by the administration of gonadotropic hormone.
2. Embryos can be reared to maturity, and adults maintained for many years, in a laboratory.
3. Many manipulations employed in experimental embryology can be carried out on eggs or embryos of this species (see section on Experimental Techniques).
4. Radioactive precursor molecules of small or large size can be introduced at any stage of development.

MANAGEMENT OF *XENOPUS LAEVIS* IN THE LABORATORY

Sources of Adults

WILD-TYPE FROGS

Adult male and female *Xenopus laevis* can be obtained direct from South African dealers, of which the following are examples: Division of Inland Fisheries, Private Bag 14, Stellenbosch, South Africa, or the South African Snake Farm, P.O. Box 6, Fish Hoek, Cape Province, South Africa. In order to ensure survival it is desirable to have the frogs sent by air. In the interest of saving the cost of air freight and of avoiding delay, many will prefer to obtain their specimens from local stockists of whom the following are examples which happen to be known to the author: in the

* The author wishes to express his sincere gratitude to Professor M. Fischberg who introduced him to *Xenopus laevis*, and who initiated his interest in the care of laboratory animals. Part of the author's experience with this species has been gained while in receipt of a research grant from the Medical Research Council.

United States, Mr. Jay Cook, Cockeysville, near Baltimore, Md.; in Europe, Drs. de Rover, Ericalaan 9, Ermelo, Holland, with agencies in other European countries.

1-*nu* MUTANTS

O-*nu* embryos homozygous for the anucleolate mutation (Elsdale, Fischberg, and Smith, 1958) are useful for certain kinds of experiments since they do not synthesize ribosomal ribonucleic acid (RNA) during embryogenesis (Brown and Gurdon, 1964). This mutation is lethal in homozygous condition and must therefore be maintained as heterozygous 1-*nu* individuals. These are not at present available commercially and must be obtained from any laboratory known to maintain a stock of 1-*nu* frogs. It is not reasonable to ask such a laboratory to supply adult 1-*nu* frogs since it is expensive and time-consuming to rear *Xenopus laevis* to maturity in the laboratory. However, it is reasonable to ask a laboratory to supply, when next convenient, a range of young tadpoles (not sorted into genotype) from any mating in which at least one of the parents was 1-*nu*.

METHODS OF TRANSPORTATION

Under natural conditions *Xenopus laevis* can move considerable distances across land from one pond to another. These frogs will therefore come to no harm if out of water for several days, so long as they are kept permanently damp by moist leaves, moss, or if sterile conditions are required, by cotton wool or paper, at a temperature within the range of 16°C to 26°C. Tadpoles on the other hand must be kept in water at all times within the above temperature range. Adult frogs, tadpoles, and embryos will tolerate air travel well so long as they are in a pressurized part of the aircraft.

Maintenance in a Laboratory

ACCOMMODATION

Xenopus may be conveniently maintained in breeding condition by accommodating the frogs in glass or transparent plastic tanks with about 10 females or 15 males in 30 liters of water. Tap water may be used, but it is desirable to allow it to stand in a large storage tank long enough for it to reach room temperature and for the concentration of chlorine to become reduced by equilibration with air. Since these frogs are capable of jumping out of water in tanks with sides several inches higher than the water level, tanks should be provided with lids heavy enough to prevent dislocation by the frogs. The water in the frog tanks does not need aeration but should be kept within the range 18°C to 24°C.

FEEDING

The frogs should be fed twice per week with fragments of ox liver small enough to be swallowed in a single mouthful. We have been unable to detect any clear improvement in breeding capacity by supplementing this diet with vitamins, etc. Within a few hours of feeding, the tanks should be cleaned and the water changed, or if this is not possible, all uneaten liver should be removed. If this routine is followed it will not generally be necessary to change the water of the tanks more often than twice per week after feeding. For this purpose taps may be screwed into plastic tanks, but an air/water suction pump is best used for glass tanks.

DISEASES

In the laboratory frogs of this species usually enjoy a low mortality rate of less than 2–3 percent per year. Of this percentage some die of cancer—usually a

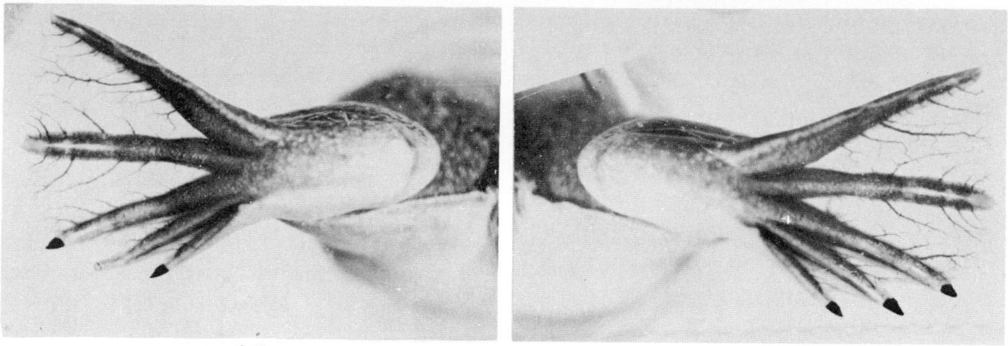

(a) (b)

FIG. 1. Hind feet of *Xenopus laevis:* (a) claw on the fourth digit has been removed; (b) natural situation with claws present on digits 3-5.

lymphosarcoma the behavior of which is consistent with viral etiology (Balls and Ruben, 1964). Fungal infection occasionally affects a colony, but this can be eliminated or at least its spread arrested by immersing affected frogs for ½ hour daily in a 0.002 percent (w/v) solution of $KMnO_4$ made up in aquarium water. Internal parasites including cestode tapeworms and trematodes are sometimes present in *Xenopus* but these do not always cause ill health. Most causes of death in the author's colony affect single individuals in a tank, are not apparently preceded by a period of illness, and are not attributable to any obvious cause. Further observations on this matter may be found in a generally informative article by Elkan (1957).

METHODS OF MARKING FROGS

Since *Xenopus laevis* can live for over 15 years in a laboratory it is often desirable to distinguish individuals kept in the same tank. Attempts to tattoo numbers onto frogs are time consuming and the results impermanent. The most satisfactory current method of marking these frogs is to clip off some of the claws from the hind feet. Each hind foot typically has three claws—on the third, fourth, and fifth digits (Fig. 1b); and the absence of one is quickly visible (Fig. 1a). By removing appropriate combinations of claws from each hind foot 64 different numbers are available as explained in Fig. 2. Claws will regenerate

FIG. 2. A system of numbering individuals of *Xenopus laevis,* by removal of claws from the hind foot digits. The left foot is used to indicate the tens, and the right foot the units. Thus the frog represented at the bottom of the diagram is number 77. All possible combinations of removed claws provide 64 different numbers.

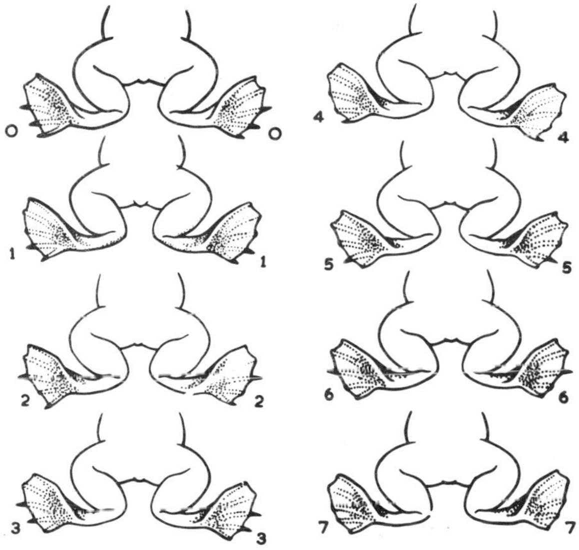

in time, and must be reclipped every 4 months in adults and about every 2 months in growing immature frogs. Infection or other embarrassment results extremely rarely from this treatment. In a large colony it will be necessary to use the complete range of 64 numbers several times, but this presents no problem so long as frogs are reliably prevented from escaping from one tank into another.

FIG. 3. Adult *Xenopus laevis:* (a) ventral view of a sexually mature male showing black nuptial pads on the arms and the absence of cloacal valves; (b) dorsal view of a sexually mature female showing protruding cloacal valves.

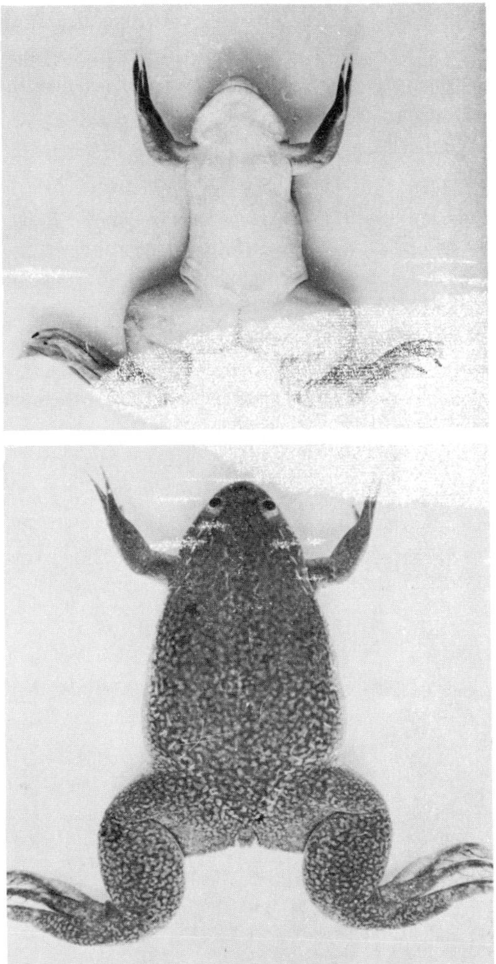

(a)

(b)

Sex Recognition and Induction of Mating

The sexes are most easily distinguished by the appearance of the cloaca and by forearm coloration. Females have a flap of tissue on each side of the cloaca, but males do not (Fig. 3). These "cloacal valves" become enlarged and reddened during oviposition. Males have a broad streak of black pigmentation on the inside of the forearm and, if in good mating condition, a thin extension of this streak along the inside of the upper arm (Fig. 3a). In females these parts of the arm are white or gray but never black. When selecting frogs for mating, males should have these "nuptial pads" on the forearm. Females should look considerably fatter than males (Fig. 3b) and should have pronounced cloacal valves. Small cloacal valves are always present on immature frogs of both sexes.

Mating can be promoted by confinement in a small aquarium tank, or by subtle temperature changes. But much the most convenient and reliable method of inducing mating is by the injection of mammalian gonadotropic hormones. In most countries a reasonably inexpensive commercial preparation of serum or chorionic gonadotropin is obtainable, for example Antuitrin (Parke Davis, U.S.A.), Pregnyl and Gestyl (Organon Laboratories, Crown House, London Road, Morden, Surrey, England), or Gonadotrophin (Ciba, Basel, Switzerland). Since the water for injection supplied with these hormones often contains a small amount of phenol which can be harmful to frogs, the hormones should be made up in a saline solution at about 500 International Units per milliliter. The hormone solution is injected through the skin into the dorsal lymph sac. The use of a fine needle makes it unnecessary to cause the discomfort of passing the needle through a muscle before releasing the contents of the syringe into the dorsal lymph sac. The doses of hormone to be injected vary with the condition of the frogs, the source of hormone, etc. The following doses are those generally used in Oxford. Males are given 50–150 I.U. 36–24 hours before mating is required. Females are given a priming dose of 50–200 I.U.; 8 hours later (at 20°C) a final dose of 300–500 I.U. is given and oviposition is expected to commence 8 hours after this. Larger doses tend to be required during the period from May or June to August, a time of year in which *Xenopus laevis* does not spawn under natural conditions. After the final hormone injection the male and female are placed in a laying tank with water at least 6 inches deep and 1 square foot in surface area. Beneath the frogs should be placed a grid or rack with holes through which the eggs will drop. The rack must be tightly fixed about 1 inch above the base of the tank so that the frogs cannot get caught underneath it and drown or disturb the eggs.

The rather large doses of hormone used to induce egg-laying (4 I.U. per gram wet weight) suggest either that mammalian hormones are rather ineffective in Amphibia, or that of the several kinds of hormone present in unpurified mammalian gonadotropins one constituting a minor part may be the one which is mainly effective in frogs. In an attempt to distinguish these possibilities, purified LH and FSH (Organon Laboratories and NIH, Washington), the major gonadotropic components of chorionic gonadotropin and pregnant mare's serum respectively, were injected into frogs. Since these highly purified preparations of hormones induced egg-laying no more or less effectively than the less purified preparations, the former of the two possibilities suggested above appears to be correct.

Expected Fertility and the Culture of Embryos

Following hormone-induced mating, 2,000–6,000 eggs are usually laid within 12 hours. Fertility varies considerably according to a number of conditions (Gurdon and Uehlinger, 1966), but the average fertility of all matings carried out in this laboratory with imported animals over the last few years is over 50 percent. In many matings it is over 95 percent.

In natural conditions eggs are laid sparsely among vegetation to which they stick until the tadpoles hatch. Eggs deposited through a laying rack in the laboratory are abnormally concentrated, and tend to become arrested or abnormal in development, especially if many of them are unfertilized. To prevent this eggs should be removed from the laying tank within 12 hours of the termination of laying, and spread out at not more than 10 per square inch under 1 inch of clean water. With proper care, over 90 percent of fertile eggs should yield normal hatching tadpoles a few days later.

Rearing Embryos into Sexually Mature Adults

About 4–6 days after fertilization, tadpoles start swimming actively around the floor of the container, a sign that they are ready to feed. In order to obtain fast growth tadpoles are fed on a suspension of finely powdered nettles (*Urtica* sp.). This is obtainable in the United States from S. B. Penick & Co., New York and Chicago, and in England from R. Brookes & Co., 27 Maiden Lane, Covent Garden, London, W.C.2. The nettle powder should be *gradually* mixed with water, at first as a thick paste (1 gm per milliliter), then by addition of water to give a final stock suspension of 1 gm per 5 ml. If too great a volume of water is added to the powder at first, a layer of unsuspended powder remains on the surface of the water and is likely to lead to some mortality of tadpoles which swallow it; 1 ml of the stock suspension is stirred into each liter of dechlorinated tap water in the tadpole rearing tanks. The resulting turbidity should be cleared by the tadpoles within a few hours. For fast growth conditions, tadpoles should be kept at 20°–24°C at a concentration of not more than ten per liter at first, and later of only one per liter. The water in which the tadpoles are kept should be changed every 2 to 3 days. Aeration of the water is not necessary since the tadpoles come to the surface to breathe air every few minutes. Under these conditions we are able to rear tadpoles to metamorphosis within 5–6 weeks from fertilization. Powdered ox liver or hens' egg can be used instead of nettle powder but growth is no faster and the water requires more frequent changing.

The onset of metamorphosis is most easily recognized by the eruption of the forelimbs which develop under the skin. At metamorphosis tadpoles cease feeding for about 7–10 days, during which time the tentacles and tail are resorbed and the larval head condenses by loss of water into a smaller and nontransparent adult head. When the tail is fully resorbed the frog is ready to start feeding. The most convenient food at this stage is small worms such as the annelid *Tubifex*, a fresh-water oligochaete. About 3 months after metamorphosis small fragments of liver are taken and this constitutes a staple diet for the frogs. They should reach sexual maturity between 1 and 2 years after fertilization.

Frogs reared in the laboratory do not always grow at the same rate, and sometimes suffer skeletal deformities. This is particularly evident when the progeny of different matings are compared. Nearly all the progeny of some matings become normal adults within a year, while several of those from other matings may remain small or may develop bent backs or projecting lower jaws. It is not clear whether these abnormalities are a consequence of laboratory rearing conditions, or whether they occur but fail to survive in wild conditions. The reproductive capacity of the skeletally deformed frogs is not necessarily inferior to that of normal frogs. The fertility of frogs reared in the laboratory is somewhat but not markedly less than that of imported frogs reared in the wild. Attempts in Oxford to improve fertility by varying the frogs' diet or supplementing it with vitamins etc. have not shown any substantial effect.

EXPERIMENTAL TECHNIQUES APPLICABLE TO EGGS AND EMBRYOS OF *XENOPUS LAEVIS*

The eggs of *Xenopus laevis* range from 1.2 to 1.5 mm in diameter, and like other amphibian eggs lend themselves to microsurgical operations. For most experiments it is desirable to rear embryos or parts of embryos in saline solutions such as those of Niu and Twitty (Flickinger, 1949), Barth and Barth (1959) as modified by Elsdale *et al.* (1960), or Steinberg (1957). It should be remembered that embryos which have been removed from the vitelline membranes or from most of their jelly tend to exogastrulate if left in a strongly hypertonic solution during the stage of gastrulation.

Variable Quality of Eggs Laid in the Laboratory

A substantial variation exists in the capacity of eggs laid in the laboratory by different females to withstand experimental manipulations. This has been particularly clearly shown by variation in the normality of development promoted by nuclei from the same group of dissociated cells after transplantation into eggs of different females (Gurdon, 1960b). This variation in resistance to experimental interference can substantially affect the results of even the simplest manipulation, but no way of overcoming this difficulty has so far been found. It may be due to the artificial induction of ovulation by hormones with the consequent laying of immature or overmature eggs.

Artificial Fertilization

In contrast to frogs like species of *Rana*, very large numbers of eggs do not accumulate in an expanded oviduct in *Xenopus laevis*. In the latter species eggs are laid within a few hours of ovulation. For this reason not more than a few hundred mature eggs will be obtained by killing a female with or without prior hormone injection. Large numbers of eggs can be obtained only by allowing a female to lay them after the usual hormone injection. However once an egg is laid the jelly coat starts to swell rapidly and when this has happened the egg cannot be fertilized. The methods of artificial fertilization usually employed in *Rana* are therefore not directly applicable to *Xenopus*, but the following method has been successfully used at Oxford. A male with black nuptial pads is killed and a small incision made in the ventral body wall through which a testis (at the base of the fat-body) is removed. The frog is wrapped in moist paper and placed in a 4°C refrigerator. The excised testis is cleaned free of blood and slightly macerated in its own volume of saline solution. As soon as 10–20 unfertilized eggs are laid by a female at about the same time, these are collected in a small dish and all water removed. The testis is laid adjacent to the eggs for about 1 minute. If fertilization has been successful the eggs will rotate within 15–20 minutes after fertilization and the area of animal pole pigment will contract. One testis can be used to fertilize several hundred eggs over a period of 3–4 hours if it is kept in a covered watch glass at room temperature whenever not in use for fertilizing eggs. As soon as fertility of the eggs drops, the other testis from the frog in the refrigerator may be used in the same way. By this means we can obtain nearly 100 percent fertility over 8 hours by killing only one frog.

Notes or References to Other Experimental Techniques

1. Microinjection of Solutions into Eggs. About 50 mμliters can be injected into fertilized or unfertilized eggs without causing abnormal development. At 20–40 minutes after fertilization a fine pipette will penetrate the vitelline membrane, but at other times or in unfertilized eggs a brief exposure to ultraviolet irradiation must be used to permit penetration as described by Gurdon (1960a).

2. Androgenetic Haploids. These can be conveniently prepared by ultraviolet (UV) irradiation of the animal pole of eggs within 15 minutes of fertilization (Gurdon, 1960a), or by irradiating unfertilized eggs with UV in the same way and then artificially fertilizing them. This effect is obtained because the eggs are laid with the second meiotic metaphase spindle on the periphery of the animal pole. By 15 minutes after fertilization or activation the second polar body has been emitted and the egg pronucleus descends toward the center of the egg out of reach of the UV irradiation.

3. Triploids and Tetraploids. Triploids can be obtained by a temperature treatment just after fertilization, a proce-

dure which suppresses the emission of the second polar body (Smith, 1958). Tetraploids can be obtained as a byproduct of nuclear transplantation especially if blastula or advanced tadpole nuclei are used as donors (Gurdon, 1959).

4. Nuclear Transplantation. This can be successfully carried out as described by Elsdale, Gurdon, and Fischberg (1960).

5. Cortical Grafts. Parts of the cortex of eggs or of early cleavage embryos can be grafted onto eggs and embryos of the same age (Curtis, 1962).

6. Germ-cell Grafts. The germ cells from a neurula can be successfully grafted into another neurula from which the germ cells have been removed (Blackler and Fischberg, 1961). The grafted germ cells produce normal gametes when the host reaches sexual maturity (Blackler, 1962).

7. Sex reversal. The addition of estradiol to the water of feeding tadpoles at a particular stage of larval life results in a change of sex (Gallien, 1953 and 1956).

Administration of Labeled Precursors

Satisfactory incorporation of labeled precursor molecules can be obtained following administration by any of the following methods:

1. A few hours before laying commences 1–2 mc of inorganic $P^{32}O_4$ may be injected intraperitoneally into a female (Kutsky, 1950). The acid-soluble pool of labeled substances disappears rather slowly during early development (Brown and Littna, 1964).

2. The incubation of embryos under appropriate conditions in medium to which $Na_2C^{14}O_3$ has been added to give a concentration of about 30 μc per milliliter results in rapid incorporation of $C^{14}O_2$ (Cohen, 1954).

3. Substantial incorporation into nucleic acids or proteins in periods of 1–2 hours may be obtained by the microinjection of labeled nucleosides or amino acids at any stage of development (Gurdon, 1966).

OTHER MEMBERS OF THE SUBFAMILY *XENOPODINAE*

Species and Subspecies of *Xenopus*

The genus *Xenopus* is composed of six species which are indigenous in central and southern Africa. Five of these are more local in distribution than *X. laevis* (Nieuwkoop and Faber, 1956); they are appreciably smaller than *X. laevis* and are most easily distinguished by reference to two structural characters (Noble, 1923). One is a fourth claw on the hind foot—the metatarsal tubercle—which is present in *X. tropicalis*, *X. fraseri*, and *X. clivii*. The other is a small tentacle just below the eye; this is more than 1 mm long in *X. tropicalis*, *X. fraseri*, and *X. mülleri*, but is absent or reduced to less than 0.5 mm in *X. laevis*, *X. clivii*, and *X. gilli*. *Xenopus tropicalis* differs from all other species in having exceptionally small eyes. Fertile eggs have been obtained from all species except *X. gilli*, either in Professor Fischberg's laboratory in Geneva or in Oxford, by the usual hormone treatment. Hybrids between species cannot be obtained, indicating that they are true species. The size of eggs is reduced approximately in proportion to adult size; thus those of *X. mülleri* are about 1 mm in diameter, and those of *X. tropicalis* about 0.7 mm diameter. These species, and especially *X. tropicalis*, appear to tolerate laboratory conditions less well than *X. laevis*, and to suffer a higher mortality rate. They are, however, invaluable for any experiments in which more pronounced genetic differences are required than are provided by the anucleolate mutation.

Subspecies are recognized only in *X. laevis*. There are 5 of these (Nieuwkoop and Faber, 1956), and they are distinguishable mainly by differences in color pattern. All can be maintained and bred in the laboratory by the treatment described above.

Hymenochirus* and *Pseudhymenochirus

Hymenochirus curtipes and *H. boettgeri* are both small aquatic species, little over an inch long, and indigenous in the Congo and Cameroon regions of Africa (Noble, 1923). The sexes are not easily distinguished, but fertile eggs are sometimes produced spontaneously if several adults are kept in the same tank. The eggs are small (less than 1 mm in diameter), and will develop without special attention into tadpoles ready to feed. However tadpoles will not grow on nettle powder and probably require small crustacea as food. Further information on breeding and rearing these species can be obtained from Sokol (1959).

Pseudhymenochirus merlini, from Guinea in Africa, is intermediate in characters between *Xenopus* and *Hymenochirus* and does not appear so far to have been reared in the laboratory.

REFERENCES

BALLS, M., and L. N. RUBEN, 1964: Variation in the response of *Xenopus laevis* to normal tissue homografts. *Devel. Biol.*, 10: 92.

BARTH, L. G., and L. J. BARTH, 1959: Differentiation of the cells of the *Rana pipiens* gastrula in unconditioned medium. *J. Embryol. Exp. Morph.*, 7: 210.

BLACKLER, A. W., 1962: Transfer of germ-cells between two subspecies of *Xenopus laevis*. *J. Embryol. Exp. Morph.*, 10: 641.

———, and M. FISCHBERG, 1961: Transfer of primordial germ-cells in *Xenopus laevis*. *J. Embryol. Exp. Morph.*, 9: 634.

BROWN, D. D., and J. B. GURDON, 1964: Absence of ribosomal RNA synthesis in the anucleolate mutant of *Xenopus laevis*. *Proc. Nat. Acad. Sci. U.S.*, 51: 139.

———, and E. LITTNA, 1964: RNA synthesis during the development of *Xenopus laevis*, the South African Clawed Toad. *J. Mol. Biol.*, 8: 669.

COHEN, S., 1954: The metabolism of $C^{14}O_2$ during amphibian development. *J. Biol. Chem.*, 211: 337.

CURTIS, A. S. G., 1962: Morphogenetic interactions before gastrulation in the Amphibian, *Xenopus laevis*—the cortical field. *J. Embryol. Exp. Morph.*, 10: 410.

ELKAN, E., 1957: *Xenopus laevis* (Daudin). In A. N. Worden and W. Lane-Petter (eds.), *UFAW Handbook on the Care and Management of Laboratory Animals*, 2nd ed., The Universities Federation for Animal Welfare, London, Eng., p. 804.

ELSDALE, T. R., M. FISCHBERG, and S. SMITH, 1958: A mutation that reduces nucleolar number in *Xenopus laevis*. *Exp. Cell. Res.* 14: 642.

———, J. B. GURDON, and M. FISCHBERG, 1960: A description of the technique for nuclear transplantation in *Xenopus laevis*. *J. Embryol. Exp. Morph.*, 8: 437.

FLICKINGER, R. A., 1949: A study of the metabolism of amphibian neutral crest cells during their migration and pigmentation *in vitro*. *J. Exp. Zool.*, 112: 465.

GALLIEN, L., 1953: Inversion totale du sexe chez *Xenopus laevis* Daud. à la suite d'un traitement gynogène par le benzoate d'oestradiol administré pendant la vie larvaire. *Compt. Rend. Acad. Sci.*, 237: 1565.

———, 1956: Inversion expérimentale du sexe chez un Anoure inférieur, *Xenopus laevis* (Daudin). Analyse des conséquences génétiques. *Bull. Biol. France Belg.*, 90: 163.

GURDON, J. B., 1959: Tetraploid frogs, *J. Exp. Zool.*, 141: 519.

———, 1960a: The effects of ultraviolet irradiation on uncleaved eggs of *Xenopus laevis*. *Quart. J. Microscop. Sci.*, 101: 299.

———, 1960b: Factors responsible for the abnormal development of embryos obtained by nuclear transplantation in *Xenopus laevis*. *J. Embryol. Exp. Morph.*, 8: 327.

———, 1966: The control of gene activity during cell differentiation in higher organisms. In R. A. Brink (ed.), *Heritage from Mendel*, University of Wisconsin Press, Madison, Wis., p. 203.

———, and V. UEHLINGER, 1966: "Fertile" intestine nuclei. *Nature*, 210: 1240.

KUTSKY, P., 1950: Phosphate metabolism in the early development of *Rana pipiens*. *J. Exp. Zool.*, 115: 429.

NIEUWKOOP, P. D., and J. FABER, 1956: *Normal Table of* Xenopus laevis (*Daudin*). North-Holland Publishing Co., Amsterdam.

NOBLE, G. K., 1923: Contributions to the herpetology of the Belgian Congo based on the collections of the American Museum Congo expedition, 1909–1915. *Bull. Amer. Mus. Nat. Hist.*, 49: 147.

SMITH, S., 1958: Induction of triploidy in the South African Clawed Frog, *Xenopus laevis* (Daudin). *Nature*, 181: 290.

SOKOL, O. M., 1959: Studien an pipiden Fröschen. *Zool. Anzeiger*, 162: 154.

STEINBERG, M., 1957: In report by J. D. Ebert; *Carnegie Institution of Washington Yearbook*, 56: 347.

Urodeles*

By G. Fankhauser

INTRODUCTION

Compared with anurans, urodeles have certain disadvantages as suppliers of eggs and embryos. In general they produce a smaller number of eggs per female, the development of the eggs is slower (which, however, may be an asset for the finer temporal analysis of certain events), and the larvae are carnivorous and must be supplied with live food of suitable size. These drawbacks are compensated in part by the frequently larger size of the individual eggs and embryos which facilitates surgical operations; furthermore, both front and hind limbs develop relatively early and are thus available for experimentation.

Several fundamental and peculiar differences exist between the two orders of amphibia with regard to the processes of fertilization. (1) The eggs of oviparous anurans are inseminated by the male at the time of their extrusion into the water. In urodeles the eggs are fertilized internally, as they pass out through the cloaca of the female, by spermatozoa that have been stored in a sperm receptacle or spermatheca. These are picked up by the cloacal lips of the female in a package perched on top of a gelatinous spermatophore which has been deposited by the male on the bottom of the pond or aquarium, at the conclusion of a complex courtship performance. (2) In anurans, fertilization is strictly monospermic under normal conditions; polyspermy can be induced by artificial means, such as concentrated suspensions of spermatozoa. It always leads to the independent division of the supernumerary spermatozoa, abnormal cleavage, and the formation of inviable mosaic (haploid-diploid) embryos. In urodeles, on the contrary, fertilization is normally polyspermic, but only one sperm nucleus participates in the development of the egg. Independent division of the accessory sperm complexes is usually suppressed by an inhibitory influence of unknown nature that seems to spread from the vicinity of the two pronuclei (see review in Fankhauser, 1948). (3) While unfertilized frog eggs can be induced to undergo parthenogenetic development by pricking with a fine needle,

* A considerable part of the material presented in this section has been taken from the author's chapter on amphibia in *Animals for Research. Principles of Breeding and Management*, pp. 475–500, 1963. Such material has been reproduced with permission of Academic Press Ltd., London and New York. The chapter contains information on some other species of urodeles and a complete list of the stage series of normal development of amphibian embryos published up to that time.

salamander eggs are completely refractory to this treatment. They can be activated by temperature or electric shocks, *viz.*, they elevate the vitelline membrane, so that the eggs can rotate in response to gravity, complete the second maturation division that had been arrested at metaphase, and form the egg nucleus. However, the treatment does not induce the formation of a new centrosome or division center, and cleavage is at best very abnormal and comes to an early halt.

At the suggestion of the editors, the most widely used American genera will be discussed in detail: the Eastern newt (*Triturus* or *Diemictylus viridescens*), the California newt (*Taricha*), and *Ambystoma*, including the Mexican axolotl. Two foreign species of newts, which are also used extensively and can be maintained in laboratory colonies, the Japanese newt (*Triturus pyrrhogaster*) and the Spanish newt (*Pleurodeles*), will be dealt with more briefly. Detailed descriptions of the American species, their life histories and breeding habits will be found in S. C. Bishop's *Handbook of Salamanders* (1943), which covers the salamanders of the United States, Canada, and Lower California, in *The Salamanders of New York* (1941) by the same author, and in R. C. Stebbins' *Amphibians of Western North America* (1951).

GENERAL INFORMATION ON URODELES AND THE DEVELOPMENT OF THEIR EGGS

Commercial Sources for Obtaining Urodeles

The following firms and professional collectors, among others, offer the species indicated:

Carolina Biological Supply Co., Burlington, North Carolina 27216: *Triturus viridescens*, *Ambystoma* eggs (*Taricha* is supplied by their Oregon laboratory, *Powell Laboratories*, Gladstone, Oregon 97027).

General Biological Supply House, 8200 S. Hoyne Avenue, Chicago, Illinois: *Triturus viridescens*.

The Lemberger Company, 1222 W. South Park Avenue, Oshkosh, Wisconsin 54902: *Triturus viridescens*, *Taricha*.

Glenn Gentry, 2816 Colonial Circle, Donelson, Tennessee 37214: *Triturus viridescens*, *Ambystoma* eggs.

Lewis H. Babbit, Petersham, Mass. 01366: *Triturus viridescens*.

Neither the Eastern nor the California newts can be maintained profitably in permanent laboratory colonies, as can the axolotl and the Spanish and Japanese newts (see sections on individual species); fresh breeding stock must be procured each season.

Rearing of Embryos and Larvae

Methods for the obtaining of eggs will be discussed under the individual species, as they vary considerably.

WATER

Eggs and embryos develop equally well in pond, spring, or well water, or in dechlorinated water from the municipal system. Dechlorination tanks installed in the laboratory and serviced regularly by a commercial concern have proven most advantageous.

TEMPERATURE

Eggs of salamanders will develop normally at a wide range of temperatures; for *Triturus viridescens* we found the upper limit for normal development to be about 27°C, the lower limit about 10°C; at the latter temperature development is almost at a standstill. Rates of development at one or more temperatures are given by the authors of various "normal tables" (see the following section).

FOOD

The most convenient diet for newly hatched larvae of all urodeles is a suspension of brine-shrimp larvae (*Artemia*). Dried eggs are obtainable from the San Francisco Aquarium Society, 1655 W. Winton Avenue. Hayward, California. They will hatch within 24 to 48 hours when sprinkled on a salt solution of suitable concentration, e.g., 8 tablespoons of sodium chloride to 1 gallon of dechlorinated water. We use rectangular Pyrex trays with a partition of a composition board that rests on the rim of the tray near one end and stops about $\frac{1}{4}$ inch from the bottom. The eggs are sprinkled on the brine behind the partition. Many of the larvae will swim under the partition toward a light source placed at the other end of the tray and thus become separated from the undigestible egg shells. The suspension of larvae is pipetted into centrifuge tubes and sedimented to allow the partial replacement of the brine with fresh water. This process is repeated twice more, and the resulting suspension fed to the urodele larvae. The *Artemia* larvae will remain alive in fresh water for several hours. When the salamander larvae are half-grown, they can be switched to a diet of *Tubifex* worms. Larvae of smaller species, such as *Triturus viridescens*, can be raised to metamorphosis on a pure diet of newly hatched *Artemia* larvae. It would be more appropriate to establish permanent *Artemia* cultures and raise the *Artemia* larvae to sizes suitable for larger urodele larvae (and adults) on a diet of algae or yeast. So far, we have not been too successful with this, nor with preliminary attempts to establish large-scale cultures of fresh-water amphipods, which would constitute an ideal food for larger larvae and adults. *Daphnia* and other Cladocera, when available, are still an excellent diet; some years ago we raised older larvae in groups of six in *Daphnia* cultures kept in 3-gallon aquaria and obtained unusually large and vigorous animals at metamorphosis, but were discouraged by the amount of work involved in keeping a sufficient number of reserve cultures available. In large containers and in the presence of abundant food, a number of larvae can be raised together without cannibalism. In the commonly used smaller culture dishes competition for food soon becomes evident. Therefore, it is advisable to isolate the individual larvae about 2 weeks after feeding begins.

METAMORPHOSED ANIMALS

As a rule, these are more difficult to feed, if they take up a permanent residence on land. With young efts of *Triturus viridescens*, we found it most convenient to place open vials with *Drosophila* cultures into the terraria so that the efts could crawl into the vials to feed on large maggots as well as on newly eclosed flies. Newly metamorphosed animals of other species, e.g., *Triturus pyrrhogaster*, can be induced more easily to return to water to feed. In *Triturus viridescens*, the "water drive," which normally does not arise until 2 to 3 years after metamorphosis, has been induced in recently metamorphosed animals by implanting one-half of a pituitary from an adult newt under the skin of the throat. The implant apparently furnishes the necessary prolactin-like hormone which seems to be responsible for the water drive. Once returned to water, the animals grow considerably faster than under the best conditions on land.

In the Princeton laboratory, we have for many years used a simpler method for avoiding the land stage of *Triturus viridescens*. At the age of 50 to 60 days the larvae are placed in a 0.04 percent solution of thiouracil which prevents the synthesis of thyroxine in the thyroid and produces a permanent larva which can grow to almost adult size within a year. The animals must be kept permanently in the thiouracil solution, since the thyroid recovers after return to water, at least in the younger animals, and metamorphosis follows. Permanent larvae may also be obtained by raising the larvae in a solution of potassium-perchlorate (0.05 percent) or of 1-methyl-2-mercapto-imidazole (0.002 percent).

Stages in Normal Development

Every worker in normal or experimental embryology needs a short-hand notation to designate and identify the various stages the embryo passes through on its way to the free-swimming larva and, to a lesser extent, from there to metamorphosis. The first series of normal stages of a urodele was developed in R. G. Harrison's laboratory at Yale but never published in its original form which consisted of large paintings of the various stages made from life by the artist Lisbeth Krause. These paintings were grouped together and photographed, and prints of these photographs were made available to embryologists. The Harrison stages were published as outline drawings by Hamburger (1942) and Rugh (1948), without verbal descriptions of the characteristics of each stage.

Normal stages for other species of urodeles were modeled after the Harrison series for *Ambystoma*, and corresponding stages designated with the same number: *Taricha torosa*, the California newt—V. C. Twitty and D. Bodenstein, published in Rugh (1962), p. 90; *Triturus pyrrhogaster*, the Japanese newt—J. Oyama (1930), P. L. Anderson (1943), Y. K. Okada and M. Ichikawa (1947); *Pleurodeles waltlii*, the Spanish newt—L. Gallien and M. Durocher (1957). Unfortunately, beginning with the tailbud stages, the embryos of different species vary sufficiently in the relative timing of various developmental events, and thus in the combination of new diagnostic features that appear at any one time, so that it becomes difficult to match the Harrison stage numbers accurately (*cf.* Table 1 and Figs. 1 to 9; see also Gallien and Durocher, 1957, Table II).

For this reason, and also in order to make finer subdivisions of the development of the embryo, a different set of symbols was used for the normal stages of *Triturus viridescens*. These were worked out at the Princeton laboratory in the thirties. Development was first divided into periods or phases designated by capital letters; a number was assigned to the individual stages within each period and a brief description of the characteristics of each stage given (see Fankhauser, 1945, p. 23). For the cleavage period the designations 1, 2, 4, 8, 16, 32 cells, early blastula (B_1), middle blastula (B_2), and late blastula (B_3) were used. Gastrulation stages were designated with G, neurulation stages with N, tailbud ("embryo") stages with E. Larval development was subdivided into two periods, the first characterized by the various stages in the formation of the forelimbs (F), the second by the stages in hind limb development (H). (In this species, there is only a slight overlap between these two periods.) Gallien and Durocher (1957) recognized the same major periods in *Pleurodeles*, adding the phase of metamorphosis, but numbered the stages consecutively according to the Harrison system.

TABLE 1. EXAMPLES OF CORRESPONDING STAGES IN NORMAL DEVELOPMENT OF FIVE SPECIES OF URODELES

PHASE OR PERIOD	DESCRIPTION OF STAGE (BASED PRIMARILY ON *Triturus viridescens* AND *Pleurodeles*)	*Triturus viridescens**	*Pleurodeles*†	*Taricha torosa*‡	*Triturus pyrrhogaster*§	*Ambystoma punctatum***
Gastrulation	Dorsal lip of blastopore forms small crescent, Fig. 1	G3	8b	11	11	10
Neurulation	Neural plate bordered with well-formed folds, Fig. 2	N3	14	15	17	15
Tailbud (embryo) stages	Prominent tailbud, flat gill-mounds, Fig. 3	E3	24½	28	21	30
	Three gill-buds indicated, numerous light-gray pigment cells, heart beat, movements, Fig. 4	E6	30	33	31	35
Larval period (Forelimb development)	Medium balancers and gills, all with circulation, prominent forelimb buds, pigment cells darker, Fig. 5	F2	32	37	37	37
	Forelimb buds longer, notched (2 fingerbuds indicated), Fig. 6, feeding begins in *Pleurodeles*	F8	38	..	40½	41
	Long third fingerbud; feeding begins in *Triturus viridescens*, Fig. 7	F15	42	..	..	46
(Hind limb development)	Hind limb buds long, 2 prominent toebuds, 3rd toebud flat, Fig. 8,	H6	50–	..	..	..
	5th toebud flat, Fig. 9	H12	53–	..	..	..
Metamorphosis	Gills reduced one-half	..	55b	..	..	..
	Metamorphosis completed	..	56	..	..	..

* G. Fankhauser, unpublished.
† L. Gallien and M. Durocher (1957).
‡ V. C. Twitty and D. Bodenstein, *see* Rugh (1962).
§ J. Oyama (1930).
** R. G. Harrison, *see* Hamburger (1960) and Rugh (1962).

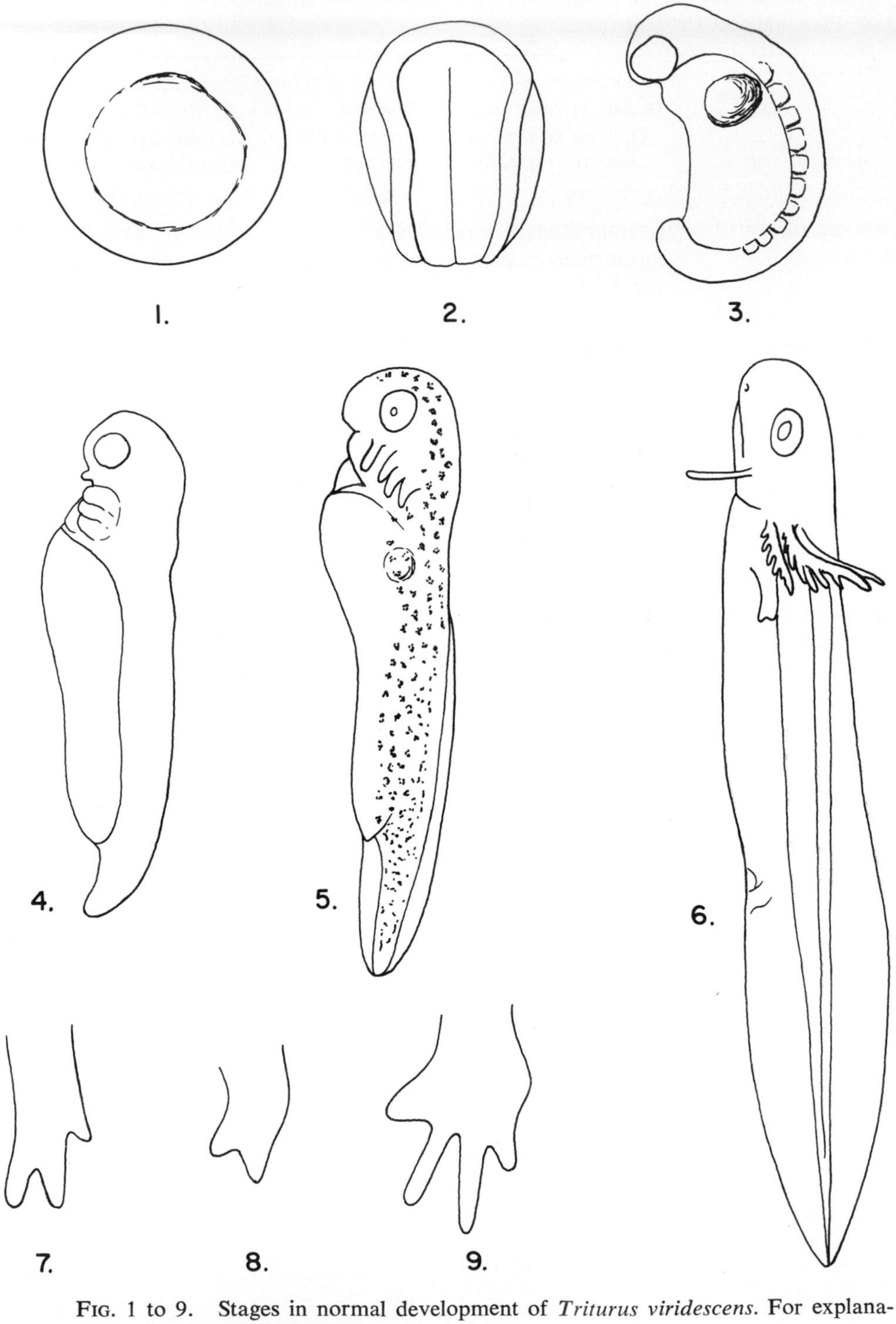

FIG. 1 to 9. Stages in normal development of *Triturus viridescens*. For explanations see column 2 in Table 1.

INDIVIDUAL SPECIES

Eastern Newt, *Triturus (Diemictylus) viridescens*[1]

Since adult newts remain in the water between breeding seasons, they can be collected easily the year round. During the normal breeding season, which lasts from the end of March to June, fertile eggs may be obtained by placing freshly collected females in large finger bowls containing sprigs of *Elodea*. The females deposit several eggs a day, for a week or longer, by attaching them singly to *Elodea* leaves which are bent together or folded with the hind legs to make a "nest." In the spring most of the females carry a supply of spermatozoa in the spermatheca which fertilize each egg as it passes through the cloaca during laying. In nature, courtship and mating begin in the autumn and continue through the winter and spring.

Before the beginning of the normal breeding season, ovulation and egg laying can be induced by implanting pituitaries from frogs, preferably females, as their glands are about twice as potent as those of males. By this method eggs may be obtained as early as the middle of October, or as soon as the larger oocytes in the ovaries have reached their full size. At that time, some of the females have not yet mated and will deposit unfertilized eggs. If a male is placed with the pituitary-implanted female, which is very eager to mate (Humphries, 1955), courtship takes place and may lead to the successful transfer of the sperm package from the spermatophore deposited by the male to the cloaca of the female.

If newts are collected in the fall or winter, they should be kept in a refrigerator at a temperature of from 3° to 7°C until they are used. At this low temperature the ovaries remain in good condition for at least 2 to 3 months, while they begin to deteriorate after about 2 weeks at room temperature. The animals are removed from the refrigerator once a week, given *Tubifex* worms, and left to feed at room temperature for a few hours before they are returned to the refrigerator.

Our standard pituitary treatment consists of implanting either the whole frog pituitary, or the anterior lobe alone, under the skin of the lower jaw, with the female newt lightly anesthetized with a solution of chloretone (3 gm in 1000 ml of dechlorinated water). A second pituitary is given 2 days later. Some females begin to lay eggs on the second or third day following the second implant; more often, during the fall and winter, a third implant is necessary which is given 4 or 5 days after the second. In some cases the period of oviposition can be prolonged by another pituitary graft made when the egg-laying activity tapers off.

[1] The legal name for this genus has been changed repeatedly; in the older literature it is referred to either as *Diemictylus* or as *Notophthalmus*. Later it was predominantly known as *Triturus* when it became important in embryological work; hence the attachment of the embryologists to this name. More recently, the name switched back officially to *Diemictylus*. However, according to Opinion 635 of the International Commission on Zoological Nomenclature (*Bulletin of Zoological Nomenclature*, 19, p. 152, 1962) the valid name (following the "first reviser principle") should be *Notophthalmus*. This change, while strictly legal, is confusing. Both names, *Diemictylus* and *Notophthalmus*, were coined by Rafinesque and first published in 1820 in the "Annals of Nature" on page 5, lines 8 and 26–27 respectively. It is commonly agreed that Rafinesque, who had an obsession to create new genera, separated the adult water form of the newt, which he called *Diemictylus*, from the terrestrial, immature red eft stage of the same species, which he named *Notophthalmus*. This last name thus did not apply to the adult newt originally, but was selected by the first reviser (Baird, 1850) as the proper genus name. The confusion created by this was clearly recognized by E. D. Cope in 1889, who in *The Batrachia of North America* says on p. 202: "What name should be applied to this genus is uncertain, and may perhaps ever remain so."

To some extent oviposition can be controlled by the simple trick of removing the *Elodea* from the dish. Properly stimulated females will hold back the eggs for several hours or overnight, until the plants are returned. Females that are overstimulated by the pituitary treatment tend to scatter the eggs on the bottom of the dish, even in the presence of *Elodea.* Such eggs are usually unfertilized; this suggests either that manipulation of the *Elodea* leaves by the hind legs to form a nest may be important in facilitating the passage of spermatozoa from the spermatheca to the cloaca as the egg passes through, or that eggs dropped on the bottom pass through the cloaca too rapidly to be fertilized.

If freshly laid, and thus newly fertilized, eggs are needed for the experiment, as for the induction of triploidy by heat- or cold-shock, the egg-laying process must be watched and the egg removed as soon as the female leaves the *Elodea*. For this purpose it is most convenient to have from six to ten implanted females available which can be observed at the same time. As the females spend from 3 to 5 minutes making the "nest" and depositing the egg, the time of insemination is known only approximately. Artificial insemination can be carried out, using eggs from the posterior part of the oviducts and concentrated sperm fluid from a vas deferens. The procedure is not recommended, however, since the female must be sacrificed and usually contains only a small number of usable eggs. Moreover, there is the danger of inducing an abnormally high degree of polyspermy in the egg which leads to abnormal cleavage, an event which is very rare if the eggs are fertilized naturally as they pass through the cloaca.

The outermost layer of the jelly capsule is adhesive and more or less opaque, the degree of "milkiness" varying with different females. It adheres to the inner clear layers over the whole surface of the capsule and can be removed in small pieces only, in contrast to the corresponding layer of eggs of Japanese or European newts which can be peeled off easily. Fortunately, the parts of the sticky layer which are in contact with the leaves usually remain behind as the egg capsule is removed from the plant and open one or more transparent windows for closer observation of the egg and embryo.

The wall of the jelly capsule consists of at least three layers. Under the adhesive layer is a transparent, tough (inelastic) layer. Inside of that is applied a thin, elastic layer. Since capsule fluid is hypertonic to water, water diffuses into the capsule and creates considerable pressure which forces the elastic inner layer against the tough outer one ("tube and tire effect"). Before an egg or embryo can be removed from the capsule, this pressure must be released carefully. This is best done by (1) forcing the egg toward one end of the oblong capsule with gentle pressure of a pair of watchmaker's forceps, and (2) puncturing the capsule at the other end with one prong of a second pair of forceps and holding this prong in position, so that the pressure is released gradually. If the prong is withdrawn immediately, the sudden release of the pressure may squirt the egg out through the opening. When the depressurized capsule is then opened with two pairs of forceps, the torn edges have a strong tendency to curl in sharply and exert local pressure on the embryo which may tear the thin wall of the blastula or early gastrula stages. It is easier to remove the capsule either when the egg is in the one-cell or an early cleavage stage and thus without a cavity, or after the tailbud stage has been reached and the embryo has become less fragile.

At the Princeton laboratory we tried to set up a more or less permanent colony of *Triturus viridescens* by keeping adult newts during the summer in a large, well-planted tank with plenty of food. In the following winter the females responded to pituitary implantations by laying an unusually large number of eggs. However, these eggs were of poor quality, as indicated by their abnormal pigmentation, and did not develop normally. It is thus necessary to return the animals to their ponds at the end of spring and to collect fresh breeding stock in the fall.

Western Newts (*Taricha*)

Of the three species of Western newts, *Taricha torosa*, the California newt, is the most widely used. Its breeding season lasts from late December to April, varying with latitude and altitude, and it lays large eggs in firm-jellied clumps, 7 to 29 per clump (see Stebbins, 1951). Miller and Robbins (1951), in a detailed study of the reproductive cycle of this species, discovered that about one-half of the adult-sized animals, dissected before the beginning of the breeding period, had unmatured gonads. They suggested that these individuals "represent a portion of the population which does not breed every year" (p. 417).

Artificial fertilization is rather simple in this species and has been used extensively by Twitty and his students in hybridization experiments with other species of *Taricha*, *T. granulosa*, the rough-skinned newt, and *T. rivularis*, the red-bellied newt. Twitty (1965) prefers to use naturally spawning females, with eggs already in their oviducts. However, ovulation can also be induced by implantation of a single pituitary gland from an adult female newt, and the eggs will accumulate in the oviducts within a few days. Their arrival in the posterior part of the oviducts can be ascertained by gentle stripping of the female's body wall which will express an egg from the cloaca. The female is decapitated, the abdominal cavity opened, and the egg-filled oviducts are removed with forceps and placed on a flat surface in a shallow puddle of water to prevent their drying. The sperm suspension is prepared by dissecting out the sperm ducts from several mature males and stripping them into 5 ml of Holtfreter's solution in a Petri dish. The concentration of sperm is not too important, but the suspension should have a slightly milky appearance.

The oviducts are now opened with watchmaker's forceps and the eggs immersed very briefly in the sperm suspension. They are then placed on the bottom of a moistened finger bowl or Pyrex baking dish where they are left for 15 to 20 minutes before they are covered with spring water or boiled tap water. Percentages of fertilization and normal development are usually quite high. The larvae are raised on *Artemia* nauplii to the mid-larval period and then switched to a diet of adult brine shrimp which are available locally. Although metamorphosed animals feed in the water, it is advisable to tilt the culture dishes to allow the animals to crawl onto dry areas.

Japanese Newt (*Triturus pyrrhogaster*)

Triturus pyrrhogaster has several advantages over *Triturus viridescens* for embryological work. (1) The adults are hardier and thrive for several years under laboratory conditions if they are kept in a large aquarium or tank on a diet of *Tubifex*, earthworms, or beef liver. Both sexes return to normal breeding condition in the fall. However, at Princeton we have had some difficulty in obtaining normal spawnings after the second year. (2) The eggs are larger and are more easily observed during development, since the adhesive and opaque outer layer of the jelly capsule can be peeled off completely. (3) There is no prolonged terrestrial stage in the life history; newly metamorphosed animals can often be induced to return to the water after a few days.

To induce spawning during the winter, we have used a pituitary implantation technique similar to that used with the American newt; two frog pituitaries are implanted at the same time, and eggs are deposited 3 or 4 days later. A single female may deposit from 30 to 90 eggs over a period of 2 weeks. Hamburger (1960) gives two injections of two pituitaries each, 1 or 2 days apart, with good results. The methods used for rearing the larvae are identical with those for *T. viridescens*. Japanese investigators have succeeded in rearing the animals to sexual maturity and have obtained normal offspring from them.

Unfortunately, it has been impossible to purchase Japanese newts from commercial sources in Japan during the past 2 or 3 years. At present they can be obtained only through personal contact with Japanese zoologists.

Spanish Newt (*Pleurodeles waltlii*)

Eggs of *Pleurodeles waltlii* are used extensively in European laboratories, particularly by Gallien and his students at the Laboratoire d'Embryologie of the Faculté des Sciences in Paris. He has been most helpful in supplying breeding stock from his large colony to investigators in this country. As far as I know, the species is not available commercially. Two years ago one of our students, a herpetologist, while traveling in Spain, collected specimens for me, with the assistance of a young Spanish collector. They are not easy to catch, since they live preferably at the bottom of deep wells. While the animals survived the plane trip, they died within a few weeks after arrival; specimens from a well-established laboratory colony appear to be hardier.

Gallien (1952, 1957, 1962) has given detailed descriptions of the optimal culture conditions for adults and embryos. He keeps ten adults in an aquarium 50 × 50 × 25 cm, with slowly running water and pebbles at the bottom, or in a cement tank 1 meter square, without pebbles. Under these conditions the animals are prevented from leaving the water. They are fed twice a week with finely chopped beef heart which is left in the tank for 8 hours, then siphoned off, together with feces and shed skins. Males and females are kept in separate tanks at a temperature of 16° to 20°C.

Spawnings are obtainable from early September to early May during which period the males are always in breeding condition. Three pairs of animals are placed in an aquarium 50 × 50 × 25 cm, divided into three compartments by glass partitions. Courtship begins almost immediately. During amplexus, the male is situated under the female, with its forelegs, which are covered with dark, heavily keratinized epidermis, hooked over those of the female. The male then deposits spermatophores which are picked up by the female with the cloacal lips. The males are removed; spawning begins 24 to 48 hours after pairing and lasts for about 2 days. The female attaches packages of about 10 eggs each to stones, at intervals of 10 to 30 minutes, and lays a total of 400 to 800 eggs. The eggs are similar in size to those of the Japanese newt.

The larvae hatch at about 10 days, at 16° to 20°C, and metamorphose between 50 and 90 days. They are first fed *Paramecium* and very small *Daphnia* (for which *Artemia* nauplii may be substituted), later hashed *Chironomus* larvae or *Tubifex*, and finally whole *Chironomus* larvae or *Tubifex*. If a small number of larvae are kept in a large volume of slowly running water, they grow to larger size and metamorphose later. At the usual time of metamorphosis, the animals measure 55 to 60 mm; at 4 months they are about 80 mm long. The first spawning can be obtained at an age of about 16 months. In Gallien's laboratory, some females and males have bred every year for 8 to 10 years, although they are most prolific at 2 to 6 years.

Spotted Salamander (*Ambystoma maculatum*) and Tiger Salamander (*Ambystoma tigrinum*)

These species usually do not spawn spontaneously in the laboratory, and pituitary treatment has not been found to be successful in inducing ovulation and normal spawning. If mating adults are collected at night during the normal breeding season they will spawn when brought to the laboratory. It is still recommended to follow the routine established long ago in Professor Ross G. Harrison's laboratory at Yale and to wait for a warm rain to occur during a night of the normal spawning season. Such conditions induce the animals to migrate to their breeding ponds, where eggs in the one-cell stage can be collected on the morning after the rain. The larvae can be raised easily to metamorphosis but are difficult to rear to maturity.

The larger tiger salamander has been maintained by Hutchinson (1950) in a breeding colony under the very special and favorable conditions of the now defunct Morris Biological Farm of the Wistar Institute. He was able to extend the breeding season into the month of June by controlling the temperature. To my knowledge this attempt has not been repeated elsewhere.

Mexican Axolotl (*Siredon mexicanum*)

The legal generic name of this species obscures its close relationship to *Ambystoma tigrinum* with which it hybridizes easily in the laboratory. Colonies have been maintained in several laboratories, most successfully by Humphrey, first at the University of Buffalo and subsequently at Indiana University. He has published extensive instructions for the maintenance and care of colonies and for the rearing of the embryos (Humphrey, 1961b, c, 1962, 1965).

Adult axolotls are kept singly in 1-gallon containers (small aquaria, glass or plastic fish bowls, or pans). They are fed three times a week with large earthworms or beef or lamb liver which is cut into thin strips and kept frozen until feeding time. Each animal is given as many strips as it will take without hesitation when offered.

Mature males show a marked enlargement of the lateral margins of the cloaca. Spawnings are obtainable from November to June, and from young animals that have just reached maturity (at 1 year) even during the summer, if the laboratory temperature is maintained at about 21°C. A male and a female are placed together in the early evening in an aquarium 30 × 45 cm, or a dishpan about 37 cm across. A thin layer of fine gravel or coarse sand on the bottom will help to anchor the spermatophores deposited by the male and to keep them upright. The water temperature should be no higher than in the tanks of the colony. The animals should be left undisturbed overnight in the dark. Ovulation usually occurs only after a successful mating and insemination of the female. Spawning may begin within 18 to 30 hours after the animals are placed together; usually, from 300 to 600 eggs are laid within 24 hours. The percentage of fertile eggs is highly variable. The spawning female may be placed in an aquarium with clean bottom to which the eggs are attached singly or in small groups. If the female is disturbed too often the spawning process may be interrupted. It is best to remove the eggs at intervals of several hours, unless freshly fertilized eggs are needed for the experiment. If a female spawns early in the breeding season she may be mated again after 6 to 8 weeks. It is best to replace the breeding animals at the end of their third year.

Artificial insemination requires the sacrifice of both male and female. Ovulation can be induced by intramuscular injection of 180 to 220 International Units of follicle-stimulating hormone (e.g., the preparation made by the Armour Company for veterinary use). When spawning begins 18 to 24 hours later, the female should be disturbed at intervals to prevent normal expulsion of the eggs, since eggs that have been in contact with water cannot be inseminated. The female is decapitated, the oviducts are exposed and the eggs transferred in groups to a dry covered watch glass. The content of a sperm duct of the decapitated male is mixed with 10 ml of 10 percent Ringer's solution, the suspension pipetted over the surface of the eggs and left in contact with the eggs for 20 minutes. The eggs are then covered with water, and the watch glasses immersed in a large bowl of water after 20 or 30 minutes more.

A shallow bowl with 1 liter of water will accommodate 50 to 60 eggs, which hatch in about 2 weeks. *Artemia* nauplii are an excellent first food but can be replaced by small *Daphnia* or pieces of small *Tubifex* or *Enchytraeus* worms. Larger larvae are fed *Daphnia* or *Tubifex*, or pieces of earthworms. Exclusive use of *Artemia* or *Enchytraeus* is not recommended since it may produce edema and small hemorrhages in the skin. Later on, hand feeding with strips of beef liver is essential to obtain animals in breeding condition within 1 year. Daily feeding of young larvae is important; feeding on alternate days is sufficient when the larvae are several months old.

The development of axolotl eggs follows closely that of *Ambystoma tigrinum* for which Harrison has pictured a few stages. Humphrey (1965) finds the *A. punctatum* stages useful up to stage 38. A complete series of normal stages of the axolotl would be helpful.

SPECIAL USES FOR URODELE EGGS AND EMBRYOS

Spontaneous and Induced Heteroploidy

In *Triturus viridescens*, deviations from the normal, diploid chromosome number occur with reasonable frequency (Fankhauser, 1938, 1945). The chromosome number of each living larva may be determined in dividing epidermis cells of amputated tail tips which are prepared as whole mounts following staining with Harris' acid haemalum. Second clippings of the regenerated tail tip may be taken if needed after 5 days. Our stages F9 to F11 are best for the first clipping since they show the largest number of metaphases. Triploid larvae are the most frequent aberration and are found in laboratory-raised animals with a frequency of about 1 percent. Pentaploid and haploid larvae appear less often, tetraploid and aneuploid larvae are rare.

A much more extensive investigation was undertaken in collaboration with Dr. R. R. Humphrey between 1942 and 1959 with thousands of tail tips from larvae of his large, pedigreed axolotl colony (Humphrey and Fankhauser, 1957; Fankhauser and Humphrey, 1959). Thanks to the availability of the recessive white mutant, combined in reciprocal crosses with the dominant black, it was possible to determine the origin of spontaneous haploids, triploids, and pentaploids, either from accidents at fertilization (haploids) or from suppression of one or both of the meiotic divisions of the egg (polyploids).

Triploidy was first induced experimentally in *Triturus viridescens* by prolonged cold-treatment of freshly fertilized eggs (Fankhauser and Griffith, 1939) and, later, by short heat-shock, 10 minutes at 36° to 37°C (Fankhauser and Watson, 1942). Both treatments suppress the formation of the second polar body in a variable percentage of the eggs. In axolotl eggs, both haploidy and triploidy may be induced by cold treatment, depending on the duration of the treatment (Fankhauser and Humphrey, 1942).

Analysis of Karyotype

The first complete analysis of the karyotype of any vertebrate animal was carried out on serial sections of haploid, diploid, and mosaic blastulae of the European newt, *Triturus palmatus* (Fankhauser, 1934). Analyses with modern squash methods were performed for the axolotl (Hauschka and Brunst, 1965; Signoret, 1965), *Pleurodeles* (Gallien *et al.*, 1965; Gallien, 1966), and *Taricha* (Seto and Pomerat, 1965).

Lampbrush Chromosomes

Oocytes of *Triturus viridescens* were used in the classic studies of Gall (1954, 1958, 1963) for the elucidation of the fine structure of these intriguing giant chromosomes which offer unique opportunities for the analysis of gene function in the developing egg. These investigations are based on the identification of the individual chromosomes and thus the determination of the lampbrush karyotype which shows structural details unavailable in the contracted somatic chromosomes.

Nuclear Transplantation (*cf.* King, pp. 737–751, this volume)

At first, transplantation of a nucleus from an embryonic cell into an unfertilized urodele egg was prevented by the impossibility of activating the egg by pricking with a needle. This difficulty was overcome by the discovery that the urodele egg can be activated by temperature shocks, as shown originally by Wagner (1944), and, more efficiently, by an electrical shock. Nuclear transplantation has been carried out successfully with eggs of the axolotl (Signoret, Briggs, and Humphrey, 1962; Briggs, Signoret, and Humphrey, 1964) and *Pleurodeles* (Gallien *et al.*, 1963a, b; Bideau, 1964).

Mutant Races of the Axolotl for Studies in Developmental Genetics and for Use as "Markers"

The pedigreed axolotl cultures propagated for many years on a very large scale by Humphrey have furnished a number of interesting mutations. The first to be discovered was a "fluid imbalance," usually lethal, which, on closer analysis, turned out to be caused by two closely linked factors with a low percentage of crossing-over (Humphrey, 1943, 1948, 1959). More recently, Humphrey (1962; Briggs and Humphrey, 1962) found a semilethal mutation producing vasodilation and other effects, a lethal factor which induces abnormalities in the renal system and other organs (1964), and a lethal which induces failure of heart function in the embryo (1965). Of great interest is his discovery of a chromosomal deletion involving the nucleolar organizer and the gene for dark color which, in heterozygous condition, produces embryos with one normal and one very small nucleolus in their nuclei that are thus conveniently marked for nuclear transplantation (Humphrey, 1961).

REFERENCES

ANDERSON, P. L., 1943: The normal development of *Triturus pyrrhogaster*. *Anat. Rec.*, 86: 59. (See also Rugh, 1962, p. 88.)

BAIRD, S. F., 1850: Revision of the North American Tailed-Batrachia, with descriptions of new genera and species. *J. Acad. Nat. Sci. Phila.*, Second Series, 1: 281.

BIDEAU, M., 1964: Manifestations cytologiques et comportement des noyaux au cours de la greffe nucléaire chez l'urodèle *Pleurodeles waltlii* Michah. *Compt. Rend. Acad. Sci.* (Paris), 259: 213.

BISHOP, S. C., 1941: *The Salamanders of New York*. 365 pp. New York State Museum Bull. No. 324.

———, 1943: *Handbook of Salamanders. The Salamanders of the United States, of Canada, and of Lower California*. 555 pp. Comstock Publishing Co., Ithaca, N.Y.

BRIGGS, R., and R. R. HUMPHREY, 1962: Studies on the maternal effect of the semilethal gene, v, in the Mexican axolotl. *Devel. Biol.*, 5: 127.

———, J. SIGNORET, and R. R. HUMPHREY, 1964: Transplantation of nuclei of various cell types from neurulae of the Mexican axolotl (*Ambystoma mexicanum*). *Devel. Biol.*, 10: 233.

COPE, E. D., 1889: *The Batrachia of North America*. 525 pp. Bull. U.S. Nat. Museum, No. 34.

FANKHAUSER, G., 1934: Cytological studies on egg fragments of the salamander Triton. V. Chromosome number and chromosome individuality in the cleavage mitoses of merogonic fragments. *J. Exp. Zool.*, 68: 1.

———, 1938: Triploidy in the newt, *Triturus viridescens*. *Proc. Am. Philos. Soc.*, 79: 715.

———, 1945: The effects of changes in chromosome number on amphibian development. *Quart. Rev. Biol.*, 20: 20.

———, 1948: The organization of the amphibian egg during fertilization and cleavage. *Ann. N.Y. Acad. Sci.*, 49: 684.

———, 1963: Amphibia. In W. Lane-Petter (ed.), *Animals for Research: Principles of Breeding and Management*. Academic Press, London and New York, p. 475.

———, and R. B. GRIFFITHS, 1939: Induction of triploidy and haploidy in the newt, *Triturus viridescens*, by cold treatment of unsegmented eggs. *Proc. Nat. Acad. Sci.*, 25: 233.

———, and R. R. HUMPHREY, 1942: Induction of triploidy and haploidy in axolotl eggs by cold treatment. *Biol. Bull.*, 83: 367.

———, and ———, 1959: The origin of spontaneous heteroploids in the progeny of diploid, triploid, and tetraploid axolotl females. *J. Exp. Zool.*, 142: 379.

———, and R. C. WATSON, 1942: Heat-induced triploidy in the newt, *Triturus viridescens*. *Proc. Nat. Acad. Sci.*, 28: 436.

GALL, J. G., 1954: Lampbrush chromosomes from oocyte nuclei of the newt. *J. Morph.*, 94: 283.

———, 1958: Chromosomal differentiation. In W. D. McElroy and B. Glass (eds.), *The Chemical Basis of Development*, Johns Hopkins Press, Baltimore, Md., p. 103.

———, 1963: Chromosomes and cytodifferentiation. *Symposium of the Society for the Study of Development and Growth*, 21: 119.

GALLIEN, L., 1952: Elévage et comportement du Pleurodèle au laboratoire. *Bull. Soc. Zool. France*, 77: 456.

———, 1962: Personal communication.

———, 1966: Le caryotype de l'urodèle Pleurodeles poireti Gervais. Étude comparative des caryotypes dans le genre *Pleurodeles*. *Compt. Rend. Acad. Sci.* (Paris), 262: 122.

———, and M. DUROCHER, 1957: Table chronologique du développement chez *Pleurodeles waltlii* Michah. *Bull. Biol.*, 91: 97.

———, M. LABROUSSE, B. PICHERAL, and J.-C. LACROIX, 1965: Modifications expérimentales du caryotype chez un amphibien urodèle (*Pleurodeles waltlii* Michah.) par irradiation de l'oeuf et la greffe nucléaire. *Rev. Suisse Zool.*, 72: 59.

———, B. PICHERAL, and J.-C. LACROIX, 1963a: Transplantation de noyaux triploides dans l'oeuf du Triton *Pleurodeles waltlii* Michah. Développement de larves viables. *Compt. Rend. Acad. Sci.* (Paris), 256: 2232.

———, ———, and ———, 1963b: Modifications de l'assortiment chromosomique chez les larves hypomorphes du triton *Pleurodeles waltlii* Michah., obtenues par transplantations de noyaux. *Compt. Rend. Acad. Sci.* (Paris), 257: 1721.

HAMBURGER, V., 1960: *A Manual of Experimental Embryology*, rev. ed., University of Chicago Press, Chicago, Ill.

HAUSCHKA, T. S., and V. V. BRUNST, 1965: Sexual dimorphism in the nucleolar autosome of the axolotl (*Siredon mexicanum*). *Hereditas*, 52: 345.

HUMPHREY, R. R., 1943: A lethal recessive character in the Mexican axolotl (*Ambystoma mexicanum*). *Anat. Rec.*, 85: 320.

———, 1948: A lethal fluid imbalance in the Mexican axolotl inherited as a simple Mendelian recessive. *J. Hered.*, 39: 255.

———, 1959: A linked gene determining the lethality usually accompanying a hereditary fluid imbalance in the Mexican axolotl. *J. Hered.*, 50: 279.

———, 1961a: A chromosomal deletion in the Mexican axolotl (*Siredon mexicanum*) involving the nucleolar organizer and the gene for dark color. *Amer. Zool.*, 1: 361.

———, 1961b: Personal communication.

———, 1961c: The Mexican axolotl (*Siredon mexicanum*): feeding, care, etc., of adults and young. 7 pp. Mimeographed. Available from Dept. of Zool., Indiana University, Bloomington, Ind.

———, 1962a: Mexican axolotls, dark and mutant white strains: care of experimental animals. *Bull. Phila. Herpet. Soc.*, April–Sept.: 21.

———, 1962b: A semilethal factor (v) in the Mexican axolotl (*Siredon mexicanum*) and its maternal effect. *Devel. Biol.*, 4: 423.

———, 1964: Genetic and experimental studies on a lethal factor (r) in the axolotl which induces abnormalities in the renal system and other organs. *J. Exp. Zool.*, 155: 136.

———, 1965: Personal communication.

———, and G. FANKHAUSER, 1957: The origin of spontaneous and experimental haploids in the Mexican axolotl (*Siredon—or Ambystoma—mexicanum*). *J. Exp. Zool.*, 134: 427.

HUMPHRIES, A. A., 1955: Observations on the mating behavior of normal and pituitary-implanted *Triturus viridescens*. *Physiol. Zool.*, 28: 73.

HUTCHINSON, R. C., 1950: Amphibia. In E. J. Farris (ed.), *The Care and Breeding of Laboratory Animals*, John Wiley & Sons, Inc., New York, p. 331.

MILLER, M. R., and M. E. ROBBINS, 1954: The reproductive cycle in *Taricha torosa* (*Triturus torosus*). *J. Exp. Zool.*, 125: 415.

OKADA, Y. M., and M. ICHIKAWA, 1947: A new normal table for the development of *Triturus pyrrhogaster*. *Exp. Morphol.* (Tokyo), 3: 1 (in Japanese).

OYAMA, J., 1930: Normentafel der frueheren Entwicklung des *Diemictylus pyrrhogaster* (Boie). *Zool. Mag.*, 23: 465 (in Japanese).

RAFINESQUE, C. S., 1820: *Annals of Nature or Annual Synopsis of New Genera and Species of Animals, Plants, etc., Discovered in North America.* 16 pp. Lexington, Ky.

RUGH, R., 1962: *Experimental Embryology. Techniques and Procedures.* 3rd ed., 501 pp. Burgess Publishing Co., Minneapolis, Minn.

SETO, R., and C. M. POMERAT, 1965: *In vitro* study of somatic chromosomes in newts, genus *Taricha*. *Copeia*, 1965: 415.

SIGNORET, J., 1965: Étude des chromosomes de la blastula chez l'axolotl. *Chromosoma*, 17: 328.

———, R. BRIGGS, and R. R. HUMPHREY, 1962: Nuclear transplantation in the axolotl. *Devel. Biol.*, 4: 134.

STEBBINS, R. C., 1951: *Amphibians of Western North America.* 539 pp. University of California Press, Berkeley, Calif.

TWITTY, V. C., 1965: Personal communication.

WAGNER, C., 1944: Experiments on artificial parthenogenesis of eggs of the newt, *Triturus viridescens*. Senior thesis, Princeton University, Princeton, N.J.

Medaka

By Toki-o Yamamoto

INTRODUCTION

In recent years, the medaka (*Oryzias latipes*) has come to be widely used as a laboratory animal in various fields in biology, especially in developmental biology and genetics. Its relatively short life cycle, capacity to reproduce, and ease of breeding are chiefly responsible for its popularity in these fields.

The medaka is indeed useful to biologists of various fields, because it is small, hardy, and prolific. It has proved to be extremely useful in the study of fertilization (Yamamoto, 1939, 1944; *cf.* also 1961) and embryology because, unlike the guppy, the platyfish, and the swordtail, the medaka is an oviparous cyprinodont fish. The medaka is particularly suitable as biological material for laboratories with limited finances and space; it can withstand cold temperatures. The medaka is also useful in the study and practices of genetics because there are various mutants of this species. In fact, among fishes, it is the first in which the Mendelian laws have been proven to be valid (Toyama, 1916) and partially Y-linked inheritance has been established (Aida, 1921). It is also the first animal in which complete reversal of sex differentiation in both directions was successfully induced by administration of sex hormones during larval life (Yamamoto, 1953, 1955, 1958).

In view of these facts, the writer presents several hints on procurement, maintenance, care, and use of the fish for convenience of researchers. Brief surveys of culture methods, secondary sexual characters, and the method of artificial fertilization are made. In addition, some precautions necessary for breeding and some advanced techniques for developmental biology are touched upon.

As to cleavage and later developmental stages, Rugh's book (1948, p. 376) is an adequate reference written in the English language. In Japanese, two articles on normal stages of development have been published, one by Matui (1949) and another by Gamo and Terajima (1963). Briggs and Egami (1959) presented the most complete bibliography on the medaka.

PROCUREMENT AND ESTABLISHMENT OF STOCKS

Although the wild type (brown or olive) fish can be found and easily collected in Japan, some color varieties such as orange-red, white, and others have been kept in Japan. The orange-red type is sometimes referred to as "golden" medaka in some quarters. Thus, Innes (1935 and later editions) stated that "In the cultivated stock a pale gold replaces the olive . . ." and that "there is said to be a deeper orange stock which the writer has never seen." This is because of the fact that orange color (carotenoid) tends to fade when the fish is cultured indoors.

The origin of orange-red and other color varieties of cultivated stocks is wrapped in a shroud of a mist. The orange-red fishes have been painted by Ukiyoē artists of the Yedo era, so the race must have arisen by mutation from the wild type more than a few hundred years ago. The orange-red stock and a few other varieties have since been kept by goldfish breeders.

Centers of farms of cultivated stocks are Yatomi near Nagoya, Kōriyama in Nara Prefecture, and Urayasu in Chiba Prefecture. It must be borne in mind that the medaka breeders have cultivated so-called "Himedaka" collectively. Hence, it is natural that so-called "Himedaka" (orange-red) stocks include a few non-orange-red varieties. The Himedaka are available at goldfish shops and night stalls in any large city in Japan. This being so, the Himedaka are not a pure orange-red variety, but are comprised of heterozygous orange-red, white, and variegated races. To establish pure strains, medaka must be bred in the laboratory. The chromatophores responsible for body color of fish are melanophores, xanthophores, and leucophores. The "brown" chromatophores described by Goodrich (1927) seem to be leucophores which are brown by transmitted light but opaque white by reflected light.

The inheritance of body color in this fish has been studied by Toyama (1916), Ishihara (1917), and Aida (1921). The excellent work by the last-mentioned author revealed that the various color effects are referred to the action of genes. When the genes are homozygous, the color varieties are assigned as follows: brown (wild type) *BBRR*; blue *BBrr*; white *bbrr*; variegated orange-red *B′B′RR*; and variegated white *B′B′rr*. The triple alleles *B*, *B′*, *b* control the formation of melanin in the melanophore and are autosomal. The gene *B*, which is dominant to both *B′* and *b*, permits full formation of melanin. *B′* is dominant to *b* and causes variegation. There are pigmented and nonpigmented areas in the genotypes *B′B′* and *B′b* producing the mottled appearance. In the orange-red (*bbRR* or *bbRr*) and white (*bbrr*), the melanin formation is so scanty that melanophores are usually invisible in an "expanded" condition.

The genes *R* and *r* govern the deposition of an orange-red carotenoid pigment in xanthophores and are partially sex-linked. Both the X and Y chromosomes have a locus for either *R* or *r*. The Y chromosome usually carries *R*. We will touch upon the occurrence of the Y^r chromosome later. When only the orange-red and white varieties are referred to, the phenotype of the former can be denoted simply as *R* and the latter *r* because both of them are carrying the common *bb* genes. The partially sex-linked *R* and *r* genes can be used as excellent marker genes.

In the cultivated stock available from dealers, a white (*bbrr*) fish is rare. In addition, rare white fishes are usually females with the constitution bbX^rX^r (*cf.* Aida, 1921). This might be because of the fact that the gene *r* must have arisen by mutation of X^R but not from the Y^R. The Y^r chromosome is produced only by crossing over between the X^r and Y^R. Both in Aida's and our breeds, white males (bbX^rY^r) have appeared by allosomal crossing over.

In consequence of this fact, the white medaka is rare and the male is even rarer than the female. As an example, we may mention our scores made in 1961 (Tomita and Yamamoto, unpublished). Of 4,000 cultivated stock obtained from a dealer at Yatomi, we found only 19 white fishes all of which were females. It follows that the white medaka in cultivated stock is usually present at the level of only 0.5 percent. By use of the Hardy-Weinberg law (Hardy, 1908; Weinberg, 1908; *cf.* also Stern, 1943), it is estimated that about 13 percent of the cultivated stock is heterozygous (*bbRr*).

When we can obtain even a single white male, it is easy to establish a pure white strain (bbX^rX^r and bbX^rY^r). To establish homozygous stock of orange-red fish, one should mate individually an orange-red fish with a white fish in order to test whether the former has the genotype *RR* or *Rr*. If their offspring are all orange-red, it is certain that the orange-red parent is homozygous. When, however, no white fish is available, breeding of a single *bR* female and *bR* male and their offspring must be continued for several generations. If no white fish appear, it is almost certain that the stock breeds true. Our d-*RR* strain has been established by the latter alternative.

Genealogy of our d-*rR* stock in which the female is white (bbX^rX^r) and the male is orange-red (bbX^rY^R), displaying father-to-son inheritance, is described in one of my papers (Yamamoto, 1958). The original progenitors of the stock were purchased in 1945 from a dealer at Yatomi near Nagoya. First, a white female (bbX^rX^r) was mated with a homozygous orange-red male (bbX^RY^R). Then, an F_1 heterozygous orange-red male (bbX^rY^R) was back-crossed to a white female (bbX^rX^r) to get equal numbers of white females and orange-red males. Thereafter, interbreeding of the offspring has been repeated generation after generation by mass matings.

The d-*rR* strain is very useful for the study of sex differentiation because the presumable sex genotype can be distinguished by body color. It is important to make a stock census before the breeding season because there appear to be some exceptions (about 0.5 percent) which are either crossover white males (X^rY^r) or X^rY^R females arising from genic outbalance of sex genes. These exceptions must be removed from the population. The crossover X^rX^R females cannot be distinguished except by test crosses.

For experimental embryology, the gene *B* of the wild type can be used as an excellent marker. This gene manifests itself within 48 hours after fertilization when eggs are kept at 25–28°C. On the yolk sac of embryos from the age of 2 days onward, there appear embryonic melanophores. Goodrich (1927) used this gene to score F_2 segregation ratios of the hybrids of *bb* × *BB* and *bb* × *Bb*. One of my students (Uwa, 1965) has performed an experiment of gynogenesis using *b*-eggs inseminated by *B*-sperm weakened by treatment with toluidine blue to ascertain that karyogamy did not take place. Thus, he has succeeded in producing haploid embryos. Use of the wild-type males (*BB*) is promising for other experimental approaches.

ANESTHESIA

For observation, operation, and sexing of immature fish or adults, anesthesia is necessary. Either phenylurethane (not ethylurethane) or Chloretone (chlorobutanol) can be used as an anesthetic. Recently, MS-222 (Tricaine methansulfonate, Sandoz Laboratories) has been widely used as a fish anesthetic. For this fish, however, phenylurethane is the best. Phenylurethane of 0.015 percent may be used satisfactorily to immobilize the fish. Since the melting point of phenylurethane is about 50°C and its solubility is low, it is wise to make 0.1 percent solution dissolved

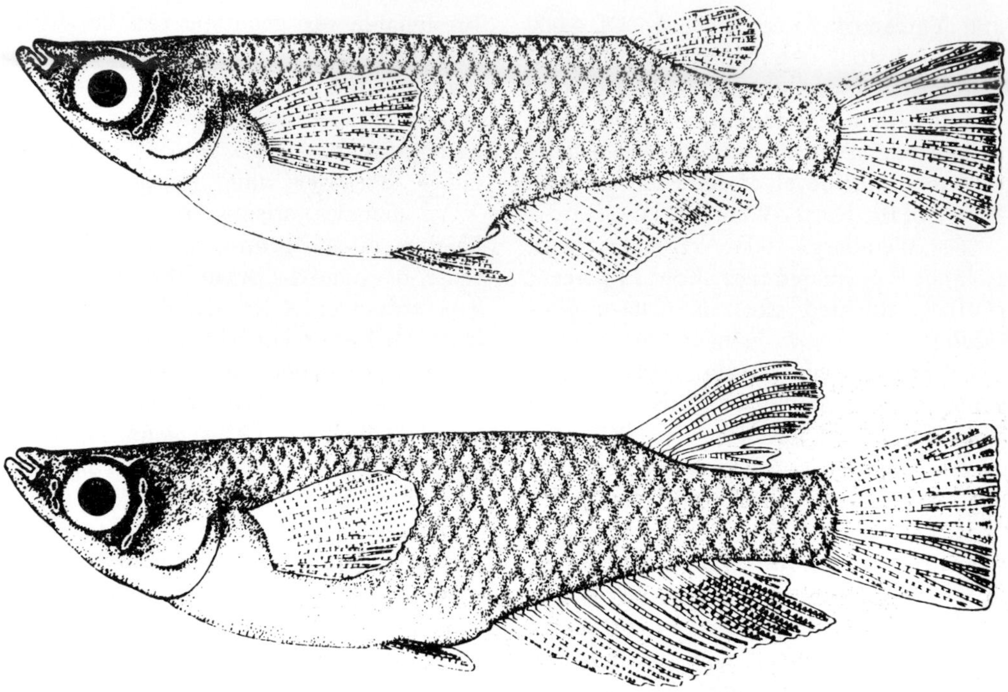

FIG. 1. Female (above) and male (below) of the medaka *(Oryzias latipes)*.

at a temperature of 60°C as a stock solution. Take 15 parts of this solution and dilute it with 85 parts of water. Chloretone (0.035 percent) is also useful.

To preserve the life of anesthetized fish, they should be returned to water before the extent of breathing movements reaches minimum as judged by over-all feebleness and irregularity of breathing. It is harmful to anesthetize fish more than once a day.

SEXING OF FISH

The sex of fully grown fish can be determined by putting the fish into a beaker of water and observing it from the side. The male and female are easily distinguished by the outline of the anal and dorsal fins (Fig. 1). It is wise and certainly safe, however, to observe an anesthetized fish under a low-power microscope. This method is especially useful for sexing an immature fish.

For detailed points of secondary sexual characters, the reader is referred to Oka (1931) and Yamamoto (1953, 1958). The female is characterized by having less developed anal and dorsal fins and well developed urinogenital papilla. In the full-grown female, all anal fin rays except the first two-to-four, are usually bifurcated. The male has enlarged anal and dorsal fins and poorly developed urinogenital papilla. The anal fin rays of the male are single except the last one, which is usually bifurcated. The margin of these fins in the male has a saw-toothed appearance, and the dorsal fin has a deep cleft between the last ray and the one preceding it.

The most prominent feature of the male sexual character is the presence of numerous small papillar processes on the posterior region of the anal fin. At the posterior margin of the caudal and at the distal margin of the anal fin, there appear a series of leucophores, which become conspicuous in the breeding season.

SPAWNING

Spawning usually takes place at dawn. Prior to spawning, the male displays a characteristic sexual maneuvering. The male approaches the female and performs swift circular movements around its mate. Then the male assumes a position slightly below and behind the female. When the female is receptive both sexes juxtapose themselves and the male embraces its mate by bending the anal and dorsal fins at the position of homologous female fins. Both dorsal and anal fins of the male are broader than those of the female, and the anal fin of the male has numerous papillar processes on the posterior half of the fin. These secondary sexual characters are undoubtedly adapted to clasping its mate firmly. During the embrace, their bodies twist in a characteristic S-curve, in which the head of the male is bent somewhat toward the female with its tail projecting outward. In this juxtaposition, accompanied by vibrating movements of the posterior parts of the pair, ova and sperm are released.

After the ova are expelled *en masse* at the time of mating, a cluster of eggs remains attached to the belly of the female for some hours, suspended from the oviduct pore by fine threads attached to the chorion. Finally, the egg mass is detached by the action of the female in swimming and contacting roots of water plants, or if there is no vegetation, by contacting the bottom of the container. The water hyacinth, *Pontederia* (*Eichhornia*) *crassipes*, by virtue of its brushlike root system serves as an admirable receiver of fish spawn. The foxtail *Myriophyllum verticillatum* can also be used as a suitable water plant.

BREEDING TECHNIQUE

In outdoor mass breeding, a number of males and females are placed in a pool with a base of concrete or in a larger earthen basin. A frame covered by a wire netting is laid over the container. This is necessary to protect fish against predatory animals, such as the kingfisher which picks up the fish, and the dragonfly, which deposits its eggs in the water. Nymphs of dragonflies are plagues for young fish. Aside from protecting the fish, the frame is useful to prevent them from leaping out and from running over the sides during heavy rains.

The detritus or mulm accumulating on the bottom should be siphoned off by a hose. It is recommended to have a water-hyacinth float on the water surface. When eggs deposited on the roots are "eyed," the plant should be removed to another container. This must be done because newly hatched fry are preyed upon by their parents. Because of this parental cannibalism, fry will usually not survive when they are allowed to live together with adults.

In indoor breeding, every care must be taken as to container, water, temperature, and lighting because indoor conditions cannot duplicate natural ones. In later pages, necessary conditions are described. Because medaka are inhabitants of stagnant waters or slowly streaming waters rather than rapidly flowing rivers, they do not need much oxygen. Hence, if fishes are not unduly crowded, aeration and filtration are unnecessary. However, mulm should be siphoned off and the coral or ramshorn snail (*Planorbis corneus*) is a useful scavenger. The more light the better.

Propagation of unicellular algae (producing so-called green water) is an indication that lighting conditions are sufficient.

For the purpose of genetic studies, one to five females of known genotype may be mated with one male. For carrying this out, the male and the females are put simultaneously into a container. When it is necessary to place the two sexes in the container at different times, it is better to introduce females to a male that has become accustomed to the container rather than the reverse, because a larger female accustomed to the container sometimes attacks the newly arrived male.

Care must be taken to avoid possible mixing of different breeds. In breeding season, the same net used to take fish out of one container should not be employed to take fish from other containers until the net is completely dried. This is to guard against allowing eggs adhering to the net to be transferred.

Some precautions with this fish are of paramount importance for an accurate genetic study. Although fertilization is usually external, internal fertilization and development of eggs may occur in extremely rare cases, as first pointed out by Amemiya and Murayama (1931). Eggs fertilized within the female are usually shed together with ripe ova at the next spawning (usually on the next day). In order to avoid the possible mixture of zygotes resulting from promiscuous mating, it is recommended that the first batch of eggs or the first hatched fry should be excluded from the container. This procedure is necessary when previously mated females are used for genetic work. It is, therefore, advisable to use virgin females when possible. In this case, however, virgin females prior to maturity, or before breeding season, should be used. A mature female does not usually lay eggs when she is kept isolated from the male. Only on rare occasions does she lay some infertile eggs in swimming in contact with the wall of the container. When a mature female is kept isolated from the male for long, her abdomen becomes greatly distended because of an accumulation of daily ovulated and decaying ova within the ovary. A female with an abnormally plump abdomen becomes barren, and even if she is given a mate she does not spawn and her death is hastened as a result of rupture of the abdominal skin.

ARTIFICIAL FERTILIZATION

The female, once it has become mature, spawns at dawn of succeeding days during breeding season. In the day time, the mature female living together with the male contains no ripe ova. In performing artificial fertilization, therefore, females which have spawned one or more times should be isolated from males during the day before the experiment is to be performed. Females are sacrificed to obtain ripe ova because the ordinary stripping method is not only harmful to fish but frequently injures ova and causes them to manifest mechanical activation.

The brain of the isolated female is pithed with a needle to immobilize it. Upon dissecting such a female, one will find in the ovary ripe eggs which would have been laid at the dawn of the day of the experiment if the female had been living with the male. The testis of the male is isolated in the same manner.

Isolated ovary and testis are separately immersed in an isotonic balanced salt solution for the medaka, composed of 0.133 M NaCl (100 parts) + 0.133 M KCl (2.0 parts) + 0.099 M $CaCl_2$ (2.1 parts) (pH adjusted to 7.3 by about 0.002 percent of $NaHCO_3$). This solution is equal to the following weight mixture: NaCl, 0.75 percent; KCl, 0.02 percent; $CaCl_2$, 0.02 percent; and $NaHCO_3$, 0.002 percent.

The isolated ovary is torn with a pair of glass needles in the solution in order to separate ripe ova from the rest. The ripe ova can be distinguished from unripe ones by their large size and translucent nature. Sperms are liberated by tearing the testis in the solution, and they are used to inseminate the ova.

The above solution was formulated by the writer on the basis of osmotic pressure of *Oryzias* eggs (Yamamoto, 1941) and is found to be most appropriate for keeping the unfertilized egg in fertilizable condition and as a medium for artificial insemination (Yamamoto, 1939, 1944, *cf.* also 1963). Moreover, this solution is better than fresh water for development of *Oryzias* eggs.

METHOD FOR REMOVING THE CHORION

The egg of the medaka is surrounded by the chorion (egg membrane). It consists of a thinner outer and a thicker inner layer. For experimental embryology it is desirable to remove the chorion. However, within a few minutes after fertilization the chorion becomes so tough and the egg proper is so delicate that mechanical removal without injuring the egg is almost always unsuccessful.

The use of hatching enzyme to dissolve the chorion proved to be satisfactory. Ishida (1944a, 1944b) found the hatching glands in the medaka while he was staying in our laboratory. If we observe advanced embryos under a low-power microscope, the upper roof of the buccal cavity looks opaque. This is due to the fact that there are numerous hatching glands in that region. If, however, we observe embryos ready to hatch or newly hatched fry the buccal cavity is clear. This indicates that the hatching enzyme has been already discharged.

A simple method for chorion removal is to put three advanced embryos with opaque buccal cavities into a deep hollow slide containing the balanced salt solution for the medaka; crush embryos to obtain a crude enzyme solution. Then, put one intact egg into the solution. Within 3 hours the outer layer may be perforated here and there, and the inner layer is dissolved. Then, the thinner outer layer may be torn easily by a pair of forceps or by gently blowing, using a pipette. The enzyme acts mainly on the inner layer.

Sakai (1961) reported another method to remove the chorion. Hardening of the chorion after fertilization is due to toughening of the thicker inner layer. Hence, if slits are made in the chorion, access of the enzyme is quickened with the result that the dissolution of the chorion becomes faster. Using this procedure and putting eggs in the balanced salt solution containing hatching enzyme and pancreatin, she has succeeded in removing the chorion not only from fertilized eggs but from unfertilized ones. Fertilization of denuded eggs of the medaka was accomplished.

Smithberg (1966) reported an enzymatic procedure for dechorionating this fish egg, using "pronase," a proteolytic enzyme of bacterial origin.

MICROINJECTION OF CHEMICALS INTO FERTILIZED EGG

Shortly after fertilization the chorion is soft. Hardening of the membrane is completed within some minutes after fertilization. After the completion of the toughening process, the chorion becomes so tough and elastic that injection is difficult. Injection of chemicals immediately after fertilization is relatively easy. At this stage it can be done without using a micromanipulator.

Artificial insemination should be accomplished by the method described in the section on artificial fertilization, and injections should be made immediately after the breakdown of cortical alveoli. A suitable tool must be devised to hold the egg tightly. A loop made of glass is recommended. Injection can be made under a binocular microscope using a micropipette with a thick gum bulb, the tip of which is 20 μ in diameter. After the injection, eggs may be kept in our 0.133 *M* balanced salt solution containing 100 I.U. of penicillin per milliliter.

Recently, microinjection of oily substances has successfully been accomplished in our laboratory. Hishida (1964) has performed the injection of a droplet of olive oil containing estrogens stained with Sudan III. About 10 percent of injected eggs hatched out and grew into larvae of 15 mm in length. Takeuchi (1965) has injected carotenoids into the egg.

CULTURE OF MEDAKA

Container

For indoor culture, all-glass vessels are the best. We use squat round glass bowls with a diameter of 30 cm. A container of this size can hold about 15 adults at a temperature of 25°–28°C. The usual rectangular aquarium with steel frames can be used only after every trace of potentially poisonous substance is completely diffused out; used aquariums are preferable.

Feeding

The medaka is omnivorous; it takes both animal and vegetable foods. As live foods, certain aquatic worms (*Tubifex*, *Limunodrilus*) and the white worm (*Enchytraeus*) are adequate. The ideal live foods for both adults and young are certain water fleas (Entomostraca) and the brine shrimp (*Artemia salina*). Among water fleas, *Moina macrocopa* has proved to be the best. It is smaller than *Daphnia*, so that it is readily taken by the fish. Although adult *Moina* cannot be eaten by young fish, it is recommended that they be put in the containers, because tiny larvae of *Moina*, which are parthenogenetically produced, are easily eaten by young fish.

For newly hatched fry, large protozoans, especially *Paramecium caudatum*, are adequate as live food. The micro worm (*Anguillula*) can also be eaten by them. In ordinary culture of fish, live foods have beneficial effects. The medaka, however, can thrive safely on dried foods provided that water contains unicellular green algae. For instance, in our experiments on the effect of sex hormones, it was necessary to force the fry to eat a standard dry diet containing hormones. The writer has formulated a standard diet which consists of the following: 60 gm shrimp powder, 30 gm toasted whole barley flour, 6 gm dried yeast preparation, 4 gm powdered green tea (Yamamoto, 1955). The mixture should be sifted by a sieve with 100–150 mesh. Fry are fed on this diet with or without hormones until they reach the 12-mm stage or older. While unicellular algae in the aquarium may be taken by fry to some extent even under this condition, it is almost certain that the main nutriments are the dried foods.

Thereafter, the fry are reared outdoors on a mixture of shrimp powder and toasted whole barley flour with the occasional addition of some live foods. Some natural live foods, such as mosquito larvae, are taken by fish under outdoor conditions. Chironomid larvae are not taken by the fish.

Water

Well or pond water is perfectly satisfactory. Tap water cannot be used immediately after it is drawn, because it is usually treated with chlorine and other chemical agents. By drawing a quantity of tap water and exposing it to sunlight for 2 or 3 days or allowing it to stand longer, it then becomes fit for use because volatile chlorine will have evaporated within that period. Bubbling of air quickens elimination of chlorine. For a rapid remedy for harmful chlorine, addition of 0.1–0.3 gm of sodium hyposulfite, $Na_2S_2O_3$, per 10 liters is generally recommended.

Although habitats of the medaka are mainly waters of low lands and brackish water, it is also known to inhabit tide pools of coasts of certain regions in Japan and Korea. The medaka withstands a wide range of salinity, and a diluted sea water is rather better than the fresh water. In indoor culture, therefore, the use of a balanced salt solution is recommended, if the tap water proves to be unsuitable.

Rugh (1948) suggested use of the following salt solution: NaCl, 1.0 gm; KCl, 0.03 gm; $CaCl_2$, 0.03 gm; $MgCl_2$, 0.08 gm; and distilled water to 1 liter. This solution is osmotically equivalent to about 0.02 *M* NaCl solution (1/25 of sea water) and is quite satisfactory. However, the use of a "bicarbonated" distilled water may be recommended (0.02 gm of $NaHCO_3$ per liter, pH 7.3) in making the above mentioned solution. Practically, it is convenient to make the following stock solution, which is osmotically equivalent to a 1 *M* NaCl solution: NaCl, 500 gm; KCl, 15 gm; $CaCl_2$, 15 gm; $MgSO_4$, 40 gm; and distilled water to 10 liters. This solution is diluted to 1/50 with "bicarbonated" distilled water of pH 7.3. For rearing of eggs, the balanced salt solution equivalent to 0.133 *M* NaCl solution (pH adjusted to 7.3) is better.

Keeping one or more extra containers filled with reservoir water is recommended. These may be placed close to fish-containing aquaria, and used for changing water. This procedure is desirable for two reasons: first, because the harmful effect of chlorine is avoided, and second, because the same temperature as that of fish-containing aquaria is obtained. For the latter reason even when using a balanced salt solution, keeping a reservoir is preferable. Any sudden change in water temperature may prove fatal to fish.

Temperature

Since the medaka is native to the Far East, it can withstand the winter in temperate zones without artificial heat. This fact gives it a higher scientific value than other tropical fishes. In temperate climates, the stock can be kept in out-of-door conditions throughout the whole year. They can survive at a wide range of temperatures, tolerating temperatures as low as 1°C. The maximal thermal point is 37°–38°C. Temperatures of 25°–28°C have been found to be suitable for breeding.

In Tokyo and Nagoya, the breeding season extends from mid-April to mid-September. If a temperature of 25°–28°C is controlled by artificial means, maturation is quickened and the seasonal reproductive habit is destroyed; spawning can then be induced in any season, even winter. The fish can stand a wide range of temperature fluctuations providing the change is gradual; sudden changes of temperature are harmful to fish.

Light

Because the medaka is probably subtropical in origin and is a typical surface swimmer, it likes plenty of sunlight. In culturing of this fish, light has a beneficial effect. In rearing the medaka indoors, containers should be placed under windows in the area where pollution of air is not serious.

In culturing the fish in the interior of a room, "day-light" fluorescent tubes or "warm white" tubes must be used. The latter, which resembles sunlight more closely, is better. Continuous lighting, however, upsets the rhythm of reproduction of the fish. The tubes must be switched on and off; 12 hours of light and 12 hours of dark are recommended.

Sufficient light induces growth of unicellular algae and turns the water greenish. Light green water is favorable for fish because unicellular algae serve not only as oxygenators but as their food.

Diseases

It is not my intention to give a detailed description of fish diseases and fish therapy, since they are common to many fresh-water fishes and may be found in any book on aquarium keeping or fish culture. Therefore, only a few hints on remedies for the most common diseases are given.

Of the many diseases, the most common ones are caused by a fungus (*Saprolegnia*) and a parasitic ciliate (*Ichthyophthirius*), or "Ich." *Saprolegnia* infects the chorion of eggs, young fish, and adults. Two methods are recommended for combating the fungus. Eggs or fish should be put temporarily in a remedial bath. One method is to bathe them in 0.02 percent (1:5,000) solution of Mercurochrome (dibromohydroxymercurifluorescein, sodium) for 30–40 minutes. The other is to bathe them in 0.0005 percent (1:200,000) solution of Malachite green for 30–40 minutes.

The "white spots," or "Ich," is a highly contagious disease and is difficult to cure. Formerly, treatment with a 0.001 percent solution of quinine sulfate for a week was recommended. Nowadays, however, effective medications for treatment may be obtained from any tropical fish shop.

REFERENCES

AIDA, T., 1921: On the inheritance of color in a fresh-water fish, *Aplocheilus latipes* Temminck et Schlegel, with special reference to sex-linked inheritance. *Genetics*, 6: 554.

AMEMIYA, I., and S. MURAYAMA, 1931: Some remarks on the existence of developing embryos in the body of an oviparous cyprinodont, *Oryzias latipes* (Temmink et Schlegel). *Proc. Imp. Acad.* (Tokyo), 7: 176.

BRIGGS, J. C., and N. EGAMI, 1959: The medaka (*Oryzias latipes*). A commentary and a bibliography. *J. Fish. Res. Bd. Canada*, 16: 363.

GAMO, H., and I. TERAJIMA, 1963: The normal stages of embryonic development of the medaka, *Oryzias latipes* [in Japanese]. *Jap. J. Ichthyol.*, 10: 31.

GOODRICH, H. B., 1927: A study of the development of Mendelian characters in *Oryzias latipes*. *J. Exp. Zool.*, 49: 261.

HARDY, G. H., 1908: Mendelian proportions in a mixed population. *Science*, 28: 49.

HISHIDA, T., 1964: Reversal of sex-differentiation in genetic males of the medaka (*Oryzias latipes*) by injecting estrone-16-C^{14} and diethylstilbestrol (monoethyl-1-C^{14}) into the egg. *Embryologia*, 8: 234.

INNES, W. T., 1935: *Exotic Aquarium Fishes*. Aquar. Publ. Co., Norristown, Pa.

ISHIDA, J., 1944a: Hatching enzyme in the fresh-water fish, *Oryzias latipes*. *Annot. Zool. Japon.*, 22: 137.

———, 1944b: Further studies on the hatching enzyme of the fresh-water fish, *Oryzias latipes*. *Annot. Zool. Japon.*, 22: 155.

ISHIHARA, K., 1917: On the inheritance of body color in *Oryzias latipes*. *Mitt. Med. Fak. Kyushu*, 4: 261.

MATUI, K., 1949: Illustration of the normal course of development in the fish, *Oryzias latipes* [in Japanese]. *Zikkenkeitaigaku* [Experimental Morphology], 5: 33.

OKA, T. B., 1931: On the processes on the fins in the male of *Oryzias latipes* and other sex characters of this fish. *J. Fac. Sci., Tokyo Univ.*, IV, 2: 171.

RUGH, R., 1948: *Experimental Embryology.* Burgess, Minneapolis, Minn.

SAKAI, Y. T., 1961: Method for removal of chorion and fertilization of the naked egg in *Oryzias latipes. Embryologia*, 5: 357.

SMITHBERG, M., 1966: An enzymatic procedure for dechorionating the fish embryo *Oryzias latipes. Anat. Rec.*, 154: 823.

STERN, C., 1943: The Hardy-Weinberg law. *Science*, 97: 137.

TAKEUCHI, K., 1965: A method of lipid injection into a fish egg. *Experientia*, 21: 736.

TOYAMA, K., 1916: Some examples of Mendelian characters [in Japanese]. Nihon Ikushugaku Kaiho, 1: 1.

UWA, H., 1965: Gynogenetic haploid embryos of the Medaka (*Oryzias latipes*). *Embryologia*, 9: 40.

WEINBERG, W., 1908: Über den Nachweis des Vererbung beim Menschen. *Jahrehefte Verein f. Naturk. in Württemberg*, 63: 368.

YAMAMOTO, T., 1939: Changes of the cortical layer of the egg of *Oryzias latipes* at the time of fertilization. *Proc. Imp. Acad.* (*Tokyo*), 15: 269.

———, 1941: The osmotic properties of fresh-water fish, *Oryzias latipes. J. Fac. Sci., Tokyo Imp. Univ.* IV, 5: 461.

———, 1944: Physiological studies on fertilization and activation of fish eggs. I. Response of the cortical layer of the egg of *Oryzias latipes* to insemination and to artificial stimulation. *Annot. Zool. Japon.*, 22: 109.

———, 1953: Artificially induced sex-reversal in genotypic males of the medaka (*Oryzias latipes*). *J. Exp. Zool.*, 123: 571.

———, 1955: Progeny of artificially induced sex-reversal of male genotype (XY) in the medaka (*Oryzias latipes*) with special reference to YY-male. *Genetics*, 40: 406.

———, 1958: Artificial induction of functional sex-reversal in genotypic females of the medaka (*Oryzias latipes*). *J. Exp. Zool.*, 137: 227.

———, 1961: Physiology of fertilization in fishes. *Intern. Rev. Cytol.*, 12: 361.

Fundulus

By J. P. Trinkaus

INTRODUCTION

Fundulus heteroclitus, Linnaeus, 1766, whose common names are killifish and mummichug, is one of the most abundant shallow water fishes of the Gulf and Atlantic coasts, ranging from Texas to the Gulf of St. Lawrence (Bigelow and Schroeder, 1953). It is found typically in inshore bays and inlets and in tidal estuaries and pools. Bigelow and Schroeder (1953) have suggested that practically all the *Fundulus* in the Gulf of Maine may be found within 100 yards of the shore.

COLLECTING

Fundulus are easily collected in minnow traps or by seining. It is said that seining is more effective on the incoming tide near high tide. The breeding season in the area of Woods Hole extends from early June until approximately the middle of July. However, some ripe adults may be found in the warmer waters of ditches and pools as early as the last part of May and in the colder waters of Cape Cod Bay and Pleasant Bay as late as the end of July. In any case there is always a certain amount of variability due to the weather. A hot, sunny June and July usually means an early end to the *Fundulus* season.

In the colder, more northern waters of the Gulf of Maine the season begins in early June and extends to the end of the first week of August. Ripe fish are found more readily in estuaries where the water temperature at low tide is 16°–18°C, as opposed to 10°–12° in the bay.

MAINTENANCE

The adult fish are easily maintained in the laboratory with minimum care. Sexes should be separated as soon as possible after collecting to prevent spawning. Aquarium water should be circulated or highly aerated and small numbers of fish placed in each aquarium. If during the spawning season *Fundulus* are kept under these conditions and fed raw quahog (*Mercenaria mercenaria*) once a day, they may be kept in good condition for weeks and will yield eggs and sperm during a good portion of that time.

DISTINGUISHING THE SEXES

Adult males and females are readily distinguished during the breeding season. Both usually measure between 2 and 4 inches in length, but may be as long as 6 inches. The male is a dull, dark green, the sides bearing narrow, ill-defined transverse bars composed of silvery spots. The dorsal fin has a black spot in its caudal aspect. The belly is predominantly yellowish. The female is pale olive and usually has no distinct bars or spots, although young females have indistinct, dark transverse bars on the sides. The dorsal fin is non-pigmented. *Fundulus majalis* often occurs with *F. heteroclitus* and its egg is also useful. It is less transparent than that of *F. heteroclitus*, however, and hence not as favorable material. Descriptions of the adults may be found in Costello, Davidson, Eggers, Fox, and Henley (1957). *Fundulus diaphanus* also is found frequently with *F. heteroclitus* and its egg is likewise useful for developmental studies.

FERTILIZATION

One of the advantages of *Fundulus* eggs is that they may be readily obtained by stripping and then fertilized at will. Gravid females can be recognized by their distended abdomens. To obtain eggs, the female is held firmly in one hand belly upward, anterior end facing the wrist, while *gentle* pressure is applied to the abdomen with the forefinger of the other hand. As the finger is pushed toward the vent the pressure forces out the eggs. When a female is viewed against the light while stripping, the eggs may be seen as they pass down the oviduct, which runs along the anal fin. If the female is ripe, eggs should strip easily, regardless of the size of the fish. A large female may yield a few hundred eggs at one stripping. If she is then returned to the aquarium, she should yield eggs again every few days for as long as 8 to 10 days. Males are stripped in the same way and the milt is expressed as a small issue of milky fluid. Small males often are more potent than larger ones.

For fertilization, eggs should be stripped first into a finger bowl whose bottom has been merely wetted with sea water. Sperm are added as soon as possible after, but no later than 10 minutes. If stripping males is unsuccessful, sperm can often be obtained quickly by opening a male, removing his testes, and mincing them in the finger bowl with the eggs. This method is used routinely in Maine. There need be no worry about adding too much sperm. Polyspermy is effectively prevented in *Fundulus* by closure of the micropylar canal immediately after sperm penetration (Huver, personal communication). Rocking the dish gently after addition of sperm will ensure fertilization. After the egg-sperm mixture has stood for 10–15 minutes, the fertilized eggs should be washed twice with fresh sea water and then left well separated in about a centimeter of sea water. The sea water should be changed daily. If the female has been stripped in properly gentle fashion all or virtually all the eggs will be fertilized.

ARTIFICIAL INDUCTION OF SPAWNING

Obtaining eggs in an advanced state of maturation prior to the onset of the normal spawning season is now standard practice in fish culture (reviewed in Pickford and Atz, 1957). There are two problems involved: (1) bringing immature fish to a prespawning condition, and (2) inducing spawning in ripe or nearly ripe fish. The former is best accomplished by regulation of environmental conditions, including food, temperature, and light. The latter is accomplished by hypophyseal injection.

Fundulus heteroclitus can be brought to maturity earlier than normal by keeping winter fish at a warm temperature (20°C) (Mathews, 1939). Spawning has been achieved by injections of *Fundulus* pituitary glands, or mammalian gonadotropin. Pickford (unpublished) obtained mature eggs early in May with a single intraperitoneal injection of bovine luteinizing hormone (LH)—(100 μg per gram weight of fish) into gravid females that had been brought to maturity at 20°C in the laboratory during the preceding winter. Lower doses and *Fundulus* pituitary glands would probably be equally effective (Pickford, personal communication). Mathews (1940) was able to mature the gonads of immature males and females by intraperitoneal implantations of adult *Fundulus* pituitary glands every third day for a month.

Pituitary glands of carp, which has been described by Russian investigators as a universal donor, may be obtained from Stoller Fisheries Inc., Spirit Lake, Iowa. Pituitary glands from various species may be obtained from the Harborton Marine Laboratory, Harborton, Virginia, and from New England Biological Associates, Inc., Sand Hill Cove Road, Narragansett, Rhode Island. Whole fresh or fresh-frozen glands are preferable, but extracts preserved in alcohol or acetone-dried will also work.

CONDITIONS FOR RAISING EMBRYOS

I know of no embryonic material easier to raise in the laboratory than the eggs of *Fundulus heteroclitus*. They are exceptionally tough and can withstand wide variations in temperature and salinity. No doubt their ability to survive in the highly variable environment of estuarial pools and ditches is due to this hardiness. In our experience development is normal at temperatures ranging from 15° to 27°C. Solberg (1938) reports normal development below 15°, to as low as 12°. We have found at Woods Hole, however, that even though embryos and eggs raised at such a low temperature appear normal superficially, they are not. For unexplained reasons they become quite fragile at these lower temperatures, wound readily upon dechorionation, heal wounds poorly, and are generally useless for operative procedures.

As befits the egg of an estuarian fish, *Fundulus* eggs are extraordinarily resistant to changes in salinity. They appear to develop best in normal sea water, especially during the first few hours after fertilization, but have been observed to develop in evaporated sea water, whose salts are saturated, and in distilled water. In the latter case, development appears to be normal up to the formation of the embryo, but after that the yolk sac swells very gradually until the perivitelline space is obliterated (Armstrong and Child, 1965). These changes occur with or without the chorion in place and are due exclusively to the permeability properties of the egg surface proper. The chorion appears to be readily permeable to all small molecules. The egg surface, on the contrary, is highly impermeable, even to water.

Fundulus eggs are highly resistant to disease, whether encased in the chorion or dechorionated. This is not so for the adult fish, however. They are susceptible to fungus when kept in aquaria, although the frequency of infection can be reduced if crowding is avoided and if the fish are handled with wet hands and as little as possible during stripping.

DECHORIONATION

Aside from its limited spawning season, the only special problem which the *Fundulus* egg presents is the difficulty of removing the chorion or shell. This is a serious matter, for it may well be the obstacle that has prevented widespread use of this otherwise excellent material for the analysis of development. Dechorionation therefore deserves detailed discussion. The chorion is a relatively thick (10–12 μ), tough membrane, which cannot be torn, like the vitelline membrane of a frog's egg, without destroying the egg. It must be cut away, a difficult and tedious procedure. There have been systematic attempts by students in the Embryology

Course at Woods Hole to circumvent this difficulty by treating eggs with enzymes and other agents which might conceivably soften or digest the chorion without adversely affecting the egg. To my knowledge all such attempts have failed. At first this was surprising, since the *Fundulus* larva manages to digest the bulk of the chorion very well prior to hatching by an enzyme produced in the mouth region (Armstrong, 1936). Inability to digest the chorion by external treatment is probably due to its peculiar structure. According to Shanklin (1959), the chorion is composed of two layers: a thick, inner compact meshwork of protein fibrils and a thin, outer more homogeneous layer. The hatching enzyme digests the inner layer, leaving the resistant thin outer layer to be rent by lashings of the larval tail. Active hatching enzyme can easily be collected by hatching many eggs in a restricted volume of sea water (Milkman, 1954, 1955; Kaighn, 1964). If a circumferential scratch were made through the resistant outer layer of the chorion, it is conceivable that such a concentrate of hatching enzyme could be utilized to digest the exposed inner layer and dechorionate the egg. An optimistic note was introduced recently by Huver's (1963) suggestion that mersalyl, applied just after fertilization, prevents the chorion from hardening and hence makes mechanical removal of the chorion a simple matter. B. B. Ganguly and I (unpublished) confirmed that the mersalyl does indeed impede hardening of the chorion, but it does not necessarily make mechanical removal easier, at least at concentrations compatible with normal development. The chorion remains soft; however, upon cutting it tends to turn in and fatally constrict the egg. At higher concentrations of mersalyl, dechorionation is easy but the egg develops abnormally. Further study seems necessary before the utility of mersalyl for dechorionation is defined.

Regretfully, therefore, we must turn to time-tested but tedious microsurgical methods. Some years ago Nicholas (1927) showed that with patience chorions can be cut away with iridectomy scissors. The eggs first are freed of the sticky fibers clinging to the chorion by rolling them on filter paper or paper toweling, and then placed in a Syracuse dish three-fourths full of sea water or double-strength Holtfreter's solution. One point of the scissors is sharpened so that it will readily penetrate the chorion. With this blade of the scissors in the perivitelline space, one may progressively cut around the egg, pulling uncut membrane over the point of the scissors with a steel needle. During this period the egg is raised off the bottom of the dish. This method has been used with success through the years by Oppenheimer and others, as soon as the perivitelline space has formed. My own method (Trinkaus, 1951) has been to cut the chorion away with two pairs of watchmaker's forceps, preferably Dumont #5. One point of one pair is sharpened, so that it will puncture the chorion with minimum pressure. The egg is held with the unsharpened pair of forceps and the sharper point of the other pair is gently shoved through the shell and as far into the perivitelline space as possible. Next, the points of these forceps are brought together to grasp the membrane, raising the egg from the bottom of the dish at the same time. From this point on, one must work above the bottom of the dish; for after puncture of the chorion the slightest pressure on the egg causes its rupture. With the chorion firmly grasped by the sharp-pointed forceps, one point of the duller forceps is rubbed against the chorion where it is held so as to cut it. The grasping forceps is then released. With the point still in the perivitelline space, the shell is rotated upon the blade with the assistance of the other forceps. The membrane is then grasped again and cut as previously. By repetition of this procedure the chorion can be cut into halves and removed from the egg. Particular care must be taken in making the last cut or so, since the egg is in danger of getting caught between the cut edges of the now gaping shell. When this happens the result is ruinous. This method also can be used to dechorionate eggs without injury as soon as the perivitelline space has formed. Both the iridectomy scissors and the forceps method can be used to dechorionate the eggs of many teleosts and both work effectively after some practice. Dechorionation by these methods is difficult only before closure of the blastopore. After that, the egg is much less readily injured and the chorion can be removed with ease.

SPECIAL QUALITIES OF FUNDULUS EGGS FOR THE ANALYSIS OF DEVELOPMENT

The eggs of *Fundulus heteroclitus* possess a number of special advantages for the study of development. The adults are readily collected and kept in the laboratory, where they may be stripped for eggs and sperm at will. The chorionic membrane is transparent and it is necessary only to remove the chorionic fibers (see p. 116) to have a clear view of the developing egg. What is more important is that the egg itself is transparent, affording observation of intimate details of development. Like the eggs of other teleosts, the *Fundulus* egg develops meroblastically. As such it is excellent material for the analysis of yolk-blastoderm relations and the epibolic spreading of the blastoderm over the yolk. Unlike the eggs of many teleosts, the *Fundulus* egg is demersal (i.e., heavier than water) and for this reason is amenable to many experimental procedures that cannot be applied to pelagic eggs. It also is a relatively large egg (a little less than 2.0 mm in diameter) and has a convenient rate of development (about like that of *Ambystoma punctatum*). Its resistance to wide fluctuations in temperature and salinity have already been discussed. In addition, it withstands mechanical manipulation admirably. Wounds heal readily, development proceeds after deletion of large amounts of yolk or cellular material, grafts are quickly incorporated, and isolates of partial or whole blastoderms develop in culture. All of these characteristics in their aggregate make the *Fundulus* egg excellent material for the analysis of development. It has but two serious deficiencies: a limited spawning season and a tough chorion which requires care and patience for its removal.

TIME TABLE OF DEVELOPMENT

The most accurate time table of development available in the literature is that of Armstrong and Child (1965). The following table is extracted from it.

TIME SEQUENCE OF DEVELOPMENT AT 20°C ± 0.2°

STAGE	AGE IN HOURS
Unfertilized Ovum	0
Formation of the blastodisc	1.75
2-Cell stage	2.50
4-Cell stage	3.25
8-Cell stage	4.25
32-Cell stage	6.00
Blastula	7–15
Beginning of epiboly	20–24
Gastrulation (to closure of blastopore)	20–46
Embryo formation (up to 4 somites)	40–52
Embryogenesis up to onset of circulation	52–84
Appearance of retinal pigment	128
Heart chambers differentiated	168
Jaw and body movements, hatching	228

STAGING

Two sets of normal stages are now available for *Fundulus heteroclitus*. Oppenheimer's (1937) stages have been in use for 30 years and are familiar to all who have worked with *Fundulus* embryos. For all their usefulness, however, they have had two deficiencies. There are not enough stages and the photographic illustrations are not sufficiently detailed. For this reason Armstrong and Child (1965) have devised another normal series with more stages and with detailed line drawings for illustrations. This series is more useful and is recommended.

TECHNIQUES FOR THE STUDY OF DEVELOPMENT

Normal Development

Fundulus eggs are activated by simple contact with sea water, where, in the absence of sperm, their cortical alveoli burst and a perivitelline space and a blastodisc form. (Development stops there, however. No one has yet succeeded in inducing true parthenogenesis in *Fundulus* eggs, in spite of many trials with treatments known to work in other forms.) In order to study the characteristics of the unfertilized egg, therefore, eggs must be stripped into dilute sea water (70 percent fresh water, 30 percent sea water), in which activation does not occur. They also should not be rolled, since the micropyle is more easily located in the presence of the chorionic fibers. Another reason to avoid rolling is that the chorion has not yet hardened at this stage; hence rolling usually bursts the egg. There is no definitive study of the unfertilized egg of *Fundulus*. The paper of Kagan (1935) is incorrect in certain important details. E. Borysko and I have shown, in an unpublished fine-structural study, that the cortical alveoli are huge and occupy the bulk of the cortical cytoplasm. Yamamoto has studied fertilization carefully in *Oryzias latipes*, whose egg is quite similar to that of *Fundulus*, and his papers should be consulted (see reviews, 1956, 1961). Huver (1960) has shown that the first polar body may be seen prior to fertilization in *Fundulus*. After one is familiar with the morphology of the unfertilized egg, the activation of eggs by sperm in normal sea water may be readily studied. The dissolution of the cortical alveoli, proceeding from the micropyle at the animal pole in a wave and followed by formation of the perivitelline space (Wessells and Swartz, 1953; Huver, 1956), is a spectacular process and well worth careful study.

A few hints that will aid observation are in order. By 1 hour after fertilization the chorion has sufficiently hardened that one may now observe the egg in any orientation by either of the following techniques. Place the eggs in depression slides with a 1.7–1.8 mm depression (slightly less than the diameter of the egg). Thus situated, the egg may be accurately rotated by simply moving the cover slip. If such slides are not available, eggs may be placed in a drop of sea water on an ordinary glass slide and covered with a thin, flexible sheet of mica. Water is then withdrawn with lens paper until capillary attraction causes pressure on the egg. It may then be rotated as in the previous method. For observation of details of structure a combination of transmitted and direct light is advisable.

The transparency of the *Fundulus* egg makes it ideal for following cleavage, epiboly, surface activities of the blastomeres and cell movements with time-lapse cinemicrography (Trinkaus and Lentz, 1967). For such purposes, the dechorionated spherical egg can be kept in position by placing it in a deep depression slide. Vibration of the egg by the shutter of the camera is prevented by placing the microscope and the egg on separate tables. Inasmuch as the lipid droplets of the yolk tend to drift to the upper region of the yolk (relative to gravity), they often come to lie under just that part of the blastoderm which is under study and thus obscure observation. We have found it convenient, therefore, to remove these droplets during early cleavage with an orally controlled micropipette. The small wounds in the yolk cytoplasmic layer close readily and little yolk is lost. Development appears to proceed normally after the operation, at least up to early embryo stages.

Fixation

Fundulus eggs and other teleost eggs are difficult to fix properly, for both the light and the electron microscopes. The following method has given us the most satisfactory paraffin sections up to a middle gastrula stage. Dechorionate the egg. Then place the whole egg in the fixative, watching it continuously under a dissecting microscope. After a minute or so, cut swiftly into the yolk just vegetal to the margin of the blastoderm or periblast with watchmaker's forceps, so that the bulk of the yolk is cut away. The blastoderm, with a thin layer of yolk fixed to its under surface, is now transferred to fresh fixative for the requisite time (as required by the fixative). This method will distort the blastoderm less than any other method I know. That is not to say, however, that the blastoderm is left undistorted. In late blastula and gastrula stages the spreading blastoderm is under great tension and tends to contract and round up immediately when exposed to fixative. This method reduces this contraction to a minimum and yields fixed blastoderms whose topography is close to that of the normal. If the technique of dechorionation has not yet been mastered, the following technique is recommended. Place the egg with chorion (cleaned of its fibers) in the fixative for several minutes so as to fix the blastoderm more completely than in the previous method. Then, with forceps or iridectomy scissors, dechorionate the egg. The dechorionation procedure is not so demanding because the partially fixed blastoderm is more resistant to tearing than a living blastoderm and loss of some yolk is of no concern. When the chorion has been removed, cut away all yolk but a thin layer beneath the blastoderm and place the blastoderm in fresh fixative. This method yields blastoderms which are more distorted than with the previous method. After middle gastrula, dechorionation of the living egg is much easier. Again it is best initially to place the whole egg in the fixative and to cut away the parts of the embryo desired in the fixative, as above.

For the electron microscope, the same basic procedure should be adopted. The special features of fixation for the EM concern the fixatives themselves, as they relate to the qualities of embryonic protoplasm. In our experience (Lentz and Trinkaus, 1966), the following procedure yields satisfactory results. The egg is dechorionated and placed directly in a solution of cold 5 percent glutaraldehyde in 0.05 *M* cacodylate buffer containing 0.4 *M* sucrose, whose pH is adjusted to 7.4. After a few minutes, the bulk of the yolk is cut away from the blastoderm and the isolated blastoderm is placed in fresh cold fixative, where fixation is allowed to proceed for 1 hour. The blastoderms (or tissues) are then placed in cold 0.05 *M* cacodylate buffer (pH 7.4), containing 0.4 *M* sucrose, overnight, followed by fixation for one hour in cold 1.0 percent osmium tetroxide, buffered with veronal acetate (pH 7.4) containing 0.4 *M* sucrose. Although fixation is carried out in a hypertonic solution, appreciable shrinkage of cells does not occur. The use of less hypertonic, isotonic, or hypotonic fixation solutions results in varying degrees of swelling and disruption of mitochondria and intercellular membrane-bounded spaces and an apparent distortion of cell relationships. The fixed tissues are rapidly dehydrated in graded concentrations of ethanol and embedded in Maraglas. If the blocks are oriented so that the blastoderms are cut transversely, one may observe the relationships of yolk, periblast, blastomeres, and enveloping layer in each section.

Operative Procedures

Oppenheimer (1936) discovered that wounds heal well if operations are carried out in double-strength Holtfreter's solution, rather than sea water. We have confirmed this (Trinkaus and Drake, 1956) and have shown further that double-strength Holtfreter's solution clearly provides a more favorable milieu for isolated blastoderms than single, triple, or quadruple strength. Sea water is actually toxic to inner blastomeres and should be avoided. The reason whole eggs develop normally in sea water is doubtless because of the protection provided by the highly impermeable egg surface.

Fundulus embryos are amenable to extirpation procedures at all stages and to transplantation after cleavage is well under way. Since the instruments and techniques are by and large the same as for amphibian and chick embryos and are well described in two standard works (Hamburger, 1960; Rugh, 1962) there is no need to describe them here. It goes without saying that before attempting an analysis an intimate knowledge of normal development is required. Two special features of the teleost embryo, the enveloping layer and the periblast or yolk syncytium, are figured in diagrammatic form for the sea bass in Wilson's (1891) well-known study and for *Fundulus* in a recent paper by Lentz and Trinkaus (1967). The normal course of the morphogenetic movements of *Fundulus* gastrulation has been described in part by Oppenheimer (1936c), but the situation needs re-examination now in the light of Ballard's recent studies of Salmo (1966a, b, c). Careful examination of these papers and those of Devillers (1961), Morgan (1895), Nicholas and Oppenheimer (1942), Oppenheimer (1947), Pasteels (1936), Rudnick (1955), Smith (1957), and Trinkaus (1951, 1967) would constitute a good introduction to *Fundulus* development.

Culturing

An advantage of a meroblastic egg is that the blastoderm, out of which the embryo and the yolk sac develop, can be separated from the yolk mass and cultured separately (Oppenheimer, 1936b). The *Fundulus* blastoderm may be completely separated from its yolk mass after formation of the syncytial periblast by merely severing the marginal connection of the two layers (Trinkaus and Drake, 1956, 1959). Such a blastoderm contains within its cytoplasm only a small quantity of nutrient material previously absorbed from the yolk (Lentz and Trinkaus, 1967) and will soon be dependent on exogenous nutrients supplied in the medium. A *Fundulus* blastoderm isolated in this manner is an excellent system in which to study the role of exogenous factors in development.

Fundulus blastoderms may also be readily dissociated into a suspension of separate cells. The following procedure works well (Trinkaus, 1963). Place a blastula or gastrula blastoderm in Ca- and Mg-free double-strength Holtfreter's solution (2 × H) for 15 minutes. Then transfer the blastoderm to 0.1 percent EDTA in Ca-Mg-free 2 × H for another 15 minutes.

(Trypsin does not work well.) After this treatment the blastoderm is transferred to the medium in which the cells are to be cultured and is dissociated into individual cells by drawing it in and out of a small-bore (0.2 mm inner diameter) micropipette. Cell locomotory activity may be studied in short-term culture by culturing cells in a standing drop of a simple nutrient medium containing 0.5 percent glucose and 0.2 percent Difco protease-peptone made up in 2 × H buffered to pH 7.4 with phosphate and bicarbonate. For longer-term culture of dissociated cells and reaggregates, a richer medium, such as those used in standard chick and mammalian cell culture, works very well. Cultures should be kept at 20°–25°C.

REFERENCES

ARMSTRONG, PHILIP B., and JULIA S. CHILD, 1965: Stages in the normal development of *Fundulus heteroclitus*. *Biol. Bull.*, 128: 143.

BALLARD, W. W., 1966: The role of the cellular envelope in the morphogenetic movements of teleost embryos. *J. Exp. Zool.*, 161: 193.

———, 1966a: Origin of the hypoblast in *Salmo* I: Does the blastodisc edge turn inward? *J. Exp. Zool.*, 161: 201.

———, 1966b: Origin of the hypoblast in *Salmo* II: Outward movement of deep central cells. *J. Exp. Zool.*, 161: 211.

BIGELOW, HENRY B., and WILLIAM C. SCHROEDER, 1953: *Fishes of the Gulf of Maine. Fish. Bull., U.S.*, 53: 1.

COSTELLO, D. P., M. E. DAVIDSON, A. EGGERS, M. H. FOX, and C. HENLEY, 1957: *Methods for Obtaining and Handling Marine Eggs and Embryos.* 247 pp. Marine Biological Laboratory, Woods Hole, Mass.

DEVILLERS, CHARLES, 1961: Structural and dynamic aspects of the development of the teleostean egg. *Adv. in Morphogenesis*, 1: 379.

HAMBURGER, VIKTOR, 1960: *A Manual of Experimental Embryology.* 219 pp. University of Chicago Press, Chicago, Ill.

HUVER, C. W., 1956: The relation of the cortex to the formation of the perivitelline space in the eggs of *Fundulus heteroclitus*. *Biol. Bull.*, 111: 304.

———, 1960: The stage at fertilization in the egg of *Fundulus heteroclitus*. *Biol. Bull.*, 119: 320.

———, 1963: A chemical technique for dechorionating teleost eggs. *Copeia*, 3: 591.

KAGAN, B. M., 1935: The fertilization period of the eggs of *Fundulus heteroclitus* and some associated phenomena. *Biol. Bull.*, 69: 185.

KAIGHN, E. M., 1964: A biochemical study of hatching in *Fundulus heteroclitus*. *Devel. Biol.*, 9: 56.

LENTZ, T. L., and J. P. TRINKAUS, 1967: A fine-structural study of cytodifferentiation during cleavage, blastula and gastrula stages of *Fundulus heteroclitus*. *J. Cell. Biol.*, 32: 121.

MATHEWS, S. A., 1939: The relationship between the pituitary gland and the gonads in *Fundulus*. *Biol. Bull.*, 76: 241.

———, 1940: The effects of implanting adult hypophysis into sexually immature *Fundulus*. *Biol. Bull.*, 79: 207.

MILKMAN, ROGER, 1954: Controlled observation of hatching in *Fundulus heteroclitus*. *Biol. Bull.*, 107: 300.

———, 1955: Further studies on the hatching of *Fundulus heteroclitus*. *Biol. Bull.*, 109: 349.

MORGAN, T. H., 1895: The formation of the fish embryo. *J. Morph.*, 10: 419.

NICHOLAS, J. S., 1927: The application of experimental methods to the study of developing *Fundulus* embryos. *Proc. Nat. Acad. Sci.*, 13: 695.

———, and J. M. OPPENHEIMER, 1942: Regulation and reconstruction in *Fundulus*. *J.*

Exp. Zool., 90: 127.

OPPENHEIMER, J. M., 1936a: Transplantation experiments on developing teleosts (*Fundulus* and *Perca*). *J. Exp. Zool.*, 72: 409.

———, 1936b: The development of isolated blastoderms of *Fundulus heteroclitus*. *J. Exp. Zool.*, 72: 247.

———, 1936c: Processes of localization in developing *Fundulus*. *J. Exp. Zool.*, 73: 405.

———, 1937: The normal stages of *Fundulus heteroclitus*. *Anat. Rec.*, 68: 1.

———, 1947: The organization of the teleost blastoderm. *Quart. Rev. Biol.*, 22: 105.

PASTEELS, J., 1936: Études sur la Gastrulation des Vertébrés Méroblastiques. I. Téléostéens. *Arch. Biol.*, 47: 205.

PICKFORD, G. E., and J. W. ATZ, 1957: *The Physiology of the Pituitary Gland of Fishes.* 613 pp. New York Zool. Soc.

RUDNICK, DOROTHEA, 1955: Teleosts and birds. In Willier, Weiss, and Hamburger (eds.), *The Analysis of Development*, Saunders, Philadelphia, Pa., p. 297.

RUGH, ROBERTS, 1962: *Experimental Embryology*. 3rd ed., *ix* + 501 pp. Burgess Publishing Co., Minneapolis, Minn.

SHANKLIN, D. R., 1959: Studies on the *Fundulus* chorion. *J. Cellular Comp. Physiol.*, 53: 1.

SMITH, SIDNEY, 1957: Early development and hatching. In M. E. Brown (ed.), *The Physiology of Fishes*, Academic Press, New York, p. 323.

SOLBERG, ARCHIE N., 1938: The development of a bony fish. *Progr. Fish Cult.*, No. 40: 1–19.

TRINKAUS, J. P., 1951: A study of the mechanism of epiboly in the egg of *Fundulus heteroclitus*. *J. Exp. Zool.*, 118: 269.

———, 1963: The cellular basis of *Fundulus* epiboly. Adhesivity of blastula and gastrula cells in culture. *Devel. Biol.*, 7: 513.

———, 1967: Morphogenetic cell movements. In Michael Locke (ed.), *Major Problems of Developmental Biology*, The 25th Symposium of the Society for Developmental Biology, Academic Press, New York, p. 125.

———, and JOHN W. DRAKE, 1956: Exogenous control of morphogenesis in isolated *Fundulus* blastoderms by nutrient chemical factors. *J. Exp. Zool.*, 132: 311.

———, and ———, 1959: Enhancement of morphogenesis in *Fundulus* blastoderms by fusion and crowding *in vitro*. *Devel. Biol.*, 1: 377.

———, and T. L. LENTZ, 1967: Surface specialization of *Fundulus* cells and their relation to cell movements during gastrulation. *J. Cell Biol.*, 32: 139.

WESSELLS, NORMAN K., and F. J. SWARTZ, 1953: Relation of the micropyle to cortical changes at fertilization in the egg of *Fundulus heteroclitus*. *Anat. Rec.*, 117: 557.

WILSON, H. V., 1891: The embryology of the sea-bass (*Serranus atrarius*). *Bull. U.S. Fish Comm.*, 9: 209.

YAMAMOTO, T., 1956: The physiology of fertilization in the medaka (*Oryzias latipes*). *Exp. Cell Research*, 10: 387.

———, 1961: Physiology of fertilization in fishes. *Int. Rev. Cytol.*, 12: 361.

Annual Fishes*

By John P. Wourms

INTRODUCTION

Unlike most of the other chapters in this book, this one will attempt to introduce a developmental system that has recently been discovered and is still in the exploratory phases of study. Annual fish eggs afford the investigator the opportunity to study vertebrate embryogenesis in a naturally occurring system characterized by phases of dispersion and reaggregation of blastomeres. At the same time, they present a unique opportunity to work with a vertebrate system in which diapause is manifested at several distinct stages during development.

ECOLOGY AND LIFE HISTORY

"Annual fishes" (Myers, 1942, 1952) is a term used to characterize a group of cyprinodontid fishes found in temporary bodies of fresh water located in savannah, llanos, campos, and pampas regions and sometimes in forest areas of South America and Africa. These fishes are common only in isolated water holes, swamps, and puddles that dry up during the dry season. They are usually rare or absent in permanent streams or ponds. The complete drying out of the aquatic habitat results in the death of all adult and juvenile individuals. The population survives for long periods only in the form of eggs buried in the mud. During the subsequent rainy season, the ponds refill, the eggs hatch, and the larvae rapidly grow to maturity and reproduce (Myers, 1942, 1952; Dahl, 1958; Carvalho, 1957; Boschi, 1953; Magis, 1963; Vanderplank, 1940). The population in a given locale is permanent in spite of fluctuations in the annual climatic cycle (Wourms, 1964, unpublished).

Recently, survival of the population in the egg form has been correlated with some unique developmental characteristics. The developmental pattern of annual fish eggs is different from that of other teleosts (Peters, 1963; Wourms, 1963). In annual fishes, embryogenesis occurs in a reaggregated mass of previously dispersed cells (Wourms, 1965). In addition, these eggs are capable of undergoing diapause at three distinct stages during the course of development. In all of the 39 species of oviparous cyprinodonts thus far studied, those fishes that are identified as "annuals" on the basis of ecology and life history

* This chapter was prepared during the tenure of U.S. Public Health Service Predoctoral Fellowship Fl-GM-15,631 from the Division of General Medical Sciences.

also possess the unique developmental pattern (Peters, 1963, 1965; Wourms, 1963, 1964, 1965). Thus, while the annual fishes were originally characterized solely on the basis of ecology and life history, their possession of a distinctive developmental pattern and eggs that can undergo multiple diapause also distinguishes them from other fishes.

SPECIAL ADVANTAGES AND USES OF ANNUAL FISH EGGS

Annual fish eggs exhibit several characteristics which are of developmental interest. Stages of normal development are summarized in Table 1 (a complete series will be published elsewhere). At the present time there is no detailed description of annual fish development. Earlier statements (Peters, 1963; Wourms, 1963) were incomplete.

As cleavage proceeds, the blastomeres segregate into three cell populations. This occurs early and relatively small numbers of cells are present (less than 200 in *Rachovia* and *Pterolebias*). Two of these populations are present in the form of thin sheets of cells one layer thick, the enveloping layer and a syncytial layer of similar thickness, the periblast. The third population is a mass of ameboid cells located beneath the thin enveloping layer at the flat blastula stage. The low number of cells involved and the arrangement of the populations permit easy study of their origin, behavior, and fate. The population of ameboid cells disperses over the surface of the egg as epiboly occurs and then reaggregates during a period of several days to form the embryo proper. The processes of dispersion and reaggregation are easily followed.

Several slight variations in developmental pattern are to be found among the annual fishes. In *Nothobranchius* the process of segregation of the cell populations is not so dynamic, nor is there a tendency for pre-ameboid cells to form a tightly consolidated mass.

In contrast, *Rachovia* and *Pterolebias* demonstrate these features with extreme clarity, since epiboly begins at a much earlier stage (120–200 cells). Here again, there is little tendency for the central blastomeres to consolidate before dispersing. *Aphyosemion* complicates the picture. Some species reveal a developmental pattern which is only a slight modification of normal teleost development, while other species, e.g. *Aphyosemion arnoldi*, duplicate the pattern just described.

It should be noted that the enveloping layer persists throughout the course of development up to the time of hatching. It is a continuous cellular layer which completely surrounds the entire embryo and yolk sac, and in later stages of development does not seem to be attached to the embryo in any way. It is essentially concentric to the inner surface of the chorion.

Annual eggs also have the ability to undergo diapause at three distinct stages in development (Table 1). Peters (1963) has stated that diapause at stage I (dispersed cell stage) and stage III (prehatching stage) is facultative. Arrest in stage I is terminated by an increase in oxygen concentration, while arrest in stage III is terminated by a decrease in oxygen concentration. Diapause at stage II (mid-somite stage) is probably obligatory in African annual fishes (*Aphyosemion*, *Nothobranchius*). The presence of obligate diapause at stage II has also been established in some South American forms (*Austrofundulus*, *Rachovia*; Wourms, unpublished). A considerable variation in the duration of diapause as seen in eggs of the same clutch from a single female, especially at stage II, has been noted. This variability may represent a survival mechanism that allows a population to escape

TABLE 1. SELECTED STAGES IN THE NORMAL DEVELOPMENT OF *Austrofundulus myersi* AT 25°

STAGE NUMBER	TIME	DESCRIPTION
1	0 hours	Unfertilized ovum. Egg ellipsoidal; 2 mm diameter; hyaline to amber; chorion flaccid with short, adhesive fibrils; cortical granules, yolk platelets, lipid droplets; central germinal vesicle.
3	1.5 hours	1-Cell stage. Cytoplasm of yolk accumulates in blastodisc; perivitelline space; chorion hardening.
8	6 hours	32-Cell stage. Group of central blastomeres, the future ameboid cells invested by an outer shell of peripheral blastomeres, the precursors of the periblast-enveloping layer.
10	8 hours	High, solid blastula. About 128 cells, all uninucleate.
11	10 hours	Flat, solid blastula. Blastomeres in outer shell flattened; central blastomeres spherical; all cells uninucleate.
12	12 hours	Early flat hollow blastula. Appearance of segmentation cavity beneath enveloping layer; cells of enveloping layer squamous and binucleate; spherical pre-ameboid cells loosely clustered in segmentation cavity; extension and retraction of lobopodia by all cells; no free periblast nuclei.
13	16 hours	Late, flat, hollow blastula. Increase in multinuclearity and flatness of enveloping layer cells; consolidation of pre-ameboid cells in segmentation cavity; free periblast nuclei.
14	20 hours	Expanding, flat, hollow, blastula. Epiboly commences; concentric rows of periblast nuclei; pre-ameboid blastomeres tightly grouped in a spherical mass in segmentation cavity; ameboid cells migrating away from periphery of mass; multiple nuclei peripherally located in cells of enveloping layer.
17	32–36 hours	½ Overgrowth. Half of yolk surface covered by epiboly of enveloping layer and periblast; mass of pre-ameboid blastomeres almost entirely dispersed as ameboid cells that actively migrate between enveloping and periblast layers.
19	44–48 hours	Completion of epiboly. Entire surface of yolk invested by concentric layers of periblast and enveloping layers; ameboid cells randomly distributed as individual, motile cells; mitosis in ameboid cell population; no indication of any multicellular organization equivalent to embryonic shield or embryo.
20	day 3 (72 hours) (Diapause 1)	Dispersed phase 1. Ameboid cells still randomly distributed, tending toward increased density in lower hemisphere; central oil droplet assuming peripheral position in upper hemisphere. *First diapause occurs here.*
21	day 4	Dispersed phase 2. Position of lipid droplet stabilized at

TABLE 1 (*continued*)

STAGE NUMBER	TIME	DESCRIPTION
		periphery of yolk in upper hemisphere; single region of increased cell density and contact, the site of reaggregation in the lower hemisphere.
22	day 5	Reaggregation 1. Definite reaggregate, consisting of a solid mass of cells, one layer thick.
23	day 6	Reaggregation 2. Increase in area of aggregate; cells tightly packed in tissue-like organization.
24	day 7	Reaggregation 3. Aggregate lenticular in shape; several cells thick.
25	day 8	Reaggregation 4. Further increase in area and volume of aggregate.
26	day 9	Reaggregation 5. Increase in size of aggregate; tendency toward elongation in direction of embryonic axis.
27	late day 9	Definitive embryonic axis. Linear organization of cells within the aggregate.
28	day 10	Solid neural keel. Forerunner of Kupffer's vesicle at posterior end; head fold at anterior end.
29	early day 11	Early somite embryo. First somites formed; Kupffer's vesicle present; little cephalic organization; no expansion of forebrain as optic vesicles.
32	day 15 (Diapause 2)	Long somite embryo. Heart as a simple contractile tube in pericardial cavity; no circulation. *Second diapause occurs here.* Minimum duration is 30 days; duration variable and may last over 150 days in aqueous incubation media.
33 to 42	During 16 days from the termination of diapause 2	Growth and organogenesis. Increase in size and complexity, establishment of circulation, pigmentation, and organogenesis all closely parallel *Fundulus,* but at a slower rate. Development of the head and central nervous system initially lags behind that of the other systems.
43	Attained about 16 days after termination of diapause 2 (Diapause 3)	Prehatching. Highly developed embryo. After attaining this stage, embryo may proceed to hatch in 2–3 days or enter diapause 3 for periods of up to 2–3 months or more.
44	2–3 days after stage 43 or immediately after termination of diapause 3	Hatching.

extinction despite inconsistent climatic cycles (Wourms, 1964). The occurrence of diapause periods, some of which can last for at least a year, raises many interesting questions about the relationship of such arrested development to the control of differentiation in cells and tissues.

A further area of interest in annual fishes is the study of the physiological mechanisms that permit the eggs to survive

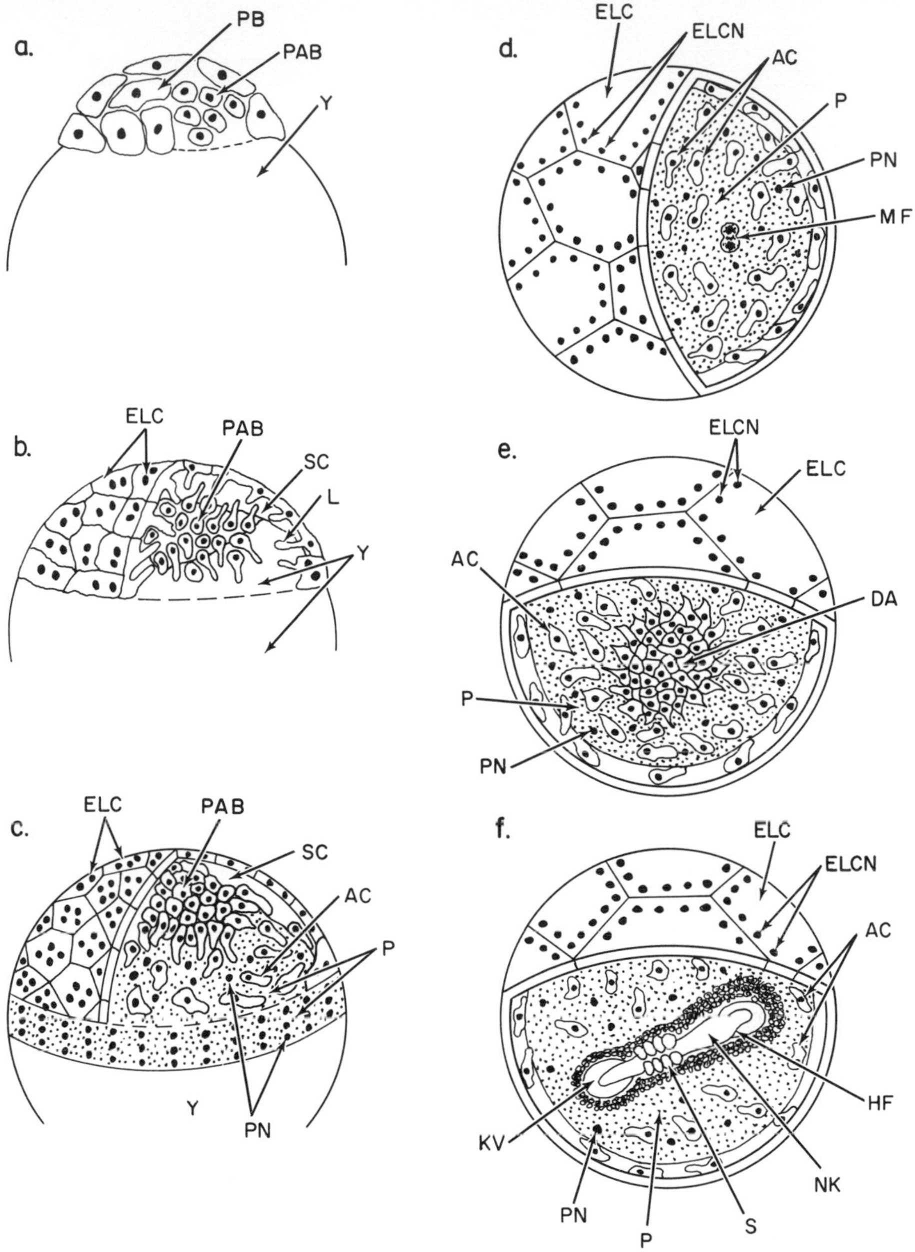

FIG. 1. Diagrammatic representation of dispersion and reaggregation in *Austrofundulus myersi.* Chorion removed; surface view of the egg with enveloping layer intact on one side; on the other side, the enveloping layer is removed to illustrate underlying ameboid cells and periblast; periblast stippled; cell numbers reduced for clarity; oil droplets not illustrated. (a) stage 10; (b) stage 12; (c) stage 14; (d) stage 19; (e) stage 22; (f) stage 29. AC, ameboid cell; DA, definitive aggregate; ELC, enveloping layer cell; ELCN, nuclei of enveloping layer cell; HF, head fold; KV, Kupffer's vesicle; L, lobopodia; MF, mitotic figure; NK, neural keel; P, periblast; PN, periblast nuclei; PAB, pre-ameboid blastomeres; PB, periphera blastomeres.

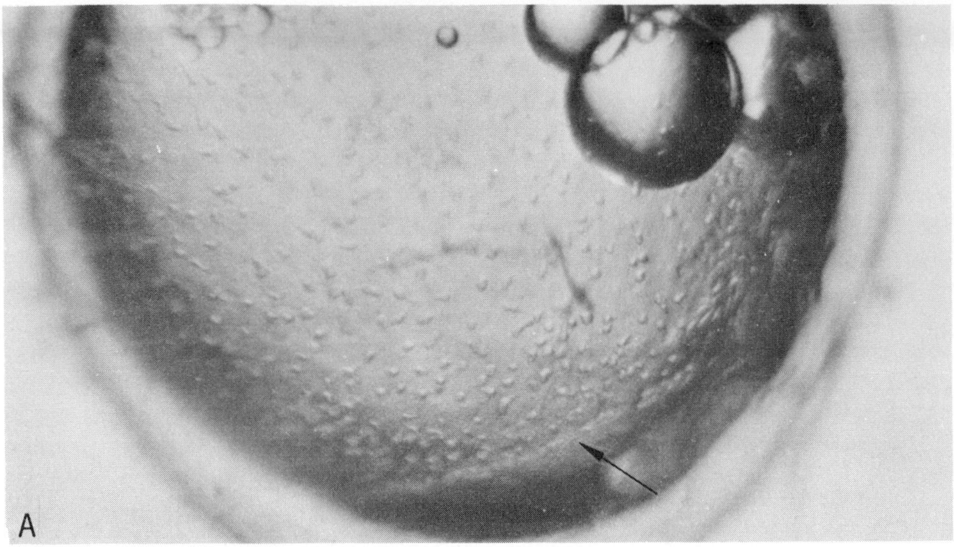

FIG. 2. Dispersed stages of *Austrofundulus myersi.* (A) Stage 18½ (⅞ epiboly, 42 hours). Ameboid cells are randomly distributed over the egg surface. The junction of the periblast-enveloping layer with the yolk is in the lower part of the photograph (→). (B) Stage 20 (day 3), side view. A region of increasing cell density (→), the future site of

various stress conditions and make them respond to environmental cues. Work on the behavior of eggs subjected to partial drying is needed. The information on diapause in the literature has been derived from eggs studied in aqueous incubation media.

Annual fishes are found in areas in which populations of a given species are isolated from one another. This fact would seem to qualify them eminently for combined studies in population genetics and development. Pertinent, perhaps, is the fact that considerable phenotypic variation is generally encountered within the relatively small, isolated adult populations. Closely linked to such studies is a consideration of the evolution of the annual fish developmental pattern. The genus *Aphyosemion* seems well suited for such work. Within this large genus, there are nonannual species from permanent bodies of water which undergo typical teleostean development. Other species which are ecologically annual possess an annual fish developmental pattern. There are also species, believed to be transitional forms, which possess an annual fish developmental pattern that apparently retains some of the characters of normal teleost development (Wourms, unpublished).

Practical advantages of annual fishes are the following. They are fresh-water forms and can be maintained almost anywhere with little need of special facilities. Eggs can be obtained through natural spawnings, as in the case of *Oryzias* (see Yamamato, this volume, pp. 105–6). Using replicate spawnings, large numbers of eggs can be obtained on a continual daily basis. There is no seasonality. When environmental conditions are properly regulated, spawning occurs throughout the year. The assurance of successful natural spawning together with promiscuous mating behavior easily facilitates genetic studies. The

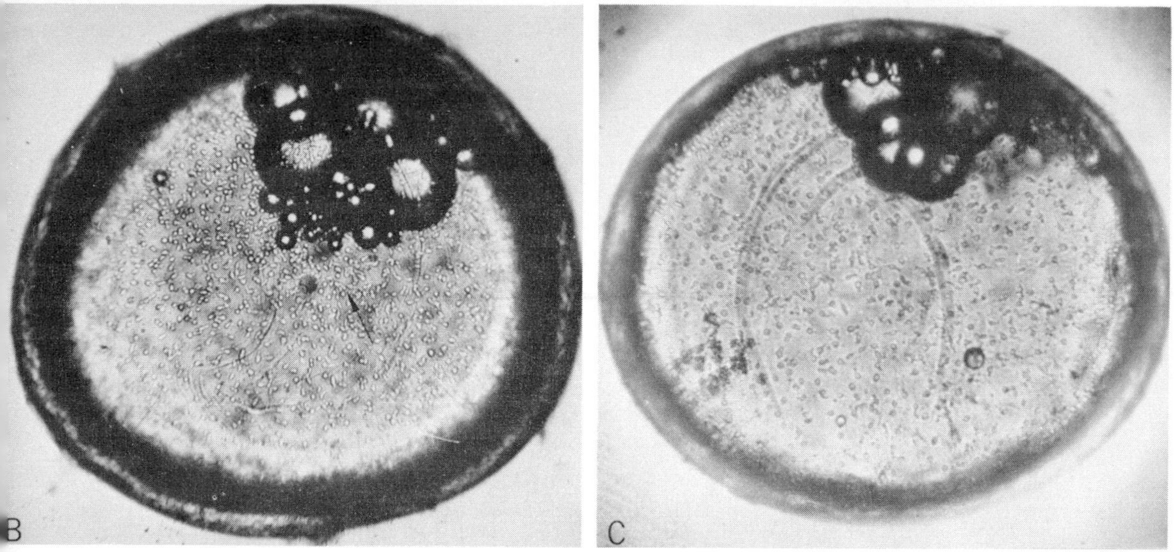

reaggregation, occurs in this egg in supraequatorial area, near the oil droplets, in contrast to the usual subequatorial position of the reaggregate. (C) Stage 20 (day 3). The same egg as B, viewed from the opposite side. The ameboid cells are randomly distributed with no indication of regions of increased density. (Fig 2A by Christensen & Wourms.)

eggs of most species are at least as hardy as those of *Oryzias* and *Fundulus*. In addition, they are transparent, demersal, usually of large size (species-dependent), and many are free of chorionic projections. Larvae hatched from eggs grow rapidly and may attain full sexual maturity in 4 to 6 weeks. The resistant properties of annual fish eggs and their ability to diapause permit them to be shipped by airmail. Populations when not needed may be stored in the egg form for well in excess of a year.

This system is not without its disadvantages, some of which are peculiar to it, some accidental, and others characteristic of teleost material in general. One disadvantage involves different aspects of a similar problem—species identification and the pedigree of laboratory material, on both the species and the population level. At the present time, the origin and pedigree of many of the annual fishes are either unknown or dubious. In addition, many of the annual fishes currently available from commercial sources have been erroneously identified (in particular, species within the genera *Nothobranchius* and *Aphyosemion*). More serious still is the taxonomic confusion with regard to the identification and validity of species within the African genera, *Aphyosemion* and *Nothobranchius* (Radda, 1963). This is especially unfortunate since *Aphyosemion*, because of its transitional species, is most interesting from an evolutionary point of view. These disadvantages may be overcome. The aid of a competent ichthyologist should be enlisted for identification of all material. Probability of gross error is reduced if one works with the more distinctive species, e.g., South American forms in general and some African species. For genetic and population studies the best solution is to obtain wild stock. Finally, it may be noted that while annual fishes are in general hardy, some forms, especially *Nothobranchius*, are highly susceptible to disease (*cf.* section on Maintenance). A final disadvantage of annual fishes, in common with *Oryzias* and *Fundulus*, is that they possess a tough chorion which must be removed for many experimental procedures. [The study of the chorion, especially its function during diapause under simulated natural conditions, is worthwhile. Its differentiation in *Cynolobias bellottii* has been elegantly described at the ultrastructural level (Sterba and Müller, 1962; Müller and Sterba,1963).]

SOURCES OF SUPPLY AND COLLECTING

At first, it might appear that annual fishes are exotic and difficult-to-obtain laboratory animals. Fortunately, however, a number of them are reasonably common aquarium fishes. I have found the most dependable sources of supply to be aquarists working with the material for pleasure, and commercial breeders supplying annual fishes to the aquarium trade. In the United States and abroad there are a sizable number of aquarists who specialize in cyprinodonts (or killifish). Many such aquarists possess a store of practical information as to sources of supply and maintenance. If approached, they are generally more than willing to make their knowledge available to the scientific community. I have listed the names of several aquarists, well known for their interest in annual fishes. These individuals may be willing to be of assistance or to suggest someone closer by, if geographically distant.

1. Mr. Robert O. Criger
   4209 Manchester Road
   Middletown, Ohio 45042
2. Mr. George J. Maier
   802 Belmont Avenue
   Chicago 14, Illinois
3. Mr. Albert J. Klee
   8280 Julie Marie Drive
   West-Chester, Ohio 45069
4. Mr. Roger Hoelter
   777 Josina Avenue
   Palo Alto, California
5. Mr. E. Roloff
   Sophienstrasse 152
   Karlsruhe, Germany
6. Colonel Jorgen Scheel
   Abrinken 95
   Virum, Denmark
7. Dr. Walter Foersch
   Mainzer Strasse 22
   Munich 23, Germany

Alternatively, a local aquarium society may prove of assistance in locating an aquarist specializing in annual fishes.

I have obtained most of my laboratory stock from: Mr. John Gonzales, 640 Pine Street, Philadelphia 6, Pa. Other sources of supply may be found in the advertisements contained in various aquarium magazines. When considering a source of supply distance is not a factor. The successful shipment of adult specimens by special delivery-airmail is feasible during most seasons of the year.

Because of the generally dubious pedigree of the fishes currently available, it would seem desirable to establish some permanent colonies based upon stock derived from well-characterized wild populations. A second fact mitigates for the establishment of such colonies, namely, that many of the known populations and species of annual fishes are in danger of extinction because of the proximity of their habitats to expanding urban centers (Myers, personal communication). It is not feasible to discuss possible collecting sites and techniques, except to note that it is essential to undertake collecting when there are populations of adult fishes available. Since spawning can be accomplished under field conditions, adults and/

or eggs can be collected for a permanent laboratory colony. Myers (1952) gives photographs of typical habitats, which are often not easy to locate without such aid.

GENERAL COMMENTS ON ANNUAL FISHES

On the basis of developmental studies, the following species have been shown to have a dispersion-reaggregation pattern of development and the ability to diapause:

1. *Aphyosemion arnoldi* Boulenger
2. *Aphyosemion caeruleum* Boulenger (Conventional use of name)
3. *Aphyosemion nigerianum* Clausen (≡ *A. calliurum* in Peters, 1963.)
4. *Aphyosemion walkeri* Boulenger
5. *Austrofundulus myersi* Dahl
6. *Austrofundulus transilis* Myers
7. *Cynolebias bellottii* Steindachner
8. *Cynolebias nigripinnis* Regan
9. *Cynolebias whitei* Myers
10. *Cynolebias* (*Cynopoecilus*) *melanotaenia* Regan
11. *Nothobranchius guentheri* Pfeffer
12. *Nothobranchius melanospilus* Pfeffer
13. *Nothobranchius orthonotus* Peters
14. *Nothobranchius palmquistii* Lönnberg
15. *Nothobranchius rachovii* Ahl
16. *Nothobranchius taeniopygus* Hilgendorf
17. *Pterolebias longipinnis* Garman
18. *Pterolebias peruensis* Myers
19. *Pterolebias zonatus* Myers
20. *Rachovia brevis* Regan
21. *Rachovia hummelincki* de Beaufort

If information obtained solely through ecological or life-history studies is taken into consideration, the above list can be extrapolated to include many other species. In general, it may be concluded that if life-history studies of a cyprinodontid indicate an incubation time of 4 to 6 weeks or more at room temperature, as opposed to 1 to 2 weeks, then there is reasonable assurance that the cyprinodont in question exhibits an annual fish developmental pattern.

The following species have proved to be the most suitable for laboratory studies:

1. *Austrofundulus myersi*: Most suitable of all. Adults large, prolific, and hardy; eggs large (2.0 mm) and without surface projections; spawns readily over silica sand, greatly facilitating egg collection.

2. *Cynolebias whitei*: Hardy; prolific; fair-sized eggs (1.25 mm); spawns in silica sand; albino strain available.

3. *Cynolebias bellottii*: Large eggs (1.5 mm); one of the more prolific forms; capable of withstanding cooler temperatures; species represented in the wild by a number of isolated populations; because of recent use in mosquito control in California, it may become quite common. It can, however, be difficult to spawn under less than ideal conditions.

4. *Aphyosemion caeruleum*: Large species; continuous production of many eggs. Annual pattern of development, but not as extreme as most species. Requires larger aquaria and is sensitive to water conditions. *Aphyosemion* in general are sensitive to water conditions and require extra attention.

5. *Nothobranchius*: *N. guentheri* and *N. palmquistii* are extremely prolific under favorable conditions. Eggs are readily collected from sand. Multiple spawnings ensure a continuous supply of eggs in large quantities. Eggs are small (1.00 mm); chorion is covered with projections. Adults often subject to fatal pandemics.

6. *Rachovia hummelincki*: Especially useful for the analysis of cleavage stages and the segregation of blastomeres into defined populations. Unfortunately, the species is uncommon and not prolific. Other species of *Rachovia* and *Pterolebias* seem to share all of the above properties.

MAINTENANCE

Some suggestions for the maintenance of annual fishes are presented here. The potential worker is referred to pertinent sections of aquarium publications (Innes, 1956; Markis, 1964; Sterba, 1962; Van den Nieuwenhuizen, 1964). Gordon (1950) presents a masterful treatment on the general methods of maintaining fishes.

General

Maintaining a colony of fishes is facilitated by the use of a windowless aquarium room in which temperature and photoperiod are automatically controlled, rather than by attempting to control the conditions in a group of individual tanks. Since annual fishes are mostly tropical or subtropical forms, the maintenance of a temperature of 20°–25°C is essential. Cooling devices may be necessary in those areas where the ambient temperature is in excess of 30°C for prolonged periods. Excessive temperatures are deleterious, reducing the fecundity of adults and the viability of eggs. Small, all-glass tanks of 2-gallon capacity are suitable for pairs of smaller fish and hatching eggs. Tanks of 5- to 10-gallon capacity, preferably of flat, shallow proportions, are used for larger forms, e.g., *Austrofundulus*, *Aphyosemion caeruleum*. Larger-sized tanks are required for raising young fish. All tanks must be covered with a well-fitted sheet of glass, since annual fish are notorious for their jumping ability. Filtration of aquarium water is both desirable and essential, because of the need for heavy feedings to promote growth and continuous spawning. Filtration prevents the establishment of conditions favorable for microbial growth. Such control is essential for disease prevention and the reduction of surface contamination of eggs. Standard inside aquarium filters are suitable for larger aquaria. For small tanks, the so-called "sponge filter" is ideal. This is essentially a fine-mesh synthetic sponge, through which the passage of water is effected by a filter stem (*cf.* Markis, 1964). Lighting should be subdued, arranged in a manner to facilitate work, but without exposing aquaria to excessive illumination. A simple timing device provides adequate control of the photoperiod.

Feeding

Live foods such as tubifex worms, adult brine shrimp, mosquito and chironomid larvae, wingless *Drosophila*, *Daphnia*, and similar small crustaceans are required for the continued maintenance of fish in spawning condition. Some species will do well on prepared foods, e.g., Gordon's (1950) formula. Fry are fed newly hatched brine shrimp nauplii until capable of taking larger food.

Water

Water conditions appear to be a critical factor in the successful maintenance of annual fishes. Generalizations are foolhardy, but unavoidable. For most species, soft to moderately hard water (not in excess of 100 ppm total hardness) is required. *Austrofundulus*, the Argentine species of *Cynolebias*, and *Nothobranchius* do better at slightly increased mineral concentrations. Most annual fish prefer water with an acid pH. This is usually produced by storing water in a glass container with peat moss (ordinary greenhouse type) until the water has become slightly amber in color. Such water has an additional advantage of inhibiting microbial growth. *Nothobranchius* and *Austrofundulus* do better in neutral or alkaline water. *Nothobranchius* is commonly found in waters with a surprisingly high content of dissolved iron (Geisler, 1959). It seems possible that the sensitivity of this genus to disease, which mitigates against its more extensive use, may be due to an unsatisfied iron requirement. In general, it would seem advisable to maintain only one or two types of water conditions in laboratory aquaria. A supply of aged, conditioned water should be kept in glass containers for emergency use. Contact of the water in aquariums or storage containers with copper, zinc, galvanized iron, or other metals must, of course, be avoided.

Diseases

Disease prevention by the avoidance of disease-promoting conditions such as dirty aquaria and chilling is essential. The principal disease which affects annual fishes is "Velvet," a term descriptive of the appearance of a fish infected by the ectoparasitic dinoflagellate *Oodinium limneticum.* A heavily parasitized fish appears to be powdered with gold. This parasite often causes fatal pandemics in laboratory populations. Treatment in the dark with 0.50 percent aqueous Malachite Green at a dosage of one drop per gallon is effective. Treatment should be repeated after 24 hours. If signs of gasping are observed, half of the tank water should be immediately replaced with aged, untreated water. If treatment is successful, half of the tank water should be replaced in 3 days, and another half after 5 days. Care should be taken to avoid the spread of the parasite via contaminated equipment, dripped water, etc.

A second disease, common in fishes which have been chilled, is "ich," caused by the protozoan *Ichthyophthirius.* Infected fish are covered with small white spots, hold their fins tightly pressed to the body, and incessantly scratch themselves against hard surfaces. Warmth and treatment in the dark with a 1 percent quinine hydrochloride solution at a dosage of 12.5 ml per gallon added in three equal parts during a 12-hour interval is effective. After 1 or 2 weeks, the aquarium water should be slowly replaced.

Some of the more sensitive annual fishes are subject to shock, and even death, if suddenly subjected to a radical change in water conditions. This problem is often met with when new fishes are acquired. The pH and hardness of the water in shipping containers should be checked. If radically different from tank conditions, shipping water and tank water should be slowly mixed. It is preferable to introduce fishes into water whose chemistry approximates that of the source.

Finally, it should be noted that the annual fishes are generally short-lived. Most species, especially if used for continuous spawning, seldom exceed an age of 8 months to a year. Fecundity and the viability of the eggs decrease sharply as senescence is attained.

An extensive treatment of diseases and prophylaxis is available in Reichenbach-Klinke (1965).

DISTINGUISHING SEXES

Distinguishing sexes in annual fish presents no problems. Sexual dimorphism is commonly so pronounced that males and females seem to belong to different species (and were so treated in early taxonomic studies). In general, the overall coloration and the patterning of males is more pronounced and more brilliant than that of the females. Males often display gaudy combinations of scarlet, blue, bright green, and yellow, while the females are patterned in drab shades of brown, gray, and green. Other ornamentation, such as elongated fins and filamentous fin rays, are pronounced in males and reduced in females. Males exhibit a high degree of aggressiveness among themselves and a lesser degree toward females.

INTRODUCTION

Echinoderm eggs, particularly those of the sea urchin, have come to play an increasingly important role in both embryology and cell biology. These eggs offer a number of advantages. They can be obtained in large numbers, handled with ease, and cultured in simple media. They are easily fertilized, and a population of eggs can be made to divide synchronously simply by fertilizing all of them at the same time. Furthermore, the eggs will take up many radioactively labeled compounds such as amino acids and nucleosides, and they are susceptible to numerous drugs. Echinoderm eggs also offer a number of experimental possibilities. Large numbers can be induced to develop parthenogenetically, interspecific hybrids can be formed, and, with the use of suitable eggs, one can separate large numbers into nucleate and anucleate halves by centrifugation. Sometimes the anucleate halves can be fertilized or division induced by means of artificial parthenogenetic techniques.

There are also some drawbacks. The eggs are easy to obtain and handle at marine laboratories where the animals are readily available and running sea water is on tap. The task of maintaining a supply of animals at laboratories far from the ocean may become a significant undertaking, but still a practical venture. Echinoderm eggs have a large amount of yolk and other cytoplasmic material, and this may make the observation of nuclear phenomena difficult in living material. A few species, such as the urchin *Lytechinus variegatus*, do have exceptionally transparent eggs. It is also very difficult to raise embryos beyond the pluteus stage. Therefore studies requiring a second generation are impractical.

Echinoderm eggs have been used in biological research for more than 100 years. During this time, a number of techniques have been developed for handling the animals and their eggs. This chapter will cover techniques the author and others have found to be reliable and of general applicability. The last section will briefly refer to some of the more specialized uses of echinoderm eggs.

Three valuable references on the use of echinoderm eggs are Harvey (1956), Costello *et al.* (1957), and Tyler and Tyler (1966). The former is primarily devoted to *Arbacia punctulata* but also contains a good deal that is applicable to other urchins. Harvey's book also contains [illegible] experimental [illegible]s and a bibliog- [illegible]ely 1,700 references [illegible]*acia* and other urchins. [illegible]ves specific directions for [illegible]dling, and fertilizing the eggs [illegible]r of east coast echinoderms, as [illegible]other marine animals. Many of [illegible]chniques have wide applicability.

The echinoderms that will primarily [illegible]e considered in this chapter are those of North America and Hawaii, though of course most of the methods will in general, and often in detail, be applicable to other species.

GENERAL

Echinoderms are found only in salt water. The phylum is divided into five classes. Three of these, the Crenoidea (sea lilies), Holothuroidea (sea cucumbers), and Ophiuroidea (brittle stars), are seldom used as research material. The Echinoidea (sea urchins and sand dollars) are by far the most popular source of experimental material. Asteroidea (starfish) are also used.

The eggs of both the sea urchin and sand dollar, unlike those of many other animals, are haploid when shed. That is, both meiotic divisions are completed prior to spawning. Starfish eggs are shed in the germinal vesicle (tetraploid nucleus) stage and undergo the two meiotic divisions, with polar body formation, after they are spawned. Usually the germinal vesicle breaks down rather asynchronously, and development after fertilization is often asynchronous. This can detract from the over-all usefulness of starfish eggs. The germinal vesicle does offer a certain number of advantages. It contains a nucleolus, which urchin eggs do not have prior to fertilization, and starfish eggs are one of the few cells from which nucleoli have been isolated (Vincent, 1952). Starfish eggs also serve as good material for the study of meiosis.

EQUIPMENT AND REAGENTS

If the animals are to be used at a marine laboratory, the necessary equipment for obtaining and handling eggs and embryos is quite simple. The basic kit includes: 5–10 ml hypodermic syringes and needles, scissors, hand centrifuge, 12-ml conical centrifuge tubes, cheesecloth, and a compound microscope. The usual assortment of common laboratory glassware, slides, and cover slips, and sea water are also necessary. If large numbers of embryos are to be raised, stirring motors may be needed. Potassium chloride is the only indispensable reagent.

If the animals are not to be kept alive, research at inland laboratories requires little more than the above. The only item normally unavailable is sea water. One source is the Marine Biological Laboratory at Woods Hole, which ships 5-gallon carboys. The author has found that a synthetic salt mixture marketed under the name "Instant Ocean"[1] is a good sea water substitute. At least in New York City, it should be made up in distilled water, not tap water as the directions specify. This product does not contain fluoride or silicate among the known ingredients, and these may have to be added when distilled water is used. For many purposes, including developmental studies, a simple synthetic mixture often works quite well. There are many formulae for such mixtures, and the one used in Dr. Mazia's laboratory is given here. Reagent grade chemicals are used. These seem to

[1] Obtained from Aquarium Systems, Inc., 1489 East 289th Street, Wickliffe, Ohio 44092.

contain enough impurities to supply needed trace elements. If necessary the pH should be adjusted to 8.2. Calcium chloride is left out for calcium-free sea water.

Synthetic Sea Water

CHEMICAL	GRAMS PER LITER
NaCl	28.32
KCl	0.77
$MgCl_2 \cdot 6H_2O$	5.41
$MgSO_4 \cdot 7H_2O$	7.13
$CaCl_2$	1.18
After the above salts are dissolved add:	
$NaHCO_3$	0.2

DISTRIBUTION, SPAWNING SEASON, AND PROCUREMENT OF SEA URCHINS

Distribution

Sea urchins, like almost all other groups of organisms, are represented by large numbers of species in warm waters and fewer species, but many individuals, in colder waters. In the Hawaiian Islands, there are nine species that can be found in fair abundance. Of these the most easily obtained and usable are *Echinometra mathaei* and *Tripneustes gratilla*. Along the west coast of the North American continent, the significant species are: *Strongylocentrotus purpuratus* (the purple urchin), *S. franciscanus*, *S. dröbachiensis* (the green urchin), and *Lytechinus pictus*. Of these, *S. purpuratus* is the most abundant and frequently used and ranges from southern California to Alaska. *Strongylocentrotus franciscanus* has roughly the same range. *Strongylocentrotus dröbachiensis* is found from Puget Sound north and *Lytechinus pictus* from southern California south. The urchin most extensively used along the east coast is *Arbacia punctulata*, which occurs from Cape Cod to Florida. *Strongylocentrotus dröbachiensis* is abundant in the northeast, and *Lytechinus variegatus* is commonly found in Florida.

Two species of sand dollar used in developmental studies and found along the coasts of North America are *Echinorachnius parma* on the east and northwest coasts and *Dendraster excentricus* on the west coast.

Spawning Season

The spawning season for any particular species can vary from year to year by a month or more and depends on geographical location. Urchins in northern waters tend to have a shorter season than those in the south. The data given here are therefore only approximate.

By the proper choice of animals or geographical locality, a researcher can keep himself supplied with eggs the year round. In fact, in the more tropical waters some urchins can often be found with a few eggs at any time of the year. The two Hawaiian urchins are examples of these. *Echinometra mathaei* has a peak season running from September to March, whereas *Tripneustes gratilla* spawns primarily from June to December; but some specimens of either can be found with eggs at any time of year. The spawning season for *S. purpuratus* is in the winter months with gametes in greatest abundance from December through February. The usable season is generally from September to May, with gametes sometimes being available in early summer. *Strongylocentrotus dröbachiensis* is ripe from January into spring. *Arbacia* has a season running from mid-June to mid-August (Harvey, 1956). The season for *Lytechinus variegatus* is from autumn to spring, and *Lytechinus pictus* from spring to autumn. The two sand dollars spawn in the summer months.

Procurement

The method for procuring urchins depends to some extent on the species. *Strongyglocentrotus purpuratus*, *Lytechinus*, and sand dollars are among those that can be collected at low tide in the appropriate environment. Many of the others are obtained by diving or dredging. Personnel at biological laboratories along the coasts usually know the best areas for collecting the endemic species, though sometimes the knowledge is a guarded secret.

The Marine Biological Laboratory at Woods Hole, Massachusetts will ship a number of marine animals to inland laboratories. There are also private collectors who ship echinoderms and other marine animals. This is more a labor of love than money; and, except for a few particularly tenacious individuals, there is a rapid turnover. The author knows of three collectors who have been in business for a number of years.[2] There are often personnel at marine laboratories who are willing to collect on a part-time basis. A letter to the director of the laboratory is the best means of contact. The location and laboratory addresses can be found in Hiatt (1963). One source of urchins that is particularly convenient in some large cities is the wholesale fish market. For example, the Fulton Fish Market in New York City has *S. dröbachiensis* throughout the winter.

STARFISH DISTRIBUTION, SEASON, AND PROCUREMENT

There are a number of starfish on both coasts of North America. Two of these have been used fairly extensively in embryological research: *Asterias forbesi* on the east coast and members of the genus *Pisaster* on the west coast. The latter can be collected at low tide; the former is often obtained by dredging or dragging. Both *Pisaster* and *Asterias* spawn during the summer months. The season for *Asterias* is rather short and lasts from May to mid-July (Costello *et al.*, 1957).

MAINTAINING LIVE ANIMALS

The best method for maintaining live animals in usable condition depends on how long one wishes to keep them. If they are to be used within a short time after collecting, that is, in less than a week, they can be kept cold at approximately 5°C and damp, but not actually in water. Alternating layers of moist sea weed and animals maintain the specimens rather well. If the animals are to be kept for longer than a week, their maintenance becomes a more complex undertaking. Echinoderms are not the easiest animals to maintain in closed systems. *Lytechinus pictus* is probably the hardiest species. It is a good scavenger and keeps well with minimum effort. It can be stimulated to spawn by electric shock, which means the egg yield can be controlled, and the animals left unharmed. However, this is a small urchin and therefore yields relatively small amounts of gametes. The other echinoderms are harder to maintain, but the author knows of several laboratories that have kept specimens of one or another species for extended periods. Most of these use recirculating sea water tanks or aquaria. Cool temperature, a large amount of clean water per animal, and control of pH are the main physical prerequisites. Most echinoderms, particularly the urchins, eat foods ranging from sea weed or lettuce to frozen shrimp. Ferguson (1966) has kept *S. purpuratus* and *Arbacia* alive for long periods on a diet of frozen Pakistan

[2] Pacific Bio-Marine Supply Company, P.O. Box 285, Venice, California. Supplies *Strongylocentrotus purpuratus* and *Lytechinus pictus*.

Stanley Becker, P.O. Box 62, Big Pine Key, Florida, supplies *L. variegatus*.

Gulf Specimen Co., P.O. Box 206, Panacea, Florida, supplies *L. variegatus* and *Arbacia punctulata*.

shrimp, a variety they seem particularly fond of. If the temperature is kept low enough, many species will survive for a month or more even without food. It should be kept in mind that there is always the danger in closed systems that all individuals in a tank will be stimulated to spawn if one starts to spawn.

In deciding whether to keep animals for long periods or to purchase them when needed, one should weigh the cost and bother of a sea water system against the cost of obtaining the animals when needed. Collectors are currently charging a dollar per specimen (plus or minus 50 cents) plus air freight.

SEXING ECHINODERMS

Sexes are separate in all the commonly used echinoderms but can seldom be identified by external features. Sometimes it is necessary to know the sex of an individual, particularly if one wishes to conserve material. A common method is to take a biopsy. A hypodermic needle is passed through the peristomial membrane of sea urchins or sand dollars and into the gonads, and a small sample of material is drawn out with a syringe and examined under the microscope. Starfish are sexed in a similar manner except that the needle is passed through the arm. This procedure does not seem to affect the animal's survival significantly. Some urchins can be induced to spawn by electric shock (see below). A short stimulation can therefore be used as a means of sexing individuals. This method does not work for all species.

Obtaining Gametes

The most widely used method for induced shedding of sea urchin and sand dollar gametes is coelomic injection of 0.5 *M* KCl. This solution is approximately isotonic with sea water. The amount injected depends on the size of the urchin and ranges from 1 ml or less for small individuals to 10 ml for large animals. Experience soon indicates the correct amount. It is simplest to inject the animals through several points around the peristomial membrane. This treatment is probably not to the organism's advantage but is usually not lethal.

Harvey (1956) uses electric shock to stimulate spawning in *Arbacia*. Line voltage is stepped down to 10 volts AC using a transformer and applied across the urchin with lead electrodes. The animal spawns until the gonads are exhausted or the stimulation is stopped. This method has two important advantages. The animals are apparently not harmed, and the yield of gametes can be controlled. The only drawback is that some urchins and all starfish fail to respond. Spawning can be induced in starfish by injection of a radial nerve extract; the paper of Chaet and Musick (1960) should be consulted for details.

The Hawaiian urchins respond irregularly to KCl injection, ripe animals sometimes not shedding; and they do not respond at all to electrical stimulation. A freshly prepared sea water-acetylcholine solution has been found to work well (Hinegardner, 1961). This is made up in sea water at a concentration of approximately 0.01 *M*. Once one knows what the correct amount of acetylcholine per volume of sea water looks like, the solution can be made up by eye. It is important that the solution be made up no more than 10–20 minutes before use. This method does not work for all urchins.

The oldest technique for obtaining gametes is surgical removal of the gonads. This method can be tedious but is applicable to all echinoderms. If the gonads are removed carefully, good egg yields can be obtained with little contamination. Gonads are removed from starfish by cutting off an arm and then making a mid-dorsal cut along the length of the arm. If the animal is ripe, the gonads will appear as two large, multibranched organs lying next to the greenish-brown digestive glands. Ovaries are usually salmon to reddish colored, and testes white to pale yellow. The ovaries should be carefully lifted out, rinsed in sea water, and placed in a dish of sea water. The eggs will extrude from the proximal end of the ovary. Generally, eggs produced during the first 5 or 10 minutes are best. The testes can be left in the arm. A small piece is removed when needed, and its sperm suspended in an appropriate amount of sea water. Sea urchins can be handled in much the same way except that the cut is made around the mouth region, the digestive organs are taken out, and the ovaries carefully removed by cutting the thin tissues holding them in place. Practically the entire contents of a ripe ovary will often consist of fertilizable eggs. The testes can be left in place or removed; in either case they are treated in the same manner as those from starfish.

Obtaining Eggs

The best method for collecting eggs from sea urchins, sand dollars, or starfish that have been stimulated by electricity or injection is to place the animal upside down over a vessel, such as a beaker, that is somewhat smaller in diameter than the animal. The vessel should be filled with enough sea water to cover the gonadopores. The eggs will flow from the pores in streams and pile up on the bottom. Depending on the species used, spawning may take from 5 minutes up to a half-hour or more. It is sometimes profitable to reinject after shedding has ceased or to shake the animal strongly. This sometimes produces a significant increase in yield.

Usually assorted pieces of debris, broken spines, and sand are collected along with the eggs. These are easily removed by passing an egg suspension through several layers of cheesecloth or appropriate mesh bolting silk or nylon. Fertilization and development appear to be adversely affected by coelomic fluid and secretions from the animal, and it is always advisable to wash the eggs several times with sea water. This is done by allowing the filtered eggs to settle, decanting or drawing off as much water as possible, and resuspending the eggs in fresh sea water. This should be repeated about three times.

Egg Longevity

A number of factors determine how long eggs can be kept until they fail to fertilize and develop normally. Eggs of *S. purpuratus* can be kept for about 24 hours at 5°C without significant loss in fertilizability. At high temperature they deteriorate more rapidly. Some workers have attempted to devise methods for increasing egg longevity (see Harvey, 1956, p. 149). Though some of these are reported to extend the usable life of eggs for up to a week, none have come into wide use; and in most cases it is easier to maintain a ripe animal rather than store the eggs.

Egg Yield

The yield of eggs from any one animal depends on its size and degree of ripeness. A large *S. franciscanus* will often produce more than 100 ml of settled eggs. A portion of this volume consists of the jelly coat surrounding each egg. During the peak of its season, *S. purpuratus* can yield more than 50 ml. At the other end of the range is the small *Lytechinus pictus*, which contains in the neighborhood of 1 ml of eggs. This is also the range for sand dollars. *Arbacia* is reported by Harvey (1956) to yield 5 ml of eggs at best and usually less.

Sperm

Unlike the eggs, sperm have a very short life. Very few sperm remain active in suspension for longer than a few hours. Like sperm of other organisms, echinoderm sperm are activated in the presence of oxygen. The easiest way to keep them inactive, and thus extend their life span, is to leave them in the gonads, or collect them under what are called "dry" conditions, i.e., in the absence of sea water. With sea urchins that have been induced to shed, this can easily be done by placing the animal upside down over a Syracuse dish or similar receptacle that is smaller in diameter than the urchin. It is advisable to have a ring of absorbent tissue between the rim of the dish and the animal. This helps prevent contamination of the sperm by liquids that run off the outside of the shell. The sperm will drip from the gonadopores into the dish. Once collected, the sperm should be covered to prevent evaporation and stored in the refrigerator until needed. They will generally remain viable under these conditions for more than a day.

FERTILIZATION

If both the eggs and sperm are viable, fertilization is a very simple task. All that is involved is adding an appropriate number of sperm to an egg suspension. Beginners have a tendency to use too much sperm. This does not affect fertilization, but leads to problems later. A large excess of sperm may produce polyspermy in a significant number of eggs. Some species are more susceptible to this than others. Furthermore, the excess sperm soon die and begin to decompose which in turn may be detrimental to embryonic development. Uniform fertilization is most easily obtained by using a sperm suspension. A drop or less of the "dry" sperm is suspended in about 10 ml of sea water, and the appropriate amount of this suspension added to the eggs. Experience will show how much sperm to add. In general, microscope examination should show something like 10 sperm surrounding each egg. This is only a rough number, but several hundred sperm is too much unless the eggs fail to become fertilized with less.

The first evidence of fertilization is the raising of the fertilization membrane. This begins at the point of sperm entry and rapidly extends over the egg. The entire process takes less than a minute. Most workers reject a batch of eggs which shows less than 90–95 percent fertilization, as determined by the presence of membranes. Developmental synchrony can often be predicted by how synchronously the membranes are raised.

If there is any doubt as to the viability of any batch of gametes, it is wise to fertilize a drop of egg suspension for microscopic examination. Infertility can be caused by a number of conditions, none of which are adequately explained. Sometimes the sperm are immotile or move very sluggishly. Such sperm seldom fertilize eggs well. If the sperm are vigorous, they are almost always usable. More frequently, eggs fail to become fertilized even though the sperm are known to be good. Some workers have attempted to treat such recalcitrant eggs in various ways to improve fertilization. Harvey (1956) should be consulted for the pertinent references. Usually, unless the eggs are particularly precious, it is easier to obtain a fresh batch of eggs and try again.

DEVELOPMENT

The developmental sequence for all echinoderm embryos normally used in experimental biology is essentially the same. The major stages are illustrated in Fig. 1 for the development of the sand dollar (Karnofsky and Simmel, 1963). The number of cells per embryo increases

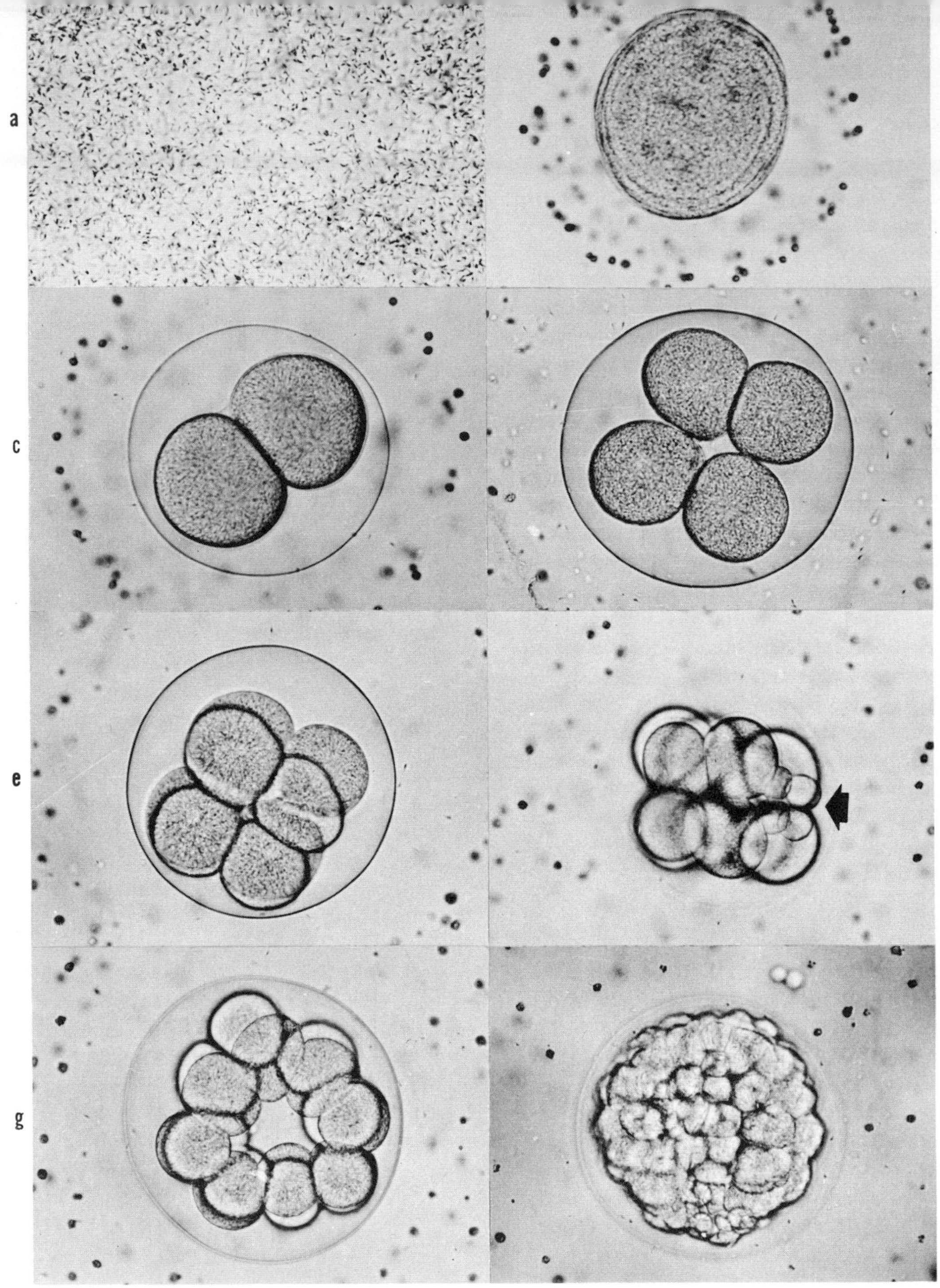

FIG. 1. Developmental stages of eggs of *Echinorachnius parma* raised at 15°C. All times are hours after fertilization. The magnification for all stages is the same and approximately 190 ×. (a) Sperm suspension. (b) Unfertilized egg. Dark bodies surrounding the egg are red pigment granules imbedded in the jelly coat. (c) Two-cells, 1.5 hours. The fertilization membrane is clearly visible. (d) Four-cells, 3 hours. (e) Eight-cells, 4 hours. (f) Sixteen-cells, 5 hours. The four micromeres are indicated by the arrow. (g) Sixteen-cell embryo, 5.5 hours. View perpendicular to f. (h) Morula, 6.5 hours. (i) Early blastula, 7 hours. (j)

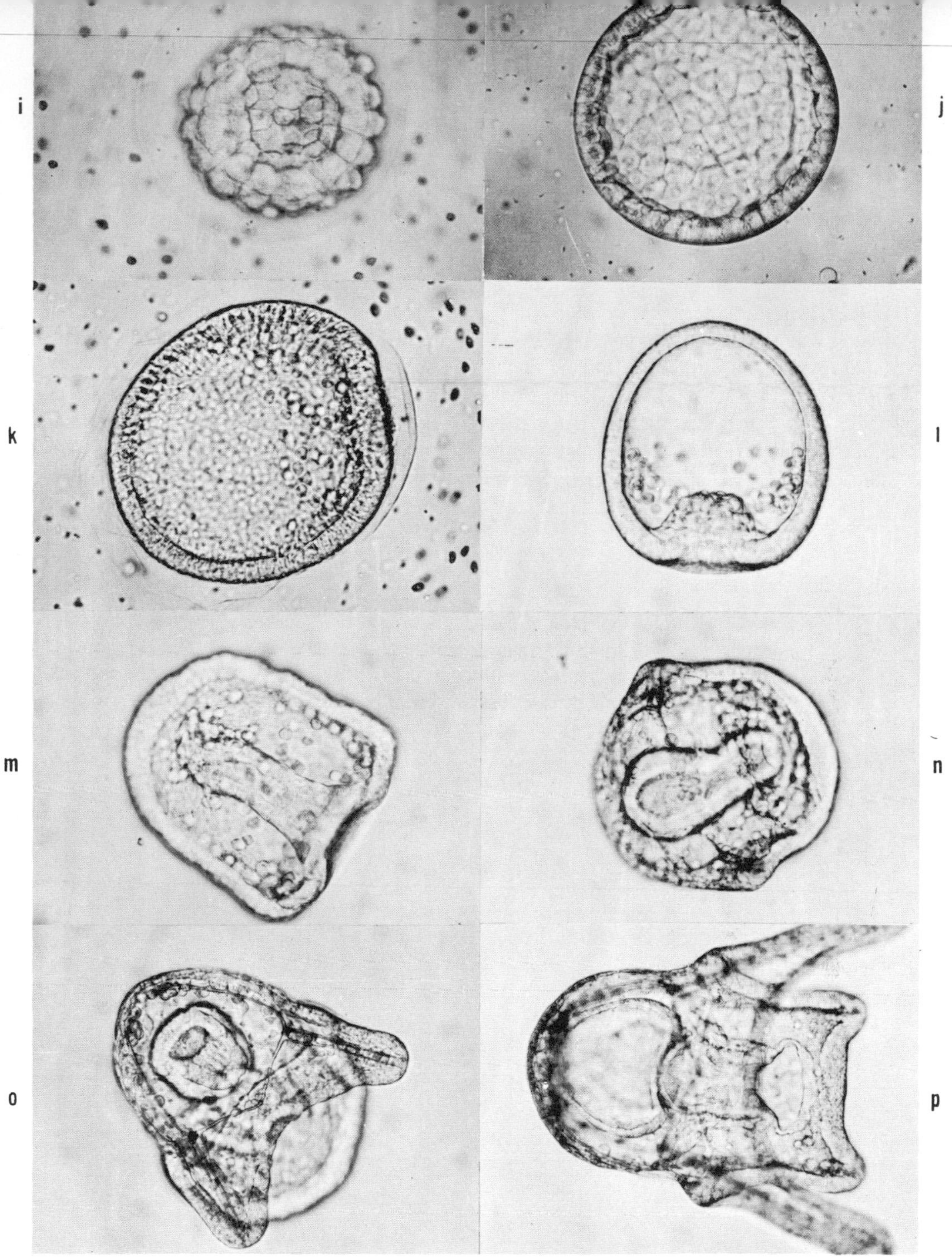

Blastula, 8 hours. (k) Late blastula in process of hatching, 12 hours. (l) Early gastrula, 25 hours. (m) Late gastrula, 31 hours. (n) Prism stage, 48 hours. (o) Early pluteus, short arms, anal or ventral view, 50 hours, (p) Late pluteus, long arms, oral or dorsal side, 72 hours. SOURCE: Karnofsky, D. A., and Simmel, Eva B.: Effects of growth-inhibiting chemicals on the Sand-dollar embryo, *Echinarachnius parma.* Progr. Exp. Tumor Res. 3: 254–295 (1963). Reprinted by permission of S. Karger, Basel/New York.

almost exponentially up to early blastula stages, after which the division rate drops. This is shown in Fig. 2, where the number of cells per embryo of *S. purpuratus* is plotted against time. The times of hatching and gastrulation are indicated.

The rate of development and, for that matter, whether the eggs develop at all depend on the temperature. *Arbacia* will develop normally at 23°C, but *S. purpuratus* begins to show abnormalities above 15°C. The rate of development for most echinoderms has a Q_{10} somewhat greater than 2. That is, a 10° lowering of the temperature more than doubles the time of development.

Raising Embryos

If relatively few embryos are being raised, or if the embryos are so fragile that agitation disrupts them, they are most easily cultivated as monolayers on the bottom of a container. This method produces abnormal embryos, or no development at all, if the layer of eggs is much more than one egg thick. If larger numbers of eggs are used, they must be

FIG. 2. A semi-log plot showing the number of cells per *Strongylocentrotus purpuratus* embryo plotted against time after fertilization at 15°C. The data points were obtained by the method outlined in the text. Each point is the average of several counts. The time at which embryos normally hatch from their fertilization membranes and the period of gastrulation are indicated.

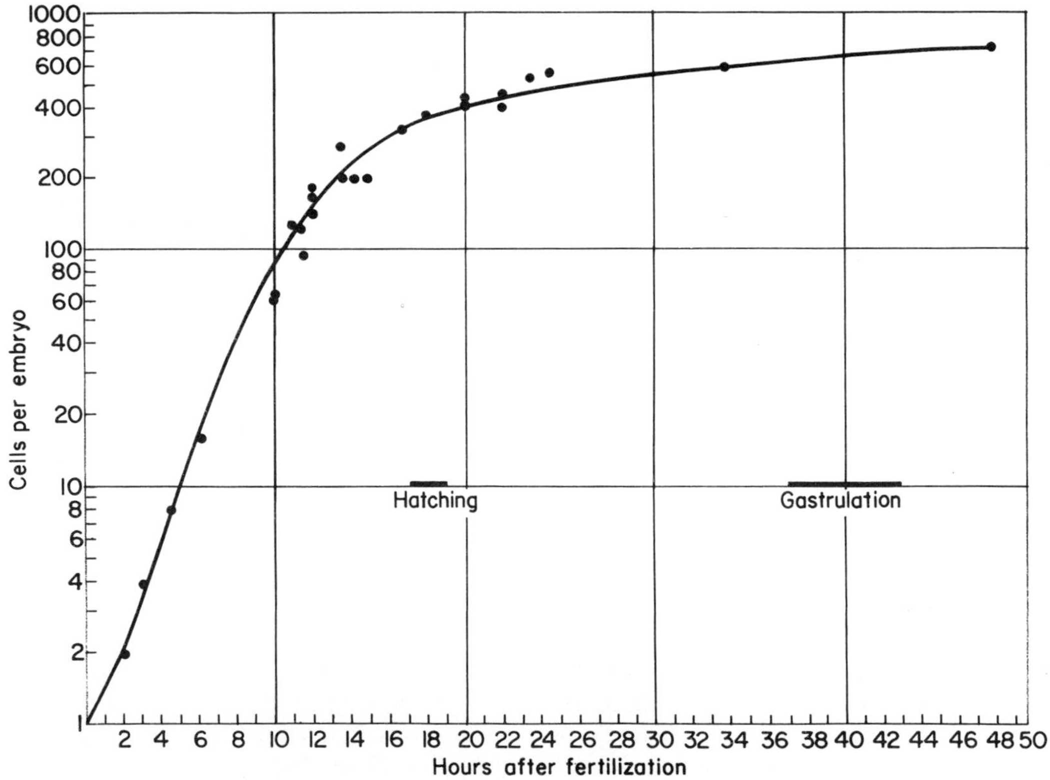

agitated. *Strongylocentrotus purpuratus* embryos develop well in beakers or buckets in which eggs are agitated by using plastic paddles attached to 60 rpm clock motors. This keeps the embryos suspended and circulates the water but is not fast enough to damage the embryos. For best development, the concentration of eggs should not be much greater than 4×10^6 eggs (2 ml packed eggs the size of those from *S. purpuratus*) per 100 ml sea water. The embryos of most echinoderms can be raised to the pluteus stage without much trouble. At this point, they have exhausted their yolk, and they soon die unless fed, and in fact, the larvae generally die even when fed. Raising embryos through metamorphosis is an undertaking in itself. Methods for doing this can be found in Harvey (1956, p. 113).

CHOICE OF EGGS

There is no echinoderm whose eggs are universally good for all research situations. However, some approach this ideal more closely than others. In the author's opinion *Strongylocentrotus purpuratus* comes closest. The eggs are strong and withstand some rather drastic treatments. They are not so pigmented that cytoplasmic phenomena can not be followed (though *Lytechinus variegatus* is better on this score), and they can be obtained in the large amounts necessary for many biochemical studies. Furthermore, this urchin has a long spawning season that coincides almost exactly with the academic year, and it can easily be shipped to inland laboratories (see footnote 2) and be maintained in aquaria. All in all, it has many advantages and few drawbacks.

Arbacia eggs have certainly been the most extensively studied, probably because this urchin is the only one in abundance on the east coast above Florida, and because it spawns during the summer when the Woods Hole Marine Laboratory is occupied. The eggs are not as hardy as those of *S. purpuratus*, and they are highly pigmented. The yield of eggs per urchin is relatively low, and the spawning season is short. This urchin does, however, keep well in aquaria, and for many embryological studies the eggs are as useful as those from *S. purpuratus*. *Strongylocentrotus franciscanus* and *S. dröbachiensis* eggs seem to offer no particular advantage over either *S. purpuratus* or *Arbacia*, though they may be easier to obtain in some localities. *Lytechinus pictus* has the advantage of being a very hardy species, but it yields small amounts of gametes. Sand dollar eggs seem to be particularly sensitive to a variety of drugs affecting deoxyribonucleic acid (DNA) and protein synthesis and are useful for studies in this area (Karnofsky and Simmel, 1963). These animals keep well at marine laboratories, but they are difficult to maintain in a closed sea water system. The two Hawaiian species of sea urchins have both advantages and disadvantages. Eggs of *Echinometra mathaei* equal those of *S. purpuratus* in ease of handling, but the urchin is small, and it may be hard to collect. The animals live in holes in rock or coral. *Tripneustes gratilla* is large and easy to obtain, but the eggs are very fragile and cannot withstand even mild agitation. Starfish eggs do not offer any general advantages over those of the urchins. The eggs are quite fragile and usually develop more asynchronously than urchin eggs. These eggs are often used in comparative studies and to test generalities resulting from studies on other eggs.

RESEARCH METHODS

Jelly Coat Removal

The jelly coat has the same index of refraction as sea water and is not directly visible under the microscope. Its presence can most easily be ascertained by observing how closely eggs will pack, or how far debris or sperm are kept from the egg. The jelly coat of sand dollar eggs contains pigment granules and is easily detected.

It is sometimes desirable to free eggs from their jelly coat. In some species the jelly is removed simply by passing the eggs through cheesecloth or fine mesh. If the jelly coat is more tenacious, it is usually removable in acid sea water. The method of Hagström (1959) is simple and has wide applicability. The pH of 50 ml of sea water is lowered with 0.1 *N* HCl to a point where the addition of 100 ml of fresh sea water will yield sea water with a final pH between 5.5 and 5.8. Then 100 ml of an egg suspension in fresh sea water is poured into the 50 ml of acid sea water, and the eggs are allowed to settle. The appropriate size container is one which gives a suspension shallow enough to permit settling of eggs in 1–3 minutes. The acid solution is then drawn off and enough fresh sea water added to bring the pH back to normal. If the eggs' sojourn in acid is kept brief, the method appears to do no harm.

Fertilization Membrane Removal

Two different methods for eliminating fertilization membranes will be described in some detail. A summary of some other methods is presented in the article by Berg in this volume, pp. 767–776. The first prevents membrane formation; the second removes the membrane once it has formed.

Moore (1930) found that eggs left for about 2 minutes in 1 *M* urea free from electrolytes failed to form a fertilization membrane or hyaline layer when subsequently fertilized in sea water. The cells cleaved properly but did not remain together as a blastula, forming irregular strands instead. Moore used small numbers of eggs and simply added a few drops of a thick egg suspension to 50 ml of 1 *M* urea. Larger volumes can be handled (Hultin, 1948). The eggs are first concentrated by hand centrifugation, then suspended in a large volume of urea solution for 30 seconds, gently hand centrifuged, and resuspended in fresh urea for 1 minute. The suspension is then diluted with sea water, the eggs again centrifuged, and finally suspended in sea water. They can then be fertilized. It is important that appreciable quantities of Mg^{++} or Ca^{++} not be present during urea treatment.

Membranes can be removed after fertilization. In some cases they can be stripped off by passing the fertilized eggs through bolting silk having a mesh size slightly less than the diameter of the eggs. Lindahl and Lundin (1948) found that the membranes of *Paracentrotus lividus* could be removed this way if the eggs were passed rapidly through the silk within 2 or 3 minutes after fertilization. The membranes of *S. purpuratus* cannot be removed satisfactorily by this method unless they are first treated (Mazia *et al.*, 1961). A rather dense suspension of eggs (e.g. 10 vol eggs/100 vol of sea water) is fertilized at 15°C. As soon as the membranes begin to rise, after about 30 seconds, two volumes of calcium-free artificial sea water containing 1 mg per milliliter MEGA (Mercaptoethylglucon-amide)[3] and 0.01 *M* EDTA (ethylenediaminetetraacetate) at pH 7.5–8.5. are added. The MEGA prevents hardening of the membranes, while lack of calcium and the presence of EDTA prevent clumping once the membranes are removed. The eggs are gently stirred in this solution for about 15 minutes. The membranes are then stripped off by passing the eggs through appropriate size

[3] Obtained from Cyclo Chemical Corp., Los Angeles 1, California.

bolting silk (25 mesh for *S. purpuratus*). Generally several passes through the silk are necessary to remove all membranes. A moderate amount of pressure is required to force the eggs through the mesh. A simple membrane stripper can be constructed by cutting off the end of a 50-ml plastic centrifuge tube and attaching the silk to the rim end of the tube with a rubber band. The eggs can then be forced through with moderate air pressure. Once the membranes have been removed, the eggs should be handled very gently. They are allowed to settle, and the supernatant, containing the membranes and excess sperm, is removed. Then the eggs are gently resuspended in Ca-free sea water, settled, and the supernatant again removed. This step is repeated once more. Sometimes the eggs clump after they settle the first time. If they do, the clumps should be resuspended more or less intact by carefully pouring the Ca-free sea water down the side of the container. Usually at the third wash the eggs will have separated. The settling period should be no longer than necessary, or one risks anoxia in the settled layer. If the eggs are to be used prior to the first division, they can be left in Ca-free sea water. If they are to be raised beyond this stage, regular sea water should be added to the suspension. As long as calcium is present in the sea water, the cells of each embryo will remain together and develop normally.

Counting Eggs

Echinoderm eggs are too large to count with any accuracy using a hemocytometer (even deep ones) and too small to count with the naked eye. They can be counted with a Coulter Counter using an appropriate aperture tube.

A less expensive technique, which is fairly accurate, is that described by Shapiro (1935). The end of a thin-walled capillary tube of known inside diameter, such as a 1-mm blood capillary, is dipped into a homogeneous egg suspension and filled by capillary action. The tube is then laid on its side under a dissecting microscope, and the eggs allowed to settle. The eggs in a measured length of the tube are counted. From this length and the diameter of the tube, the volume containing the counted eggs is calculated. The concentration in the original solution can then be determined. For ease of counting, the egg concentration in the suspension should not be too great.

Counting Cells per Embryo

A fairly simple technique for counting the number of cells per embryo will be described here. This was developed for use with *S. purpuratus* embryos, but it is probably applicable to other species. The only requirement is that the fertilization membrane not be present. After hatching this is no problem. If cell counts are to be made prior to hatching, membranes should be removed by the method of Lindahl and Lundin (1948) or Mazia *et al.* (1961).

A sample containing about 0.1 ml of packed embryos is hand centrifuged, the supernatant removed, and about 6 ml of a 1.5 *M* dextrose solution containing approximately 10^{-3} *M* EDTA is added. The embryos are quickly suspended in this solution. A small drop of the suspension is placed on a microscope slide, covered with a cover slip, and left undisturbed for 3–10 minutes. Enough liquid is withdrawn with bibulous paper to flatten the embryos slightly. One then slides the cover slip sideways several millimeters. If the time of exposure to and concentration of EDTA are correct, and the right amount of liquid has been removed, the cells of an embryo will form a monolayered streak. With a little practice, this can be done with no significant cell loss. The cells in a number of streaks can be counted or photographed and counted later. The data for Fig. 2 were obtained in this way.

The precautions to be observed are these: there should not be too many embryos in the dextrose-EDTA, or it will be difficult to tell where one streak ends and the next begins. If too much EDTA is used, or embryos are left in the dextrose-EDTA too long or handled too roughly, the cells will tend to fall apart before streaking. Cells will also tend to disintegrate under these conditions. Conversely, if not enough EDTA is used, the cells will not streak properly.

A variation on this method is to disassociate the embryos in dextrose-EDTA. Then by determining the concentration of disassociated cells with a hemocytometer and the number of embryos these cells came from, the number of cells per embryo can be calculated. In the author's experience this gives somewhat less accurate results than the first method.

Visualizing Chromosomes

It is often of great advantage to be able to determine readily the mitotic state of developing eggs. This is difficult with living material because chromosomes are seldom visible under phase contrast optics or similar systems. A simple, yet very effective, technique using fixed material has been developed by Mazia and is briefly described by Mazia *et al.* (1960). A more complete description is given here.

A sample containing about 0.1 ml packed embryos is hand centrifuged and the sediment fixed overnight at room temperature, or for 5–10 minutes at 70°C, in 4 or 5 ml of 3:1 alcohol:acetic acid. Twelve-milliliter conical centrifuge tubes serve as good containers. After fixation the tubes are centrifuged and as much fixative as possible is drawn off. It is important that essentially no alcohol remain. This can be accomplished by rotating each tube so that the embryos are spread over the lower portion of the tube. The alcohol is allowed to evaporate to the point where the embryos no longer flow but still appear damp. Then about 6 ml of 50 percent acetic acid is added. If fixed properly, the embryos will become transparent. A sample of this suspension is placed on a slide, covered, and enough liquid drawn off with bibulous paper to partially flatten the preparation. The cells should be examined with phase contrast optics. Under positive phase the chromosomes will appear much darker than the cytoplasm, and mitotic stages can easily be recognized. In favorable preparations, it may even be possible to count the chromosomes.

Artificial Parthenogenesis

Harvey (1956) lists something like 90 different ways for inducing some form of artificial activation in sea urchin eggs alone. These range from techniques that simply induce formation of the fertilization membrane to ones that yield some normal larvae. Much of the early work, and in fact much of what is known about artificial parthenogenesis even today, can be found in Loeb's classic book on the subject (Loeb, 1913). Loeb's method, which seems to work for most echinoderm eggs, the so-called "double method," will be described here.

To each 50 ml of an egg suspension 2 ml 0.1 *N* butyric acid are added. The suspension is stirred to insure a uniform solution. After 2 minutes, the eggs are hand centrifuged, and the supernatant removed. The eggs are then resuspended in sea water and stirred for 10 minutes. Then 8 ml of 2.5 *M* NaCl per 50 ml egg suspension is added, and the eggs again stirred. The eggs can either be allowed to settle as a monolayer, or stirred. After 30 minutes, this hypertonic sea water is removed, and fresh sea water added.

Butyric acid and similar substances cause the fertilization membrane to form, but the eggs seldom cleave. The hypertonic sea water induces aster formation, and some form of cleavage usually follows. Whether or not an egg cleaves in the normal manner depends on how many asters form and where they lie in the cytoplasm. Anywhere between 1 and 6 asters may form, and any number of these may become attached to the chromosomes. If more than two asters are involved in chromosome movement and division, cells are produced with abnormal chromosome numbers, and abnormal development follows. Cells with two asters frequently show normal cleavage and development. Not all eggs, of course, behave identically; and the researcher may find that exposure times in butyric acid or hypertonic sea water have to be modified to suit the particular species being used. Dirksen (1961) describes slight modifications of this technique for use with *S. purpuratus*.

Interspecific Hybrids

There are several techniques for fertilizing the eggs of one species with sperm from another. Sometimes it is possible to produce a significant number of hybrids simply by adding a large excess of sperm to eggs of a closely related species. Chaffee and Mazia (1963) were able to achieve 18 percent fertilization by adding *S. franciscanus* sperm to *S. purpuratus* eggs and 9 percent for the reverse cross. These are unusually good yields; generally the percent fertilization is much less, frequently less than a few percent. However, by treating eggs, a high yield of hybrids can often be produced.

Loeb found that short treatment at high pH was an effective way for increasing cross fertilization. One version of this method, used by Baltzer and Bernard (1955), is the following. Eggs are suspended in sea water containing 2.5 percent by volume 0.1 *N* NaOH and left for 5–10 minutes. Sperm from another species are then added to the eggs. After an additional 5–10 minutes the eggs are settled, the basic sea water removed, and fresh sea water added. The eggs are settled once more, the water removed, and fresh sea water again added. This is repeated one more time. The pH should now be that of sea water. The resultant embryos can be treated and cultured in the usual manner.

Hultin (1948) found that eggs freed of their jelly coat, then treated with 0.5 percent trypsin for 30 minutes and subsequently washed with sea water, could be fertilized by sperm from several species. He was able to obtain up to 80 percent cross fertilization with several European urchins. Simply removing the jelly coat will sometimes permit interspecific hybridization (Harding and Harding, 1952).

All these methods are probably acting on the egg's surface, and more specifically, probably on the vitelline membrane which is believed to be the normal barrier to foreign sperm. The extent of hybrid development does not seem to depend on the method used to produce it but rather on genetic factors. Some crosses, such as those between the two species of *Strongylocentrotus*, develop to the pluteus stage. Crosses between less closely related species generally do not develop beyond late blastula or early gastrula. One of the first indications of faulty development is the appearance of abnormal cells in the blastocoel.

EXPERIMENTAL TECHNIQUES

This section gives a short list of some basic experimental techniques that have been applied to echinoderm eggs and embryos. The references cited are not necessarily to the first workers in an area but sometimes to more recent papers where a number of techniques have been integrated.

The older work on cell lineage and manipulation of cells is reviewed by Hörstadius (1939 and 1949).

A summary of the recent literature on echinoderm development and its biochemistry can be found in Karnofsky and Simmel (1963).

Centrifugation of eggs into nucleate and anucleate halves and the use of these in experimental embryology is extensively covered by Harvey (1956).

Disassociation of embryo cells and the subsequent reconstitution of the embryo is described by Giudice (1962).

Gross and Cousineau (1964) describe the application of autoradiographic techniques to the study of synthetic processes in sea urchin material.

The cortical layer can be isolated from eggs by the method of Sakai (1960).

The isolation of cell constituents and their changes during development are covered in the article by Wilt in this volume, pp. 659–670.

REFERENCES

BALTZER, F., and M. BERNHARD, 1955: Weitere Beobachtungen über Letalität und Vererbungsrichtung beim Seeigelbastard *Paracentrotus* ♀ × *Arbacia* ♂. *Exp. Cell Res.*, Suppl. to Vol. 9: 16.

CHAET, A. B., and R. S. MUSICK, JR., 1960: A method for obtaining gametes from *Asterias forbesi*. *Biol. Bull.*, 119: 292.

CHAFFEE, R. R., and D. MAZIA, 1963: Echinochrome synthesis in hybrid sea urchin embryos. *Dev. Biol.*, 7: 502.

COSTELLO, D. P., M. E. DAVIDSON, A. EGGERS, M. H. FOX, and C. HENLEY, 1957: *Methods for Obtaining and Handling Marine Eggs and Embryos.* 247 pp. Marine Biological Laboratory, Woods Hole, Mass.

DIRKSEN, E. R., 1961: The presence of centrioles in artificially activated sea urchin eggs. *J. Biophys. Biochem. Cytology*, 11: 244.

FERGUSON, R., 1966: Personal communication.

GIUDICE, G., 1962: Restitution of whole larvae from disaggregated cells of sea urchin embryos. *Dev. Biol.*, 5: 402.

GROSS, P. R., and G. H. COUSINEAU, 1964: Macromolecular synthesis and the influence of actinomycin on early development. *Exp. Cell Res.*, 33: 368.

HAGSTRÖM, B. E., 1959: Further experiments on jelly-free sea urchin eggs. *Exp. Cell Res.*, 17: 256.

HARDING, C. V., and D. HARDING, 1952: Cross fertilization with the sperm of *Arbacia lixula*. *Exp. Cell Res.*, 3: 475.

HARVEY, ETHEL B., 1956: *The American Arbacia and Other Sea Urchins.* Princeton University Press, Princeton, N. J.

HIATT, R. W., 1963: *World Directory of Hydrobiological and Fisheries Institutions.* American Institute of Biological Sciences, Washington, D.C.

HINEGARDNER, R. T., 1961: The DNA content of isolated sea urchin egg nuclei. *Exp. Cell Res.*, 25: 341.

———, 1962: The isolation of nuclei from eggs and embryos of the sea urchin. *J. Cell Biol.*, 15: 503.

HÖRSTADIUS, S., 1939: The mechanics of sea urchin development, studied by operative methods. *Biol. Rev.*, 14: 132.

———, 1949: Experimental researches on the developmental physiology of the sea urchin. *Pubb. Staz. Zool. Napoli*, Suppl. to Vol. 21: 131.

HULTIN, T., 1948: Species specificity in fertilization reaction. I. The role of the vitelline membrane of sea urchin eggs in species specificity. *Arkiv für Zoologi*, 40A(12): 1.

KARNOFSKY, D. A., and E. B. SIMMEL, 1963: Effects of growth inhibiting chemicals on the sand dollar embryos *Echinorachnius parma*. *Progr. Exp. Tumor Res.*, 3: 254.

LINDAHL, P. E., and J. LUNDIN, 1948: Removal of the fertilization membranes from large quantities of sea urchin eggs. *Science*, 108: 481.

LOEB, J., 1913: *Artificial Parthenogenesis and Fertilization.* University of Chicago Press, Chicago, Ill.

MAZIA, D., P. J. HARRIS, and T. BIBRING, 1960: The multiplicity of the mitotic centers and the time-course of their duplication and separation. *J. Biophys. Biochem. Cytology*, 7: 1.

———, J. M. MITCHISON, H. MEDINA, and P. HARRIS, 1961: The direct isolation of the mitotic apparatus. *J. Biophys. Biochem. Cytology*, 10: 467.

MOORE, A. R., 1930: Fertilization and development without membrane formation in the egg of the sea urchin, *Strongylocentrotus purpuratus*. *Protoplasma*, 9: 9.

SAKAI, H., 1960: Studies on sulfhydryl groups during cell division of sea urchin egg. II. Mass isolation of the egg cortex and change in its —SH groups during cell division. *J. Biophys. Biochem. Cytology*, 8: 603.

SHAPIRO, H., 1935: The validity of the centrifuge method for estimating aggregate cell volume in suspensions of the egg of the sea urchin, *Arbacia punctulata*. *Biol. Bull.*, 68: 363.

TYLER, A., and B. S. TYLER, 1966: The gametes; some procedures and properties. In R. A. Boolootian (ed.), *Physiology of Echinodermata*, Interscience Publishers, New York, Chap. 27; see also Chap. 28.

VINCENT, W. S., 1952: The isolation and chemical properties of the nucleoli of starfish oocytes. *Proc. Nat. Acad. Sci., U.S.*, 38: 139.

Marine Annelids: *Sabellaria*

By John E. Winesdorfer

INTRODUCTION

The tubiculous polychaete annelid, *Sabellaria cementarium*, is a widely distributed sedentary annelid of Puget Sound. It and the related genus *Idanthyrsus* are described by the Berkeleys (1952) as being widespread throughout the Pacific basin. *Sabellaria vulgarius* is the east coast species that has been thoroughly described previously (Costello, 1957). Animals used in our laboratory are obtained by dredging in Puget Sound over a wide variety of depths, and are found in masses of sand tubes attached to rock or shell. Although *Sabellaria* has rarely been recorded as an intertidal animal, *Idanthyrsus* is often found intertidally as a reef builder.

Animals are maintained in holding tanks with running sea water and retain mature gametes for as long as 6 months. However, animals retained in standing sea water tanks with a common charcoal aquarium filter will remain reproductive for at least 3 months. Optimal water temperature will vary with the region, but 10°C is the normal temperature for maintaining and culturing the animals from such a body of water as Puget Sound. No attempt at feeding has been made, as the animals appear to obtain sufficient nutrient particles in either the running or standing sea water systems.

Large numbers of animals appear to be ripe at all times of the year. Spawning is induced by breaking the brittle sand tubes and freeing the worms. Females are readily identifiable by the dark magenta color of eggs filling the abdominal segments. In contrast, male segments are a creamy white. No such distinction can be made in the case of *Idanthyrsus* as eggs are also rather opaque and white in color.

GAMETES, FERTILIZATION

Eggs when spawned are irregular in shape and possess an intact germinal vesicle and intact nucleolus. The chromatin and spindle material lie closely associated with the nucleolus. Exposure of eggs to sea water at 10°C leads during an average period of 50 minutes to the following events. (1) Prominent vitelline membranes are raised as cortical granules break down and contribute their contents to the perivitelline space. (2) Prominent dendritic microvilli elongate and terminate immediately beneath the outermost vitelline layer. (3) The nucleolus is dispersed and germinal vesicle walls disintegrate. (4) Chromosomes come to lie at the animal

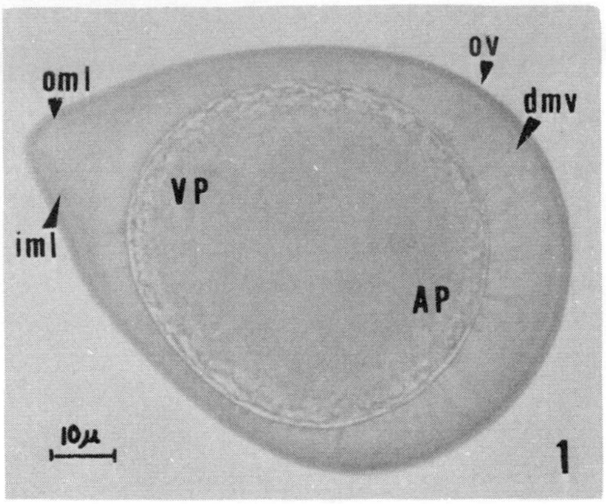

FIG. 1. Mature unfertilized egg; Interference Phase, original magnification 400 ×: *ov* – outer vitelline membrane; *oml* – outer middle vitelline layer; *iml* – inner middle vitelline layer; *dmv* – dendritic microvilli; *VP* – vegetal pole; *AP* – animal pole.

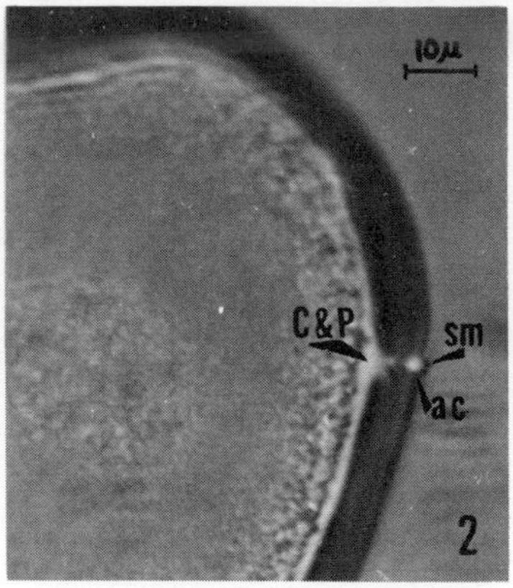

FIG. 2. Sperm penetration; egg slightly compressed. Interference Phase, original magnification 400 ×: *sm* – sperm midpiece; *ac* – sperm acrosome; *C & P* – entrance cone and coalescing processes of microvilli.

pole with the ends of the spindle fixed in the cortical cytoplasm. Thus meiosis is arrested at first meiotic metaphase, and only subsequent fertilization will induce reduction division. Figure 1 shows an unfertilized egg in which the above reactions have occurred.

Two major difficulties in obtaining good synchronous *Sabellaria* cultures arise in getting active sperm suspensions and in preventing polyspermy. A first precaution is to use only glassware that has been cleaned in sulfuric acid-nitric acid cleaning solution and to avoid all detergent contamination. Males are spawned individually in separate Syracuse dishes containing small quantities of filtered sea water. Sperm suspensions should stand for 15 minutes before examination under a high-dry objective. A useful habit when checking sperm activity or egg fertilization is to lick cover slips before application. This prevents premature activation of the acrosome reaction and sperm inactivation. Often sperm suspensions can be activated by application of 10^{-3} *M* EDTA-treated sea water (pH should be readjusted to 8.2),. Fertilization is then carried out in the same medium. An alternative, but less generally satisfactory, method is to carry out fertilization in pH 9.5 sea water. Potassium hydroxide is the preferred reagent for pH adjustment.

Unripe eggs are rarely spawned unless the female is broken in removing her tube. In any event eggs from such animals should be discarded, as coelomic fluid contaminants may be deleterious to development. Eggs should be allowed to settle and then be washed at least twice. While eggs may be fertilized at any time in the post-spawning maturation period, for most purposes it is convenient to allow maturation to occur, so that fertilization may be viewed as a separate event. If eggs are required to show synchronous maturation they may be spawned into water at 3°–5°C. This inhibits vesicle breakdown until the temperature is raised and does not appear to harm the eggs. The sign most indicative of fertilization is the sperm entrance cone shown in Fig. 2. While phase contrast or interference phase observations are useful, any light microscope can be used to follow the events described. It may prove useful to close down the field diaphragm to increase contrast. Sperm attachment and entry is normally effected in 20–30 minutes if eggs are fully mature when inseminated. Production of the entrance cone is initiated as the sperm contacts a microvillus. The cone can be seen to arise from an out-pocketing of the cortical plasm and the coalescence of several microvilli adjacent to the point of contact. Early entry is slow as the sperm lyses away the outer vitelline layer, but later phases are rapid as the sperm and cone sink through the inner vitelline layers. Most details of this process would seem to parallel those observed by the Colwins (1957) in the polychaete *Hydroides*.

As first recognized by Novikoff (1938) sperm suspensions must be quite dilute if polyspermy is to be avoided. Sperm obtained from one male should be diluted to 50 ml and two drops of this then added to 300 ml of washed and suspended matured eggs. Quantities of eggs obtained will vary depending upon the size and ripeness of the spawning female. One or 2 ml of eggs, measured after light packing by hand centrifugation, should be suspended in the 300 ml of fertilization medium. In 15 minutes and again at 1 hour, supernatant sea water should be decanted from the settling eggs and fresh filtered sea water added. This washing should be especially thorough if either method of sperm activation described above has been used. Rationalization for the low sperm concentration recommended can be found if microvilli adjacent to the entry cone are observed. First these and then all remaining cell processes can be seen to retract to the egg surface in a 15-minute period following sperm attachment. A short while later scattered microvilli again appear; these microvilli can be seen crossing the perivitelline area in Fig. 3. Thus, while polyspermy may be presumed to be prevented by the retraction of available attachment sites, the block is slow, and not nearly so efficient as that observed in echinoderm material.

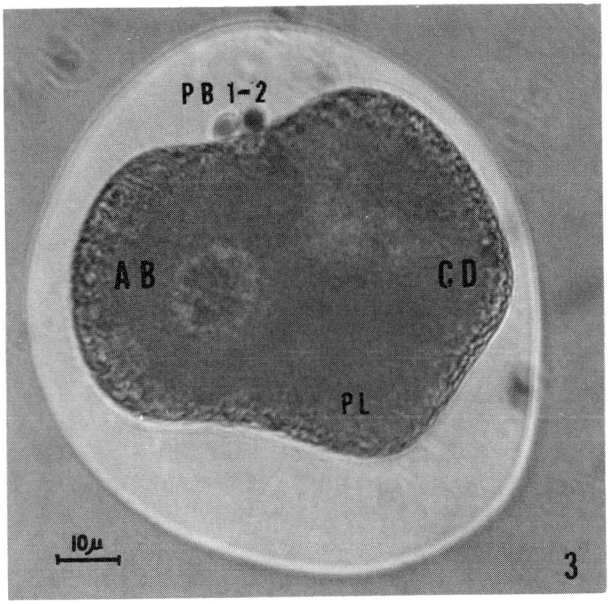

FIG. 3. Egg from normally developing culture, late polar lobe prior to first cleavage, original magnification 400 ×: *AB* and *CD* – potential first blastomeres; *PL* – retracting polar lobe; *PB* 1-2 – polar bodies from reduction divisions.

Some or all of the distinctive features of *Urechis* development—oocyte growth in the absence of nurse or follicle cells, postponement of maturation divisions until after fertilization, spiral cleavage, and rapid development—are shared by many invertebrates. It is their happy combination, however, in an animal whose gametes are plentiful through all seasons, whose oocytes are easily separated from other cells and other stages in oogenesis, and whose embryos develop in synchrony, that makes *Urechis* a potentially rich source of information for the biochemical embryologist in particular.

Although this chapter concerns the use of *Urechis caupo* only, other members of the phylum Echiuroidea have interested embryologists. Dawydoff's (1959) comprehensive account of the echiuroids contains many references to published work, and includes descriptions of the varied reproductive biologies within this group which might be exploited for comparative studies.

DISTRIBUTION AND COLLECTING

Urechis caupo is an inhabitant of sandy mud flats unspoiled by pollution or silt. Each worm lives in a U-shaped burrow. The two openings are commonly $1\frac{1}{2}$–3 feet apart, and the base lies one or more feet below the mud surface. When the flats are exposed at low tide, worms can easily be collected with a small shovel and two 3- to 4-foot lengths of moderately flexible tubing, 1 cm or less in diameter. By inserting one end of a tube into a hole and blowing, the other end of the burrow is revealed. The two tubes, pushed into the burrow from either end, provide a guideline for digging. The pink, sausage-shaped worm has a soft body, so the shovel should be used cautiously.

Urechis has been collected from a number of places along the California coast: Tomales Bay, Bodega Bay, Elkhorn Slough, Newport Bay, and Morro Bay; other unreported sites may exist. To my knowledge, there are three other *Urechis* species similar to *U. caupo* in habitat and reproductive biology. These are *U. unicinctus* in Japan (Embleton, 1900), *U. novae-zealandiae* (Knox, 1957), and *U. chilensis* in the Strait of Magellan (Seitz, 1907).

LABORATORY MAINTENANCE OF ADULT WORMS

Conditions that will ensure a long-term supply of gametes in good condition from laboratory-kept animals are not clearly defined. The worms will live for months in vigorously aerated, standing sea water at a density of one worm per gallon, but after about a month under these conditions, the eggs in the storage sacs begin to decline in quality, showing spontaneous activation, reduced fertilizability, and abnormal development. The number of immature oocytes in the coelom decreases also. This is probably a result of starvation. For laboratories near a collecting place, it is convenient to collect fresh worms once a month and return the old ones to the mud flats.

Urechis caupo is a filter feeder, and traps its food by pumping water through a mucous net secreted across the burrow entrance (Fisher and MacGinitie, 1928b). The net and its contents, which can be as small as 1 μ in diameter, are swallowed together. In nature, the bulk of this diet may be detritus (MacGinitie, 1935b), but diatoms are also ingested. Since diatoms are easily cultured in the laboratory (Needham, 1959), they might provide a convenient source of food. The worms may thrive on bacteria also; MacGinitie (1932) reports measurable growth in two worms fed *Pseudomonas* for 2 months.

Artificial burrows should be provided for the worms in laboratory aquaria. Without them, they are unable to feed and tend to develop infected lesions in the body wall from lying in the bottom sediment. One-inch diameter glass or lucite tubing, bent into a U with each segment at least 8 inches long, serves admirably. Sexually mature worms are best kept at 15°C or less, since they occasionally spawn in the laboratory if the water temperature rises higher.

Besides the problem of obtaining a continuous supply of healthy gametes from worms kept in captivity, which may be solved by feeding, there appear to be no major obstacles to successful maintenance of *Urechis* in an inland laboratory. The worms are able to carry sufficient oxygen reserve in their blood cells for several hours of deprivation during low tides (Redfield and Florkin, 1931) and this could be drawn upon during transportation. Additional information on the natural history of *Urechis* (Fisher and MacGinitie, 1928a; Hall, 1931; MacGinitie, 1935b, 1938) may be useful to those interested in maintaining the worms in the laboratory.

OBTAINING GAMETES

Gametes from the Storage Organs (Fertilizable)

Urechis can be stimulated to extrude eggs or sperm by inserting a blunt-tipped probe into a storage sac through the external pore and gently rotating it. A glass rod or pipette pulled to a tip diameter of about $\frac{3}{4}$ mm, and flamed at the end, is suitable. If the probe is too thick or too sharp, it will injure the delicate tissue of the storage organ. The probe stimulates the muscular walls of the storage organ to contract, expelling eggs or sperm onto the surface of the worm where they can be collected with a pipette or the lip of a test tube. Gentle pressure on the body of the worm facilitates extrusion. Since the sperm are white, and the eggs pale pink to peach colored, this is a convenient method for sexing the worms.

Animals collected from Elkhorn Slough contain mature gametes at all times of the year, but considerably fewer during the late summer and early fall. Ricketts and Calvin (1960) report that animals are usually spawned out in the summer at Newport Bay, in southern California. Since animals will frequently spawn in the laboratory if the water temperature rises above 15°C, it is likely that increased temperatures are the stimulus for natural spawning.

Occasionally in freshly collected females, and frequently in those which have been probed before, the storage organs contain a small number of blood cells, immature oocytes, or pieces of cellular debris. The latter are easily removed by filtering the eggs through nylon mesh with a pore size just large enough to allow the eggs to pass through.[1] Blood cells and immature oocytes (except the large ones, which are seldom present unless the storage organ has been damaged) can be eliminated by repeatedly suspending the eggs in sea water and pouring off the supernatant after the large oocytes have settled by gravity.

Gametes from the Coelom (Immature)

The coelomic fluid, which does not clot, can be drained from an incision in the body wall, or withdrawn into a syringe. The loss of a few milliliters of fluid by the latter method does little apparent damage to the worm; the small wound usually closes quickly and proceeds to heal. (It is best to keep the worm in filtered sea water

[1] "Nitex," the trade name for a nylon monofilament screen cloth available in a variety of mesh-opening sizes, has been very useful for a number of separatory procedures. Prices and specifications can be obtained from: Tobler, Ernst & Traber, Inc., 71 Murray Street, New York, N.Y.

with antibiotics added.) Before making an incision, *Urechis* can be relaxed by a half-hour immersion in isotonic $MgCl_2$ (67 gm per liter tap or distilled water).

A mature worm contains 15–30 cc coelomic fluid, up to 50 percent of which may be cellular. The most numerous cells are nucleated, hemoglobin-containing (Redfield and Florkin, 1931) blood cells, 16–35 μ in diameter. These comprise about 25–50 percent of the coelomic fluid volume. Immature oocytes of all sizes usually account for 3–4 percent of the fluid volume. Ameboid cells, which are frequently clumped, are the third major cell type.

Low-speed centrifugation (for instance, several minutes at the high speed setting on a table-model International Clinical Centrifuge) will effect a crude separation of oocytes from blood cells in coelomic fluid or sea water. The blood cells sediment at the bottom, and the oocytes form a layer between them and the fluid. Repeated recentrifugation of the resuspended oocyte layer will remove most of the blood cells. All remaining blood cells can be removed by gently filtering the eggs through two thicknesses of Nitex # 20 (see footnote 1). Single and clumped ameboid cells are retained by two thicknesses of Nitex # 86, through which all the oocytes will pass.

Some further separation of immature oocytes according to size can be accomplished by filtration through a graded series of Nitex cloths with mesh openings between 20 and 86 μ. (Since the eggs are somewhat deformable, they will pass through cloths with smaller specified mesh openings.) The separation accomplished by the nylon cloths is frequently not very sharp, however. Preliminary work with bovine albumin gradients indicates that centrifugation of immature oocytes through discontinuous density gradients will segregate them into more homogeneous classes. It might also be convenient to remove the fertilizable oocytes by adding sperm, since the formation of the fertilization membrane and the swelling of the egg as it becomes spherical after fertilization increase its diameter considerably.

STERILITY

By observing a few simple precautions, fertilizable eggs and sperm can be obtained free of any microorganisms detectable in isotope incorporation experiments. The posterior end of the worm is wrapped in paper towels to absorb the jets of water it emits from its anus when disturbed, and the anterior end, particularly around the storage sac pores, is wiped free of mucus and detritus with a clean tissue. Dipping the anterior end very briefly into distilled water may lyse some marine microorganisms remaining on the body wall. The distilled water treatment should be followed by rinsing in sterile sea water (filtered and autoclaved) because hypotonicity will cause eggs to activate (see section on artificial activation). The excess water is blotted from the region around the pores with another tissue, and a sterile probe is used to stimulate spawning. If the worms are being fed, it may be useful to give them heat-killed organisms to reduce the possibility of contamination from the body wall during gamete collection.

When obtaining coelomic contents, it is extremely important to avoid puncturing any part of the gut. In any event, antibiotics should probably be added to coelomic fluid during long-term incubations.

INCUBATING UNFERTILIZED AND IMMATURE OOCYTES

Unfertilized eggs from the storage organs of healthy females will keep for long periods in sterile sea water containing

0.1 mg per milliliter each of penicillin and streptomycin without degeneration, spontaneous activation, or loss of fertilizability. Eggs kept at 17°C for up to 2 weeks, and one batch at 13°C for 2 months, showed virtually 100 percent fertilization and almost as high a percentage of normal development, at the end of these times. During manipulations of the unfertilized eggs, such as swirling or filtering, allowing them to be trapped in a surface film should be avoided, since the resultant damage appears to produce an abortive activation.

Immature oocytes do not fare as well in sea water as they do in coelomic fluid. Several hours' incubation in sea water seems to have little effect on their appearance or ability to incorporate isotopes into macromolecules, but during overnight incubation significant numbers degenerate. The inadequacy of sea water for long-term incubation is not surprising, since it differs in so many respects from coelomic fluid: for instance, pH (coelomic fluid is more acid, around pH 7.5) and nutrient supply (an amino acid analysis of *Urechis* coelomic fluid is reported by Giordano, Harper, and Filice, 1950).

FERTILIZATION

Eggs can be fertilized in either sea water or coelomic fluid, but postfertilization events are delayed in the latter, developmental synchrony is poor, and many eggs develop abnormally (see also MacGinitie, 1935c). For normal, synchronous development, incubation at 17°–18°C in sea water is recommended.

"Dry" sperm (as it comes from the storage organ) diluted with sea water 1:400,000 in an egg suspension made by diluting "dry" eggs, or eggs packed by gentle centrifugation, 1:100, is adequate for 100 percent fertilization with a minimum of excess sperm. At this concentration, virtually 100 percent of the eggs will develop normally, and with excellent synchrony, to trochophore larvae, if adequate respiratory exchange is provided by incubating them in shallow sea water (up to 1 or 2 cm, depending on vessel diameter). With mechanical stirring, the egg concentration could probably be increased.

Events immediately following fertilization have been described in a number of publications (e.g., Tyler, 1931a; Newby, 1940; see also Table 1). Tyler (1965) has followed sperm penetration by electron microscopy. *Urechis* eggs can be multiply inseminated (Tyler and Schultz, 1932). A discussion of their polarity is included in papers by Holt (1934), and Morgan and Tyler (1935). The role of fertilizing is discussed by Tyler (1941).

ARTIFICIAL ACTIVATION

Urechis eggs can be activated by exposure to dilute, ammoniacal, or acid sea water. A detailed analysis of the conditions for activation in dilute sea water, and response of the eggs, is contained in a series of papers by Tyler (1931a, b; 1932a, b). According to Tyler, most eggs respond in one of two ways to dilute sea water: one class activates normally and produces two polar bodies, but fails to cleave; the second class fails to produce polar bodies, but cleaves after some delay. The proportion of eggs in either class can be controlled by choosing particular dilutions and exposure times. This behavior is related to the distribution of chromosomes and centrosomes (Tyler, 1932b). Eggs activated to polar-body formation can be fertilized, and will then undergo normal cleavage, presumably because the sperm supplies a second aster (Tyler and Schultz, 1932).

Hiraiwa and Kawamura (1936) report that *U. unicinctus* eggs treated with ammoniacal sea water (approximately

TABLE 1. TIMETABLE OF NORMAL DEVELOPMENT IN *Urechis caupo* AT 17°C

STAGE	TIME
Sperm addition	0
Nucleolar breakdown	10–12 minutes
Germinal vesicle breakdown complete	15 minutes
First polar body	35 minutes
Second polar body	45 minutes
Two cells	90 minutes
Ciliated blastula (64 cells)	7 hours
Gastrulation (148 cells at start)	16–18 hours
Feeding larva	about 40 hours
Metamorphosis	about 60 days

0.005 *N* NH_4OH) will form polar bodies and proceed to cleave. A few *U. caupo* eggs treated in this manner behave similarly, but most show the inverse correlation between polar-body formation and cleavage (Tyler and Bauer, 1937). A similar response to acid sea water is given by *U. caupo* eggs, and the proportion of eggs in the two classes can be controlled by length of exposure (Tyler and Bauer, 1937).

Scheer and Scheer (1947) have experimented with the effects of a number of ions and drugs on artificial activation. A number of chemical agents are reported by Isaka and Aikawa (1963) to cause elevation of the fertilization membrane in *Urechis unicinctus* eggs. The paper is not concerned, however, with the effects of these treatments on subsequent activation or fertilizability of the eggs.

DEVELOPMENT

As mentioned above, *Urechis* eggs cleave spirally. The first two cleavages are equal, but the four vegetal cells resulting from the third cleavage are slightly larger than the rest. Through ensuing cleavages the four vegetal blastomeres remain larger than the others, and additional inequalities in cell size arise. Sixty-four cell blastulae "hatch" about 7 hours after fertilization (at 17°C) by pushing cilia through the fertilization membrane. Gastrulation takes place during the sixteenth through eighteenth hours, and the trochophore larvae begin feeding at about 40 hours. A brief timetable of normal development is given in Table 1.

The normal development of *Urechis caupo* from fertilization to the metamorphosing larva (about 60 days) has been covered thoroughly by William Newby (1940) in a monograph entitled "The Embryology of the Echiuroid Worm, *Urechis caupo*." The book provides detailed descriptions, drawings, and timetables of cell lineage, gastrulation, and organogenesis. The care and feeding of larvae, a comparison of *Urechis* development with that of other echiuroids and invertebrates, and a discussion of the phylogenetic position of the Echiuroidea are also included. A portion of this work, covering fertilization through the 64-cell stage, has been published separately (Newby, 1932).

If *Urechis* eggs at 2–3 minutes after fertilization are immersed in 1 *M* urea (freshly made up in unbuffered distilled water) until the fertilization membrane swells and bursts, and then returned to normal sea water, the cleavage blastomeres can be separated by shaking. However, with the fertilization membrane gone, the arrangement of cells, even in undisturbed controls, becomes very disorganized.

PUBLISHED EXPERIMENTAL WORK

Urechis caupo eggs have provided the material for a variety of embryological studies. Since these are somewhat scattered in the literature, they are referred to below for a representative bibliography.

Some papers have been omitted, either because of low information content or because references to them are included in related papers cited.

Respiration

Determinations of oxygen consumption, temperature coefficients, and respiratory quotients for *Urechis* eggs and embryos are reported in a series of papers by Tyler and others (Horowitz, 1940a; Tyler, 1936a, b; Tyler and Horowitz, 1938; Tyler and Humason, 1937). Cytochrome is present in the eggs (Black, Epstein, and Tyler, 1958). Horowitz and Baumberger (1941) describe some properties of a hematoporphyrin-like pigment, which is peculiar to the eggs, and may be important in respiration. (Egg pigments are also discussed briefly by Baumberger and Michaelis, 1931.)

Tyler and Humason (1937) report the important finding that oxygen consumption in *Urechis* eggs actually decreases slightly following fertilization. Increased respiratory rates after fertilization occurred only in eggs from females kept in the laboratory for long periods of time. Unfertilized eggs from these animals consumed oxygen at lower absolute rates than did those from freshly collected worms; and the absolute level reached after fertilization was more nearly constant, regardless of the source of the eggs.

Chemistry

For a long time, almost nothing was known about the biochemistry of *Urechis* eggs or embryos. Linderstrøm-Lang and Holter (1933) described changes in dipeptidase activity upon fertilization, and Horowitz (1939) catalogued nitrogen partition in developing eggs. Recently, however, it has been demonstrated that fully grown unfertilized *Urechis* eggs are synthesizing both RNA and protein (Gould, 1965; Das, Luykx, and Alfert, 1965, have also published autoradiographic evidence of RNA synthesis). Further information on RNA and protein metabolism in *Urechis* oocytes and embryos is in preparation.

SPECIAL USES

Features that recommend *Urechis* to the attention of developmental biologists have been described in the Introduction. No particular obstacles to biochemical studies exist. Radioactive precursors (amino acids, nucleotides, $P^{32}O_4$) are readily taken up by eggs and embryos in either sea water or coelomic fluid, and standard extraction procedures can be applied with little or no modification.

Urechis eggs are also excellent for following fertilization and early development in the classroom. Cytological details, such as the germinal vesicle and nucleolus, are clear under low power with transmitted light. Following fertilization, the sperm entrance cone, elevation of the fertilization membrane, nuclear breakdown, and the formation of maturation and cleavage spindles are all easily followed.

If there is one area in development for which *Urechis* may provide classic material, it is the study of oogenesis. The year-round abundance of developing oocytes floating singly in a large body cavity has already been mentioned. Oocytes can be exposed *in vivo* to radioactive precursors or other materials injected into the coelom, or can be isolated and incubated *in vitro*. Long-term culture of various oocyte stages may be possible *in vitro*, or *in vivo* (injecting them into males, for instance).

REFERENCES

BAUMBERGER, J., and L. MICHAELIS, 1931: The blood pigments of *Urechis caupo*. *Biol. Bull.*, 61: 417.

BLACK, R., S. EPSTEIN, and A. TYLER, 1958: The oxidation of carbon monoxide by fertilized eggs of *Urechis caupo* shown by use of a C^{13} label. *Biol. Bull.*, 115: 153.

DAS, N., P. LUYKX, and M. ALFERT, 1965: The nucleolus and RNA metabolism in *Urechis* eggs. *Dev. Biol.*, 12: 72.

DAWYDOFF, C., 1959: Classe des Echiuriens. In P. Grassé (ed.), *Traité de Zoologie*, Masson et Cie, Paris, vol. 5, p. 855.

EMBLETON, A., 1900: On the structure and affinities of *Echiurus* (*Urechis*) *unicinctus*. *Trans. Linnaean Soc. London, Zoo.*, 8: 77.

FISHER, W., and G. MAC GINITIE, 1928a: A new Echiuroid worm from California. *Ann. Mag. Nat. Hist. Ser. 10*, 1: 199.

———, and ———, 1928b: The natural history of an Echiuroid worm. *Ann. Mag. Nat. Hist. Ser. 10*, 1: 204.

GIORDANO, M., H. HARPER, and F. FILICE, 1950: The amino acids of the blood of *Urechis caupo* (Echiuroidea). *Wasman J. Biol.*, 8: 1.

GOULD, M., 1965: RNA and protein synthesis in *Urechis caupo* oocytes. *Amer. Zool.*, 5: 635.

HALL, V., 1931: The muscular activity and oxygen consumption of *Urechis caupo*. *Biol. Bull.*, 61: 400.

HIRAIWA, Y., and T. KAWAMURA, 1936: Relation between maturation division and cleavage in artificially activated eggs of *Urechis unicinctus* (von Drasche). *Biol. Bull.*, 70: 344.

HOLT, V., 1934: Further observations on the polarity of the eggs of *Urechis caupo*. *Biol. Bull.*, 67: 341.

HOROWITZ, N., 1939: The partition of nitrogen in the developing eggs of *Urechis caupo*. *J. Cell. Comp. Physiol.*, 14: 189.

———, 1940a: The respiratory metabolism of the developing eggs of *Urechis caupo*. *J. Cell. Comp. Physiol.*, 15: 299.

———, and J. BAUMBERGER, 1941: Studies on the respiratory pigment of *Urechis* eggs. *J. Biol. Chem.*, 141: 407.

ISAKA, S., and T. AIKAWA, 1963: Separation of the fertilization membrane in *Urechis* and sea urchin eggs as a phenomenon caused by breakage of hydrogen bonds. I. Action of mercaptide-forming, alkylating, oxidizing and protein-denaturing agents. *Exptl. Cell Res.*, 30: 139.

KNOX, G., 1957: *Urechis novae-zealandiae* (Dendy): a New Zealand Echiuroid. *Trans. Roy. Soc. N. Zealand*, 85: 141.

LINDERSTRØM-LANG, K., and H. HOLTER, 1933: Beiträge zur enzymatischen Histochemie. IV. Der peptidasegehalt einiger mariner Invertebraten. *Zeit. Physiol. Chem.*, 215: 167.

MACGINITIE, G., 1932: The role of bacteria as food for bottom animals. *Science*, 76: 490.

———, 1935a: Normal functioning and experimental behavior of the egg and sperm collectors of the echiuroid, *Urechis caupo*. *J. Exptl. Zool.*, 70: 341.

———, 1935b: Ecological aspects of a California marine estuary. *Amer. Midl. Nat.*, 16: 629.

———, 1935c: The fertilization of eggs and the rearing of the larvae of *Urechis caupo* within the blood cavity of the adult animal. *J. Exptl. Zool.*, 71: 483.

———, 1938: Notes on the natural history of some marine animals. *Amer. Midl. Nat.*, 19: 207.

MORGAN, T., and A. TYLER, 1935: Effects of centrifuging eggs of *Urechis* before and after fertilization. *J. Exptl. Zool.*, 60: 301.

NEEDHAM, J., 1959: *Culture Methods for Invertebrate Animals.* Dover Publications, Inc., New York.

NEWBY, W., 1932: The early embryology of the Echiuroid, *Urechis*. *Biol. Bull.*, 63: 387.

———, 1940: *The Embryology of the Echiuroid Worm*, Urechis caupo. *Memoirs of the American Philosophical Society*, vol.

16. Independence Square, Philadelphia, Pa.

REDFIELD, A., and M. FLORKIN, 1931: The respiratory function of the blood of *Urechis caupo*. *Biol. Bull.*, 61: 185.

RICKETTS, E., and J. CALVIN, 1960: *Between Pacific Tides*, 3rd ed., Stanford University Press, Stanford, Calif., p. 308.

SCHEER, B., and M. SCHEER, 1947: Some interrelations of drug and ion actions in the artificial activation of marine eggs. *Physiol. Zool.*, 20: 15.

SEITZ, P., 1907: Der Bau von *Echiurus* (*Urechis*) *chilensis*. *Zool. Jahrb.* (*Anat.*), 24: 323.

TYLER, A., 1931a: The production of normal embryos by artificial parthenogenesis in the Echiuroid, *Urechis*. *Biol. Bull.*, 60: 187.

———, 1931b: The relation between cleavage and total activation in artificially activated eggs of *Urechis*. *Biol. Bull.*, 61: 45.

———, 1932a: Production of cleavage by suppression of the polar bodies in artificially activated eggs of *Urechis*. *Biol. Bull.*, 63: 218.

———, 1932b: Chromosomes of artificially activated eggs of *Urechis*. *Biol. Bull.*, 63: 212.

———, 1936a: On the energetics of differentiation. III. Comparison of the temperature coefficients for cleavage and later stages in the development of the eggs of some marine animals. *Biol. Bull.*, 71: 59.

———, 1936b: On the energetics of differentiation. IV. Comparison of the rates of oxygen consumption and of development at different temperatures of eggs of some marine animals. *Biol. Bull.*, 71: 82.

———, 1941: The role of fertilizin in the fertilization of eggs of the sea urchin and other animals. *Biol. Bull.*, 81: 190.

———, 1965: The biology and chemistry of fertilization. *Amer. Nat.*, 99: 309.

———, and H. BAUER, 1937: Polar body extrusion and cleavage in artificially activated eggs of *Urechis caupo*. *Biol. Bull.*, 73: 164.

———, and N. HOROWITZ, 1938: On the energetics of differentiation. VII. Comparison of the respiration rates of parthenogenetic and fertilized *Urechis* eggs. *Biol. Bull.*, 74: 99.

———, and W. HUMASON, 1937: On the energetics of differentiation. VI. Comparison of the temperature coefficients of the respiratory rates of unfertilized and fertilized eggs. *Biol. Bull.*, 73: 261.

———, and J. SCHULTZ, 1932: Inhibition and reversal of fertilization in eggs of the echiuroid worm, *Urechis caupo*. *J. Exptl. Zool.*, 63: 509.

Cecropia

By William H. Telfer

INTRODUCTION

A laboratory fortunate enough to have a dependable commercial supplier of Cecropia moth cocoons can study the physiology of diapause, the transformation of the diapausing pupa into a reproductively mature moth, and the development of the egg into a caterpillar, with none of the distractions of a rearing operation. Once the caterpillar has spun its cocoon, it transforms into a pupa and no longer requires food. The pupa, having entered diapause, can be readily shipped by a supplier, and will remain viable in a laboratory refrigerator without additional care for up to 18 months. After 3 or more months of chilling, the pupa, on removal from the refrigerator, can be depended on to initiate adult development. The moth also is unable to feed, but will readily mate and lay fertile eggs before dying a week or two after its emergence from the cocoon.

Lamentably, quantity suppliers of Cecropia and other saturniids having a pupal diapause are limited in number, and the few established laboratories relying on them are understandably reluctant to identify them to potentially competing buyers. Even if a dependable source of cocoons is available, however, both larval development and the larval-pupal transformation can only be studied with a caterpillar rearing operation close at hand.

RAISING CATERPILLARS

To obtain caterpillars, and in the absence of a supplier, experimentally useful numbers of pupae, there is no fully reliable substitute for a summer in the field. Despite efforts in a number of enterprising laboratories to devise artificial diets or to store leaves in freezers, fresh leaves still on the tree remain the most satisfactory food and the vigor of the culture is highly dependent on leaf quality.

The most serious hazard to a rearing operation is reputed to be epidemic disease; even the most successful culturers have had the anguishing experience of seeing a major proportion of their caterpillars languish and die just before reaching the hardy pupal stage. There are grounds for believing, however, that susceptibility to disease is usually a consequence of nutritional inadequacy and it is far easier to correct this than to raise animals in a sterile environment. By raising native larvae on trees for which they are naturally adapted, and by taking steps to ensure the vigor of the food tree, the procedure described here has yielded a supply of robust pupae annually for 10 successive years with negligible loss to disease.

The operation utilizes a small orchard of *Prunus serotina*, the black cherry native to eastern North America. In southeastern Pennsylvania, the locus of this operation, black cherry trees are often defoliated by tent caterpillars in late May or early June, and the trees are thus adapted to the sort of abuse to which caterpillar culture subjects them. Provided that they share with the black cherry an ability to form new leaves continuously throughout the summer, there is no reason to believe that other species of *Prunus*, a genus that is well represented throughout the Northern Hemisphere, would not do equally well.

A few young trees, 4 to 8 feet tall, are transplanted from surrounding fields to the orchard each year in late fall or early spring. Their root configuration is such that it is impossible to obtain more than two or three primary branches, and these are unavoidably denuded of soil. Regeneration of functional roots is apparently quite rapid, since foliation invariably begins vigorously the following May. To compensate for root loss, about seven-eighths of the branches bearing leaf buds are removed by pruning. Two years after transplantation, the trees are usually large enough to be useful.

The spacing between trees is 12 feet. Although the orchard is not cultivated, the ground cover is mowed several times each summer and the trees are mulched every 2 or 3 years with wood chips to a radius of about 4 feet from the trunk. In addition the trees are fertilized in late spring or early summer every other year, either with ammonium nitrate, which is reputed to encourage foliation rather than flowering, or with "10-6-4,"[1] both obtainable from agricultural supply stores. The dry fertilizer is poured into four to eight holes, each about 15 inches deep and 1 inch in diameter, and spaced within a 4-foot radius of the trunk.

Pruning is necessary each spring to keep the foliage compact enough to fit within the nets described below. After 5 or 6 years the trees have usually become so stout that several branches can be individually netted. Several of the older trees in the orchard, though defoliated annually for 10 years, now support close to a hundred caterpillars apiece every summer.

Aside from the innovation of a well regulated orchard, the rearing procedure is basically that used for many other lepidoptera throughout the world and adapted for large-scale rearing of Cecropia by C. M. Williams. In order to control the time of emergence of moths to be used as breeding stock, the diapausing pupae are "overwintered" at 6°C (Williams, 1956). Chilling activates the endocrine mechanism that starts the animal on its adult molt, and 6°C is sufficiently cool so that activated animals do not commence development in the refrigerator for at least a year.

The pupae should be removed from the refrigerator 6 to 7 weeks before hatching caterpillars are desired. The pupal-moth molt usually commences within 2 weeks after the termination of chilling, though the exact time varies with the individual and with the duration of chilling. Once the molt is initiated, 3 weeks more are required at 25°C for the emergence of the moth. Mating and egg laying can be completed within another 5 days, and the caterpillars hatch about 11 days after the eggs are laid. For the operation described here, six or more chilled female pupae are placed at 25°C weekly from early April to late May. If a pupa has been removed from its cocoon for sexing and weighing, it should be

[1] "10-6-4" is commercial shorthand for the ratio of readily soluble nitrogen, phosphorus, and potassium, by weight.

reinserted with the anterior end toward the valves of the cocoon. Emergence from the cocoon, which is possible only through the valves, serves to scrape the pupal cuticle off the moth and thus reduces the loss of animals due to unsuccessful eclosion.

Because inbred lines have been reported to yield puny animals, some North American laboratories try to obtain outbreeding with endemic males by tying female moths from the breeding stock out of doors. In the Philadelphia region outbreeding can be achieved from late May till early July, though the frequency of matings varies greatly from year to year, presumably due to fluctuations in the native population. The male characteristically arrives well after midnight and copulation continues throughout the following day. Unless one arises at daybreak and brings the pair indoors (it is convenient to tie the female to a portable screen), he is apt to find, rather than mating moths, a well-breakfasted catbird.

In order to ensure against those years when the local males fail to answer the call, it is prudent to prepare for laboratory breeding as well. While a few skilled lepidopterists are able to initiate mating by apposing the moths' genitalia manually, the nonspecialist can obtain more consistent results with Cecropia by placing about four males and two females in a 2 × 2 × 2-foot screened cage in a well ventilated room or greenhouse. Four or five matings per week can be expected from the procedure, and these will yield well over a thousand caterpillars per week. Because of a natural tendency for the culturer to use a system that he knows will work, there has been little systematic investigation of the method and it is therefore likely that substantial improvements are possible. There are indications, for instance, that a cage may become less productive after a week or so of use, presumably due to saturation with the pheromone produced by the female to attract the male, and it may therefore be advisable to have an uncontaminated cage available as a substitute.

With either outbreeding or cage mating, the male usually releases the female shortly after sunset. The female should be immediately placed in a box lined with paper. She will ordinarily deposit fifty to a hundred or more fertile eggs within an hour or so, and will repeat this flurry of activity every evening until her ovaries have been emptied of their several hundred eggs. The paper linings on which the eggs have been laid should be hung from a food tree within 10 days after laying begins. The caterpillar emerges from its egg through a hole eaten in the chorion around the micropyle, and shortly crawls off the paper onto a neighboring leaf.

To keep out birds, mice, and parasitic insects, and to keep the caterpillars from wandering off to spin their cocoons, it is essential that the tree be netted. Because of its ability to withstand mechanical abrasion and weathering, a successful material for this purpose is the cotton mosquito netting manufactured for the United States military services and sometimes available at military surplus depots.[2] When sewed into bags with flat dimensions of about 5 × 9 feet, the netting will enclose enough leaves for up to thirty-five caterpillars on a tree that has been trimmed to form compact foliage. The net must be firmly tied with a rope around the trunk of the tree so that there is absolutely no route of ingress or egress. With gentle laundering and some minor patching of holes, a cotton net should be good for at least three summers.

[2] A comparable material can be obtained from James Thompson and Co., Inc., 112–114 Prince St., New York 12, N.Y.

Probably the most imperative rule of all is to avoid overstocking the nets. The caterpillars have formidable appetites and grow exponentially until at 6 weeks of age they weigh up to five thousand times their hatching weight (15 gm as opposed to 3 mg). The rearer must either discipline his inclinations to get the most out of a tree by never placing more than twenty-five or thirty eggs under a net, or be prepared to visit the nets daily as the caterpillars approach maturity so that they can be promptly transferred from trees showing signs of premature defoliation. While there are reports that transferring caterpillars increases susceptibility to disease, this has never been observed in the fertilized orchard described here.

Since neither the fertility of the unhatched eggs nor the number of leaves on a tree can be easily determined, an estimate of the maximum number of eggs that can be safely put under a net is apt to be wide of the mark. The uncertainties can be greatly reduced by first placing all of the eggs from a single moth under one net, where the caterpillars usually grow luxuriantly for several weeks, and then transferring what is hopefully the definitive number of caterpillars to freshly netted trees. To avoid undue handling, the animals should be transferred on trimmings of the tree if possible, rather than being plucked off their branch or leaf. This warning applies especially to molting caterpillars which are unable to shed their old cuticle if the silken pad to which they cling is loosened.

At the cessation of feeding the caterpillars move down the tree where, failing to escape, they spin their cocoons in the folds of the net. It is best to leave the cocoons undisturbed for several days until they have stiffened and preferably for an additional 2 weeks when the pupal molt has been completed. Within a month after pupation, it is advisable to place the cocoons at 6°C in case some of the pupae have failed to enter a stable diapause. At this point the year's rearing operation can be considered complete.

There are a number of special problems that vary with the year and the site. In New England, it has been reported that pentatomid bugs, which can impale the maturing caterpillars with their proboscis through the mesh of the net, frequently injuring them irreparably, become particularly abundant during late summer. Their predations are reduced by using double layers of netting or by attempting to complete the annual rearing operation early in the summer. In Pennsylvania lace bugs that are unavoidably trapped inside the net can multiply rapidly enough in 6 weeks to cause severe damage to the foliage. Since natural predators effectively control them in unnetted trees, the simplest solution, and one consistent with the procedure of redistributing caterpillars half way through their growth period, has been to reduce by 2 or 3 weeks the length of time during which the trees are under nets. Caterpillars spinning at the bottom of the net attract mice which can chew holes in the mesh and enjoy a feast. Trimming the trees so that the net can be tied 2 feet or higher above the ground appears to reduce this problem significantly, and putting crumpled newspaper in the bottom of the nets has been suggested. While some operations have had trouble with birds tearing their way through the netting, the well policed Pennsylvania orchard has never been afflicted with this event, despite the fact that catbirds and mockingbirds frequently perch on the nets. Other problems guaranteed to educate the laboratory experimenter in natural history and animal behavior are bound to arise, but as long as the operation remains productive these can be as entertaining and informative as they are traumatic. Finally, there is the problem of a progressive local official deciding to control mosquitoes by broadcasting insecticides. By very good fortune, rural Pennsylvania is loath to spend its tax dollars on anything as frivolous as mosquito control as long as there are no questions of public health involved, but the possibility of spraying should definitely be investigated before setting up a new orchard.

OTHER LEPIDOPTERA

The basic procedures described here for Cecropia should be applicable to many other species of saturniids, though a different food tree would presumably be required in each case (Collins and Weast, 1961), and, in facultatively diapausing species, the photoperiod must be taken into account in planning the rearing operation (Danilevski, 1965). A laboratory method for the nondiapausing saturniid *Samia cynthia ricini* is described in an article by Schneiderman, which is included in this chapter.

A chemically defined diet for the laboratory rearing of the tobacco horn worm, a large sphingid with a facultative pupal diapause, has been developed by Yamamoto, and is described in a volume on the rearing of economically important insects edited by Smith (1966). This species has thus become potentially important material for the study of diapause and metamorphosis.

Two small and easily cultured moths that have been useful in developmental studies are *Ephestia kuehniella* (Whiting, 1937) and the wax moth, *Galleria mellonella*, which has now been cultured axenically (Waterhouse, 1959).

SELECTION OF EXPERIMENTAL ANIMALS

There is a tremendous spread in the size of Cecropia pupae yielded by culture methods, the pupal weight often ranging from well under 4 gm to over 9 gm. The extent to which such differences have genetic or nutritional origins has never been systematically investigated. Whatever the cause, variability in experimental results can often be significantly reduced by using animals within a restricted size range.

Two other precautions in the selection of experimental material are necessary. Many of the changes undergone during molting, metamorphosis, and the transitions into and out of diapause, are so rapid and extreme that physiological and morphological observations have little meaning unless correlated very carefully with the stage of development. For this purpose, a detailed description of the external morphology of the five larval instars can be found in a monograph by Packard (1912) and, if this is not available, more cursory descriptions written for amateur lepidopterists are available in Collins and Weast (1961) and in Eliot and Soule (1902). Information helpful in the staging of the larval-pupal transformation has been provided by Williams (1952). Finally, a detailed timetable of the morphological changes occurring in the transformation of the male pupa into a moth was published by Schneiderman and Williams (1954) and supplemental information necessary in staging the corresponding female molt was added by Telfer and Rutberg (1960) (see Table 1).

As early as the last larval instar there are some fundamental sexual differences in the physiology and growth of a number of tissues, particularly the blood and fat body, in addition to the reproductive organs. There are also significant differences in size. The median body weight of six hundred female pupae raised in one operation in 1965, for instance, was 6.4 gm, while that of their sibling males was 4.9 gm, though there was a substantial

TABLE 1. TIMETABLE FOR THE DEVELOPMENT OF CECROPIA AT 25°C AS WITNESSED IN PUPAE EQUIPPED WITH FACIAL AND ABDOMINAL WINDOWS*

DAY	CHARACTERS
	Part 1: Males†
0	Initiation of hypodermal retraction just ventral to imaginal disc of genitalia; no retraction elsewhere
1	Hypodermal retraction under terminal window extends half way up each side; the aedeagus and harpal lobes have tripled in size and migrated slightly toward center of window; hypodermal retraction under facial window has occurred only along posterior margin and is restricted to the midline and the lateral angles; *no retraction of leg hypodermis*
2	*Initiation of retraction of leg hypodermis*, harpes show considerable enlargement and sharply defined outer edges; beginning of midventral fold between harpes; the aedeagus has migrated about half way to center of window
3	Facial retraction nearly complete; eye lobes partially visible; terminal retraction complete except dorsally; midventral fold of genitalia extends dorsally to aedeagus; harpes show considerable molding and beginning of subdivision into upper and lower lobes; tips of dorsal harpal lobe slightly forked
4	Facial and terminal retraction complete; eye lobes well developed but unpigmented; further subdivision of harpes into dorsal and ventral lobes; aedeagus has a cone-shaped, transparent, undivided membranous tip
5	Palps and "stalks" of antennae visible for first time. Harpes considerably enlarged and show well developed upper and lower fleshy, semitransparent lobes; no pubescence; no eye pigment
6	Membranous tip of aedeagus subdivided into two or three semitransparent processes; harpal lobes with sharp edges; extremely delicate transparent pubescence along outer edge of upper harpal lobes; no pubescence of lower lobes; no eye pigment
7	Initiation of pink eye pigment; transparent pubescence now extends along outer edge of lower harpal lobes; genitalia deeply telescoped into preceding segment
8	Generalized reddish brown eye pigment; genitalia fully formed but fleshy and unpigmented; pubescence generally distributed over outer side of all harpal lobes, but longer and "silky" along edge of upper lobes
9	Dark reddish brown eye pigment; long silky hairs on upper harpal lobes and shorter silky hairs on lower lobes
10	Dark brown eye pigment; long silky hairs on all harpal lobes; membranous tip of aedeagus with fleshy spine
11	No further change

* Characters printed in italics are visible without windows and can be seen by moistening the overlying cuticle with 70% alcohol. The adult genitalia of Cecropia have been described and figured by Michener (1952).

† Source: Schneiderman and Williams (1954), Table 1, *Biol. Bull.*, 106: 239–40.

overlap in the size ranges of the two sexes. There is, finally, the extraordinary concentration of juvenile hormone occurring in the abdomen of male moths (Williams, 1963) to illustrate that, for many purposes, it is prudent to use experimental and control animals of the same sex.

The male Cecropia moth can be easily distinguished by its large feathery antennae, which are nearly twice as wide

DAY	CHARACTERS
12	Tan streak of pigment present on each side of mouth opening; white hairs on upper harpal lobes and on face; earliest tan pigment on genitalia along surface of gnathos and on ridge connecting upper and lower harpal lobes on each side
13	*Tarsal claws black;* facial cuticle with pale diffuse tan pigmentation; coarse white hairs on harpes; tannish pigmentation of triangular plate (annulus) below base of aedeagus, the pigment extending bilaterally to lower tip of lower harpal lobes; the latter, in turn, show minute black punctate spots; tip of aedeagus dark brown; tan pigmentation of upper harpal lobes; spine on membranous tip of aedeagus still transparent
14	Spine on tip of aedeagus black; *black, fully-formed antennal rami*
15} 16}	Persistence of coarse white hairs
17	*Three black spots along posterior edge of each forewing;* the coarse white hairs on genitalia show initiation of pale pink pigmentation
18	*Generalized but incomplete wing pigmentation;* red, pink, and white hairs on genitalia; cuticle "soft" only in region of forewings
19	*Complete wing pigmentation; softening of cuticle extends to dorsum of abdomen*
20	*Cuticle "soft" throughout but not crisp;* molting fluid partially absorbed under facial and abdominal windows
21	*Cuticle crisp throughout; molting fluid fully resorbed except under abdominal window; cuticle semitransparent*
22	*Animal distended; adult emergence*
	Part 2: Females‡
13	*Tarsal claws darken*
13–14	*Antennal rami darken*
15–16	Spines on genitalia turn from white to reddish brown
16–17	Developing ovarian tracheae become lined by a cuticular thread demonstrable by teasing the tracheae apart
18	Ovarian tracheae become air-filled and thus appear silvery
18–19	*Initiation of forewing pigmentation: lateral spots appear*
19	*Advanced wing pigmentation; lateral abdominal pigmentation visible*
21	*Cuticle softened over facial region*
22	*Cuticle crisp*
23	*Adult emergence*

‡ Except for the irrelevance of the characteristics involving the structure of the genitalia, the timetable for males is applicable to females for the first 13 days of development. Source: Telfer and Rutberg (1960), Table 1, *Biol. Bull.*, 118: 353.

and one and a half times as long as those of the female, and by the small size of the abdomen, which contrasts with that of the female swollen with eggs. The external genitalia also differ conspicuously, the male having a pair of harpes adapted to gripping the end of the female abdomen during mating and a heavily cuticular aedeagus through which the spermatophores are introduced into the vulva. The end of the female abdomen, by contrast, is relatively membranous and everts under pressure into a conical structure adapted for oviposition. In the pupa also the antennae, which are at this stage a pair of flattened sacs partially concealing the legs and wings on the ventral side of the thorax, are substantially larger in the male than in the female. External genitalia are minute relative to those of the moth but sexual differences are already clear. The male genitalia appear as a pair of small lobes on the ventral side of the ninth abdominal segment. (As a clue to segment number, there are six functional spiracles on each side of the pupal abdomen, one each on segments two through seven, while the residuum of an additional larval spiracle that was covered over with cuticle during the pupal molt is visible on the eighth segment.) In the female pupa a median ventral slit extends through both the eighth and ninth segments.

Distinguishing the sex in caterpillars is more difficult but, following the suggestions of Ishewata (1928) for other saturniids, we have found that Cecropia males and females in the last two larval instars can be sorted provisionally in the field, and with considerable reliability by examination through a dissecting microscope. The imaginal disc of the male genitalia is manifested midventrally as a transparent area in the cuticle at the anterior border of the ninth abdominal segment. The female caterpillar lacks this marker and has instead an indentation lying a few millimeters on each side of the ventral midline of the eighth abdominal segment. The indentations are paler in color than the green cuticle surrounding them and are particularly conspicuous shortly after molting. The validity of these markers can be readily confirmed either be separating the caterpillars that exhibit the two patterns and checking their sex after pupation, or by dissecting them to reveal the gonads. There are always a few individuals in which the patterns are ambiguous and these should be avoided in experimental work requiring sexual distinctions in caterpillars.

ADDITIONAL LITERATURE

Michener (1952) has published an excellent monograph which includes the classification and phylogeny of saturniids and a general description of the external morphology of the moth stage. Questions of anatomical terminology are conveniently resolved by consulting either this or the morphological treatise of Snodgrass (1935), which deals with the internal anatomy of insects as well. Michener's new name for Cecropia, *Hyalophora cecropia* (Linnaeus), now appears rather frequently in the literature, though, with the exception of the entomological journals, many editors will accept the common name, Cecropia moth, as sufficient, in view of the fluidity of its nomenclature. Earlier literature, including most of that cited here, uses the generic names, *Platysamia* and *Samia*.

REARING OF *Samia cynthia ricini*

(*prepared by Howard A. Schneiderman*)

A nondiapausing strain of *Samia cynthia ricini* has been raised in our laboratory for sixteen generations. These insects are inbred and uniform in their rate of development. A method for raising them in the laboratory is described below. It is a modification of a method originally developed by Claude Rivers of Cambridge, England. The food plant employed is *Ligustrum* (sp.) or privet which can be easily grown in a greenhouse.

New eggs are placed on paper towels in plastic containers in an incubator at 25°C and 70 percent relative humidity. A photoperiod with 12 hours of light is used (8:00 A.M. to 8:00 P.M.). The eggs become indented and slightly gray 1 day before hatching. At this time the paper is moistened with a few drops of water to soften the shells so that the larvae may crawl out more easily. Between 50 and 75 first instar larvae are placed on damp filter paper in covered plastic containers (4 × 5 × 4 inches) with a few branches of privet. Older leaves which are carefully washed should be used. Fresh green leaves are to be avoided. Change and dampen the filter paper every other day and replace wilted leaves with new ones. The leaves in the containers may be easily cleaned off with a small brush. Do not, however, disturb or touch the larvae. Larvae of all stages should be raised at 25°C with a high humidity.

Second instar larvae, which are more yellow than first instar larvae, are placed in larger plastic containers (8 × 4 × 4 inches) on a damp paper towel. Third instar larvae, which are white due to wax secretion, are placed on frames of hardware cloth in large plastic containers (12 × 11 × 4 inches) lined with a damp paper towel. About twenty larvae may be kept in each container until pupation. Fourth and fifth instar larvae should be fed twice daily, and cleaned once daily.

Dry towels are used to line the containers when the larvae commence spinning. Cocoons are kept in a partially open container until they are dry. The cocoons are kept at 25°C until emergence of the adults.

A covered gallon cardboard container, lined with dry towels, is used as the mating chamber. Each day a damp towel is placed in the container. Two or three females and five males are put in each container. When one pair of adults begin to mate, the others are removed to keep fertile eggs separate, and to keep track of progeny of a single individual. The mating adults should not be disturbed for 12 hours. The mated pair should be separated after 1½ days. The male is returned to a container with unmated females, and the mated female is left in the original container for 2 or 3 days. The eggs are then placed at 25°C as already described.

Hatching of eggs requires 11 days. The duration of larval life depends in part upon the quality of the food plants. With good food larval life lasts for about 34 days (hatching to spinning), prepupal life 4 days (start of spinning to pupation), adult development 15 days (pupation to eclosion).

REFERENCES

COLLINS, M. C., and R. D. WEAST, 1961: *Wild Silk Moths of the United States. Saturniinae.* Collins Radio Co., Cedar Rapids, Iowa.

DANILEVSKI, A. S., 1965: *Photoperiodism and Seasonal Development of Insects.* Oliver and Boyd, Edinburgh, Scotland.

ELIOT, S. M., and C. G. SOULE, 1902: *Caterpillars and Their Moths.* The Century Co., New York.

ISHEWATA, S., 1928: Sexual differences in the larvae of silkworms and some other moths. *Proc. 3rd Panpacific Science Congress*, 2: 2171.

MICHENER, C. D., 1952: The Saturniidae (Lepidoptera) of the western hemisphere. *Bull. of the American Museum of Natural History*, 98: Article 5.

PACKARD, A. S., 1912: *Monograph of the Bombycine Moths of North America,*

Including Their Transformations and Origin of the Larval Markings and Armature. Part III. Families Ceratocampidae (exclusive of Ceratocampinae), Saturniidae, Hemileucidae, and Brahmaeidae. *Memoirs, National Academy of Science.* 12: Part 1.

SCHNEIDERMAN, H. A., and C. M. WILLIAMS, 1954: The physiology of insect diapause. IX. The cytochrome oxidase system in relation to the diapause and development of the Cecropia silkworm. *Biol. Bull.*, 106: 238.

SMITH, C. N. (ed.), 1966: *Insect Colonization and Mass Production.* Academic Press, New York.

SNODGRASS, R. E., 1935: *Principles of Insect Morphology.* McGraw-Hill, New York.

TELFER, W. H., and L. D. RUTBERG, 1960: The effects of blood protein depletion on the growth of the oocytes in the Cecropia moth. *Biol. Bull.*, 118: 185.

WATERHOUSE, D. F., 1959: Axenic culture of wax moths for digestion studies. *Ann. N.Y. Acad. Sci.*, 77 (Art. 2): 283.

WHITING, P. W., 1937: Rearing *Ephestia kuehniella* larvae in quantity. In P. S. Galtshoff *et al.* (eds.), *Culture Methods for Invertebrate Animals*, Comstock, Ithaca, N.Y.

WILLIAMS, C. M., 1952: The physiology of insect diapause. IV. The brain and prothoracic glands as an endocrine system in the Cecropia silkworm. *Biol. Bull.*, 103: 120.

———, 1956: The physiology of insect diapause. X. An endocrine mechanism for the influence of temperature on the diapausing pupa of the Cecropia silkworm. *Biol. Bull.*, 110: 201.

———, 1963: The juvenile hormone. III. Its accumulation and storage in the abdomens of certain male moths. *Biol. Bull.*, 124: 355.

The Honeybee Embryo*

By E. J. DuPraw

INTRODUCTION

Recently the embryo of the common hive bee has proved especially suitable for a variety of analytical techniques, including micrurgy (reviewed by Gurdon, 1964), time-lapse cinemicrography (DuPraw, 1963a, 1965a), and whole-mount electron microscopy (DuPraw, 1965a, b, c). Although this embryo is not in wide use at the present time, it is certainly one of the most convenient of all eggs from the point of view of availability, size, transparency, and ease of laboratory manipulation; for those interested specifically in insect embryos (i.e., the prelarval stages), it is perhaps unsurpassed by any other material.

Except in mid-winter, honeybee embryos of all stages may be obtained readily from any normal bee colony. The eggs are found in the honeycombs near the center of the nest, one egg in each wax cell. Normally only the queen lays eggs, but she is capable of laying continuously at the rate of 1,000 or more per day. Combs containing several hundred eggs apiece can be removed from a single colony, brushed free of bees, and brought into the laboratory, where the embryos may be sorted and experimentally manipulated with no danger of stings to the investigator or his technicians. Honeybee maintenance also presents relatively few problems, since the bees are able to feed themselves, warm, humidify, and clean their own nests. Because beekeeping equipment and procedures vary considerably in different places, depending on climate, honey plants, and regional traditions, newcomers to apiculture should seek advice and instruction from a local expert.

Normal embryogenesis in the honeybee was extensively described in a monograph by Nelson (1915), whose figures of sectioned eggs are still the best available for many developmental stages. Nachtsheim (1913) also published a definitive study of chromosome numbers and behavior during oogenesis, spermatogenesis,

* Special thanks are due to Prof. Ruth Horsting, who contributed her time and talents for nearly a year while drawing the standard stages of honeybee embryogenesis (Figs. 6 through 17). Special contributions have also been made by Mr. Rick Jahn, who provided exceptionally capable assistance in the laboratory. The author wishes to acknowledge the participation of many students, including Mr. Michael Fry, Mr. Peter Rae, Mr. Ira Handelsman, Mr. Morris Wong, Mr. Phil Held, Mr. Dan Kurtak, and Miss Barbara Horsting. Earlier investigations with honeybee embryos were supported by grants from the American Philosophical Society and the National Institutes of Health; more recently the author's research has been supported by National Science Foundation grant GB-1924.

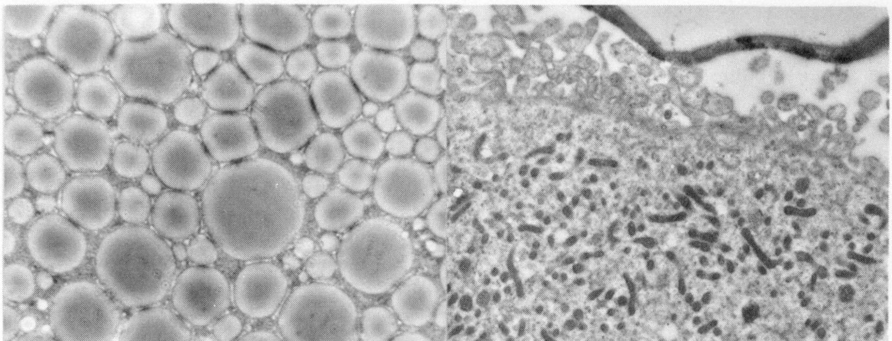

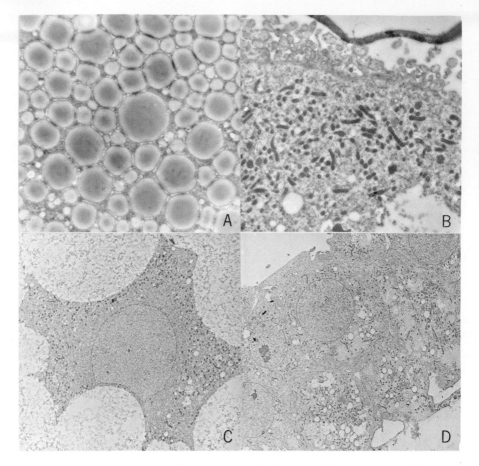

FIG. 1. (A) Yolk spheres embedded in a mitochondria-rich plasm; squash preparation of stage 1 embryo, seen by phase contrast. About 500 ×. (B) Thin-section of stage 2 embryo, showing mitochondria-rich periplasm; fixed in glutaraldehyde, embedded in methacrylate. About 5000 ×. (C) Thin-section of stage 2 embryo, showing an energid or cleavage "cell." Note the close contact of the energid plasm with yolk spheres on all sides, and the exclusion of mitochondria from the vicinity of the nucleus. Fixed in glutaraldehyde, embedded in methacrylate. About 1800 ×. (D) Thin-section of stage 6 embryo, showing several blastoderm cells. Note that the nuclei are apical in position, and that the base of the central cell is open to the underlying yolk. Fixed in glutaraldehyde, embedded in vestopal. About 1400 ×.

fertilization, and cleavage in worker (2n = 32) and drone (n = 16) eggs. Several precise statistical analyses of morphogenesis were produced later by Seidel's students and grand-students, Schnetter (1934a), Muller (1957), and Reinhardt (1960). More recently DuPraw (1963a) has employed time-lapse cinemicrography to film the entire course of honeybee embryogenesis, and has extended the morphological analysis to the level of ultrastructure (DuPraw, 1965a, b, c). The first experimental analysis with living honeybee embryos was carried out by Schnetter

(1934b), who developed fundamental techniques for incubating and ligaturing the eggs; Schnetter's student, Sauer (1954), continued the ligature experiments, and ligatured eggs have also been filmed side by side with unligatured controls by DuPraw (1963a). The effects of X-irradiation on honeybee embryos have been studied by Bertzbach (1960) and by DuPraw (1964a). Finally, techniques for injecting honeybee embryos, for transplanting cleavage nuclei, and for observing living embryonic cells *in vitro* have been introduced by DuPraw (1958, 1963a, b, 1965a, b).

GENERAL PROPERTIES OF HONEYBEE EMBRYOS

The eggs of the honeybee are characteristically sausage-shaped, their dimensions and proportions varying somewhat from queen to queen and with seasonal or nutritional factors; the usual range for total egg length is about 1.6–1.8 mm, while the maximum diameter varies around 0.35 mm. When laid, the eggs are attached to the honeycomb by their presumptive posterior ends, which are slightly smaller than the anterior ends and are thinly coated with an adhesive substance; it is also possible to distinguish the presumptive dorsum, which is slightly concave, from the convex ventral side. The egg therefore has a visible bilateral symmetry, as well as anterior-posterior polarity, both of which correspond to those of the larva-to-be.

Roughly speaking, the newly laid honeybee egg is a two-phase system, consisting primarily of yolk spheres (10–30 μ in diameter) embedded in a mitochondria-rich matrix (Figs. 1A, 1B). This plasm-yolk system is highly fluid and is enclosed in a transparent, proteinaceous egg membrane which, as seen in electron micrographs, possesses a double-layered structure. The outer layer is less than 0.1 μ thick, dissolves in weak solutions of sodium hypochlorite (Clorox), and corresponds to the much heavier "shell" or chorion of other insect eggs; the inner layer is about 0.25 μ thick, resists attack by Clorox, and represents a vitelline membrane. The fact that both membranes together are less than half a micron thick makes the honeybee embryo unusually amenable to ligatures or micropipette penetration at any developmental stage, but it also means that these embryos are highly susceptible to accidental rupturing or less serious forms of mechanical damage.

The gross composition of whole honeybee embryos has been investigated by Dr. F. E. Strong and the author (unpublished); preliminary findings for groups of sibling embryos just after laying and just before hatching are given in Table 1. In agreement with Nelson and

TABLE 1

	STAGES 1 AND 2 (n = 37)		STAGES 9 AND 10 (n = 18)	
	AVERAGE WT. PER EMBRYO (μg)	PERCENT FRESH WT.	AVERAGE WT. PER EMBRYO (μg)	PERCENT FRESH WT.
Total	142	100	102	100
Water	125	88	85	83
Lipid	10	7	3	3
Nonlipid (by difference)	7	5	14	14

Sturtevant (1924), these observations indicate that the total mass (and volume) of the honeybee embryo decreases by about 28 percent during the 3 days of development. Most of the weight loss is at the expense of water, and there is also a net increase in nonlipid dry mass at the expense of lipid. The density of honeybee embryos at all stages corresponds closely to the density of a 12 percent sucrose solution (1.044 mg per microliter); from this relationship the volume of the egg immediately after laying can be estimated as about 0.135 μl. In newly laid eggs, somewhat over half of the lipid fraction is accounted for by polar lipids, primarily phosphatidyl choline (lecithin) and phosphatidyl ethanolamine, while the remainder includes triglycerides, free fatty acids, and free sterols.

If a honeybee embryo adhering to a fragment of honeycomb base is placed upside down on the surface of a 12 percent sucrose solution, subsequent centrifugation at 18,500 *g* for 1 hour causes the embryo to separate from its base (which goes to the bottom of the tube), to float vertically in the middle of the sucrose solution, and to stratify internally into a number of transverse layers. In eggs centrifuged *immediately* after laying, the yolk spheres form the most centripetal layer in the egg and account for over 70 percent of the total egg volume. Within 3 hours after laying, however, a new centripetal layer appears, which occupies the light pole of the egg and displaces the yolk sphere layer into the second position. Since the egg is about 88 percent water and yolk spheres make up 70 percent of its volume, it is clear that both the yolk sphere and plasm phases must be aqueous; they are evidently kept separate by unit membranes around the yolk spheres, which may be derived from oocyte pinocytosis vacuoles (Telfer, 1963). Further changes in the number and relative volumes of the centrifuge layers, which characterize various stages of development, will be described elsewhere.

In the embryogenesis of insects, the plasm-yolk mass plays a part which is morphologically, physiologically and, indeed, conceptually dissimilar from any of the processes familiar to vertebrate and marine invertebrate embryologists. The insect yolk has been compared to a template on the surface of which the embryo is assembled (Seidel, 1961), and it is also true that construction proceeds largely by a differential recruitment of both plasm and yolk from the interior of the egg. Most of the plasm in the newly laid egg is interspersed among the yolk spheres (Fig. 1A), with a small amount concentrated just under the surface membrane as a thin "periplasm" layer (or *Keimhautblastem*). Later the periplasm increases in thickness at the expense of the interior plasm net (Fig. 1B), while in the egg interior the replicating cleavage nuclei also recruit their own surrounding islands of plasm (Fig. 1C). Eventually the periplasm gives rise to a surface layer of uninucleate blastoderm cells by the unique process of "superficial cleavage" (Fig. 1D). Still later a second, inner periplasm (*innere Keimhautblastem*) forms beneath the blastoderm and is ultimately assimilated by the blastoderm cells. As these morphological redistributions of plasm and yolk proceed, the plasm-yolk "template" changes shape by so-called "yolk contractions," which occur both locally and *en masse*. Although initially the protoplast (i.e., the plasm-containing parts of the embryo) occupies the entire volume enclosed by the chorion, at later stages it shortens markedly, giving rise to one or more clear, fluid-filled spaces between the outside surface of the periplasm (or blastoderm) and the inside surface of the egg membrane (Figs. 7, 8, 11, 12). These contractions are reversible, so that at later stages the protoplast again occupies the full volume of the egg (Figs. 9 and 10).

The sequence of redistributions between plasm, yolk, and extraembryonic spaces is very precisely timed and appears to be governed largely by interactions between physiological centers localized at different levels in the plasm-yolk mass. Counce (1961) and Krause and Sander (1962) have provided excellent English reviews of the many experiments, performed primarily by Seidel and his students in Germany, which have revealed the existence and properties of these control centers. In the egg of the honeybee, Schnetter (1934a, b) demonstrated a "differentiation center" lying in the region of the presumptive thorax, between the 20 percent and 30 percent levels measured from the anterior pole. A second type of control center (activation center) was found by Sauer (1954) in 12-hour honeybee embryos at the 64 percent level; some factor from this center is required for the differentiation of presumptive mesoderm cells, since in its absence such cells give rise to endoderm. Finally, a "cleavage center" is sometimes said to occupy the 10 percent level near the anterior pole of the honeybee egg, primarily because the zygote nucleus migrates to this position for the early cleavage mitoses.

LABORATORY INCUBATION OF HONEYBEE EMBRYOS

Since the optimum temperature for honeybee development is 34°–36°C, it is necessary to incubate the embryos when they are maintained outside the colony. Total development time from oviposition until hatching is 70–76 hours, but this is subject to variations of some hours even at constant temperature. Precise timing data, together with a detailed description of the various developmental stages, is provided in the Appendix.

Two alternative methods have been developed for maintaining honeybee embryos in the laboratory. In the first method (Schnetter, 1934b), the eggs are removed from the comb by cutting a small wax disc from the bottom of the honeycomb cell with the egg adhering in its center. Wax discs and eggs are then placed in a dry, beeswax-lined Petri dish together with enough wet cotton to maintain a high atmospheric humidity; finally, the covered dish is incubated at 35.5°C. Eggs are most easily removed from old combs in which the cells are lined with several layers of cocoon from previous brood cycles; in such combs the queen lays her eggs on the cocoon lining, which can be cut readily with a sharpened dental tool and lifted out with watchmaker's forceps.

The second method of incubating honeybee embryos involves immersing the eggs in paraffin oil (Reinhardt, 1960; DuPraw, 1963b, 1965a). Since heavier oils sometimes induce anomalies, particularly when eggs are crowded, a relatively light paraffin oil is recommended for this purpose (Fisher Scientific Co., viscosity 125/135, cat. no. 0-119). Eggs are usually removed from the comb by cutting out individual cocoon discs, after which both disc and egg are immersed in a small dish of warm oil under a dissecting microscope; while the disc is held in watchmaker's forceps, the egg is gently nudged off its base with a blunt glass microtool (fabricated by drawing out 1-mm glass capillary tubing over a microflame, then flaming the tip to produce a small terminal sphere of glass). Whereas the surface of a dry egg resembles frosted glass, an immersed egg becomes beautifully transparent, and individual cells or even nuclei may be resolved. Paraffin oil also eliminates the need to control humidity, so that embryos are ordinarily incubated in uncovered 60-mm Petri dishes; the eggs may be pipetted from one dish to another with an ordinary eyedropper.

Most losses during laboratory incubation are the result of mechanical damage, which occurs easily in the earlier stages and may not be detectable until later.

In this respect, the dry culture method of Schnetter is the safer, since the egg itself need not be touched at all. The process of immersing newly laid eggs in oil, even when carried out by an experienced operator, usually damages a few individuals at their (attached) posterior ends; after immersion in oil such damaged eggs leak very slowly, forming an aqueous "bubble" at the point of rupture. Immersed eggs which are to be filmed or used in other critical ways should always be observed for at least 10–20 minutes until it has been established that they are not leaking.

In addition to mechanical damage, honeybee eggs are also very sensitive to temperature shock and to drying. When brood combs are removed from the hive, care must be taken not to expose them to the heat of the sun, and combs that are not in use should be packed in moist paper towels and incubated; when eggs are removed from a comb, they should also be transferred directly into a covered Petri dish with wet cotton. As long as such obvious precautions are exercised, it will not harm the embryos to be cooled at room temperature for an hour or more during the process of removing them from the comb or while observing them under a microscope. Injured eggs sometimes show progressive internal changes that can be mistaken for normal developmental stages, e.g., a gradual alteration in the plasm-yolk distribution, resulting in irregular cloudy regions within the embryo (appearing white by oblique light and brownish by transmitted light).

For certain experimental purposes it is necessary to have a number of early embryos, the ages of which are known to within a few minutes. The standard method used since the time of Petrunkewitsch (1903) for obtaining timed embryos is to confine a queen to a single comb containing no eggs; the queen and her bees are then left undisturbed for an hour or more, after which the comb is removed and searched. Provided that the queen is vigorous and the colony healthy, about 20–40 eggs are commonly obtained, and their ages are then known to within ±30 minutes. Not all methods of confining the queen are equally effective; the author has obtained best results with a comb-size, rectangular cage made of "queen excluder wire" (obtainable commercially), in which the bars of the cage are so spaced that the worker bees can pass through but the larger queen cannot. Since the queen occasionally refuses to lay or lays only a few eggs, it is sometimes desirable to start two or more queens at once (each in its own colony). A queen lays eggs only when she is fed sufficient "bee milk" by the nurse bees and when the colony can maintain its brood nest temperature in the vicinity of 34°C. For these reasons, laying is enhanced if the queen is confined to a comb containing fresh pollen and nectar plus a few young larvae (which attract nurse bees). The queen cage should be placed in the center of the brood nest closely flanked by other brood-containing combs.

MICRURGICAL TECHNIQUES

The earliest micrurgy performed with honeybee embryos was Schnetter's (1934b) series of ligature experiments, in which infant hair was used to tie off 12-hour (early stage 4) and 24-hour (late stage 4) embryos at different levels (for stage numbers, see Appendix). Schnetter demonstrated that the blastoderm cells retain considerable regulative ability up to early stage 4, but that embryos ligatured during or after the end of stage 4 develop in mosaic fashion. Even during the regulative development of 12-hour embryos however, the *ectoderm* and *mesoderm* respond as if the egg contains transverse regions or sensitive levels corresponding to the head, thorax, and abdomen of the future larva. For example, a ligature as far back as 21 percent of the egg length from the anterior pole permits development of a complete dwarf larva (although the same ligature at late stage 4 would remove the labrum, stomodaeum, and brain), while a ligature anywhere between the 27–33 percent levels results in a larva which lacks a head but possesses a normal, 13-segmented trunk. If the ligature crosses the 34 percent boundary, then the three thoracic segments are lost as a unit (*Ganzbildung*) and only a normal 10-segmented abdomen develops; finally, a ligature posterior to the 40 percent level results in a defective or partial abdomen. On the basis of his physiological and morphological analyses, Schnetter (1934a, b) concluded that early embryos contain a "differentiation center" located between the 20 percent and 30 percent levels (presumptive thorax region); after the 32-nuclei stage, this region stains preferentially with thionin and seems to initiate many developmental events. With regard to the *endoderm* and *mesoderm* Sauer (1954) showed that anterior and posterior midgut rudiments usually develop on both sides of a ligature. In fact, anteriorly even the presumptive mesoderm develops as endoderm until a boundary is crossed at the 64 percent level (activation center); only in eggs ligatured posterior to the 64 percent level is mesoderm able to develop on both sides. Embryos ligatured at various stages have been filmed side by side with unligatured controls (DuPraw, 1963a); this technique has demonstrated that an anterior ligature at stage 1 prevents migration of the cleavage nuclei and effectively enucleates the main part of the egg.

Several materials have been used by the author for successful ligatures, including baby hair, wool, nylon, and cashmere; however, by far the most useful material is a single cotton fiber plucked from a mass of common sterile absorbent cotton. Only the longest, unkinked fibers are selected, and these are formed into simple overhand loops under a dissecting microscope by means of watchmaker's forceps. Those loops which are most nearly circular provide the best chance of success. Eggs to be ligatured are always incubated dry and are mounted in upright positions on an operating block. A circular cotton loop is then lowered over the anterior end of the egg (which is usually at room temperature), positioned at the desired level, and pulled tight with watchmaker's forceps. Although this operation requires practice, it does not present heroic difficulty; especially if a cotton fiber is used, the ligature has strength and flexibility without resiliency (i.e., once pulled shut the ligature does not spring open). Most failures are caused by rupturing of the egg's surface membranes, either through pulling the loop too tight or through positioning the loop too obliquely relative to the egg's long axis (which tends to stretch the chorion). Oil-immersed eggs almost invariably rupture upon ligaturing, but a dry egg which has already been ligatured may afterwards be immersed for filming or microscope observation.

The suitability of the honeybee embryo for such ligature operations also confers on it a suitability for micropuncture or micropipette experiments. Provided that the embryo is punctured or injected at the anterior pole, the "wound" may be artificially healed by placing a ligature just behind the anterior end. This type of procedure was introduced by DuPraw (1958, 1960) for the transplantation of cleavage nuclei from one embryo to another; in the original work, core plasm containing a variable number of energids was pipetted from timed mid-stage 2 embryos to timed early stage 1 embryos and the recipients were then ligatured at the anterior ends (Fig. 2). It was found that a small proportion of these injected embryos completed development and hatched as dwarf larvae. Uninjected control embryos, ligatured at the same stage and level, showed no development at all. Although time-lapse films subsequently confirmed that an anterior ligature effectively enucleates an uninjected stage 1 embryo, it is not entirely certain that the injection procedure itself may not displace the recipient's own nucleus into the interior, preventing enucleation.

The most successful micropipette

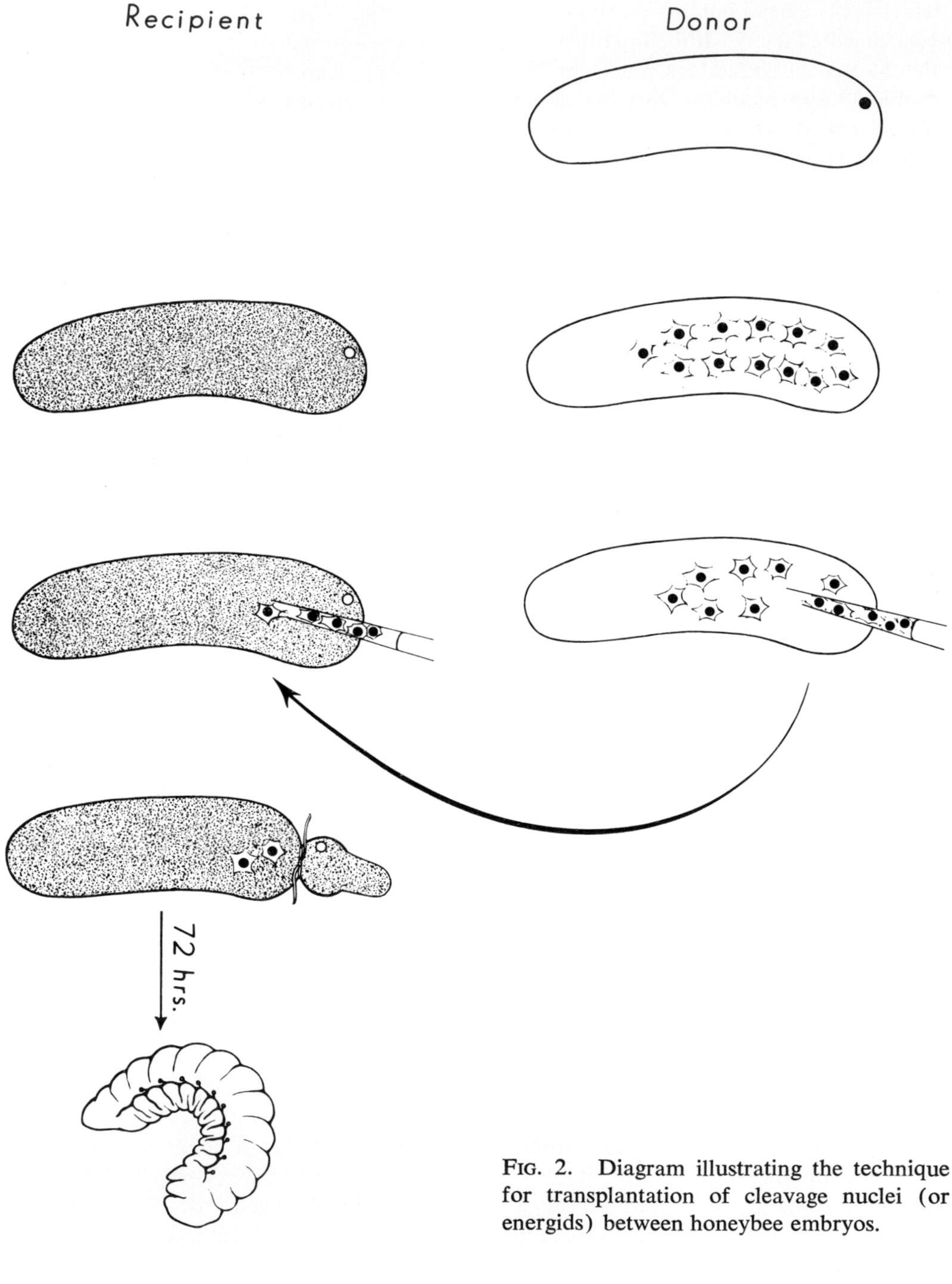

FIG. 2. Diagram illustrating the technique for transplantation of cleavage nuclei (or energids) between honeybee embryos.

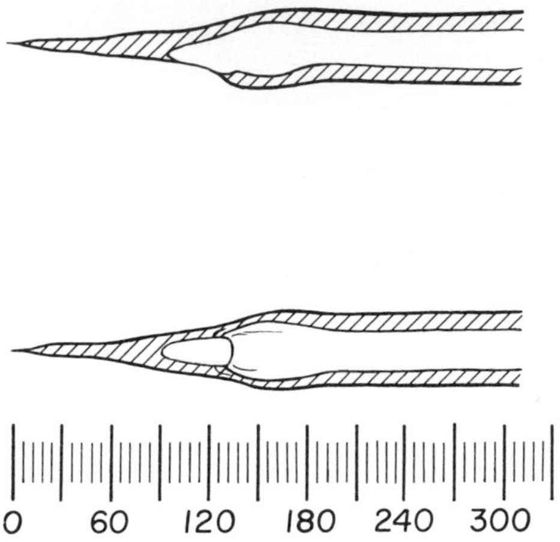

FIG. 3. A pipette of the type used for nuclear transplant or injection of honeybee embryos. Scale is calibrated in microns (1 unit = 6μ).

experiments carried out so far with honeybee embryos have involved the injection of colchicine, H^3-thymidine or H^3-uridine. For instance, if a 10^{-3} *M* colchicine solution (N.B. Co., 4 mg per 10 ml) is injected into the core of a late stage 2 or early stage 3 embryo, the ensuing cleavage mitosis is blocked at metaphase in several thousand nuclei; this method has been used to obtain large numbers of metaphase chromosomes for whole-mount electron microscopy (DuPraw, 1965b). Similarly, injection of a 1.5×10^{-5} *M* solution of H^3-thymidine (New England Nuclear, 6.78 C/mmole) into the core of a stage 6 embryo leads to extensive labeling of nuclear DNA, which is detectable in smear preparations by autoradiography. In both types of experiment, operated embryos are incubated for only 1 or 2 hours after injection, and since drying is not a problem, the postinjection ligature may be omitted.

As in the nuclear transplant work, microinjection is performed under a dissecting microscope with a specially fabricated glass micropipette mounted in a low-power micromanipulator (Brinkmann model 3050). The pipettes are of the type called "pipette à bec massif" by DeFonbrune (1949), which have approximately the shape of a hypodermic needle with a needle-sharp tip and the pipette mouth on one side (Fig. 3). Although such pipettes may be manufactured by hand, they are easier to construct using a DeFonbrune microforge (procedure given by DeFonbrune, 1949). The pipette is held in an air-tight seal by a Brinkmann pipette holder connected through thin-walled rubber tubing to a 2-ml syringe. During the microinjection procedure it is helpful if the pipette, pipette contents, and the embryo itself are all incubated at or near the optimum developmental temperature (35.5°C), and such incubation is essential for successful transplantation of nuclei or cytoplasm into early stage embryos. Transplantation operations may be performed in a walk-in incubator; for greater convenience, however, a special, thermostatically controlled operating chamber has been designed, which rests on the stage of a dissecting microscope and has convenient controls for orienting the embryo and micropipette (Fig. 4).

Several dry embryos of appropriate developmental stage are premounted on a beeswax operating block, their cocoon bases stuck firmly on the wax. After the micropipette has been charged with the solution to be injected (prewarmed to 35.5°C), one embryo is oriented with its long axis parallel to the pipette axis and its anterior pole centered in opposition to the pipette tip (Fig. 2). A one-dimensional thrust with the manipulator is then sufficient to penetrate the chorion, bringing the pipette opening inside the embryo. The solution is injected by depressing the syringe plunger, which increases the air pressure in the micropipette system. Finally the pipette is removed by a brisk, one-dimensional withdrawal movement, and a new egg may be oriented for

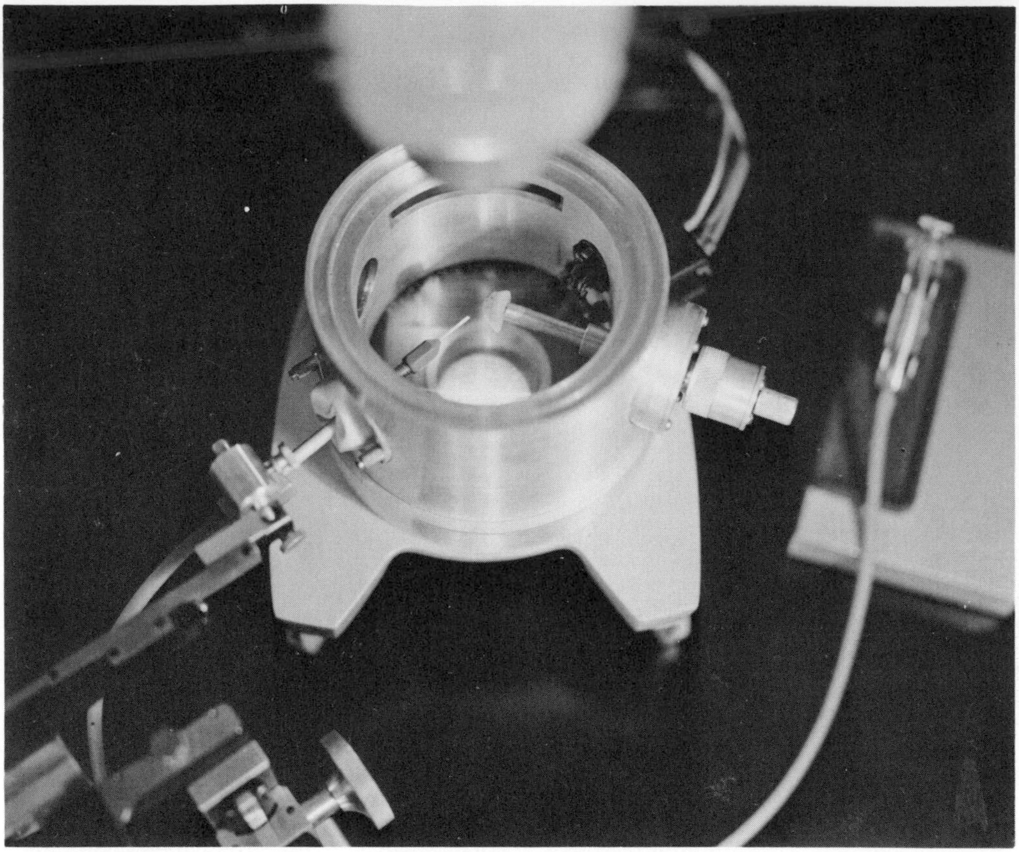

FIG. 4. A thermostatically-heated operating chamber designed by the author for transplantation of honeybee nuclei. The chamber sits on the stage of a dissecting microscope; embryos are mounted on the small wax cone near the center of the photograph, and the micropipette is held in the micromanipulator at bottom left.

injection with the same instrument. A similar technique is used for transplantation of cleavage nuclei, except that the micropipette is not "charged" in advance with an artificial solution; instead one or more donor embryos are mounted in marked positions near the recipients, energid-containing plasm is withdrawn with a dry micropipette, and the pipette is then immediately inserted into a recipient embryo for injection (this procedure has been filmed by DuPraw, 1963a). In these operations, movements of the micropipette are kept to a minimum and most of the necessary reorientation is accomplished by adjusting the operating block.

Provided that the pipette tip is sharp enough, its shank fine enough, and its opening large enough, these injection procedures are not unusually difficult and a series of three or four premounted embryos may often be injected with the same "charged" pipette. However, problems sometimes arise in withdrawing the pipette from the recipient embryo. In the most fortunate cases, the embryo permits the pipette to withdraw smoothly without stickiness, and there seems to be a clotting or gelation in the wound as the pipette leaves; the result is that both cytoplasm and injected material remain inside the chorion with no significant exovate. Occasionally, however, the edges of the wound tend to stick to the pipette, resisting its withdrawal, and the embryo may sometimes be pulled away from its cocoon base. Even if the withdrawal is smooth, injected material and egg cytoplasm occasionally run out of the wound as the pipette tip emerges.

Depending on the purpose of the injection and the development stage of the embryo, these difficulties may or may not spoil the injected embryo for experimental purposes. In the case of stage 6 embryos injected with tritium thymidine, operated individuals remain useful even when some of the injected solution comes out again; if such embryos are incubated for an hour, then smeared on a slide and autoradiographed, considerable labeling of nuclear DNA is found. On the other hand, the noncellular stages 1, 2, and 3 do not continue development very long after exovating. In either case it is of little help to ligature a wound after exovation has occurred. Postinjection ligatures are of value mainly in preventing desiccation if the experimental embryo is to be maintained over a period of days (as in the nuclear transplant technique). Sometimes a punctured embryo, such as a stage 2 nuclear transplant donor, is observed to develop and hatch normally even without ligaturing, but such embryos much more commonly shrivel up after a few hours to a day of incubation.

POSTEMBRYONIC DEVELOPMENT

Newly hatched larvae in the honeybee colony remain at the bottoms of their cells, where nurse bees provide them with "bee milk" or worker jelly; this is a fairly fluid secretion containing a wide variety of nutrients and closely related to royal jelly, the food of the queen larva. Within a short time the larva literally floats in a puddle of bee milk and lies on one side in a C-shaped position, respiring rhythmically through its 10 uppermost spiracles. At the end of a 5-day feeding period (6 days for drones) it ceases to eat, defecates, spins its cocoon and pupates; meantime the cell is capped with wax by helpful adult worker bees. The duration of the "capped" pupal period varies for the different castes, being 14–15 days for drones, 13 days for workers, and only 7–8 days for queens; pupation ends with removal of the wax cap and the emergence of a typical adult bee (imago). Myser (1954) has provided a careful description of external morphology and internal histogenesis during honeybee metamorphosis.

Drone, worker, and queen larvae are readily distinguishable in the colony by differences in the size and orientation of their honeycomb cells (illustrated by Grout, 1963). Eggs laid in drone cells are normally unfertilized and genetically haploid (Petrunkewitsch, 1901; Nachtsheim, 1913), and there is good evidence that the sex of an egg is in fact usually determined by whether or not it is fertilized. However, a high degree of inbreeding and genetic homozygosity can lead to production of diploid males (Woyke 1963, 1965). Merriam and Ris (1954) also found that the amount of DNA per nucleus in tissues of normal adult drones is not notably less than in the corresponding tissues of workers and queens. Differentiation of female larvae into either worker or queen bees depends on events during the larval feeding period, and is not irreversibly established until about the third day after hatching (Weaver, 1957). Even the fully formed workers are not completely asexual, since in queenless colonies a certain proportion of workers are able to lay viable eggs that develop parthenogenetically into drones; in some races, unfertilized worker or queen eggs can also develop a small percentage of parthenogenetic diploid females (see Tucker, 1958). Commercial techniques for rearing queens from young worker larvae are widely used (for details see Grout, 1963), and it is therefore practical to raise queens from experimental eggs by transferring the hatchlings into a strong, queenless colony. Using these methods, the author has reared apparently normal queens from dwarf larvae which hatched from eggs ligatured at early stage 4. Unfortunately, experimental larvae are sometimes eaten rather than reared by the nurse bees, and therefore a convenient technique for laboratory rearing of postembryonic honeybee stages is badly needed.

Although some partial success has been obtained in rearing larvae in the laboratory (Michael and Abramovitz, 1955; Weaver, 1955; Smith, 1959; Jay, 1959; Dixon and Shuel, 1963; Woyke, 1963), present techniques are both tedious and accompanied by high larval and pupal mortality. The difficulty may be summarized by stating that no defined medium has yet been devised which is nutritionally equivalent either to worker jelly or to royal jelly. Even the storage and feeding of royal jelly in bulk, which is the basis of most laboratory rearing methods, produces notably slower growth and higher mortality under laboratory conditions than in nature. The problem of queen-worker differentiation is closely linked with the problem of rearing honeybee larvae *in vitro*, and it is very likely that the solution to both problems will depend on the unraveling of a complex balance among several nutritional factors.

"SQUASH CULTURE" TECHNIQUE

A fairly simple method has been devised by DuPraw (1965a) for filming or observing mitosis and ameboid activity in individual living honeybee embryonic cells. A single, oil-immersed embryo of appropriate developmental stage is pipetted in a small drop of oil to the surface of a clean, standard microscope slide; next, a 24 × 50-mm glass cover slip is applied with an exaggerated "smear" motion, which bursts the chorion and spreads the embryonic cells in monolayers or isolated cells and cell groups. If such a preparation is viewed by phase contrast or interference microscopy, the cells and yolk spheres are found to be protected from the paraffin oil by an almost invisible coating of aqueous plasm, whereas the paraffin oil itself surrounds the cell groups and protects them from desiccation. Such squash culture preparations remain viable for 6 hours or more; if the slide is incubated during observation, the cells show a variety of ameboid, saltatory, and mitotic activity.

In squash cultures prepared from advanced stage 6 embryos, it is possible to distinguish at least two classes of tissue: large ectodermal cells with nuclei 10–11 μ in diameter and much smaller mesodermal cells with nuclei 6.5–7.5 μ in diameter; in addition, from late stage 6 on, sheets of serosal cells with nuclei 12–14 μ in diameter may be found. In all cases the nuclei are very clear and vacuole-like, containing one or more prominent, dense nucleoli. Very active pseudopod formation and saltatory movements of cytoplasmic granules occur in stage 6 preparations. Mitosis has been observed in squash cultures derived from early stage 4, stage 6, and especially stage 7 embryos. Usually if cell division appears in a preparation at all, it can be found in different cells over a period of hours; however, mitotic, saltatory, and pseudopodal activity quickly cease when a preparation is chilled to room temperature, and begin again on reincubation. The author has determined from time-lapse films that the metaphase pause in stage 6 squash cultures lasts about 17 minutes, anaphase requires only 3–7 minutes (until cytokinesis), and telophase lasts about 15–20 minutes.

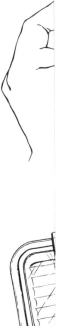

Just as intact stage 6 embryos actively incorporate H^3-thymidine and H^3-uridine, stage 6 cells in squash cultures also show incorporation of labeled deoxyribonucleic acid and ribonucleic acid precursors. In this modification of the squash culture technique, a small drop of isotopically labeled precursor solution (100 μc per ml) is placed on a clean microscope slide and one or several embryos enclosed in a drop of paraffin oil are deposited directly on the aqueous droplet. The preparation is then smeared under a cover slip in the usual way and incubated for 1–3 hours. Following incubation, the cover slip is removed, the slide is fixed in 25 percent ethanol for 10 minutes, then dehydrated through an ethanol series (10 minutes each in 50, 75, 85, 95, and 100 percent) and cleared in toluene. Finally, the preparation is dried in a desiccator for 2 days or more before being covered with stripping film or liquid emulsion (Kodak NTB-2; see Weston, this volume, pp. 723–736). Autoradiographs are exposed for 3 weeks, then developed in D-19 for 5 minutes. Active incorporation of both DNA and RNA precursors has been observed, but it is not known whether the same cell can exhibit both.

Stage 2 energids apparently do not continue mitosis after squashing. Often it is difficult to recognize the energids at all since the nuclei are very clear, about 10 μ in diameter, lack nucleoli, and are nearly identical in appearance with numerous nearby yolk spheres. Nevertheless, comparison of the yolk spheres themselves in stages 1, 2, and 3 squash cultures has revealed a striking physical change which evidently accompanies the migration of energids in stage 2. Whereas immediately after laying, the yolk spheres do not contain visible inclusions (Fig. 1a), several types of weirdly shaped granular inclusions (lipochondria) may be found from stage 2 on, and by stage 3 these have become quite frequent. Some differential staining of spheres and inclusions has been achieved with Nile blue; an aqueous solution of the dye is applied to a microscope slide, drained, and permitted to dry as a thin film. If the slide is then used to squash a stage 2 embryo in paraffin oil and viewed in white light, the preparation shows a light blue staining of some but not all the yolk spheres, intense staining of ovoid inclusions, and some variable color in filamentous and crown-shaped inclusions.

FIXED PREPARATIONS FOR LIGHT AND ELECTRON MICROSCOPY

Two major difficulties must be overcome in fixing honeybee embryos: (1) the egg membranes, though thin, are relatively impermeable to aqueous solutions and resist rapid, uniform penetration of fixing agents; (2) the egg, since it contains nearly 90 percent water, is very prone to crenate during alcohol dehydration and more especially during clearing. Although these difficulties are sometimes helped by removing the outer chorion with weak sodium hypochlorite solution (Clorox), the inner vitelline membrane is actually the thicker of the two egg coats and cannot be removed without totally dispersing the embryo. So far, the most practical solution has been a combination of tedious procedures: the embryos, after immersion in a dish of fixative solution, are punctured repeatedly with a fine glass microneedle and left in fixative overnight; thereafter the dehydration and clearing are carried out in gentle steps, sometimes involving a drop-wise replacement of solutions over a period of many hours. Even with these precautions it sometimes happens that, as two apparently identical embryos are passed through the reagents side by side, one will crenate and the other usually in anaphase (Nachtsheim, 1913). The two maturation divisions take place in a conelike thickening of the periplasm (*Richtungsplasma* or maturation plasm) very near the anterior pole toward the ventral side of the egg. These divisions do not separate polar bodies as such, but form four groups of chromosomes, the innermost of which migrates dorsally into the egg interior as the female pronucleus. The remaining three chromosome masses stay in the maturation plasm, where two of them fuse and go through further divisions until they disappear at late stage 2 or early stage 3. In living eggs one can sometimes detect a faint brownish spot in the region of the maturation plasm; the visible color presumably is due to a higher density of mitochondria and their contained cytochrome pigments.

In fertilized eggs there are usually three to seven sperm, all of which form male pronuclei. The female pronucleus generally encounters one of these early in its migration (near the maturation plasm), fuses with it, and initiates the first cleavage mitosis. In unfertilized (male) eggs, on the other hand, the female pronucleus continues to migrate until it reaches the dorsal surface of the egg, where it initiates cleavage. Chromosome counts during and after the first cleavage mitosis show 32 chromosomes in fertilized eggs, 16 in unfertilized ones. These chromosomes are very tiny and consequently some authors have been led into serious errors regarding chromosome number; however, the reliable karyotype descriptions of Nachtsheim (1913) served to clarify most of the important relationships. One major source of confusion was the fact that, during the egg maturation divisions, only 8 bipartite chromosomes are visible (instead of 16 tetrads); according to Nachtsheim, each of these 8 morphological pairs is equivalent to two highly compact tetrads. Similarly, in the primary spermatocytes (which are haploid), the 16 dyads sometimes lie together as 8 pairs.

During the last half of stage 1, three mitotic divisions occur in the anterior 10 percent of the egg (cleavage center), producing a cluster of eight cleavage nuclei. As is characteristic in insects, these cleavage mitoses are not accompanied by cytoplasmic division of the egg as a whole; each nucleus recruits its own plasm island, forming a "cleavage cell" or "energid," but all the plasm islands remain in continuity with the plasm net surrounding the yolk spheres and thereby with one another (Fig. 1C). Up to the eight-nuclei stage the energids show relatively little tendency to migrate and remain together in a cluster. At this time in the living egg it is often possible to distinguish one large or several small brownish masses in the anterior part of the protoplast, but the early cleavage divisions are usually difficult to follow exactly *in vivo*.

In sectioned material the mitotic figures show two unusual features throughout cleavage: (1) during each anaphase and telophase a peculiar "midplate" forms, which is Feulgen negative but at an early time consists of phase-dense granules superficially resembling metaphase chromosomes in size, position, and affinity for hematoxylin (Fig. 18); (2) in contrast to the maturation spindles, which lack centrioles, the cleavage spindles during and after cleavage I exhibit prominent polar centrioles that persist during interphase and "replicate" in typical fashion. These centrioles cannot be derived from the sperm because they develop identically in both fertilized and unfertilized eggs (Nachtsheim, 1913). Also in fertilized eggs during cleavage, the supernumerary sperm form spindles which lack centrioles and do not divide. Since the centrioles seem not to be present in the egg during the maturation stages, their origin remains unexplained.

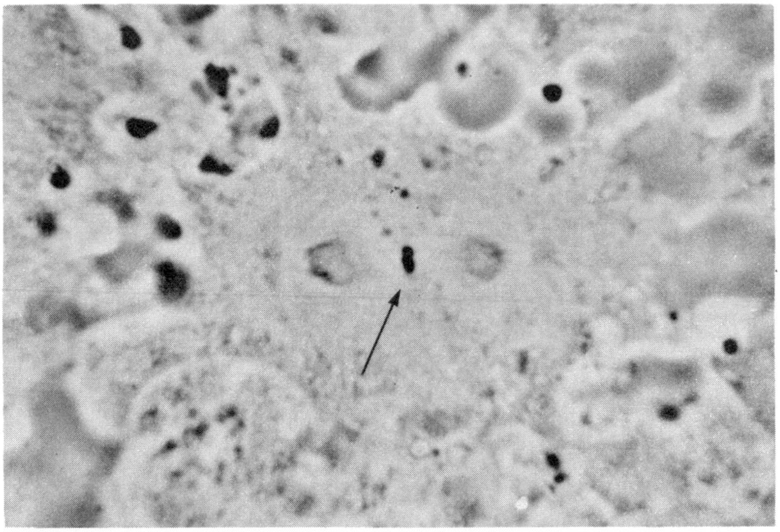

FIG. 18. Telophase in a late stage 2 energid. Arrow indicates the characteristic mid-body lying between the two daughter nuclei. Phase contrast micrograph of a methacrylate embedded thick-section. About 1200 ×.

Stage 2 (Fig. 7). Duration about 3.6 hours

Stage 2 is characterized by a sudden, rapid, and energetic migration of the energids, many of which leave their anterior (stage 1) positions and move toward the posterior pole of the egg; from external aspect, the beginning of this stage is signaled by the appearance of a clear space at the posterior pole, due to a posterior yolk contraction which is essentially a slow continuation of the anterior contraction begun in stage 1. As the nuclei migrate they pause at rhythmic intervals for further mitotic divisions, and the direction of migration in its later phase shifts toward the egg periphery. The result is that near the end of stage 2 about 1,000 nuclei enter the periplasm over the entire surface of the embryo. As they do, the periplasm divides itself by "superficial cleavage" into typical uninucleate cells. The end of the stage is recognizable by the appearance of conspicuous "bumps" over the anterior surface as superficial cleavage begins (Fig. 8).

At the beginning of stage 2 a cluster of eight energids lies near the 10 percent level (measured from the anterior pole), about equidistant from the dorsal, ventral, and lateral surfaces. Cleavage IV occurs as migration begins, and three further mitoses (V–VII) take place at approximately equal intervals while the energids are moving toward the posterior pole. In this first phase of migration, the energids appear to stream through the central core of the protoplast, some moving more rapidly than others, and there is a noticeable pause or slowing at each mitosis; by the 128-nuclei stage the posteriad migration is complete and nuclei are distributed at all levels in the core of the embryo. At this point a new phase of migration begins, when almost all the energids start to move radially from the protoplast core out toward the periplasm. It is during this phase that cleavages VIII–X take place at blastoderm at any given moment are found in widely different stages of transition, at least until the inner periplasm is completed near the end of stage 4. At that time the plasm layer has a very grainy appearance and an extremely regular profile, tapering in thickness both from the differentiation center toward the anterior and posterior poles, and from the ventral midline toward the dorsolateral areas. This tapering has been regarded as a visible manifestation of anterior-posterior, mediolateral, and ventro-dorsal gradients in the embryo, and was very carefully mapped by Schnetter (1934a) and Reinhardt (1960).

Concerning the origin of the inner periplasm and the relationship between its appearance and the transition to a columnar blastoderm, relatively little information is available; in fact, previous investigators have failed to emphasize that the two events are closely related both temporally and spatially. Timed sibling embryos fixed and sectioned at hourly intervals from 12 to 22 hours after laying show that, in any given region of the blastoderm, the nuclei begin the transition to a single-layered (apical) condition soon *after* the inner periplasm appears beneath the basement membrane; while this transition is still in progress, the cytoplasm of the blastoderm cells suddenly becomes continuous with the inner periplasm. In some preparations there is an indication that the lateral as well as basal plasma membranes may disappear briefly during these events, so that a transient condition occurs resembling the situation immediately before superficial cleavage, i.e., free nuclei migrate apically through an acellular outer periplasm. In fact, during late stage 4 the structure of the honeybee blastoderm is very much like that of the *Drosophila* periplasm during superficial cleavage (Sonnenblick, 1950; Mahowald, 1963), with incomplete columnar cells rising stalklike from the inner periplasm and separated by flask-shaped furrows.

After the appearance of the inner periplasm until the last half of stage 6, no further mitosis is observed in the embryo. Since there are only about half as many nuclei in worker embryos as in drones, each blastoderm cell in the workers occupies nearly twice as much surface area as in comparable drone embryos. This relationship makes it possible to distinguish the sexes with great certainty in living embryos at late stage 4 and early stage 5, simply by observing the surface of the oil-immersed egg at about 500 ×.

Stage 5 (Fig. 11). Duration about 8.3 hours

When the embryo is approximately 24 hours old a new yolk contraction begins, accompanied by the slow reappearance of clear, fluid-filled spaces at the anterior and posterior poles (Fig. 11). This change is detectable first at the anterior end, where its appearance signals the beginning of stage 5. As in the previous stage, relatively little change takes place in the external appearance of the embryo during stage 5, but this period is the prelude for many striking morphogenetic movements during the next stage. In fact the transition to stage 6 is marked by a ventral movement of cells over the anterior pole, leading to formation of a conspicuous thickening (the anterior midgut rudiment) in the anterior ventral blastoderm (Fig. 12).

Internally, the primary change which takes place during this stage is the re-establishing of basal plasma membranes to complete the separation of the blastoderm cells. As this occurs, the inner periplasm is apportioned more or less equally to the overlying cells, and in fact at mid-stage 5 traces of the periplasm layer are still conspicuous in the distinctively granular basal cytoplasms of neighboring blastoderm cells. By the end of the stage this granular plasm is no longer distinguishable, but is apparently replaced in many or all cells by a single large vacuole lying basal

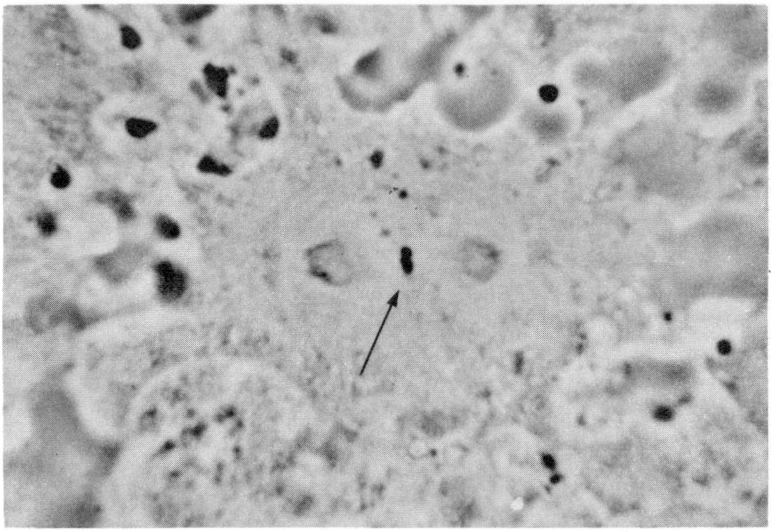

FIG. 18. Telophase in a late stage 2 energid. Arrow indicates the characteristic mid-body lying between the two daughter nuclei. Phase contrast micrograph of a methacrylate embedded thick-section. About 1200 ×.

Stage 2 (Fig. 7). Duration about 3.6 hours

Stage 2 is characterized by a sudden, rapid, and energetic migration of the energids, many of which leave their anterior (stage 1) positions and move toward the posterior pole of the egg; from external aspect, the beginning of this stage is signaled by the appearance of a clear space at the posterior pole, due to a posterior yolk contraction which is essentially a slow continuation of the anterior contraction begun in stage 1. As the nuclei migrate they pause at rhythmic intervals for further mitotic divisions, and the direction of migration in its later phase shifts toward the egg periphery. The result is that near the end of stage 2 about 1,000 nuclei enter the periplasm over the entire surface of the embryo. As they do, the periplasm divides itself by "superficial cleavage" into typical uninucleate cells. The end of the stage is recognizable by the appearance of conspicuous "bumps" over the anterior surface as superficial cleavage begins (Fig. 8).

At the beginning of stage 2 a cluster of eight energids lies near the 10 percent level (measured from the anterior pole), about equidistant from the dorsal, ventral, and lateral surfaces. Cleavage IV occurs as migration begins, and three further mitoses (V–VII) take place at approximately equal intervals while the energids are moving toward the posterior pole. In this first phase of migration, the energids appear to stream through the central core of the protoplast, some moving more rapidly than others, and there is a noticeable pause or slowing at each mitosis; by the 128-nuclei stage the posteriad migration is complete and nuclei are distributed at all levels in the core of the embryo. At this point a new phase of migration begins, when almost all the energids start to move radially from the protoplast core out toward the periplasm. It is during this phase that cleavages VIII–X take place at rhythmic intervals, so that when the energids enter the periplasm the embryo is at a 1,024-nuclei stage (Schnetter, 1934a).

The diameters of the interphase nuclei during cleavage are approximately 10 μ, and of the energids themselves about 20 μ. Near the margins of the cytoplasm surrounding each nucleus many small vacuoles are often seen (Fig. 1c), suggesting that the energids take up material from the adjacent yolk spheres by active pinocytosis. In time-lapse films the cleavage mitoses appear to be synchronous and are spaced at intervals of about 30–35 minutes, while the posteriad migration requires a total of 110–115 minutes and the radial migration about 100–115 minutes. However, mitotic synchrony is not quite perfect since in fixed material some energids are found to be in telophase while others are in metaphase. In the living egg at the beginning of stage 2 the energids are only dimly detectable, but they gradually become more conspicuous as they increase in number and distribution; by transmitted light they appear as faint brownish spots (Fig. 7), while in oblique light they stand out as bright regions. In the second phase of migration, when the energids begin to rise toward the surface, they give the embryo a "speckled" appearance which is quite conspicuous and characteristic for this stage.

In time-lapse films it is clear that the movement of energids through the core of the protoplast in a posterior direction is accompanied by a local movement (streaming) of the peripheral protoplast in an anterior direction (DuPraw, 1963a). The posterior contraction of the protoplast, which accompanies the posteriad migration, also contributes to the massive redistribution of egg contents occurring at this time. After the energids begin to move radially toward the periplasm, they form a flame-shaped perimeter with the widest part in the presumptive thorax region (differentiation center, where the energids enter the periplasm first). The yolk inside the energid perimeter has a strikingly different consistency from that outside, i.e., in fixed-sectioned material it appears granular and does not show the spheroid plasm net still seen in the region between the energids and the egg surface (Nelson, 1915; Schnetter, 1934a; Muller, 1957). The development of this granular yolk seems to coincide with the appearance of lipoid inclusions in the yolk spheres, as seen in stage 2 squash cultures, and with the advent of a centripetal "fat cap" in centrifuged eggs (see preceding section).

Stage 3 (Fig. 8). Duration about 2.5 hours

Stage 3 represents the period of "superficial cleavage" or blastoderm formation; it begins with the indentation of the periplasm around each cleavage nucleus, a process that is most conspicuous at the anterior pole of the protoplast where for a short period large, gemlike protuberances may be seen (Fig. 8). As in the case of the advanced cleavage mitoses, blastoderm formation is not perfectly synchronous, but occurs first in the presumptive thoracic region near the anterior end (i.e., in the differentiation center); this region is also characterized by an unusual tendency to stain with thionin. In Fig. 8 only the anterior half of the egg shows periplasm indentations, while the remainder of the protoplast exhibits a "speckled" appearance caused by energids that are just approaching the surface. Soon after the energids enter the periplasm the protoplast begins to expand again, taking up the clear fluid at both poles of the egg, until at the end of stage 3 it once again occupies the entire volume enclosed by the chorion (Fig. 9).

Superficial cleavage does not interrupt

the rhythmic progress of nuclear cleavage, which continues through two more mitotic cycles with spindles oriented tangentially to the protoplast surface (cleavages XI and XII; Schnetter, 1934a). In time-lapse films the stage 3 mitoses appear to be near-synchronous and are spaced at about the same intervals as previous cleavages. It should be noted that the twelve cleavage mitoses take place autonomously and at regular 35-minute intervals throughout stages 1, 2, and 3, requiring about 7 hours of the 10.6 hours between oviposition and the beginning of stage 4. Although theoretically the blastoderm after cleavage XII should contain 4,096 cells, a certain number of energids never enter the periplasm, but remain in the interior of the protoplast as "yolk nuclei" or primary vitellophages. About 10 percent of all the nuclei at the 1,024-nuclei stage represent vitellophages (Schnetter, 1934a), and these are thought to mediate further transformations in the yolk during the later embryonic stages (Muller, 1957).

It would appear that the periplasm itself carries out the formation of cell boundaries around the cleavage nuclei. The contact of the energids with the periplasm, as seen in time-lapse films, is marked by an immediate, striking "twitch" or contraction that is most conspicuous at the anterior end of the embryo; at the same time, numerous cleavage furrows invaginate into the periplasm between neighboring nuclei (Fig. 19A and Mahowald, 1963). In honeybee eggs enucleated at stage 1, a process of "pseudocleavage" also occurs, during which the plasm subdivides even though no nuclei are present (Reinhardt, 1960; DuPraw, 1963a, 1964a; see Seidel, 1961 for a review of pseudocleavage in other insects). Since this pseudocleavage is delayed relative to blastoderm formation in control honeybee embryos, it appears that the cleavage nuclei do play a regulatory role in normal superficial cleavage.

Stage 4 (Figs. 9 and 10). Duration about 14 hours

The transition from the end of stage 3 to the beginning of stage 4 is marked by the resorption and disappearance of the clear, fluid-filled spaces at the two poles of the egg. At this time the embryo closely resembles a newly laid egg in its external aspect, and it is only by detecting the blastoderm cells along the profile boundary with the chorion that the correct stage can be recognized (Fig. 9). Developmental changes during the next 14 hours are extremely subtle, both internally and externally. The most conspicuous event from external aspect is the appearance of a dense line or layer between the blastoderm and the yolk mass (Fig. 10), which is first detectable in the anterior ventral part of the protoplast (differentiation center) about 5.5 hours after stage 4 begins (16-hour embryo). This line, which represents a granular, "inner periplasm" layer (*innere Keimhautblastem*), gradually extends itself around the poles of the egg to the dorsal side (Fig. 10). Early stage 4 embryos are those that lack an inner periplasm, mid-stage 4's are those that have developed the inner periplasm ventrally, and late stage 4's are those embryos in which the inner periplasm extends around the poles. The end of this stage is signaled by the reappearance of an anterior protoplast contraction, accompanied by a clear cap at the anterior pole (Fig. 11).

As stage 4 begins, the protoplast is entirely covered by a single layer of cells. These blastoderm cells possess nuclei approximately 7 μ in diameter, and they are separated from the central yolk by a distinct basement membrane (Fig. 19B). A similar description applies to the embryo

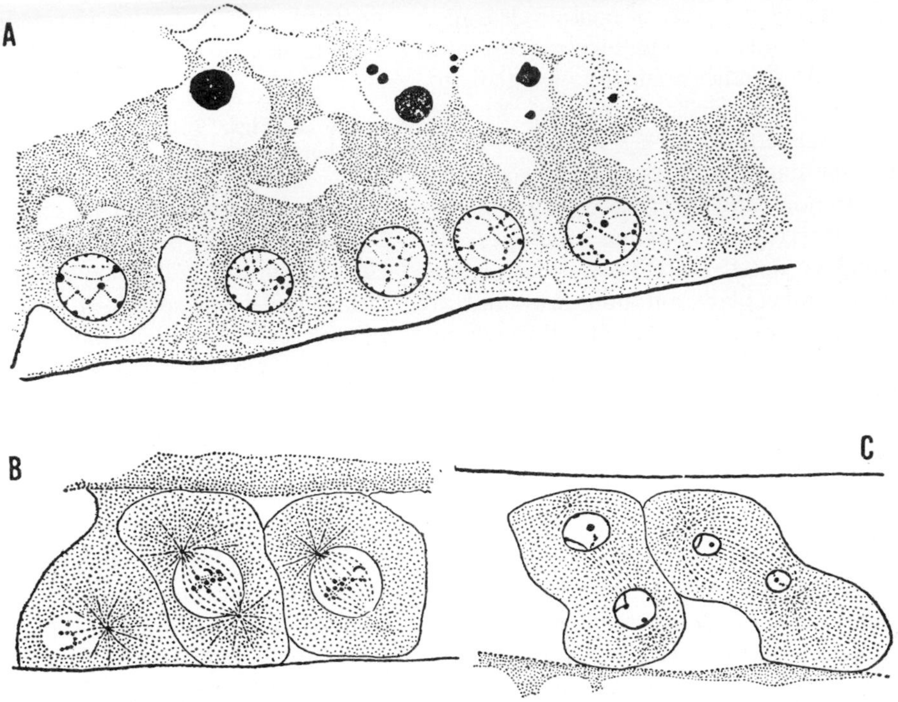

FIG. 19. (A) Stage 3 blastoderm. (B) and (C) Early stage 4 blastoderm, with well-defined cells and basement membranes. (D) Mid-stage 4 blastoderm, with nuclei at two levels. (E) Late stage 4 blastoderm, with inner periplasm fusing with blastoderm cells and nuclei moving to apical positions. (F) Early

at the end of stage 5 some 22 hours later, although in the meantime a proliferation of nuclei and several specific rearrangements take place among the blastoderm cells. The fact that the honeybee embryo spends over one-third of its total development time in blastoderm stages is one of its most remarkable features.

Soon after stage 4 is under way, most of the blastoderm cells undergo a series of nonsynchronous mitoses in which the spindles are oriented more or less obliquely to the protoplast surface, resulting in a transition from a single layer of cell nuclei to a double-layer arrangement (Figs. 19B, C). Meanwhile the cells themselves do not form two layers, but display an interdigitating pattern, in which short cells alternate with long, teardrop-shaped cells (Fig. 19D). The only part of the blastoderm which does not participate in this rearrangement is a narrow longitudinal strip along the dorsal midline, which never forms part of the embryo proper but may contribute to the extraembryonic membrane (amnion-serosa); in this region only a single layer of spheroid or cuboid cells is found in most or all of the blastoderm stages. The double-layer phase lasts about 4 hours, during which the cells are confined to a sharply delimited, false-bottom-like space between the outer chorion and the inner basement membrane. During this period the total number of nuclei increases

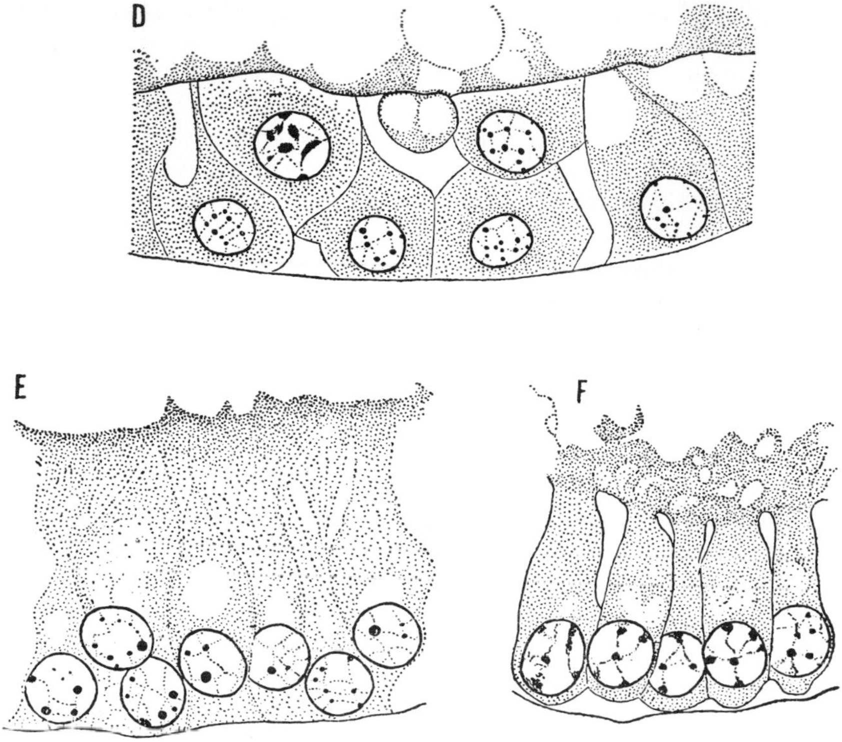

stage 5 blastoderm, with nuclei at a single level just beneath the chorion, and cells in continuity through the inner periplasm. SOURCE: J. A. Nelson, *The Embryology of the Honeybee,* Princeton University Press, 1915.

to about 19,500 in diploid worker embryos and to 34,000 in haploid drone embryos (Reinhardt, 1960), equivalent to 2–3 mitotic divisions per cell; however it is difficult to determine whether all of the blastoderm cells participate equally in the proliferation.

Beginning at about 16 hours, two major changes develop more or less simultaneously in the structure of the blastoderm: (1) the inner periplasm makes its appearance beneath the basement membrane in the presumptive thorax region; and (2) in the same region the blastoderm cells begin to rearrange themselves as a single layer of nearly identical columnar cells possessing uniformly apical nuclei (Fig. 19E). Both these changes progress slowly until they converge in the disappearance of the basement membrane, followed by fusion between the inner periplasm (now some 5–7 μ thick) and the cytoplasm of the blastoderm cells. At this stage the blastoderm cells, which previously were discrete, typical uninucleate cells, are found to be once more in continuity with one another through the inner periplasm layer (Fig. 19F). Eventually the entire blastoderm achieves this transition, with the exception of the narrow, longitudinal middorsal strip; even in the late stage 4 embryos, the inner periplasm tapers to an end on either side of this strip. The other parts of the blastoderm at any given moment are found in widely different stages of transition, at least until the inner periplasm is completed near the end of stage 4. At that time the plasm layer has a very grainy appearance and an extremely regular profile, tapering in thickness both from the differentiation center toward the anterior and posterior poles, and from the ventral midline toward the dorsolateral areas. This tapering has been regarded as a visible manifestation of anterior-posterior, mediolateral, and ventro-dorsal gradients in the embryo, and was very carefully mapped by Schnetter (1934a) and Reinhardt (1960).

Concerning the origin of the inner periplasm and the relationship between its appearance and the transition to a columnar blastoderm, relatively little information is available; in fact, previous investigators have failed to emphasize that the two events are closely related both temporally and spatially. Timed sibling embryos fixed and sectioned at hourly intervals from 12 to 22 hours after laying show that, in any given region of the blastoderm, the nuclei begin the transition to a single-layered (apical) condition soon *after* the inner periplasm appears beneath the basement membrane; while this transition is still in progress, the cytoplasm of the blastoderm cells suddenly becomes continuous with the inner periplasm. In some preparations there is an indication that the lateral as well as basal plasma membranes may disappear briefly during these events, so that a transient condition occurs resembling the situation immediately before superficial cleavage, i.e., free nuclei migrate apically through an acellular outer periplasm. In fact, during late stage 4 the structure of the honeybee blastoderm is very much like that of the *Drosophila* periplasm during superficial cleavage (Sonnenblick, 1950; Mahowald, 1963), with incomplete columnar cells rising stalklike from the inner periplasm and separated by flask-shaped furrows.

After the appearance of the inner periplasm until the last half of stage 6, no further mitosis is observed in the embryo. Since there are only about half as many nuclei in worker embryos as in drones, each blastoderm cell in the workers occupies nearly twice as much surface area as in comparable drone embryos. This relationship makes it possible to distinguish the sexes with great certainty in living embryos at late stage 4 and early stage 5, simply by observing the surface of the oil-immersed egg at about 500 ×.

Stage 5 (Fig. 11). Duration about 8.3 hours

When the embryo is approximately 24 hours old a new yolk contraction begins, accompanied by the slow reappearance of clear, fluid-filled spaces at the anterior and posterior poles (Fig. 11). This change is detectable first at the anterior end, where its appearance signals the beginning of stage 5. As in the previous stage, relatively little change takes place in the external appearance of the embryo during stage 5, but this period is the prelude for many striking morphogenetic movements during the next stage. In fact the transition to stage 6 is marked by a ventral movement of cells over the anterior pole, leading to formation of a conspicuous thickening (the anterior midgut rudiment) in the anterior ventral blastoderm (Fig. 12).

Internally, the primary change which takes place during this stage is the reestablishing of basal plasma membranes to complete the separation of the blastoderm cells. As this occurs, the inner periplasm is apportioned more or less equally to the overlying cells, and in fact at mid-stage 5 traces of the periplasm layer are still conspicuous in the distinctively granular basal cytoplasms of neighboring blastoderm cells. By the end of the stage this granular plasm is no longer distinguishable, but is apparently replaced in many or all cells by a single large vacuole lying basal to the nucleus and equaling or exceeding the nucleus in diameter (7 μ); these vacuoles persist into stages 6 and 7, surviving longer in the ectoderm than in the mesoderm. A distinct basement membrane is also present at this time, which once again separates the blastoderm as a whole from the central yolk mass.

The author's preparations suggest that the inner periplasm is not so much "taken up" as "included in" the blastoderm cells when the basal cell membranes are reestablished. During this process fairly large, flask-shaped spaces are seen between neighboring cells, and the cells themselves are prism- or teardrop-shaped with their narrow ends attached to the inner periplasm (Fig. 19f). The over-all morphology suggests that the flask-shaped spaces may act as cleavage furrows, which cut through the inner periplasm in a manner similar to the process of superficial cleavage in *Drosophila* (Mahowald, 1963).

Stage 6 (Figs. 12 and 13). Duration about 6.2 hours

At the beginning of stage 6 the embryo is already some 32 hours old, yet shows remarkably little evidence of developmental change. Longitudinal sections show an ellipse of several hundred virtually identical columnar cells enclosing the central yolk mass; in these cells the nuclei are so uniformly apical in position that they seem to occupy a very regular "nuclear layer" just beneath the protoplast surface. The most obviously differentiated cells in the embryo are those which form a cap over the anterior pole and which have a distinctively transparent, vacuolate cytoplasm. At this time there are also a great many vitellophage nuclei scattered through the yolk mass. Schnetter (1934a) has noted that the blastoderm "fate map" at the beginning of stage 6 consists of six longitudinal strips: a midventral strip occupying about one-sixth of the egg circumference, which will form endoderm at its anterior and posterior ends, and mesoderm between; two ventrolateral strips of ectoderm, occupying about one-third of the egg circumference each, which will migrate ventrally during stage 6 and cover the midventral mesoderm; two dorsolateral strips which form the dorsal part of an extraembryonic membrane (the amnion-serosa) and which are "stretched" into a squamous epithelium as the ectoderm migrates ventrally; and the narrow middorsal strip, which according to Nelson (1915) forms a syncytium at the surface of the yolk mass.

The beginning of stage 6 is marked by a sudden, ventrally-directed migration of blastoderm cells over the anterior pole of the protoplast; this movement is associated with the appearance of a conspicuous, platelike thickening in the ventroanterior blastoderm, the anterior midgut rudiment (AMR; Fig. 12). Not long afterward an essentially similar, but less conspicuous posterior midgut rudiment (PMR) begins to develop near the posterior pole of the embryo. The formation of the anterior midgut rudiment by cell migration was first inferred by Nelson (1915) from the absence of mitosis as the number of AMR cells exhibits its early increase, and it is directly confirmed by time-lapse films, which show a contemporary movement in the blastoderm cells at the anterior pole (DuPraw, 1963a). Later in stage 6 both the AMR and PMR begin to proliferate by mitosis, and at stage 8 these cells will migrate out over the surface of the yolk mass, forming the anterior and posterior halves of a sausage-shaped midgut (endoderm).

Soon after the appearance of the AMR, the cap of vacuolate cells lying over the anterior pole lifts away from the yolk mass (which is still covered by the basement membrane) and forms a hoodlike cell monolayer between the chorion and the protoplast (Figs. 13 and 14); this is the anterior part of the amnion-serosa, which is continuous with the two dorsolateral membrane rudiments. More or less simultaneously with the separation of the anterior serosa, the two ventrolateral sheets of ectoderm begin to migrate ventrally over the mesodermal plate. In early stage 6 these ectodermal folds are visible as short longitudinal borders lying ventrolaterally just behind the AMR (Fig. 12); however, the folds gradually become longer in a posterior direction while at the same time they move slowly toward the ventral midline. From ventral aspect the embryo at this time exhibits a conspicuous hourglass pattern which is clearly visible even in unimmersed embryos (seen best with oblique lighting). By mid-stage 6 the ectodermal folds from either side meet ventrally in the anterior one-third of the embryo (differentiation center; Fig. 13), where a fully two-layered condition is first established (ectoderm overlying mesoderm). Finally the line of junction lengthens from the thoracic region farther and farther posteriad in a process that resembles the "zipping up" of an overcoat. As stage 6 progresses the hourglass pattern changes to a "Gothic arch" design (Fig. 13), and the protoplast contraction that began in stage 5 gradually becomes more extreme. Finally the Gothic arch becomes shorter and narrower until it disappears at the posterior pole, signaling the completion of the ectodermal migration and the end of stage 6.

The massive cell movements during stage 6 apparently depend on a form of ameboid progression. DuPraw (1965a) has shown that honeybee embryonic cells *in vitro* exhibit pseudopodal activity at this stage, in addition to saltatory movements of their cytoplasmic particles. Time-lapse films of whole embryos in oblique light also show clearly that the ectodermal sheets move ventrally almost *in toto*, resulting in a net concentration of the original blastoderm cells in the ventral half of the embryo; as the ectoderm moves ventrally, the dorsolateral serosa cells apparently stretch out, abandoning their original columnar configuration to establish a squamous epithelium over the vacated surface of the protoplast. By the end of stage 6, only a thin amnion-serosa covers the yolk mass in the dorsal half of the embryo. As a result of these migrations the true embryonic tissues become confined to the ventral and lateral surfaces of the protoplast, where the configuration of the midplate (endoderm + mesoderm) resembles that of a canoe (Schnetter, 1934a); the bow and stern correspond to the solid midgut rudiments, while the concave hull between them is the thin inner layer of mesoderm. Although columnar ectoderm lies external to the mesoderm, it does not yet extend over the midgut rudiments. Finally, the amnion-serosa forms a kind of dorsal canopy, whose ventral margins are exactly fitted to the corresponding dorsal margins of the ectoderm (Fig. 14).

During stage 6 the originally uniform blastoderm cells also differentiate in accordance with their ectoderm-mesoderm-endoderm fates. Changes are apparent in the diameters of the nuclei, which attain 10 μ in the columnar ectoderm, 7.5 μ in the anterior and posterior endoderm masses, and only about 6 μ in the mesoderm (measured after fixation); the relative sizes of the cells themselves are also approximately in the same proportion. Posteriorly, where ectoderm has only recently come to lie over mesoderm, the basal vacuoles of the ectoderm cells appear to be greatly enlarged, often exceeding the nucleus in diameter. Since the vacuoles are immediately adjacent to the neighboring mesoderm layer, the appearance strongly suggests that material from the mesoderm vacuoles is being transferred to the ectoderm vacuoles; furthermore, these vacuoles are lacking in the anterior mesodermal cells, which have been in contact with ectoderm for a longer time. Sauer (1954) has shown that the differentiation of mesoderm in the region between the AMR and PMR is dependent on factors which are localized at the 64 percent level in early stage 4 embryos (nearer the posterior end). There is also good evidence that at later stages the lateral ectoderm induces specific organ differentiations in the underlying mesoderm, both in beetles (Bock, 1942) and in honeybee embryos (Bertzbach, 1960).

Stage 7 (Fig. 14). Duration about 5.7 hours

Stage 7 is the time when the ventral amnion-serosa separates from the embryonic tissues. In profile view, embryos of this stage exhibit a conspicuous "dent" or transverse groove in the ventral surface, which marks the posterior margin of the amnion-serosa (Fig. 14). Early in stage 7, just after the ectoderm migration is complete, the position of this dent is slightly posterior to the AMR, but as the stage progresses the dent also moves slowly toward the posterior pole. The position of this surface feature therefore provides a linear scale or natural clock by which early, middle, and late stage 7 embryos may be distinguished. Anterior to the ventral dent, the amnion-serosa completely encloses the protoplast, while behind the dent the serosa is present only dorsally, where it is still attached to the lateral margin of the ectoderm. When the dent nears the tail end of the embryo a cap of cells lifts off the posterior pole in a manner reminiscent of the anterior serosa separation early in stage 6. This posterior cap rapidly joins the ventral membrane at the dent, after which the formation of the amnion-serosa is complete and the embryo is entirely enclosed by a sausage-shaped cell monolayer. The end of stage 7 can be recognized by the presence of the amnion-serosa at *both* poles of the egg, where it occupies the fluid-filled spaces between the protoplast and the chorion (Fig. 15).

The single honeybee extraembryonic membrane has been variously designated as an "amnion" by some authors and a "serosa" by others. In point of fact, this membrane has a compound origin: the dorsal and polar regions are derived from dorsal and polar blastoderm cells, thus corresponding to the serosa of other insect species; the ventral region, on the other hand, separates during stage 7 in a process resembling amnion formation in other insects. In honeybees this process evidently involves recruitment of membrane cells from the underlying ectoderm layer, since sections of the ventral dent region occasionally show a cell which belongs to the margin of the amnion-serosa but is still partly embedded in the ectoderm. In the ventral dent region, relatively little mitosis is seen during separation of the amnion.

Protoplast shortening continues during stage 7, while correspondingly the canoe-shaped embryo curves dorsally around the anterior and posterior poles to such an extent that the two midgut rudiments come to lie on the dorsal surface of the yolk mass. At the same time the outer ectoderm also extends farther and farther dorsally, both in the lateral regions (under the serosa) and at the poles (covering the midgut rudiments). Throughout this stage mitotic figures are observed in the midgut rudiments, the mesoderm, and the ectoderm, where mitosis seems to be much more frequent than it was in stage 6.

Stage 8 (Fig. 15). Duration about 3 hours

The appearance of the amnion-serosa at the posterior pole, which signals the end of stage 7, also marks the beginning of stage 8. At this time the protoplast has shortened to its minimum length and the embryo from external aspect resembles a little sausage, without any obvious head or paired appendages. Just dorsal to the anterior pole, however, the ectoderm has thickened into an unpaired protuberance which is the rudiment of the labrum. Stage 8 in its manner of definition may be regarded as an interim stage, lasting only 2–4 hours and ending when the head and segments become readily apparent, i.e., when the embryo first acquires the profile of a larva (Fig. 16).

The most notable event that occurs during this stage is the formation of the midgut from the anterior and posterior midgut rudiments. The cells of these two dorsal masses migrate out over the surface of the yolk, between the yolk basement membrane and the serosa (dorsally) or the mesoderm (ventrally). By early stage 9 they have formed a closed cell monolayer which entirely covers the central yolk mass.

Stage 9 (Fig. 16). Duration about 19.5 hours

Stage 9 includes all those periods of honeybee embryogenesis in which a recognizable larva form has already developed, but the embryo is not yet capable of active muscular contractions. Defined in this way, stage 9 includes several widely different types of organogenesis, and, with a duration in the order of 20 hours, it is also the longest of the standard stages. Some further subdivision of this period would be desirable (Nelson, 1915; Schnetter, 1934a). However, from external aspect the changes in the embryo are undramatic ones, reflecting many simultaneous yet gradual processes of growth and differentiation. This absence of sharp transitions dictates that in practice only an informal distinction between early, middle, and late stage 9 can be recognized.

At the beginning of the stage, a well defined head and thirteen body segments are apparent, the three anterior segments being thoracic and the remaining ten abdominal; the unpaired labrum, which is the most obvious appendage, projects forward like a unicorn's horn. Gradually, as stage 9 progresses, the labrum swings ventrally (compare Figs. 16 and 17), while the stomodaeum develops just beneath it as an ectodermal invagination. Three pairs of head appendages, the mandibles and two maxillae, also become prominent as knobs of tissue along the ventral sides of the head (Fig. 16). About midway through stage 9 the larva begins to increase in length again at the expense of the fluid-filled spaces at the poles of the egg. As the extraembryonic fluid is taken up, the midgut and other organs become more clearly delineated. Since the amnion-serosa does not increase in length, this membrane eventually becomes stretched taut over the head and tail of the larva (Fig. 17). Dorsal to the stomodaeum, a fairly massive brain develops and is connected to a large ganglion beneath the stomodaeum by two circumesophageal connectives. In the trunk a ventral nerve cord and segmental ganglia also develop. The midgut remains a closed sack until stage 10, when the stomodaeal invagination finally breaks through the anterior wall during the hatching process. Although a proctodaeal invagination occurs near the posterior tip of the abdomen, it does not open into the midgut until the end of the larval feeding period, just before pupation occurs.

Toward the end of stage 9 the tracheal (i.e., respiratory) system can be detected as a faint longitudinal zigzag line in the midlateral region; this line represents a longitudinal tube (one on each side) connected to the exterior by 10 short branches to the 10 spiracles on segments II–XI (Fig. 17). The two longitudinal tracheal trunks are also connected to one another by various transverse connectives. Just before stage 10 the profile of the tail region also changes from its earlier rounded configuration (Fig. 16) to a more pointed one (Fig. 17).

Stage 10 (Fig. 17). Duration about 3 hours

The appearance of active muscular contractions marks the end of stage 9 and the beginning of stage 10; because such muscular movements form an integral part of the hatching process this may be regarded as the hatching stage, which ends with the emergence of the larva. Its total duration varies from 2 to 5 hours and is highly sensitive to temperature.

Muscular movements are first apparent in the head region as an intermittent and very faint "nodding"; gradually the nodding becomes more vigorous and communicates itself to the more anterior segments until eventually the entire larva shows a kind of rhythmic pulsing. As soon as the larva has acquired enough freedom of movement it begins a 180-degree rotation around its long axis, bringing its ventral side to the concave surface of the chorion (Fig. 17); this reversal in dorsoventral orientation, which is an invariable feature of hatching, is sometimes carried out very rapidly, sometimes more slowly, and different larvae may rotate either to the left or to the right.

After rotation has been accomplished, the peristalsis-like movements become even more vigorous and the larva again expands noticeably in volume; presumably this is due to a further uptake of the clear fluid which still occupies the spaces between the larva and the chorion. At this time the amnion-serosa, though still intact, becomes visibly stretched each time the larva moves its tail. Finally the serosa breaks up into fragments which eddy about in the currents created by the larval movements. Soon after fragmentation of the serosa the tracheal tubes very rapidly fill with air, an event which makes the tracheal system opaque and transforms it into one of the larva's most conspicuous features (Fig. 17). Since this change occurs even in immersed embryos, the air is evidently drawn from solution by some still undetermined mechanism; furthermore it does not appear in all parts of the tracheal system at once, but is seen first at a variable point of origin (usually in one of the longitudinal trunks), from which it progresses sequentially throughout the system. After tracheal "clearing" the larva continues its strong muscular movements, and within a few minutes the chorion suddenly ruptures at one or more places, discharging the internal fluids onto the surface of the egg. Finally the hatchling worms its way out of the chorion through a gradually enlarging hole (DuPraw, 1963a).

As first noted by DuPraw (1961, 1963b), the hatching process in honeybees involves lysis of the chorion by a hatching enzyme. The presence of this enzyme can be assayed by placing a newly laid egg in a "hatching puddle" (the fluid remaining after emergence of the larva), whereupon the egg lyses within 5 to 10 minutes. Lytic activity can also be mimicked by a protease (0.01 percent trypsin) and is destroyed by incubation at 65°C for 30 minutes. Although the source of the hatching enzyme is not known, the author has ligatured stage 10 eggs at different levels and observed chorion dissolution on one or both sides of the ligature (depending on the level). These experiments indicate that the enzyme arises from a fairly broad region of the trunk, corresponding approximately to the spiracle-bearing segments (II–XI). The author has also investigated hatching in related Hymenoptera (*Melissodes*, Anthrophoridae; *Nomia*, Halictidae; *Nomadopsis*, Andrenidae; *Megachile*, Megachilidae; *Polistes*, Vespidae), all of which exhibit either partial or complete dissolution of the chorion. In *Melissodes*, *Nomia*, and *Megachile*, the initial dissolution is strikingly localized to two longitudinal bands along the lateral rows of spiracles, and in some cases an independent dissolution may occur around the head (unpublished

TABLE 2

	STAGE DURATION (HOURS)				TYPICAL VALUES (HOURS)	
STAGE	*1963–1*	*1963–2*	*1965–1*	*1965–2*	DURATION	AGE AT BEGINNING
1	4.2 ±0.5	4.7 ±0.5	ca 4.5	4.7 ±0.9	4.5 ±0.2	0
2	3.7	3.5	3.7	3.5	3.6 ±0.1	4.5 ±0.2
3	1.8	2.9	2.7	2.7	2.5 ±0.4	8.1 ±0.1
4	13.4	19.9	15.5	13.4	14.1 ±0.8	10.6 ±0.5
5	8.0		8.1	8.7	8.3 ±0.3	24.5 ±1.4
6	6.0	6.6	5.9	11.0	6.2 ±0.3	32.3 ±1.4
7	6.0	5.5	5.6		5.7 ±0.3	38.3 ±1.4
8	2.0	3.8	3.1	23.4	3.0 ±0.9	44.0 ±1.1
9	18.6	19.6	20.2		19.5 ±0.9	46.9 ±2.0
10	3.2	5.1	2.0	2.7	3.2 ±1.2	66.6 ±2.6
Total	66.8	71.3	71.2	70.0		70.0 ±2.0

observations). Since the honeybee enzyme lyses a stage 1 egg within 5 to 10 minutes, it apparently is released not more than 10 minutes before the normal hatching rupture. Possibly the fragmentation of the amnion-serosa plays a role in activating the hatching enzyme.

THE TIMING OF HONEYBEE EMBRYOGENESIS

Development of techniques for filming embryos by time-lapse cinemicrography (DuPraw, 1963a, b) has made it possible not only to define developmental stages with precise beginning and end points, but also to investigate the duration of these stages under controlled temperature conditions. Table 2 summarizes data for four worker embryos, two of which were filmed by transmitted light in a walk-in incubator ("1963," eggs illustrated by DuPraw, 1963a) and two by oblique light in a thermistor-controlled microscope incubator ("1965"); for the first two embryos, temperatures generally fluctuated between 34.5° and 35.5°C (except for rare thermostat malfunctions), while for the last two the temperature was held at 35.5° ± 0.25°C throughout development. In the thermistor system, a large plastic bag is used as a microscope incubating chamber, and the embryos are immersed in a 60-mm Petri dish filled with paraffin oil; the temperature of the oil is then continuously monitored and controlled by means of a temperature control unit (Yellow Springs Model 73TK) with a thermistor probe (YSI #401) immersed in the same paraffin oil near the embryos. High precision is thus obtained in monitoring temperatures actually experienced by the embryos on the microscope stage.

Although the values given in Table 2 differ considerably from data published by previous authors, this is due in part to the earlier practice of incubating embryos in the honeybee colony itself, where temperatures are far from constant (e.g., Petrunkewitsch, 1903; Nachtsheim, 1913; Nelson, 1915). Moreover, even at constant temperature, different embryos vary among themselves by a matter of a few minutes to some hours (Table 2). The longer stages (4 and 9) are more variable than the shorter ones (e.g., stage 2); also, among unknown (random) embryos stages 4 and 9 are generally the most often encountered because they make up the largest fraction of the total development time. By contrast, the most difficult stages to find are the earliest ones, since the transitions are rapid and the embryos progress to more advanced stages while the search is in progress. Early stages can often be found near the queen, provided that she can be located before she becomes disturbed (methods are also available for obtaining timed eggs; see preceding section). As a guideline for predicting the development of unknown embryos, the last columns in Table 2 summarize these observations in a semisubjective estimate of typical stage durations, cumulative ages, and ranges of variability.

With respect to drone (haploid) eggs, Seidel and Reinhardt (1959) and Reinhardt (1960) have reported fundamental differences in the egg structure and timing of development relative to sibling worker (diploid) eggs. Although some of these distinctions are certainly real, other differences in timing reported by Reinhardt (1960) do not exceed the variability commonly encountered among various worker eggs (Table 2). It is likely that first cleavage is delayed in unfertilized eggs, and this would introduce a consistent lag in development relative to worker eggs. Preliminary films of development in drone and worker embryos lying side by side indicate that the durations of stages 2 to 8 are very similar in both types.

REFERENCES

ANDERSON, T., 1951: Techniques for the preservation of three-dimensional structure in preparing specimens for the electron microscope. *Trans. N.Y. Acad. Sci.*, (II) 13: 130.

BERTZBACH, R., 1960: Experimentelle Untersuchungen über den Einfluss von Rontgenstrahlen auf die Embryonalentwicklung der Honigbiene. *Roux' Arch. f. Entwick. mech.*, 152: 524.

BOCK, E., 1942: Wechselbeziehungen zwischen den Keimblättern bei der Organbildung von *Chrysopa perla* L. *Roux' Arch. f. Entwick. mech.*, 132: 159.

BUTLER, C. G., 1955: *The World of the Honeybee.* 226 pp. Macmillan Co., New York.

COUNCE, S. J., 1961: The analysis of insect embryogenesis. *Ann. Rev. Ent.*, 6: 295.

DE FONBRUNE, P., 1949: *Technique de Micromanipulation.* 203 pp. Monograph of the Pasteur Inst., Masson et Cie, Paris.

DEODIKAR, G. B., C. V. THAKAR, and P. N. SHAH, 1959: Cytogenetic studies in Indian honeybees. I. Somatic chromosome complement in *Apis indica* and its bearing on evolution and phylogeny. *Proc. Ind. Acad. Sci.*, 49: 194.

DIXON, S. E., and R. W. SHUEL, 1963: Studies in the mode of action of royal jelly in honeybee development. III. The effect of experimental variation in diet on growth and metabolism of honeybee larvae. *Can. J. Zool.*, 41: 733.

DU PRAW, E. J., 1958: Supporting evidence for nuclear transplant using eggs of the honeybee. *Anat. Rec.*, 132: 429.

———, 1960: Further developments in research on the honeybee egg. *Glean. Bee Cult.*, 88: 104.

———, 1961: A unique hatching process in the honeybee. *Trans. Am. Microscop. Soc.*, 80: 185.

———, 1963a: Analysis of embryonic development in the honeybee I. 16-mm sound film, available from the Library of Congress, Washington, D.C.

———, 1963b: Techniques for the analysis of cell function and differentiation using eggs of the honeybee. *Proc. 16th Intern. Congr. Zool.*, Washington, D.C., Vol. 2, p. 238.

———, 1964a: X-ray enucleation and the honeybee nuclear transplant technique. *Amer. Zool.*, 4: 288.

———, 1964b: Non-Linnean taxonomy. *Nature*, 202: 849.

———, 1965a: The organization of honeybee embryonic cells. I. Microtubules and amoeboid activity. *Devel. Biol.*, 12: 53.

———, 1965b: The organization of nuclei and chromosomes in honeybee embryonic cells. *Proc. Nat. Acad. Sci. U.S.*, 53: 161.

———, 1965c: Macromolecular organization of nuclei and chromosomes: A folded fibre model based on whole-mount electron microscopy. *Nature*, 206: 338.

———, 1965d: Non-Linnean taxonomy and the systematics of honeybees. *Syst. Zool.*, 14: 1.

———, 1965e: The recognition and handling of honeybee specimens in non-Linnean taxonomy. *J. Apic. Res.*, 4: 71.

FYG, W., 1959: Normal and abnormal development in the honeybee. *Bee World*, 40: 57, 85.

GROUT, R. A., 1963: *The Hive and the Honey Bee.* 556 pp. Dadant & Sons, Hamilton, Ill.

GURDON, J. B., 1964: The transplantation of living cell nuclei. *Adv. Morphogen.*, 4: 1.

JAY, S. C., 1959: Factors affecting the laboratory rearing of honeybee larvae (*Apis mellifera* L.). M.S. thesis, University of Toronto, Toronto, Canada.

KERR, W. É., and H. H. LAIDLAW, 1956: General genetics of bees. *Adv. Genet.*, 8: 109.

KRAUSE, G., and K. SANDER, 1962: Ooplasmic reaction systems in insect embryogenesis. *Adv. Morphogen.*, 2: 259.

LAIDLAW, H. H., 1949: Development of precision instruments for artificial insemination of queen bees. *J. Econ. Ent.*, 42: 254.

———, and K. W. TUCKER, 1964: Diploid tissue derived from accessory sperm in the honey bee. *Genetics*, 50: 1439.

———, M. A. EL BANBY, and K. W. TUCKER, 1964: Five new eye-color mutants in the honey bee. *J. Hered.*, 55: 207.

———, ———, and ———, 1965a: Further linkage studies in the honey bee. *J. Hered.*, 56: 39.

———, ———, and ———, 1965b: Three wing mutants of the honey bee. *J. Hered.*, 56: 84.

MAHOWALD, A. P., 1963: Electron microscopy of the formation of the cellular blastoderm in *Drosophila melanogaster*. *Exp. Cell Res.*, 32: 457.

MERRIAM, R. W., and H. RIS, 1954: Size and DNA content of nuclei in various tissues of male, female and worker honeybees. *Chromosoma*, 6: 522.

MICHAEL, A. S., and M. ABRAMOVITZ, 1955: A method of rearing honey bee larvae *in vitro*. *J. Econ. Ent.*, 48: 43.

MORGENTHALER, H. U., 1952: Nucleic acid content of the ovary of the queen bee. *Arch. Julius-Klaus-Stiftung*, 27: 206.

MULLER, M., 1957: Entwicklung und Bedeutung der Vitellophagen in der Embryonalentwicklung der Honigbiene. *Zool. Jahrb.*, 67: 111.

MYSER, W. C., 1954: The larval and pupal development of the honey bee *Apis mellifera* Linnaeus. *Ann. Entom. Soc. Amer.*, 47: 683.

NACHTSHEIM, H., 1913: Cytologische Studien über die Geschlechtsbestimmung bei der Honigbiene (*Apis mellifica* L.). *Arch. Zellforsch.*, 11: 169.

NELSON, J. A., 1915: *The Embryology of the Honeybee.* 282 pp. Princeton University Press, Princeton, N.J.

———, and A. P. STURTEVANT, 1924: The rate of growth of the honeybee larva. *U.S.D.A. Bull.* #1222, Pt. 1.

PEASE, D. C., 1964: *Histological Techniques for Electron Microscopy.* 381 pp. Academic Press, New York.

PETRUNKEWITSCH, A., 1901: Die Richtungskorper und ihr Schicksal im befruchteten und unbefruchteten Bienenei. *Zool. Jahrb., Anat.*, 14: 573.

———, 1903: Das Schicksal der Richtungskorper im Drohnenei. *Zool. Jahrb., Anat.*, 17: 481.

REINHARDT, E., 1960: Kernverhältnisse, Eisystem und Entwicklungsweise von Drohnen und Arbeiterinneneiern der Honigbiene (*Apis mellifera*). *Zool. Jahrb., Anat.*, 78: 167.

ROTHENBUHLER, W. C., 1958: Progress and problems in the analyses of gynandromorphic honey bees. *Proc. 10th Intern. Cong. Ent.*, 2: 867.

RUTTNER, F., 1959: Technik und Ziel der kunstlichen Insemination von Bienenköniginnen. *Orion Zeit. Nat. Tech.*, 6: 467.

SAUER, E., 1954: Keimblätterbildung und Differenzierungsleistungen in isolierten Eiteilen der Honigbiene. *Roux' Arch. f. Entwick. mech.*, 147: 302.

SCHNETTER, M., 1934a: Morphologische Untersuchungen über das Differenzierungszentrum in der Embryonalentwicklung der Honigbiene. *Zeit. Morph. Okol. d. Tiere*, 29: 114.

———, 1934b: Physiologische Untersuchungen über das Differenzierungszentrum in der Embryonalentwicklung der Honigbiene. *Roux' Arch. f. Entwickl. mech.*, 131: 285.

———, 1936: Die Entwicklung von Zwerglarven in geschnurten Bieneneiern. *Zool. Anz. Suppl.*, 9: 82.

SEIDEL, F., 1961: Entwicklungsphysiologische Zentren im Eisystem der Insekten. *Zool. Anz. Suppl.*, 24: 121.

———, and E. REINHARDT, 1959: Kern-Plasma-Relation und Unterschiede in der Eistruktur bei Drohne und Arbeiterin der Honigbiene (*Apis mellifica*). *Naturwiss.*, 46: 411.

SMITH, M. V., 1959: Queen differentiation and the biological testing of royal jelly. 56 pp. *Cornell Univ. Agric. Expt. Stat. Memoir* #356.

SONNENBLICK, B. P., 1950: The early embryology of *Drosophila melanogaster.* In M. Demerec (ed.), *Biology of Drosophila*, John Wiley & Sons, New York.

TELFER, W. H., 1963: The physiology of oocyte differentiation in the cecropia moth. In V. J. Brookes (ed.), *Insect Physiology*, Oregon State University Press, Corvallis, Oreg.

TUCKER, K. W., 1958: Automictic parthenogenesis in the honey bee. *Genetics*, 43: 299.

WEAVER, N., 1955: Rearing of honeybee larvae on royal jelly in the laboratory. *Science*, 121: 509.

———, 1957: Effects of larval age on dimorphic differentiation of the female honey bee. *Ann. Entom. Soc. Amer.*, 50: 283.

WOYKE, J., 1963: Rearing and viability of diploid drone larvae. *J. Apic. Res.*, 2: 77.

———, 1965: Genetic proof of the origin of drones from fertilized eggs of the honeybee. *J. Apic. Res.*, 4: 7.

*Drosophila**

By Winifred W. Doane

INTRODUCTION

Developmental processes are ultimately under the control of the genome. Therefore, the more knowledge at hand concerning the heredity of an organism, the more useful will that organism be to the developmentalist. Since its introduction into the laboratory by T. H. Morgan in 1911, *Drosophila melanogaster* Meig. has been the subject of more genetic investigations than any other diploid animal. This unique situation is well substantiated by the four volumes of *Bibliography on the Genetics of Drosophila*, compiled by Muller (1939) and Herskowitz (1953, 1958, 1963). These compilations, which contain over twelve thousand entries, give invaluable aid to the newcomer in the field by acquainting him with the wealth of information at his disposal. With recent refinements in micromethods of assay and manipulation, there is a renewed interest in the development and biochemistry of *Drosophila*, especially in terms of the genetic control of differentiation.

The purpose of this chapter is to provide the investigator who is relatively unfamiliar with the use of "fruitflies" for developmental studies with some routine methods for procurement, maintenance, and handling. A brief outline of the life cycle of *D. melanogaster* is presented in addition to techniques for collecting various developmental stages and some general purpose histological procedures. *The Biology of Drosophila* (Demerec, 1950) supplies much of the background material for this.

It is assumed that the reader is acquainted with ways of setting up experimental matings to demonstrate fundamental principles of genetics such as dominance, independent assortment, linkage, and genic interaction. Examples may be found in any standard textbook on genetics and are provided by several laboratory guides (e.g., Demerec and Kaufmann, 1961; Strickberger, 1962). Explicit directions for the conditions required to rear flies for linkage experiments are given in *The Mutants of Drosophila melanogaster* (Bridges and Brehme, 1944). This volume lists alphabetically all the known mutants in *D. melanogaster* up to 1944, with explanations for nomenclature and symbolism. The description of mutants, their location on crossover maps (and cytological maps, when possible), as well as references to the literature on

* The author is grateful to Professor D. F. Poulson and to Dr. C. C. Doane for their helpful criticisms of the manuscript. Preparation of the manuscript and development of certain techniques described in it were supported in part by National Science Foundation Grant GB-1718.

them, are among the useful items provided by this volume. A long overdue revision of this catalog is currently being prepared by D. Lindsley and E. Grell. Meanwhile, most mutants discovered since the first edition are described in various issues of *Drosophila Information Service* (*D.I.S.*)[1] and basic symbols used for them are summarized in Volume 38. *D.I.S.* supplies lists of mutants in other species, stock listings, current bibliographies, a directory of *Drosophila* workers, and research and technical notes.

Mutants are known that affect almost every part of the body (Braver, 1956, lists some by part affected), as well as developmental, physiological, and biochemical processes. This array of genetic tools is augmented by many elaborately synthesized stocks (balanced by inversions, attached X's, etc.) and intricate breeding techniques that simplify both stock maintenance and screening procedures for lethals and other mutants. Many of these techniques for "genetic engineering" are found among the selected papers of H. J. Muller (1962); newer ones have been reviewed by Muller and Oster (1963). With these breeding techniques at his disposal, it is possible for the experimentalist to manipulate the genetic background of his material and so eliminate much uncontrolled variability (e.g., Doane, 1960b, 1961).

PROCUREMENT

Upwards of two thousand different strains of *D. melanogaster* are available from stock centers established in the United States of America. These centers, supported by the National Science Foundation, maintain and distribute wild and mutant strains suitable for research and teaching needs. Stock lists are provided by the centers and are also kept up to date by *D.I.S.* Requests may be addressed to Drosophila Stock Center I (West):

Dr. E. B. Lewis
Division of Biology
California Institute of Technology
Pasadena, California 91109

or Drosophila Stock Center II (East):

Dr. Irwin I. Oster
Department of Biology
Bowling Green State Univ.
Bowling Green, Ohio 43402.

Laboratories throughout the world list their various strains and species of *Drosophila* in *D.I.S.* and these are generally available upon request. Many of these strains are not in the permanent collections at the stock centers. For species other than *D. melanogaster*, a Type Culture Collection of *Drosophila* species has been established at the Instituto di Genetica, Via S. Epifanio 14, Pavia, Italy. Stocks are distributed freely under the support of the International Union of Biological Sciences. The largest collection of species stocks in the United States, however, is to be found at the Department of Zoology, University of Texas, Austin. The *University of Texas Publications*, found in most university libraries, supply much of the information pertaining to their taxonomy and distribution. A listing of species for the United States, accompanied by suitable references to their descriptions, is provided by Strickberger (1962, Appendix 4).

Field collections of *Drosophila* are generally made by using a mash of overripe fruits, especially bananas, as bait. A variety of traps have been designed (e.g., see Spencer, 1950, technical notes in *D.I.S.*, and bibliographies of *Drosophila*).

[1] *D.I.S.*, distributed among *Drosophila* workers the world over, is not a publication in the strict sense. However, copies are in the libraries of most major universities and colleges and may be obtained on interlibrary loan or by writing to the present editor, Prof. E. Novitski (Dept. of Biol., Univ. of Oregon, Eugene, Oregon).

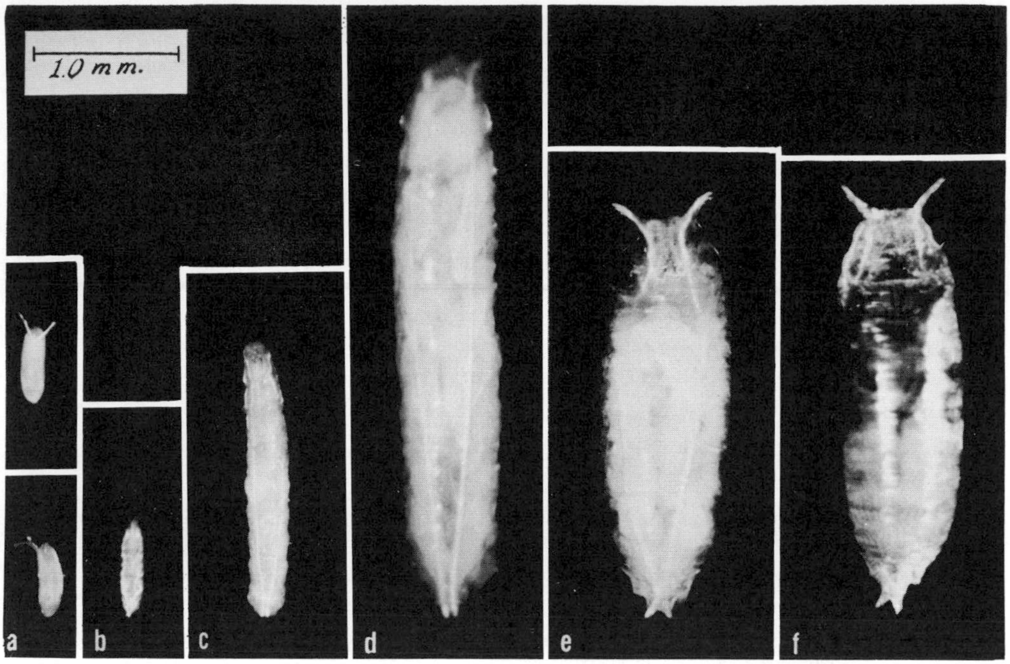

FIG. 1. Developmental stages of *D. melanogaster:* (a) eggs; (b), (c), and (d) larval instars I, II, and III, respectively; (e) "prepupa"; (f) late pupa, with developing adult seen inside pupal case. All have the same magnification; all are viewed dorsally except the lower egg which is shown in lateral view.

LIFE CYCLE

Developmental Stages

Drosophila is a holometabolous insect with the typical sequence of developmental stages: egg, larva, pupa, and adult. The relative sizes of these stages in *D. melanogaster* are shown in Fig. 1. During development two systems are established, the larval and the imaginal. The former is the product of embryogenesis, which occurs within egg membranes. The latter is derived primarily from the undifferentiated cells of imaginal discs which appear in larval stages, but only a few of which have morphologically distinguishable rudiments prior to hatching from the egg. The following account is based on the life cycle and development of *D. melanogaster*. The investigator may consult the contributed papers by Sonnenblick (1950), Poulson (1950), and Bodenstein (1950) in *Biology of Drosophila* for a more thorough understanding of the subject. References to recent findings appear in various review papers on insect development (e.g., Counce, 1961; Anderson, 1962, 1966; Agrell, 1964) and in Herskowitz's bibliographies. A cinematographic study (Ede and Counce, 1956) of embryonic development is available for distribution (from Film Unit, Institute of Animal Genetics, Edinburgh, Scotland) and is a valuable tool in visualizing dynamic aspects of early development.

THE EGG

Eggs appear oval in dorsal view and have an average length of less than 0.5 mm.

Viewed laterally, the dorsal side is flattened (Fig. 1a). They are covered with an opaque white chorion that bears a pair of filaments toward the anterodorsal end. The chorion is easily removed, revealing beneath it a shiny, transparent, relatively impervious vitelline membrane that surrounds the egg proper. A small conical projection at the anterior end contains the micropyle, through which a spermatozoan enters the egg. Contrary to earlier views, monospermy rather than polyspermy appears to be the rule (Hildreth and Lucchesi, 1963). After mating, spermatozoa are stored in the female's seminal receptacle and paired spermathecae. The sperm inseminate eggs as they pass through the uterus. Insemination is accompanied by

TABLE 1. TIMETABLE OF EMBRYONIC STAGES IN *Drosophila melanogaster*

STAGE NO.	TIME (HOURS)	DEVELOPMENTAL EVENT (AT 23°–25°C)
1	0–1½	Premigration; completion of meiosis and fusion of pronuclei; 8 synchronous cleavage mitoses
2	1½	Migration of cleavage nuclei; preblastoderm; pole cell formation
3	2	Syncytial blastoderm; synchronous blasteme mitoses completed
4	2½	Cleavage furrows; blastoderm cell formation
5	3	Cellular blastoderm; pregastrular cell movements
6	3½	Early gastrulation; ventral furrow; posterior plate thickens beneath pole cells
7	3¾	Cephalic furrow; ventral furrow deep; extension of germ band begins
8	4	Invagination of posterior and anterior midgut rudiments; germ band extension continues; embryonic membranes formed
9	4½	Transitory dorsal folds; flattening of mesoderm as germ band continues to extend
10	5	Germ band extension complete; large neuroblasts discrete; yolk mass enclosed by primitive gut
11	5½	Invagination of proctodaeum and stomodaeum begins; neuroblast mitoses
12	6	Segmentation of mesoderm; stomodaeum and proctodaeum deep
13	7	Tracheal invaginations; salivary gland plates
14	8	Segmentation of head and trunk; attachment of muscles
15	9	Shortening of embryo begins; salivary glands moved internally
16	10	Head involution and dorsal closure begin
17	11	Gonad primordia compact; head involution and dorsal closure continue
18	12	Midgut saclike, unconstricted; frontal sac deep
19	13	Constriction of midgut; chitinization begins
20	14	Condensation of ventral nervous system; first muscular movements
	16	Condensation of nervous system continues; regular muscular movements
	18	Larval differentiation nearly complete; active movements
21	20	First air in tracheae; active movements continue
22	22–24	Hatching from egg

completion of meiosis with the innermost product destined to become the female pronucleus. Insemination is not a prerequisite for the completion of meiotic divisions as was formerly believed (Doane, 1960a).

Egg cytoplasm is highly vacuolated and rich in yolk granules except for a thin layer of periplasm at the surface and the cytoplasmic islands that surround nuclei. At the posterior end are darkly staining polar granules, most of which become included in the pole cells. Mahowald (1962) has examined them with the electron microscope. Oviposition usually follows immediately after fertilization, making it possible to time developmental stages accurately. Conjugation of male and female pronuclei within 15 minutes after egg deposition initiates cleavage divisions and nuclear and cytoplasmic movements. By these, three lines of nuclei are established: blastoderm, pole cell, and yolk cell nuclei. Most of the embryo derives from the blastoderm, which is at first syncytial but soon cellularizes. Mahowald (1963a, b) described the ultrastructure of blastoderm differentiation; Poulson (1950) mapped presumptive areas (see discussion by Anderson, 1966). Pole cells present the first visible sign of cellular differentiation and are destined to become germ cells or specialized midgut cells, according to Poulson and Waterhouse (1960). (Opposing views are expressed by Jura, 1964a, b.) Subsequent highlights in embryogenesis, especially those relating to morphogenetic movements, are summarized chronologically in Table 1. Although the suggestion of Imaizumi (1958) that embryonic stages be standardized by numbering them is a good one, there seems little reason to depart from Poulson's timed categories. The latter have been assigned stage numbers in the table, with some minor changes.

THE LARVA

The transparent, whitish larva is an active feeder whose burrowing activities leave behind tunnels and furrows in the food medium, a useful criterion, within a few days, of the success of a new culture. The active larval phase, interrupted by two molts, is divided into three instars. Larval size ranges from little more than the length of an egg at the beginning of the first instar to about 4.5 mm by the late third instar (Fig. 1b, c, d). A movable pair of black mouth hooks distinguish the anterior end at a glance; their size and the number of teeth reveal the larval instar. Paired spiracles protrude at both ends of the larva.

For orientation, some of the larval internal morphology is shown in Fig. 2. Paired salivary glands lie laterally in the anterior region, just behind the pharynx. Anlage of testes, or ovaries, appear as transparent beads embedded in the opaque white fat bodies (omitted in figure) in a dorsolateral position at about one-third the distance from the posterior end. As indicated in the figure, testes are considerably larger than ovaries of a comparable age. Gonad size is used to sex larvae; the relative sizes for different ages are given by Cooper (1950, Table 1). Two Malpighian tubules, whose distal extremities are deleted in the figure, are attached to the intestine just in front of the juncture between mid- and hindguts. Many eye color mutants (e.g., *v*, *ltd*, *ma*) reduce the yellow pigmentation typical of wild type tubules. These provide some of the few useful genetic markers employed to identify larvae of given genotypes for experimental work.

At each larval molt the entire cuticle and its associated structures are shed and a new integument is laid down within which the next instar grows and expands.

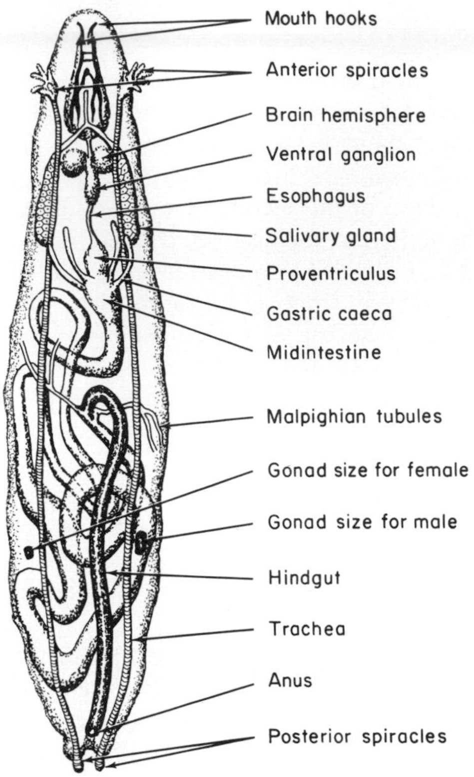

FIG. 2. Internal structure of larva. Reprinted by permission from M. W. Strickberger, *Experiments in Genetics with Drosophila* (New York: John Wiley & Sons, 1962), p. 6.

Internal larval organs in the meantime grow gradually through an increase in cell size and are characterized by a constancy in cell number. By contrast, the imaginal discs increase in size primarily through cell multiplication. Neither a description of these discs and their subsequent growth and differentiation nor a discussion of endocrine controlling mechanisms involved in the molting cycle and metamorphosis will be attempted here. Bodenstein (1950) has provided much of the background material on these subjects, including a diagram (p. 289) to aid in locating and identifying the organ discs. A timetable that includes the major postembryonic stages is given here in Table 2.

THE PUPA

Larvae leave the food medium at the close of the third instar and crawl to some fairly dry surface such as the walls of culture bottles. Once there, the anterior spiracles evert and the body shortens, ceases to move, and attaches. The larval cuticle transforms into a puparium which is at first soft and white (Fig. 1e), but soon hardens and turns tan, and eventually forms the outer pupal case. Shortly after puparium formation, the larva within detaches from the puparium by means of a fourth molt to become the headless "prepupa" with no external wings or legs. Pupation is evidenced by the eversion of head structures, wings, halteres, and legs. The prepupal cuticle is shed and a new pupal cuticle formed so that the pupa comes to lie within a total of three membranes.

The greatest changes associated with metamorphosis occur during the pupal stage when certain larval tissues and organs are histolyzed while adult structures are organized, to a large extent, from imaginal discs. These discs provide excellent material for experiments designed to demonstrate factors that control the growth and differentiation of cells into tissues and organs (see this volume, Ursprung, pp. 485–492, and Schneider, pp. 543–554). They are easily removed by dissection and, in *D. melanogaster*, offer suitable targets not only for standard techniques of expermenital embryology but for a host of genetic tools as well (e.g., see Hadorn, 1965).

Duration of Developmental Stages

The rate of development of *D. melanogaster* is very rapid when compared with most other insects. The accompanying timetables (Tables 1 and 2) are based on those compiled by Poulson (1950) for embryonic stages and by Bodenstein (1950) for postembryonic development. The latter author also provided more detailed timings which were not included, as did Sonnenblick (1950) for early embryology.

While these tables give a general indication of the duration of various stages and the occurrence of major events in many normal strains under so-called standard conditions, they cannot be taken too literally. Many factors, both environmental and genetic, influence the duration of a given stage. The most easily controlled of these is temperature. At 25°C, it takes 9 days for a zygote to reach adulthood, whereas its rate of development is progressively retarded at lower temperatures. (Continuous exposure to temperatures over 28°C may cause sterility or death.) Undefined ingredients in the diet contribute to variations in developmental rates, as does the degree of crowding. Harker (1965) discusses the importance of a biological clock to the developmental rate of pupae. Embryonic rates differ for different populations of flies (King, 1959); larval rates have an estimated heritability of 20–25 percent (Sang, 1962). Thus, the investigator often finds it necessary to establish the time it takes for a particular event to occur in strains with which he is working before experimenting with them.

REARING OF DROSOPHILA

Standard techniques for rearing and handling *D. melanogaster* are presented below. For more details and alternative methods, see Sturtevant, 1937; Spencer, 1950; Demerec and Kaufmann, 1961; and Strickberger, 1962. Although many species are successfully cultured by these methods, others may have very different developmental rates and environmental requirements. Information about optimal conditions for given species may be found by consulting the various bibliographies of *Drosophila* and *D.I.S.* reports.

Manipulation of Adults

ANESTHETIZING FLIES

Ether is used for routine examination and transfer of flies. Etherizers are easily constructed or obtained commercially.

TABLE 2. TIMETABLE OF GENERAL POSTEMBRYONIC STAGES IN *Drosophila melanogaster*

TIME		
HOURS	DAYS	DEVELOPMENTAL EVENT (AT 25°C)
0	0	Hatching from egg; first larval instar begins
25	1	First molt; second instar begins
48	2	Second molt; third instar begins
96	4	Puparium formation; puparium white
98	4	Puparium fully colored
100	4.2	"Prepupal" molt
108	4.5	Pupation; cephalic complex, wings, legs everted
145	6	Eye pigmentation begins
165	6.9	Bristle pigmentation begins
192	8	Adult ready to emerge from pupa case

The simplest consists of a quarter-pint milk bottle fitted with a cork that has a wad of cotton nailed to its inner end. A few drops of ether are applied to the cotton; flies are shaken into the bottle; and the stopper is inserted. A foam rubber pad or plastic sponge provides a good tapping surface upon which the bottle may be emptied. When movement ceases, flies are quickly shaken out and examined. This etherizer can be modified to fit the mouths of culture bottles and vials of all sizes by lodging a plastic funnel in the stopper. Of the commercially available models, the Burco Drosophila Anesthetizer (Drosophila Supply, 250 Lincoln St., West Lafayette, Indiana) is recommended for its ease of handling and speed.

A few drops of ether in the anesthetizer are enough to immobilize a large batch of flies for 20 or so minutes. Should they revive too soon, a re-etherizer is inverted over them until they stop moving again. This is made by gluing some blotting paper to the inside half of a small Petri dish and dropping ether on it. Avoid trying to count or examine too many flies at once or some may escape. Set some aside in a vial to be anesthetized as needed. Care must be taken not to overetherize, a condition easily recognized by flies assuming a rigid posture with legs extended straight below the body and wings held downward at a 45-degree angle or flexed vertically upward. Overetherized flies usually die, but may survive in a partially paralyzed state or with reduced fertility.

Etherized flies often get stuck if put directly on moist food, so it is advisable to place them on a strip of sterile toweling in fresh culture bottles or to allow them to revive first in an empty vial before shaking them into a food container. When food is sticky in bottles after flies have emerged, a bright light may be used to attract flies away from the mouth of the bottle during transfer. During humid weather, flies will get stuck in the moisture that accumulates inside an etherizer, unless it is left open when not in use.

Ether is not always recommended as an anesthetizing agent. It temporarily inhibits egg production and may alter other physiological processes. Some strains and species are very susceptible to overetherization. Carbon dioxide may be used when ether is inappropriate. A convenient CO_2-anesthetizer may be constructed from a porcelain Buchner-type suction funnel mounted level with the stage of the microscope. The funnel's lower end is attached by tubing to a CO_2 tank equipped with a reduction valve. Gas seeps upward through the perforated filter plate which is covered by filter paper to prevent flies from dropping into the pores. If icing becomes a problem, a heating coil may be wrapped around the base of the funnel. Dry ice may also be substituted as a source of CO_2.

TOOLS FOR HANDLING FLIES

Flies are most easily examined on a white surface under a dissecting microscope. A 3×5-inch file card taped between two pieces of glass, or a white ceramic tile, makes an excellent counting plate. A camel's hair brush (no. 1) serves for pushing flies about while classifying or counting them and for sweeping them into vials or bottles. A pair of watchmaker's forceps (no. 5) is useful for manipulating individuals and, with practice, may prove more satisfactory for counting than the brush. Static electricity becomes a problem in handling flies when the relative humidity is low, but can be dissipated by gently exhaling over the etherizer or counting plate. Flies of no further use are discarded in a morgue. This is a jar or finger bowl containing a

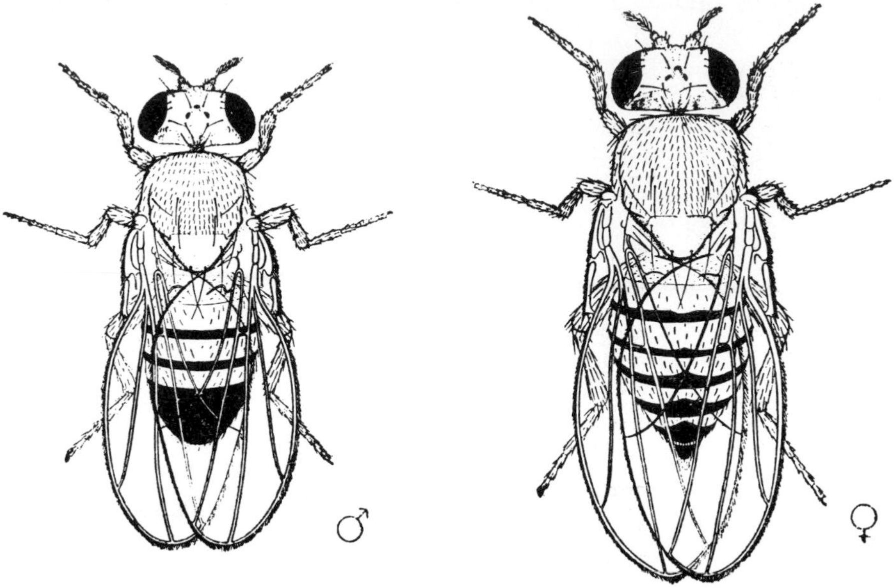

FIG. 3. Adult flies of *Drosophila melanogaster:* male at left, female at right. Reprinted by permission from *Drosophila Guide,* ed. B. P. Kaufmann and M. Demerec, Carnegie Institution of Washington, 7th ed., 1965. Drawing by T. H. Morgan.

fluid into which flies will quickly sink, e.g., motor oil, alcohol, or water saturated with detergent.

General Maintenance

RECOGNIZING ADULT SEXES

Accurate and rapid separation of sexes is important for breeding purposes. Fortunately, *D. melanogaster* is readily sexed by traits that are visible with little or no magnification. The abdomen (Fig. 3) shows the most obvious differences between the sexes. In females, it is: (1) longer, with seven superficially distinct dorsal segments (males have only six); (2) much broader when distended with eggs; (3) more pointed at the tip (rounded in males); and (4) less melanized than in males of most strains. Genitalia of the two sexes are distinctive (Fig. 4). A "sex comb" is characteristically found at the distal end of the most proximal tarsal joint of the male foreleg (Fig. 5). Further details of external and internal morphology are presented by Ferris (1950) and Miller (1950), respectively. The external structures shown in Fig. 4 are helpful in recognizing new adult mutant types.

COLLECTING VIRGIN FEMALES

It is essential to use virgin females when setting up experimental matings or maintaining special stocks that are inadequately balanced. The easiest method is to clear all flies from a culture bottle in which adult emergence has begun. Males will not mate for several hours after emergence, so any females that emerge over the next 8–12 hours will remain virgins if separated from males within this period. Pigmentation in both sexes will be light in young flies, so care should be exercised in classifying them.

If only a few virgins are needed, an

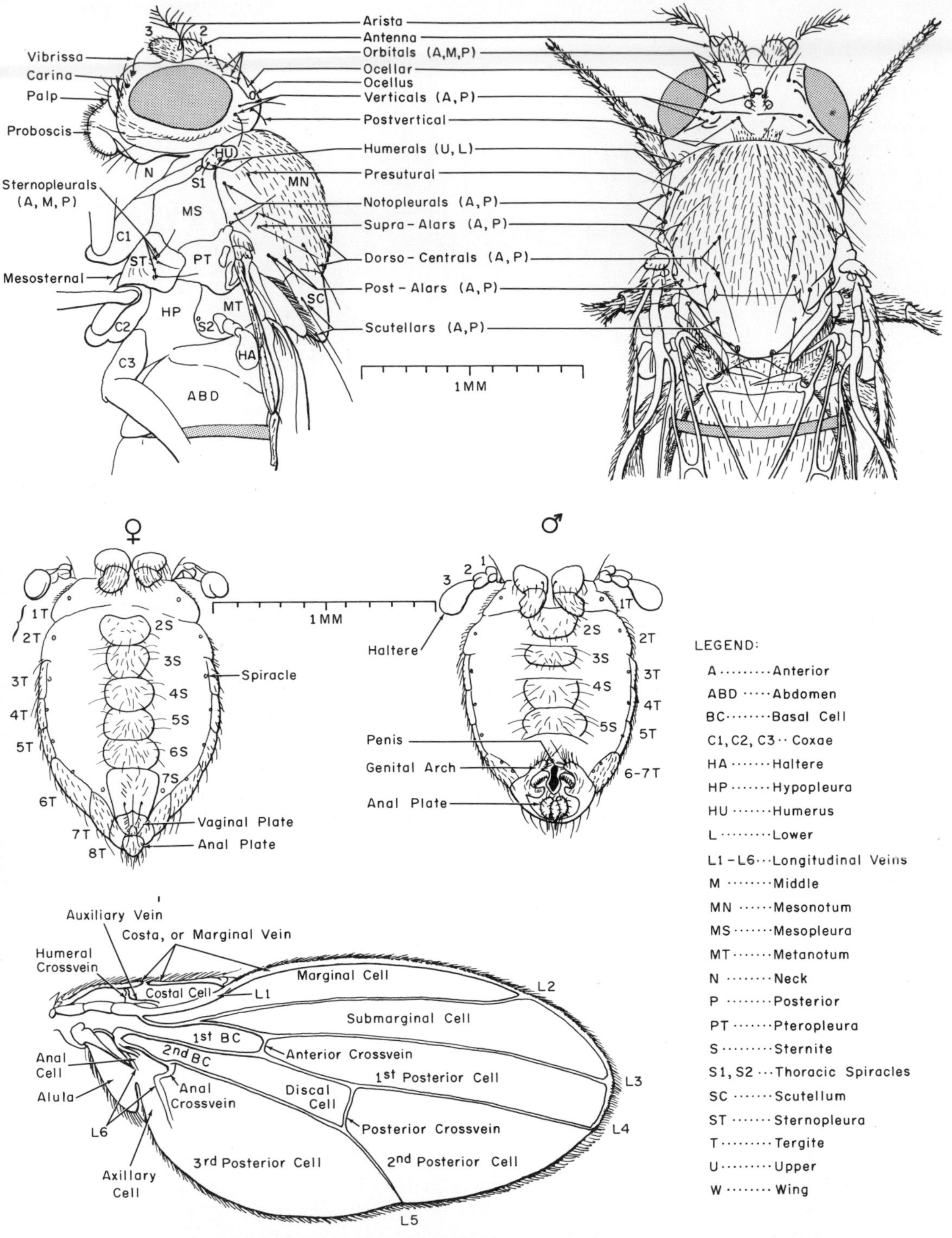

FIG. 4. External morphology of *Drosophila melanogaster*. Drawing by C. B. Bridges in *Drosophila Information Service*, No. 3, 1935, Worksheet No. 1. Reprinted by permission.

alternative method may be employed. Newly emerged females, usually recognizable by their pale coloration, will generally remain unmated at least as long as the meconium is still present. The meconium represents the shed epithelial lining of the larval midgut and gastric cecae and persists throughout pupal development as a greenish-yellow body in the midgut (Bodenstein, 1950). It can be seen through the body wall of newly emerged adults as a dark spot in the left anteroventral region of the abdomen. It migrates posteriorly and within an hour or two is eliminated through the anus. The meconium appears in young flies of both sexes, so males must be separated from virgin females collected this way.

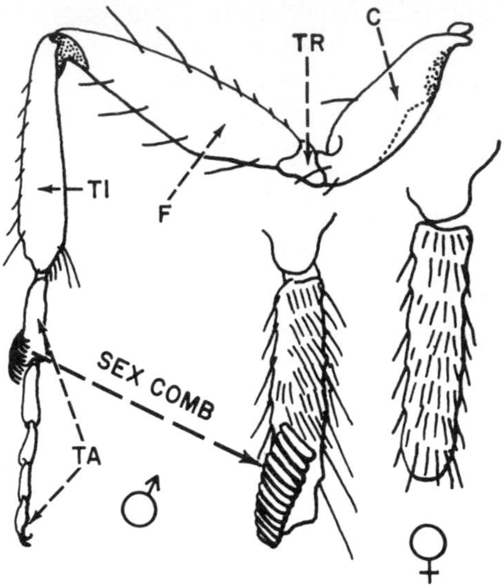

FIG. 5. Diagram of left foreleg of male *Drosophila melanogaster.* C, coxa; TR, trocanter; F, femur; TI, tibia; TA, tarsus. Detail at lower right shows metatarsus of male with metatarsal comb (sex comb) and metatarsus of female, which lacks the sex comb. Drawing by G. F. Ferris, in *The Biology of Drosophila,* ed. M. Demerec (New York: John Wiley & Sons, 1950), p. 406. Reprinted by permission.

FOOD CONTAINERS

Stock cultures and experimental crosses from mass matings may be reared in half-pint or quarter-pint glass milk bottles. Some laboratories prefer shell vials because they take up less space and require less food. However, they are easily broken and yield fewer progeny. [Disposable paper containers have also been recommended (Moyer *et al.*, 1961).] Plugs, made of cotton batting wrapped in two layers of cheesecloth and tied with a string, are made to fit snugly in bottles or vials and can be used repeatedly after autoclaving. Another type commonly used is the plastic "Dispo" plug (Scientific Products Co.) of the size for a 35–45 mm opening.

Single pair matings are set up either in shell vials (25 × 95 mm) or in three-quarter-ounce glass creamers of the type used in restaurants. Creamers are cheap, durable, not easily knocked over, and may be stacked on trays. Plain cardboard caps with stapled pull-tabs are used as covers and they provide space for labeling. Etherized flies can be placed on the underside of the cap and the creamer inverted over it until the flies revive.

"STANDARD" CULTURE MEDIA

Drosophila melanogaster normally abounds on fermenting soft fruits such as bananas, grapes, plums, apples, deriving nutrition primarily from yeasts associated with the fermentation process. Fermenting crushed bananas thus provide the simplest and earliest used adequate diet for culturing both larval and adult stages. Such media, however, are generally difficult to handle and costly. Spencer (1950) reviewed earlier literature on culture methods and indicated the essentials of a good general-purpose medium. Several media are now in use in various laboratories that fulfill these requirements. The recipes for two such "standard" media are given below. Others commonly in use are described by Demerec and Kaufmann (1961), Strickberger (1962), and various technical notes in *D.I.S.*

CORNMEAL-MOLASSES-AGAR. This medium, originating at the California Institute of Technology, has been used successfully in our laboratory for many years. The formula given in Table 3 provides food sufficient for 100 half-pint bottles, 200 quarter-pint bottles, or 500 creamers. Ingredients are prepared in two separate vessels, I and II, as follows:

1. Boil water and agar in container I until agar dissolves (10–20 percent more agar may be needed in hot weather). Add molasses and bring it to a boil again.
2. Mix contents of vessel II, using cold water, until all lumps are removed.
3. Add contents of II to I and boil until the mixture is a sirupy consistency, about 5 minutes. Stir constantly while cooking to prevent sticking and burning.
4. Stir in one of the following mold inhibitors and pour: (a) 60 ml of a stock solution of Tegosept M (methyl-*p*-hydroxybenzoate) prepared by dissolving 10 gm in 100 ml of 95 percent ethanol; or (b) 34 ml of propionic acid, after medium has cooled to about 60°C.

Prior to putting flies into bottles, the food should be seeded with living yeast. Add a pinch of dried baker's yeast (Fleischmann's) or a drop of yeast suspension. The latter is made by stirring enough yeast into a flask of sterile water to get a milky consistency (refrigerate and discard when yeastlike odor is lost). Insert a strip of sterilized paper toweling, 1 inch wide, into the medium by means of an ordinary table knife so that the paper forms a bridge over the food.

SUCROSE-AGAR. This simple medium, developed at the University of Wisconsin by James F. Crow (Mittler and Bennett, 1962), eliminates the need for adding live yeast to the food. Live yeast, in excess, forms a sticky layer over the surface and may produce harmful amounts of carbon dioxide. The gas may kill larvae and/or loosen food and push it out of the container. The formula, presented in Table 3, has the added advantage of omitting molasses and cornmeal, both of which vary greatly with the source of supply. Amounts indicated should supply enough food for approximately the same number of bottles as in the preceding formula. Prepare as follows:

1. Add dry ingredients to water while it is being brought to a boil and mix until thoroughly dissolved.
2. Boil 5–15 minutes to kill all yeast cells. Additional water may be added, if needed, should too much escape as vapor.
3. Cool medium to about 60°C, stir in 30 ml of propionic acid and pour.

Both of the above media are poured while still warm and thin into clean culture bottles previously autoclaved 20 minutes at 15 pounds per square inch of pressure. Fill bottles, vials, or creamers with about 1 inch of food (automatic dispensers are commercially available), cover temporarily with a sheet of cheesecloth and allow to cool and jell. Sterile plugs are then inserted. Under ordinary circumstances no further precautions need be taken against contamination. Let food sit overnight before introducing flies so that excess water will evaporate from the inside walls of bottles. Food should be used within a few days of its preparation.

SETTING UP STOCK CULTURES

When setting up stocks, it is wise to examine each fly carefully. Contamination by flies from extraneous sources will thus be avoided as well as the introduction of some unwanted parasites. A dozen or so pairs of healthy young parents are generally

TABLE 3. STANDARD CULTURE MEDIA

MEDIUM		INGREDIENTS	AMOUNT
Cornmeal-Molasses-Agar		Water	4,200 ml
	I	Agar	45 gm
		Molasses (unsulfured)	600 ml
		Cornmeal	490 gm
	II	Brewer's Yeast*	65 gm
		Water	1,450 ml
Sucrose-Agar		Water	6,000 ml
		Agar	114 gm
		Sucrose	324 gm
		Brewer's yeast*	192 gm

* Brewer's yeast is supplied by Standard Brands, Inc. (specify Fleischmann's pure, dry, inactivated 2019) and by the Schlitz Brewing Co. (indicate nondebittered, dried).

mated in a half-pint food bottle, but more may be needed for strains of reduced viability or fertility. An excess of males is often helpful. Virgin females are selected when there is any question of contamination or if a balanced line shows signs of breaking down, e.g., appearance of cross-over types.

At least two culture bottles should be set up initially for each strain. In subsequent generations, one old bottle is saved when a fresh one is set up after each transfer. Each bottle is labeled with the date of transfer and the stock's name in symbols. Although 25°C is generally used in experimental matings of *D. melanogaster* (see David and Clavel, 1966, for physiological optimum), stocks are usually stored at 18°–19°C. Development is retarded at the latter temperature so bottles require changing only every 3 to 4 weeks. Many species thrive at this temperature, but no higher, and may take considerably longer to pass through a complete life cycle. The maintenance of a minimum relative humidity of 40 percent will ensure that food in culture bottles will not dry out prematurely.

Selection of parents for the next generation at each transfer is time consuming. Instead, the same parents may be shaken over again into fresh bottles at 2-week intervals, i.e., before their progeny has emerged. This is repeated three or four times, depending on the vigor of the strain. The last bottle shaken into is left to hatch and the emerging offspring then selected for parents of the following generation. This method not only prolongs the length of a generation and its yield, but also saves considerable time in stock maintenance. It decreases the amount of mold and/or bacteria that tend to accumulate in old food bottles. In general, the latter should be discarded and cleaned as soon as feasible; old food bottles may become infested with mites.

CONTROL OF MOLDS, BACTERIA, PESTS, AND PARASITES

Only those organisms known to associate with *Drosophila* that are likely to become a problem in laboratory cultures will be discussed. Others, such as parasitic hymenopterans and nematodes, may occasionally appear but are either rare or easily eliminated from stocks.

MOLDS. Culture medium heavily contaminated by molds becomes covered by a dense mat of hyphae that prevents flies from feeding and females from laying eggs. Developing larvae and adults may actually be harmed by the mold, especially strains that are slow to mature or develop. Incorporation of a mold inhibitor in the medium eliminates much of this problem. Tegosept M or propionic acid, in proportions indicated earlier, are very effective. Caution must be taken, however, to limit amounts to the minimum required to control mold growth. Otherwise the growth of yeast and flies will be impaired.

During warm, humid weather, molds tend to build up in spite of the presence of inhibitors in the food. When this happens, flies should be shaken into fresh bottles daily for several days. This usually controls the mold, but sterile techniques in food preparation may be warranted. Periodic swabbing of etherizers, counting plates, desk tops, etc., with 70 percent alcohol is helpful. As a last resort, eggs may be collected and surface-sterilized to rid a culture of contaminants. The build-up of resistant strains of molds or bacteria can often be averted by routinely switching from one inhibitor to another.

BACTERIA. Certain bacterial contaminants in or on the medium are detrimental to stocks. Those that produce a slimy exudate trap flies and are an especial nuisance. In general, the same techniques used to control molds are effective here. Bacteria that impart a dark reddish-brown color to the food are common contaminants, but relatively benign. However, they can interfere with the maintenance of some strains. Their control is effected by repeated transfers, surface-sterilization of eggs, or the use of antibiotics (Hendrix and Ehrlich, 1965) in the medium.

PROTOZOANS. Certain microsporidians can be dangerous parasites of *Drosophila* (Wolfson *et al.*, 1957; Stalker and Carson, 1963). Heavily infected flies become sterile and infections may kill larvae, pupae, or adults. Several species are known to be susceptible to the same sporozoan, including *D. melanogaster*. Spores are readily seen in parasitized adults dissected in saline and are found associated with reproductive organs, fat bodies, and the gut. Two types of spores have been described (Stalker and Carson, 1963); one type is 4 to 5 μ in length and ovoid, the other is larger and banana-shaped. As yet no good method of control is known other than discarding infected stocks. The avoidance of adult crowding, a rapid transfer schedule, and a low rearing temperature are suggested.

MITES. Mite infestations may present serious problems. They reduce the number of progeny and may destroy less vigorous strains. Among species that infest *Drosophila* cultures, the most dangerous is the parasitic "laboratory mite," *Histiostoma laboratorium* Hughes (Hughes, 1950). It has a tiny brown hypopus stage that attaches to adult flies, usually on legs, wings, or genitalia, and sucks body fluids. Fruitfly cultures provide excellent conditions for breeding these mites and they rapidly increase in numbers in old food bottles. As active crawlers, they spread from culture to culture, bypassing plugs. They spring at and attach to moving objects such as flies and are readily carried over into fresh bottles.

Other relatively harmless mites, which lack hypopi, may infest cultures and live on the food medium. The commonest is the "white" mite whose long white hairs on an ovate body easily distinguish it from the laboratory mite, whose body is more squatty and does not bear long hairs (see Spencer, 1950, Fig. 5).

The sources of mite infestations are flies received from other laboratories, wild collections, and various insects or animals entering the laboratory. Adult flies from newly acquired cultures should be carefully inspected and isolated from other stocks until they are proven free of mites. If mites appear, their life cycle can be disrupted by repeated transfers of flies to fresh bottles every few days for 3 to 4 weeks. Old bottles should be discarded and heat sterilized as soon as larvae appear in new ones. Etherizers, equipment to handle flies, trays, tables, etc., may be wiped with a weak solution (1:100) of phenol or Lysol. If these precautions are followed, there is little trouble in controlling mites.

Should these measures be inappropriate or inadequate, administration of a miticide may be necessary. Brown (1965) suggests the use of Kelthane®. The wettable powder containing 18.5 percent active ingredient (1,1-bis(*p*-chlorophenyl)-2,2,2-trichlorethanol) is readily available. Before pouring food into clean, sterile bottles, rinse them in a suspension of Kelthane, 230–463 ppm, and allow them to drain dry. Transfer flies from infested stocks into treated bottles and, as soon as their progeny emergy, shake offspring into fresh bottles prepared the same way. By the third generation, all mites should be gone. Heavily infested bottles may be treated directly as follows: remove adults, quickly pour a 75 ppm suspension in and out of bottles, stopper them, and collect adults that emerge (Brown, 1966). MacIntyre (personal communication) administers Kelthane-AP in the food medium for population cages at the rate of 1 gm dry powder in 3,800 ml of medium, with no noticeable detriment to progeny yield, developmental time, or fertility. Nonetheless, miticides must be used with caution since strains and species vary markedly in their tolerance to them.

Axenic Culture Methods

SURFACE-STERILIZATION OF EGGS

Sterile egg surfaces are a prerequisite to the establishment of axenic cultures of *Drosophila* or for aseptic collection of developmental stages. An elaborate device was designed by Sang (1956) for handling large numbers of eggs with a minimum of damage to embryos. Should this procedure be employed, the substitution of 0.1 percent cetyl dimethyl benzyl ammonium chloride for Cetavlon, followed by a wash of 3 percent sterile sucrose, then sterile water, is now recommended (Sang, personal communication). This technique, however, is somewhat involved and time consuming, so the following alternative is offered for general purposes:

1. Either place eggs in a lens-paper sack whose edges are tied with a cotton thread, or collect them on a piece of finely woven Fiberglas cloth laid over the usual egg-collecting medium. Peel off Fiberglas and draw it into a sack by means of a thread.

2. Dechorionate eggs in the sack by placing it for several minutes in 3 percent sodium hypochlorite (Clorox and water, 1:1, will do).

3. Rinse well with sterile distilled water.

4. Wash thoroughly with a 0.1 percent solution of cetyl dimethyl benzyl ammonium chloride. [A solution containing 0.25 percent peracetic acid and 0.1 percent Naccanol is also effective (Doll *et al.*, 1963).]

5. Rinse in 3 percent sterile sucrose, then in two rinses of sterile distilled water.

6. Using aseptic techniques and working under a hood, transfer eggs to a sterile culture vial by cutting open the sack inside the vial. For some studies, it may prove simpler to permit eggs to hatch in a sterile Petri dish and transfer the larvae to culture vials with a sterile brush.

7. With each transfer of flies from an axenic culture, an assay is made for the presence of microbes. Mix together samples of old culture medium with some flies and larvae. Inoculate two tubes of each of the following microbiological media with each sample: nutrient broth, thioglycolate broth, and mycological agar. Incubate bacterial assay tubes 48 hours at 37°C, those for mycological assay for 96 hours at 25°C, and discard fly cultures shown to be contaminated.

SYNTHETIC MEDIA

It is not possible to formulate a single defined synthetic diet adequate for normal growth and development of all strains of *D. melanogaster* (e.g., Sang, 1959). Thus, several media are in use that satisfy nutritional requirements as determined for the strains in given laboratories. A bibliography of pertinent references to nutritional studies made prior to 1964 was compiled by Fuchs (1965).

BACTO-HINTON DROSOPHILA MEDIUM. Commercially available preparations, based on the chemically defined medium of Hinton, Noyes, and Ellis (1951) are supplied by Difco Laboratories. Although this medium has been the basis of much experimentation on nutritional needs of *D. melanogaster*, it has been our experience that relatively few strains grow well on it and development is retarded.

SANG'S MEDIUM C. More success is had using the Medium C formula of Sang (1956). This diet, or modifications of it, is commonly used in nutritional and genetic studies with good results. It is easily prepared and allows larval development to proceed at nearly normal rates. Unfortunately, some of its components are not defined, such as casein, which supplies the nitrogen. Salt requirements are also not entirely defined, some essential elements being provided by contaminants in casein and agar. But since the medium provides a good basic diet upon which to elaborate, its formula is given in Table 4. Prepare as follows:

1. Bring all ingredients to a boil and dissolve the agar.
2. Autoclave mixture 20 minutes at 15 pounds of pressure.
3. Add 2.6 ml of Tween 80 and swirl while cooling to about 60°C in a cold water bath. (Ellis, personal communication, suggests the use of Tween 80, a surface active agent, to help disperse casein, cholesterol, and lecithin throughout the medium.)
4. Pour 5 ml of medium into each culture tube under a hood, using sterile methods. Tubes (25 mm O.D. × 150 mm long) are previously sterilized and covered with metal caps or polypropylene Bacti-Capall® caps. Insert a sterile cotton plug wrapped in cheesecloth under the cap, after introduction of eggs or larvae,

TABLE 4. SANG'S SYNTHETIC DIET, MEDIUM C

INGREDIENTS	AMOUNT (mg)
Agar	3,000
Casein (low vitamin)	5,500
Fructose	750
Cholesterol	30
Lecithin	400
Yeast nucleic acid	400
Thiamine HCl (Aneurin)	0.2
Riboflavin	1.0
Nicotinic acid	1.2
Ca pantothenate	1.6
Pyridoxine HCl	0.25
Biotin	0.016
Folic acid	0.3
$NaHCO_3$	140
KH_2PO_4	183
Na_2HPO_4	189
H_2O to	100 ml

otherwise larvae may escape.

Sang's medium is slightly modified for the culture of adults on a defined medium. The method is described by Sang and King (1961), who also determined the amino acid requirements in adult nutrition. Ellis (personal communication) suggests that organic components of Sang's medium be obtained in the United States from Difco Laboratories (Bacto-Agar, fructose), and Nutritional Biochemical Corp. or Sigma Chemical Co. (remaining ingredients).

OTHER SYNTHETIC DIETS. Various workers have proposed other completely defined, synthetic media (e.g., Geer, 1966, and Ellis, 1959). These include amino acid requirements, thus eliminating casein. Texts of these reports may be consulted for the amounts to be used and for other modifications.

Microbes, yeasts, etc., can be a source of uncontrolled variability in enzyme assays or in the expression of traits such as quantitative characters. Axenic culture of flies is advisable, but a defined diet is not always warranted. For such purposes, a simple and sufficient diet can be provided by doubling or tripling the content of brewer's yeast in one of the standard media, preparing it aseptically and introducing surface-sterilized eggs. Antibiotics may be included (5,000 units each of a penicillin-streptomycin mixture in 100 ml of medium), if they do not interfere with assay procedures.

TECHNIQUES FOR HANDLING DEVELOPMENTAL STAGES

Collecting Eggs

There are many ways to collect eggs, some more elaborate than others (see Sonnenblick, 1950, and *D.I.S.* notes). Whatever technique is employed, it is helpful to keep certain points in mind. Females reach a peak in egg production early in adult life and this is when collections are most easily made. The appearance and extent of this period varies with the species; in *D. melanogaster*, it occurs roughly between 4 and 7 days after emergence. Eggs are laid more or less continuously, although slight diurnal rhythms exist and in some species a more pronounced periodicity may occur (King and Wolfsberg, 1957). Rates vary but in most normal strains of *D. melanogaster* the average is 50–70 eggs per female per day during the peak of production. In order to obtain maximum egg size and production, uncrowded rearing conditions should be maintained.

Females lay eggs one at a time and embryonic stages are timed from the moment of deposition. However, eggs may be held within a female's uterus following fertilization, develop there, and be laid at any stage up to the completion of larval differentiation. Thus, in order to get precise timings it is necessary to collect eggs from only those females that are laying rapidly, thereby clearing the uterus. Preliminary collections should be discarded. Flies lay best under conditions that supply ample moisture and the products of fermentation. The collection interval for pre- and post-meiotic stages is usually from 5 to 15 minutes because of the speed with which early developmental events occur; the interval for later stages may be extended to 1 or 2 hours. *Drosophila melanogaster* eggs are usually collected and aged at 25°C.

The choice of collecting chamber depends somewhat on how the eggs will be used. Mass collections generally suffice. (Sonnenblick describes methods for collecting from single females for early stages when greater accuracy in timing is needed.) The simplest chamber is an empty culture bottle turned on its side. It will accommodate about forty pairs of flies. At suitable intervals, cardboard spoons spread with standard medium topped with a fermenting yeast paste, attractive to females, are inserted and later removed. The paste is made by mixing baker's yeast with food medium (1 gm in 100 ml) 2 days in advance and allowing it to ferment at room temperature. (If eggs are needed immediately, fermentation may be simulated by making a thick aqueous yeast suspension and adding a few drops of ethanol and diluted acetic acid.) When removing or replacing food spoons, it helps to attract flies away from the mouth of the bottle by means of a bright light.

When very large numbers of eggs are required, a more elaborate chamber may be constructed (Yoon and Fox, 1965). A type that yields a fair degree of accuracy in egg timing is made from a clear plastic cylinder (45 mm long, 22 mm in diameter) sealed at one end by Dacron gauze whose mesh is large enough for the passage of eggs, but not flies (Hildreth and Lucchesi, 1963). Collections are made as follows:

1. Separate the sexes upon emergence and age them 3–4 days on standard food sprinkled with dried baker's yeast.

2. Mate 3 hours before collecting eggs by shaking flies into cylinders (40 pairs in each); plug open end with cotton; push plug to within 0.5 cm of sealed end to force flies down when collecting. (As ether inhibits egg production, it must not be used just before collecting.)

3. Place fermenting yeast paste in Petri dish halves and cover with Kleenex-type tissue, overlaid with a piece of blotting paper that has been previously soaked in vinegar solution (1 part in 9 parts water). Moist blotting paper provides a good collecting surface and dark blue is apparently the color preference of laying females.

4. Set a tube of flies, gauze end down, on the blotting paper in a dish; allow females to oviposit through the gauze; gently lift tube at end of desired intervals to remove paper bearing eggs and replace paper with a fresh one.

For hatchability and eclosion tests, the use of darkened culture medium, against which the white eggs stand out, will make counting simpler. Charcoal or grape juice (one 12-ounce can of frozen concentrate in 2 liters of food) is added to the medium before it is poured.

Handling Eggs

A steel needle, flattened on two opposite sides and blunted at the tip, makes a good scoop for picking up eggs. When collected on blotting paper, eggs may be whisked off with a camel's hair brush. Ringer solutions are unnecessary when handling and aging eggs, as long as the vitelline membrane is laid down normally and remains intact. Eggs must be kept moist while aging, either on wet blotting paper or in a small dish of water (Syracuse watch glass, 27 mm diameter; or Columbia Culture Dish, 42 mm square).

Removal of the chorion allows one to observe developmental dynamics such as morphogenetic movements. Chorions may be removed by gently stroking eggs with a needle. However, the quickest method in handling large numbers is to submerge eggs in a dish of Clorox diluted with an equal part of water. Swirling the dish constantly, observe under a dissecting microscope as the chorions dissolve. When the filaments become transparent, quickly pipette off the Clorox solution containing bits of chorion and other debris, and rinse eggs several times with distilled water. Pipettes and dishes should be siliconized to prevent eggs from sticking to them. Egg development may be followed in a hanging drop slide.

Unfertilized or lethal eggs are usually

recognizable a few hours after deposition or death. Those that are unfertilized (and zygotes that die in early cleavage stages) remain opaque white. Cytoplasmic abnormalities develop and these increase progressively after the third hour. Fissures appear on the surface that divide the cytoplasm into several parts, while internally a characteristic necrosis may be demonstrated histologically (Sonnenblick, p. 77). Embryonic lethality is generally recognized by progressive melanotic darkening of dead tissues, often in discrete patches.

Manipulation or treatment of large numbers of eggs is simplified by placing them in a lens paper or Fiberglas sack, as described earlier. Sacks can be transferred from one solution to the next (e.g., for Feulgen whole mounts), thus avoiding the tedious operation of pipetting fluids on and off eggs. It may prove more convenient to make a basket for eggs out of brass strainer cloth (100–200 mesh) or from a plastic tube sealed at one end with tightly woven Dacron cloth.

Collecting and Handling Postembryonic Stages

Larvae of specific ages are obtained from eggs collected in mass, incubated, and allowed to hatch. First instars are then picked off at given intervals and subsequent developmental stages determined from the time of hatching. Creamers or Petri dishes containing standard food sprinkled with extra yeast are used to raise them (no more than 25 per creamer or 125 per dish). Since newly emerged larvae are fragile and easily injured, they must be handled with care. A camel's hair brush (no. 1), brought to a point with water, is less damaging than a blunted needle or forceps. Forceps may be used without harm to harvest later stages. Larvae can be forced out of the food at collection time by flooding it with water. Pupae are gently eased from the walls of containers with a moist brush.

If desired, the three larval instars may be separated from one another by wire screens. Eighty mesh will screen second instar from first and sixty mesh will separate third from the other two. The sieving must be done quickly or larvae will squeeze through smaller openings than those indicated.

Postembryonic stages of *D. melanogaster* and other species have been used extensively in transplantation experiments, particularly in regard to factors controlling imaginal disc differentiation. Techniques employed in such studies are given by Ursprung in this volume, pp. 485–492 (see also Bodenstein, 1950), tissue and organ culture methods are discussed by Schneider in this volume, pp. 543–554.

ROUTINE HISTOLOGICAL TECHNIQUES

Penetration of Fixatives

It is necessary to puncture the vitelline membrane of eggs in order to ensure rapid and uniform penetration of fixatives. Removal of the chorion is not essential and, in fact, its presence makes pricking eggs somewhat easier since they are less slippery. The chorion also aids in the orientation of eggs during embedding and later in orienting sections. (Dechorionation is required, of course, for whole mounts.) Tungsten needles, sharpened by dipping them into melted sodium nitrite, are best for puncturing eggs. Heat the sodium nitrite to a slow rolling boil in a nickel crucible. Needles can be made from 2-cm lengths of black tungsten wire (0.01-inch diameter, supplied in 2-foot lengths by General Electric Co., Cleveland

Wire Works) embedded in glass rods or held in pin vises.

Although postembryonic stages are not confined by a vitelline membrane, it is nevertheless necessary to puncture the hypodermis in a number of places to ensure proper penetration of fixatives. Older pupae are best dissected free of the puparium before fixation. Larvae should be forced to relax before puncturing them: put them in a dish (stendor) of Ringer solution containing 4 percent $MgSO_4$ and place the dish on a hot plate set for 60°C. As they are warmed, they first become very active but within a few minutes cease to move and stretch out (Gottlieb, 1966). When this happens, immediately transfer them to a watch glass containing fixative and puncture them. (Anesthetizing larvae will not prevent their contraction when punctured.)

Gottlieb (1966) developed a method for fixing postembryonic stages without the need of puncture, thus eliminating distortions caused by the needle. His technique employs a modification of Ammerman's chrom-alum fixative containing dimethyl sulfoxide (DMSO) which aids penetration. The proposed schedules for dehydration and infiltration, however, are tedious and we find the following routine provides sectioned material of comparable, if not superior, quality:

1. Place specimen in fixative (formalin, 95 percent ethanol, glacial acetic acid, water, DMSO, in proportions of 6:16:1 26:4) warmed to 60°C, 5 minutes. Remove promptly to room temperature and allow fixative to penetrate another 10–15 minutes. (Larvae should be relaxed prior to fixation.)

2. Rinse in distilled water.

3. Dehydrate in Smith's alcohol series (see below), modified as follows: (a) add intermediate steps between each graded concentration of alcohol by mixing each grade with the next in equal parts; (b) allow ½ hour for each step, except for the mixture of solutions I and II, and II alone, which require 12 hours each. Infiltrate and embed as usual.

Whole Mount Preparations

A relatively quick and easy method for preparing whole mounts of embryos was recommended by Counce (1966). Results are sufficiently good for it to be used in screening mutants that affect specific embryonic stages, or in determining the gross effects of experimental treatments. It may be applied to postembryonic stages as well by lengthening the time for each step in relation to the increase in body size. Whole mounts of organs or organ discs may also be made this way by dissecting them out in Ringer solution and placing them directly into fixative. The procedure follows.

1. Dechorionate eggs in diluted Clorox and wash.

2. Puncture in F.A.A. fixative (formol-ethyl alcohol-acetic acid, 6:16:1, plus 30 parts water); fix ½ to 2 hours, or overnight.

3. Transfer to 30 percent ethanol, 15 minutes, then 70 percent, 15 minutes.

4. Stain 24–48 hours in alcoholic borax carmine. (Grind together 2–3 gm carmine and 4 gm borax; dissolve them by slowly heating in 100 ml distilled water. Cool. Add 100 ml 70 percent ethyl alcohol. Let stand 1 week, shaking frequently. Filter.)

5. Destain with acid alcohol (a few drops of concentrated HCl in 70 percent alcohol) for desired contrast, usually 24–48 hours. Embryos should be pale cherry red but deepen in color on clearing.

6. Dehydrate through alcohols to absolute, clear in xylol, and mount. Support cover slips with glass chips and seal with fingernail polish to prevent shrinkage of mounting medium.

Preparation of Sectioned Material

For detailed histological and cytological studies, sectioned material is required. The following method incorporates the schedule for fixation, dehydration, and infiltration of Smith (1940). Excellent sections of *Drosophila* eggs may be obtained in spite of their yolkiness, particularly in early stages. Postembryonic stages may also be prepared this way with fine results.

1. Fix in F.A.A. as in step 2 for whole mounts.

2. Dehydrate in the order shown in Table 5. (Change Solution V after $\frac{1}{2}$ hour; store in Solution II.) Add eosin to Solutions I–IV so that eggs and larvae are more easily seen during subsequent steps.

3. Infiltrate in equal parts of Solution V and paraffin, 16 hours. Transfer to fresh paraffin (60°C, melting point) for 40–45 minutes with three changes. A vacuum oven will remove air from tracheae in larvae, pupae, and adults.

4. Embed in a small watch glass coated with glycerin or in a paper boat. (Reorient eggs in block under a microscope with a hot needle, without touching them. Align about six in a row and trim block so they are cut in unison in 5- to 8-μ thick sections. A single ribbon containing complete series of all six embryos will fit nicely under a single cover slip.)

5. Stain eggs as follows: run sections through xylol and alcohols to water; mordant with 4 percent iron alum, 1 hour; wash several minutes; stain 1–2 hours in Heidenhain's iron hematoxylin; carefully destain in 2 or 4 percent iron alum. Dehydrate, clear, and mount in Canadian balsam. Tap water, instead of distilled water, in rinses and in alcohols will improve the blue color. Postembryonic stages are better stained with Harris' or Delafield's hematoxylin, counterstained with eosin.

Salivary Gland Chromosome Squashes

Use of the large, paired, polytene chromosomes in the salivary glands for the construction of cytological maps is well known. Reference maps to the nomenclature of bands in these chromosomes are provided by Bridges and Brehme (1944) for *D. melanogaster*. Various regions of the maps have been revised from time to time (e.g., Slizynski, 1944). The advantage of being able to correlate a genetic factor with a given band on a chromosomal map is obvious; it is also important to know whether or not the developmental effects attributed to a given mutant are the result of a chromosomal aberration (inversion, translocation, deficiency, or duplication). Position effects, lethal deficiencies, etc., have been the subject of many interesting studies in developmental genetics. (Recently devised techniques for analysis of factors that control metabolic activities,

TABLE 5.

SOLUTION	TIME (HR)	WATER (%)	ETHYL ALCOHOL (%)	*n*-BUTYL ALCOHOL (%)	PHENOL (%)*
I	1	30	50	20	..
II	24	15	50	35	4
III	1	5	40	55	..
IV	1	..	25	75	..
V	1	..	..	100	4

* % Phenol dissolved in alcoholic solution.

puffing, etc., of loci in polytene chromosomes are beyond the scope of this paper.)

The following method for the routine analysis of salivary gland chromosomes is based on the technique of J. Schultz, as described by Nicoletti (1959). Baker's (1952) method for making permanent mounts is included. Further details and alternative procedures are provided by Demerec and Kaufmann (1961), Strickberger (1962), and various technical notes in *D.I.S.*

1. Raise larvae at 18°C on standard medium enriched with extra yeast; collect them as they crawl onto walls of bottle just before puparium formation.

2. Dissect out salivary glands in a drop of Shen's solution (9 gm NaCl, 0.42 gm KCl, 0.25 gm $CaCl_2$ in 1 liter H_2O) on a siliconized slide under 25 × magnification as follows: using two rust-free needles (e.g., no. 9 sewing needles mounted in wooden holders), hold rear half of larva with one and place tip of other just behind mouth parts; drag second needle away from first in order to decapitate and pull out the glands, which usually remain attached to the head end; separate glands from other tissues and strip off fat bodies attached to them.

3. Transfer to a drop of 45 percent acetic acid on same slide, 1 minute.

4. Quickly remove to a small drop of stain in center of slide, 10–15 minutes. The stain consists of 2 percent powdered natural orcein (C. T. Gurr Ltd., London, England) in equal parts of lactic and glacial acetic acids.

5. Lower a siliconized cover slip (22 × 22 mm) over the drop and, holding it in place with two fingers, tap cover glass several times directly over the glands with a small rubber hammer or the eraser end of a pencil.

6. Fold a piece of bibulous paper around slide and press firmly with thumb in a rocking motion, without moving cover slip.

7. Allow 24 hours for maximum coloration and examine under a phase microscope with a green filter. If chromosomes are not well spread, reapply pressure. Preparations will last several weeks without sealing.

8. To prepare permanent mounts, stain glands on a siliconized cover slip; squash by inverting cover slip on an unsiliconized, well cleaned slide. Freeze preparation on a block of dry ice; flick off cover glass with a razor blade wedged under one corner. Before tissue can melt, place slide in 95 percent ethanol, 2–3 minutes, and then in absolute alcohol, 1 minute. While still wet, place a drop of euparal to one side of the smear and drag the mounting medium over the smear with a clean cover slip wetted in absolute alcohol. Gently lower cover slip.

CONCLUDING REMARKS

Drosophila is used extensively in experiments that exploit genetic approaches to problems of development. While it is not possible to do justice here to the literature in the field of developmental genetics, certain references will serve as an introduction. The classic paper of Poulson (1945) on the use of lethal deficiencies to demonstrate chromosomal control of embryonic processes provided the stimulus for many subsequent investigations in which lethal and female sterility mutants were employed as "built-in-experiments" to analyze normal development. Simultaneously, Hadorn and his co-workers undertook analyses of postembryonic stages. The uses of genetic techniques, coupled with those of experimental embryology, are discussed in his book, *Developmental Genetics and Lethal Factors* (Hadorn, 1955); newer methods applied to imaginal disc differentiation were alluded to earlier (Hadorn, 1965; Ursprung, this volume). Implications of a genetic approach that utilizes mutants in a pseudoallelic series to analyze problems of growth and differentiation are summarized by Lewis (1964). Counce (1961), in reviewing literature on insect embryogenesis, indicated many unsolved problems in the causal analysis of early development; her bibliography contains numerous references to *Drosophila* (see also Bodenstein, 1953, for later stages, and Anderson, 1962, 1966). Goldschmidt (1955) has provided much interesting and relevant material in *Theoretical Genetics*. Recent bibliographies on *Drosophila* (Herskowitz, 1963; Fuchs, 1965; current issues of *D.I.S.*) show a growing emphasis on biochemical aspects of differentiation and particularly on the control of gene action and protein synthesis. Since developmental problems often touch on evolution and speciation, the following works may be of help for background reading: Dobzhansky (1951), Patterson and Stone (1952), Stone (1955), and Sturtevant (1961).

REFERENCES

AGRELL, I., 1964: Physiological and biochemical changes during insect development. In M. Rockstein (ed.), *The Physiology of Insecta*, Vol. I, Academic Press, New York, p. 91.

ANDERSON, D. T., 1962: The epigenetics of the larva in Diptera. *Acta Zool.* (Stockholm), 43: 221.

———, 1966: The comparative embryology of the Diptera. *Ann. Rev. Entomol.*, 11: 23.

BAKER, W. K., 1952: Permanent slides of salivary and ganglion chromosomes. *D.I.S.*, 26: 129.

BODENSTEIN, D., 1950: The postembryonic development of Drosophila. In M. Demerec (ed.), *Biology of Drosophila*, John Wiley & Sons, New York, p. 275.

———, 1953: Postembryonic development. In K. D. Roeder (ed.), *Insect Physiology*, John Wiley & Sons, New York, p. 822.

BRAVER, N. B., 1956: *The Mutants of Drosophila melanogaster Classified According to Body Parts Affected.* 36 pp. Carnegie Instn. of Wash. Publ., 552A.

BRIDGES, C. B., and K. S. BREHME, 1944: *The Mutants of Drosophila melanogaster*. 257 pp. Carnegie Instn. of Wash. Publ., 552.

BROWN, R. V., 1965: Control of *Histiostoma laboratorium* in *Drosophila* cultures. *J. Econ. Entomol.*, 58: 156.

———, 1966: Use of Kethane to control mites in *Drosophila*. *D.I.S.*, 41: 190.

COOPER, K. W., 1950: Normal spermatogenesis in *Drosophila*. In M. Demerec (ed.), *Biology of Drosophila*, John Wiley & Sons, New York, p. 1.

COUNCE, S. J., 1961: The analysis of insect embryogenesis. *Ann. Rev. Entomol.*, 6: 295.

———, 1966: Whole mounts of *Drosophila* eggs. *D.I.S.*, 41: 195.

DAVID, M. J., and M.-F. CLAVEL, 1966: Essai de définition d'une température optimale pour le développement de la Drosophile. *C. R. Acad. Sc. Paris*, 262: 2159.

DEMEREC, M. (ed.), 1950: *Biology of Drosophila*. 1st ed., 632 pp. John Wiley & Sons, New York. 1965: 2nd ed. Hafner Publishing Co., New York.

———, and B. P. KAUFMANN, 1961: *Drosophila Guide. Introduction to the Genetics and Cytology of Drosophila melanogaster*. 7th ed., 47 pp. Carnegie Instn. of Wash.

DOANE, W. W., 1960a: Completion of meiosis in uninseminated eggs of *Drosophila melanogaster*. *Science*, 132: 677.

———, 1960b: Developmental physiology of the mutant *female sterile (2) adipose* of *Drosophila melanogaster*. II. Effects of altered environment and residual genome on its expression. *J. Exp. Zool.*, 145: 23.

———, 1961: Developmental physiology of the mutant *female sterile (2) adipose* of *Drosophila melanogaster*. III. Corpus allatum-complex and ovarian transplantations. *J. Exp. Zool.*, 146: 275.

DOBZHANSKY, T., 1951: *Genetics and the Origin of Species*. 3rd ed., 364 pp. Columbia University Press, New York.

DOLL, J. P., P. C. TREXLER, L. I. REYNOLDS, and G. R. BERNARD, 1963: The use of peracetic acid to obtain germ free invertebrate eggs for gnotobiotic studies. *Amer. Midland Natural.*, 69: 231.

EDE, D. A., and S. J. COUNCE, 1956: A cinematographic study of the embryology of *Drosophila melanogaster*. *Roux' Arch. für Entwmech.*, 148: 402.

ELLIS, J. F., 1959: Reversal of an adenine and a cytidine requirement in axenic *Drosophila* culture. *Physiol. Zool.*, 32: 29.

———: Personal communication.

FERRIS, G. F., 1950: External morphology of the adult. In M. Demerec (ed.), *Biology of Drosophila*, John Wiley & Sons, New York, p. 368.

FUCHS, M. S., 1965: Bibliography of the biochemical genetics of *Drosophila*. *D.I.S.*, 40: 105.

GEER, B. W., 1966: Comparison of some amino acid mixtures and proteins for the diet of *Drosophila melanogaster*. *Trans. Ill. State Acad. Sci.*, 59: 3.

GOLDSCHMIDT, R. B., 1955: *Theoretical Genetics*. 563 pp. University of California Press, Berkeley and Los Angeles, Calif.

GOTTLIEB, F. J., 1966: Punctureless preparation of insect specimens. *J. Roy. Micr. Soc.*, 85: 369.

HADORN, E., 1955: *Developmental Genetics and Lethal Factors*. (English transl.) 355 pp. John Wiley & Sons, New York.

———, 1965: Problems of determination and transdetermination. In *Genetic Control of Differentiation. Brookhaven Symp. in Biol.*, 18: 148.

HARKER, J. E., 1965: The effect of a biological clock on the developmental rate of *Drosophila* pupae. *J. Exp. Biol.*, 42: 323.

HENDRIX, N., and E. EHRLICH, 1965: A method for treating bacterial contamination of *Drosophila* cultures with antibiotics. *D.I.S.*, 40: 99.

HERSKOWITZ, I. H., 1953: *Bibliography on the genetics of Drosophila*. II. 212 pp. Alden Press, Oxford, Eng.

———, 1958: *Bibliography on the genetics of Drosophila*. III. 296 pp. Indiana University Press, Bloomington, Ind.

———, 1963: *Bibliography on the genetics of Drosophila*. IV. 344 pp. McGraw-Hill Book Co., New York.

HILDRETH, P. E., and J. C. LUCCHESI, 1963: Fertilization in *Drosophila*. I. Evidence for the regular occurrence of monospermy. *Devel. Biol.*, 6: 262.

HINTON, T., D. T. NOYES, and J. F. ELLIS, 1951: Amino acids and growth factors, in a chemically defined medium for *Drosophila*. *Physiol. Zool.*, 24: 335.

HUGHES, R., 1950: The genetics laboratory mite *Histiostoma laboratorium*, n. sp. (Anoetidae). *J. Wash. Acad. Sci.*, 40: 177.

IMAIZUMI, T., 1958: Recherches sur l'expression des facteurs létaux héréditaires chez l'embryon de la drosophile. V. Sur l'embryogénèse et le mode des létalités au cours du développement embryonnaire. *Cytologia*, 23: 270.

JURA, C., 1964a: Cytological and experimental observations on the origin and fate of the pole cells in *Drosophila virilis* Sturt. Part I. Cytological analysis. *Acta Biol. Crac., Zool.*, 7: 59.

———, 1964b: Cytological and experimental observations on the origin and fate of the pole cells in *Drosophila virilis* Sturt. Part II. Experimental analysis. *Acta Biol. Crac., Zool.*, 7: 89.

KING, J. C., 1959: Differences between populations in embryonic developmental rates. *Amer. Nat.*, 93: 171.

KING, R. C., and M. F. WOLFSBERG, 1957: Oogenesis in adult *Drosophila melanogaster*. VI. A comparison of oogenesis among *Drosophila melanogaster, virilis, pseudoobscura* and *gibberosa. Growth,* 21: 281.

LEWIS, E. B., 1964: Genetic control and regulation of developmental pathways. In M. Locke (ed.), *The Role of Chromosomes in Development*, Academic Press, New York, p. 231.

MAC INTYRE, R. J.: Personal communication.

MAHOWALD, A. P., 1962: Fine structure of pole cells and polar granules in *Drosophila melanogaster. J. Exp. Zool.*, 151: 201.

———, 1963a: Electron microscopy of the formation of the cellular blastoderm in *Drosophila melanogaster. Exptl. Cell Res.*, 32: 457.

———, 1963b: Ultrastructural differentiations during formation of the blastoderm in the *Drosophila melanogaster* embryo. *Devel. Biol.*, 8: 186.

MILLER, A., 1950: The internal anatomy and histology of the imago of *Drosophila melanogaster.* In M. Demerec (ed.), *Biology of Drosophila*, John Wiley & Sons, New York, p. 420.

MITTLER, S., and J. BENNETT, 1962: A simple food medium that requires no live yeast with the minimum of variables. *D.I.S.*, 36: 131.

MOYER, S. E., R. E. COMSTOCK, and L. H. BAKER, 1961: Efficient procedures for culturing *Drosophila* in disposable paper containers. *D.I.S.*, 35: 106.

MULLER, H. J., 1939: *Bibliography on the genetics of Drosophila.* 132 pp. Oliver and Boyd, Edinburgh.

———, 1962: *Studies in Genetics: The selected papers of H. J. Muller.* 618 pp. Indiana University Press, Bloomington, Ind.

———, and I. I. OSTER, 1963: Some mutational techniques in *Drosophila.* In W. J. Burdette (ed.), *Methodology in Basic Genetics*, Holden-Day, Inc., San Francisco, Calif., p. 249.

NICOLETTI, B., 1959: An efficient method for salivary gland-chromosome preparations. *D.I.S.*, 33: 181.

PATTERSON, J. T., and W. S. STONE, 1952: *Evolution in the Genus Drosophila.* 610 pp. The Macmillan Co., New York.

POULSON, D. F., 1945: Chromosomal control of embryogenesis in *Drosophila. Amer. Nat.*, 79: 340.

———, 1950: Histogenesis, organogenesis, and differentiation in the embryo of *Drosophila melanogaster* Meigen. In M. Demerec (ed.), *Biology of Drosophila*, John Wiley & Sons, New York, p. 168.

POULSON, D. F., and D. F. WATERHOUSE, 1960: Experimental studies on pole cells and midgut differentiation in Diptera. *Aust. J. Biol. Sci.*, 13: 541.

SANG, J. H., 1956: The quantitative nutritional requirements of *Drosophila melanogaster. J. Exp. Biol.*, 33: 45.

———, 1959: Circumstances affecting the nutritional requirements of *Drosophila melanogaster. Annals N.Y. Acad. Sci.*, 77: 352.

———, 1962: Selection for rate of larval development using *Drosophila melanogaster* cultured axenically on deficient diets. *Genet. Res., Camb.*, 3: 90.

———, and R. C. KING, 1961: Nutritional requirements of axenically cultured *Drosophila melanogaster. J. Exp. Biol.*, 38: 793.

SLIZYNSKI, B. M., 1944: A revised map of salivary gland chromosome 4. *J. Hered.*, 35: 322.

SMITH, S. G., 1940: A new embedding schedule for insect cytology. *Stain Tech.*, 15: 175.

SONNENBLICK, B. P., 1950: The early embryology of *Drosophila melanogaster.* In M. Demerec (ed.), *Biology of Drosophila*, John Wiley & Sons, New York, p. 62.

SPENCER, W. P., 1950: Collection and laboratory culture. In M. Demerec (ed.), *Biology of Drosophila*, John Wiley & Sons, New York, p. 535.

STALKER, H. D., and H. L. CARSON, 1963: A very serious parasite of laboratory *Drosophila.* Second report. *D.I.S.*, 38: 96.

STONE, W. S., 1955: Genetic and chromosome variability in *Drosophila. Cold Spr. Harb. Symp. Quant. Biol.*, 20: 256.

STRICKBERGER, M. W., 1962: *Experiments in Genetics with Drosophila.* 141 pp. John Wiley & Sons, New York.

STURTEVANT, A. H., 1937: Culture methods for Drosophila. In P. S. Galtsoff, F. E. Lutz, P. S. Welch, and J. G. Needham (eds.), *Culture Methods for Invertebrate Animals*, Comstock Publishing Co., New York, p. 437. 1959: 2nd ed., Dover Publications, Inc., New York.

———, 1961: *Genetics and Evolution: The selected papers of A. H. Sturtevant.* 334 pp. W. H. Freeman and Co., San Francisco, Calif.

WOLFSON, M., H. D. STALKER, and H. L. CARSON, 1957: A serious parasite of laboratory *Drosophila*. *D.I.S.*, 31: 170.

YOON, S.-B., and A. S. FOX, 1965: Permeability of premature eggs from *Drosophila* collected with the "ovitron." *Nature*, 206: 910.

Rotifers*

By C. W. Birky, Jr.

INTRODUCTION

Rotifers are small aquatic micrometazoans which possess well developed but simple digestive, reproductive, excretory, muscular, and nervous systems. As with other members of the phylum Aschelminthes, their body cavity is a pseudocoel filled with fluid. The class Rotifera includes three subclasses or orders: Monogononta, Bdelloidea, and Seisonidea. Useful general discussions of these organisms are given by Remane (1929), Hyman (1951), and de Beauchamp (1965). This article deals only with the monogonont and bdelloid rotifers, which possess a unique combination of unusual features making them ideally suited for certain types of studies in embryology and genetics. These include the ability to reproduce both asexually and sexually, extremely rapid and regular development, and ease of culturing large numbers of animals. The monogonont *Asplanchna* has been utilized most intensively for developmental genetics, and its culture and handling will be emphasized.

REPRODUCTION: LIFE CYCLES AND EMBRYOLOGY

The life cycle of the monogonont rotifers is outlined in Fig. 1. Two types of females are found in most species; these two types, mictic and amictic, are practically indistinguishable unless they either lay fertilized eggs or bear older embryos whose sex can be recognized. The maturing oocytes of the amictic female undergo an equational maturation division, similar to mitosis, so that the resulting ovum has a full diploid chromosome complement and is genetically identical to its parent. Such embryos develop by diploid parthenogenesis into diploid adult females. This amictic or asexual reproduction can be repeated indefinitely, resulting in the formation of large clones of females. Certain environmental stimuli, such as a change in the diet, cause amictic females to produce mictic female offspring. Maturing oocytes in mictic females undergo typical meiosis, forming haploid eggs. If the eggs are not fertilized, they develop by haploid parthenogenesis into haploid males. The males, which are usually very small and lack a digestive system, produce

* A major portion of the cytological and autoradiographic techniques described for use with *Asplanchna* were developed by Dr. Rossana Bignami; her work, and the collaboration of Sister M. Jacinta Bentfeld, is gratefully acknowledged. These studies were supported in part by Public Health Service Research Grant GM 12183, from the National Institutes of Health.

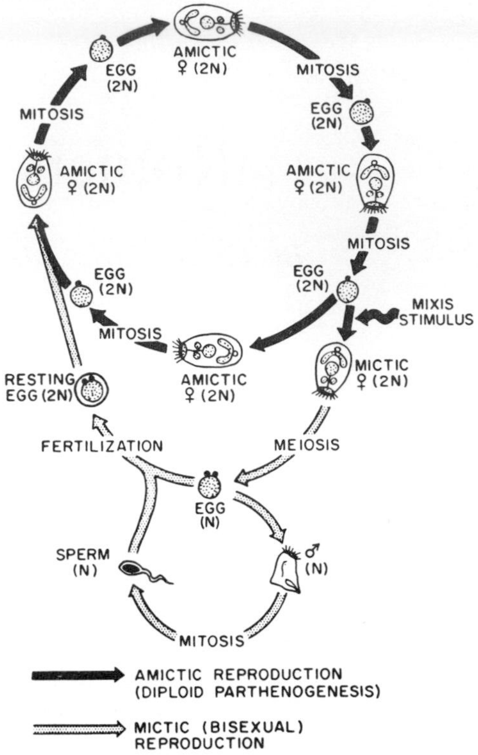

FIG. 1. Life cycle of the monogonont rotifers. "Mitosis" and "meiosis" refer to the oocyte maturation divisions in amictic and mictic females, respectively. SOURCE: Fig. 2 in C. W. Birky, *J. Exp. Zool.,* 155:275. Reprinted by permission.

sperm by a single equational maturation division. If the haploid eggs are fertilized, diploid zygotes with thick shells result. Such eggs may lie dormant over the winter and are called resting eggs. The zygote in a resting egg invariably becomes an amictic female. Among the bdelloid rotifers, there are no mictic females and no males, and consequently the sexual mode of reproduction appears to be lacking completely.

The reproductive system of the female monogononts and bdelloids consists of three main parts: (1) the germarium, a group of primary oocytes; (2) the vitellarium, which synthesizes "yolk" and cytoplasm and delivers them to maturing oocytes in the manner of the nurse cells of some other organisms; and (3) the oviduct. In most rotifers, male and female parthenogenetic embryos have a shell formed around them; the eggs are laid and mature outside the body of the female. The process of oogenesis is extremely rapid, requiring a few hours, and the transfer of materials from vitellarium to maturing oocyte can be readily observed in living females. The male reproductive system consists of a testis and copulatory organ. During copulation, the male injects sperm through the female's body wall into the pseudocoel.

The development of rotifer embryos has been described by Nachtwey (1925) in great detail, and also by Zelinka (1891), Jennings (1896), Tannreuther (1919, 1920), de Beauchamp (1956), and Pray (1965). Development is mosaic (Lechner, 1966), and begins with a highly modified spiral cleavage. Detailed cell lineages have been worked out for the reproductive system and less complete lineages have been proposed for the other organs. Mitosis ceases about half way through development, although cell differentiation and morphogenesis continues. Rotifers show the phenomenon of eutely: each adult organ or tissue (with certain exceptions; cf. Birky and Field, 1966) contains a constant, species-specific number of nuclei. An adult female contains less than 1,000 nuclei in most species. Late in development, cell membranes break down and disappear, so that most tissues in the adult are syncytial.

Both the physiological and morphological aspects of the phenotype of many rotifer populations are highly responsive to the environment. In nature, this polymorphism may lead to seasonal changes in morphology (cyclomorphosis). In general, the phenotype of an adult rotifer is stable, but environmental influences such as qualitative changes in food supply may cause the offspring of the females subjected to the influences to have a phenotype different from that of their mothers (e.g., Gilbert, 1966). The induction of mixis is an example of such a physiological polymorphism. This responsiveness to the environment makes the detection of mutants difficult, but it offers the investigator a tool for the study of non-Mendelian hereditary influences on development.

Members of the genus *Asplanchna* are particularly useful as experimental organisms for several reasons. They are among the largest of the rotifers (adult females 600 μ or more in length, embryos about 100 μ in diameter). Adults do not have the tough lorica found in many rotifers, and are thus easily dissected. They are ovoviviparous; the parthenogenetic female and male embryos undergo complete development *in utero* and are not enclosed in a shell. These animals are completely planktonic, and because they lack a foot they cannot attach to the walls of culture vessels or pipettes and are easily handled.

OBTAINING STOCKS

Rotifers may be collected from almost any body of fresh water. *Asplanchna brightwelli* and *A. girodi* prefer small ponds with a slightly alkaline pH and rich in organic matter. A small plankton net on a long pole is useful for collecting planktonic rotifers. When collections are made, a quantity of water from the source should be taken to the laboratory for use in initial culture attempts. Collections must be kept from overheating or freezing during transportation; a Thermos jug is useful. In the laboratory the samples of plankton or of vegetation in water are placed in shallow dishes and examined with a stereoscopic dissecting microscope. Rotifers are picked up in micropipettes and isolated in filtered water from the source of the collection. In initial culture attempts, it may be desirable to acclimate rotifers to the culture medium by rearing several asexual generations in culture medium diluted with such filtered water. Useful references for the identification of rotifers include Edmondson (1959), Pennak (1953), and Voigt (1957). Stocks of *Asplanchna*, as well as information about possible sources of other species, may be obtained by writing to the author of this article.

MATERIALS

Stereoscopic microscopes with magnifications of 10× to 90× are indispensable for routine observation and handling of cultures and of embryos; the microscopes should have substage mirrors for transmitted light. A compound phase-contrast microscope is extremely useful for cytological examination of the highly transparent, living rotifers. Animals are immobilized (for observation) by compressing them under a cover slip supported by thin glass fibers, or better, in a microcompression chamber (Biological Institute, Philadelphia, Pa.).

In general, rotifers may be conveniently handled using materials and methods similar to those used with protozoa (e.g., Sonneborn, 1950). Individual adult rotifers and very small cultures are most easily grown in thick Pyrex triple depression slides with the sides ground for labeling with a charcoal pencil. Slide cultures must be kept in moist chambers to avoid evaporation and bacterial contamination. Larger cultures are maintained in plastic tissue culture dishes, culture tubes, or flasks. Glassware used for cultures must not be used for toxic chemicals, and preferably glass used for cultures should be washed separately. Culture glassware may be washed with soap, but it must be rinsed thoroughly with hot tap water and distilled water; the final rinses should be in water from a glass still. Pasteur pipettes are used for handling large numbers of animals. Micropipettes for handling individuals or eggs are drawn from Pasteur pipettes to bore diameters slightly larger than the diameter of the animals. Bulbs for the pipettes must be of soft rubber to allow accurate control and avoid fatigue. To avoid accidental transfer of animals and contamination of cultures with foreign microorganisms, pipettes are rinsed after each use in boiling distilled water. If it is important to avoid bacterial contamination of cultures, a transfer hood with plastic front is desirable. The hood encloses the microscope (with the oculars projecting to the outside), hot plate with boiling water, and instruments; the hood may be sterilized with a germicidal ultraviolet lamp. Glassware should be autoclaved; pipettes are plugged with cotton and autoclaved in suitable containers, after which the rubber bulbs are added.

METHODS FOR CULTURING AND GENETICS

Asplanchna

The following methods have been developed for culturing *A. brightwelli* and *A. girodi* (Birky, 1964, 1965). The basic medium is a culture of the food organism *Paramecium aurelia*, which has been grown on *Aerobacter aerogenes* in an infusion of baked lettuce leaves according to the methods of Sonneborn (1950). Fresh lettuce leaves are washed in distilled water, spread on filter paper, and baked in an oven at 180°C until they are brown. Blackened and green portions of the leaves are discarded and the remainder ground to a powder with a mortar and pestle. The powder is boiled in distilled water at a concentration of 1.5 gm per liter for 15 to 20 minutes, allowed to cool, and filtered through paper in a Buchner funnel. Calcium carbonate ($CaCO_3$) is added to saturation (0.1 gm per liter) as a buffer and the baked lettuce infusion is autoclaved. The pH should be about 6.8. The medium is inoculated with *Aerobacter* (maintained on nutrient agar slants at 31°C) and incubated 48 hours at 31°C. The cloudy bacterized fluid is decanted off the $CaCO_3$ and the pH adjusted to 6.8, if necessary, with sterile saturated $Ca(OH)_2$ or 1 *N* HCl. Paramecia are added at such a concentration that they will "clear" the bacteria from the culture medium in about 24–36 hours at 27°C, and the culture is used after 48 hours. A portion of the cleared culture is added to a fresh batch of bacterized lettuce medium for future use and the remainder adjusted to pH 7.5 ± 0.1. The concentration of paramecia is approximately doubled by adding concentrated paramecia centrifuged from a portion of the same culture. The resulting fluid, called Medium 29, should contain $3\text{–}4 \times 10^3$ paramecia per milliliter.

Concentrated paramecia for feeding rotifer cultures are obtained by centrifuging a paramecium culture at low speed in an International Oil Testing Centrifuge until most of the paramecia are loosely packed in the bottom of the pear-shaped 125-ml tube. About 2 ml of fluid containing the pellet are removed with a pipette. The "cleared" baked lettuce infusion remaining after removal of the paramecia may be filtered through paper and then through a sterile Millipore filter (type HA), and retained for use with *Eudorina*, etc., in the induction of mixis.

Slide cultures of *Asplanchna* are initiated by introducing 1 to 20 female rotifers into 0.5 to 1.0 ml of Medium 29 in a slide depression. Tube and flask cultures are usually begun at concentrations of 10 to 20 females per milliliter. If higher initial concentrations are used, the rotifers and their progeny may "clear" the culture (consume all paramecia) in less than 24 hours. In crowded cultures, cannibalism may follow exhaustion of the food supply. Cultures at concentrations of up to about 50 females per milliliter can be maintained by adding an excess of concentrated paramecia once or twice daily. Tubes and flasks are filled no more than two-thirds full in order to maintain a favorable surface:volume ratio. Our cultures are routinely kept at 23°C in constant light.

Cultures are usually fed every 1 to 3 days, or when cleared. At the same time, the population density is adjusted to the desired level. Slide cultures are fed by transferring the rotifers to fresh culture fluid with micropipettes or by adding a drop of concentrated paramecia. Mass cultures in tubes or flasks may be fed in one of several ways: (1) concentrated paramecia are added to the cleared culture; (2) the volume of the culture is doubled or trebled by the addition of Medium 29 with about twice the usual concentration of paramecia; (3) a micropipette is used to remove fluid with a minimum of animals and the remaining animals are fed Medium 29; (4) the culture is placed in a centrifuge tube and chilled to about 4°C. At this temperature the rotifers swim sluggishly and settle to the bottom, after which they are collected with a pipette and placed in fresh fluid. To insure recovery of all animals, the chilled culture may be centrifuged briefly. Whatever feeding methods are used, the animals should be put in completely fresh Medium 29 once a week to insure healthy cultures. If cultures are kept at 16°C, the reproductive rate is lowered and feeding may be required only about once every 4 days.

The fertilized resting eggs produced by bisexual reproduction settle to the bottom of culture containers and lie dormant for a minimum of about 1 day before hatching. It is thus possible to maintain pure clones even in the presence of bisexual reproduction by pipetting culture fluid from the bottom of tube cultures daily to remove resting eggs, or by transferring animals and fluid from the top of the culture to a fresh container. Resting eggs are removed from large flask cultures after the contents of the flasks have been concentrated by centrifugation.

Occasionally, cultures of *Asplanchna* show a marked decline in reproductive rate for unknown reasons. Such depressed cultures may sometimes be "cured" by daily transfer to fresh culture fluid. Contamination of cultures with certain filamentous bacteria which entangle the rotifers and prevent feeding may result in loss of stocks. Filamentous bacteria and some other contaminants may be eliminated by growing the rotifers for 1 to 2 days in the presence of 500 μg per milliliter of penicillin. Contaminants may also be eliminated by washing the paramecia (procedure given by Sonneborn, 1950) and the rotifers. Only newborn female rotifers may be washed effectively, in the following manner: resting eggs, or mature amictic females bearing older embryos, are washed five times through Medium 29 with penicillin. The eggs or adults are left in the fifth wash and, at frequent intervals, newborn females are collected and washed five more times.

The baked lettuce infusion used to prepare Medium 29 may be replaced by similar infusions made with Cerophyl (obtained from Cerophyl Laboratories, Inc., Kansas City, Mo.) or Scottish grass (Meadow, 1965; obtained from M. McIntyre Co., Edinburgh, Scotland). The $CaCO_3$ buffer may be replaced by 0.4 gm per liter Na_2HPO_4. If desired, *Asplanchna* can be reared in saline solutions to which are added concentrated paramecia or other food organisms. Suitable solutions are those of Dryl (1959), Gilbert (1963), and Pace (Hopkins and Pace, 1937). De Beauchamp (1938) and Pourriot (1965) found that some stocks of *A. brightwelli* and *A. girodi* could not be reared indefinitely on a diet of *Paramecium caudatum*. They were able to culture these species on small rotifers (*Rhinops*, *Anuraea*, *Brachionus*, or *Keratella*) which in turn were raised on algae (see below). The very common species *A. priodonta* has never been successfully reared in the laboratory on any diet.

Cultures of *A. brightwelli* and *A. girodi* fed Medium 29 usually consist predominantly or entirely of amictic females. Occasionally, such cultures produce mictic females for unknown reasons. In the absence of such "spontaneous" mixis, cultures of *A. brightwelli* can be induced to produce large numbers of mictic females by feeding them the alga *Eudorina elegans*. The algae are collected by centrifugation from cultures in soil water, washed by centrifugation through sterile cleared lettuce infusion, and suspended in the same medium at about 10^4 colonies per milliliter. A slightly more effective mixis-inducing stimulus is *Paramecium bursaria* with symbiotic zoochlorellae. These paramecia are reared in baked lettuce infusion on *Aerobacter cloacae* in continuous light. Female rotifers are introduced into a suspension of *Eudorina* or *P. bursaria*; after about 1 week, a large number of males are observed in the culture, denoting the presence of a high percentage of mictic females which can be used for breeding. After mixis induction, it may be desirable to feed the culture *P. aurelia* for a few days, as the animals reproduce rather slowly on the inducing organisms.

Appropriate methods of mixis induction must be worked out by trial and error for each stock or species of *Asplanchna*, and the above methods may not be suitable for all. These methods are, for example, not effective with any of my stocks of *A. girodi*, and frequently fail with a stock of *A. sieboldi*. Lechner (1966) describes a culture technique which allows control of mixis in *A. girodi*. Gilbert (1965) induces mixis in *Asplanchna* by feeding them paramecia which have previously ingested large numbers of *Chlamydomonas* or *Euglena*. The latter are easily grown on plates of Difco Euglena Agar, from which they are washed into Gilbert's (1963) solution. This indirect method is necessary because the rotifers will not utilize small, unicellular algae directly as a food source.

After one has obtained a clone with a high percentage of mictic females, selfing is carried cut by simply allowing the males to fertilize the females in the same clonal culture. For crosses between two different clones, newborn virgin females must be obtained (females which have begun to reproduce cannot be fertilized). Mature females bearing older embryos are selected from a mictic culture and placed in a separate dish. Newborn females are removed from this dish at frequent intervals. If males are found in the container, they are removed immediately and newborn females also present are used for selfing or discarded, as they may not be virgin. The virgin females are placed immediately in a few drops of Medium 29 in depressions with males of the appropriate type. Males and females may be left together overnight; on the following day the impregnated mictic females are recognized by the presence of resting eggs or by a brownish coloration of their vitellaria.

Resting eggs may be hatched by leaving them at 23°C in Medium 29; newborn females should be removed daily. The eggs may also be stored indefinitely at 4°C in Dryl's (1959) solution or other suitable saline solution without hatching. They may subsequently be induced to hatch by placing them in Medium 29 at room temperature. There is some decrease in hatchability after eggs have been stored at 4°C for several months.

Other Rotifers

Unlike the carnivorous *Asplanchna*, most rotifers may be reared in the laboratory on bacteria and/or small algae. Handling methods may be similar to those described above, with suitable modifications required for animals which attach to the walls of culture containers and routinely lay eggs. Special mention should be made of *Epiphanes* (formerly *Hydatina*) *senta*, one of the most useful and intensively studied monogononts. These animals may be grown on the colorless alga *Polytoma*, in which case most of the animals are amictic. Feeding *Chlamydomonas* to the cultures induces mixis with great reproducibility. Hertel (1942) gives some methods for culturing and doing crosses with this species. Meadow (1965) grows the monogonont *Philodina* directly on *A. aerogenes* in baked lettuce infusion or, in isolation cultures, in bacterized Scottish grass infusion diluted with an equal volume of Gilbert's (1963) solution. A variety of other bacteria-supporting media have been used, such as infusions of malted milk (Finesinger, 1926), wheat grains (Kwasikpui, 1960), or oat grains (Miller, 1931). Alternatively, many species may be reared on algae in inorganic media such as filtered pond or spring water (Lansing and Lamy, 1961; Nathan and Laderman, 1959), Loomis' BVC medium (Laderman and Guttman, 1963), soil water (Buchner, 1941), diluted Knop's solution (Lansing, 1942), or diluted Bennecke's solution (Miller, 1931; de Beauchamp, 1938). Many of these solutions also serve directly as culture media for the algae. For example, de Beauchamp (1938) grew a number of rotifer species by simply adding them directly to dense cultures of *Chlorella* in 5–20 percent Bennecke's solution. Though *Chlorella* may be the most generally useful algal food for the smaller rotifers, it is not suitable for some. Among the most extensive and useful studies on rotifer nutrition are those of Pourriot (1957, 1958, 1963, 1965), who has attempted to rear many different species on a variety of green algae, brown algae, and diatoms.

In most cases, no attempt has been made to eliminate contaminating microorganisms from rotifer cultures. However, dixenic and monoxenic cultures on bacteria or bacteria plus *Chlorella* have been reported by Miller (1931), Nathan and Laderman (1959), and Dougherty (1963). Finally, Dougherty's group has had some success with axenic culture in an undefined medium (see Dougherty and Harris, 1964).

IN VITRO METHODS FOR EMBRYOS

Experimental studies on rotifer embryos have been limited almost entirely to *Asplanchna*. Attempts to operate on embryos *in utero* have failed, as it is difficult to immobilize the females; also, puncture wounds made by inserting needles through the body wall fail to heal and the animals die of sepsis and/or osmotic shock. Lechner (1966) avoided these problems by using an ultraviolet microbeam to destroy regions of embryos selectively *in utero*. Preliminary attempts to devise an artificial culture medium for embryos have failed. However, the following simple method gives good results for short-term *in vitro* growth of embryos, and can probably be utilized for any ovoviviparous rotifer.

A small number (10–20) of females bearing embryos in the desired stages are washed by transferring them through two to five changes of sterile Dryl's solution and finally through one change of distilled water. Penicillin may be included in the early washes. The animals are then placed in a small drop of water on a clean microscope slide within a low wall of wax. The water is removed with a very fine pipette and then with a small triangle of bibulous paper. The remaining fluid is allowed to evaporate, until the animals are very slightly wrinkled. The live, but externally dry, rotifers are now covered with a layer of high-viscosity (no. 10) Kel-F oil (Minnesota Mining and Manufacturing Company, St. Paul, Minn.) or paraffin oil, which prevents further evaporation. Each female is then carefully ripped open with fine glass or steel needles (the latter can be made by grinding insect pins on a fine stone). Pseudocoel cavity fluid (PCF) is thus liberated from the females and forms a drop under the oil, adhering to the slide. Embryos or adult organs are dissected out into the PCF and the remaining maternal tissue is removed with the needles.

Embryos in this environment develop normally for several hours, and are accessible to mechanical or chemical operations. Adult muscle tissue will retain contractility and cilia will beat for up to 24 hours. For observation at high magnifications, the embryos in the PCF may be transferred to an oil-filled culture chamber made by sealing a cover slip with wax over a circular hole drilled through an ordinary microscope slide. Embryos lying on the cover slip in such a chamber may be observed with bright-field or phase-contrast illumination in an inverted microscope; the behavior of nuclei and spindles during mitosis is clearly visible. Transfers of embryos are made with fine glass pipettes drawn from Pyrex tubing (O.D. 1 mm, I.D. 0.8 mm) to a diameter slightly greater than that of the embryos. The tips of the pipettes should be broken straight across and fire-polished if possible; the de Fonbrune microforge is convenient for this purpose. Pipettes are inserted in a Leitz microtool holder, which in turn is attached to an 0.2 ml Gilmont micrometer syringe (Cole-Parmer), or similar instrument, by plastic tubing. The entire system is filled with the same oil used in the culture chambers.

The period of normal development *in vitro* may be lengthened by the following modifications in procedure. The donor females under oil are covered, prior to dissection, with a large volume of PCF obtained previously from a separate group of females (50–100 if possible). Such extra PCF may be frozen under oil and stored at −20°C; freezing also kills most or all bacteria and thus helps to eliminate troublesome bacterial contamination of the cultures. Contamination may also be retarded in cultures infected with bacteria by removing most of the PCF and replacing it with fresh fluid. Dissection of embryo donor females should be as gentle as possible; repeated handling of embryos, as in transfers to different containers, is detrimental. If the animals are to be observed repeatedly in a compound microscopc, an infrared-absorbing filter should be placed between the microscope lamp and the culture to avoid heating the pseudocoel cavity fluid. If these precautions are taken, most embryos at any stage of development will develop normally *in vitro* for 8 to 10 hours. Thereafter, development slows and cytological abnormalities appear. Complete normal development from egg to adult has not been achieved; it would require about 20 hours.

AUTORADIOGRAPHY OF ADULTS AND EMBRYOS

Adult *Asplanchna* rapidly take up small molecules from their environment. Deoxyribonucleic acid (DNA) in adult vitellarium nuclei and cytoplasm, and in embryos in the mitotic stage of development, may be labeled by exposing female rotifers to 100 μc per milliliter of tritiated thymidine in Dryl's solution for 1 to 5 hours. The monogonont *Philodina* will not incorporate radioactive amino acids or nucleosides directly from the medium. Meadow (1965) uses the following method for labeling adult and embryonic tissues in this species. Labeled amino acids or nucleosides with specific activity of about 10 c per millimole are added directly to sterilized Scottish grass infusion at about 5–10 μc per milliliter. This medium is inoculated with *Aerobacter* and incubated 1 day. The rotifers are then allowed to feed on the labeled bacteria for several hours before fixation.

Asplanchna embryos and vitellaria may also be labeled *in vitro*. A spherical drop of tritiated thymidine or uridine in distilled water is injected into the oil of a culture chamber. The floating drop may be measured with an ocular micrometer before it is pushed down to the cover slip with a needle and fused to the glass. A drop of PCF of appropriate volume and containing the embryo(s) to be labeled is attached to the cover slip adjacent to the precursor. When the embryo is in an appropriate stage, the two drops are pushed together with a needle. Label uptake is stopped by addition of fixative. Labeling for 1 minute with 100 μc per milliliter of tritiated thymidine will produce adequate grain densities if the embryo is labeled during the DNA synthetic period. For longer periods of exposure of adult or embryonic tissues, donor females under oil are simply ripped open gently, but not dissected, and the labeled precursor added. This method permits normal functioning of tissues *in vitro* for longer periods of time, and is especially useful for labeling vitellaria which are easily damaged if removed completely from the donor animals.

After labeling, animals are fixed and either squashed or sectioned for autoradiography. For squashes, embryos labeled *in vitro* are fixed 10 minutes in ice-cold 45 percent acetic acid. They are then placed on a subbed slide in a very small drop of the acetic acid, covered with a silicone-coated cover slip, and left for 10 minutes. The embryos are then squashed gently and left for another 10 to 20 minutes. The slide is now placed on a block of dry ice or on an aluminum bar previously chilled by immersion in liquid nitrogen. When the slide is covered with frost, the cover slip may be flipped off with a razor blade. The slide is placed in 3:1 methanol:acetic acid for 10 minutes, then transferred to 50 percent and 30 percent ethanol and water for 5 minutes each. The slides are now hydrolyzed 10 minutes in 1 *N* HCl at 60°C, rinsed in water, stained for 5 minutes in aceto-orcein, and finally rinsed in water and air dried.

For sections, animals may be fixed in Carnoy's fluid, formaldehyde, glutaraldehyde, or osmic acid. Adult rotifers usually contract strongly and permanently upon contact with fixatives. *Asplanchna* usually expand again during dehydration, but other species should be narcotized before fixation. Meadow (1965) gets a high percentage of extended *Philodina* by concentrating the animals in a small volume of culture fluid and adding about 1/10 volume of 1 percent cocaine hydrochloride in 50 percent methanol. The animals are then immediately fixed by freeze substitution. *Asplanchna* may be narcotized, if necessary, by exposure to 0.1 percent Novocain for about 15 minutes; after this treatment, most or all females remain viable and reproduce if they are washed free of the narcotic. Other narcotization procedures are given by Pennak (1953) and Voigt (1957). It is extremely difficult to embed small numbers of rotifers or embryos in paraffin successfully. They are easily embedded in

Epon or methacrylate; techniques are given by Pease (1964). A very soft methacrylate mixture is easiest to section and gives adequate preservation of structure for light microscopy. Meadow (1965) embeds rotifers in pure butyl methacrylate. Pieces of methacrylate with individual animals are then cut out of the block and embedded in any desired orientation in a very hard paraffin (Fisher's 61°C Tissuemat). The resulting paraffin-Epon block is sectioned with an ordinary steel microtome knife; the outer layer of paraffin allows ribbons to be formed. Plastic-embedded sections are usually cut at 0.5–2 μ and transferred to subbed glass slides. If methacrylate is used, the plastic may usually be removed from sections with organic solvents such as xylol and then subjected to enzyme extraction or stained. Epon is difficult to remove from sections. Adult *Asplanchna* which are to be embedded in this plastic can be punctured with needles after fixation and treated with acid or enzymes prior to embedding. After sections or squashes have been prepared, they may be subjected to autoradiography [techniques are given by Caro and others in Prescott (1964)].

REFERENCES

BEAUCHAMP, P. DE, 1938: Les cultures de Rotifères sur Chlorelles. Premiers résultats en milieu septique. *Trav. Stat. Zool. Wimereux*, 13: 27.

———, 1956: Le développement de *Ploesoma Hudsoni* (Imhof) et l'origine des feuillets chez les rotifères. *Bull. Soc. Zool. France*, 81: 374.

———, 1965: Classe des Rotifères. In P. Grassé (ed.), *Traité de Zoologie*, 4 (3), Masson et Cie, Paris, p. 1225.

BIRKY, C. W., JR., 1964: Studies on the physiology and genetics of the rotifer, *Asplanchna*. I. Methods and physiology. *J. Exp. Zool.*, 155: 273.

———, 1965: Studies on the physiology and genetics of the rotifer, *Asplanchna*. II. The genic basis of a case of male sterility. *J. Exp. Zool.*, 158: 349.

———, and BONNIE FIELD, 1966: Nuclear number in the rotifer *Asplanchna:* intraclonal variation and environmental control. *Science*, 151: 585.

BUCHNER, H., 1941: Experimentelle Untersuchungen über den Generationswechsel der Rädertiere. II. *Zool. Jahrb.*, 60: 279.

DOUGHERTY, E. C., 1963: Cultivation and nutrition of micrometazoa. III. The minute rotifer *Lecane inermis* (Bryce, 1892) Harring, 1913. *J. Exp. Zool.*, 153: 183.

———, and L. C. HARRIS, 1964: Renewed axenic cultivation of the monogonont rotifer, *Lecane inermis*. *Am. Zoologist*, 4: 286 (abstr.).

DRYL, S., 1959: Antigenic transformation in *Paramecium aurelia* after homologous antiserum treatment during autogamy and conjugation. *J. Protozool.*, 6 (suppl.): 25 (abstr.).

EDMONDSON, W. T. (ed.), 1959: *Fresh-water Biology*. 2nd ed., John Wiley & Sons, Inc., New York.

FINESINGER, J. E., 1926: Effect of certain chemical and physical agents on fecundity and length of life, and on their inheritance in a rotifer, *Lecane* (*Distyla*) *inermis* (Bryce). *J. Exp. Zool.*, 44: 63.

GILBERT, J. J., 1963: Mictic female production in the rotifer *Brachionus calyciflorus*. *J. Exp. Zool.*, 153: 113.

———, 1965: Personal communication.

———, 1966: Rotifer ecology and embryological induction. *Science*, 151: 1234.

HERTEL, E. W., 1942: Studies on vigor in the rotifer *Hydatina senta*. *Physiol. Zool.*, 15: 304.

HYMAN, L., 1951: *The Invertebrates.* Vol. III: Acanthocephala, Aschelminthes, *and* Entoprocta. McGraw-Hill, New York.

HOPKINS, D., and D. PACE, 1937: The culture of *Amoeba proteus* Leidy *Partim* Schaeffer.

In J. Needham (ed.), *Culture Methods for Invertebrate Animals*, Comstock Publishing Company, Inc., Ithaca, N.Y.

JENNINGS, H. S., 1896: The early development of *Asplanchna Herrickii* de Guerne. *Bull. Mus. Comp. Zool. Harvard*, 30: 1.

KWASIKPUI, D. B., 1960: Suggested method for the maintenance of rotifer culture. *Turtox News*, 38: 267.

LADERMAN, A. D., and H. N. GUTTMAN, 1963: Induction of sexuality by alteration of photoperiod in the rotifer *Brachionus rubens*. *J. Exp. Zool.*, 152: 5.

LANSING, A. I., 1942: Some effects of hydrogen ion concentration, total salt concentration, calcium, and citrate on longevity and fecundity of the rotifer. *J. Exp. Zool.*, 91: 155.

———, and F. LAMY, 1961: Fine structure of the cilia of rotifers. *J. Biophys. Biochem. Cytol.*, 9: 799.

LECHNER, M., 1966: Untersuchungen zur Embryonalentwicklung des Rädertieres *Asplanchna girodi* de Guerne. *Roux' Arch. Entwickl.-mech.*, 157: 117.

MEADOW, N., 1965: Personal communication.

MILLER, H. M., 1931: Alternation of generations in the rotifer *Lecane inermis* Bryce. *Biol. Bull.*, 60: 345.

NACHTWEY, R., 1925: Untersuchungen über die Keimbahn, Organogenese und Anatomie von *Asplanchna priodonta* Gosse. *Zeit. wiss. Zool.*, 126: 239.

NATHAN, H. A., and A. D. LADERMAN, 1959: Rotifers as biological tools. *Ann. N.Y. Acad. Sci.*, 77: 96.

PEASE, D. C., 1964: *Histological Techniques for Electron Microscopy*. 2nd ed., Academic Press, New York.

PENNAK, R. W., 1953: *Fresh-water Invertebrates of the United States.* Ronald Press Company, New York.

POURRIOT, R., 1957: Sur la nutrition des Rotifères à partir des Algues d'eau douce. *Hydrobiologia*, 9: 50.

———, 1958: Sur l'élevage des Rotifères au laboratoire. *Hydrobiologia*, 11: 189.

———, 1963: Utilisation des Algues brunes unicellulaires pour l'élevage des Rotifères. *C.R. Acad. Sci.*, 256: 1603.

———, 1965: Recherches sur l'Écologie des Rotifères. *Vie et Milieu*, Supp. #20: 1.

PRAY, F. A., 1965: Studies on the early development of the rotifer *Monostyla cornuta* Müller. *Trans. Am. Microsc. Soc.*, 84: 210.

PRESCOTT, D. M. (ed.), 1964: *Methods in Cell Physiology*, Vol. I. Academic Press, New York.

REMANE, A., 1929: In *Bronn's Klassen und Ordnungen des Tier-Reichs*, 4: 2: 1: 1–4: 1.

SONNEBORN, T. M., 1950: Methods in the general biology and genetics of *Paramecium aurelia*. *J. Exp. Zool.*, 113: 87.

TANNREUTHER, G. W., 1919: Studies on the rotifer *Asplanchna Ebbsbornii*, with special reference to the male. *Biol. Bull.*, 37: 194.

———, 1920: The development of *Asplanchna Ebbsbornii* (rotifer). *J. Morph.*, 33: 389.

VOIGT, M., 1957: *Rotatoria: die Rädertiere Mitteleuropas.* Gebrüder Borntraeger, Berlin-Nikolassee.

ZELINKA, C., 1891: Studien über Rädertiere. III. Zur Entwicklungsgeschichte der Rädertiere nebst Bemerkungen über ihre Anatomie und Biologie. *Zeit. wiss. Zool.*, 53: 1.

Coelenterates

By Sears Crowell

INTRODUCTION

Developmental biologists have used coelenterates for many kinds of studies. Since nearly all species are marine, most investigators have worked at coastal stations. A suitable species has often meant merely the one available at Woods Hole, Naples, or other similar stations. No attempt has been made here to show which species can be obtained at each marine laboratory. The forms specifically mentioned are widely distributed and they also are among those which have been cultured successfully inland.

Hydra, hydroids, and other coelenterates seem to be the simplest of the true metazoa. The body can be visualized as a sac or cylinder with inner and outer epithelia between which lies a secreted, mostly noncellular mesoglea. The internal cavity is a digestive space with a single opening, usually surrounded by tentacles.

Actually great diversity of form and life history is found among coelenterates and the explanation of this diversity is one of the tasks of the experimental morphologist. The life cycle of coelenterates is so variable that generalizations are almost absurd. In the case of hydrozoans and scyphozoans, medusae (jellyfish) produce gametes; and sometimes the zygotes then develop almost directly into medusae without there being any long-lived larval or juvenile stage. More commonly a zygote develops into a polyp, and the polyp produces further polyps by budding. If, as commonly happens, these remain attached to one another, a "colony" results. In the case of hydrozoa we call these hydroids, or hydroid colonies, or colonial hydroids. There may be polymorphism of the "individuals" (polyps or zooids) of the "colony." There can be much coordination within such an organism, and precise arrangement of the component members. In many species the polypoid form produces medusae by budding, but it is even more common for the medusa to be incompletely developed, or entirely suppressed (as in hydra). Whether the series sketched above represents the evolutionary history is uncertain. It is, however, pertinent that most studies of morphogenetic processes have been carried forward using hydroid organisms which are clearly not adult in organization.

It may be added that "completion" of a life cycle to the sexual phase may be unnecessary in some species. Hydra appears to be able to continue indefinitely only by budding. We have observed a natural population of *Craspedacusta* for 17 years which produces only female medusae and is presumably kept going only by asexual methods. We have kept a culture of scyphozoan polyps for 10 years.

SOME PROPERTIES OF COELENTERATES

Embryology

The experimental morphologist is likely to associate coelenterates with studies of regeneration (polarity, gradients) and reconstitution, rather than with work on developing eggs. However, at a marine station eggs may be obtained from a wide variety of species, at least seasonally. At Woods Hole *Pennaria* and *Hydractinia* have been used most.

Normal development of eggs, settling and metamorphosis of planulae, separation of blastomeres, and similar studies have rarely been attempted inland. However, *Hydractinia* was successfully carried through several sexual generations by Hauenschild (1954); Miller obtained good sperm and both he and I obtained good planulae from *Campanularia*. (See directions below.)

Regeneration

Scores of investigators have sought a clearer understanding of the events of regeneration, the guiding agencies, and the phenomenon of polarity through the use of hydra and hydroids. The stems of almost any hydroid can be cut into sections for simple experiments on regeneration suitable for a beginning zoology class. Most pieces will produce a hydranth at one end within 2 days, and nearly always in correspondence with the original polarity. Modifications may be introduced to cause reversal of polarity: placing one end in sand, capping one end with a fine capillary, putting the two ends at different O_2 tensions—using a barrier between two sides of a culture dish.

Grafting experiments may be carried out to combine parts at different levels. Perhaps the first demonstration of induction or organizer action was by Browne in 1909. A bit of hypostome transplanted to the column of hydra led to production of a secondary hydranth by the host tissue. The words used by Browne (later E. B. Harvey or Mrs. E. N. Harvey) are of some historical interest: *stimulate*, *instigate*, and *call forth*.

Normal Growth

We now have scores of reports dealing with nearly all aspects of hydra's morphogenetic behavior: the general patterns of growth and budding (Brien and Reniers-Decoen, 1949), localization of mitosis (Burnett, 1959; Campbell, 1965), fine structure (Lentz and Barrnett, 1965), control of sexuality (Loomis, 1954), other biochemical aspects (Lenhoff, 1965).

Much less is known of the control of form in hydroids. A formal explanation of the diverse patterns seen in the different species can be obtained by a concept of localized growth zones ("animal meristems") but recent reexamination of this question by use of vital stains makes this whole proposition seem unlikely (Hale, 1964; Wyttenbach, 1965; Crowell, Wyttenbach, and Suddith, 1965).

Fulton (1961) developed a simple mathematical model or formula for the growth of *Cordylophora*, and Braverman and Schrandt (1964) have gone a step further by feeding rules to a computer and letting it make models of colonies of *Podocoryne*.

Polymorphism

In many hydroids there are ordinary polyps (hydranths, gastrozooids) and reproductive polyps (gonangia, gonozooids). In some species there are additional forms (dactylozooids, tentaculozooids, sarcostyles, etc.). The factors which lead to the production of one or another of the types are incompletely understood. *Hydractinia* (see below) has been most often used in this connection.

Reconstitution

Long ago Wilson (1911) demonstrated that disorganized clumps of cells of hydroids can reorganize to form normal small polyps. More recently close analyses of the phenomenon have been made by Beadle and Booth (1938), Zwilling (1963), and others. One need only obtain clean bits of stem, then squeeze out the living tissues from the enclosing perisarc using tweezers, a bent glass rod, or a "bit of shaped Tygon tubing held in a pair of forceps" (Zwilling). The tissue may be subdivided with fine instruments and then small clumps pushed into a pile. Often ectoderm and entoderm are separated during the squeezing-out process. Zwilling was able to obtain reconstitution from purely ectodermal cells in *Cordylophora*, and Steinberg (1963), using the polyp of a scyphozoan, has had similar results. The separation of layers was carried out merely by using fine dissecting instruments.

Tissue Culture

There are only a few studies in which coelenterate cells have been kept in tissue culture, but there appear to be no serious obstacles. Phillips (1961) may be consulted for methods.

Techniques

Operations with coelenterate polyps are comparatively easy. For any particular situation the investigator will quickly work out details himself. When necessary, marine forms can be narcotized with $MgSO_4$ or $MgCl_2$. Tissues can be held in place by tiny skewers of glass needles. Usually only brief contact between recently cut surfaces is adequate to make grafts adhere.

Nile blue sulfate, neutral red, or methylene blue may be used to stain specimens (1/10,000 or less concentration). Nile blue sulfate (probably the other vital stains as well) is useful for marking. The dye may be added to a 2 percent agar solution which is poured onto a glass plate while hot. After it sets and dries, flakes may be cut off and placed against the tissue to be stained. Hale (1964) used cellophane soaked in Nile blue sulfate for his marking studies. Green hydra may be "decolorized" by keeping them in 0.5 percent glycerine solution for 1 to 3 weeks (see Lenhoff and Muscatine, 1963). By this method identical stock of two colors can be obtained.

CULTURE METHODS

These general directions are known to apply to the following marine hydroids: *Bougainvillea*, *Hydractinia*, *Podocoryne*, *Obelia*, *Clytia*, *Campanularia*, and to the polyp stage of *Aurelia*. New cultures are initiated by putting a small piece of a colony (a stem, piece of stolon, or a few polyps) on a glass slide. This may be held in place by a thread tied around the slide. Alternatively a piece may be merely placed on a slide in an undisturbed dish until it attaches. Once stolons grow out and fasten themselves to the slide the old part can be removed. The water should be replaced at least twice a week. Most hydroids must be fed once a day to ensure good growth but can be maintained with less frequent feedings.

Feeding

Newly hatched larvae of the brine shrimp *Artemia* are the universal solution to the problem of feeding nearly any coelenterate. The exceptions are: the polyps of the fresh-water jellyfish, *Craspedacusta* (see below), colonial hydroids with tiny hydranths, *Schizotricha* for example, and probably some other untried species. Eggs may be purchased from dealers including the following:

Brine Shrimp Sales Company, Inc.
San Francisco Aquarium Society, Inc.
1655 West Winton Avenue
Hayward, California

Aquarium Stock Company, Inc.
27 Murray Street
New York, New York

Westchester Aquarium Supply Company
454 Mamaroneck Avenue
White Plains, New York

Brine shrimp eggs can be hatched out in sea water, synthetic sea water, or in sodium chloride solution. Loomis and Lenhoff (1956) prepared a stock solution by dissolving 5 pounds of commercial table salt in 2 gallons of hot tap water (= 360 gm per liter). This stock solution is diluted 100 × with tap water to make the solution for hatching eggs. Our own practice is to use sea water which has been discarded after use for hydroid culture.

Ten-inch finger bowls with water 3 cm deep are convenient. Loomis and Lenhoff (1956) recommend flat Corning 3-quart utility dishes. If one uses a floating ring of glass or rubber tubing the eggs can be placed within the ring; on hatching the nauplii escape from the enclosure and one can then pipette them off without getting unhatched eggs and egg shells. They nearly all collect on the lighted side of the dish. This method will work only if the eggs float. In the trade there are "San Francisco eggs" which float and "Salt Lake eggs" which do not. When the latter are used, the practice is to raise eggs in flasks through which air is bubbled.

Feeding may be managed by moving hydroids to a special feeding dish containing an excess of *Artemia* and then returning them to the culture dish, or *Artemia* in the "right" amount can be put into the culture dish. In hydra and *Campanularia*, egestion occurs 3–5 hours after feeding, hence it would be best if water were changed about 6 hours after feeding; however I know of no one who has found this necessary.

Sea Water

A useful compilation of articles on circulating sea water systems is available (Clark and Clark, 1964). For some purposes such systems may be inappropriate or unnecessary. The suggestions which follow apply to the latter condition.

Sea water may be obtained from the Supply Department, Marine Biological Laboratory, Woods Hole, Massachusetts or from other coastal dealers. Recent experience shows that synthetic sea water may be better than natural sea water. Synthetic sea salts are currently available from the following:

"Instant Ocean"
Aquarium Systems
1489 East 289th Street
Wickliffe, Ohio 44902

"Rila Salts"
Rila Products
P.O. Box 114
Teaneck, New Jersey

"Neptune Salts"
Westchester Aquarium Supply Company
454 Mamaroneck Avenue
White Plains, New York

If a circulating system is not used, it is probably less expensive to make new water than to purify the old. However, our practice has been to filter once-used water (through ordinary filter paper) and to use this in the dishes in which animals are fed.

This water, in turn, is filtered and used for the culture of *Artemia*.

Hauenschild (1954) used pasteurized sea water obtained by heating to 80°C for a half-hour on successive days. For most purposes this is probably unnecessary.

Some movement of water is desirable if animals are kept in small dishes (in contrast to an aquarium with constant circulation); they seem to do better if placed on a tray which can be moved gently to and fro. Ours moves 4 inches, 35 times a minute (Hauenschild, 1954).

For raising both polyps and medusae, Rees and Russell (1937) had a device by which a glass plate in a beaker was moved back and forth every minute or so to stir the water slightly. A magnetic stirrer may be used if it is not too close to the specimens.

NOTES CONCERNING MOST COMMONLY USED AND AVAILABLE FORMS

Most of the forms mentioned are available from the Supply Department, Marine Biological Laboratory, Woods Hole, Massachusetts and from other sources.

Hydractinia and *Podocoryne*. These hydroids live on shells occupied by hermit crabs, and have four types of polyps: gastrozooids, gonozooids, dactylozooids (spiral zooids), and (rarely) tentaculozooids. They have been used in analysis of factors which cause development of one zooid type rather than another, of transformation from one type to another, etc. (see Braverman, 1962). Both may be used in the study of individual specificity in respect to stolon fusion (Hauenschild, 1954).

Hydractinia. This is the genus of hydroids whose eggs have most commonly been used in the embryology and invertebrate courses at Woods Hole. Shedding of gametes is light-dependent. After a period of darkness of several hours a brief exposure to light results in shedding of eggs and sperms in 30–60 minutes (Costello *et al.*, 1957; Ballard, 1942).

Hauenschild successfully cultured *Hydractinia* for several years. Specimens were fastened to glass rods suspended at both ends by nylon threads. These colonies reached sexual maturity in a few months and usable gametes were obtained. Planulae settle in glass dishes and some transform to small polyps. Polyps at first are too small to feed on whole *Artemia* larvae and so must be hand-fed with fragments of larvae for a few days.

Cordylophora. This is a fresh-water athecate more easily cultured than most (Fulton, 1960). It is excellent for studies of tissue dissociation and reaggregation, and suitable for demonstration of polarity in stems. Although it can be kept in pond water, I have used and recommend 1 part sea water to 2 or 3 parts pond or distilled water. Fulton (1962) used a defined solution: $NaCl$, 0.05 *M*; KCl, 0.001 *M*; $CaCl_2$, 0.005 *M*; $MgCl_2$, 0.005 *M*; $NaHCO_3$, 0.001 *M*. ($KHCO_3$, 0.001 *M* may be substituted for the KCl and $NaHCO_3$.)

Bougainvillea. This is an athecate form which is easily kept. It produces a free medusa.

Tubularia. Because it has long, large stems this genus has probably been used more often than any other hydroid for studies of regeneration. Most investigators have been unable to keep it in culture.

Campanularia flexuosa. This hydroid is suitable for studies of patterns of growth (Crowell, 1957). It can be used for dissociation and regeneration experiments. Miller obtained usable sperm from material in culture. The eggs remain in the gonangia where, if fertilized, they develop to the planula stage. A newly started colony of *Campanularia* begins to produce gonangia after about 10 days.

Obelia geniculata. This is similar to *Campanularia* except that medusae are produced.

Laomedea. Some of the European authorities use this name for what are called *Campanularia* and *Obelia* by most Americans. The confusion is compounded by the use of *Campanularia* for what we call *Clytia*.

Aurelia. The polyp stage of this scyphozoan is hardy and easily cultured. New polyps are produced by budding. Feeding may be as infrequent as once a week. Spangenberg (1965) has obtained strobilization but the factors which induce it are not so well specified that reproducible results can be assured.

Hydra. Loomis and Lenhoff (1956) have described methods for raising hydra in mass cultures; for culture of smaller numbers their methods may easily be modified (see also Ham and Eakin, 1958). For the culture medium one may use pond water known to be satisfactory, or tap water if properly treated. Loomis added 20 gm $NaHCO_3$ and 10 gm Versene disodium salt to 1 liter of tap water; 20 ml of this stock solution was added to each gallon of tap water before use. If the tap water lacks sufficient calcium, 50 mg per liter $CaCl_2$ should be added. Alternatively, one may use distilled water to which is added $CaCl_2$ and $NaHCO_3$ each in 10^{-3} M concentration. Hydra are fed once a day with living brine shrimp larvae. The larvae are removed into a fine net (125 mesh) where they are washed briefly with tap water. They are then placed in fresh water and fed to the hydra promptly. After feeding, the water is poured from the dishes containing hydra and replaced with new water; this should be repeated. Unattached hydra that pour off in the culture water may be collected either by swirling the decanted water in round bowls (the hydra collect in the center as the water comes to rest), or by using a 38-mesh net which will retain the hydra but allow the shrimp to pass through. For maximum growth, water should also be changed about 6 hours after feeding by which time egestion has occurred. Bowls should be completely cleaned once a week.

Craspedacusta. Polyps of this fresh-water jellyfish grow well in culture. Lytle (1961) found that they do better in moving water, and that hand-feeding, using separately cultured *Aeolosoma*, gave good reproduction, including medusa production. The *Aeolosoma* were raised on rice agar plates which contained a mixture of bacteria and were prepared in the following manner. A thin layer of 1 percent agar was poured into sterile Petri dishes and five to eight rice grains (preheated in a dry test tube suspended in boiling water for 10 minutes) were added to each dish. A buffered salt solution was prepared from a stock solution containing 1.20 gm NaCl, 0.03 gm KCl, 0.04 gm $CaCl_2$, and 0.02 gm $NaHCO_3$ per liter. For use on the rice agar plates the stock solution was diluted 1:10 with glass-distilled water, poured into the plates after the agar hardened and then left to stand for 3 days. Then the plates were inoculated with about a dozen worms apiece and kept in moderate light. The density of the worm population becomes adequate as a food supply in about 2–4 weeks at 18.5°C. Small amounts of dechlorinated tap water and a few grains of preheated rice can be added from time to time. The plates provided thousands of worms in 1- to 2-month periods when maintained in this way.

I don't know of a reliable source for *Craspedacusta* polyps. Lytle and I obtained them by placing glass slides in racks in a quarry hole where medusae were known to be abundant (June and July are probably the best months). Payne found them merely by close inspection of rocks. At present there is a culture at Wisconsin and also at Pennsylvania State.

Sea Anemones. Most species are readily kept in aquaria, and may be fed with brine shrimp. For studies of regeneration I particularly recommend *Nematostella*, a small, simple, burrowing form, which is hardy and lives well even when unable to burrow.

REFERENCES

BALLARD, W. W., 1942: The mechanism for synchronous spawning in *Hydractinia* and *Pennaria. Biol. Bull.*, 82: 329.

BEADLE, L. C., and F. A. BOOTH, 1938: The reorganization of tissue masses of *Cordylophora lacustris* and the effect of oral cone grafts, with supplementary observations on *Obelia gelatinosa. J. Exp. Biol.*, 15: 303.

BRAVERMAN, M. H., 1962: *Podocoryne carnea*, a reliable differentiating system. *Science*, 135: 310.

———, and R. C. SCHRANDT, 1964: Computer generation of hypothetical hydroid colonies. *Amer. Zoologist*, 4: 380.

BRIEN, P., and M. RENIERS-DECOEN, 1949: La croissance, la blastogénèse, l'ovogénèse chez *Hydra fusca* (Pallas). *Bull. Biol. France et Belg.*, 83: 293.

BROWNE, E. N., 1909: The production of new hydranths in Hydra by the insertion of small grafts. *J. Exp. Zool.*, 7: 1.

BURNETT, A., 1959: Histophysiology of growth in hydra. *J. Exp. Zool.*, 140: 281.

CAMPBELL, R. D., 1965: Cell proliferation in Hydra; an autoradiographic approach. *Science*, 148: 1231.

CLARK, J. R., and R. L. CLARK, 1964: *Sea Water Systems for Experimental Aquariums.* U.S. Dept. of Interior. Fish and Wildlife Research Report No. 63. 190 pp. U.S. Government Printing Office.

COSTELLO, D. P., M. E. DAVIDSON, A. EGGERS, M. H. FOX, and C. HENLEY, 1957: *Methods for Obtaining and Handling Marine Eggs and Embryos.* Marine Biological Laboratory, Woods Hole, Mass.

CROWELL, S., 1957: Differential responses of growth zones to nutritive level, age, and temperature in the colonial hydroid *Campanularia. J. Exp. Zool.*, 134: 63.

———, C. R. WYTTENBACH, and R. L. SUDDITH, 1965: Evidence against the concept of growth zones in hydroids. *Biol. Bull.*, 129: 403.

FULTON, C., 1960: Culture of a colonial hydroid under controlled conditions. *Science*, 132: 473.

———, 1961: The development of *Cordylophora.* In H. M. Lenhoff and W. F. Loomis (eds.), *The Biology of Hydra and of Some Other Coelenterates*, University of Miami Press, Coral Gables, Fla., p. 287.

——— 1962: Environmental factors influencing the growth of *Cordylophora. J. Exp. Zool.*, 151: 61.

HALE, L. J., 1964: Cell movements, cell division, and growth in the hydroid *Clytia johnstoni. J. Embryol. Exp. Morph.*, 12: 517.

HAM, R. G., and R. E. EAKIN, 1958: Time sequence of certain physiological events during regeneration in hydra. *J. Exp. Zool.*, 139: 33.

HAUENSCHILD, C., 1954: Genetische und Entwicklungsphysiologische Untersuchungen über Intersexualität und Gewebeverträglichkeit bei *Hydractinia echinata* (Flemm). *Arch. EntwMech. Org.*, 147: 1.

LENHOFF, H. M., 1965: Some physicochemical aspects of the macro- and micro-environments surrounding *Hydra* during activation of their feeding behavior. *Amer. Zoologist*, 5: 515.

———, and L. MUSCATINE, 1963: Symbiosos: On the role of algae symbiotic with Hydra. *Science*, 142: 956.

LENTZ, T. L., and R. J. BARRNETT, 1965: Fine structure of the nervous system of *Hydra. Amer. Zoologist*, 5: 341.

LOOMIS, W. F., 1954: Environmental factors controlling growth in hydra. *J. Exp. Zool.*, 126: 223.

———, and H. M. LENHOFF, 1956: Growth and sexual differentiation of hydra in mass culture. *J. Exp. Zool.*, 132: 555.

LYTLE, C. F., 1961: Patterns of budding in the freshwater hydroid *Craspedacusta*. In H. M. Lenhoff and W. F. Loomis (eds.), *The Biology of Hydra and of Some Other Coelenterates*, University of Miami Press, Coral Gables, Fla., p. 317.

PHILLIPS, J. H., 1961: Isolation and maintenance in tissue culture of coelenterate cell lines. In H. M. Lenhoff and W. F. Loomis (eds.), *The Biology of Hydra and of Some Other Coelenterates*, University of Miami Press, Coral Gables, Fla., p. 255.

REES, W. J., and R. S. RUSSELL, 1937: On rearing the hydroids of certain medusae, with an account of the methods used. *Journ. Mar. Biol. Assoc.*, 22: 61.

SPANGENBERG, D. B., 1965: Cultivation of the life stages of *Aurelia aurita* under controlled conditions. *J. Exp. Zool.*, 159: 303.

STEINBERG, S., 1963: The regeneration of whole polyps from ectodermal fragments of scyphistoma larvae of *Aurelia aurita*. *Biol. Bull.*, 124: 337.

WILSON, H. V., 1911: On the behavior of dissociated cells in hydroids, *Alcyonaria*, and *Asterias*. *J. Exp. Zool.*, 11: 281.

WYTTENBACH, C. R., 1965: Sites of mitotic activity in the colonial hydroid, *Campanularia flexuosa*. *Anat. Record*, 151: 483.

ZWILLING, E., 1963: Formation of endoderm from ectoderm. *Biol. Bull.*, 124: 368.

Sponges

By Paul E. Fell

INTRODUCTION

Sponges have been used to a very limited extent by developmental biologists. There are two features of sponge material which make it difficult to work with and which account, at least in part, for its limited use. First, many sponges are difficult to maintain in the laboratory and show signs of degeneration after only one to several days in aquaria. Second, both sexual and asexual development usually take place within the mesenchyme of the parent sponge, making certain types of analysis difficult or impossible.

COLLECTION AND MAINTENANCE OF LIVING MATERIAL

Collection

Sponges should be carefully freed from their substrate and, except when they are exposed, transferred to a bucket under water. The sponges should be uncrowded during transport and should be placed in suitable aquaria as soon as possible.

MARINE SPONGES

There are a large number of sponge species available along both the Atlantic and Pacific coasts which might be of interest to developmental biologists (see Miner, 1950; Hartman, 1958; and Light *et al.*, 1961). Only a few species, which have been used in some of the more recent studies, will be mentioned here.

Microciona, a bright orange-red sponge, may occur in either of two growth forms. In shallow water where there is pronounced water movement, this sponge forms thin encrustations on rocks and shells. In deeper, quieter water and on wharf piles, it frequently develops into large clusters of close-set, fingerlike lobes which branch and reunite. Although this sponge is only rarely exposed by the tide, it may be easily collected in shallow water. *Microciona prolifera* is abundant along the Atlantic coast from New England to Cape Hatteras and the West Indies, and is reproductive during the summer (July and August). *Microciona microjoanna* is common in bays and harbors along the Pacific coast of the United States. It reproduces during the late spring and early summer. Then at least in some years the mature sponges die, and large specimens do not reappear until late autumn. Reproduction apparently is sexual.

Halichondria panicea, a greenish-yellow

to orange sponge, is found from the Arctic Ocean to New England, along the north Pacific, and in Europe. This sponge is quite resistant to desiccation and, unlike *Microciona*, is frequently completely exposed at low tide. In rocky intertidal regions, it forms thin encrustations with oscula scattered irregularly over the surface. This sponge may be found in among the mussels and stalked barnacles along the outer, surf-swept California coast. In the yacht harbors, where it may be extremely abundant on the floats and pilings, it frequently forms large masses with tall, erect oscular tubes. On the Pacific coast *Halichondria* reproduces during the late summer and early autumn. Reproduction is sexual.

Haliclona is another cosmopolitan genus with representatives on both the Atlantic and Pacific coasts. *Haliclona* (*Chalina*) *occulata* is abundant along the Canadian and New England coasts and along the coasts of England and western Europe. This sponge, which is purple-brown, has a bushy habit. The large subdivided branches are supported on a slender stalk, and numerous oscula are scattered over the surface. This sponge is found in deeper water and on wharf piles and is exposed only by the lower low tides. *Haliclona permollis* and *Haliclona ecbasis* are common along the central California coast. *Haliclona permollis* may be found encrusting rocks in the upper intertidal zone and may be collected at most low tides. It is usually situated under rock ledges or in crevices among the rocks, in places shaded from the sun. This light purple sponge forms thin encrustations with regularly spaced, volcano-like oscular tubes. It reproduces during the spring and early summer. *Haliclona ecbasis* may be abundant in some yacht harbors at certain times of the year. It occurs attached to the floats, frequently forming thick encrustations on the masses of mussels, but never to the pilings. It may also be found occasionally in rocky intertidal regions. This sponge is usually a rich golden brown; however, surfaces exposed to bright sunlight are frequently lavender. Like many sponges, it has no single growth form. Frequently it occurs in thick masses of stout, closely set oscular tubes; but it may also occur in the form of irregular tubes which branch and reunite, of club-shaped lobes with oscula opening at various points along their length, or of a thin sheet with low oscular tubes scattered over its surface. This sponge has two reproductive seasons, one in the spring and another in the fall. It appears that the sponge is not normally reproductive during the winter and that mature specimens usually die after the spring reproductive season. However, under favorable conditions (water temperature may be important) there may be one long reproductive season which begins in the spring, continues through the summer, and ends in late autumn. Reproduction is sexual.

FRESH-WATER SPONGES

Fresh-water sponges are common in clean, relatively quiet bodies of water where they may be found attached to rocks, logs, aquatic plants, floats, and other stable substrates. They are easily collected in shallow water. *Spongilla lacustris*, *Spongilla fragilis*, and *Ephydatia* (*Meyenia*) *fluviatilis* have a worldwide distribution. The two species of *Spongilla* and another species of *Ephydatia*, *E. mülleri*, are among the most common species in the United States. Most of the fresh-water sponges reproduce sexually during the summer (primarily during July and August) and asexually, by gemmulation, at any time during the growing season. *Spongilla lacustris* is the only common species that regularly forms gemmules in September and October (Pennak, 1953).

Maintenance

INTACT SPONGES

Freshly collected material should be used whenever possible, for in many cases attempts to maintain sponges in the laboratory for an extended period of time have been unsuccessful. Marine sponges should be placed in sea-table aquaria supplied with running sea water. (Other aquarium systems are mentioned below.) It is usually advisable to pass the sea water through a coarse filter, such as glass wool, since sponges are particularly subject to fouling by material suspended in the water. Even under these conditions, many marine sponges remain healthy for only a few days. Certain fresh-water sponges seem to keep very well in aquaria. Penney (1933) found that specimens of *Spongilla discoides* remained healthy for several months when kept in pond water if fresh pond water was added occasionally to replace that lost by evaporation. However, this is an exceptionally long period. Usually fresh-water sponges remain healthy for only 1 to 3 weeks even when there is a continuous flow of water through the aquarium (Pennak, 1953).

Although large, intact specimens from the field frequently do not keep well in aquaria, there are several methods available for the culture of small sponges. While such cultures have not been used extensively in studies of development, they should make feasible certain kinds of experiments which are impractical or impossible to do with large specimens. Furthermore, in very small sponges the tissues are sufficiently transparent to allow for direct observation of the processes that take place within the mesenchyme where both sexual and asexual reproduction occur.

EXPLANTS

Penney (1932), using *Spongilla discoides*, found that when a small, healthy sponge or a small piece of a larger sponge is placed on a glass slide in pond water, it soon adheres to the slide and grows out on the glass as a thin encrustation. When the piece of sponge is small, all of the tissue moves out on the slide; however, when the original piece is large, a thick central portion remains. This may be carefully cut away without damaging the encrusting region. If the water is replaced daily with fresh pond water, these small sponges may be kept indefinitely. Using this procedure, Penney (1933) studied the formation of reduction bodies in small explants. Each small sponge usually forms one and never more than three reduction bodies, and many details of the process may be observed in the living material and in whole mounts.

Simpson (1963) has modified this procedure for growing explants of *Microciona prolifera*. Explants are prepared by freeing the edge of an encrusting specimen with a razor blade and tying square centimeter sections to glass slides with the original basal portion in contact with the glass. The explants are placed in sea-table aquaria or hung in coarse wire containers in the harbor. In the first situation, the explants are fed a mixture of marine algae two or three times a week, although at certain seasons of the year it may not be necessary to feed the explants. Simpson (personal communication) has used *Isochrysis galbana* and *Dunaliella euchlora*, feeding the explants 50 ml of each alga from a log phase culture in 6 liters of sea water every other day. The algae are mixed, centrifuged, and resuspended three times in sea water before they are fed to the explants. The sea water is changed prior to each feeding. The method of Davis and Ukeles (1961) may be used (probably on a smaller scale) for growing the algae.

RECONSTITUTED SPONGES

When pieces of sponge are broken up into their component cells (see below), the cells reaggregate, forming small masses which adhere to the glass and which may subsequently re-form small functional sponges.

Microciona prolifera readily reconstitutes under certain conditions; and the small sponges may be kept indefinitely (Wilson, 1907; Wilson, 1937; and Warburton, 1960). Upon reaggregation, the dissociated cells of this species usually form a coarse reticular mass. When pieces of this reticulum are partially freed from the glass, they round up into globular masses, the size of which is easily controlled. These masses may then be transferred to glass slides and placed in aquaria supplied with running sea water or in dishes of standing sea water. In the former situation, the slides should be supported near the surface of the water and protected from the current entering at the bottom; in the latter, the water should be changed two to three times a day. Under laboratory conditions, complete sponges usually form within 6 to 7 days. When the cultures are suspended in coarse wire containers from a dock, development is more rapid; and the sponges keep well for long periods of time and may even reproduce.

Galtsoff (1925) found that masses which are smaller than about 200 μ in diameter never form complete sponges. Canals frequently appear, but these do not join and form a single system. Furthermore, oscula fail to develop. On the other hand, larger masses rapidly transform into small sponges with a perfect canal system and a single central osculum. Similarly, Spiegel and Metcalf (1957b) found that when the dissociated cells of *Microciona* are placed in filtered sea water or in artificial sea water, reconstitution is incomplete. Canals and flagellated chambers form, but neither oscula nor water currents are seen. However, when the cells are cultured in 0.5 percent boiled, dried yeast in Tyler's artificial sea water[1] at pH 8.2, functional sponges with canals, flagellated chambers, and raised oscular tubes are produced. Other media (sugar solutions, amino acid mixtures, and albumin solutions made up in artificial sea water) were also tried, but were found to be unsatisfactory.

Other marine sponges, *Haliclona permollis* for example, do not normally reconstitute in sea water. However, under more favorable conditions, perhaps in the presence of nutrients, these sponges may also be capable of reconstitution.

As in the case of the marine sponges, certain of the fresh-water sponges appear to reconstitute more readily than others. However, it is not clear to what extent these differences reflect differences in the culture conditions (natural nutrients in the water, the size of the aggregates, etc.). The reconstitution of *Spongilla lacustris* and *Ephydatia mülleri* has been described by Müller (1911), and that of *Ephydatia fluviatilis*, by Brien (1937). The aggregates attach to the substrate after about 4 days and form small sponges in about a week. Müller found that only aggregates with a diameter greater than 0.7 mm reconstitute, and Brien found 1.0 to 1.5 mm in diameter to be the optimal size. Much larger aggregates disintegrate. It is best to keep

[1] 1,000 ml 0.55 *M* NaCl, 22 ml 0.55 *M* KCl, 195 ml 0.37 *M* $MgCl_2$, 103 ml 0.37 *M* NaH_2SO_4, 6 ml 0.55 *M* $NaHCO_3$, and 35 ml 0.37 *M* $CaCl_2$ adjusted to pH 8.2 (Tyler, 1953).

the cultures in running, well-aerated water. In standing water the cultures rapidly become infested with bacteria and protozoa, unless the water is changed frequently.

Ganguly (1960) was unable to grow sponges from the aggregates of *Ephydatia* sp. The aggregates remained healthy for up to a month and frequently formed canals and flagellated chambers, but development did not progress beyond this point.

GROWTH OF SMALL SPONGES FROM LARVAE (SEE WILSON, 1937, AND BRIEN AND MEEWIS, 1938)

Freshly collected specimens of reproductive sponge are transferred to finger bowls containing sea water (or pond water, depending on the sponge) as soon as possible. The release of the larvae is apparently stimulated by confinement and may occur from within a few minutes to several hours. When the larvae are released, they are transferred with a pipette to large Petri dishes containing glass slides or other suitable substrate. If histological sections of the metamorphosing and young sponges are to be made, it is convenient to coat the bottom of the dishes with a thin layer of 2 percent agar or of paraffin. Cellophane may also be used. The fixation and development of the larvae on these various substrates are essentially the same. It is necessary to change the water several times a day. The larvae attach within a day or two, and the slides may then be transferred to wire containers and hung from a dock.

SPONGES PRODUCED FROM GEMMULES (SEE RASMONT, 1961 AND 1962)

The gemmules of fresh-water sponges are sterilized superficially by immersing them in a dilute solution of hydrogen peroxide (Perhydrol Merck diluted 1/25) for 5 minutes. They are then washed six times in mineral medium[2] and placed in Petri dishes containing 25 ml mineral medium at 120 gemmules per dish. The gemmules of *Ephydatia fluviatilis* germinate in 3 to 4 days. At 5 days when the gemmules are fixed to the substrate by the young sponges encrusting them, the cultures are placed in a dark incubator at 20°C. Young sponges of different sizes may be obtained by grouping the gemmules into clusters (2, 3, 4, etc.).

The sponges are fed suspensions of washed and killed bacteria. The bacteria[3] are washed three times in mineral medium and are heated at 60°C for 30 minutes on 3 successive days. Prior to Tyndallization an aliquot of each suspension is mineralized and its total nitrogen determined by micro-Kjeldahl. The heat-killed suspensions are diluted to 50 or 100 μg per milliliter total nitrogen, and 1-ml aliquots (a normal feeding dose) are distributed in test tubes and frozen until needed. The sponges are fed three times a week and the medium is changed prior to each feeding.

Small sponges maintained in this way frequently form gemmules within a few weeks. Many of the sponges produce a single gemmule; however, in the larger sponges, two or three gemmules are sometimes produced. The onset of gemmulation depends in a complex way on the size of the young sponges and on the quantity of their diet (Rasmont, 1963).

While it has been emphasized that many sponges do not keep well under ordinary laboratory conditions and that

[2] Ca^{++}, 2.00 meq per liter; Mg^{++}, 1.00 meq per liter; Na^{+}, 1.00 meq per liter; K^{+}, 0.05 meq per liter; Cl^{-}, 2.05 meq per liter; So_4^{--}, 1.00 meq per liter; SiO_3^{--}, 0.50 meq per liter; and HCO_3^{-}, 0.50 meq per liter.

[3] Rasmont used *Staphylococcus aureus* and *Escherichia coli* grown in Roux flasks on bouillon agar.

cultured sponges generally do best when they are kept in their normal environment (in open water), efforts should be made to define conditions which are optimal for the maintenance, growth, and development of these animals. Improved aquarium systems, which utilize a complete artificial sea water (Clark and Clark, 1964), are now commercially available.[4] The filter and circulation systems are designed to promote the rapid removal of wastes, to maintain the desired pH value, and to ensure efficient gas exchange. Furthermore, temperature may be rigorously controlled. The artificial sea water employed is a carefully formulated mixture of twenty salts which does not exactly duplicate the salts found in sea water, but which has been found to be optimal for maintaining marine animals under laboratory conditions. These systems have been useful in maintaining a number of marine animals, many of which go through their entire life cycle. By employing systems of this sort and by careful feeding procedures, it may be possible to keep many marine sponges and, in particular, small cultures of these sponges under controlled conditions.

DEVELOPMENT

Among the siliceous sponges two forms of development are widespread—sexual reproduction and gemmulation. While there are numerous accounts of the development of both marine and fresh-water sponges, few of these accounts are complete. In many cases emphasis has been placed on the description of the parenchymula larva and its metamorphosis into a small sponge. In some instances it has not been established whether the larvae described are sexually or asexually produced (see Webb, 1935; Hyman, 1940; and Levi, 1956, for reviews).

[4] Instant Ocean, Aquarium Systems, Inc. 1489 East 289 Street, Wickliffe, Ohio.

Sexual Reproduction

Halichondria (Meewis, 1941), *Haliclona* (Meewis, 1939), and the fresh-water sponges (see Brien and Meewis, 1938, for an account of *Ephydatia fluviatilis*) reproduce sexually, although some of these sponges also reproduce by gemmulation. In many sponges spermatozoa apparently develop from archeocytes. According to Fincher (1940), in *Stylotella heliophila* spermatozoa develop in aggregates of archeocytes in which the peripheral cells flatten and form an envelope about the inner cells which undergo a series of divisions. As the cells divide, they become progressively smaller; and finally the smallest cells differentiate into spermatozoa. In *Reniera* (Tuzet, 1932) and in the Spongillidae (Leveaux, 1941 and 1942), spermatozoa apparently develop from choanocytes which lose their collar and flagellum and increase in size. In *Reniera* the sperm-mother cells divide producing a sheath cell and a spermatogonial cell, and the former gradually envelops the nest of spermatogonia which is produced by division of the latter. In the Spongillidae (*Spongilla lacustris* and *Ephydatia fluviatilis*) a number of sperm-mother cells aggregate and form a mass which becomes surrounded by a single layer of flattened mesenchymal cells.

Similarly, in some sponges (*Stylotella* and the Spongillidae) oocytes apparently develop from amebocytes, while in others (*Reniera*) they apparently develop from choanocytes. In the Spongillidae large yolk-laden nurse cells aggregate about the growing oocyte, cytolize, and are engulfed by them. In *Haliclona permollis* and *Haliclona ecbasis* (Fell, in preparation), the major growth of the oocytes is accomplished by the engulfment of whole nurse cells. Although the nucleus of the nurse cells disappears either as or immediately after the cells are engulfed, the cytoplasm remains intact. Consequently the fully developed oocytes are filled with a large number of nurse cells. During cleavage of the egg, the cytoplasm of the nurse cells is incorporated progressively into the cytoplasm of the blastomeres. Finally in *Tedanione foetida* (Wilson, 1894) and in *Halichondria panicea* (Fell, unpublished observations), the nurse cells, which apparently supply the oocytes with yolk precursors, are separated from them by a thin follicular epithelium.

In the few cases where fertilization has been observed (see Tuzet, 1932, for an account of fertilization in *Reniera*), it was found that the spermatozoan does not fuse with the egg directly, but enters an archeocyte near the egg. This "carrier cell" approaches the egg and adheres to it, and the engulfed spermatozoan, which loses its tail, is then transferred to the egg.

Cleavage of the zygote produces a solid mass of cells, in which nucleolate nuclei re-form after each division. During the early cleavage stages nuclear division may proceed more rapidly than cell division, so that binucleate and plurinucleate blastomeres are formed. As development proceeds spicules appear at the periphery of the embryo and are subsequently brought into the interior and concentrated toward the posterior pole. At the same time the peripheral cells align and form a pseudostratified columnar epithelium in which there are three to eight nuclear layers and in which each cell possesses a single long flagellum. Beneath this epithelium there are many fibroblast-like cells, and centrally among the spicules there are numerous archeocytes (see Levi, 1964, for an account of the ultrastructure of the larva of *Mycale contarenii*, and Borojevic, 1966, for an analysis of the developmental capacities of its cells). Finally the solid parenchymula larva breaks free and leaves the parent sponge in the excurrent stream.

Asexual Reproduction

In the fresh-water sponges (see Rasmont, 1956 and 1962, for an account of gemmulation in *Ephydatia fluviatilis*), gemmules are formed by the aggregation of archeocytes. The initial aggregates grow by cell division and probably also by the immigration of new archeocytes. At the same time yolk-laden cells (trophocytes) enter the aggregates, cytolize, and are engulfed by the archeocytes. Finally the fully developed aggregates become encased within a resistant capsule consisting of an inner and an outer collagen layer and an intervening layer of spicules. The formation of the capsule is a highly ordered process, beginning at one pole and progressing around to the opposite pole where a micropyle is formed. Under favorable environmental conditions, the gemmules germinate and develop into small sponges. The gemmules of *Ephydatia fluviatilis* are able to germinate immediately following their formation. On the other hand, those of *Ephydatia mülleri* undergo a diapause, and their ability to germinate is greatly enhanced by vernalization.

A number of marine sponges, including *Haliclona* (*Haliclona loosanoffi*, Hartman, 1958; and *Haliclona ecbasis*, Fell, in preparation), also produce gemmules. However, in most cases the process of gemmulation has not been studied in detail.

DISSOCIATION, AGGREGATION, AND CULTURE OF SPONGE CELLS

Dissociation

Mechanical dissociation and chemical dissociation are the methods most frequently employed. Enzymatic procedures have not been very effective.

MECHANICAL DISSOCIATION (SEE WILSON, 1907)

The tissue is cut into small pieces which should be no more than a few millimeters in diameter, and the pieces are dissociated by forcing the cells through bolting silk (no. 25 standard quality cloth) into sea water. This may be done by placing the pieces of tissue on a square of bolting silk, folding the edges of the cloth around the tissue so as to form a bag, and then squeezing the bag immersed in sea water with a pair of blunt forceps. Alternatively, a disc of silk may be supported on a stainless steel screen in a 50-ml syringe, and the cells may be forced through the silk by means of the plunger. A Swinny adapter[5] with silk supported on a screen may be added to the tip of the syringe for more complete dissociation. In the resulting suspension most of the cells occur in small clusters. Filtering the suspension through several layers of bolting silk excludes the larger clusters, but does not break up the smaller ones.

Simons (1963) found that fresh-water sponges may be readily dissociated by flushing the tissue in and out of a syringe. A 1-cc piece of sponge is placed with 2 ml of water into a small hypodermic syringe and is broken up by repeatedly forcing the tissue in and out through the tip. The fragments are then dissociated by forcing them in and out through successively smaller gauge needles (19, 23, and 26). In the resulting suspension there are a few clusters of cells and some debris, but dissociation is much more complete than when bolting silk is used.

CHEMICAL DISSOCIATION (SEE HUMPHREYS *et al.*, 1960a, AND HUMPHREYS, 1963)

For *Microciona prolifera*[6] 1 gm of blotted tissue is immersed in 80 ml of calcium- and magnesium-free artificial sea water[7] (CMF-SW) at pH 7.2 and 0°C. The tissue is cut into pieces approximately 3 mm on a side and is soaked for 30 minutes. Soaking the tissue for this period of time loosens the cells, but does not free the numerous spicules, which are released from their matrices with prolonged treatment. The cells are then dissociated by forcing them through bolting silk into 80 ml of fresh CMF-SW at 0°C (see section on Mechanical Dissociation). The concentration of the resulting suspension is estimated by hemocytometer counts. For *Microciona prolifera* Humphreys (1963) obtained between 10 and 40 × 10^6 cells per milliliter of suspension depending upon the time of year. The cells and cell clusters are then sedimented by centrifugation at 500 *g* for 2 minutes and are resuspended in fresh, cold CMF-SW at a concentration of 20 × 10^6 cells per milliliter. Dissociation is completed by swirling 15-ml aliquots of the suspension in 100-ml beakers at 80 rpm on a gyratory shaker with a $\frac{3}{4}$-inch diameter of rotation for 6 to 9 hours. Three-milliliter aliquots of the resulting suspension are transferred to 12-ml conical centrifuge tubes, and the loose clusters of cells are dispersed into single cells by flushing them briskly 10 to 15 times through the tip of a pipette with a 1-mm orifice. Frothing of the solution should be avoided. The dissociated cells are then sedimented by centrifugation at 120 *g* for 2 minutes and are resuspended in cold artificial sea water[8] or in natural sea water. The cell concentration may be determined again and the suspension diluted as required.

[5] Millipore Filter Corporation, Bedford, Massachusetts.

[6] This procedure requires some modification for other species (see Humphreys, 1963).

[7] NaCl, 27 gm per liter; Na_2SO_4, 1 gm per liter; KCl, 0.8 gm per liter; and $NaHCO_3$, 0.18 gm per liter of glass-distilled water.

[8] NaCl, 24.7 gm per liter; KCl, 0.7 gm per liter; $CaCl_2$, 1.0 gm per liter; $MgCl_2 \cdot 6H_2O$, 4.7 gm per liter; $MgSO_4 \cdot 7H_2O$, 6.3 gm per liter; and $NaHCO_3$, 0.18 gm per liter glass-distilled water (Humphreys, 1963).

Using a modification of this procedure it has been possible to isolate the solubilized adhesives and to partially characterize them (see below). Solutions of the adhesive material(s) may be prepared in the following way. Five to ten grams of blotted sponge are immersed in 150 ml of cold CMF-SW, cut into 1-cc pieces, and soaked for 10 minutes in each of four changes of 150 ml of CMF-SW at 0°C. Then the cells are forced through bolting silk into 50 ml of cold CMF-SW, and the suspension is swirled on a gyratory shaker at 80 rpm for 4 hours at 0°C. At the end of this period the suspension is centrifuged at 6,780 *g* for 10 minutes at 0°C. The supernatant is then recentrifuged at 14,500 *g* for 90 minutes at 0°C. Finally one part 18.5 m*M* $CaCl_2$ solution is added to 9 parts of the second supernatant. This preparation is mixed 1:1 with chemically dissociated cells in artificial sea water at 5°C (Humphreys, 1963, and Moscona, 1963).

An alternative procedure for dissociating the cells (Curtis, 1962), which has not been as thoroughly worked out as the first, employs ethylenediaminetetraacetic acid (EDTA). Small pieces of sponge are immersed in 0.004 *M* EDTA in 0.55 *M* NaCl buffered with 0.004 *M* tris-hydrochloric acid (2-amino-2-hydroxymethyl 1,3-propanediol-hydrochloric acid) for 24 minutes. At the end of this period the cells are dispersed as in mechanical dissociation.

ENZYMATIC DISSOCIATION

Spiegel and Metcalf (1957a) tested a number of enzyme preparations for their effectiveness in dissociating the cells of *Microciona prolifera*. In each case 0.2 ml of suspension, obtained by expressing 2 gm of sponge through bolting silk into 20 ml of artificial sea water, was added to 3 ml of enzyme solution. Of the enzymes tested (2 percent crude protease at pH 7.6, 0.2 percent crystalline trypsin at pH 7.7, 0.2 percent crystalline chymotrypsin at pH 7.7, 2 percent crude papain containing 100 mg cysteine per 100 ml at pH 7.0, 2 percent steapsin at pH 7.0, and the stomach juices of several crabs, all made up in Tyler's artificial sea water) only the stomach juice of the blue crab, *Callinectes sapidus*, was effective. However, even with the stomach juice prolonged treatment (18 hours) was required.

Aggregation

Aliquots of the cell suspension may be placed in Petri dishes and the cells allowed to self-aggregate. The cells rapidly settle to the bottom of the dish and begin to move about. When the cells come into contact with one another in the course of their random movements, they stick together so that progressively larger masses are formed.

For studies of the nature of cell adhesion, a method of aggregation which does not depend upon cell migration is preferable. Rotation-mediated aggregation has been employed by Humphreys *et al.* (1960b). Three-milliliter aliquots of the cell suspension (adjusted to 10×10^6 cells per milliliter) are placed in 25-ml Erlenmeyer flasks and rotated at 80 rpm on a gyratory shaker with a $\frac{3}{4}$-inch diameter of rotation. At 22°C the cells of *Microciona* begin to adhere immediately. After about 1 hour incorporation of cells into aggregates is complete, and between 3 and 6 hours the aggregates attain their ultimate size. Under these conditions approximately 2,000 globular masses averaging 140 μ in diameter are formed. Aggregates have been maintained in rotating flasks, the sea water being changed every other day, for over 2 months. After about 2 weeks canals appear in some of the aggregates (Humphreys, 1963).

At 5°C there is a striking difference in the behavior of chemically dissociated and mechanically dissociated cells. The mechanically dissociated cells form aggregates, but the chemically dissociated cells do not. However, when supernatants from chemical dissociation are added with Ca^{++} to chemically dissociated cells, these cells also form aggregates at 5°C (Humphreys, 1963, and Moscona, 1963).

When the dissociated cells of two different species are mixed, they sort out from one another. That is, cell adhesion is species-specific. To demonstrate this specificity, different colored species are used. When the cells of *Microciona* (red) are mixed with the cells of *Haliclona* (purple-brown), all of the aggregates formed are either red or purple-brown; there are none of intermediate color.

It is interesting that the supernatants show species specificity. When a supernatant obtained from *Microciona* is added to the chemically dissociated cells of *Haliclona* at 5°C, no aggregation occurs, even though the supernatant is effective with the cells of *Microciona*. In fact, when a supernatant obtained from one species is added to a mixture of cells from both species, only the cells of the homologous species form aggregates (Humphreys, 1963, and Moscona, 1963). Preliminary evidence suggests that the active materials are glycopeptides (MacLennan, 1963; Margoliash *et al.*, 1965; Humphreys, 1965a and b; and Gasic and Galanti, 1966).

Cell Culture

Only a few attempts to culture sponge cells have been reported. The work of Spiegel and Metcalf (1957b) has already been mentioned. Rasmont (1961) has tried several nutrient media for culturing germinating sponge gemmules. His media consisted of a mineral medium (see footnote 2, page 269), penicillin (400 μg per milliliter), streptomycin (200 μg per milliliter), and either the organic constituents of Eagle's (complex mixture of amino acids and vitamins) or those of Hanks' (hydrolyzate of lactalbumin) added to yeast extract at a concentration 0.1 or 0.01 that normally used for the culture of vertebrate tissues. These media were toxic, and the young sponges were abnormal. Huxley (1921) tried to culture isolated choanocytes of the calcareous sponge, *Sycon coronatum*. Solutions of peptone, 0.1 percent ammonium lactate, and sponge broth (3 ml of sponge chopped up in 20 ml of sea water) were tried without success. Conditions which favor reconstitution of sponges from suspensions of single cells have been discussed in a previous section. However, it is very likely that the conditions which favor reconstitution are quite different from those necessary for maintaining cells in culture.

REFERENCES

BOROJEVIC, R., 1966: Étude expérimentale de la différenciation des cellules de l'éponge au cours de son développement. *Dev. Biol.*, 14: 130.

BRIEN, P., 1937: La réorganisation de l'éponge après dissociation par filtration et phénomènes d'involution chez *Ephydatia fluviatilis*. *Arch. Biol.*, 48: 185.

———, and H. MEEWIS, 1938: Contribution à' l'étude de l'embryogénèse des Spongillidae. *Arch. Biol.*, 49: 177.

CLARK, J. R., and R. CLARK (eds.), 1964: *Sea Water Systems for Experimental Aquariums.* U.S. Fish and Wildlife Service

Research Report #63. 190 pp. Can be obtained from Supt. of Documents, Washington 25, D.C.

CURTIS, A. S. G., 1962: Pattern and mechanism in the reaggregation of sponges. *Nature*, 196: 245.

DAVIS, H. C., and R. UKELES, 1961: Mass culture of phytoplankton as foods for metazoans. *Science*, 134: 562.

FINCHER, J. A., 1940: The origin of the germ cells in *Stylotella heliophila* Wilson (tetraxonida). *J. Morph.*, 67: 175.

GALTSOFF, P. S., 1925: Regeneration after dissociation (an experimental study on sponges). II. Histogenesis of *Microciona prolifera*. *J. Exp. Zool.*, 42: 223.

GANGULY, B., 1960: The differentiating capacity of dissociated sponge cells. *Roux' Arch. Entwmech. Org.*, 152: 22.

GASIC, G. J., and N. L. GALANTI, 1966: Proteins and disulfide groups in the aggregation of dissociated cells of sea sponges. *Science*, 151: 203.

HARTMAN, W. D., 1958: Natural history of the marine sponges of southern New England. *Bull. Peabody Mus., Yale*, 12: 155. (This paper gives the breeding seasons of many American and European sponges.)

HUMPHREYS, T., 1963: Chemical dissociation and *in vitro* reconstruction of sponge cell adhesions. *Dev. Biol.*, 8:27.

———, 1965a: Cell surface components participating in aggregation. Evidence for a new cell particulate. *Exp. Cell Res.*, 40: 539.

———, 1965b: Aggregation of chemically dissociated sponge cells in the absence of protein synthesis. *J. Exp. Zool.*, 160: 235.

———, S. HUMPHREYS, and A. A. MOSCONA, 1960a: A procedure for obtaining completely dissociated sponge cells. *Biol. Bull.*, 119: 294.

———, ———, and ———, 1960b: Rotation-mediated aggregation of dissociated sponge cells. *Biol. Bull.*, 119: 295.

HUXLEY, J., 1921: Restitution bodies and free tissue culture in *Sycon*. *Quart. J. Micros. Sci.*, 65: 293.

HYMAN, L. H., 1940: *The Invertebrates: Protozoa through Ctenophora*, Vol. I. McGraw-Hill Co., New York.

LEVAUX, M., 1941 and 1942: Contribution à l'étude histologique de l'ovogénèse et de la spermatogénèse des Spongillidae. *Ann. Soc. Roy. Zool. Belg.*, 72: 251 and 73: 33.

LEVI, M. C., 1956: Étude des Halisarca de Roscoff. Embryologie et systématique des Démosponges. *Arch. Zool. Exp. Gén.*, 93: 1.

———, 1964: Ultrastructure de la larve parenchymella de Démosponge I. *Mycale contarenii* (Martens). *Cah. Biol. Mar.*, 5: 97.

LIGHT, S. F., R. I. SMITH, F. A. PITELKA, D. P. ABBOTT, and F. M. WEESNER, 1961: *Intertidal Invertebrates of the Central California Coast*. University of California Press, Berkeley, Calif.

MAC LENNAN, A. P., 1963: The sponge cell surface in relation to aggregation specificity. *Biochem. Journal*, 89: 99 p.

MARGOLIASH, E., J. R. SCHENCK, M. P. HARGIE, S. BUROKAS, W. R. RICHTER, G. H. BARLOW, and A. A. MOSCONA, 1965: Characterization of specific cell aggregating materials from sponge cells. *Biochem. and Biophys. Res. Comm.*, 20: 383.

MEEWIS, H., 1939: Contribution à l'étude de l'embryogénèse de Chalinidae: *Haliclona limbata*. *Ann. Soc. Roy. Zool. Belg.*, 70: 201.

———, 1941: Contribution à l'étude de l'embryogénèse des éponges siliceuses—Développement de l'oeuf chez *Adocia cinerea* (Grant) et *Halichondria coalita* (Bowerbank). *Ann. Soc. Roy. Zool. Belg.*, 72: 126.

MINER, R. W., 1950: *Field Book of Seashore Life*. G. P. Putnam's Sons, New York.

MOSCONA, A. A., 1963: Studies on cell aggregation: demonstration of materials with selective cell-binding activity. *Proc. Nat. Acad. Sci.*, 49: 742.

MÜLLER, K., 1911: Das Regenerationsvermögen der Süsswasserschwämme insbesondere über die bei ihnen vorkommende Regeneration nach Dissociation und Reunition. *Roux' Arch. Entwmech. Org.*, 32: 397.

PENNAK, R. W., 1953: *Fresh-water Invertebrates of the United States*. Ronald Press Co., New York.

PENNEY, J. T., 1932: A simple method for the study of living fresh-water sponges. *Science*, 75: 341.

———, 1933: Reduction and regeneration in fresh-water sponges. *J. Exp. Zool.*, 65: 475.

RASMONT, R., 1956: La gemmulation des Spongillides. IV. Morphologie de la gemmulation chez *Ephydatia fluviatilis* et *Spongilla lacustris*. *Ann. Soc. Roy. Zool. Belg.*, 86: 349.

———, 1961: Une technique de culture des éponges d'eau douce en milieu controlé. *Ann. Soc. Roy. Zool. Belg.*, 91: 147.

———, 1962: The physiology of gemmulation in fresh-water sponges. In D. Rudnick (ed.), *Regeneration. 20th Growth Symposium*, Ronald Press Co., New York.

———, 1963: Le rôle de la taille et de la nutrition dans le déterminisme de la gemmulation chez les Spongillides. *Dev. Biol.*, 8: 243.

SIMONS, J. R., 1963: The adhesion and coalescence of sponge cells after dissociation. *Proc. Linn. Soc. New South Wales*, LXXXVIII 28.

SIMPSON, T. L., 1963: The biology of the marine sponge *Microciona prolifera* (Ellis and Salander). I. A study of cellular function and differentiation. *J. Exp. Zool.*, 154: 135.

SPIEGEL, M., and C. METCALF, 1957a: Enzymatic dissociation of sponge cells. *Biol. Bull.*, 113: 355.

———, and ———, 1957b: The reaggregation of *Microciona* cells in culture media. *Biol. Bull.*, 113: 356.

TUZET, O., 1932: Recherches sur l'histologie des éponges *Reniera elegans* (Bow) et *Reniera simulans* (Johnston). *Arch. de Zool. Exp. et Gén.*, 74: 169.

TYLER, A., 1953: Prolongation of life-span of sea urchin spermatozoa, and improvement of the fertilization-reaction, by treatment of spermatozoa and eggs with metal-chelating agents (amino acids, Versene, DEDTC, oxine, Cupron). *Biol. Bull.*, 104: 224.

WARBURTON, F. E., 1960: Influences of currents on form of sponges. *Science*, 132: 89.

WEBB, D. A., 1935: The histology, cytology, and embryology of sponges. *Quart. Jour. Micros. Sci.*, 78: 51.

WILSON, H. V., 1894: Observations on gemmule and egg development in marine sponges. *J. Morph.*, 9: 277.

———, 1907: On some phenomena of coalescence and regeneration in sponges. *J. Exp. Zool.*, 5: 245.

———, 1937: Notes on the cultivation and growth of sponges from reduction bodies, dissociated cells, and larvae. In J. G. Needham (ed.), *Culture Methods for Invertebrate Animals*, Cornell University Press (Comstock), Ithaca, N. Y., reprinted by Dover, New York, 1959.

Early-Flowering Plants

By Bruce G. Cumming

INTRODUCTION

There are several recent reviews on the physiology of flowering (Hillman, 1962; Searle, 1965), including one that is particularly useful as a reference because of its comprehensiveness (Lang, 1965).

Plants that flower at an early stage in growth can be particularly valuable for critical studies of flowering. They are also valuable when large populations of successive generations are required in as short a time as possible, for example, in genetic studies (Langridge, 1955, 1957a,b; Murray and Craig, 1965; Rédei, 1962). With early flowering, there can be considerable economy in time, space, and labor, and more effective use of controlled environmental facilities. The increased replication that is made possible by using smaller individuals can increase the precision of experimentation. Simple fast methods for controlling and detecting developmental changes have been devised for such material.

This chapter refers particularly to higher plants that can be induced to flower at a very early stage in growth, that is, essentially in the cotyledonary stage of the seedling. However, a few primary leaves may be present in the embryo and/or be produced after germination before there is initiation of a floral primordium. To assess the earliness of flowering, the minimum primary leaf number preceding the formation of a terminal flower may be used when frequent critical observations are impossible, but the most accurate method is to observe the time of floral initiation by microdissection.

The main characteristics and origin of some of the presently known early-flowering plants are summarized in Table 1. These include plants belonging to the three main photoperiodic classifications (Garner and Allard, 1920): short-day plants (SDP), e.g., *Chenopodium* spp., *Pharbitis nil* [synonym *Ipomoea nil*], *Sporobolus* spp.; long-day plants (LDP), e.g., *Arabidopsis thaliana*, *Baeria chrysostoma*, *Chenopodium murale*; day-neutral plants (NDP), e.g., *Chenopodium foetidum*. There are other plants that probably belong with these, but experimental work is lacking at present.

Possible sources of seeds are listed in Table 1 but these are in no sense comprehensive. Apart from the natural distribution of such species, which can be determined from the published "Flora" of different regions (e.g., Wahl, 1953), the seed lists (Index Seminum) of botanical gardens in different parts of the world indicate sources of seeds of many species

TABLE 1. CHARACTERISTICS AND ORIGIN OF SOME EARLY-FLOWERING SHORT-DAY, LONG-DAY, AND DAY-NEUTRAL PLANTS (SDP, LDP, NDP, RESP.)*

SPECIES	IDENTIFICATION	PHOTOPERIODIC TYPE	MINIMUM LEAF NUMBER	EARLIEST FLORAL INITIATION (DAYS)	SPECIAL FEATURES	ORIGINAL SPECIMEN (EX) OR BOTANIC GARDEN SEED SOURCE	REF. TO PHOTOPERIODIC RESPONSE
Arabidopsis thaliana (L.) Heynh	Landsberg	LDP	?	10–12 days (flower buds)	"Wild type"	Ecotype seeds from F. Laibach (1951)	Rédei, 1962
	Race Enkheim	LDP	?	14 ("flowering")	Early-flowering but less uniform than Estland	Langridge cites Laibach (1943) as an original source for seeds	Langridge, 1957b
	Race Estland	LDP	11	22 ("flowering")	GA hastens flowering in SD (Langridge, 1957). Chromosome number n = 5	Langridge cites Laibach (1943) as an original source for seeds	Langridge, 1957b
Baeria chrysostoma F. and M.		LDP, if temp. <25°C; sensitive to LD 5 days after germination	4–6	10–11	Early-flowering desert ephemeral (Loo, 1946)	Rancho Santa Ana Botanic Garden, California, U.S.A.	Sivori and Went, 1944
Chenopodium album L.	No. 132	SDP	4	23	Earlier flowering than most selections of sp.	ex. Cumming and Bassett No. 132. 5 mi. east of Clear Lake, Man., Can.‡	†
C. album L. var. *lanceolatum* (Muhl.) Coss and Germ.	No. 142	SDP	4	24		ex. Cumming and Bassett No. 107. Kootenay Lake, B.C., Can.‡	†
C. album L. var. *stevensii* Aellen	No. 149	SDP	4	17		ex. Cumming and Bassett No. 50. Battleford, Sask., Can.‡	†
C. aristatum L.	No. 601	SDP	2	7		Dieust voor Parken en Plantsoenen, Gerard Legrellelaan 5, Antwerp, Belgium	†

	No. 606	SDP	2	5–6	Single D in LL when cotyledons extruded induces flowering; reveals endogenous rhythm	Bot. Garden, Univ. of Warsaw, Poland	†	
C. berlandieri Moq. var. *zschakei* (Murr.) Murr.	No. 148	SDP	4	19		ex. Cumming and Bassett No. 111. Fernie, B.C., Can.‡	†	
C. botrys L.	No. 8	SDP	4	20	Also valuable for germination studies (Cumming, 1963b)	ex. Shumovitch No. 1460. Smith's Falls, Ont., Can.‡	†	
	No. 217	SDP	4	14		Univ. of London, U.K.	†	
C. foetidum Schrad.	No. 65	NDP	2–4	7	Low leaf number only when starved	Bot. Garden, Leopoldstraat, Belgium	†	
	No. 114	NDP	2–4	8	Low leaf number only when starved	Bot. Garden, Univ. of Warsaw, Poland	†	
C. fremontii S. Wats.	No. 166	SDP	6	18		ex. Cumming and Bassett No. 49. Pike Lake, Sask., Can.‡	†	
C. gigantospermum Aellen	No. 18	SDP	4	14	Large seeds red pericarp. Difficult to germinate	ex. Frankton No. 5717. Crooked River, Sask., Can.‡	†	
	No. 19	SDP	4	14	Large seeds green pericarp. Difficult to germinate	ex. Frankton No. 5716. S. of Graham Bay, Ottawa, Ont., Can.	†	
C. glaucum L.	No. 21	SDP	3	24	Closely related to *C. salinum* but in LD *C. glaucum* flowers earlier than *C. salinum*	ex. Bassett and Bragg No. 3209. Collingwood, Ont., Can.‡	†	Cumming, 1959
	No. 130	SDP	2	20		ex. Frankton No. 57/187. Between Chesterville and Winchester, Ont., Can.‡	†	

TABLE 1 (*continued*)

SPECIES	IDENTIFICATION	PHOTOPERIODIC TYPE	MINIMUM LEAF NUMBER	EARLIEST FLORAL INITIATION (DAYS)	SPECIAL FEATURES	ORIGINAL SPECIMEN (EX) OR BOTANIC GARDEN SEED SOURCE	REF. TO PHOTOPERIODIC RESPONSE
C. macrospermum Hook	No. 192	SDP	2	20		ex. Howell, California Acad. Sci., Santa Barbara County, Calif., U.S.A.	†
C. murale L.	No. 197	LDP	4–6	about 28	Slow growing in Petri dish (light may retard root growth). Non-rosette annual	ex. Calif. Acad. Sci., Santa Barbara County, Calif., U.S.A.‡	†
	No. 557	LDP	5–6	about 28		ex. Frankton and Bassett No. 1793. Rock Island, Stanstead Co., P.Q., Can.‡	†
C. polyspermum L.		SDP	4–6	about 9		Source unknown, used by Jacques (1957)	Jacques, 1957
	No. 120	SDP	4–5	12		Bot. Garden, Coimbra, Portugal	†
	No. 205	SDP	4–5	10		Royal Bot. Garden, Kew, U.K.	†
C. rigidum Lingelsh	No. 219	SDP	5–6	10		Royal Bot. Garden, Kew, U.K. (No. 2174)	†
C. rubrum L.	No. 372	SDP at 20°C. Ambiperiodic at 25° to 35°C	2	7	At 20°C single D in LL when cotyledons extruded induces flowering	ex. Calder and Kukkonen No. 28093. Dawson-Whitehorse Rd., Yukon, Can. 62°46′N, 136°36′W‡	† Cumming, 1961, 1963a
	No. 373	SDP	2	6-7	Single D in LL when cotyledons extruded induces flowering	ex. Calder and Kukkonen No. 28020 A. Mile 945, Alaska Highway, Yukon, Can. 60°52′N, 135°42′W‡	† Cumming, 1961

	No. 374	SDP	2	6–7	Single D in LL when cotyledons extruded induces flowering; reveals endogenous rhythm	ex. Calder and Kukkonen No. 28112. 2 mi. north of Haines Jct., Alaska Highway, Yukon, Can. 60°47′N, 137°32′W‡	Cumming, 1961, 1963a; Cumming, Hendricks, and Borthwick, 1965
	No. 184	SDP	2	6–7	Not induced by single D as readily as more northern selections	ex. Best. Swift Current, Sask., Can. 50°10′N, 105°35′W	† Cumming, 1961, 1963
	No. 28	SDP	2	6–7		ex. Stevenson, No. 415. Brandon, Man., Can. 49°58′N, 100°00′W‡	† Cumming, 1959, 1961; Kasperbauer, Borthwick, and Hendricks, 1963, 1964
	No. 194	SDP	2	10	Not induced by single D	ex. Pollard, Calif. Acad. Sci., Santa Barbara County, Calif., U.S.A. Cachuma Lake, Santa Ynez Valley, Calif. 34°20′N, 119°50′W‡	† Cumming, 1961, 1963a
C. salinum Standley	No. 22	SDP	2	8	Can be induced by single D when older	ex. Stevenson No. 416. Brandon, Man., Can.‡	† Cumming, 1959
	No. 69	SDP	2	8		ex. Cumming and Bassett No. 69. nr. Banff, Alberta, Can.‡	†
C. strictum Roth var. *glaucophyllum* (Aellen) Wahl	No. 29	SDP	4	13		ex. Stevenson No. 1035. Brandon, Man., Can.‡	†
C. urbicum L.	No. 53	SDP	4	15		ex. Mulligan. Dominion Arboretum, Ottawa, Can.‡	†
	No. 124	SDP	4	15		Tech. Hogeschool Cult. Gervassen. Julianalaak. Delft. The Netherlands.	†

TABLE 1 (*continued*)

SPECIES	IDENTIFICATION	PHOTOPERIODIC TYPE	MINIMUM LEAF NUMBER	EARLIEST FLORAL INITIATION (DAYS)	SPECIAL FEATURES	ORIGINAL SPECIMEN (EX) OR BOTANIC GARDEN SEED SOURCE	REF. TO PHOTOPERIODIC RESPONSE
Pharbitis nil Choisy [synonym *Ipomoea nil* (L.) Roth]	Strain Violet and Tenden (others not clearly identified)	SDP According to light quality and intensity can show ambiperiodic response (Mathon and Stroun, 1962)	about 2	>14 (earliest time not clear from literature)	Single D in LL when cotyledons extruded induces flowering; reveals endogenous rhythm, c̄ correct L and D temperature e.g., near 20°C (Takimoto and Hamner, 1964, 1965d)	H. Kihara, Kyoto Univ., Japan cited (in Imamura, 1953) as supplying seeds of plants sensitive to single D	Imamura, 1953; Kujirai and Imamura, 1958; Marushige and Marushige, 1963; Takimoto, 1960; Takimoto, Tashima, and Imamura, 1960
Sporobolus neglectus Nash	Sn 101 Sn 111	SDP SDP	4 4	28 28	No anthers formed on plants in Petri dish but seed formed: cleistogamy	ex. Dore and Gillett No. 17511. Along Madawaska River nr. Camel Chute, P.Q. No. 17478. Braeside, Renfrew Co., Ont., Can.‡	†
Sporobolus vaginiflorus (Torr.) Wood	Sv 102	SDP	3	24	Cleistogamous	ex. Dore No. 17581. Roadside by Rideau Lake, Westport, Leeds County, Ont., Can.‡	†

* NOTE: "ex" refers to original collector(s) and herbarium specimen(s) that provided seed. SD = short day, LD = long day. D = dark, LL = continuous light.
† Cumming, B. G., unpublished. Photoperiodic response type, primary leaf number, and earliest floral initiation determined by growing plants in Petri dishes in 8-hour, 16-hour, and 24-hour daily photoperiods (with not less than 8 hours at 1,200 ft-c using fluorescent and incandescent light). Seed stocks being maintained by author, so far as possible. The Carolina Biological Supply Co., Burlington, North Carolina, U.S.A., will also start stocks of some of these selections, depending on demand.
‡ DAO: Dried specimens preserved in the herbarium, Plant Research Institute, Canada Department of Agriculture, Ottawa, Ontario.

that are available for distribution or exchange (see for example Howard *et al.*, 1963; Tsitsin, 1959). Other potentially valuable sources are dried herbarium specimens that may possess viable seeds. Unless the source of seeds is identical to the listed reference (Table 1) a similar photoperiodic response should not be assumed. It is known, for example, that the photoperiodic response of plants within a species can differ according to their latitude of origin (Cumming, 1961, 1963a).

Certain other plants show characteristics related to the foregoing, and although they are not considered here in detail, they may provide additional relevant references.

In *Arachis hypogea*, the peanut, variety Schwarz, young plants show simultaneous growth of the main axis and of cotyledonary buds (Fortanier, 1957; Van Rossem and Bolhuis, 1954). While the main axis remains vegetative, the two cotyledonary buds are borne on lateral leafy stems in the axils of which are inflorescences. The least number of days from germination to floral initiation reported for variety Schwarz is about 19 days when grown at an optimum temperature of 35°C day and 32°C night (Fortanier, 1957). The initiation of flowers is apparently independent of photoperiod and thermoperiodicity, but the formation of floral buds and the amount of flowering is highly dependent on external conditions such as temperature, light intensity, and water supply (Fortanier, 1957).

In *Triticum aestivum*, wheat, variety Marquis, an LDP, floral initiation can be obtained in 11–12 days with a minimum primary leaf number of 6.5–7 when plants are grown from germination in continuous light of 2,500 ft-c (fluorescent plus BCJ incandescent) at 30°C (Friend, 1964).

An aquatic plant, *Lemna perpusilla* 6746, duckweed (Hillman, 1959; Landolt, 1957), is an SDP that can be induced to flower in response to a single dark period interrupting long days. Methods of cultivation of this plant and its value for studies of development are discussed elsewhere in this book by Posner, pp. 301–317.

Short-day plants such as *Xanthium pennsylvanicum*, cocklebur (Hamner and Bonner, 1938), *Glycine max*, soybean (Borthwick and Parker, 1938), and the LDP *Lolium temulentum*, darnel (Evans, 1958, 1960), have been used intensively in studies of photoperiodism and flowering but they have not been reported to flower early in their life cycle. Generally, they require about 4 to 5 weeks growth after germination to attain fully their sensitivity to a limited number of inductive photoperiodic cycles (perhaps synonymous with "ripeness-to-flower" [Klebs, 1918]). When full photoperiodic sensitivity is reached, at least one strain of *Xanthium pennsylvanicum* will flower in response to a single long dark period interrupting long days or continuous light. Similarly, in at least one population of *Lolium temulentum*, exposure of 5-week-old plants to a single long light period interrupting short days will result in flowering (Evans, 1960). Floral initiation can be detected in such plants soon after the start of inductive cycle(s), that is, after about 5 days in *X. pennsylvanicum* and 8 days in *L. temulentum*.

Possession of full photoperiodic sensitivity at an early seedling stage is a considerable advantage in studies of flowering. At least three SDP: *Chenopodium rubrum*-374 (Cumming, Hendricks, and Borthwick, 1965), *Chenopodium aristatum*-606 (Cumming, 1965b), and *Pharbitis nil*, Japanese morning glory, strain "Violet" (Kujirai and Imamura, 1958; Takimoto and Hamner, 1964) are photoperiodically responsive to a single dark period and show an endogenous circadian rhythm in flowering response as soon as the cotyledons are expanded from the seed coat after germination. Using *C. rubrum*-

374, for example, when a single dark period is imposed 4 days from the beginning of seed imbibition, floral initiation is detectable 3 to 4 days after plants are returned to continuous light (Cumming *et al.*, 1965). Thus, individual experiments on rhythmic flowering responses and phytochrome control can be completed in 10 to 14 days. So far, no LDP has been found that shows a response equivalent to the foregoing, that is, very early flowering induced by a single long light period interrupting short days, with plants maintained in small Petri dishes. Undoubtedly, the discovery of such an LDP would be very useful.

The discovery of a strain of *Brassica campestris* L. that responds to a single long day (photoinductive cycle) interrupting 8-hour short days, as early as 4 days after sowing, was recently reported by Friend and Helson (1966). Further details are given in another publication (Friend, in press). *Brassica campestris* is a quantitive long-day plant, because flowering occurs quite rapidly even in short days. Temperature requirements for germination and for flower induction are fairly unspecific. Extending the photoperiod from 8 to 22 or 24 hours during 1 photocycle (with incandescent light of ca. 40 ft-c) induced inflorescences in 90 percent of the plants. Inflorescence development was visible on dissection 5 or 6 days after photoinduction. Floral induction increased with duration and intensity of the supplementary light. This plant is therefore a valuable addition to the short list of long-day plants induced by 1 long day. Both *Lolium temulentum* (Evans, 1958) and *Sinapsis alba* (Bernier, 1963) become sensitive to 1 long day only when about 4 or 5 weeks old, by which time the plants are quite large. *Anagallis arvensis* (Ballard and Grant Lipp, 1964) has the advantage of being photoinductive in the seedling stage so that small flowering plants can be obtained, but the amount of floral initiation induced by one long day is slight, if any. Also *A. arvensis* plants become harder to induce as they age.

The following sections provide fuller details of some selected early-flowering plants and refer to techniques that are appropriate for them.

SEEDS AND STORAGE, PRETREATMENT OF SEEDS, GERMINATION AND SUBSEQUENT GROWTH

Seeds and Storage

The recommended temperature for storing many seeds is 0° to 5°C; in this temperature range water in the seeds does not freeze and enzyme activities are retarded. The moisture content of seeds should not be much in excess of 10 to 15 percent (Stanley and Butler, 1961). Lower temperatures may be suitable if the water content of the seeds is low so that ice crystals do not damage the cells. To prevent excessive moisture in the air one simple method is to store seeds in a desiccator or other enclosed vessel with a drying agent: e.g., silica gel, calcium chloride, activated alumina, or anhydrous calcium sulfate (Brandenburg, Simons, and Smith, 1961). Saturated solutions of different chemicals can be used to control the relative humidity in small, closed spaces; values for nearly one hundred substances are given in one reference (Winston and Bates, 1960). Seeds of *Arabidopsis* may remain viable for 3 years (Laibach, cited by Langridge, 1957b), seeds of many *Chenopodium* spp. for at least 5 years (Cumming, 1965b).

Pretreatment of Seeds

Some seeds are difficult to germinate even when completely "after-ripened."

Several pretreatments may ensure subsequent maximum uniform germination in the shortest possible time.

TREATMENT OF PARENTAL PLANTS FROM WHICH THE SEED STOCKS ARE HARVESTED

Seeds harvested from SDP of *Chenopodium* spp. grown in long days or continuous light may be smaller and more dormant than seeds from plants grown in short days (Cumming, 1965b; Jacques, 1957; Lona, 1947). The difference in germination may be due to the formation of thicker seed integuments in long days (Lona, 1947).

TREATMENT OF SEEDS BEFORE PLANTING

The main purpose of these treatments is to hasten imbibition of water and rupturing of the seed coat and to reduce the contamination by microorganisms of subsequently planted seeds.

MECHANICAL SCARIFICATION. Seeds will normally germinate readily if a portion of the seed coat overlying the radicle is abraded or ruptured, for example with emery paper or a scalpel. Such manual methods are tedious except for small numbers of seeds. Machines can perform the same function but may reduce viability.

CHEMICAL SCARIFICATION. Good germination of *Chenopodium polyspermum* (92 percent at 30°C in light) has been obtained by soaking seeds for 1 hour in concentrated sulfuric acid then washing in water (Jacques, 1957). Periods as short as 1.5 to 5 minutes in concentrated sulfuric acid have improved the subsequent germination of *Chenopodium rubrum* and *C. aristatum* at 30°C in light but some embryos were damaged (Cumming, 1965b). Much better results have been obtained by diluting concentrated H_2SO_4 in water to 75 or 50 percent of the original concentration then immersing the seeds for periods of from 4 to 30 minutes, using the lower concentration for seeds with thinner coats. The seeds should be examined with a binocular dissecting microscope at intervals to ensure that the seed coats are not penetrated by acid and underlying tissue damaged. The seeds can be conveniently washed with sterile water on filter paper in a funnel. Immersion for 12 to 24 hours in sterile or running tap water can improve imbibition and, for this, seeds can be wrapped in fine mesh cheesecloth (Cumming, 1965b). The small seeds of *Chenopodium* spp. are normally dried before planting to facilitate their handling. Such treatments can substitute for an alternating temperature of about 32.5°/10°C that may otherwise be required (Cumming, 1963a, b; Cumming *et al.*, 1965) for optimum germination. With suitable acid treatment and imbibition at 30°C, a high percentage germination can be obtained within 1 to 2 days.

Seeds of *Pharbitis nil* are normally soaked in concentrated H_2SO_4 for 30 to 45 minutes, then washed in running water for 2 to 24 hours before planting (Kadman-Zahavi, 1963; Kujirai and Imamura, 1958; Nakayama *et al.*, 1960; Takimoto and Hamner, 1964).

Prolonged immersion of seeds in sterile, aerated, or running water, apart from encouraging imbibition, may leach germination inhibitors from the seed coat and thus hasten germination.

WETTING AGENTS. These may hasten imbibition of water by seeds. One method that has been applied to *Chenopodium rubrum*-374 (Hollis, 1965) is to soak seeds for 20 minutes in 1 percent "Aerosol" Solution ("wetting agent—preventive water spot," from, e.g., Fisher Scientific Co.) at 30°C, wash them in three or more changes of tap water, then dry on filter paper.

STERILIZATION OF SEEDS. Seeds of *Arabidopsis thaliana* have been sterilized by soaking them for 10 minutes in a (1:1) solution of absolute ethanol and "20 volumes" hydrogen peroxide, before planting under sterile conditions on agar (Langridge, 1957b).

Seeds of *Chenopodium* spp. have been surface-sterilized by soaking them for 20 to 30 minutes either in a filtered saturated solution of calcium hypochlorite or in a 1–2 percent solution of Javex (Cumming, 1965b).

Seeds of *Pharbitis nil* have been surface-sterilized by soaking them in 10 percent calcium hypochlorite for 40 minutes before, and for 10 minutes after, prolonged immersion in sterile water, prior to planting in aseptic culture (Takimoto, 1960).

Germination and Subsequent Growth

Arabidopsis thaliana

Completely afterripened seeds may germinate within 2 days at 22° to 26°C, with not less than 16 hours light per day. Similar germination was obtained when seeds were taken from siliqua 12 days after fertilization; thereafter a dormancy period followed lasting until about 2 weeks after "full ripening" (Langridge, 1957b). A standard procedure after sterilization of seeds and planting has been to place cultures at low temperature (0° to 5°C) for 24 hours, then transfer them to 25°C, using continuous light of 800 ft-c fluorescent and relative humidity of more than 60 percent. Since exposure of the root system to light delayed flowering by 1–1.5 days, silica gel was favored as the medium for germination and growth when large-scale sterile cultures were required for genetic work; up to 50 plants can be grown on 75 ml of the silica gel medium in 9 × 5-cm crystallizing dishes (Langridge, 1957b). Agar, darkened with charcoal to absorb light, was used in smaller experiments, but differential heating of this medium in light and darkness can create errors (Langridge, 1957b).

Chenopodium spp.

Conditions that are suitable for germination of *Chenopodium* spp. are outlined in a number of references (Cumming, 1959, 1963a, b, 1965a; Cumming *et al.*, 1965; Herron, 1952; Jacques, 1957). One very convenient and economical method that provides satisfactory semisterile conditions for germination, subsequent growth, and floral initiation, is to place seeds in small Petri dishes (6 × 1.5 cm or 9 × 2 cm) on filter paper (4.25 cm or 9 cm respectively) moistened with water (tap, demineralized, or distilled). Some stimulation of germination may be obtained using a 0.1–0.2 percent solution of potassium or sodium nitrate, or 0.034 percent hydrogen peroxide. An additional effect of KNO_3 or of nutrients can be to stimulate growth of the seedlings at an early stage; this may alter photoperiodic sensitivity, not necessarily in a way that is desired, in species such as *C. aristatum*, *C. rubrum*, and others (Cumming, 1965b). Other substances can be added in solution to the filter paper as required and, once the seeds have germinated, different solutions can be added to the filter paper and washed off at a given time, if desired. A simple method that can be employed for semisterile germination and maintenance of seedlings for early-flowering experiments is to add an excess amount of the imbibition solution to eight layers of Whatman No. 2 filter paper in each Petri dish, then autoclave for asepsis, pour off excess liquid from each dish, mark the lids of dishes according to treatment number, then plant the seeds. Seeds of *C. aristatum*, *C. foetidum*, and *C.*

rubrum can be planted at a rate as high as 150 per 6-cm dish, using 4.25-cm diameter filter paper. Special vacuum planters can be used but it is a simple operation to plant a fairly uniform number of seeds by hand using a small seed package.

The germination of many *Chenopodium* species is stimulated by light, particularly at high temperature (Cumming, 1959, 1963b). For earliest flowering, germination should be accomplished as quickly as possible and, when plants are to be grown in small Petri dishes, hypocotyl elongation should be kept to a minimum to prevent the cotyledons touching the glass lid. Many *Chenopodium* spp. have some light requirement and their germination is stimulated most by light of high red/far-red ratio (Cumming, 1963b). Thus fluorescent light is more stimulatory than incandescent and, very conveniently, it results in least hypocotyl elongation. A high percentage germination of some species, including *C. aristatum* and *C. foetidum*, can be obtained within about 2 days at 30°C in continuous low intensity fluorescent light of about 100–600 ft-c, provided that the seeds lack dormancy. A constant temperature is easier to apply than alternating temperatures and may be preferable in critical experiments where the number of variables should be reduced to a minimum. However, seeds of *C. rubrum* from plants grown in long day lengths may not germinate uniformly at constant high temperature unless they are treated with sulfuric acid. Complete germination of untreated seeds of *C. rubrum* can be obtained in $2\frac{1}{2}$ to $3\frac{1}{2}$ days at an alternating temperature of 32.5°/10°C in low intensity fluorescent light (Cumming *et al.*, 1965).

Germination is faster if imbibition is started at the higher temperature. To hasten expansion of the cotyledons the last 24 hours of the "germination period" can be at 32.5°C. When different photoperiods are imposed at alternating temperatures it is preferable that the dark period should coincide with the lower temperature, because the light requirement for germination generally increases with temperature and a high temperature during darkness can be inhibitory to floral induction. Dark periods can be imposed by various means other than relying entirely on darkened germinators that may, in any case, need to be opened to light. For example, Petri dishes can be wrapped in aluminum foil or in black cloth, or they can be placed in 35-mm motion picture film cans. When dark periods differ by more than 12 hours in a single experiment, the germination period for half the total number of dishes can be started 12 hours before the other so that each successive 24 hours of dark period(s) can be applied within a 12-hour period each day (Cumming *et al.*, 1965). An inductive dark period interrupting continuous light and applied $2\frac{1}{2}$ to 3 days after wetting seeds of *C. aristatum*-606 (Cumming, 1965b) or $3\frac{1}{2}$ to 4 days after wetting seeds of *C. rubrum*-374 (Cumming *et al.*, 1965), can result in floral initiation.

To avoid contamination, when seedlings are to be maintained on filter paper in Petri dishes, water lost by evaporation should be replaced by boiled water and this can be applied with a large capacity plastic plunger syringe.[1] Application of nutrient solution to seeds prior to germination may be inhibitory, but, as soon as radicle extension has started, nutrient can be added to the medium. Either 50 to 100 percent Hoagland's No. 1 solution (Hoagland and Arnon, 1939), modified by providing the 10 ppm iron as Sequestrene (sodium ferric ethylenediamine tetraacetate), or about 1–1.5 ml (solid volume) of a proprietary 20-20-20 compound fertilizer

[1] Tomac irrigating syringe, 2-ounce capacity. Cat. No. 15902. American Hospital Supply, Evanston, Ill.

(containing trace elements and iron chelate) in 1 liter of distilled water, is satisfactory. The solution should be boiled before use, and, if contamination is a problem, a trace of Captan 50 W (N-trichloromercapto-4-cyclohexene-1,2-dicarboximide) can be added as an antifungal agent—add this to the solution just after boiling (Cumming, 1963a; Cumming *et al.*, 1965).

For completely aseptic germination and continued growth, an agar culture medium developed by Miller (1965) has proven to be very satisfactory for germination and subsequent growth of *C. rubrum* and *C. aristatum*-606, and for production of callus from different tissues (Cumming, 1965b). Some methods for such culture media are discussed elsewhere in this volume (Miller, pp. 613–622).

For spectrographic work using *C. rubrum*-28 (Kasperbauer *et al.*, 1963, 1964) seeds have been planted in a 2:1 mixture of heat-sterilized soil and sphagnum in shallow furrows in plastic boxes. The furrows corresponded with given wavelengths on the spectrograph. Seeds were not covered with soil but the planted boxes were covered with transparent lids and kept under continuous fluorescent light at 27°C. A high percentage of seeds germinated in 3 days.

Pharbitis nil

Seedlings of "Japanese morning glory" are bigger than those of *Arabidopsis thaliana* and *Chenopodium* spp. and this is a disadvantage if it is desirable to grow a large number of individuals in small containers. After treating dry seeds with sulfuric acid for about 30 minutes and washing them for 16 to 24 hours in running water, the swollen seeds are generally sown on moist sand or perlite for a further 24 hours in darkness at temperatures between 20° and 30°C (Marushige and Marushige, 1963; Nakayama *et al.*, 1960; Takimoto and Hamner, 1964). At the end of this period the radicles should have emerged and the seedlings can then be transferred to appropriate growing conditions.

FLOWERING

Arabidopsis thaliana is an autogamous facultative long-day plant. Recent international cooperation on *Arabidopsis* research attests to the value of this plant (Röbbelen, 1965). Selected races, e.g., Enkheim, Estland (Langridge, 1957b), are described as small and rapidly growing with a 28-day life cycle, a low chromosome number ($n = 5$) and a high fertility of about 150 seeds under sterile conditions. The small size and rapid growth of the plants enable them to be grown throughout their life cycles on sterile nutrient agar in ordinary test tubes or in larger numbers on silica gel in crystallizing dishes. The consequent precision of environmental control can facilitate the study of growth and development, gene-environment interactions, and the effects of organic substances added to the medium. Furthermore the small seeds with their low nutrient reserves make the plants sensitive to mineral deficiencies, thus offering valuable material for mineral bioassay (Langridge, 1957b).

For optimal growth, the trace element cations should be chelated and light should be excluded from the roots. Exposure of roots to light has delayed flowering by 1–1.5 days. When supplied with sucrose, plants absorbed only the glucose portion (Langridge, 1957b). Other studies have shown that the inclusion of sucrose or glucose in a sterile culture medium can promote flower induction (Rédei, 1962).

Adaptively superior hereditary changes (supervital mutants) have been studied using X-rays (Rédei, 1962); this work was partly based on ecotypes studied by

Laibach (1943, 1951). It was found that a great variety of useful genetic markers can easily be induced by X-rays, the complete life cycle taking 5–6 weeks under suitable conditions. Seeds, presoaked 24 hours, were given 8,000–12,000 r of X-rays at approximately 160 kv, 5 mA, 207 r per minute. After genetic tests, the homozygous progeny of a single individual of the early ecotype "Landsberg" was used in particular. "Landsberg," planted in pots and maintained in long days in a greenhouse with supplemental incandescent illumination, showed flower primordia (visible through a watchmaker's magnifier) in 10–12 days. Some of the mutants obtained in this study flowered much later in both long and short days.

Chenopodium spp.

The photoperiodic reactions of a considerable number of *Chenopodium* spp. are summarized in Table 1. Early flowering can be obtained by germinating seeds and maintaining the seedlings on moistened filter paper or some other sterile medium in Petri dishes or other small containers.

Floral initiation or later stages in flowering can be determined very readily using a binocular dissecting microscope. Detection of floral initiation involves an error of less than 1 day, since the apex can be readily observed, if necessary without damaging any tissues. The seedling to be observed can be held gently under the cotyledons with a pair of bent forceps while the cotyledons and any young leaves are bent to expose the apex, using a pair of very fine-tipped forceps or a mounted needle.

The transition of a vegetative to a floral primordium is similar throughout the genus *Chenopodium*. In *C. rubrum*, for example (Fig. 1, and Cumming, 1963a), an apical vegetative primordium is visible as an undifferentiated spherical dome of cells which can produce leaves and axillary bud primordia (spiral phyllotaxy). Note, in Fig. 1a, the youngest leaf initial (primordium) produced from the (upper left) side of the vegetative apex. Floral initiation involves swelling of the dome of cells and the formation of a peripheral ridge of tissue that encircles an inner area with an apical protuberance (Fig. 1b); the latter eventually forms the stigma surmounting the monocarpous ovary, while the peripheral ridge grows up to surround the ovary but not the stigma. Histological transformations of the apical meristem of *Chenopodium album*, during floral initiation, have been studied in detail (Gifford, 1964).

Anthers and perianth (Fig. 1f) which are derived respectively from axillary bud and leaf initials (Fig. 1a) may be reduced or absent (Fig. 1e) when there is precocious flowering and/or when nutrients are lacking. Plants of many *Chenopodium* spp. may be self-fertile and can be selfed or cross-pollinated to produce seed in Petri dishes (Fig. 1g), in sterile culture, etc.

Selected plants of *C. rubrum* are particularly valuable for studies of floral initiation in response to environment (Cumming, 1959, 1963a, 1965), for studies of phytochrome (Cumming, 1963; Cumming *et al.*, 1965; Kasperbauer *et al.*, 1963, 1964), endogenous rhythms (Cumming *et al.*, 1965), and the effects of chemical mutagens such as ethyl sulfate (Murray and Craig, 1965). Photoperiodic response curves of six different latitudinal selections of *C. rubrum* are shown in Fig. 2. Twenty-five seeds of a selection were germinated and grown to maturity in each section of a Felsen quadrant 9 × 2-cm Petri dish (Fig. 1d) on six layers of Whatman No. 1 filter paper, 7 cm in diameter, previously cut into 4 equal-sized quadrants. The filter paper was moistened with 50 percent Hoagland's No. 1 solution with 10 ppm iron as Sequestrene (chelated iron). Petri

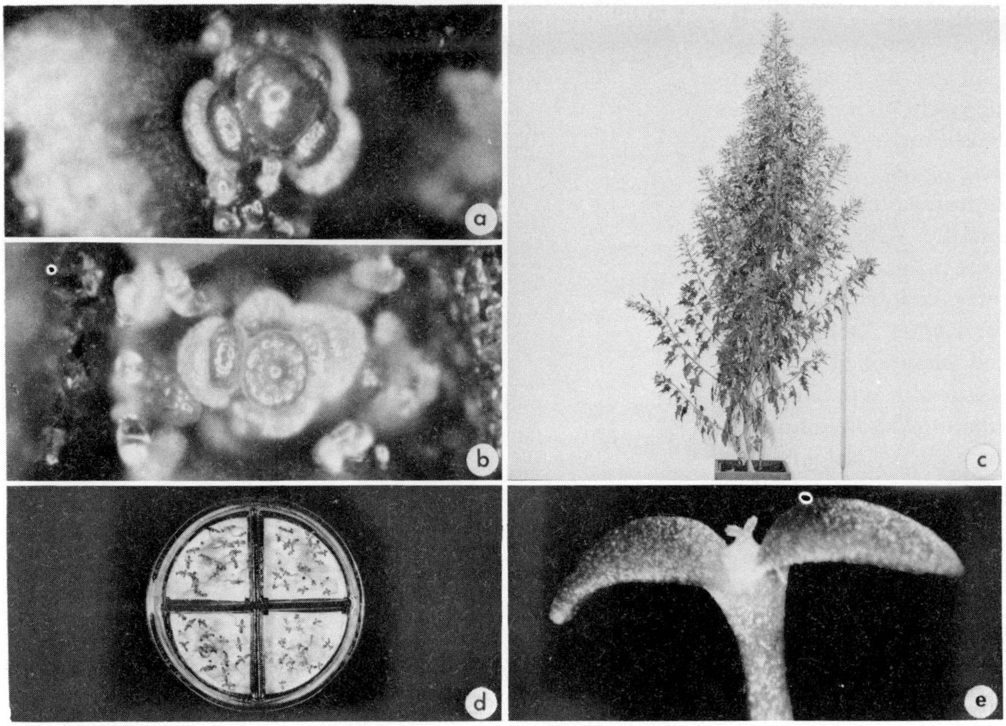

FIG. 1. Flowering in the genus *Chenopodium* (Tourn.) L. (a) and (b) Transition of apical primordium of *C. rubrum* — 372 from vegetative (a) to floral state (b). (c) Vegetative plant of *C. rubrum* — 28 grown in continuous light for 250 days (scale: 1 m rule). (d) Four different selections of *C. rubrum* maintained in a 9 × 2-cam Felsen quadrant Petri dish for flowering. (e) Very early flowering of *C. rubrum* — 28 at low nutritional level in 8-hour day lengths; all floret parts except ovary were rudimentary or absent. (f) Early flowering of *C. rubrum* — 28 with stamens, ovaries, and perianth members, when grown with

dishes were kept in 35-mm motion picture film cans in lightproof cabinets for the appropriate dark periods. The initial temperature was 15°/30°C (15°C for 16 hours, 30°C for 8 hours) to stimulate germination, after which dishes were transferred to constant temperatures of 15°, 20°, 25°, and 30°C, respectively. Floral initiation was recorded when at least 4 plants out of 25 within a treatment showed a peripheral ridge (Fig. 1b). In selection *a*, ambiphotoperiodism was shown at high temperatures: earliest initiation at 25°C was in 12-hour and 24-hour photoperiods so that a bimodal response curve was obtained, while, at 30°C, initiation was earliest in continuous light but there was a secondary optimum in short photoperiods (see also Cumming, 1963a). These results show that a distinction can be made between selections, first, on the basis of sensitivity of flowering response to small differences in daily photoperiod, the order being selection $f > e > d > c > b > a$ where selection *f* is the most sensitive and *a* the least. Thus, the ability to flower in a wide range of photoperiods, including extremely long ones is correlated with latitudinal origin, the most northern selections flowering in

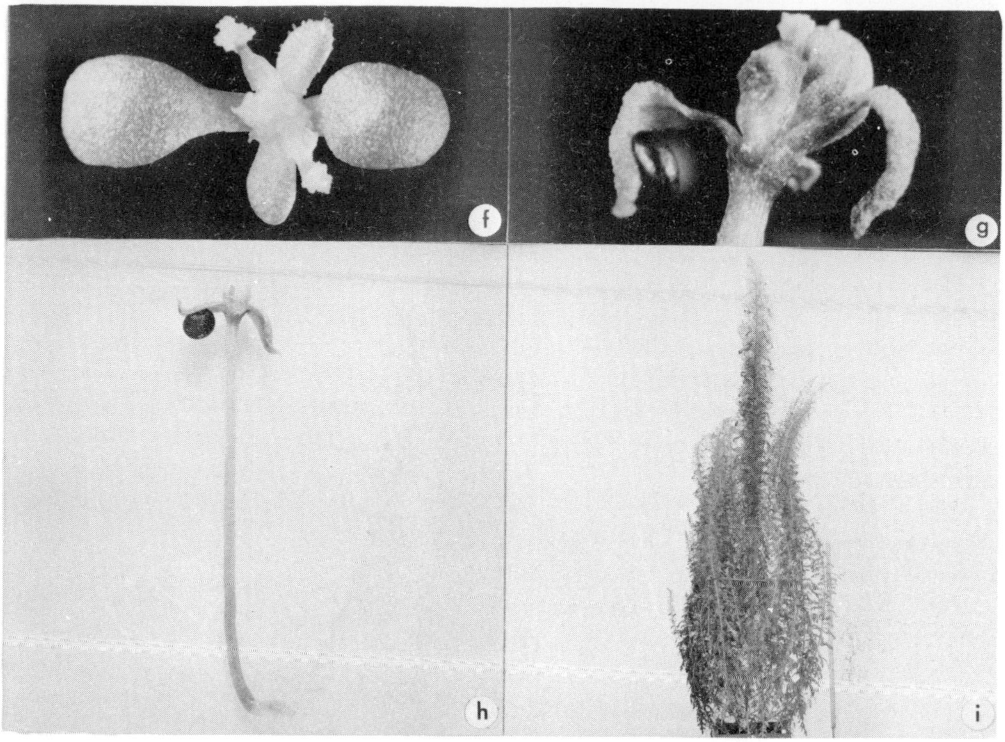

Hoagland's solution in 8-hour day lengths. (g) Subsequent seed formation resulting from selfing of (f). (h) Early flowering of day-neutral *C. foetidum* – 114 grown in continuous light in a Petri dish at low nutritional level; testa 0.5 mm diameter adhering to cotyledon. (i) Flowering plant of *C. foetidum* – 114 grown in continuous light at high nutritional level in soil (scale: 1 m rule). SOURCE: *a, b:* B. G. Cumming, 1963, *Can. J. Botany,* 41:901; *c, d, e, f:* based on results of B. G. Cumming, 1959, *Nature,* 184: 1044; *g, h, i:* previously unpublished.

the widest range of photoperiods. Selections such as *f*, *e*, and *d* will produce giant vegetative plants when grown in soil for prolonged periods in continuous light (Fig. 1c). A second distinction can be made on the basis of sensitivity of response to a limited number of photoinductive cycles (Cumming, 1961, 1965b; Cumming *et al.*, 1965; Kasperbauer *et al.*, 1963), the order being in general $a > b > c > d > e > f$. Thus, selections *a*, *b*, and *c* can be induced to flower quite readily in response to a single dark period interrupting continuous light.

The effects of a single dark period interrupting continuous light can be studied more precisely using selection *c*, 60°47′N = *C. rubrum*-374 (Cumming *et al.*, 1965), because selection *a*, 62°46′N = *C. rubrum*-372, flowers fairly rapidly even in continuous light. *Chenopodium rubrum*-372 shows ambiphotoperiodic response and reversal of photoperiodic response at high temperature in light of low intensity (Fig. 2 and Cumming, 1963a). It is particularly valuable for culture on sterile media, because of its ability to flower at an early stage, even in continuous light (Cumming, 1965b).

Photoperiodic response curves of *C.*

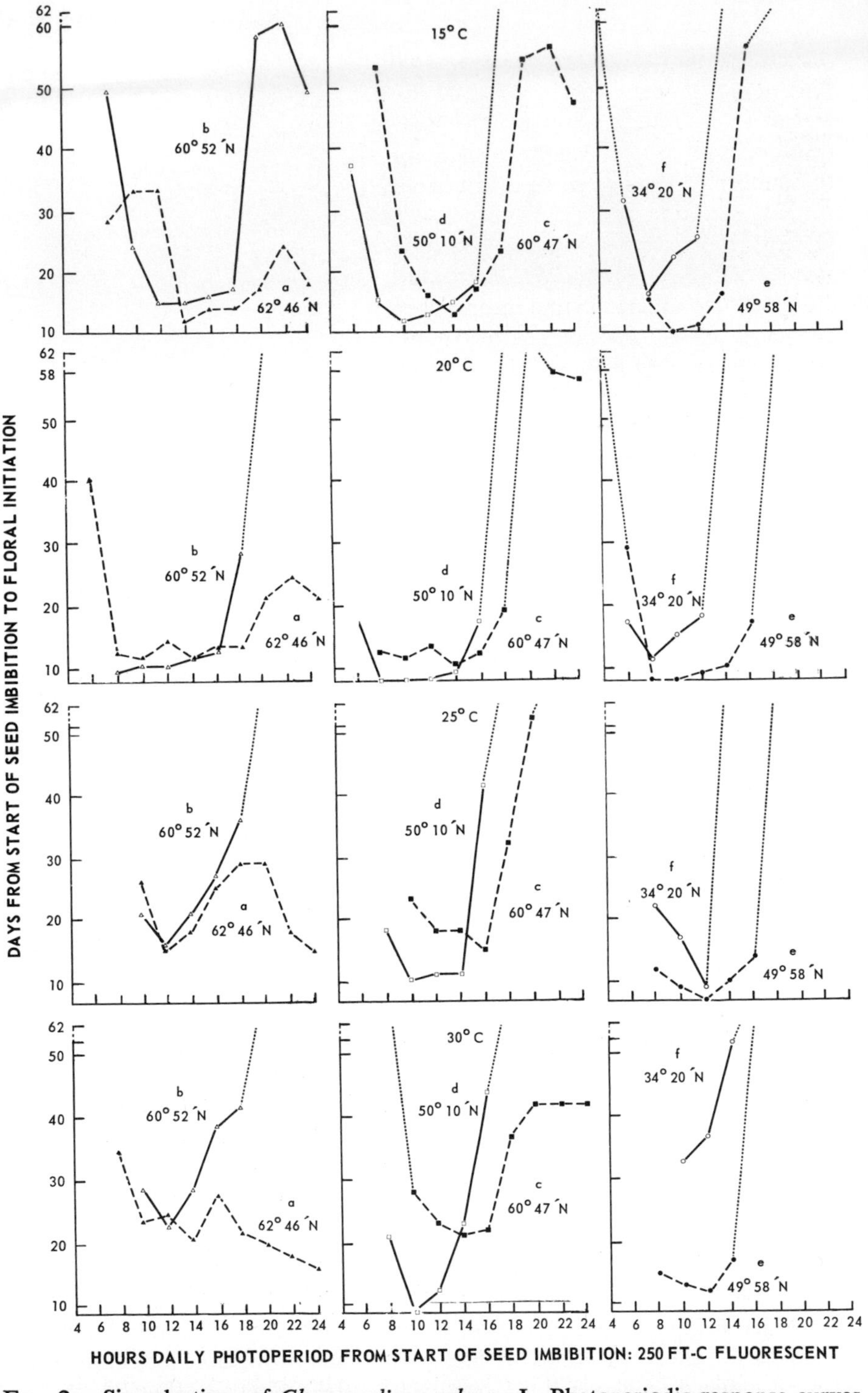

FIG. 2. Six selections of *Chenopodium rubrum* L. Photoperiodic response curves for days from seed imbibition to floral initiation in Felsen quadrant Petri dishes at temperatures of 15°, 20°, 25°, 30°C, light of 250 ft-c cool white fluorescent. Extension of response curves by dotted line indicates plants were still vegetative in respective photoperiods at 62 days. Missing values at photoperiods <10 hours indicates plants died while vegetative. (Previously unpublished.)

rubrum-372 and *C. aristatum*-606, both SDP, and *C. foetidum*-114, a virtually day-neutral plant, are shown in Fig. 3. These were obtained by plotting mean values of the number of days from seed imbibition to floral initiation at 20°C, in response to different daily photoperiods at light intensities of 250 ft-c (cool white fluorescent) and 2,500 ft-c (quartz-iodine incandescent filament). Advantages of the quartz-line lamp ("sun guns") are discussed elsewhere (Voisey and Cumming, 1962). Floral initiation was comparatively earlier in the high intensity incandescent light, but the optimum photoperiods were almost the same in both light treatments. Note, however, that both of the SDP flowered earlier in continuous low intensity fluorescent than in high intensity incandescent light.

Chenopodium aristatum-606, although only recently investigated (Cumming, 1965b) is very sensitive to induction by a single dark period interrupting continuous light, as soon as the cotyledons are extruded. Thus, floral initiation has been detected 5–6 days after wetting seeds, when one 16-hour dark period at 20°C ($2\frac{1}{2}$ days after wetting) interrupted continuous white fluorescent light of 3,500 ft-c at 30°C. In general, both *C. rubrum* and *C. aristatum* can be induced to flower more readily if the light is of high rather than low intensity, before and after a single dark period of appropriate length. Nevertheless, flowering can be obtained with a dark period interrupting continuous fluorescent and/or incandescent light of about 400–800 ft-c at 20°C.

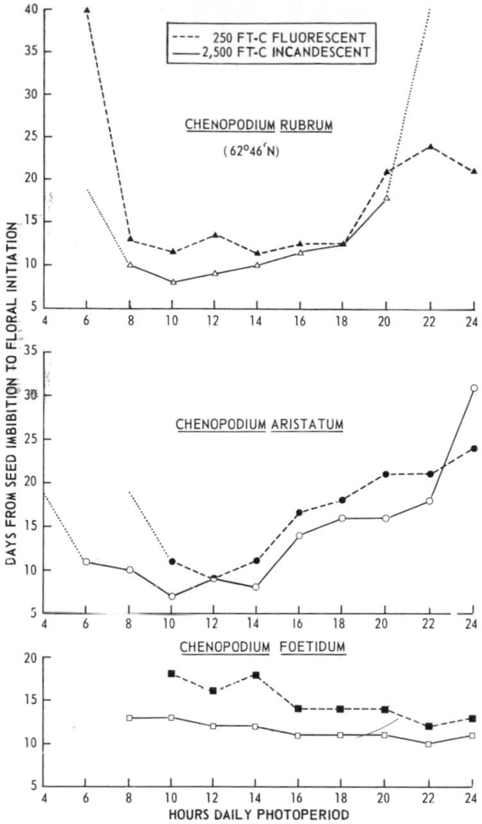

FIG. 3. Photoperiodic response curves of *C. rubrum* – 372, *C. aristatum* – 606, and *C. foetidum* – 114. Days from seed imbibition to floral initiation in Felsen quadrant Petri dishes at 20°C, light of 250 ft-c cool white fluorescent and 2,500 ft-c quartz-iodine incandescent filament, respectively. Dotted line extension indicates no floral initiation before termination of experiment. (Previously unpublished.)

Chenopodium foetidum may be particularly valuable for studying the effect(s) of inorganic and organic compounds on flowering, and for investigations of the basis of "phenotypic plasticity." If the nutritional level is low, *C. foetidum* can be induced to flower in 8–10 days, with a minimum leaf number of 2–4, more or less independently of photoperiod (Fig. 3), when grown in high intensity light in Petri dishes on filter paper or in sand (Fig. 1h). Conversely, the minimum primary leaf number is greater and floral initiation is later when seedlings are germinated and grown in soil (Fig. 1i), or at a higher inorganic nutritional level in sand. The plant illustrated in Fig. 1i produced nearly half a million seeds.

Flowering can also be recorded as the percentage of the total number of plants sampled that show at least the first signs of floral initiation on the apical primordium, within a given time (Cumming *et al.*, 1965). This method is most applicable to experiments of short duration which involve different treatments that may cause flowering ranging between 0 and 100 percent. Examples of such experiments are found in Cumming *et al.* (1965) in which flowering of *C. rubrum*-374 was examined with respect to an endogenous circadian rhythm, the state of phytochrome, and the result of changing the form of phytochrome, during a single dark period of 2 to 96 hours interrupting continuous light. Darkness was imposed either 4 or 5 days after seeds were placed on moist filter paper in Petri dishes. Dark periods as long as 5 days are not excessively detrimental at 20°C for plants of *C. rubrum*-374 and *C. aristatum*-606 grown in Petri dishes. This attribute, together with extreme sensitivity of the red/far-red photoreaction in controlling flowering, makes these selections particularly suitable for the study of rhythmic flowering responses.

A further method of assaying flowering has been applied to *C. rubrum*-28 (49°58′N) in studies of the phytochrome system (Kasperbauer *et al.*, 1963, 1964). Seedlings of this selection require repeated photoinductive cycles for optimal induction (Cumming, 1961, 1963a). These cycles, and special irradiations interrupting darkness, were imposed when the cotyledons were fully spread and before the first true leaves appeared (Kasperbauer *et al.*, 1963, 1964). The seedlings were then returned to noninductive 16-hour day lengths in the greenhouse for about 7 days. The stage of inflorescence development was then established by dissection of the terminal apex of the main axis of each plant.

Each plant was assigned a number from 0 to 9 according to the stage of development of the inflorescence. Completely vegetative plants were assigned 0, while an inflorescence barely visible to the unaided eye was recorded as 9. Stages 0 through 8 were determined with a dissecting microscope at 60 × magnification (Kasperbauer *et al.*, 1963).

Other *Chenopodium* species, including those listed in Table 1, can be maintained on moistened filter paper in Petri dishes for completion of their life cycle. Their particular value can only be revealed by further work. *Chenopodium murale* may be somewhat unusual within the genus, since it is a facultative long-day annual that does not produce a rosette and will flower within about 28 days in continuous light (Table 1). Several other species within the genus are LDP that initially form a rosette even in long days, and these will flower earliest in response to gibberellic acid treatment, e.g., *C. ambrosioides*, *C. capitatum*, *C. foliosum*. The flowering of *C. murale* in long days is not comparable in earliness to that of SDP such as *C. aristatum* and *C. rubrum* in response to short day(s). This raises the question whether later flowering and a higher minimum leaf number is a characteristic of the earliest LDP as compared with the earliest SDP.

When a plant has flowered precociously in a Petri dish, it is sometimes desired to obtain seeds from it. Even though the apical floret may die without producing pollen or seeds, it is often possible to obtain some vegetative growth of higher order lateral buds simply by transferring the plant(s) to better nutritional conditions (e.g., soil) in noninductive photoperiods. To preserve the identity of a genotype or selection, plants should be grown in isolation to avoid cross pollination from any other source. Many species appear to be capable of setting selfed seed either by isolating or bagging single plants. To obtain greater seed production from a single plant that can be prevented from flowering precociously, vegetative propagation in noninductive photoperiods is recommended; the clone can then be transferred to inductive photoperiods for seed production.

Pharbitis nil

One long dark period will induce floral initiation of selected strains or varieties (Imamura, 1953; Kujirai and Imamura, 1958; Marushige and Marushige, 1963; Takimoto, 1960; Takimoto and Hamner, 1964). "Violet" has been the most commonly used strain, requiring a minimum dark period of about 8–10 hours for floral initiation (Kujirai and Imamura, 1958). "Tenden" will flower in longer day lengths and has a critical inductive dark requirement of less than 8 hours; it is a strain adapted to the longer day lengths of northern China (Kujirai and Imamura, 1958).

In assessing flowering, the intensity of photoperiodic induction has a direct bearing on the choice of an assay. With strong induction there is floral initiation on the primary apex as well as the laterals, thus terminating all vegetative growth (Imamura, 1953; Kujirai and Imamura, 1958). The "amount of flowering" may therefore be a misleading assay of floral induction if some treatments are strongly inductive while others are not—since weakly inductive treatments can result in a greater "amount" of flowering. With weak induction there can be later "reversion" to vegetative growth on higher order lateral buds (Imamura, 1953). Some of the measurements that may be applicable include (Kujirai and Imamura, 1958): number of plants bearing floral apices; number of floral apices per 10 plants; number of plants with terminal flowers. A "flowering score" has also been used (Kadman-Zahavi, 1963): a linear scale of arbitrary values was assigned to progressive stages in floral development, the total values of all flowers on a plant were then summated for the flowering score.

Seeds of *P. nil* have been germinated and grown in sterile culture. In one such experiment (Takimoto, 1960), seeds of "Violet" were immersed for 40 minutes in concentrated H_2SO_4, then washed in running water for 1 hour, sterilized in 10 percent calcium hypochlorite for 40 minutes, washed three times in sterile water, left in sterile water until the next day, then 10 minutes in 10 percent calcium hypochlorite, then sown in 18-mm diameter test tubes on White's medium with and without 5 percent sucrose at 10° and 20°C. There were the following results: (1) all plants on sucrose at 10°C flowered independently of day length; (2) plants without sucrose at 10°C flowered in short days but not in continuous light; (3) plants on sucrose at 20°C flowered in continuous darkness or short days but did not flower in continuous light; (4) plants without sucrose at 20°C flowered in short days but not continuous light. A light requirement has been shown for optimal initiation at higher temperatures. Thus (Kadman-Zahavi, 1963), seedlings grown at 23°–25°C in culture solution with 3 percent sucrose, 75 percent Hoagland's, and 25 ppm sulfanilamide did not flower in darkness, but there was 100 percent flowering in daily light treatments of $8\frac{1}{2}$ minutes red every 30 minutes for 6 hours, with darkness for 18 hours; 70 percent flowering resulted when there was 17 minutes red light of 200 ft-c per day. Neither gibberellic acid nor kinetin induced flowering in darkness.

For nonsterile culture, germinated seeds, after selection for uniformity, are normally planted in pots or boxes of soil. At temperatures near 20°C, on the first day after germination in light, plants have unseparated cotyledons and can respond only weakly or not at all to darkness (Kujirai and Imamura, 1958). The photoperiodic reaction was stronger on the second day, and became progressively greater on succeeding days, reaching a maximum in 8–12 days. At constant 30°C, plants reached a maximum in photoperiodic sensitivity 4 days after germination, and then showed a gradual decline (Kujirai and Imamura, 1958).

A standardized procedure has been used with considerable success in studies of the flowering of strain "Violet" in response to a single dark period (Takimoto and Hamner, 1964, 1965). Seeds are soaked in concentrated H_2SO_4 for 25–30 minutes, then washed in running water overnight. Seeds are then placed on moistened sand in Petri dishes at room temperature for 24 hours. By then the radicles have emerged. Seeds are selected for uniformity and planted in 10 × 10 × 6-cm plastic pots in soil with fertilizer added, nine seeds per pot. The temperature for the next 24–30 hours is 30°–32°C and by that time all seedlings are above ground. Plants are then transferred to continuous white fluorescent light of 400 ft-c at 20°C ± 1°C, and, 4 days after planting, they are subjected to the experimental treatment(s). These may be a single dark period, irradiations interrupting short or long periods, etc. After the experimental treatment(s), plants are returned to continuous 400 ft-c fluorescent light, at 20°C, for not less than 24 hours, then to a greenhouse in 18-hour photoperiods having supplemental incandescent light of 500 ft-c, temperature 15° to 35°C. Two weeks after the experimental treatment(s), plants are dissected.

In strain "Violet," grown at 25° to 30°C, there was no circadian rhythm evident in the flowering that was caused by a single dark period applied 4 days after planting seeds with extruded radicles (Takimoto and Hamner, 1964). When plants were grown at 20° ± 1°C, in continuous fluorescent light of 400 ft-c, and given a single dark period at 18°C 4 days after planting, there was a linear increase in flowering with increased duration of darkness. But if 8 hours of darkness then 8 or 12 hours of light was applied before the main dark period, flowering response increased stepwise with longer duration of darkness—that is, an endogenous rhythm was shown (Takimoto and Hamner, 1964). Using these procedures, detailed studies have been conducted on the effects of light and temperature and the time of application of such treatments, in relation to an endogenous rhythm for flowering (Takimoto and Hamner, 1964; 1965a, b, c, d).

For the determination of action spectra (Nakayama *et al.*, 1960), seedlings have been maintained singly in test tubes with Knop's solution, at 25°C. To facilitate irradiation in the spectrograph at predetermined wavelength stations, only one cotyledon was left on each seedling.

REFERENCES

BALLARD, L. A. T., and A. E. GRANT LIPP, 1964: Juvenile photoperiodic sensitivity in *Anagallis arvensis* L. subsp. foemina (Mill.) Schinz and Thell. *Austral. J. Biol. Sci.*, 17: 323.

BERNIER, G., 1963: *Sinapsis alba* L., a new long-day plant requiring a single photoinductive cycle. *Naturwiss.*, 50: 101.

BORTHWICK, H. A., and M. W. PARKER, 1938: Effectiveness of photoperiodic treatments of plants of different age. *Botan. Gaz.*. 100: 245.

BRANDENBURG, N. R., J. W. SIMONS, and L. L. SMITH, 1961: Why and how seeds are dried. In *Seeds. The Yearbook of Agriculture 1961.* U.S.D.A., U.S. Government Printing Office, Washington 25, D.C., p. 295.

CUMMING, B. G., 1959: Extreme sensitivity of germination and photoperiodic reaction in the genus *Chenopodium* (Tourn.) L. *Nature*, 184: 1044.

———, 1961: Photoperiodic response in the genus *Chenopodium* as related to geographical distribution. *Plant Physiol.*, 36, Suppl. li.

———, 1963a: Evidence of a requirement for phytochrome-Pfr in the floral initiation of *Chenopodium rubrum. Can. J. Botany*, 41: 901.

———, 1963b: The dependence of germination on photoperiod, light quality, and temperature, in *Chenopodium* spp. *Can. J. Botany*, 41: 1211.

———, 1965a: Environment and the genus *Chenopodium.* In *Research Problems in Biology: Investigations for Students.* Series 4. Anchor Books, Doubleday and Co. Inc., Garden City, N.Y., p. 19.

———, 1965b: Plant Research Institute, Canada Department of Agriculture, Ottawa; and Department of Botany, The University of Western Ontario, London, Canada. Unpublished.

———, S. B. HENDRICKS, and H. A. BORTHWICK, 1965: Rhythmic flowering responses and phytochrome changes in a selection of *Chenopodium rubrum. Can. J. Botany*, 43: 825.

EVANS, L. T., 1958: *Lolium temulentum* L., a long-day plant requiring only one inductive photocycle. *Nature*, 182: 197.

———, 1960: Inflorescence initiation in *Lolium temulentum* L. Effect of plant age and leaf area on sensitivity to photoperiodic induction. *Australian J. Biol. Sci.*, 13: 123.

FORTANIER, E. J., 1957: De beinvloeding van de bloei bij *Arachis hypogea* L. *Mededel. Landbouwhogeschool Wageningen.*, 57: 1.

FRIEND, D. J. C., 1964: The promotion of floral initiation of wheat by far-red radiation. *Physiol. Plant.*, 17: 909.

———, in press: *Brassica campestris.* In L. T. Evans (ed.), *The Induction of Flowering. Some Case Histories.* The Macmillan Company, New York.

———, and V. A. HELSON, 1966: *Brassica campestris* L.: floral induction by one long day. *Science*, 153: 1115.

GARNER, W. W., and H. A. ALLARD, 1920: Effect of the relative length of day and night and other factors of the environment on growth and reproduction in plants. *J. Agr. Res.*, 18: 553.

GIFFORD, E. M., JR., 1964: Meristems and differentiation. In *Report of Symposium held June 3–5, 1963.* Biology Dept., Brookhaven National Lab., Upton, N.Y. Office of Technical Services, Department of Commerce, Washington 25, D.C., p. 126.

HAMNER, K. C., and J. BONNER, 1938: Photoperiodism in relation to hormones as factors in floral initiation and development. *Botan. Gaz.*, 100: 388.

HERRON, J. W., 1952: *Study of Seed Production, Seed Identification, and Seed Germination of Chenopodium Species.* 24 pp. Cornell University Agric. Exptl. Station, Ithaca, N.Y.

HILLMAN, W. S., 1959: Experimental control of flowering in *Lemna.* I. General methods. Photoperiodism in *L. perpusilla* 6746. *Amer. J. Bot.*, 46: 466.

———, 1962: *The Physiology of Flowering.* 164 pp. Holt, Rinehart and Winston, New York.

HOAGLAND, D. R., and D. I. ARNON, 1939: *The Water-Culture Method for Growing Plants without Soil.* 39 pp. Circ. Calif. Agr. Exptl. Sta., 327.

HOLLIS, C. A., 1965: Duquesne University, Pittsburgh, Pennsylvania. Personal communication.

HOWARD, R. A., B. L. WAGENKNECHT, and P. S. GREEN, 1963: *International Directory of Botanical Gardens.* 120 pp. *Regnum Vegetabile*, vol. 28. International Bureau for Plant Taxonomy and Nomenclature. 106 Lange Niewstraat, Utrecht, Netherlands.

IMAMURA, S., 1953: Photoperiodic initiation

of flower primordia in Japanese morning glory, *Pharbitis nil* Chois. *Proc. Japan. Acad.*, 29: 368.

JACQUES, R., 1957: Quelques données sur le photopériodisme de *Chenopodium polyspermum* L.; influence sur la germination des graines. Publ. No. 34. Sér. B. de l'U.I.S.B., p. 125. Colloque Int. sur le photo-thermopériodisme. Parma, Italy.

KADMAN-ZAHAVI, A., 1961: The growth of plants under very low light intensities. *Bot. Soc. Israel. Proc. 4th Congress Sci. Soc. Israel.*

———, 1963: Effects of light, kinetin and gibberellic acid on flower initiation in *Pharbitis nil* Chois. *Bull. Research Council Israel*, 11D: 191.

KASPERBAUER, M. J., H. A. BORTHWICK, and S. B. HENDRICKS, 1963: Inhibition of flowering of *Chenopodium rubrum* by prolonged far-red radiation. *Botan. Gaz.*, 124: 444.

———, ———, and ———, 1964: Reversion of phytochrome 730 (Pfr) to P660 (Pr) assayed by flowering in *Chenopodium rubrum. Botan. Gaz.*, 125: 75.

KLEBS, G., 1918: Über die Blutenbildung von *Sempervivum. Flora* 111/112: 128.

KUJIRAI, C., and S. IMAMURA, 1958: Über die photoperiodische Empfindlichkeit der Kotyledonen von *Pharbitis nil* Chois. *Bot. Mag. Tokyo*, 71: 408.

LAIBACH, F., 1943: *Arabidopsis thaliana* (L.) Heynh. Als Objekt für genetische und entwicklungsphysiologische Untersuchungen. *Bot. Archiv.*, 44: 439.

———, 1951: Über sommer und winterannuelle Rassen von *Arabidopsis thaliana* (L.) Heynh. Ein Beitrag zur Atiologie der Blutenbildung. *Beitr. Biol. Pflanz.*, 28: 173.

LANDOLT, E., 1957: Physiologische und ökologische Untersuchungen an Lemnaceen. *Ber. Schweiz. Bot. Ges.*, 67: 271.

LANG, A., 1965: Physiology of flower initiation. In W. Ruhland (ed.), *Encyclopedia of Plant Physiology*, Vol. XV, Part 1. Springer-Verlag, Berlin, Heidelberg, New York, p. 1380.

LANGRIDGE, J., 1955: Biochemical mutations in the crucifer *Arabidopsis thaliana* (L.) Heynh. *Nature*, 176: 260.

———, 1957a: Effect of day-length and gibberellic acid on the flowering of *Arabidopsis. Nature*, 180: 36.

———, 1957b: The aseptic culture of *Arabidopsis thaliana* (L.) Heynh. *Austral. J. Biol. Sci.*, Ser. B., 10: 243.

LONA, F., 1947: L'influenza delle condizioni esterne durante l'embriogenesi in *Chenopodium amaranticolor* Coste et Reyn. Sulle qualità germinative dei semi e sul vigore delle plantule che ne derivano. In *Lavori di botanica*. G. Gola Jubilee Vol. Padova, Italy, p. 324.

LOO, S. W., 1946: Preliminary experiment on the cultivation of *Baeria chrysostoma* under sterile conditions. *Amer. J. Bot.*, 33: 382.

MARUSHIGE, K., and Y. MARUSHIGE, 1963: Photoperiodic sensitivity of *Pharbitis nil* seedlings of different ages in special reference to growth patterns. *Bot. Mag. Tokyo*, 76: 92.

MATHON, C-C., and M. STROUN, 1962: Mise à fleur en jour continu et changement du type de réaction photopériodique en fonction de la qualité et du niveau de l'éclairement le *Pharbitis nil* Choisy. *Compt. Rend. Acad. Sci. Paris*, 254: 1478.

MILLER, C. O., 1965: Evidence for the natural occurrence of zeatin and derivatives: compounds from maize which promote cell division. *Proc. Nat. Acad. Sci. U.S.*, 54: 1052.

MURRAY, B., and I. CRAIG, 1965: Research Branch, Canada Department of Agriculture, Ottawa. Unpublished.

NAKAYAMA, S., 1958: Photoreversible control of flowering at the start of inductive dark period in *Pharbitis nil. Ecol. Rev.*, 14: 325.

———, H. A. BORTHWICK, and S. B. HENDRICKS, 1960: Failure of photoreversible control of flowering in *Pharbitis nil. Bot. Gaz.*, 121: 237.

RÉDEI, G. P., 1962: Supervital mutants of *Arabidopsis. Genetics*, 47: 443.

RÖBBELEN, G. (ed.), 1965: *Arabidopsis Research.* Report of International Symposium, University of Göttingen, Germany, April, 1965. Suppl. Vol. I of "Arabidopsis Information Service." Institut für Pflanzenbau und Pflanzenzüchtung, University of Göttingen.

SEARLE, N. E., 1965: Physiology of flowering. *Ann. Rev. Plant Physiol.*, 16: 97.

SIVORI, E., and F. W. WENT, 1944: Photoperiodicity of *Baeria chrysostoma. Botan. Gaz.*, 105: 321.

STANLEY, R. G., and W. L. BUTLER, 1961: Life processes of the living seed. In *Seeds. The Yearbook of Agriculture 1961.* U.S.D.A., U.S. Government Printing Office, Washington 25, D.C., p. 88.

TAKIMOTO, A., 1960: Effect of sucrose on flower initiation of *Pharbitis nil* in aseptic culture. *Plant and Cell Physiol.*, 1: 241.

———, and K. C. HAMNER, 1964: Effect of temperature and preconditioning on photoperiodic response of *Pharbitis nil. Plant Physiol.*, 39: 1024.

———, and ———, 1965a: Studies on red light interruption of timing mechanism involved in the photoperiodic response of *Pharbitis nil. Plant Physiol.*, 40: 852.

———, and ———, 1965b: Effect of double red light interruptions on the photoperiodic response of *Pharbitis nil. Plant Physiol.*, 40: 855.

———, and ———, 1965c: Effect of far-red light and its interaction with red light in the photoperiodic response of *Pharbitis nil. Plant Physiol.*, 40: 859.

———, and ———, 1965d: Kinetic studies on pigment systems concerned with the photoperiodic response in *Pharbitis nil. Plant Physiol.*, 40: 865.

———, Y. TASHIMA, and S. IMAMURA, 1960: Effect of temperature on flower initiation of *Pharbitis nil* cultured *in vitro. Botan. Mag. Tokyo*, 73: 377.

TSITSIN, N. V., 1959: *Botanicheskie sadi mira* (*Botanical Gardens of the World*). 103 pp. Academy of Sciences U.S.S.R., Moscow.

VAN ROSSEM, A., and G. G. BOLHUIS, 1954: Some observations on the generative development of the peanut. *Neth. J. Agric. Sci.*, 2: 302.

VOISEY, P. W., and B. G. CUMMING, 1962: Note on a small high intensity light unit for use in plant research. *Can. J. Plant Sci.*, 42: 392.

WAHL, H. A., 1953: A preliminary study of the genus *Chenopodium* in North America. *Bartonia*, 27: 1.

WINSTON, P. W., and D. H. BATES, 1960: Saturated solutions for the control of humidity in biological research. *Ecology*, 41: 232.

Aquatic Vascular Plants*

By Herbert B. Posner

DESCRIPTION OF THE LEMNACEAE

The Lemnaceae (duckweeds) are small, rapidly growing, aquatic flowering plants with a relatively simple morphology. Thus, precise control of temperature, light, nutrition, and aseptic conditions during the entire life cycle is easier than with higher plants of the more usual size and morphology. Since reproduction is usually vegetative, the use of a single clone eliminates genetic variability in experiments. In addition, radiation-induced aberrants can be produced (Posner, 1962b), and these may prove useful in developmental studies.

The family has four genera: *Spirodela*, *Lemna*, *Wolffiella*, and *Wolffia*. They are composed of floating or partially submerged green structures ("fronds"), usually less than 1 cm long. Fronds of *Spirodela* and *Lemna* are flat, somewhat oval, leaf-like structures with a short strand of vascular tissue extending from the proximal end. Each frond of *Lemna* has a single root arising beneath the lower epidermis. Fronds of *Spirodela* have two or more roots. The fronds of *Wolffiella* and *Wolffia* are smaller, thalloid, and have no roots. In *Spirodela* and *Lemna*, new ("daughter") fronds are produced alternately from meristematic tissues within two pockets, one on each side of an older ("mother") frond. Daughter fronds also produce fronds, sometimes while still attached to their mothers; a group of attached fronds is called a colony (see Fig. 1A). Fronds of *Wolffiella* and *Wolffia* have one pocket.

A frond usually produces only a single flower which in *Lemna* and *Spirodela* arises in the same meristematic region that produces daughter fronds. The flower has one pistil and one or more stamens, all enclosed by a thin sack ("spathe") which is torn toward maturity. Flowers of *Wolffiella* and *Wolffia* do not have a spathe; a single stamen emerges from a furrow appearing on the surface of the frond. For details of morphology and development of frond and flower, see appropriate references in the review by Hillman (1961b).

PROCUREMENT OF THE LEMNACEAE

Members of the Lemnaceae are found in still fresh waters of tropical, subtropical, or temperate regions. Various means may be used to obtain aseptic

* During the preparation of this article I was supported in part by Grant GB-3715 from the National Science Foundation.

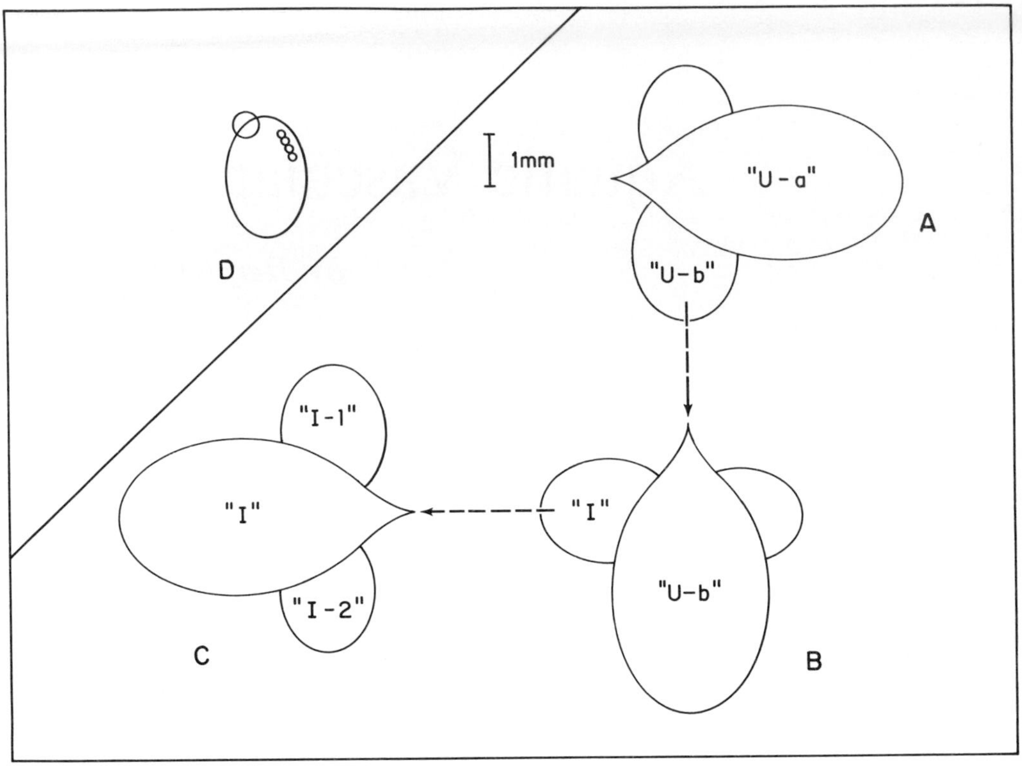

FIG. 1A–C. Diagrams illustrating isolation of I-frond of *Lemna* which is to be used as mother frond in single-frond culture experiments. (A) Initial 3-frond colony inoculum. (B) About 2 days later, U-b becomes detached from U-a; the latter is discarded. U-b now has two visible daughters, the larger of which is I-frond. (C) About 2 days later, I becomes detached from U-b; the latter is discarded. The colony remaining is the mother frond (I) with two visible daughters; the larger is I-1 and the smaller is I-2. See text for details. (D) Young flowering frond. Anther primordia in "minus" (right) pocket, frond primordium in "plus" (left) pocket. See text for details.

fronds. Hillman (1961b) gives the following procedure:

Wash fronds of the desired strain in tap water and then place for several days in mineral medium (see next section) supplemented with 0.2 percent sucrose and tryptone at 600 mg per liter. This brings resistant bacterial spores into actively growing stages which are more sensitive to subsequent sterilization. Immerse fronds for 30 seconds to 5 minutes in 0.5 percent hypochlorite solution (e.g., 1/10 dilution of Clorox). Transfer fronds to sterile medium. The survival of a single aseptic frond ensures production of an axenic clone which can be subcultured indefinitely.

Clones already in aseptic culture may be obtained from a variety of sources. The largest collection known to the author is maintained by Dr. Jerry W. McClure, Dept. of Botany, Miami University, Oxford, Ohio 45056. The clones, listed in Table 1, are available to interested investigators. Included in this collection are strains isolated and in some cases partially

TABLE 1. CULTURE COLLECTION OF *Lemnaceae* (ALL IN AXENIC CULTURE)*

COLLECTION NUMBER	TAXON	ORIGIN	CULTURED BY (SOURCE)
1	*Lemna minima*	Texas, Travis Co.	McClure
4	*L. minor*	Missouri, Atchison Co.	McClure (McNaughton)
5	*L. minor*	Minnesota, Benton Co.	McClure (McNaughton)
6	*L. minor*	Nebraska, Platte Co.	McClure (McNaughton)
7	*Spirodela oligorhiza*	Texas, San Patricio Co.	McClure
8–62	*L. minor*	Saskatchewan, Saskatoon	Perry (Steeves)
9	*L. valdiviana*	Texas, Brewster Co.	McClure (Bold)
10	*S. polyrhiza*	(with collection #9)	
10–62	*L. minor*	Washington, Thurston Co.	Perry (Phillips)
11	*L. minor*	Illinois, Peoria Co.	McClure (Curtis)
13–62	*L. minor*	Washington, Mercer Island	Perry (Phillips)
14–62	*L. minor*	Unknown	Perry (Hillman)
15–62	*L. minor*	Unknown	Perry (Hillman)
18	*L. minima*	Texas, Hays Co.	McClure
20	*Wolffiella floridana*	Texas, Travis Co. (aquarium at Univ. of Texas, of unknown origin)	McClure
21	*S. oligorhiza*	Texas, Travis Co.	McClure
22	*Wolffia papulifera*	Texas, Hays Co.	McClure
23	*S. polyrhiza*	(with collection #22)	McClure
24	*S. polyrhiza*	Louisiana, Rapides Parish	McClure (Alston)
25	*S. polyrhiza*	Florida, Suwannee Co.	McClure (Alston)
26	*Wolffia columbiana*	(with collection #25)	
27	*L. perpusilla*	Florida, Taylor Co.	McClure (Alston)
28	*L. perpusilla*	Georgia, Echols Co.	McClure (Alston)
29	*Wolffia columbiana*	Mississippi, Adams Co.	McClure (Alston)
30	*S. polyrhiza*	(with collection #29)	

* Available from Miami University. Complete collection data may be obtained from Prof. J. W. McClure, Department of Botany, Miami University, Oxford, Ohio 45056. The author is indebted to Dr. McClure for supplying the information given in this table.

TABLE 1 (*continued*)

COLLECTION NUMBER	TAXON	ORIGIN	CULTURED BY (SOURCE)
31	*L. minima*	(with collection #29)	
32	*Wolffia papulifera*	Texas, Hays Co.	McClure (F. McClure)
34–62	*L. minor*	British Columbia, Vancouver	Perry (Stein)
35	*L. perpusilla*	Unknown	Wilkes (Hillman)
36	*Wolffia papulifera*	Texas, Bexar Co.	Wilkes
38	*L. gibba*	South Dakota, Clay Co.	McClure (McNaughton)
40	*L. trinervis*	Texas, Travis Co.	McClure
41	*L. gibba*	Colorado, Grand Co.	McClure (Douglas)
42	*L. gibba*	Colorado, Grand Co.	McClure (Douglas)
44	*L. minor*	California, Tulare Co.	McClure
46	*L. gibba*	Illinois, Knox Co.	McClure (Curtis)
47	*L. gibba*	Oregon, Klamath Co.	McClure (Smith)
48	*L. gibba*	Illinois, Will Co.	McClure (Richards)
49	*L. minor*	Massachusetts, Barnstable Co.	McClure (Cox)
50	*L. minor*	Vermont, Grand Isle Co.	McClure (Walne)
51	*S. oligorhiza*	Louisiana, Orleans Parish	McClure (Youngman)
53	*Wolffiella lingulata*	(with collection #51)	
54	*L. minor*	Indiana, Putnam Co.	McClure (Welch)
55	*Wolffia punctata*	(with collection #54)	
56	*L. minima*	North Carolina, Brunswick Co.	McClure (Beal)
57	*Wolffiella floridana*	(with collection #56)	
58	*S. polyrhiza*	(with collection #56)	
59	*L. minor*	Denmark, Fredenborg Castle	McClure (Alston)
60	*L. minor*	England, Surrey Co.	McClure (Alston)
62	*Wolffia columbiana*	Illinois, Will Co.	McClure (Richards)
63	*Wolffia columbiana*	North Carolina, Wright Brothers National Memorial	McClure (Beal)
64	*S. oligorhiza*	(with collection #63)	
70	*S. oligorhiza*	Brazil, near São Paulo	McClure (Joly)

COLLECTION NUMBER	TAXON	ORIGIN	CULTURED BY (SOURCE)
70A	*S. oligorhiza*—Clones 70A through 70I were selected from the same "wild" collection as number 70.		
70B			
70C			
70D			
70E			
70F			
70G			
70H			
70I			
72	*Wolffiella gladiata*	(with collections 70–70I)	
74	*L. obscura*	Texas, Harris Co.	McClure (Alston)
76	*Wolffia papulifera*	Texas, Fayette Co.	McClure (Mabry)
77	*L. perpusilla*	Nigeria, Ibadan	McClure (Hopkins)
79	*Wolffiella lingulata*	Louisiana	McClure (Daubs)
81	*S. biperforata*	Puerto Rico	McClure (Daubs)
82	*S. oligorhiza*	Illinois	McClure (Daubs)
83	*Wolffia papulifera*	Illinois	McClure (Daubs)
86	*S. polyrhiza*	Texas, Harrison Co.	McClure (Thompson)
87	*Wolffia papulifera*	(with collection #86)	
88	*S. polyrhiza*	Louisiana	McClure (Baetcke)
89	*L. gibba*	Nairobi, Thange River	McClure (Bramblett)
91	*L. obscura*	Florida, Dade Co.	McClure
94	*S. oligorhiza*	Louisiana, Orleans Parish	McClure (Thomerson)
95	*S. oligorhiza*	Louisiana, Orleans Parish	McClure
96	*Wolffiella lingulata*	(with collection #95)	
97	*L. obscura*	Louisiana, Orleans Parish	McClure
98	*S. polyrhiza*	(with collection #97)	
98-H	*L. perpusilla*	X-Ray aberrant of 6746	Posner
99	*L. obscura*	Florida, Sarasota Co.	McClure (R. Daubs)
99-B-1	*L. perpusilla*	X-Ray aberrant of 6746	Posner
100	*L. obscura*	Florida, Charlotte Co.	McClure
101	*S. polyrhiza*	(with collection #100)	
102	*L. obscura*	Florida, Glades Co.	McClure (R. Daubs)

TABLE 1 (*continued*)

COLLECTION NUMBER	TAXON	ORIGIN	CULTURED BY (SOURCE)
103	*S. polyrhiza*	(with collection #102)	
104	*Wolffiella oblonga*	(with collection #102)	
105	*Wolffiella oblonga*	Florida, Collier Co.	McClure
107	*L. perpusilla*	Guatemala, Quezaltenango	McClure (Nelson)
108	*S. polyrhiza* (var. masonii *fide* Daubs)	Netherlands, Utrecht	McClure (Florschütz)
109	*L. gibba*	(with collection #108)	
111	*Wolffia arrhiza*	Netherlands, Rotterdam	McClure (Alston)
112pol	*S. polyrhiza* (var. masonii *fide* Daubs)	(with collection #111)	
112min	*L. minor*	(with collection #111)	
113	*S. polyrhiza* (var. masonii *fide* Daubs)	Netherlands, Utrecht	McClure (DeWilde)
115	*S. intermedia*	Uruguay	McClure (Izaquirre)
1073	*L. perpusilla*	X-Ray aberrant of 6746	Posner
4130	*L. perpusilla*	X-Ray aberrant of 6746	Posner
5104	*L. perpusilla*	X-Ray aberrant of 6746	Posner
5280	*L. perpusilla*	X-Ray aberrant of 6746	Posner
6566	*L. gibba*	California, San Luis Obispo Co.	Landolt (Stebbins)
6568	*L. minor*	Washington, Skagit Co.	Landolt (Nobs)
6570	*L. minor*	Washington, Lincoln Co.	Landolt (Nobs)
6573	*L. gibba*	Montana, Lincoln Co.	Landolt (Heisey)
6578	*L. minor*	Switzerland, Zurich Kt.	Landolt
6579	*L. minor*	Denmark, Copenhagen	Landolt (Clausen)
6580	*L. minor*	New Jersey, near Harrington	Landolt
6581	*S. polyrhiza*	(with collection #6580)	
6582	*L. minor*	California, San Mateo Co.	Landolt
6583	*L. gibba*	(with collection #6582)	
6584	*L. valdiviana*	California, Alameda Co.	Landolt
6587	*L. minor*	California, Victoria Island	Landolt
6589	*L. valdiviana*	California, San Joaquin Co.	Landolt
6591	*L. minor*	California, San Joaquin Co.	Landolt
6592	*Wolffia columbiana*	California, Stanislaus Co.	Landolt
6600	*L. valdiviana*	California, Mono Co.	Landolt
6601min	*L. obscura*	California, Mono Co.	Landolt
6601tri	*L. trisulca*	(with collection #6601min)	
6602	*L. gibba*	California, San Mateo Co.	Landolt
6609	*L. perpusilla*	California, Fresno Co.	Landolt

COLLECTION NUMBER	TAXON	ORIGIN	CULTURED BY (SOURCE)
6612	*L. perpusilla*	California, Fresno Co.	Landolt
6613	*S. polyrhiza*	(with collection #6612)	
6619	*L. obscura*	California, Madera Co.	Landolt
6623	*L. minor*	Switzerland, Egelsee Kt.	Landolt
6624	*L. trisulca*	Switzerland, Schaffhausen Kt.	Landolt
6625	*L. minor*	(with collection #6624)	
6626	*L. minor*	Switzerland, Egelsee Kt.	Landolt
6631	*S. oligorhiza*	California, Alameda Co.	Landolt (Nobs)
6711	*L. valdiviana*	California, San Mateo Co.	Landolt (Heisey)
6717	*L. valdiviana*	Guatemala, Dept. Chimaltenango	Landolt (Norvell)
6722w	*Wolffia columbiana*	Nebraska, Sherman Co.	Landolt (Kiener)
6722tri	*L. trisulca*	(with collection #6722w)	
6726	*L. valdiviana*	California, Kern Co.	Landolt
6727	*L. obscura*	California, Kern Co.	Landolt
6732	*L. minor*	Oregon, near The Dalles	Landolt
6734	*L. gibba*	Oregon, Umatilla Co.	Landolt
6735	*L. gibba*	(with collection #6734)	
6736	*L. gibba*	Washington, Columbia Co.	Landolt
6737	*L. valdiviana*	Washington, Asotin Co.	Landolt
6742	*L. minor*	Pennsylvania, Bellefonte	Landolt
6744	*L. valdiviana*	California, Tuolumne Co.	Landolt
6745	*L. gibba*	California, Tuolumne Co.	Landolt
6746	*L. perpusilla*	California, Merced Co.	Landolt
6747	*L. valdiviana*	California, Mariposa Co.	Landolt
6751	*L. gibba*	California, Monterey Co.	Landolt
6752	*L. valdiviana*	Nebraska, Garden Co.	Landolt (Kiener)
6861	*L. gibba*	Italy, Lucca	Landolt (Sulger-Büel)
6863	*L. valdiviana*	California, Madera Co.	Landolt
7000	*Wolffiella floridana*	Texas, Travis Co.	Landolt
7001	*L. perpusilla*	Texas, Liberty Co.	Landolt
7002	*L. minima*	Louisiana, St. Mary Parish	Landolt
7003	*S. polyrhiza*	(with collection #7002)	
7004	*L. minor*	Louisiana, St. Mary Parish	Landolt
7005	*L. valdiviana*	Florida, Wakulla Co.	Landolt
7006	*L. perpusilla*	South Carolina, Sumter Co.	Landolt
7007	*L. gibba*	Italy, Ponzana	Landolt
7009	*L. minor*	(with collection #7007)	
7010	*S. polyrhiza*	(with collection #7007)	
7013	*L. trisulca*	Germany, Dannenberg	Landolt (Tüxen)

TABLE 1 (*continued*)

COLLECTION NUMBER	TAXON	ORIGIN	CULTURED BY (SOURCE)
7014	*Wolffia arrhiza*	(with collection #7013)	
7015	*L. minor*	New Zealand, Banks Peninsula	Landolt
7016	*L. minor*	England, Surrey Co.	Landolt
7017	*S. polyrhiza*	(with collection #7016)	
7018	*L. minor*	Turkey, Anatolia	Landolt
7019	*L. minor*	Switzerland, Zurich Kt.	Landolt
7130pos	*L. perpusilla*	X-Ray aberrant of 6746	Posner
G1	*L. gibba*	Germany, Berlin	Kandeler
G3	*L. gibba*	Germany, Berlin	Kandeler
L.1-4-3-1 through L.1-4-3-13	*L. perpusilla*	Thirteen different progeny of selfed clone 6746	Hillman
Lms	*L. minor*	Kansas, Kansas City	Hillman (Saeger)
Lmy	*L. minor*	Connecticut, Middlesex Co.	Hillman (Castle)
Lpm	*L. perpusilla*	India, New Delhi	Hillman (Maheshwari)
Lty	*L. trisulca*	Connecticut [aquarium in New Haven (of unknown origin)]	Hillman
Soh	*S. oligorhiza*	Massachusetts [aquarium at Harvard (of unknown origin)]	Thimann
Sps	*S. polyrhiza*	Kansas, Kansas City	Hillman (Saeger)
Spy	*S. polyrhiza*	Connecticut [aquarium in New Haven (of unknown origin)]	Hillman
War	*Wolffia arrhiza*	India, New Delhi	Maheshwari

characterized by Landolt (1957), Kandeler (1955, 1956), Hillman (1957, 1961a), Posner (1962b), McClure (1966), and others.

MAINTENANCE OF LEMNACEAE

Of the various media used, Hutner's medium (Hutner, 1953) seems to be the best for maintaining vigorous growth for long periods. Hillman (personal communication) suggests the following method for preparation of stock solutions:

While stirring about 200 ml distilled water, add: $Ca(NO_3)_2{\cdot}4H_2O$, 17.7 gm; ethylenediaminetetraacetic acid (EDTA), 25.0 gm; K_2HPO_4, 20.0 gm; NH_4NO_3, 10.0 gm. To dissolve the EDTA, add 12–13 gm KOH (85 percent pellets). This makes Solution A.

To another volume of water (about 150 ml), add the following with constant stirring: $ZnSO_4{\cdot}7H_2O$, 3.295 gm; H_3BO_3, 0.710 gm; $Na_2MoO_4{\cdot}2H_2O$, 1.260 gm; $CuSO_4{\cdot}5H_2O$, 0.197 gm. At this point add 1 *N* HCl (about 13 drops) until the cloudiness disappears. Then add: $Co(NO_3)_2{\cdot}$

$6H_2O$, 0.010 gm; and $MnCl_2 \cdot 4H_2O$, 0.897 gm. This makes Solution B.

To a third volume of water (about 50 ml) add $FeSO_4 \cdot 7H_2O$, 1.245 gm. This makes Solution C.

Now, with constant stirring, combine Solutions A, B, and C. Take to 1,000 ml with distilled water. This makes Stock Solution I. Keep refrigerated.

To make Stock Solution II, take 25 gm of $MgSO_4 \cdot 7H_2O$ to 1,000 ml with distilled water.

For full-strength medium, use 20 ml of Stock Solution I plus 20 ml of Stock Solution II per liter of medium. Adjust pH to 6.1–6.4 with 5 *N* KOH.

Another medium used, designated M (Hillman, 1961a), is described in Table 2. This is a modification of a modified Hoagland's medium (see Gorham, 1950). For certain studies, the level of cupric ion in M-medium is critical. See the footnote in Table 2 for details. For information on other media, see references in Hillman (1961b).

Distribute media to either tubes or flasks (see below). Plug with cotton and autoclave for 10–15 minutes at 15 lb per square inch. Use standard microbiological aseptic techniques for subculturing fronds.

To insure the availability of sterile material, maintain permanent clonal stocks on Hutner's medium supplemented with sucrose (1 percent), tryptone (600 mg per liter), and yeast extract (100 mg per liter). Keep under low-intensity light (about 10 ft-c) at room temperature, and subculture them every 1–2 months.

EXPERIMENTAL MANIPULATION OF LEMNACEAE

Stock Cultures

Inocula for experiments are obtained from stock cultures. These may be grown

TABLE 2. COMPOSITION AND PREPARATION OF M-MEDIUM

STOCK SOLUTION	COMPOUND	AMOUNT	USE PER LITER OF MEDIUM
A	KH_2PO_4	13.6 gm/liter	50 ml
B	KNO_3	50.5 gm/liter	30 ml
C	$Ca(NO_3)_2 \cdot 4H_2O$	118.0 gm/liter	10 ml
D	$MgSO_4 \cdot 7H_2O$	49.2 gm/liter	10 ml
E	Trace elements (all in 1 liter)		
	* $CuSO_4 \cdot 5H_2O$	48.0 mg	
	$ZnSO_4 \cdot 7H_2O$	22.0 mg	
	$MnCl_2 \cdot 4H_2O$	362.0 mg	10 ml
	H_3BO_3	286.0 mg	
	$Na_2MoO_4 \cdot 2H_2O$	12.0 mg	
F	$FeCl_3 \cdot 6H_2O$	540 mg/100 ml	1 ml
G	Tartaric acid	300 mg/100 ml	1 ml

Adjust pH of medium anywhere from 4.0 to 5.0.

* Cupric ion is required for certain flowering responses, and the amount that should be added to the medium may vary depending on the amount of copper contaminating the other reagents and the water. The amount shown here is sufficient to cause long-day flowering in *L. perpusilla* 6746 under the conditions used in this laboratory: continuous cool-white fluorescent light (200 ft-c); temp. of medium, 24°–27°C; reagent-grade chemicals; water produced by glass-distilling deionized water (see Hillman, 1962).

in 125-ml Erlenmeyer flasks with about 50 ml of medium. Conditions for growing vegetative stock cultures depend on the clone being investigated (see Table 3). Most species remain vegetative on Hutner's medium diluted to 7/10 × standard concentration (see below) with 1 percent sucrose, at about 27°C under continuous cool-white fluorescent light (about 150 ft-c). Other species, such as *Lemna gibba* G3, require M-medium with 1 percent sucrose under an 8-hour photoperiod of mixed warm- and cool-white fluorescent light (about 700 ft-c) at about 27°C (Hillman, 1961a).

Another factor to be considered is the concentration of the medium. Full-strength medium is too concentrated for many of the Lemnaceae. For example, full-strength Hutner's medium is toxic for *Wolffia columbiana* 6722, but growth is healthy and rapid in a 1/5 dilution of the same medium (Hillman, 1960). For many Lemnaceae, growth in Hutner's medium diluted to 1/3 × standard concentration is better than on full-strength medium (Hillman, 1961b). See Landolt (1957) for further details on the effects of medium concentration, light intensity, and sugar supplementation.

Batch Cultures

For experiments with nongrowing cultures, fronds may be placed in distilled water (see, for example, Furuya and Thimann, 1964). For studies on vegetative growth, start cultures with single colonies. With *Lemna perpusilla* 6746, for example, use 3-frond colonies taken from stock cultures 7–10 days old. Vessels for the experimental cultures can be Erlenmeyer flasks (e.g., 50-ml flasks with about 25 ml medium) or tubes (e.g., 20 × 150-mm tubes with 15–20 ml medium).

Growth may be expressed as increases in fresh weights, dry weights (but see Gorham, 1950), and frond areas. However, a more simple and reliable measure of growth is obtained by counting all visible fronds at various intervals of time. Growth can then be expressed in one of the following ways:

1. The percentage increase in frond number during a given period.

2. Under conditions giving exponential increases, a growth constant, K (Clark, 1925), may be calculated from the equation

$$K = \frac{\log N_d - \log N_o}{d}$$

where N_o is the original number of fronds, N_d the number on day d, and d the number of days involved.

3. The Multiplication Rate (MR), which is K multiplied by 1,000. For example, an MR_{2-4} of 301 (that is, $K = 0.301$) means that frond number doubled each day from day 2 to day 4.

Since the pattern of frond production and development has been interpreted as branching in a sympodial system of unelongating shoots (Ashby *et al.*, 1949), MR values might be described as average rates of node production (Hillman, 1960). For a discussion on the kinetics of growth in duckweed cultures, see Hillman (1961b).

Single-Frond Cultures

Growth measurements on batch cultures do not give the life span of any given frond, the number of nodes (i.e., daughter fronds) it is capable of producing, or the rate at which they are produced. Such information has been obtained by using single-frond cultures, a technique first employed by Ashby *et al.* (1949) for developmental studies on meristem aging. In flowering plants of the more usual morphology, meristem aging might be responsible for the regular changes in shape and area of successive leaves. It is possible, however, that these changes are effected by slight differences in the external environment at different nodes, or to differences in the distance between the nodes and the roots (Wangermann and Ashby, 1950). With *Lemna*, these variables are eliminated.

The studies of Ashby and his group on meristem aging in *Lemna* have demonstrated a senescence-rejuvenation cycle. That is, a given frond has a definite life span during which a definite number of daughters are produced. Each daughter is smaller and produces fewer daughters (however, see Posner, 1962a) than the daughter preceding it (senescence). A small late-formed daughter produces a first daughter larger than itself; in addition, this first daughter produces more fronds than does the late-formed daughter (rejuvenation). The effects of various factors on this cycle have been studied, but its biochemical basis has not been elucidated (see Hillman, 1961b).

Another aspect of meristem aging worthy of attention involves the ability of fronds to maintain asymmetry. Most species of *Lemna* produce daughter fronds in an asymmetric, alternating order which is consistent within a clone (see, for example, Landolt, 1957). That is, all fronds of a given clone produce their first daughter frond on the same side of the longitudinal frond axis, this side being designated "plus." For example, in *L. perpusilla* 6746, the "plus" side is to the left if the frond is regarded as lying lower surface down with the proximal (pointed) end directed away from the observer (Hillman, 1959). Thus, this clone can be described as normally "left-handed." Under flowering conditions, a flower is produced in the "minus" ("right-hand") pocket.

Spontaneously shifted (in the above case, "right-handed") fronds are produced rarely, and then usually by senescent mothers. Both the position and number of flowers in a frond can also be affected. As examples, fronds with a flower in the "plus" pocket or with two flowers, one in each pocket, have been observed (Posner, 1962a; Witztum, 1966). Batch cultures may be used to survey the effects of various treatments on these phenomena (see, for example, Posner and Hillman, 1960), but for more detailed studies single-frond cultures are necessary.

The following method (Posner, 1962a) has been used successfully with *L. perpusilla* 6746 (for other methods, see Ashby *et al.*, 1949; Pirson and Göllner, 1953). Grow stock batch cultures on half-strength Hutner's medium. These cultures are used as sources of 3-frond colonies. Inoculate tubes (25 × 150 mm) containing about 20 ml of the above medium with single 3-frond colonies. Incline the tubes at a 30-degree angle under the experimental conditions. Examine daily, and remove detached daughter fronds. Note any changes in their handedness. Detached daughters are discarded or subcultured depending on the particular experiment. Note the numbers of daughters removed, and of those still attached to the mother frond. The number of days between the appearance of the mother frond and its complete loss of chlorophyll is the life span. Transfer all mother fronds to fresh medium about every 5 days.

The following criteria may be used to distinguish between a mother (the single frond being observed) and its detached daughter(s).

1. When only one daughter becomes detached, the mother frond has attached to it a relatively mature daughter (sometimes in the form of a 2- or 3-frond colony) as well as one or two other daughter fronds.

2. The root of the mother is longer, thinner, and less green than those of any of its daughters.

3. The root of the mother loses its cap, usually by the time the first two

daughters become detached.

4. As the mother ages it at first becomes dark green, then slowly loses its chlorophyll and turns yellow, and finally becomes white.

Those criteria involving the root are the most reliable during the early part of the mother's life, at which time loss of chlorophyll is not yet detectable.

The following terminology may be used in recording data. A mother frond designated by a Roman numeral is a first-daughter frond; the value of the numeral indicates the generation. As examples, Roman numeral I is a first-generation first-daughter frond, that is, the first daughter produced by a frond of an unknown. The first daughter produced by I is II, that is, a second-generation first-daughter frond. The daughters produced by a first-daughter (mother) frond are designated by that mother's Roman numeral followed by an Arabic numeral. Thus, the first daughter of I is I-1. If the latter is used as a mother frond, it is more convenient to designate it as II (as explained above). More than one Arabic numeral may follow the Roman numeral: II-6-2 is the second daughter of the sixth daughter of a second-generation first-daughter frond.

To isolate, for instance, a first-daughter frond (i.e., a I-frond) to be used as a mother, the following technique is used (see Fig. 1, A–C). First inoculate a tube with a 3-frond colony from a stock culture (Fig. 1A). This colony consists of a mother, designated as U-a (Unknown-a), and two daughters. The larger daughter is U-b (Unknown-b). When U-b becomes detached, remove and discard U-a. Unknown-b now has two visible daughters. The larger daughter is I (Fig. 1B). When I detaches from U-b, discard the latter. The colony remaining consists of I with two visible daughters; the larger is I-1 and the smaller, I-2 (Fig. 1C). Uniform populations of such colonies are obtained if the initial inocula are carefully selected for uniformity.

Flowering

The Lemnaceae are especially useful for studies on flowering, since experiments require very little space and in many cases can be completed in about 1 week. Unequivocal experimental control of flowering has been achieved for at least two species of *Lemna* (Kandeler, 1955; Hillman, 1961a) and for two of *Wolffia* (Maheshwari and Chauhan, 1963; Maheshwari and Seth, 1966). Some of the factors affecting flowering are light intensity and quality, photoperiod, and chelating agents. A summary of the effects of the last two is given in Table 3. See Hillman (1966) and Esashi and Oda (1966) for light quality effects, and Nakashima (1964) and Umemura and Oota (1965) for effects of amino acids and antimetabolites.

Flowering in *Lemna* may be evaluated with the following method (Hillman, 1959): Arrange the fronds from an experimental batch culture in a circle or spiral in a Petri dish. Separate larger colonies into groups of three or fewer fronds. Count all fronds projecting visibly beyond their mother fronds. Under 20 × power of a binocular dissecting microscope, eject or expose the contents of the pockets by pressing or tearing with a slightly flattened needle. Vegetative primordia are circular transparent disks; flower primordia resemble two or four small appressed spheres (Fig. 1D). Express the degree of flowering as the Flowering Percent (Fl%). To determine this value, divide the number of fronds with flowers at any stage of development by the total number of fronds and multiply by 100.

Flowering may also be expressed in terms of arbitrarily assigned stages, as follows (Esashi and Oda, 1964). Dissect

TABLE 3. EFFECTS OF ETHYLENEDIAMINETETRAACETIC ACID (EDTA) AND PHOTOPERIOD ON FLOWERING IN THREE SPECIES OF DUCKWEED*

SPECIES	EDTA	RESPONSE UNDER 8-HR DAY	RESPONSE UNDER CONTINUOUS LIGHT	REFERENCES
Lemna perpusilla 6746	−	Fl†	Fl	Hillman, 1961a, and
	+	Fl	Veg‡	Esashi and Oda, 1964
Lemna gibba G3	−	Veg	Veg	Hillman, 1961a and 1962
	+	Veg	Fl	
Wolffia microscopica	−	Veg	Veg	Maheshwari and
	+	Fl	Fl	Chauhan, 1963

NOTE: Medium plus 1% sucrose for *Lemna*, no sucrose for *Wolffia*. See references cited for details.
* See footnote to Table 2. † Fl designates flowering. ‡ Veg designates the vegetative state.

only maximally developed fronds and record floral stages. Floral Stage 0: vegetative; Floral Stage 1: only anther primordia present; Floral Stage 2: anther and pistil primordia present; Floral Stage 3: filaments, stigma, and style present; Floral Stage 4: anther filaments elongated; Floral Stage 5: anthers and/or stigma emerged from pocket. The degree of flower development is expressed as the average floral stage of the culture.

In *Wolffia*, flowering can be evaluated without dissection (Maheshwari and Chauhan, 1963). Fix fronds in alcohol until the chlorophyll is removed. Flower primordia are easily identified under a binocular scope since daughter frond primordia are located at a different place on the mother (see description of lemnaceae, p. 301).

If more detailed examination is required, the following method is suggested (Witztum, 1966). Fix fronds in FPA (5 ml 40 percent formaldehyde, 5 ml propionic acid, 90 ml 50 percent ethanol). Wash for a few minutes with water. Mordant in 2 percent ferric chloride for 10–15 minutes. Wash in running water. Stain in hematoxylin (0.5 percent) for 2–24 hours. Destain with 2 percent ferric chloride until the meristematic tissue shows good contrast with the rest of the frond (black against light orange). Wash with water. Run fronds through an ethanol series, then through xylene: absolute ethanol (1:1), then through pure xylene twice. Mount in suitable resin, such as Canada Balsam. Also see Cope *et al.* (1965).

Dormant Stages

SEEDS

The following methods (Posner and Hillman, 1962) have been used for aseptic production, collection, and germination of seeds of *L. perpusilla* 6746. Inoculate 125-ml flasks (1/2 × Hutner's medium plus 0.5 percent sucrose) with about 60 flowering fronds and place in an 8-hour photoperiod (1,500 ft-c; 23°C during night, 28°C during day). The yield, about 100 seeds per flask in 1 month, is more than doubled if the cultures are shaken for 90-minute periods every 12 hours.

Aseptic collection of seeds is simplified by the fact that seeds sink to the bottom of the flask, while most of the fronds remain afloat. The collection apparatus is made as follows: Insert the stem of a cylindrical separatory funnel through the cotton plug and into the neck of a 250-ml flask containing about 150 ml of appropriate medium (see below). Plug the opening of the funnel with cotton. Cap with a 100-ml beaker. Wrap aluminum foil around the stopcock of the funnel as well as the neck of the flask. Autoclave and allow to cool. In a sterile-transfer cabinet, remove aluminum foil, beaker, and cotton plug. Pour the contents of a culture into the separatory funnel. Replace the beaker and gently rotate the apparatus until the seeds fall to the bottom of the funnel. Open the stopcock until the seeds (together with a small amount of the old medium) enter the flask. Remove the funnel and plug from the latter. Insert a fresh sterile plug.

Another collection method (Hillman, personal communication) is to pour sterile water into the culture until the overflow carries the fronds out of the flask. The seeds remain at the bottom of the flask. Decant the water, add appropriate medium, and insert a sterile plug.

Upon germination, the seedlings float to the surface of the medium. They may then be removed and cultured individually if, for example, isolation of the F_1 clones is desired. For such studies, Hutner's medium can be used.

The only species for which germination requirements have been published is *L. perpusilla* 6746 (Posner and Hillman, 1962). Germination does not occur in the dark, even in the presence of sucrose plus kinetin, gibberellic acid, or yeast extract and casein hydrolyzate. Conditions for rapid rates of germination are dark pretreatment for 4 days followed by continuous light, all at about 26°C. Close to 100 percent germination occurs by the second day of light. Rapid germination also occurs under an 8-hour photoperiod. In both cases, a light intensity of 200 ft-c (cool-white fluorescent) is sufficient if certain supplements (e.g., casein hydrolyzate at 600 mg per liter) are added to the medium. Otherwise, about 800 ft-c is required. A study on the effects of temperature and light quality is in a dissertation by Glickman (1966).

TURIONS

Under certain conditions unfavorable for growth, many species produce specialized dormant fronds (turions). The most specialized and widely studied turions, those of *S. polyrhiza*, are lens-shaped organs about 1.5 mm in diameter.

High yields of turions are obtained as follows (Czopek, 1959, 1963). Inoculate 200-ml flasks containing 100 ml medium (Czopek used the medium described by Pirson and Seidel, 1950) plus 1 percent sucrose. Keep at about 28°C under continuous light (150 ft-c). Turions begin to form in about 3 weeks and number about 1,000 per flask in 7 weeks. Most of the turions sink to the bottom of the flask and thus may be collected aseptically using methods similar to those described for seeds of *Lemna* (see above). Wash the turions with sterile distilled water. Store in sterile water in the dark at about 3°C.

Germination is affected by storage and poststorage conditions (Czopek, 1959, 1962, 1964). For rapid rates of germination, store turions at 0°–3°C for 1 month. Transfer to 50-ml flasks with 25 ml medium. Incubate under continuous light (about 200 ft-c) at 28°C. Upon germination, turions form roots and a daughter frond, and then float to the surface of the medium.

DESCRIPTION OF *AZOLLA*

Techniques similar to those described for duckweeds can be used for culturing the aquatic fern, *Azolla* (mosquito fern). This small, free-floating plant, often found in habitats that include duckweeds, consists of pinnately branched, horizontally-floating stems with adventitious roots on the underside. Alternately arranged along the stem are small, overlapping, bilobed leaves. Within the upper lobe, there is a chamber containing a nitrogen-fixing blue-green alga, *Anabaena azollae*, possibly in symbiotic association.

Growth of the stem involves successive divisions of a three-sided apical cell. Abscission of lateral branches and death of mature portions of stems result in multiplication of individual plants. Sporocarps are produced in the axils of the upper lobes. For details, see Smith (1955).

STERILIZATION OF *AZOLLA*

The following method for isolation of an aseptic clone of *A. caroliniana* is given by Nickell (1958):

Place plants in a solution of potassium penicillin G (50 ppm). Transfer daily to fresh solutions of penicillin (number of transfers not specified). Transfer to nutrient medium (see below) for 1 week. Then place plants in the following solutions, each for 1 week: (1) nutrient medium with oxytetracycline (Terramycin) HCl (1 ppm); (2) nutrient medium; (3) nutrient medium plus streptomycin sulfate (5 ppm). Then subculture into nutrient medium.

EXPERIMENTAL MANIPULATION OF *AZOLLA*

To maintain stock cultures, place either small pieces (excised with a scalpel) or entire plantlets into 125-ml flasks with 50 ml medium. There is little information on the effects of media or environmental conditions on *Azolla*. Nickell (1958, 1961) grew aseptic cultures of *A. caroliniana* at 22.5°C under "diffuse light" on medium described in Table 4. Growth rates were measured by fresh weight determinations on replicate cultures at various intervals. Under the conditions described there was a long lag, so experiments required about 6 weeks to complete. Nonaseptic cultures of *A. filiculoides*, grown in one-quarter strength Hoagland's medium, gave maximum increases in fresh weight under 200 ft-c (gas-filled Mazda lamps) at about 22°C (Ahmad, 1941).

TABLE 4. COMPOSITION OF MEDIUM FOR *Azolla caroliniana* AS DESCRIBED BY NICKELL (1958, 1961)

COMPOUND	CONCENTRATION
KNO_3	0.002 *M*
$Ca(NO_3)_2$	0.003 *M*
KH_2PO_4	0.001 *M*
$MgSO_4$	0.001 *M*
$CaCl_2$	0.003 *M*
KCl	0.002 *M*
$MgCl_2$	0.001 *M*
Thiamine	100 μg/liter
Pyridoxin	800 μg/liter
Nicotinamide	800 μg/liter
B	0.1 ppm
Mn	0.1 ppm
Zn	0.3 ppm
Cu	0.1 ppm
Mo	0.1 ppm
Fe	0.5 ppm
EDTA	20 ppm
Sucrose	2%

(Adjust pH to 5.0)

RECENT GROWTH STUDIES ON *AZOLLA*

Most of the early work on *Azolla* dealt with the question of its symbiosis with *Anabaena* (see Schaede, 1948). The few recent growth studies reported have been on the effects of various chemical supplements. Nickell (1961) describes effects of growth regulators and antibiotics on aseptically grown cultures. Dusels and Bonde (1965) report that gibberellic acid (0.1 mg per liter) inhibits vegetative multiplication (i.e., fragmentation) in crude (nonaseptic) cultures of *A. mexicana.*

Clearly, there is a paucity of experimental growth studies on either crude or aseptic cultures of *Azolla.* There is a need for a careful survey of various culture conditions. The ability to grow *Azolla* rapidly under aseptic conditions would greatly enhance its usefulness as an experimental organism for studies on the initiation and development of leaves, roots, and sporocarps. Furthermore, since growth is from a *single* meristematic cell, radiation-induced morphological aberrants might be relatively easy to produce.

REFERENCES

AHMAD, G., 1941: Effect of light intensity and temperature on the growth of *Azolla filiculoides. J. Indian Bot. Soc.*, 20: 213.

ASHBY, E., E. WANGERMANN, and E. J. WINTER, 1949: Studies in the morphogenesis of leaves. III. Preliminary observations on vegetative growth in *Lemna minor. New Phytol.*, 48: 374.

CLARK, N. A., 1925: The rate of reproduction of *Lemna major* as a function of intensity and duration of light. *J. Phys. Chem.*, 29: 935.

COPE, B. T., S. BOSE, H. L. CRESPI, and J. J. KATZ, 1965: Growth of *Lemna* in H_2O–D_2O mixtures: Enhancement by kinetin. *Bot. Gaz.*, 126: 214.

CZOPEK, M., 1959: Researches on the physiology of formation and germination of turions in *Spirodela polyrhiza* (L.) Schleiden. *Acta Biol. Crac. Ser.:* Bot. Vol. II, 75.

———, 1962: The oligodynamic action of light on the germination of turions of *Spirodela polyrhiza* (L.) Schleiden. *Acta Soc. Bot. Pol.*, 31: 703.

———, 1963: Studies on the external factors inducing the formation of turions in *Spirodela polyrhiza* (L.) Schleiden. *Acta Soc. Bot. Pol.*, 32: 199.

———, 1964: The action of kinetin, gibberellic acid and red light on the germination of turions of *Spirodela polyrhiza. Bull. L'Acad. Pol. des Sci.*, Cl. II, Vol. XII: 177.

DUSELS, W. A., and E. K. BONDE, 1965: Effects of gibberellic acid, indoleacetic acid and maleic hydrazide on *Azolla mexicana. Phyton* [Argentina], 22: 51.

ESASHI, Y., and Y. ODA, 1964: Effects of light intensity and sucrose on the flowering of *Lemna perpusilla. Plant and Cell Physiol.*, 5: 513.

———, and ———, 1966: Two light reactions in the photoperiodic control of flowering of *Lemna perpusilla* and *L. gibba. Plant and Cell Physiol.*, 7: 59.

FURUYA, M., and K. V. THIMANN, 1964: The biogenesis of anthocyanins. XI. Effects of gibberellic acid in two species of *Spirodela. Arch. Biochem. Biophys.*, 108: 109.

GLICKMAN, L. T., 1966: Some factors affecting the dark processes in the germination of seeds of *Lemna perpusilla* 6746. M. A. thesis, State University of New York at Binghamton, N.Y.

GORHAM, P. R., 1950: Heterotrophic nutrition of seed plants with particular reference to *Lemna minor* L. *Can. J. Res. C.*, 28: 356.

HILLMAN, W. S., 1957: Nonphotosynthetic light requirement in *Lemna minor* and its partial satisfaction by kinetin. *Science*, 126: 165.

———, 1959: Experimental control of flowering in *Lemna*. I. General methods. Photoperiodism in *L. perpusilla* 6746. *Amer. J. Bot.*, 46: 466.

———, 1960: Growth promotion by kinetin of *Wolffia columbiana* grown in excessively concentrated medium. *Phyton* [Argentina], 14: 43.

———, 1961a: Experimental control of flowering in *Lemna*. III. A relationship between medium composition and the opposite photoperiodic responses of *L. perpusilla* 6746 and *L. gibba* G3. *Amer. J. Bot.*, 48: 413.

———, 1961b: The Lemnaceae, or duckweeds. *Bot. Rev.*, 27: 221.

———, 1962: Experimental control of flowering in *Lemna*. IV. Inhibition of photoperiodic sensitivity by copper. *Amer. J. Bot.*, 49: 892.

———, 1966: Photoperiodism in *Lemna:* reversal of night-interruption depends on color of the main photoperiod. *Science*, 154: 1360.

HUTNER, S. H., 1953: Comparative physiology of heterotrophic growth in plants. In W. E. Loomis (ed.), *Growth and Differentiation in Plants*, Iowa State College Press, Ames, Iowa.

KANDELER, R., 1955: Über die Blütenbildung bei *Lemna gibba* L. I. Kulturbedingungen und Tageslängenabhängigkeit. *Zeit. Bot.*, 43: 61.

———, 1956: Über die Blütenbildung bei *Lemna gibba* L. II. Das Wirkungsspektrum von blühförderndem Schwachlicht. *Zeit. Bot.*, 44: 153.

LANDOLT, E., 1957: Physiologische und ökologische Untersuchungen an Lemnaceen. *Ber. Schweiz. Bot. Ges.*, 67: 271.

MAHESHWARI, S. C., and O. S. CHAUHAN, 1963: *In vitro* control of flowering in *Wolffia microscopica*. *Nature*, 198: 99.

———, and P. N. SETH, 1966: Photoperiodic control of flowering in *Wolffia papulifera*. *Plant and Cell Physiol.*, 7: 163.

MC CLURE, J. W., and R. E. ALSTON, 1966: A chemotaxonomic study of Lemnaceae. *Amer. J. Bot.*, 53: 849.

NAKASHIMA, H., 1964: Effects of exogenous amino acids on the flower and frond production in duckweed, *Lemna gibba* G3. *Plant and Cell Physiol.*, 5: 217.

NICKELL, L. G., 1958: Physiological studies with *Azolla* under aseptic conditions. I. Isolation and preliminary growth studies. *Amer. Fern J.*, 48: 103.

———, 1961: Physiological studies with *Azolla* under aseptic conditions. II. Nutritional studies and the effects of chemicals on growth. *Phyton* [Argentina], 17: 49.

PIRSON, A., and E. GÖLLNER, 1953: Beobachtungen zur Entwicklungsphysiologie der *Lemna minor* L. *Flora*, 140: 485.

———, and F. SEIDEL, 1950: Zell- und stoffwechselphysiologische Untersuchungen an der Wurzel von *Lemna minor* L. unter besonderer Berücksichtigung von Kalium- und Kalziummangel. *Planta*, 38: 431.

POSNER, H. B., 1962a: *Permanent and Temporary Effects of X Rays on the Reproduction and Aging of Lemna perpusilla.* Ph.D. thesis, Yale University, New Haven, Conn.

———, 1962b: Characteristics of x-ray-induced aberrants of *Lemna perpusilla* 6746. *Plant and Cell Physiol.*, 3: 275.

———, and W. S. HILLMAN, 1960: Effects of x-irradiation on *Lemna perpusilla*. *Amer. J. Bot.*, 47: 506.

———, and ———, 1962: Aseptic production, collection and germination of seeds of *Lemna perpusilla*. *Physiol. Plant.*, 15: 700.

SCHAEDE, R., 1948: Untersuchungen über *Azolla* und ihre Symbiose mit Blaualgan. *Planta*, 35: 319.

SMITH, G. M., 1955: *Cryptogamic Botany*, 2nd ed., McGraw-Hill, New York, Vol. II.

UMEMURA, K., and Y. OOTA, 1965: Effects of nucleic acid- and protein-antimetabolites on frond and flower production in *Lemna gibba* G3. *Plant and Cell Physiol.*, 6: 73.

WANGERMANN, E., and E. ASHBY, 1950: Morphogenesis in *Lemna minor*. *Proc. Linn. Soc. London*, 162: 10.

WITZTUM, A., 1966: *A Descriptive and Experimental Study of Symmetry in* Lemna. Ph.D. thesis, Cornell University, Ithaca, N.Y.

Ferns*

By W. M. Laetsch

INTRODUCTION

Ferns have played a prominent role in the field of plant morphogenesis (reviewed by Verdoorn, 1938; Wardlaw, 1965; Cutter, 1965). There are many reasons why they have been favorite subjects for experimental work in development, and some of these reasons, such as their suitability for surgical experiments and the ease with which their organs can often be cultured, will be dealt with elsewhere in this volume. A primary reason why ferns are interesting to developmental biologists is that they exhibit a heterothallic alternation of generations with free-living sporophyte and gametophyte generations. This alternation of generations is one of the most fascinating and unexplored morphogenic phenomena in biology. This chapter will be devoted to a general discussion of the use of fern gametophytes as experimental systems and to a detailed examination of the use of both gametophytes and sporophytes of the heterosporous water fern *Marsilea*. The latter fern will be emphasized because it is the most suitable member of this group for many experimental studies and because it is the fern with which I am most familiar.

It might be useful as a prelude to this discussion to review the fern life cycle as illustrated in Fig. 1. Elementary texts frequently give the impression that the morphological difference between the gametophyte and sporophyte generations is that the former is haploid and the latter diploid. This is not an adequate explanation, since gametophytes frequently arise spontaneously from sporophytic tissue (apospory) and in many species it is not difficult to induce gametophytes experimentally. Likewise, sporophytes can develop from gametophytes (apogamy), as a result of the proliferation of vegetative gametophyte tissue or from unfertilized eggs. Aposporous gametophytes and apogamous sporophytes can have the same genotype as the tissue from which they developed, even though the phenotype is very distinct. It has also been found that gametophytes can develop from spores which are diploid as a result of the failure of reduction division.

The sporophyte is the "fern" of common usage, and in temperate zones it consists of a leaf-bearing axis which is either a prostrate rhizome or a short erect stem. Most sporophytes are perennials and frequently propagate themselves vegeta-

* I wish to express my appreciation to Miss Charollete Mentges for making the line drawings.

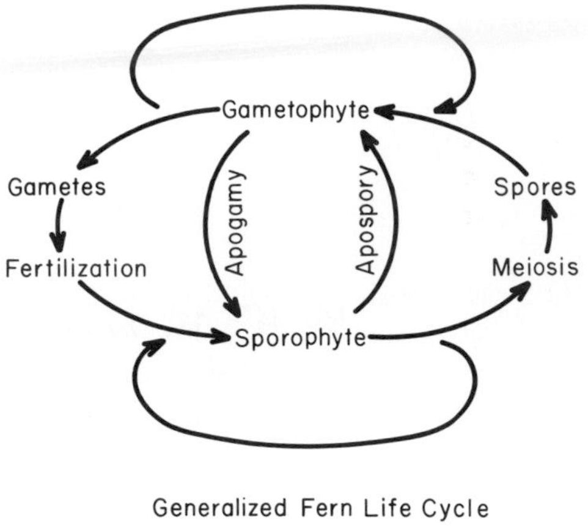

FIG. 1. Generalized fern life cycle. The recurved lines from the sporophyte and gametophyte indicate vegetative reproduction.

tively. The spores are usually the result of meiosis and are borne on the undersides of leaves or on leaves modified exclusively for spore production. The spore germinates and forms a short filament consisting of a single file of cells. Cell division in two planes is soon initiated in the apical cell and a flat plate of cells results. The gametophyte or prothallus has an apical meristematic region, and vegetative propagation of the thallus is usually more successful if part of the apical region is included in the explant. The underside of the gametophytic thallus bears rhizoids and gametangia. The latter consist of antheridia and archegonia, and their localization and induction can often be altered experimentally (Verdoorn, 1938; Voeller, 1964). The antheridia produce flagellated sperm which fertilize a single egg located at the base of the flask-shaped archegonium. The fine experiments of DeMaggio and Wetmore (1961), and DeMaggio (1963) have shown that at least in one species, *Todea barbara*, the zygote is weakly attached to the gametophyte and can be excised from the archegonium. When these excised zygotes are cultured, they develop into forms morphologically similar to gametophytes. The fern embryo develops a primary leaf, primary root, a stem apex, and an absorbing organ called the foot, since the young sporophyte lives at the expense of the gametophyte. Smith (1955) is an excellent general source for the morphology of the gametophyte, embryo, and mature sporophyte in the various taxonomic groups.

GAMETOPHYTES AS EXPERIMENTAL ORGANISMS

Fern gametophytes possess many of the criteria required of a successful experimental organism. Their structure is simple, their growth rate is fairly rapid, and they are easily established and maintained in sterile culture. They are also susceptible to cloning. The gametophyte generation has been used in many types of experimental problems. The most noteworthy of these have been studies on spore germination (Mohr 1956a; Pietrykowska, 1962, 1963), on one-dimensional versus two-dimensional growth (Mohr, 1956b; Hotta, 1960; Miller and Miller, 1964; Raghavan, 1965a, 1965b), on gametangia induction (Voeller, 1964), and on the induction of sporophytic tissue (Bristow, 1962; Whittier, 1962).

The advantages of using fern gametophytes would be less impressive if this material were difficult to obtain. This is not the case, because ferns are everywhere, and the spores are easily collected. In addition to forests, fields, and marshes, ferns are readily found on road cut embankments, vacant lots, and in backyards. Spores can also be obtained from ferns in nurseries, parks, and botanical gardens. Information on spore sources is often found in the *American Fern Journal*. Spores are collected by placing fronds on paper for a few days, whereupon spores are released from the sporangia onto the paper. This method does not work well for some species such as the sensitive fern *Onoclea sensibilis* (a common Eastern weed), which bears its spores in specialized fruiting structures. Miller and Miller (1961) describe the method for handling this problem.

Sterile gametophyte cultures of most ferns can be obtained by sterilizing the spores in 1.0–2.0 percent sodium hypochlorite (Clorox is 4.0–5.0 percent sodium hypochlorite) and rinsing with sterile distilled water. The optimum time for sterilization must be determined for the specific material, but 2–5 minutes is generally sufficient. The sterile spores are plated out onto liquid or solid medium in an appropriate container. Plastic Petri dishes are convenient, since their optical properties are excellent for microscopic observation of the germinating spores and developing gametophytes. Spores of many species have a light requirement for germination (Pietrykowska, 1962), so they should be given light during the germination period until their light requirements have been ascertained. The sensitivity of the spores to light has made them favorite subjects for investigating the photoreversible phytochrome pigment system (Miller and Miller, 1964; review by Mohr, 1963). Germination time is variable, but in the common bracken fern, *Pteridium aquilinum*, it occurs within 4–5 days. Gametangia will usually develop on the gametophytes in culture, and fertilization and sporophyte development will result. Gametophytes have been cultured as long as 8 years if the young sporophytes were excised (Mottier, 1931). With the exception of the case to be described later, sterile sporophyte cultures are best established from sterile gametophyte cultures. The work of Gottlieb and Steeves (1965) is an example of the use which can be made of sporophytes cultured in this manner.

A word should be said about fern identification, since any investigator should know the species he has collected. Ferns are a rather small, well-defined taxon, and the common species are easily identified by means of the many manuals on this group. If difficulty is experienced, send your material to the closest herbarium.

The spore has enough food material to maintain the gametophyte during early stages of development, so water is the only medium required for short-term experiments. An appropriate salt solution is required for continued growth in the light. There are many types of salt solutions, and it is probably not important which one is used as long as good growth is obtained. Two solutions commonly used for gametophytes are described by Näf (1956) and by Miller and Miller (1961). The composition of the medium used by the latter authors is as follows:

$CaNO_3 \cdot 4H_2O$	0.8 gm per liter
KNO_3	0.2 gm per liter
KH_2PO_4	0.2 gm per liter
$MgSO_4 \cdot 7H_2O$	0.2 gm per liter
Ferric tartrate	trace

The pH is adjusted to 5.2

Organic components are not required for the medium unless the gametophytes are maintained in the dark or at low light intensities. Liquid and solid media are both suitable for growth, but growth rate and gametangia development are often influenced by the respective substrates. I am not aware of any extensive work on the growth of gametophyte tissue in liquid shake cultures, but this method works well for liverwort thalli (Machlis and Doyle, 1962), and there is no reason why it would not be satisfactory for ferns. The natural habitat of fern gametophytes is one of high humidity and low light intensity, so laboratory cultures should not be subjected to high light intensity (over about

500 ft-c) until their ability to prosper has been ascertained.

The use of fern gametophytes in a number of investigations was mentioned above, but I would like to discuss one of these investigations in greater detail. The development of multicellular organisms usually includes morphogenesis or changes in form. Most of these changes are highly complicated, and it is not clear yet how our knowledge of gene action can be used to ask significant questions about their mechanisms. It is imperative to utilize morphogenic systems where the switching point in change of form is clearly delineated and susceptible to experimental treatment. There is evidence that the switch from one-dimensional to two-dimensional growth in the fern prothallus is such a system. The young gametophyte is a filament and this filamentous or one-dimensional growth form can be maintained in the dark or in certain light regimes (Mohr, 1956b; Miller and Miller, 1961). In white light, however, the apical cell of the filament divides parallel to the axis of the filament, and two-dimensional growth is initiated. Hotta (1960) found that the growth forms were characterized by different species of RNA (ribonucleic acid). In addition, the two-dimensional growth could be reversed to one-dimensional growth by the use of 8-azaguanine, and the RNA of the gametophytes treated with this purine analog was similar to the RNA of the normal one-dimensional form. This approach has been adapted by Raghavan (1965a, 1965b), and he has extended the morphological observations to other genera and has demonstrated that the two-dimensional growth is inhibited by a variety of RNA inhibitors, including actinomycin D. Nakazawa and Tanno (1965) have localized RNA in the prothallus and have correlated the region of growth with the maximum concentration of RNA. They have indirect evidence that the switch from one-dimensional to two-dimensional growth is induced by the localized accumulation of messenger RNA. Kato (1964), on the other hand, has evidence that nutritional and osmotic factors can regulate the plane of growth.

This system would be even more exciting if mutants exhibiting one-dimensional growth could be found, and Professor Pray of the University of Southern California has recently observed (personal communication) the frequent occurrence of such forms in certain species. This problem is but one of many awaiting the developmental biologist electing to utilize fern gametophytes as experimental organisms.

MARSILEA AS AN EXPERIMENTAL ORGANISM

The rest of this contribution will be devoted to a plant which is one of the most interesting of all ferns, if not of all vascular plants. This is the aquatic fern *Marsilea*, which has long been a favorite for morphological and physiological investigations. Leitgeb (1878) was one of the first to use *Marsilea* for experimental purposes, and in recent years it has been used in a similar fashion by Allsopp (work reviewed 1963), Laetsch and Briggs (1961, 1962, 1963), and Gaudet (1965).

Marsilea is an excellent experimental organism for many of the same reasons presented for fern gametophytes. It is easily established and maintained indefinitely in sterile culture in the light or dark, and it is small so that large numbers can be raised in a few culture vessels. The products of each sporocarp are very uniform, and additional uniformity can be obtained by cloning. This is done by excising nodes from a single sporeling. *Marsilea* is an aquatic plant, so the uptake of various chemicals is not the problem it is with so many vascular land plants. The ability to maintain it in liquid culture in a test tube means that a very high degree of environmental control can be maintained. The following discussion on the specialized life cycle of *Marsilea vestita* will demonstrate that the gametophyte generation of *Marsilea* is only a few hours long and that the gametophyte is almost entirely gamete-producing tissue. The sequence of gamete differentiation, therefore, can be well defined. The microspores and megaspores of this heterosporous fern can be separated with ease, so fertilization can be precisely controlled. The embryo and sporeling are very plastic and respond well to surgical treatment.

A casual look at this fern would convince the observer that it was a four-leaf clover, and indeed, it was often the four-leaf clover in good luck charms until methods for uniformly inducing four leaves on real clover were developed. The sporophyte produces two different kinds of spores (heterospory) in a hard structure called a sporocarp. This structure is homologous to leaf segments. The spores within the dried sporocarp are viable indefinitely. When the sporocarp is cut open and placed in water, a mucilaginous wormlike structure called a sorophore emerges. This structure bears transparent megasporangia and microsporangia in laterally arranged indusial sacs. The spores are rapidly released into the medium and germinate to initiate the gametophyte generations. The egg-shaped megaspore is 0.7–0.75 mm long and the round microspore is 0.075 mm in diameter. The gametophyte generation is short, since fertilization occurs within 10 hours at room temperature in *M. vestita*. The spores initially sink to the bottom, but soon rise and float on the surface due to the hydration of an enveloping gel. They are embedded in a gel in a manner not unlike the eggs of amphibians. The megaspore is a large cell packed with starch and oil except

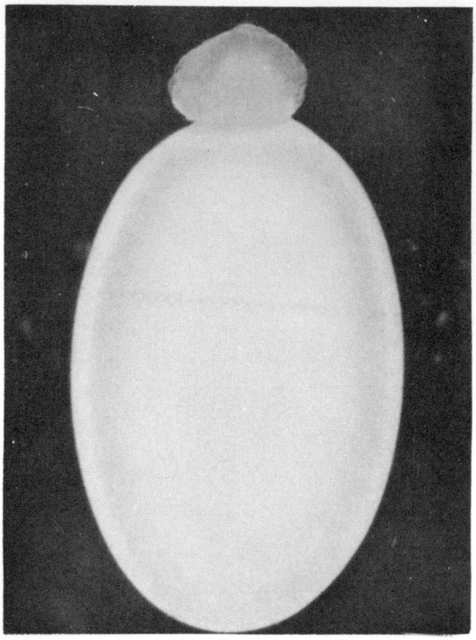

FIG. 2. Embryo of *Marsilea vestita* about 24 hours after fertilization. The large egg-shaped structure is the food storage cell of the megagametophyte. This cell is within the original megaspore wall. The globular embryo is clearly seen within the archegonium at one end of this cell. The original neck of the archegonium can be seen at the end of the archegonium. × 120.

for one end where gametophyte cells will be formed. The megagametophyte consists of a large storage cell and single archegonium containing the egg cell. The microgametophyte develops within the microspore wall and consists of two antheridia each of which produces 16 sperm. Fertilization occurs soon after sperm discharge. During the fertilization period the gel around the megagametophyte becomes full of trapped sperm. Embryogenesis is rapid (Figs. 2 and 3), and within 4 days the sporeling has a well developed primary root and leaf. Within 3 weeks seven or eight leaves and roots are

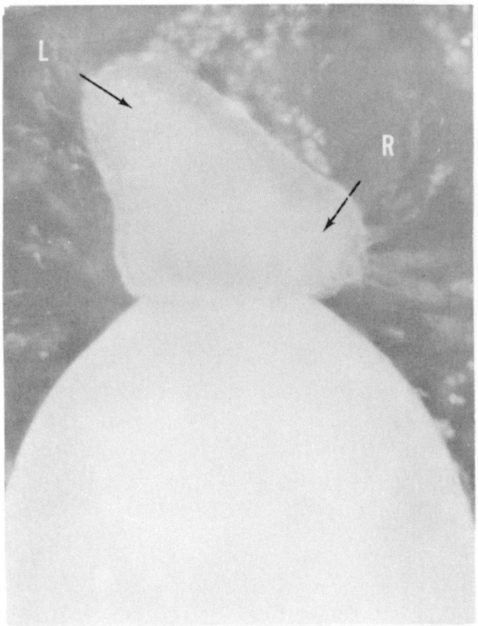

FIG. 3. Embryo of *M. vestita* about 48 hours after fertilization. The embryo is the triangular mass within the archegonial tissue. The archegonium proliferates and forms a covering for the embryo during the first 3 days of its growth. The primordia of the first leaf (L) and first root (R) are indicated by arrows. The filamentous structures emerging from the archegonium at the right are rhizoids. × 184.

produced on a short rhizome (Laetsch and Briggs, 1961). *Marsilea* exhibits a pronounced heterophylly in that several juvenile leaf forms appear before the four-parted or quadrified adult leaf develops (Fig. 4). The development of the juvenile leaf series can be experimentally manipulated, and some interesting preliminary work on this problem performed by Allsopp (1953, 1959) implicates both nutritional and hormonal factors. The adult leaf has a different form depending upon whether the plants are grown submerged in water (Fig. 4e) or in the air (Fig. 4f), and this phenomenon has been investigated by Allsopp (1955) and Gaudet (1965).

The various species of *Marsilea* are not uncommon in occurrence, but the uninitiated often mistake this fern for a flowering plant. It is frequently found on the margins of vernal pools, seasonal lakes, and roadside ditches. Local herbariums will usually have locations recorded. Mature plants are easily transplanted and they grow well in the greenhouse if they are well watered. Cultivated plants will produce a continuous supply of sporocarps. The latter should not be picked until they are relatively hard, and they must be stored after harvesting until completely dry. Sporocarps can also be obtained from some of the biological supply houses (they are expensive), and the author can supply limited quantities. A colony of plants should be established if large numbers of sporocarps are required.

Sterile cultures are established by soaking the sporocarps in 1.0 percent sodium hypochlorite for 5 minutes and rinsing them several times in sterile distilled water. We usually sterilize and rinse in a 125-ml Erlenmeyer flask with a piece of cheesecloth fastened over the mouth of the flask with a rubber band. Do not use a sporocarp unless it is well rounded and regularly shaped. The ones with an irregular shape are usually not viable. The sporocarps are transferred one at a time by sterile forceps to individual sterile Petri dishes where they are cut in half with a single-edged razor blade which has been dipped in alcohol and flamed. The two halves of a single sporocarp are transferred to a Petri dish containing 10 ml of sterile salt solution. Fertilization occurs within 10 hours at room temperature, and the embryos can then be transferred to the appropriate culture media by means of Pasteur pipettes. Five to ten embryos is a reasonable number to put into each culture tube. It is important not to mix the progeny of different sporocarps in any particular experiment because the variability between sporocarps is much greater than that found within any one sporocarp.

It is frequently desirable to separate the megaspores and microspores after they have been released into the medium. They are easily separated by flushing them through a wire screen of an appropriate size (40 mesh). The megaspores are 0.7–0.75 mm long and 0.5 mm wide while the microspores are 0.075 mm in diameter. The release of the spores is facilitated by cutting the sporocarp into four pieces and stirring them with a magnetic mixer after they are placed in water or salt solution.

We have found the following culture medium to be the most satisfactory. It is modified from that of Gautheret (White, 1963) by using NaFeEDTA instead of $Fe_2(SO_4)_3$, by decreasing the calcium and magnesium by half, and by adding molybdenum.

STOCK I

$Ca(NO_3)_2 \cdot 4H_2O$	0.75 gm
KNO_3	0.25 gm
$MgSO_4 \cdot 7H_2O$	0.25 gm
KH_2PO_4	0.25 gm

Glass-distilled H_2O to 1 liter

STOCK II

$MnSO_4 \cdot H_2O$	2.20 gm
KI	0.50 gm
$ZnSO_4 \cdot 7H_2O$	0.18 gm
H_3BO_3	0.10 gm
H_2SO_4	1.0 ml
$Ti_2(SO_4)_3$	0.20 gm
$NiSO_4 \cdot 6H_2O$	0.09 gm
$CuSO_4 \cdot 5H_2$	0.09 gm
$ZnCl_2$	0.11 gm

Glass-distilled H_2O to 1 liter

STOCK III

NaFeEDTA (Sequestrene, Geigy Chem. Corp.)
3.8 gm/100 ml glass-distilled H_2O

STOCK IV

MoO_3 15 mg/100 ml glass-distilled H_2O.
Dilute this 1:1,000

COMPLETE MEDIUM

Stock I	100 ml
Stock II	1.0 ml
Stock III	0.5 ml
Stock IV	1.0 ml

Glass-distilled H_2O to 1 liter

The pH is adjusted to 6.4 by the addition of NaOH. The vigor and growth rate of the sporelings is greatly increased by the addition of 3.0 percent sucrose. Some workers have used glucose, but we have found it much less satisfactory than sucrose.

This medium will also support the growth of excised apical and lateral buds. The embryo is supplied by the nutrients of the storage cell of the megagametophyte during the first 5 days of growth, and added sugar and salts do not aid growth during this time (Laetsch and Briggs, 1963). *Marsilea* grows well over a wide range of light intensities and photoperiods, and growth in the dark can be maintained indefinitely on the above salts and sucrose medium. The growth of the sporeling in the dark and its photomorphogenetic

FIG. 4. Juvenile and adult leaves of *Marsilea.* (a) to (d) juvenile leaves; (e) adult leaf of sporeling grown in water; (f) adult leaf of sporeling grown in air.

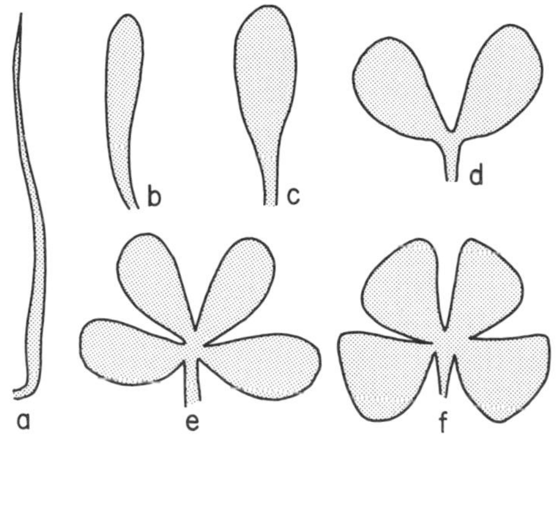

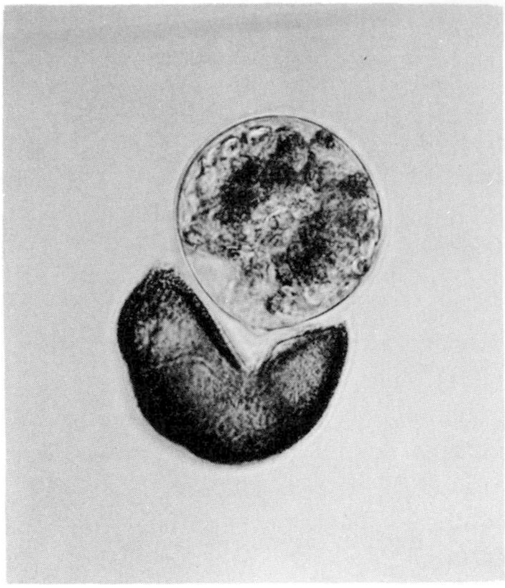

FIG. 5. Dehiscing microspore of *M. vestita.* The endospore has just been released from the exospore. Within a few seconds the sperm will be released from the two antheridia. The two dark areas are the centers of the respective antheridia. × 466.66. Photo courtesy of Harbert Rice.

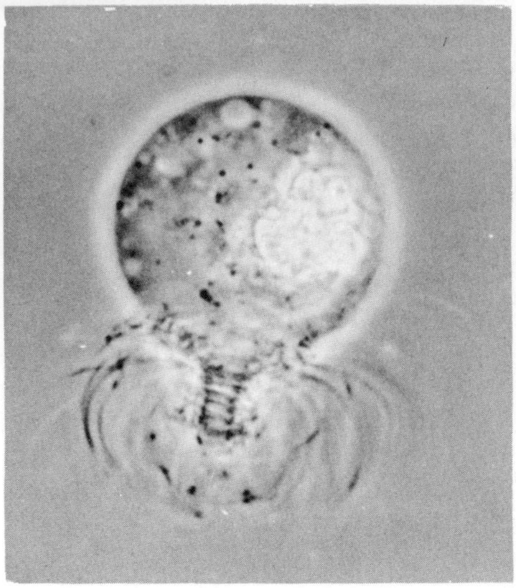

FIG. 6. Mature sperm of *M. vestita.* The sperm consists of a large vesicle containing starch (white mass) lipid bodies, and mitochondria. The nucleus is contained in the flagella-bearing coil. The sperm swims coil first, and previous to fertilization the vesicle is lost and the coil stretches. × 1800. Photo courtesy of Harbert Rice.

responses have been described in detail by Laetsch and Briggs (1962). The dark-grown plant is extremely sensitive to light and is particularly suitable for photobiological investigations.

Like many of the ferns (see chapter by Cutter, this volume), *Marsilea* lends itself to surgical treatments. The single archegonium can be surgically manipulated, as can the embryo at all stages of development (Figs. 2 and 3). It is wise to remove the contents of the storage cell of the megagametophyte when working with the gametophyte or young sporophyte because the contents of this large cell are under pressure and will often gush out through the tissue being manipulated. The contents of the cell are best released by pricking the wall with a fine, sharp-pointed needle. The shoot apex is easily exposed by cutting away the enveloping hairs, and small apical fragments (about 200 μ) will grow in the salts and sucrose medium outlined above (author's unpublished data). Sharpened watchmaker's forceps, iridectomy scissors, and glass microneedles are the most useful surgical instruments for this plant.

Most morphological and all previous experimental work with *Marsilea* has been with the sporophyte. We have initiated work with the microgametophyte and feel it shows great promise as a system for studying cell differentiation. As related above, the microgametophyte consists of two antheridia, each producing 16 flagellated sperm. The starting, or zero point, for differentiation is very exact, since the single-celled microspores do not begin metabolic activity until they are hydrated. This zero point permits the precise scheduling of a highly differentiated cell type. The time sequence for differentiation, life span, and death of sperm has been worked out in considerable detail by Harbert Rice in this laboratory. He observed the products of individual microspores and found that the differentiation of sperm is temperature dependent with discharge (Fig. 5) occurring in 5 hours from hydration at 30°C. The sperm can be separated from the microspores as soon as they are discharged by means of a 300 mesh screen[1] and subjected to the desired treatments. The individual sperm (Fig. 6) live for 30–45 minutes, so in 5½ hours the differentiation, life, and death of a highly differentiated cell can be studied. It is also significant that this differentiation goes on in the absence of growth. There are very few organisms which offer such a fine system for investigating this kind of cell differentiation under such controlled conditions.

In conclusion, it can be stated that while ferns have been used to great advantage by some investigators, they have not been fully utilized by developmental biologists. Their potential as experimental organisms is great, and they are literally waiting underfoot to be exploited.

[1] Electron microscope grid 300 mesh, nickel, 7 × 3½ inches. Ernest F. Fullum, Inc., P.O. Box 444, Schenectady, N.Y.

REFERENCES

ALLSOPP, A., 1953: Experimental and analytical studies of pteridophytes. XXI. Investigations on *Marsilea*. 3. The effect of various sugars on development and morphology. *Ann. Bot.*, N.S. 17: 447.

———, 1955: Experimental and analytical studies of pteridophytes. XXVII. Investigations on *Marsilea*. 5. Cultural conditions and morphogenesis, with special reference to the origin of land and water forms. *Ann. Bot.*, 19: 247.

———, 1959: Effects of gibberellic acid on juvenility in *Marsilea* and certain other plants. *Nature*, 184 (suppl. 20): 1575.

———, 1963: Morphogenesis in *Marsilea*. *J. Linn. Soc.* (Bot.) 58: 417.

BRISTOW, J. MICHAEL, 1962: The controlled *in vitro* differentiation of callus derived from a fern, *Pteris cretica* L., into gametophytic or sporophytic tissues. *Develop. Biol.*, 4: 361.

CUTTER, ELIZABETH G., 1965: Recent experimental studies of the shoot apex and shoot morphogenesis. *Bot. Rev.*, 31: 7.

DE MAGGIO, A. E., 1963: Morphogenetic factors influencing the development of fern embryos. *J. Linn. Soc.* (Bot.), 58: 361.

———, and R. H. WETMORE, 1961: Morphogenetic studies on the fern *Todea Barbara*. III. Experimental Embryology. *Amer. Jour. Bot.*, 48: 551.

GAUDET, J. J., 1965: The effect of various environmental factors on the leaf form of the aquatic fern *Marsilea vestita*. *Physiol. Plant.*, 18: 674.

GOTTLIEB, J. E., and T. A. STEEVES, 1965: Experimental control of the shoot system in sporelings of *Pteridium aquilinum*. *Amer. Jour. Bot.*, 52: 359.

HOTTA, Y., 1960: The role of protein and ribonucleic acid in the differentiation of fern gametophyte. *Jap. Jour. Bot.*, 17: 214.

KATO, YKIO, 1964: Physiological and morphogenetic studies of fern gametophytes in aseptic culture. II. One- and two-dimensional growth in sugar media. *Bot. Gaz.*, 125: 33.

LAETSCH, W. M., and WINSLOW R. BRIGGS, 1961: Kinetin modification of sporeling ontogeny in *Marsilea vestita*. *Amer. Jour. Bot.*, 48: 369.

———, and ———, 1962: Photomorphogenetic responses of sporelings of *Marsilea vestita*. *Plant Physiol.*, 37: 142.

———, and ———, 1963: Correlative inhibition and the primary organs of *Marsilea vestita*. *Bot. Gaz.*, 124: 317.

LEITGEB, H., 1878: Zur Embryologie der Farne. *Sitzgsber. Akad. Wiss. Wien. Math. naturw. Kl.*, 77: 222.

MACHLIS, LEONARD, and WILLIAM T. DOYLE, 1962: Submerged growth of pure cultures of the liverwort *Sphaerocarpos donnellii*. *Physiol. Plant.*, 15: 351.

MILLER, JOHN H., and PAULINE M. MILLER, 1961: The effect of different light conditions and sucrose on the growth and development of the gametophyte of the fern, *Onoclea sensibilis*. *Amer. Jour. Bot.*, 48: 154.

———, and ———, 1964: Blue light in the development of fern gametophytes and its interaction with far-red and red light. *Amer. Jour. Bot.*, 51: 329.

MOHR, H., 1956a: Die Beeinflussung der Keimung von Farnsporen durch Licht und andere Faktoren. *Planta*, 46: 534.

———, 1956b: Die Abhängigkeit des Protonemawachstums und der Protonemapolarität bei Farnen vom Licht. *Planta*, 46: 127.

———, 1963: The influence of visible radiation on the germination of archegoniate spores and the growth of the fern protonema. *J. Linn. Soc.* (Bot.), 58: 287.

———, 1964: The control of plant growth and development by light. *Biol. Rev.*, 39: 87.

MOTTIER, DAVID M., 1931: Development of sex organs of fern prothallia under prolonged cultivation. *Bot. Gaz.*, 92: 218.

NÄF, U., 1956: The demonstration of a factor concerned with the initiation of antheridia in Polypodiaceous ferns. *Growth*, 20: 91.

NAKAZAWA, SINGO, and NORIKO TANNO, 1965: Concentration gradients of RNA in fern protonema in relation to m-RNA. *Die Naturw.*, 15: 1.

PIETRYKOWSKA, J., 1962: Investigations on the germination of spores of the fern *Matteucia struthiopteris* (L.) Tod. *Act. Soc. Bot. Pol.*, 31: 437.

———, 1963: Investigations on the action of light on the germination polarity of fern spores. *Act. Soc. Bot. Pol.*, 32: 677.

RAGHAVAN, V., 1965a: Action of purine and pyrimidine analogs on the growth and differentiation of the gametophytes of the fern *Asplenium nidus*. *Amer. Jour. Bot.*, 52: 900.

———, 1965b: Actinomycin D: Its effects on two-dimensional growth in fern gametophytes. *Exptl. Cell. Res.*, 39: 689.

SMITH, G. M., 1955: *Cryptogamic Botany*. Vol. II, *Bryophytes and Pteridophytes*, 2nd ed. McGraw-Hill Book Co., Inc., New York.

WARDLAW, C. W., 1965: *Organization and Evolution in Plants*. Longmans, London, Eng.

WETMORE, R. H., A. E. DE MAGGIO, and G. MOREL, 1963: A morphogenetic look at the alternation of generations. *Jour. Indian Bot. Soc.*, 42: 306.

WHITE, PHILLIP, 1963: *A Handbook of Plant and Animal Tissue Culture*. Ronald Press, New York.

WHITTIER, D. P., 1962: The origin and development of apogamous structures in the gametophyte of *Pteridium* in sterile culture. *Phytomorph.*, 12: 10.

VERDOORN, F. (ed.), 1938: *Manual of Pteridology*. Martinus Nijhoff, The Hague, Netherlands.

VOELLER, BRUCE R., 1964: Gibberellins: Their effect on antheridium formation in fern gametophytes. *Science*, 143: 373.

Mosses and Liverworts*

By William T. Doyle

INTRODUCTION

Bryophytes offer many opportunities for the developmental biologist interested in problems basic to growth and development. Although they are relatively simple organisms (compared to the higher plants) there is an amazing variety in form, structure, and development in this group of higher cryptogams. They are also easy to handle in the laboratory. The dominant vegetative phase of growth is haploid (gametophytic); the diploid (sporophytic) stage is relatively short-lived and is morphologically dissimilar to the haploid (gametophytic) plant. However, it is possible to obtain (by regeneration) diploid or higher polyploid plants of mosses that are morphologically and functionally identical to the haploid plants. Bryophytes are readily obtained and maintained in pure culture on a defined inorganic medium, with or without added agar, and it is possible to get the complete life cycles of several bryophytes in aseptic culture. In addition, clonal cultures are easily obtained via regeneration from detached plant parts.

The protonemal-gametophore transition in mosses is an extremely interesting developmental system and one that merits further investigation. The protonemal or juvenile phase of growth consists of an extensive and often highly differentiated development of branched, uniseriate filaments. The leafy plants (gametophores) that we recognize in the field as moss arise as outgrowths from specific cells of the protonema. The induction of these gametophore initials and their subsequent development is an interesting developmental system and one that is readily amenable to study in the laboratory. Bopp (1961) has reviewed and discussed much of what is known about this system. Of more recent interest is the report by Szweykowska (1963) that kinetin induces the formation of gametophores in dark-grown mosses. So far, only kinetin has been found to have the ability to induce gametophore development in dark-grown cultures.

Mention should here be made that this chapter is not intended to represent a comprehensive review of techniques for bryophyte culture. Instead only selected procedures are discussed, mainly those that we have found useful in my laboratory. It is clearly recognized that there are almost as many variations in techniques as there are investigators.

* Contribution Number 1 from the Division of Natural Sciences.

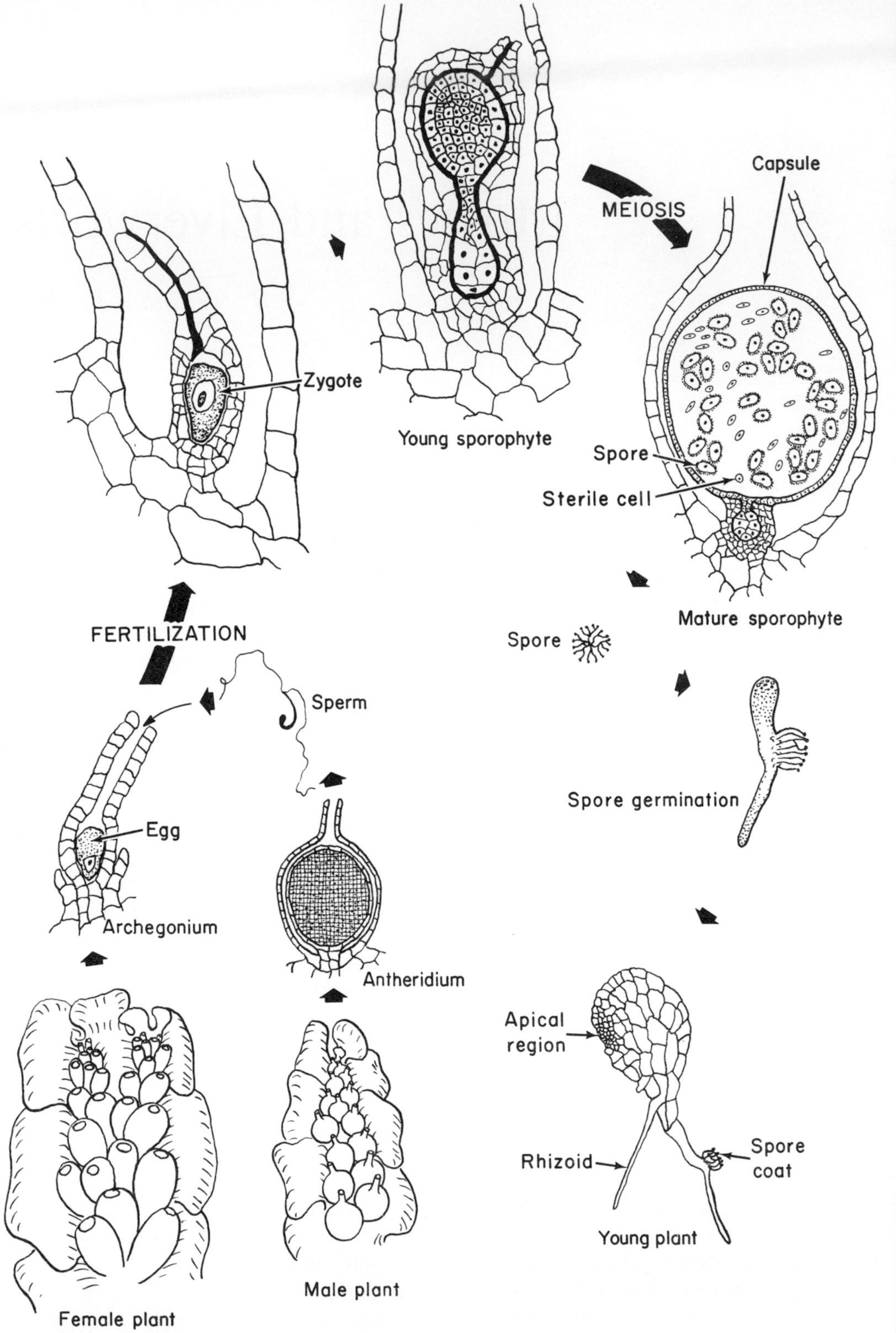

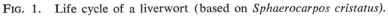

FIG. 1. Life cycle of a liverwort (based on *Sphaerocarpos cristatus*).

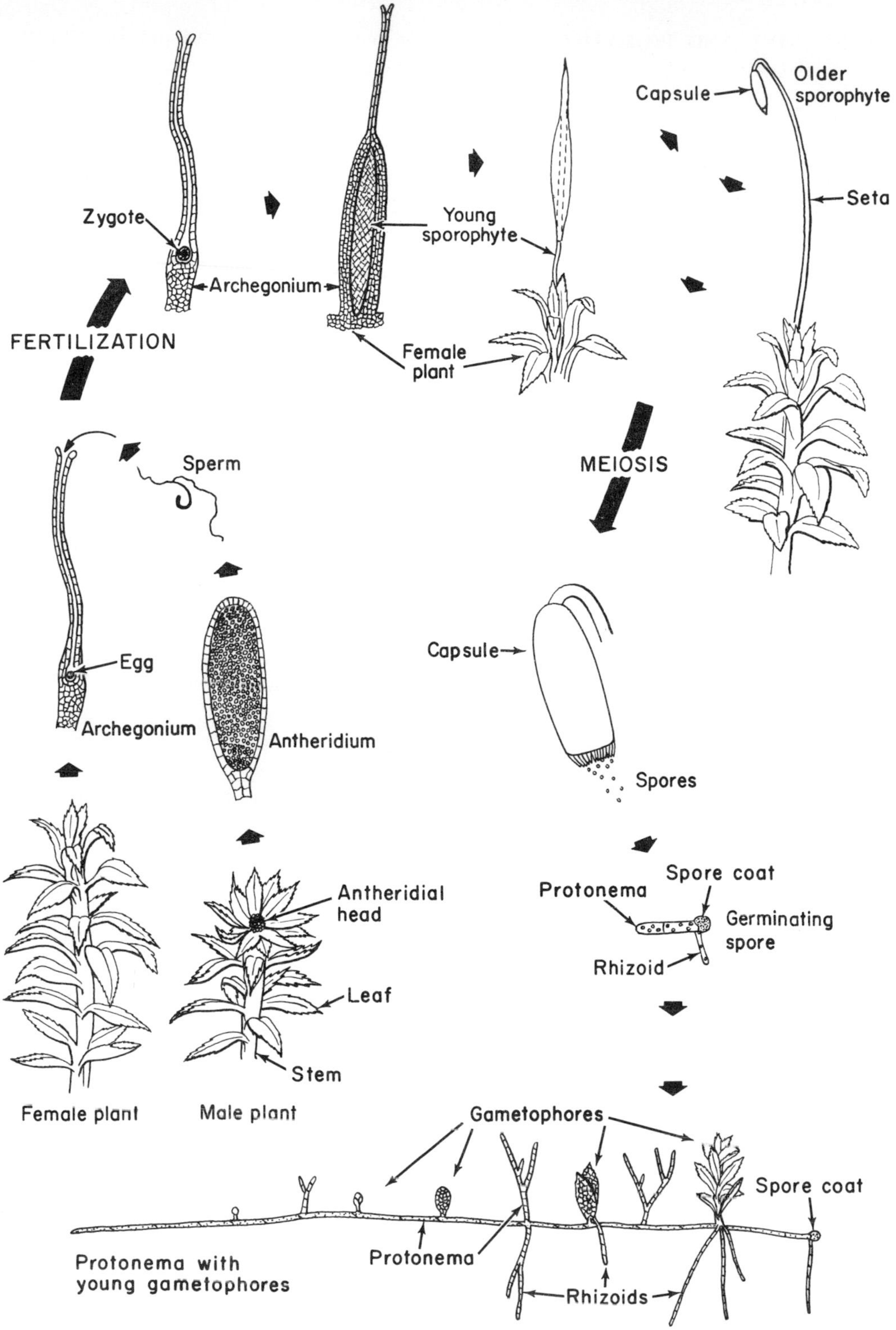

FIG. 2. Life cycle of a moss (based on *Mnium cuspidatum*).

COLLECTIONS AND ISOLATION INTO CULTURE

Collections

PURE CULTURE COLLECTIONS

There are relatively few collections of bryophytes maintained in pure (axenic) culture, in contrast to the large number of microbiological ones. The Culture Collection of Autotrophic Organisms, Czechoslovakia (a list of over 300 bryophytes is available upon request from the Culture Collection of Autotrophic Organisms, Institute of Experimental Botany, Czechoslovak Academy of Science, Viničná 5, Praha 2, Czechoslovakia), contains the most extensive collection of living bryophytes. In addition, stock cultures of bryophytes of research and teaching interest are maintained by many bryologists. For example, Hatcher (1965; Dr. Raymond E. Hatcher, Department of Botany, University of Wisconsin, Milwaukee, Wisconsin) recently published a list of 58 species of liverworts he has in pure culture; the author has about 80 single spore isolates in pure culture in his collection. Whatever the source, the sterility of organisms obtained should be checked as a matter of precaution.

FIELD COLLECTIONS

The relative paucity of pure cultures available occasionally dictates the necessity of field collections. Pure cultures must then be started from this material. Bryophytes are found in almost all habitats and they grow on an amazing variety of substrates. Many have remarkable resistance to desiccation and can be collected and stored in the dry state for years. Whenever possible plants with mature or nearly mature sporophytes should be collected because it is easier to obtain pure cultures when starting with the spores. Plants with immature sporophytes are placed in a large moist chamber and put in indirect sunlight near a north- or east-facing window in a cool room, or put in a controlled light (200 to 400 ft-c) and temperature (17° to 20°C) room until the spores mature. Since most teem with prolific populations of mites and other animal pests, field collections should not be kept in the same room with pure cultures.

Naturally occurring aneuploid and polyploid strains in bryophytes are not uncommon; it is reasonable to expect that physiological races also occur. It is important, therefore, that adequate records be made of field-collected material. These data should contain a description of the definitive features of the habitat, including substrate, exposure, type of plant community, elevation, location (as exact as possible), name of collector, and date of collection. It is also recommended that a portion of the pure culture, along with the collection data, be sent to an established pure culture collection.

Identification

Local (if available) and regional manuals of bryophytes are found in most university libraries. However, species identification can be time consuming and sometimes nearly impossible for the nonspecialist. To prevent misunderstandings in interpreting experimental results only a culture whose identity is known beyond any doubt should be used. Identifications made by competent specialists are recommended. To this end, inquiry can be directed to a nearby herbarium or to one of the officers of the American Bryological Society (addresses of current officers are given in the most recent issues of the *Bryologist*).

Isolation Methods

For developmental and biochemical studies it is desirable, if not mandatory, to work with pure cultures of genetic homogeneity. Such cultures are started from a single parent plant or cell and maintained in such a manner as to preclude contamination by other organisms. Two methods of isolating bryophytes from contaminating organisms are in general use: (1) surface sterilization of plant parts and (2) spore isolation. Adequate tests of purity of plants obtained as a result of surface sterilization or spore isolation should be conducted before experimental work begins.

SURFACE STERILIZATION

The technique of surface sterilization has enjoyed wide use and a few of the many variations on this procedure have been described by Hatcher (1965), Iverson (1957), and Miller (1964).

Materials

- 10 ml of a 5 percent Clorox solution in distilled water with a small amount of added detergent (as a wetting agent)
- Test tube or vial
- 40 ml of sterile distilled water
- Forceps or transfer loop
- Petri dish containing sterile nutrient medium (see Culture Media) solidified with 1.5 percent agar
- Bunsen or alcohol burner

Procedure

1. Pour 10 ml of the Clorox solution into the test tube.
2. Add the plant fragment, shake well, and set aside for 3 to 5 minutes.
3. Decant Clorox solution and wash plant fragment in 4 changes of sterile distilled water, 5 minutes each change.
4. Flame-sterilize and cool forceps or transfer loop and transfer plant to nutrient medium.

Comments

This method generally is more successful with plant parts with smooth surfaces, such as gemmae of *Marchantia*, than with leafy plant parts or plants that contain endophytic fungi as normal symbionts. It has also been used to decontaminate sporophyte capsules prior to spore isolation, generally an unnecessary procedure as pointed out below.

SPORE ISOLATION

The technique of spore isolation has been described by Machlis and Doyle (1962). Spores within the mature but unopened capsule are uncontaminated and it remains simply to maintain this sterility during subsequent handling. The use of this method is not restricted to unopened capsules; pure cultures are also easily obtained from opened capsules of mosses, liverworts, and hornworts from which spores have partially discharged. (Moreover, pure cultures of the horsetail fern *Equisetum* are readily started by use of naturally discharging strobili.)

Materials

- 9.0 cm filter paper
- Bunsen or alcohol burner
- Forceps
- Needles (sewing needles embedded in one end of glass rods or kitchen matches)
- Petri dishes containing sterile nutrient media (see Culture Media), solidified with 1.5 or 2 percent agar

Procedure

1. Place capsule on filter paper and open with flame-sterilized and cooled forceps and needle.
2. Pick up and discard capsule wall fragments and other detritus.

3. Tap edge of filter paper to disperse spores on paper surface.

4. Remove Petri dish lid, invert filter paper and tap lightly about an inch above Petri dish.

5. Cover Petri dish and incubate in the light at 17° to 20°C.

6. In 4 or 5 days observe under dissecting microscope for contaminants.

7. Transfer uncontaminated spores to fresh sterile agar medium.

Comments

The above method is both simple and efficient. Usually only one or at the most a few pure cultures of any species are needed. The degree of contamination in the Petri dish is rarely so great that it is impossible to isolate from a few to well over a hundred uncontaminated spores, obviating the need for surface sterilization of the entire capsule prior to spore harvest.

TABLE 1. NUTRIENT MEDIA FOR BRYOPHYTE CULTURE

PRÁT MEDIUM

COMPOUND	GRAMS/LITER
KH_2PO_4	0.1
$MgSO_4 \cdot 7H_2O$	0.1
$CaCl_2$	0.1
NH_4NO_3	0.2
Micronutrient solution	1 ml

MACHLIS MEDIUM

COMPOUND	GRAMS/LITER
KH_2PO_4	1.36
$MgSO_4 \cdot 7H_2O$	0.25
$CaCl_2$	0.11
KNO_3	1.52
Dextrose	10
Micronutrient solution	1 ml

It should also be noted that the spores within an individual bryophyte capsule are not genetically identical. The sporophyte capsule is diploid; meiosis occurs immediately prior to spore development. For this reason, sophisticated developmental and biochemical studies should be carried out on subcultures of a plant utimately derived from the germination of a single spore, not on the pooled isolates from one or more capsules.

HANDLING OF CULTURES

Media

One finds in the literature media on which a large number of bryophytes thrive, although the range of salt concentrations in these media varies considerably. A list of seventeen media that have been used in bryophyte research has been compiled by Nehira (1964). It appears that the composition of the medium is not critical for most bryophytes, although the nutrient requirements have not been studied in great detail in all respects. For example, many bryophytes seem able to get along with considerably less calcium in the medium than is usually supplied. The media shown in Table 1 are those routinely used in my laboratory. The Prát (1948) medium supports good growth of all bryophytes we have tried to culture and our stock cultures are maintained on this medium. It is not to be implied, however, that the Prát medium is necessarily the best for all bryophytes, only that we have found it to be exceedingly useful. We use the Machlis (1962) medium primarily for submersed growths of the liverwort *Sphaerocarpos;* this medium (without sugar) also supports good surface growths of bryophytes in general.

Either glass-distilled or deionized water should be used in preparation of nutrient media. The calcium, sulfate, and phosphate compounds must be added one at a time and be completely dissolved prior to the addition of the next compound, otherwise an insoluble precipitate is likely to form. The micronutrient solution mentioned above, chelated with ethylenediaminetetraacetate (EDTA) as described by Stein (1958), is listed in Table 2. However, it is likely that any trace element solution that supports growth of the higher green plants will also satisfy bryophyte micronutrient requirements.

TABLE 2. MICRONUTRIENT SOLUTION FOR BRYOPHYTE CULTURE

COMPOUND*	GRAMS
H_3BO_3	1.00
$CuSO_4 \cdot 5H_2O$	0.15
EDTA	5.00
$ZnSO_4 \cdot 7H_2O$	2.20
$CaCl_2$	0.50
$MnCl_2 \cdot 4H_2O$	0.50
$FeSO_4 \cdot 7H_2O$	0.50
$CoCl_2 \cdot 6H_2O$	0.15
$(NH_4)_6Mo_7O_{24} \cdot 4H_2O$	0.10

* The above salts are added to 75.0 ml of glass-distilled water, boiled, and then cooled slightly. Adjust the pH to about 6.5 by the addition of solid KOH pellets and dilute the resulting solution to 100.0 ml by the addition of glass-distilled water. Store in a brown bottle in the refrigerator.

Stock Cultures

Stock cultures of plants are most simply maintained in 2-ounce prescription bottles, the type obtainable at drug stores. To the Prát medium with micronutrients add agar to make a 1 percent solution. Melt the agar, then cool to about 50°C. Fill the prescription bottles about one-third full with the partially cooled agar medium. Cap bottles loosely with Bakelite or other autoclavable caps and autoclave. After sterilizing, slant the prescription bottles in order to increase surface area for plant growth and to facilitate handling during culture transfer. Slanting the bottles with the flat side up results in a more satisfactory optical surface for observation of the cultures in the bottles. When the agar has cooled to room temperature, tighten the caps and store bottles on their sides.

Stock cultures are started by aseptically transferring a plant fragment onto the slanted agar surface. These cultures are kept (in my laboratory) in a culture room with a 14-hour day, 10-hour night photoperiod regime and a 20°C day temperature. Cool-white fluorescent tubes without supplemental tungsten bulbs provide about 150 ft-c at shelf level. Under these conditions many bryophytes can be maintained in the capped prescription bottles for over a year before they need transfer. Some, such as *Riccia trichocarpa*, require more frequent attention. We routinely transfer all cultures every 6 to 8 months. The tightness of the cap does not appear to affect growth markedly; plants grow well in tightly or loosely capped bottles. Tightly capped bottles have the advantage of decreasing the possibility of contamination.

Preparation of Inoculum

Stock cultures are cloned for experiments either by fragmenting the parent plant or by harvesting gemmae (vegetative reproductive bodies formed by some bryophytes). The simplest fragmentation method is to break off pieces of the parent plant by means of a stiff transfer needle that has been flattened at the end. By this means it is possible, indeed desirable, to obtain pieces of approximately equal sizes for use as inoculum. Each fragment then regenerates to produce one or more complete plants. It is not necessary to ensure that growing points are included in each fragment, since new ones are differentiated. (See Stange, 1964, for a discussion of the processes involved in regeneration in lower plants, including the bryophytes.) The minimum size of the fragment capable of giving rise to regenerants has not been thoroughly studied in bryophytes. On simple inorganic media solidified with agar we have been unable to get regenerants from leaf fragments of *Sphaerocarpos donnellii* containing fewer than 13 to 16 cells. With most mosses one has to decide whether to use as the inoculum the filamentous (protonema) growth stage or the leafy (gametophore) growth stage. The choice obviously depends upon the intent of the experiment. Generally gametophore fragments regenerate the juvenile or protonemal phase of development; gametophore fragments therefore should be used when the experiment concerns the developmental physiology of this phenomenon. On the other hand, protonema should be used as the initial inoculum in experiments designed to study the initiation and subsequent development of gametophores and changes in the biochemical machinery during this developmental process. Mitra, Allsopp, and Wareing (1959) found that moss plants cultured under blue light do not initiate gametophores, although there is extensive and apparently otherwise normal development of the protonemal mat. (Gametophores are initiated only when plants are cultured under red or white light.) Investigations concerned with the protonema-to-gametophore transition should use protonemal inoculum from a stock culture grown under blue light. This precaution will ensure that gametophore initials are not present in the inoculum prior to the experimental treatment. Protonema can be transferred much as one would filamentous fungi, by scraping the agar surface or by cutting out small agar blocks.

A method whereby large quantities of inoculum can be readily obtained has been described by Machlis and Doyle (1962).

Materials

- Surface or submersed cultures of bryophytes
- Containers (e.g., 250-ml Erlenmeyer flasks) with experimental media
- One liter of sterile distilled water
- Sterile tea strainer (about 12 square openings per centimeter)
- Blender (e.g., Waring Blendor) with sterile cup
- Sterile 10-ml syringe equipped with a number 13 hypodermic needle

Procedure

1. Harvest cultures and transfer plants to blender cup.
   (a) Agar cultures: remove plants with a minimum of adhering agar.
   (b) Submersed cultures: drain off medium and wash plants with sterile water.
2. Add 50 ml of sterile distilled water to the blender cup and run 5 to 15 seconds until fragments pass through a number 13 hypodermic needle.
3. Pour plant fragments into tea strainer and wash with 500 ml of sterile distilled water.
4. Transfer washed material back to blender cup or other suitable sterile container and add water to provide the desired volume of inoculum.
5. Suspend fragments and draw into syringe; expel air and then inoculate flasks with 1 or 2 ml of inoculum.

Comments

This method was originally devised for submersed growths of the liverwort *Sphaerocarpos donnellii*, but has also been used with a few other liverworts. In the procedure as outlined above the sizes of the fragments in the inoculum are not uniform. Uniformity is increased by sequentially washing the material on two strainers, first a large-pored strainer to eliminate the very large fragments (that also tend to clog the hypodermic needle), and then the filtrate through a second, smaller-pored strainer (described above) to eliminate the contents of broken cells and very small plant fragments. The plant fragments retained by the second strainer are resuspended and used as the inoculum as described in (5) above.

Gemmae may be harvested by any one of several methods. Miller (1964) described a procedure whereby gemmae of the liverwort *Marchantia polymorpha* are readily harvested from the gemmae cups by placing a drop of 3 percent hydrogen peroxide solution on each cup. The gemmae rise to the surface of the cup in about 2 minutes. If the culture is aseptic the gemmae are directly transferred one at a time (by use of a hammer-flattened platinum needle) to the experimental medium. Contaminated gemmae, on the other hand, are transferred by means of a pointed watercolor brush from the drop to a sterile vial where they are surface sterilized as described earlier in this chapter. This procedure, or slight modifications of it, should work equally well with gemmae of the liverworts *Lunularia* and *Blasia* and the moss *Tetraphis*. Basile (1964), working with the leafy liverwort *Scapania nemorosa*, simply flooded an agar-grown culture that was forming gemmae abundantly. After shaking the culture the gemmae suspension was taken up into a syringe.

Culture Techniques

A wide variety of culture apparatus and techniques is described in the literature; only a few will be mentioned here. For other than aquatic organisms a solid substrate is normal and, because submersed growths of land plants often show abnormal form and development, should be used whenever possible. Media solidified with 1.5 percent or 2 percent agar generally is satisfactory. We use the Prát medium as the basic nutrient solution in most of our experimental work. Plastic Petri dishes are useful for short-term experiments; for longer growth periods we use Pyrex Petri dishes, 100 mm × 20 mm, or Pyrex Storage dishes (A. H. Thomas Co., Philadelphia, Pa.), 100 mm × 80 mm. Plants are harvested for analysis by pulling or cutting them free of the supporting agar substrate. However, it is difficult to free moss protonema from this relatively hard substrate. In this regard, Gorton and Eakin (1957), working with the moss *Tortella caespitosa*, found that the protonema readily could be washed free of agar when the medium was solidified with only 0.35 percent agar; the moss seemed to grow satisfactorily on this semisolid medium.

However, submersed cultures are extremely useful for many types of physiological studies and, unlike agar-grown plants, there is less danger of contamination of the plants by the substrate during harvest. This type of culture method is also useful for growing plants for analysis of cell wall carbohydrates. The Machlis medium, containing 1 percent dextrose, supports luxuriant growths of the liverwort *Sphaerocarpos donnellii* and the several other liverworts tested, but the effectiveness of this medium in sustaining growth of a wide variety of bryophytes has not been investigated. We generally add 50 ml of this medium to 125-ml Erlenmeyer flasks and 100 ml to 250-ml flasks. The flasks are cotton-plugged and capped with uncoated paper cups (uncoated so that they are autoclavable). The caps prevent dust from falling directly on the cotton plugs. DeLong culture flasks with Morton stainless steel closures (from Bellco, Vineland, N.J., U.S.A.) also are useful, although I feel that I get less contamination in cotton-plugged flasks during long-term experiments. Best growth is obtained when the cultures are shaken on a rotary or gyratory shaker. Plants also grow well, albeit more slowly, in standing cultures.

Basile (1964) described a useful procedure for the alteration of the culture medium during the course of growth. He used 60-ml serum bottles or other suitable bottles capped with serum-type bottle stoppers. Acid-washed white quartz sand was used as the substratum. A cotton-plugged hypodermic needle, to facilitate gas exchange, was permanently inserted through the rubber stopper. A second hypodermic needle attached to a syringe was used to introduce measured amounts of new material into the culture bottle with minimum exposure to potential contaminants. By noting the volume of the initial medium in the bottle it is possible to determine the final concentration of newly introduced compounds. This procedure is useful in that it allows for the establishment of the plant fragments on the basic medium before an experimental compound or solution is tested. We have used a slightly different procedure in my laboratory, a procedure that is useful for cultures maintained in continuous dark. A test tube, e.g., 10 mm × 100 mm, is attached to the upper part of a 250-ml Erlenmeyer flask, just below the neck of the flask. The tube is attached at an acute angle about 45 degrees from the vertical. During an experiment the flask is cotton-plugged and sterilized. A measured amount of sterile basic medium is added to the flask proper. To the side-arm is added a measured amount of sterile basic medium containing the experimental compound of a concentration to result in the desired final concentration when added to the medium in the base of the flask. The plant material is then added to the medium in the base of the flask. After a specified period of growth the experimental solution in the side-arm is added to the plant culture simply by tipping the whole apparatus on its side. This self-contained unit has obvious advantages for use in experiments dealing with the handling of cultures in the dark.

Culture Conditions

Growth chambers of the type used in higher plant research represent, for bryological investigations, an inefficient utilization of space. Several shelves each with a subtending bank of fluorescent lights make a more useful unit. It is also generally unwise to share a growth chamber with higher plants since these plants, rarely being in aseptic culture, represent an unending source of potential contamination. Fortunately, smaller growth cabinets are on the market and can be modified for bryophyte culture. Although lighted cabinets are available from several companies, they usually have the fluorescent tubes attached to the door or to the top of the chamber. Cabinets with adjustable shelves and with two or three fluorescent lights mounted under each shelf make useful and flexible growth chambers for small photosynthetic plants such as bryophytes. The excellent article by Matzke (1964) can be consulted for details concerning the conversion of commercially available growth cabinets into bryotrons. The possession of at least four of these units results in experimental flexibility.

It is impossible to generalize on the temperature, light intensity, and photoperiod regimes optimal for bryophyte growth. For example, temperatures from 18° to 30°C, photoperiodic regimes from a

10-hour day, 14-hour night to continuous light, and light intensity from about 200 ft-c to over 1,400 ft-c have been used for the culture of the same bryophyte (*Funaria hygrometrica*). In my laboratory we generally grow experimental cultures at about 20°C (day temperature), on a 14-hour day, 10-hour night photoperiod cycle and at about 450 to 500 ft-c. Illumination is provided by cool-white fluorescent lights; daylight bulbs are also satisfactory (see Downs and Bailey, this volume, pp. 635–644, for discussion of lighting). We have not yet used Sylvania Gro-Lux lamps, although they have been used by others for bryophyte culture. The environmental parameters mentioned above that we use, imposed more by limitations in our facilities than by reason, have resulted, nevertheless, in satisfactory bryophyte growth and reproducible results.

REFERENCES

BASILE, D. V., 1964: New procedures of bryophyte culture which permit alternation of the culture medium during the life cycle. *Bryologist*, 67: 141.

BOPP, M., 1961: Morphogenese der Laubmoose. *Biol. Rev.*, 36: 237.

GORTON, B. S., and R. E. EAKIN, 1957: Development of the gametophyte in the moss *Tortella caespitosa*. *Bot. Gaz.*, 119: 31.

HATCHER, R. E., 1965: Towards the establishment of a pure culture collection of Hepaticae. *Bryologist*, 68: 227.

IVERSON, G., 1957: Pure culture of *Frullania*. *Bryologist*, 60: 348.

MACHLIS, L., 1962: The effects of mineral salts, glucose and light on the growth of the liverwort *Sphaerocarpos donnellii*. *Physiol. Plant.*, 15: 354.

MACHLIS, L., and W. T. DOYLE, 1962: Submerged growth of pure cultures of the liverwort *Sphaerocarpos donnellii*. *Physiol. Plant.*, 15: 351.

MATZKE, E. B., 1964: The aseptic culture of liverworts in microphytotrons. *Bryologist*, 67: 136.

MILLER, M. W., 1964: A technique for isolating and culturing gemmae of *Marchantia polymorpha* L. under aseptic conditions. *Bryologist*, 67: 317.

MITRA, G. C., A. ALLSOPP, and P. F. WAREING, 1959: I. The effects of light of various qualities on the development of the protonema and bud formation in *Pohlia nutans* (Hedw.) Lindb. *Phytomorphology*, 9: 47.

NEHIRA, K., 1964: Culture media for bryophytes. *Bull. Biol. Soc. Hiroshima Univ.*, 31: 15.

PRÁT, S., 1948: *Algarum, Hepaticarum, Muscorumgue in culturis collection.* Plantarum Institutum Universitatis Carolinae, Prague.

STANGE, L., 1964: Regeneration in lower plants. *Advan. Morphogenesis*, 4: 111.

STEIN, J. R., 1958: A morphologic and genetic study of *Gonium pectorale*. *Amer. Jour. Bot.*, 45: 664.

SZWEYKOWSKA, A., 1963: Kinetin-induced formation of gametophores in dark cultures of *Ceratodon purpureus*. *J. Exptl. Bot.*, 14: 137.

Aquatic Fungi*

By James S. Lovett

INTRODUCTION

Within the large assemblage of fungi composing the aquatic Phycomycetes there are many of potential utility for developmental study. Perhaps the greatest virtue of these fungi is that they provide systems combining both morphological simplicity and ease of manipulation. The use of nonfilamentous water molds for the analysis of synchronously developing cultures has been the subject of a recent review (Cantino and Lovett, 1964). Despite the obvious potential of these fungi, however, only a very few species have been the object of any extensive work. Two that have been studied continuously over a period of several years will be described below. Both belong to the same family (Blastocladiaceae) of posteriorly uniflagellate fungi: *Allomyces*, a filamentous organism with alternating haploid and diploid generations, and *Blastocladiella*, a simple nonfilamentous fungus. Each presents special problems and advantages for study and each has certain limitations, some of which will become self-evident in the descriptions to follow. The emphasis in this article will be on the methods for isolating, growing, and manipulating these water molds. For this reason reference to reviews and research papers will be essential for discussions and details of the special developmental problems presented by each system. Such references will be cited at the appropriate places in the text. For the benefit of those unfamiliar with the aquatic fungi, brief descriptions of the life cycle and development of both *Allomyces* and *Blastocladiella* will be provided.

A few additional species, not described here, nevertheless do deserve mention. The biflagellate, filamentous water mold, *Achlya*, has been the subject of interesting work on the hormonal regulation of sexual development (Raper, 1951; Barksdale, 1963). And, among the nonfilamentous species, both *Rhizidiomyces apophysatus* (Fuller, 1962) and *Rhizophlyctis rosea* (LeJohn and Lovett, 1966; Chambers and Willoughby, 1964) have already been shown to have considerable promise. The latter, in particular, is a ubiquitous, readily isolated, and easily cultured organism.

* The writer would like to acknowledge his great debt to Dr. Ralph Emerson and to Dr. Edward C. Cantino, whose pioneering work with *Allomyces* and *Blastocladiella*, respectively, made these water molds popular as organisms for developmental study. Some work of the author described for *Blastocladiella* was supported by grant No. AI-04783 from the National Institute of Allergy and Infectious Disease, National Institutes of Health.

Further details on the isolation and culture of aquatic fungi will be found in a monograph on the *Aquatic Phycomycetes* by Sparrow (1960) and in a paper by Emerson (1958).

BLASTOCLADIELLA

Introduction

The main features of the life cycle of *Blastocladiella emersonii* were described soon after the fungus was originally isolated by Cantino (1951). He immediately recognized the unusual opportunity this organism provided for experimental study, and most of our present knowledge concerning the details of development in *B. emersonii* has come from the extensive and imaginative work of Dr. Cantino and his co-workers. This has been thoroughly reviewed (Cantino and Turian, 1959; Cantino, 1961; Cantino and Lovett, 1964) and the reader is therefore referred to these papers and the original articles discussed therein for detailed descriptions to supplement the brief summary below.

Life Cycle and Development

The main features in the life cycle of *B. emersonii* are illustrated in Fig. 1. The uninucleate zoospore of *Blastocladiella* has a single posterior flagellum, a conspicuous nuclear cap, and a single large mitochondrion. The unusual penetration of the flagellum and "rootlets" through channels in the mitochondrion and the lipid granules associated with the mitochondrion to form the acentric "side body," have already been described (Cantino *et al.*, 1963). The ribosome-filled nuclear cap surrounding the anterior two-thirds of the nucleus has also been isolated and partially characterized (Lovett, 1963). At germination, the zoospore rounds up, retracts its flagellum, and produces a fine tubular outgrowth or rhizoid. Before the latter occurs, the nuclear cap becomes disorganized and the cap contents are released to the surrounding cytoplasm (Lovett, unpublished) in a manner entirely similar to that described for *Allomyces* zygotes (Blondel and Turian, 1960). The young germling then grows rapidly; during this stage the spore body increases in size with nuclear division in the absence of cytokinesis, while the basal rhizoids develop into a restricted branching system of tapering filaments.

The subsequent developmental pathway of a young plant depends upon its environment. If it is grown in a PYG medium (a dilute peptone-yeast extract-glucose medium, see section on Culture) with a low population density and adequate aeration, the germling will form a colorless, thin-walled, zoosporangium (OC plant). At maturity, cross-wall formation converts this simple saclike plant into a terminal zoosporangium with one or more discharge papillae and a typically obscure empty basal cell bearing the rhizoids. The mature plant then rapidly differentiates its coenocytic protoplast to produce a large number of zoospores. These are immediately released to reinitiate the cycle leaving the parent plant a dead and empty hulk. The time required for a plant to complete the entire cycle varies from about 10 to 24 hours depending upon cell density, temperature, and other factors. On PYG agar, at 20°C, it requires about 24 hours.

Zoosporangia growing on solid medium with a dry surface will develop in a normal fashion. However, in the absence of fluid, the released spores cannot swim away and are forced to germinate and grow *in situ*. The result, after a generation or two, is a densely packed colony with hundreds of crowded plants. In such a colony the plants typically grow in an elongate fashion, but otherwise appear similar to ordinary OC thalli. When they mature, however, they form a very different

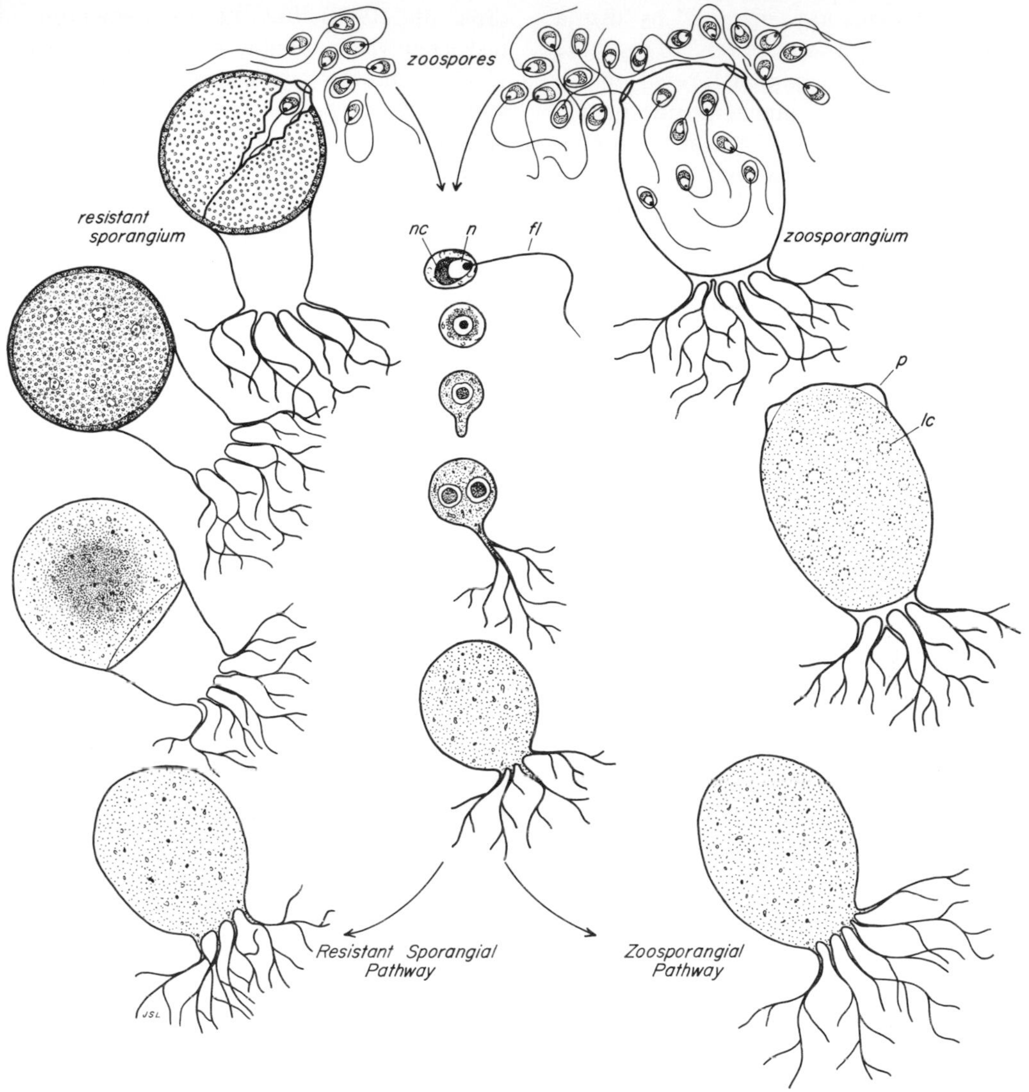

FIG. 1. Life cycle and development of *Blastocladiella emersonii.* To show more detail, the stages illustrating zoospore germination and early development have been drawn on a larger scale than the rest of the cycle. (fl) flagellum; (lc) lipid-crown droplets surrounding the prespore nuclei; (n) nucleus; (nc) nuclear cap; (p) discharge papilla.

type of plant with a terminal brown, thick-walled resistant sporangium (RS). This also results from migration of the cytoplasm and septation to leave an empty basal cell. It differs from the OC by the formation of the thick melanized wall within and separate from the original plant cell wall. The RS require considerably longer to develop than the OC, have a very low metabolic rate, and remain viable for years in an air-dry state.

When mature RS are placed in water they germinate in a two-step process whereby the thick outer wall splits open and the contents are "cleaved" to form a large number of zoospores. These are released through a papilla formed on the slightly protruding inner membrane exposed by the cracks. There is, at present, no evidence to suggest that these spores differ in any significant way from the zoospores of the OC plant. Thus, for most practical purposes, the *B. emersonii* life cycle just described is asexual. Nevertheless, the regular production of small, orange, thin-walled plants by about 0.5 percent of the zoospores has in the past raised the question of sexual reproduction. Careful examination of these plants clearly showed that their progeny had limited viability and could not fuse with other *Blastocladiella* spores. From this and other evidence, Cantino (1961) concluded that the orange plants were probably nonfunctional "males" (see discussion of sex in *Allomyces*).

Cantino's (1951) recognition of the potential value of this simple organism for experimental morphogenesis was enhanced by his early discovery that the two main paths of development could be controlled by the simple addition of bicarbonate to the basic medium (to induce RS versus OC). The evolution of techniques for growing large-scale synchronized single-generation cultures of OC and RS plants has, in recent years, allowed the application of biochemical techniques to the study of any stage in either cycle (Cantino, 1965; Cantino and Lovett, 1964; Domnas and Cantino, 1965; Horenstein and Cantino, 1964). These methods will be described in the section on Experimental Methods.

Isolation from Nature

Knowledge of the actual geographic distribution of *Blastocladiella* species is still very limited. They have been reported from England, France, the Dominican Republic, Mexico, and the United States (Sparrow, 1960), but the nonfilamentous restricted growth habit of *Blastocladiella* would tend to make it inconspicuous and easily overlooked without a deliberate search. In most instances, species of *Blastocladiella* have been "trapped" from soil-water cultures baited with such esoteric items as boiled paspalum grass, boiled corn-seedling leaves, fly eggs, a dead fly, and a hempseed radical (Sparrow, 1960); *B. emersonii* was trapped on a Petri dish of silica gel submerged for several days in a fresh-water pond (Cantino, 1951).

For isolation, 3 or 4 gm of soil and/or mud from the edge of a fresh-water stream, pond, or ditch are placed in a deep crystallizing dish (Mason jar, finger bowl, etc.) with 400–500 ml of sterile $\frac{1}{2}$ DS solution[1] or PD (1 part filtered pond water: 2 parts distilled water; Emerson, 1958). As soon as the dirt has settled, small pieces of bait are floated on the surface and the container is loosely covered. After 2 days at 20°–25°C the bait should be examined under a dissecting microscope. If a finger bowl or crystallizing dish is used the bait can usually be examined for growth without removal from the dish. When plants of *Blastocladiella* have been found, the bait can be washed a few times with sterile water (a series of 5-cm Petri dishes with 10 ml of water) and transferred to a new dish with fresh bait. The growth on the second piece of bait is usually less grossly contaminated and a better source for isolation into pure culture. With such a nonfilamentous water mold, however, it is also wise to attempt immediate isolation.

To obtain the fungus in pure culture it is usually necessary to dissect out one or more mature plants (e.g., zoosporangia with papillae or brown RS) under the

[1] A dilute inorganic salt solution containing 2.5×10^{-5} *M* $MgSO_4$ and $CaCl_2$, and 2.5×10^{-4} *M* NH_4NO_3, K_2HPO_4, and KH_2PO_4 at pH 7.0 (Murphy and Lovett, 1966).

dissecting microscope. After gently freeing the plants of as much debris as possible with fine needles (drawn from small glass rod or made of fine platinum wire embedded in glass), they are washed by transfer with a sterile capillary pipette (Pasteur pipette) through several drops of sterile ½ DS (or PD) in depression slides. After washing, the plants are left, one or more per drop, on depression slides held in a moist chamber at 20°–25°C. A sterile Petri dish with several drops of sterile water and a glass-rod triangle to support the slide works well. It has the advantage that the slide can be checked under the dissecting scope without removal from the chamber. Periodic examination is then necessary to determine when discharge occurs.

As soon as possible after the zoospores have been released, small droplets are transferred individually to plates of PYG agar and spread with a sterile bent glass rod. It is important that the plates be poured 2 days ahead to ensure a dry surface and prevent the spread of contaminants. The agar should not be *so* dry that the water is immediately absorbed or the delicate spores will be killed before they can germinate. If the washing was adequate, isolated plants should be present after about 24 hours at 25°C. The position of those that are well separated from the nearest bacterial colonies should be marked for removal at maturity. This is done by cutting out the plant on a tiny block of agar with a fine spatula (a transfer needle hammered flat at the tip, bent at an angle, and filed to a point works well). The block is transferred as before to a drop of ½ DS or PD to discharge. A pure culture should be obtained when the resulting zoospores are spread on fresh plates of PYG agar. Once this has been accomplished, the population can be increased by inducing several of the plants to discharge in a small volume and using this to inoculate plates or slants.

Culture of *Blastocladiella*

Stock cultures of *Blastocladiella emersonii* are conveniently maintained as colonies of RS on PYG[2] plates or slants. These are prepared by plating drops of a zoospore suspension diluted to yield small numbers of well separated colonies (5–10 per slant or 10–50 per plate). Desiccation and contamination of stocks on Petri plates can be minimized by sealing them with large rubber bands made for this purpose or with masking tape. Slant cultures in tubes with snug metal closures keep equally well and require less storage space. Resistant sporangia can be stored this way for several months at normal room temperatures. They can also be kept on sterile filter paper strips for an indefinite period (see the procedure described for *Allomyces* under section on Culture).

Working cultures of *Blastocladiella* are normally carried by daily transfer of zoospores to fresh PYG plates and incubation at 18°–20°C. As noted above, the time required varies as a function of cell density and temperature; crowded plants discharge earlier but reach a smaller size than those that are well separated. To transfer zoosporangial cultures, 2 to 5 ml of sterile distilled water are added to the plate when about 5 to 10 percent of the plants have started to release spores and most of the remainder have formed papillae. Two or three drops of the turbid spore suspension obtained after 15–30 minutes are then transferred by pipette to a fresh plate of PYG with a few drops of sterile water. A total volume of 0.5 ml on a freshly poured 10-cm plate will ensure the retention of a film of moisture without making it overly wet. It is

[2] PYG is a medium devised for the growth of *Blastocladiella* by E. C. Cantino and contains 1.25 gm peptone, 1.25 gm yeast extract, and 3.0 gm D-glucose per liter at pH 6.8. It is available commercially as Difco-Cantino PYG broth or agar.

advisable to check the zoospore suspension each time for obvious bacterial contamination since distinct colonies are not formed on plates with a moist surface.

When OC cultures are maintained for long periods by daily transfer they may occasionally start to behave erratically. To avoid this apparent degeneration (the cause has not been investigated) it is a good practice to start fresh cultures from RS stocks every month or two. The RS (see above) are induced to discharge spores by cutting out a few mature colonies with a minimum of agar and immersing them in about 5 ml of sterile distilled water in a small Petri dish. After discharge occurs (4–8 hours at 20°C) several drops of the dilute zoospore suspension are spread on each plate of PYG agar. Two or three subsequent transfers will usually bring the population density to adequate levels if the volumes used to harvest the spores are minimal. Each time new zoosporangial cultures are started it is convenient to prepare fresh RS stocks using drops of the already dilute RS spore suspension.

Experimental Methods

Methods will be described in this section for harvesting, washing, and counting *Blastocladiella* zoospores and for growing synchronized cultures of OC and RS plants.

PREPARATION OF ZOOSPORES

The zoospore suspensions required for each type of culture are harvested in basically the same way but the procedures differ somewhat in detail depending upon the purpose for which they are to be used. Optimal yields of spores are recovered from fresh first-generation cultures of OC plants grown under conditions where a thin film of water remains at the time of discharge. The mature OC plants should be evenly distributed and close together on the agar surface for optimum yield and uniformity of discharge time. Zoospore formation and release is stimulated by flooding the plants at the papilla stage with small volumes of sterile distilled water. Flooding when 5–10 percent of the plants have started discharge will usually give the best results. Repeated washing with small volumes induces better discharge than fewer large ones (e.g., 3 ml per 10-cm plate or 5 ml per 15-cm plate). It also keeps the cell density high and the extracted PYG results in a less drastic change in the environment of the delicate spores. For inoculating cultures one such harvest from a few plates is often adequate.

The spore suspension is removed after 10–15 minutes with a sterile blow-out pipette and filtered to remove any plants through a fluted porous filter paper (No. 500, E. H. Sargent Co., Chicago, I11.; Goldstein and Cantino, 1962) or a loose wad of cotton stuffed into the stem of the funnel. If the spores are not to be used at once, the receiving flask is packed in crushed ice to chill the cells. In preparing sterile suspensions the author uses an autoclaved assembly with a short-stem funnel inserted through a cotton plug into an Erlenmeyer of the appropriate size. A double thickness of aluminum foil covers the funnel and upper portion of the flask and can be raised to pipette in the spores. A second sterile plug to fit the flask is exchanged for the funnel assembly after filtration.

The density of zoospore suspensions is determined by counting suitably diluted aliquots with a Coulter electronic cell counter (Model B, Coulter Electronics, Inc., Hialeah, Fla.). The spores are suspended in BSM[3] at a concentration of less than 1×10^4 per milliliter and counted

[3] An inorganic salts solution composed of 1×10^{-3} *M* $MgSO_4$, 1×10^{-3} *M* $CaCl_2$, 2.5×10^{-3} *M* NH_4NO_3, 8×10^{-3} *M* KCl, and 5×10^{-3} *M* KH_2PO_4–K_2HPO_4 at pH 6.6. Just before use it is filtered through a 1.2-μ Millipore filter (Type RA, Millipore Filter Corp., Bedford, Mass.) to reduce the background count (Murphy and Lovett, 1966).

using a 100-μ aperture. The spores are diluted volumetrically with cold BSM and the counts are made immediately (with frequent mixing) to avoid germination and clumping. The zoospore concentration can also be determined by measuring the optical density at 420 μ of suspensions in a photoelectric colorimeter or spectrophotometer. This requires visibly turbid suspensions, correction for absorption by the suspending fluid (a serious error if much PYG has been extracted during harvest), and preparation of a standard curve. In the absence of a cell counter, the spore density can be estimated by counting drops of suspension in a hemocytometer after fixing for 15 seconds. With either method of counting it may be necessary to prepare a correction factor for viability, particularly if the spores are used in plating experiments.

Synchronous OC and RS cultures in liquid PYG medium are routinely inoculated with suitable volumes of sterile zoospore suspensions prepared in the manner just described. When larger numbers of spores are required for fractionation, physiology, or mass germination, the procedure is slightly modified. A much larger surface area of plant growth is used (30–40 15-cm Petri plates; several large 23 × 36-cm foil-covered Pyrex baking dishes; and Roux bottles have also been used successfully), sterile technique is usually unnecessary, and the spores are concentrated and washed by low-speed centrifugation in the cold. Large yields can be obtained by flooding such cultures several times over a period of an hour or more while holding the filtered suspension on ice. The spores are concentrated by centrifugation in 30-ml plastic tubes at 4°–10°C. The rotor is rapidly brought up to speed (755 *g*, or 2,500 rpm in a No. SS-1 or SS-34 head of the Servall Refrigerated Centrifuge), run for exactly 2 minutes, and allowed to decelerate. The supernatant is decanted from the very loose pellet of spores, 2 or 3 ml of cold BSM (or other medium) are added to each tube, and the spores are quickly resuspended by using a Pasteur pipette with a rubber bulb to force the liquid gently over the pellet. The concentrated zoospores are washed by pooling the resulting suspensions and repeating the procedure. After washing, the cells are taken up in 10–20 ml of the desired buffer, or medium, with subsequent treatment dependent upon the purpose of the experiment. A procedure for zoospore homogenization and isolation of the nuclear caps has been described (Lovett, 1963).

SYNCHRONOUS OC CULTURES

Conditions for the growth of OC plants in synchronous single-generation cultures have been provided by Goldstein and Cantino (1962). The medium contains 5.5 gm Difco-Cantino PYG per liter with 5×10^{-3} *M* phosphate buffer at pH 6.7. A total volume of 1.2 liters with a little added Antifoam A (Dow Corning Corp., Midland, Mich.) is autoclaved (35 minutes at 120°C and 16 pounds pressure) in a 2-liter Erlenmeyer flask equipped with two aeration tubes. The culture is inoculated with 8.3×10^6–2.5×10^8 spores per liter and incubated with aeration (5 liters air per minute) in a water bath at 24°C. Under these conditions, generation times (defined as the stage when 5 percent of the plants have formed discharge papillae; Goldstein and Cantino, 1962) of 16 hours and 17½ hours were obtained for dark- and light-grown cultures, respectively. A modified medium with a citrate-phosphate buffer (3×10^{-3} *M* citric acid plus 1.1×10^{-2} *M* $NaHPO_4$, pH 6.7) has also been used (Cantino, 1965; Domnas and Cantino, 1965).

ZOOSPORE DIFFERENTIATION

The above method has been modified by Murphy and Lovett (1966) for the study of synchronous zoospore differentiation. One liter of the PYG-phosphate medium is sterilized and cooled in a 1-liter water-jacketed spinner flask (No. 3007, Bellco Glass, Inc., Vineland, N.J.) equipped with a magnetic stirrer bar. An aeration tube (with an inline sterile cotton filter) is inserted through one access port and the second is plugged with cotton; the entire assembly is mounted over a large magnetic stirrer and the jacket connected to a constant temperature bath at 24°C. The culture is started by inoculation with 1.34×10^7 spores prepared as described above and used as soon after harvesting as possible. The culture is aerated with a mixture of 0.5 liter tank oxygen and 1.8 liter air per minute (separate flow meters) and stirred with the stirrer (Jumbo Magnetic Stirrer, Fischer Sci. Co., Chicago, Ill.) set at position eight. The plants are grown under ordinary laboratory light conditions.

The culture of synchronously developing plants is induced to form zoospores after $15\frac{1}{2}$ hours of growth. This is just before the end of the growth phase at a stage when no papillae have been formed. Aeration and mixing are stopped, the plants are allowed to settle for 5 minutes, and 75 percent of the medium is removed by suction with a stick filter (a fritted glass sparger). The volume is returned to 900 ml (the volume at $15\frac{1}{2}$ hours) with $\frac{1}{2}$ DS and the culture briefly stirred and aerated to mix. The exchange process is repeated, the volume finally adjusted with $\frac{1}{2}$ DS to that at $15\frac{1}{2}$ hours, and aeration and mixing are resumed. The two changes require 20 minutes and remove 94 percent of the original growth medium. With this procedure the plants remain unclumped after the change and undergo zoospore differentiation in a highly synchronized (96 percent) fashion. Papillae are formed between the seventeenth and eighteenth hours after inoculation; visible cleavage to form the spores occurs at $18\frac{3}{4}$ hours with discharge 15–20 minutes later (Murphy and Lovett, 1966). With an increase in scale, this method can also be used to produce large populations of zoospores.

SYNCHRONOUS RS CULTURES

The growth of large-scale synchronized cultures of *Blastocladiella* resistant sporangial plants has been reported by Lovett and Cantino (1960). The medium is prepared with 5.5 gm per liter of Difco-Cantino PYG broth and 8.9×10^{-3} *M* $NaHCO_3$. Ten liters of medium are autoclaved (45 minutes, 15 pounds pressure, 120°C) in a 12-liter flat-bottomed Florence flask equipped with a large (1-cm inside diameter) aeration tube (with cotton filter) and a sealed siphon tube for removing plants. After sterilization, the flask is removed from the autoclave and quickly cooled in a water bath with aeration to minimize caramelization of the medium.

The culture is started by inoculation with 1.4×10^6 zoospores per liter and incubated in a water bath at 24°C with very vigorous aeration. The resulting plant development is well synchronized and during exponential growth the mass doubling time (2.5 hours) is about twice that of OC plants in PYG. Exponential growth ends at 26–28 hours; the decelerating growth phase between 28 and 48 hours is accompanied by septation and many physiological changes associated with the switch to irreversible RS development. The RS themselves reach maturity at 80–83 hours. The use of the siphon to remove samples (discarding the material in the siphon each time) permits multiple sampling over this long period without danger of contamination.

The induction of RS by a high potassium ion concentration in continuous and batch cultures of *Blastocladiella* growing in PYG, or a peptone-glucose medium, has been reported by Griffin (1965). The degree of synchrony in the batch cultures was not described.

ALLOMYCES

Introduction

The variation between the life cycles displayed by species of *Allomyces*, and the diversity of the reproductive structures produced in the life cycle of a single species, has intrigued mycologists for many years. The distribution, taxonomy, and morphology of this interesting and widespread genus was reported in a very comprehensive paper by Emerson (1941). However, only two species have been investigated in any experimental detail, *Allomyces arbuscula* and *A. macrogynus*. Both species have a life cycle composed of two separate generations, the diploid sporophyte which produces zoosporangia (mitosporangia) and resistant sporangia (meiosporangia), and the haploid gametophyte which forms pairs of orange male and colorless female gametangia.

An excellent discussion of the life cycles and development of *A. macrogynus* and *A. arbuscula*, including a series of color and phase-contrast photomicrographs of important stages[4] may be found in Emerson's paper on "The Biology of the Water Molds" (1954). The same article includes an extensive review of the morphological problems presented by *Allomyces* and the status of their experimental exploitation at that time. In a subsequent review, Cantino and Turian (1959) discussed in detail the cytochemical and physiological work on differentiation and development in *Allomyces* through 1958. In the following paragraphs the developmental system will be briefly summarized; information will be provided concerning the details of isolation, culture, and manipulation of *Allomyces*; and, since the subject has not been reviewed recently, some of the interesting areas for experimental study will be mentioned.

Life Cycle and Development

The important stages in the alternating sporophytic and gametophytic generations of *A. arbuscula* are illustrated in Fig. 2. The sporophytic generation results from the germination of either a posteriorly uniflagellate diploid zoospore, or a biflagellate zygote (produced as the result of gametic fusion). In either case the motile cell rounds up, retracts its flagellum(a), and begins germination by the outgrowth of a rhizoidal tube. The rhizoid system increases by growth and branching, while at the same time the initial hyphal tube begins to form at the opposite pole of the encysted spore. The rhizoidal system of delicate tapering elements is usually localized and limited in extent. The larger initial hypha elongates and, as apical growth continues, branches in a regular dichotomous fashion to form a continually expanding coenocytic mycelial system. Soon after this growth system is established, the asexual reproductive structures begin to appear, i.e., the thin-walled, colorless, papillate zoosporangia and the thick-walled, brown, resistant sporangia. Each originates as a multinucleate region of a hyphal tip cut off from the remainder of the mycelium by a cross wall. A detailed cytological examination of the "cleavage" process to form the individual uninucleate zoospores with their nuclear caps and flagella was reported by Ritchie (1947). The zoosporangia produce one or more discharge papillae which appear to "dissolve" and release the fully differentiated zoospores. After a period of

[4] Some of these were taken from a film "Syngamy and Alternation of Generations in *Allomyces*, a Watermold," available commercially from Phase Films, Ross, California.

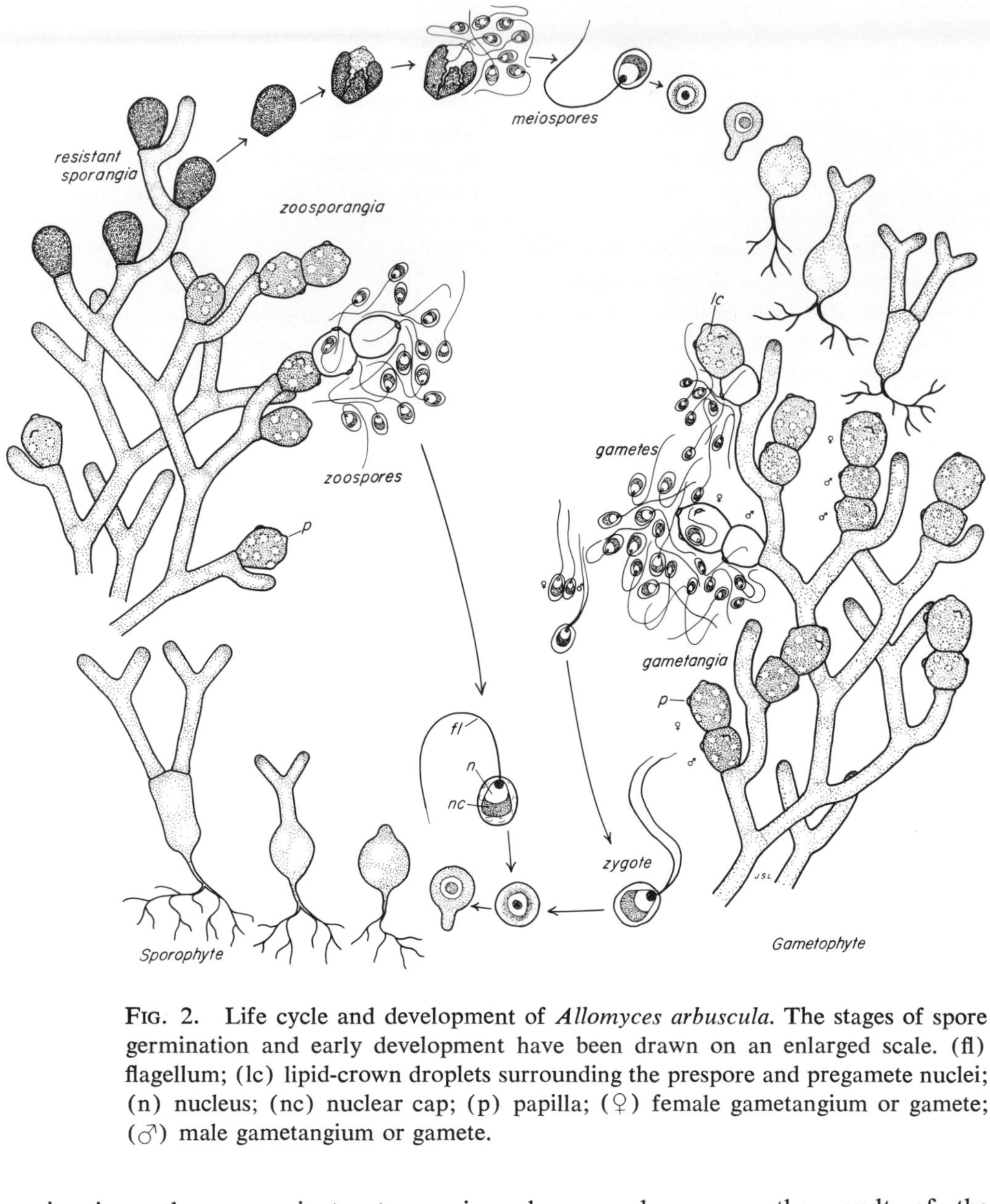

FIG. 2. Life cycle and development of *Allomyces arbuscula.* The stages of spore germination and early development have been drawn on an enlarged scale. (fl) flagellum; (lc) lipid-crown droplets surrounding the prespore and pregamete nuclei; (n) nucleus; (nc) nuclear cap; (p) papilla; (♀) female gametangium or gamete; (♂) male gametangium or gamete.

swimming, these germinate to again produce the asexual sporophyte.

The RS appear similar to zoosporangia immediately after septation. However, they subsequently form a new, much thicker wall within and separate from the original hyphal wall. This new wall contains numerous pits and gradually becomes brown as the result of the deposition of melanin pigments. In contrast to the zoosporangia the development and maturation of these dormant and resistant structures requires some time, and without treatment they frequently will not germinate until at least a few weeks after their formation (Emerson, 1941).

The RS are typically produced in large numbers and give the sporophytic culture a distinct brown color. Each mature RS contains about 12 nuclei arrested at prophase of the first meiotic division. When the RS germinate they take up water rapidly, the thick outer wall cracks open, and a discharge papilla is formed on the protruding inner membrane. This is accompanied by the completion of meiosis to yield about 48 haploid nuclei, and subsequent cleavage to form as many uninucleate flagellated spores (meiospores). These are released by the deliquescence of the papilla and swim away. Except for their smaller size the meiospores appear identical to mitospores and, upon germination, these haploid spores give rise to a branching coenocytic mycelium in an identical manner. The haploid gametophytic character of the mycelium becomes apparent only when the paired male and female gametangia are formed at the tips of the growing hyphae.

The first stage in gametangial development is septation to form two unequal-sized multinucleate chambers at the hyphal tip. Mitotic divisions continue to occur in the smaller section and the resulting male gametangium has about four times as many nuclei as the larger female gametangium. When no free moisture is present (as on a dry agar surface) the gametangia do not immediately differentiate their gametes but remain in what is known as the "lipid-crown" stage (Blondel and Turian, 1960) where each nucleus is clearly outlined by a sphere of refractile lipid droplets and the discharge papillae have formed. The small male gametangia contain γ-carotene and traces of other pigments and give the gametophytic culture its characteristic rosy, yellow-orange color. The large female gametangia and mycelium remain colorless. Gametangia in this stage will remain viable for many days at room temperature. When "lipid-crown"-stage gametangia are placed in water, the gametes are rapidly (1 to 1½ hours) cleaved out and discharged via the papillae. The cellular organization of the gametes appears to be essentially the same as that of the zoospores and meiospores, though the latter have not been as well characterized. The smaller, actively motile male gametes are attracted to the undischarged female gametangia and the larger, sluggish female gametes by means of a chemotactic substance named "sirenin" (Carlile and Machlis, 1965). Fusion of the gametes in pairs occurs in a short time to yield biflagellate diploid zygotes which are also motile. These, upon germination, give rise to new sporophytic mycelia. Since there are no genetic compatibility factors, any male gamete can, apparently, fuse with a female gamete of sufficiently similar genetic constitution, i.e., the fungus is self-compatible or homothallic.

The above description of the life cycle applies equally well to either *A. arbuscula* or *A. macrogynus*. These two species differ from one another primarily in the arrangement of the paired gametangia. The orange male is terminal (epigynous) in *A. macrogynous* and subterminal below the female (hypogynous) in *A. arbuscula*. The two also differ somewhat in the relative size of the gametangia and the intensity of pigmentation. The story is further complicated by the occasional parthenogenetic germination of unfertilized female gametes to produce a new gametophyte, or, by doubling the chromosome complement, to form a new sporophyte (particularly common with certain strains of *A. arbuscula*; Emerson and Wilson, 1954).

The potential significance of *Allomyces* as an organism for the experimental study of development was clearly recognized some years ago by Emerson (1941, 1950, 1954). It grows readily on synthetic media and is easily manipulated using only slight modifications of standard microbiological techniques. Both the haploid and diploid phases can be cultured indefinitely as such and, of course, the presence of sexuality permits genetic analysis. The lack of a genetic mating control also means that desirable haploid strains can be selfed to produce completely homozygous stable diploids (Emerson and Wilson, 1954).

Isolation from Nature

Species of *Allomyces* have been isolated from many areas of the tropical and temperate regions of the world, being most common in warmer climates. The best source for isolation is dirt or mud from the edges of fresh-water ponds, ditches, or slowly flowing streams where the soil is subject to periodic flooding. The isolation procedure outlined below is essentially that described by Emerson (1941) for *Allomyces*, but has been used over the years to isolate a variety of filamentous aquatic fungi.

To trap *Allomyces* a few grams of soil are placed in a deep crystallizing dish or straight-sided quart container about two-thirds full of sterile PD (a mixture of one-third fresh filtered pond water and two-thirds distilled water; Emerson, 1941, 1958). After the soil has settled, one or two sterile hemp seeds are added for bait. These are prepared by boiling the seeds of *Cannabis sativa* (see Emerson, 1958) for about 15–20 minutes to sterilize them, rupture the seed coats, and cause the white hypocotyl to protrude. They may also be cut in half with a razor blade, but this exposes an unnecessarily large surface area. To avoid excessive growth of undesirable microorganisms, it is important to keep the liquid volume-to-bait ratio large. If viable RS of *Allomyces* are in the soil or mud, growth normally appears as a tuft of mycelium on the exposed portion of the hemp seed within 2 or 3 days at 25°C. As soon as such growth appears it is advisable to examine it for the presence of *Allomyces* and, if present, to wash the seed (or even better a tuft of mycelium) through at least four tubes of sterile water and place it in another water culture with a new hemp seed.

Immediately after growth is established on the new seed and its identity rechecked, it should be isolated in pure culture. The simplest method is to wash the mycelial tuft as before and then aseptically break off a few hyphal filaments with a fine dissecting needle. Using a drawn-out glass capillary (Pasteur pipette) these are transferred through a series of drops of sterile PD in depression slides. Finally, each hypha is placed on a plate of Y_pS_s agar (see section on Culture of *Allomyces*) poured 48 hours ahead of time to ensure a dry surface. The developing mycelia will usually grow away from any bacterial contaminants since their spread is restricted by the dry surface.

A second method of isolation, particularly useful when contamination is persistent, is to isolate and plate the motile spores. To do this, a few mature zoosporangia, or RS, are broken from the washed mycelium with a fine dissecting needle. These are then washed by transfer through a series of 6–8 small dishes, with about 2 or 3 ml of sterile PD in each. This is most easily done with a Pasteur pipette under a dissecting microscope. The sporangia are allowed to remain in the last dish (or a drop or two of liquid on a depression slide in a moist chamber) until one or more of the sporangia discharge. Small drops of the resulting spore suspension are spread with a bent glass rod over the surface of Y_pS_s agar (see footnote 5) plates (2 days old). Small plantlets (germlings) should be visible under the dissecting microscope within about 24 hours at 25°C. Any of these which are well removed from the nearest bacterial colonies can be cut out on a tiny block of agar with a small spatula and transferred to a fresh plate of medium. Hyphal tip isolations and zoospores will give rise to colonies of the sporophyte while meiospores will produce the gametophyte. A detailed description of procedures for isolating sporangia and zoospores by this method will be found in Emerson and Cantino (1948). Emerson has also successfully used antibiotics (25–100 mg per liter streptomycin sulfate, 50–200 mg per liter penicillin G) to reduce bacterial contamination during isolation (Emerson, personal communication).

Culture of *Allomyces*

Stock cultures of *Allomyces arbuscula* and *A. macrogynus* are maintained in either of two ways, depending on whether the sporophytic or gametophytic phase is desired. The sporophyte can be cultured at room temperature, or at 10°–12°C, by transfer of small blocks of mycelium to fresh slants of Y_pS_s[5] medium every 6 weeks, or 3–4 months, respectively. Emerson (1941) has also described a procedure for storing air-dried resistant sporangia which remain viable for several years. Such stocks are easily prepared by scraping the surface of mature brown sporophytic colonies (i.e., on plates of solid Y_pS_s) with a flat sterile blade to collect the RS. These are suspended in distilled water and drops of the resulting suspension applied to sterile strips of filter paper. The strips are then air dried and stored in sterile vials.

The gametophyte can be maintained only by periodic transfer of the mycelium to new slants as indicated above for the sporophyte. However, to avoid gamete discharge and consequent reversion to the sporophyte, the slants should be prepared a week in advance of transfer, and the small blocks of mycelium placed right side up at or above the middle of the slant to avoid any traces of free moisture. Despite these precautions, brown diploid patches will sometimes appear and care should be taken to transfer only from the yellow-orange areas of pure gametophyte. With attention to these details, cultures of the haploid phase can be carried successfully for years. If necessary, the gametophyte can be obtained (or recovered) by "germinating" mature RS (from either stored filter strips or sporophyte cultures) and plating the meiospores on 2- or 3-day-old Y_pS_s plates. If fresh RS are to be used, it is necessary to free them of viable diploid mycelium and zoosporangia. This can be accomplished by pipetting suspensions of RS onto filter paper (in the manner described for their storage) and incubating them at 30°–35°C for a few weeks, or at 50°–60°C for 24 hours (Emerson, 1941). This serves not only to kill the vegetative structures but also to speed up RS maturation and increase germination. Machlis and Ossia (1953) have provided information on the cultural factors which affect the time required for their maturation.

The diploid sporophyte can be obtained either by plating zygotes derived from the gametophyte or, less directly, via meiospores plated to yield the gametophyte and the subsequent production of zygotes. To obtain zygotes, numbers of the paired gametangia are scraped from the surface of haploid cultures and placed in a few milliliters of distilled water to induce discharge. After allowing time for discharge and fusion to occur (2–4 hours), the zygotes in a drop or two of suspension

[5] A medium developed by Emerson (1941) which contains 4 gm yeast extract, 15 gm soluble starch, 1 gm K_2HPO_4, 0.5 gm $MgSO_4$, and 20 gm agar per liter at pH 7.0. This is available commercially as Difco-Emerson Y_pS_s agar.

will form sporophytic colonies after plating on Y_pS_s agar. For routine work it is simpler to carry both growth phases in culture, but from the above it is obvious that it is much easier to obtain the sporophyte from a gametophyte culture than vice versa.

The Y_pS_s medium of Emerson is simple to use and very satisfactory for maintaining stock cultures, but a simple chemically defined medium is desirable for physiological or biochemical experiments. Such a medium was devised for *Allomyces* by Ingraham and Emerson (1954) and modified by Machlis (1953).[6] The undesirably long lag in the growth of *Allomyces* on this synthetic medium can be reduced by the inclusion of 500 μmoles per liter of glutamic acid (Machlis, 1957).

Problems of Development in *Allomyces*

Emerson (1954) outlined three basic developmental problems presented by *Allomyces*: the formation and differentiation of gametangia; the development, maturation, and germination of resistant sporangia; and the mechanisms which control the regular alteration of the sporophyte and gametophyte generations. The zoosporangia should be added to this list. Emerson also stressed the extent to which these are related rather than independent problems.

Despite the fact that the gametophyte is haploid and the sporophyte diploid, at present only the reproductive structures provide a clear-cut distinction between the two. The basic organization of the motile cells appears much the same, the developmental stages and final organization of the mycelia are essentially identical (Emerson, 1941, 1954), and no significant differences have been found between the nutritional requirements of the two growth phases (Machlis and Craseman, 1956). Furthermore, with the exception of the thick-walled RS, each of the reproductive organs is formed by a very similar series of events including septation, the lipid crown stage, papilla formation, flagellum synthesis, nuclear cap organization, cleavage, and method of discharge. Some of these also occur during RS "germination." There is ample evidence that the development of reproductive structures can be modified considerably by alteration of the external environment (Cantino and Turian, 1959; Turian, 1964). Even with this apparent morphological plasticity there are, as yet, no well established cases where a sporophyte has been induced to produce diploid gametangia, or a gametophyte haploid zoosporangia. Resistant sporangia do occasionally form spontaneously on the gametophyte (Emerson, 1954), and can apparently be induced (Turian, 1964), but few of the RS formed in this way have been carefully analyzed.

The most obvious features of swarmers, the flagellum and nuclear cap, are shared by all four of the motile stages and it seems reasonable to assume that these organelles may have little to do with the *unique* function of a given spore type. In point of fact, these organelles seem more likely to represent the functions that all spores share in common, i.e., motility and conservation of the ribosomes during the nongrowing stage (Lovett, 1963; Murphy and Lovett, 1966; Turian, 1962).

Most recent work on the development of *Allomyces* has been confined to the gametangia. Blondel and Turian (1960) have provided an excellent electron micrograph series of stages during gametangial differentiation in *A. macrogynus*. A detailed study of flagellum formation by one of the two centrioles has been reported

[6] The synthetic medium B of Machlis contains only glucose, methionine, thiamine, and inorganic salts (including trace elements). For details refer to Machlis (1953).

for the same stage in *A. arbuscula* by Renaud and Swift (1964). Comparable information is not yet available for zoospores or meiospores.

Emerson and Wilson (1954) have examined the genetic basis for gametangial arrangement in crosses between *A. macrogynus* and *A. arbuscula* and their work clearly demonstrated that the inheritance was complex. Numerous intermediate hybrid types were obtained varying both in the orientation (epigyny versus hypogyny) and in the numerical ratios of the male and female gametangia. Some of the latter were very nearly unisexual male (99 percent ♂ gametangia) and female (91 percent ♀ gametangia) strains. These, like the albino mutants (apparently ♀ gametophytes) produced by Foley (1958), have considerable potential usefulness for biochemical work on development.

Turian has taken advantage of the male and female hybrids in an investigation of the physiological basis of gametangium formation. This has been directed along two lines. The first is a study of the changing ribonucleic acid (RNA), deoxyribonucleic acid (DNA), and protein content, and RNA composition, during stages leading to the formation of the large female gametes with big nuclear caps, and the more numerous small male gametes with very small caps. Primary emphasis has been placed on the concept that gradients must be set up which in some way cause increased DNA synthesis (and mitosis) in the male region and higher rates of RNA synthesis (without nuclear division) in the female region (Turian, 1963a, 1965). The second and related approach concerns other physiological parameters but primarily the role of respiratory metabolism. The basic working hypothesis has been that a weak oxidative metabolism in the presumptive "male" region causes the shunting of metabolic pathways toward increased production of DNA precursors (glycine, ribose, etc.) and potential carotenoid precursors such as acetate. This is postulated to induce male development in some way (Turian, 1960, 1961, 1963b).

Experimental Methods

A limited number of special techniques have been reported for the study of *Allomyces* development. These are outlined below.

PRODUCTION OF UNISEXUAL HYBRIDS

The complete details for the crossing of *A. arbuscula* and *A. macrogynus*, and the isolation and characterization of the resulting hybrids, will be found in the paper of Emerson and Wilson (1954).

PRODUCTION OF ZOOSPORES IN LIQUID CULTURE

Carlile and Machlis (1965) have described a procedure for producing large numbers of *Allomyces* zoospores. Erlenmeyer flasks (125 ml) with 50 ml of liquid Y_pS_s medium are inoculated with zoosporangia scraped from the surface of young (1–2 weeks old) sporophyte cultures on Y_pS_s agar. The zoospores released from the sporangia produce abundant growth after 3 days on a shaker at 25°C. The Y_pS_s medium is then decanted aseptically and replaced with an equal volume of sterile DS.[7] The cultures are returned to the shaker for 24 hours, by which time numerous zoosporangia have formed. These are induced to discharge large numbers of zoospores by transferring the mycelium to fresh DS in Petri plates. Dense suspensions are produced

[7] A 1:10 dilution of the inorganic salts of synthetic medium B (Machlis, 1953), DS contains 5×10^{-5} *M* $MgCl_2$ and $CaCl_2$, 5×10^{-4} *M* KH_2PO_4, K_2HPO_4, and $(NH_4)_2HPO_4$ at pH 7.0.

in about 2 hours. Since the spores tend to settle on the bottom of the dish it is necessary to stir them up for good recovery. Although there are no reports of the technique being used for this specific purpose, slight modification of the procedure should provide good material for the study of synchronized zoospore formation.

PRODUCTION OF GAMETANGIA IN LIQUID CULTURE

A method for inducing the semisynchronous development of gametangia in liquid culture has been described by Turian (1963a). Three media have been used that differ mainly in the time required for gametangial formation to begin: G_2Y, containing 6 gm glucose and 0.5 gm Difco-Yeast extract per liter; GCY, containing 3 gm glucose, 0.1 gm Difco-Yeast extract, and 3 gm Difco-Casein hydrolyzate per liter; and synthetic medium B (Machlis, 1953) with 0.5 percent glucose and 0.005 percent yeast extract. The cultures are inoculated with small blocks of mycelium cut from the edge of a 6- to 8-day gametophyte culture on solid Y_pS_s medium. From six to twelve blocks are added to 50 ml of medium in a 125-ml Erlenmeyer flask and the culture incubated on a rotary shaker at 25°C. Each block produces a colony in the form of a dense ball with the hyphal tips close together. The first stages of gametangium formation appear in G_2Y at 2 days, GCY at 3 to 4 days, and in the semisynthetic medium at 4 to 5 days. Only the balls formed by the inoculum blocks are used in experiments because the small "satellite" colonies are often diploid or mixed (i.e., as the result of gamete release and fusion).

Gametangial differentiation is induced by gently washing the mycelium with sterile DS and resuspending it in Petri dishes of the same solution. The time required from this point depends upon the developmental stage of the starting material. If lipid-crown-stage gametangia are used, the process of gamete formation in DS requires approximately 2 hours at 25°C.

Lipid-crown-stage gametangia have also been harvested from cultures grown on solid synthetic medium B supplemented with a mixture of vitamins (Turian, 1963a). Gram quantities (fresh weight) of male or female gametangia can be obtained by scraping the surface of several such cultures and inducing differentiation in DS. Except for the earliest stages, this material has a great advantage over the liquid cultures because only the gametangia themselves are used. The work with the mycelial spheres has all been based on the tacit assumption that the differences observed were due to the type of gametangia produced. In addition to the problem of the relative contribution of mycelium versus gametangia they also required correction for the presence of the agar blocks used to start the colonies. Turian (1964) observed the production of small gametophyte plants, with precocious gametangial development, by female gametes germinated parthenogenetically in 0.033 *M* H_3BO_3 and grown in 0.1 percent yeast extract. It is possible that this method might be developed to eliminate or minimize the problems associated with the block-inoculated liquid cultures.

REFERENCES

BARKSDALE, A. W., 1963: The role of hormone A during sexual conjugation in *Achlya ambisexualis*. *Mycologia*, 55: 627.

BLONDEL, B., and G. TURIAN, 1960: Relation between basophilia and fine structure of cytoplasm in the fungus *Allomyces macrogynus* Em. *J. Biophys. Biochem. Cytol.*, 7: 127.

CANTINO, E. C., 1951: Metabolism and morphogenesis in a new *Blastocladiella. Ant. v. Leeuwenhoek*, 17: 59.

———, 1961: The relationship between biochemical and morphological differentiation in non-filamentous aquatic fungi. *Symp. Soc. Gen. Microbiol.*, 11: 243.

———, 1965: Intracellular distribution of ^{14}C during sporogenesis in *Blastocladiella emersonii*. Effect of light on hemoprotein. *Archiv Mikrobiol.*, 51: 42.

———, and J. S. LOVETT, 1964: Non-filamentous aquatic fungi: model systems for biochemical studies of morphological differentiation. *Adv. Morphogenesis*, 3: 33.

———, ———, L. V. LEAK, and J. LYTHGOE, 1963: The single mitochondrion, fine structure, and germination of the spore of *Blastocladiella emersonii. J. Gen. Microbiol.*, 31: 393.

———, and G. F. TURIAN, 1959: Physiology and development of lower fungi (Phycomycetes). *Ann. Rev. Microbiol.*, 13: 97.

CARLILE, M. J., and L. MACHLIS, 1965: The response of male gametes of *Allomyces* to the sexual hormone sirenin. *Amer. J. Bot.*, 52: 478.

CHAMBERS, T. C., and L. G. WILLOUGHBY, 1964: The fine structure of *Rhizophlyctis rosea*, a soil Phycomycete. *J. Roy. Mic. Soc.*, 83: 355.

DOMNAS, A., and E. C. CANTINO, 1965: The fate of arginine prior to sporogenesis in synchronized ordinary colorless cells of *Blastocladiella emersonii. Biochem. Biophys. Acta*, 97: 300.

EMERSON, R., 1941: An experimental study of the life cycles and taxonomy of *Allomyces. Lloydia*, 4: 77.

———, 1950: Current trends of experimental research on the aquatic Phycomycetes. *Ann. Rev. Microbiol.*, 4: 169.

———, 1954: The biology of the water molds. In D. Rudnick (ed.), *Aspects of Synthesis and Order in Growth*, Princeton University Press, Princeton, N.J., p. 171.

———, 1958: Mycological organization. *Mycologia*, 50: 589.

———, and E. C. CANTINO, 1948: The isolation, growth, and metabolism of *Blastocladia* in pure culture. *Amer. J. Bot.*, 35: 157.

———, and C. M. WILSON, 1954: Interspecific hybrids and the cytogenetics and cytotaxonomy of *Euallomyces. Mycologia*, 46: 393.

FOLEY, J. M., 1958: The occurrence, characteristics, and genetic behavior of albino gametophytes in *Allomyces. Amer. J. Bot.*, 45: 639.

FULLER, M. S., 1962: Growth and development of the water mold *Rhizidiomyces* in pure culture. *Amer. J. Bot.*, 49: 64.

GOLDSTEIN, A., and E. C. CANTINO, 1962: Light-stimulated polysaccharide and protein synthesis by synchronized, single generations of *Blastocladiella emersonii. J. Gen. Microbiol.*, 28: 689.

GRIFFEN, D. H., 1965: The interaction of hydrogen ion, carbon dioxide, and potassium ion in controlling the formation of resistant sporangia in *Blastocladiella emersonii. J. Gen. Microbiol.*, 40: 13.

HORENSTEIN, E. A., and E. C. CANTINO, 1964: An effect of light on glucose uptake by the fungus *Blastocladiella britannica. J. Gen. Microbiol.*, 37: 59.

INGRAHAM, J. L., and R. EMERSON, 1954: Studies of the nutrition and metabolism of the aquatic Phycomycete, *Allomyces. Amer. J. Bot.*, 41: 146.

LE JOHN, H. B., and J. S. LOVETT, 1966: Ribonucleic acid and protein synthesis in *Rhizophlyctis rosea* zoospores. *J. Bacteriol.*, 91: 709.

LOVETT, J. S., 1963: Chemical and physical characterization of "nuclear caps" isolated from *Blastocladiella* zoospores. *J. Bacteriol.*, 85: 1235.

———, and E. C. CANTINO, 1960: The relation between biochemical and morphological differentiation in *Blastocladiella emersonii*. II. Nitrogen metabolism in synchronous cultures. *Amer. J. Bot.*, 47: 550.

MACHLIS, L., 1953: Growth and nutrition of water molds in the subgenus *Euallomyces*. II. Optimal composition of the minimal medium. *Amer. J. Bot.*, 40: 450.

———, 1957: Factors affecting the lag phase

of growth of the filamentous fungus *Allomyces macrogynus. Amer. J. Bot.*, 44: 113.

———, and J. M. CRASEMAN, 1956: Physiological variation between generations and among strains of water molds in the subgenus *Euallomyces. Amer. J. Bot.*, 43: 610.

———, and E. OSSIA, 1953: Maturation of the meiosporangia of *Euallomyces.* I. The effect of cultural conditions. *Amer. J. Bot.*, 40: 358.

MURPHY, SR. M. N., and J. S. LOVETT, 1966: RNA and protein synthesis during zoospore differentiation in synchronized cultures of *Blastocladiella. Dev. Biol.*, 14: 68.

RAPER, J. R., 1951: Sexual hormones in *Achlya. Am. Sci.*, 39: 110.

RENAUD, F. L., and H. SWIFT, 1964: The development of basal bodies and flagella in *Allomyces arbusculus. J. Cell Biol.*, 23: 339.

RITCHIE, D., 1947: The formation and structure of the zoospores in *Allomyces. J. Elisha Mitchell Sci. Soc.*, 63: 168.

SPARROW, F. K., 1960: *Aquatic Phycomycetes.* 2nd ed., 1187 pp. University of Michigan Press, Ann Arbor, Mich.

TURIAN, G., 1960: Déficiencies du métabolisme oxydatif et différenciation sexuelle chez *Allomyces* et *Neurospora.* Activité d'une DPN-deshydrogénase lactique chez *Allomyces. Path. Microbiol.*, 23: 687.

———, 1961: Cycle glyoxylique, transaminase alanine-glyoxylate et différenciation sexuelle chez *Allomyces* et *Neurospora. Path. Microbiol.*, 24: 819.

———, 1962: Cytoplasmic differentiation and dedifferentiation in the fungus *Allomyces. Protoplasma*, 54: 323.

———, 1963a: Synthèse différentielle d'acide ribonucléique et différenciation sexuelle chez l'*Allomyces. Dev. Biol.*, 6: 61.

———, 1963b: Sur le méchanisme de l'induction isocitratasique chez *Allomyces* et *Neurospora. Path. Microbiol.*, 26: 553.

———, 1964: Compléments sur la morphogenèse normale et anormale de l'*Allomyces. Bull. Soc. Bot. Suisse*, 74: 242.

———, 1965: Différenciation biochimique d'*Allomyces:* bases nucléiques libres et composition de l'acide ribonucléique. *Path. Microbiol.*, 28: 58.

Cellular Slime Molds*

By James H. Gregg

INTRODUCTION

The cellular slime molds (Acrasiales) provide experimental material for a variety of approaches to problems of developmental physiology. The nature of this organism compels the use of bacteriological procedures at the earlier stages in its development. At the later multicellular stages they may profitably be handled as single units or small groups of pseudoplasmodia.

It is the object of this report to describe the technique of manipulating slime molds such that they may be analyzed by any procedure desired. Thus with few exceptions specific analytical techniques have not been described in detail.

Individual slime mold pseudoplasmodia are of optimal size for the application of ultramicromethodology. The capability of analyzing single or small numbers of pseudoplasmodia is of distinct advantage in that the problem of collecting large amounts of material which is synchronized in developmental stage may be avoided. Also the problem of obtaining material uncontaminated with bacteria, dead cells, excess isotopes, etc. is considerably decreased with the selection of small numbers of pseudoplasmodia.

While it is beyond the scope of this article to present a course in the fundamentals of ultramicrotechniques the author highly recommends the reviews by Glick (1961, 1963) and Kirk (1950). Furthermore, the commercial availability of ultramicroequipment enhances the investigator's opportunity to work at this level.

CULTURE PROCEDURES

Bonner (1947)

In this conventional method of culturing slime molds 15 mm × 90 mm Pyrex or plastic Petri plates are prepared with a medium of the following formula:

Bacto-peptone	10.0 gm
Bacto-dextrose	10.0 gm
$Na_2HPO_4 \cdot 12H_2O$	0.96 gm
KH_2PO_4	1.45 gm
Bacto-agar	20.0 gm
Distilled H_2O	1,000 ml

This medium which is buffered at about pH 6.6 provides nutrient for *Escherischia coli*, the bacteria upon which

* This investigation was supported in part by Public Health Service Research Career Programs Award 5-K_3-HD-15, 780, and Research Grant GM-10138 from the National Institutes of Health.

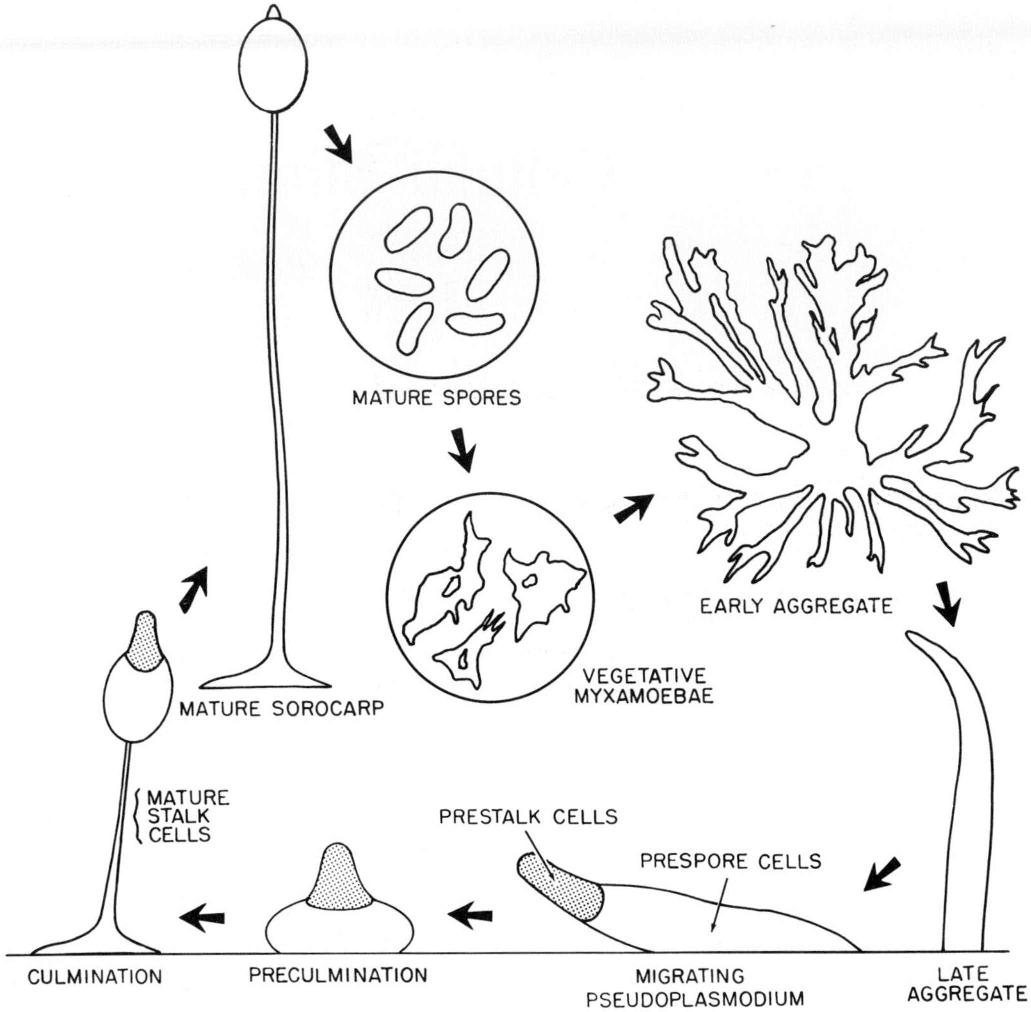

FIG. 1. The stages in the development of *Dictyostelium discoideum*.

the vegetative myxamoebae depend for food. Although a variety of bacteria will sustain growth, *E. coli* or *Aerobacter aerogenes* are the common species employed (Raper, 1937).

The mature spores of a slime mold and bacteria are transferred with a bacteriological loop to the agar plates which should have a moist but not excessively wet surface. The cultures are maintained preferably in a controlled temperature-humidity chamber. The optimal temperature range is 22°–24°C with the relative humidity within the chamber at approximately 70–75 percent for *Dictyostelium discoideum*. *Dictyostelium mucoroides* and *Polysphondylium violaceum* seem to thrive on a slightly lower humidity.

Germination of the spores occurs and the vegetative myxamoebae increase by binary fission (Bonner, 1944). Aggregation begins after approximately 36–48 hours of growth followed by the appearance of migrating pseudoplasmodia. Cultures prepared in this fashion are not closely synchronized and consequently will be composed of a variety of developmental stages. Culmination and the formation of mature sorocarps usually occur between 48 and 72 hours (Fig. 1).

Shaffer (1957)

Escherischia coli or *A. aerogenes* grown on nutrient agar are spread in a thin layer on nonnutrient agar containing 0.5 percent NaCl (pH 6.5). The plates are then inoculated with *Dictyostelium* or *Polysphondylium* spores. Growth of the myxamoebae under these conditions continues until the bacteria are exhausted at which time they enter the morphogenetic phase of development.

Gerisch (1959)

This method consists of growing *D. discoideum* in liquid media composed of 0.0167 *M* phosphate buffer (pH 6.0) and washed *E. coli* or *A. aerogenes.* The bacterial cells are present in a concentration of 1.0×10^{10} cells per milliliter of medium. The cultures are inoculated with mature slime mold spores, aerated and shaken at $23° \pm 0.5°C$. Under these conditions synchronous growth of the myxamoebae results. Myxamoebae cultured by this technique may be washed and plated out on nonnutrient agar to continue development.

Hohl and Raper (1963)

It is possible to culture certain strains of *Polysphondylium pallidum* on a complex liquid medium, the components of which may be obtained by referring to the above report. The development of such a medium provides the opportunity to culture slime molds in the absence of bacteria. This is advantageous in physiological or biochemical analyses in that interference from bacterial contamination can be avoided. It also provides a future opportunity to detect and study nutritional mutants.

Special Conditions

In the event that it is desirable to mark or label cells in order to trace their movements within a cell mass two methods are available.

LABELING WITH VITAL DYES

Dictyostelium discoideum vegetative myxamoebae have been stained with vital dyes such as Nile blue sulfate, Bismarck brown, and neutral red (Bonner, 1952). This is accomplished by suspending the cells in H_2O with the dye. The cells are placed on nonnutrient agar to continue development. Eventually migrating pseudoplasmodia appear which retain intense staining in the prestalk cells although the prespore cells alter the dyes to relatively colorless forms. Thus, the prestalk areas are delineated from the prespore regions. The colored prestalk areas may be used in grafting experiments on noncolored migrating pseudoplasmodia.

LABELING WITH ISOTOPES

Nutrient agar plates are prepared in the conventional fashion. An additional thin layer of nutrient agar containing 1.0–10.0 μc tritiated thymidine per milliliter agar or other isotopes desired is poured on the surface of the plates. Approximately 8 ml of isotope agar are required to cover the surface of one 15-mm $\times$ 90-mm plate completely. The plates are inoculated with bacteria and slime mold spores in the conventional manner.

The vegetative myxamoebae become labeled probably both from contact with the agar and from ingesting bacteria which have incorporated thymidine. Cells labeled in this fashion may be used in experiments involving scintillation spectrometers or other counting devices or in autoradiography.

MUTANT PRODUCTION

Sussman and Sussman (1953) described methods for the production and isolation of mutants. The steps in one of their procedures are as follows:

1. The slime molds are grown from single clone isolates on bacteria on nutrient agar medium.
2. The vegetative myxamoebae or mature spores are harvested and distributed on nutrient agar plates. The cells numbering 2–6 × 10^5 per plate are irradiated with a GE germicidal lamp at 10.5 cm distance for 90 seconds. Irradiation of this intensity resulted in 99.99 percent death.
3. Immediately following irradiation the plates are covered with a thin layer of bacteria from a broth culture and incubated.
4. The plates are scanned after 4–5 days growth for plaques which are abnormal.
5. Plaques which appeared abnormal are then plated clonally for several generations in order to assess the stability of the variant.
6. Aberrant forms which formed spores may be lyophilized for preservation although aggregateless and similar forms have to be maintained in the log phase of growth by transferring each week or every 10 days.

HARVESTING TISSUE FOR ANALYSES

Vegetative Myxamoebae

The myxamoebae are removed from the culture dishes by gently rubbing the agar surfaces with a glass rod in the presence of 5–10 ml of distilled H_2O or selected buffer. The bacteria-myxamoebae suspension is filtered into 15-ml centrifuge tubes through a small funnel covered with 93-μ mesh nylon screen (Nitex)[1] or simply a thin screen of absorbent cotton. This procedure removes any chips of agar or clumps of bacteria which may be present. The myxamoebae may be separated from their bacterial associate by two gentle centrifugation washes. The bacteria which remain in the supernate are conveniently removed with a fine-tipped pipette and a filter pump. Not more than two Petri plate cultures should be transferred into one centrifuge tube as an excess of cells will prevent a good separation of bacteria. The process may be conducted using reagents around 10°C and a refrigerated centrifuge if desired.

Myxamoebae harvested in this manner may be used for biochemical analyses or aliquots may be transferred to nonnutrient agar plates to continue development. Cells obtained in this fashion may also be used to extract and assay acrasin or rate substance. This entire procedure has recently been described in detail by Bonner *et al.* (1966).

Migrating Pseudoplasmodia or Preculmination Stages

Any stage in the development of the cellular slime molds may be harvested in mass by the procedures described for vegetative myxamoebae. However due to the size and shape of the multicellular stages the initial filtration through Nitex must be eliminated for obvious reasons.

It is desirable, however, in certain studies to utilize single or small numbers of pseudoplasmodia. Individual pseudoplasmodia intended for immediate biochemical analyses may be picked up by

[1] Tobler, Ernst and Traber, Inc., 71 Murray St., New York 7, N.Y.

means of a hair loop cemented to a small glass tube. They may be transferred into a centrifuge tube filled with buffer or directly to the desired container for further preparation or analysis.

If it is necessary to remove individual pseudoplasmodia from the agar with the least possible disturbance the following procedure is recommended: Clear away the debris from around the pseudoplasmodium with a fine spatula making certain that the slime track is cut a few millimeters from the pseudoplasmodium. Cut out a 5- to 10-mm square of agar bearing the pseudoplasmodium and transfer it to a beaker filled with distilled water or buffer. Slowly immerse the agar square and allow the surface tension to remove the pseudoplasmodium. The pseudoplasmodium which now floats upon the surface may be picked up by slowly raising a small disc of fine-grained filter paper held by fine-tipped forceps until the paper and the pseudoplasmodium are engaged. All procedures must be conducted with sufficient speed to prevent drying of the pseudoplasmodium. This method is of value in transferring a pseudoplasmodium into the chamber of a microrespirometer and subsequently in providing a means of recovering it for further analyses (Gregg, 1950).

A convenient way to transfer individual pseudoplasmodia to another culture dish for transectioning or grafting involves the use of a 25- to 30-mm section of 5-mm diameter thin-walled brass tubing (a cork borer provides suitable stock). The brass tube is connected to a short length of gum rubber tubing (3.0 mm inside diameter) which serves as a mouth tube. Using a stereomicroscope at low magnification (3 ×–6 ×) a pseudoplasmodium is selected, and the surrounding debris removed before the brass tube is punched over the slime mold through the agar to the bottom of the dish. The agar plug bearing the cell mass is raised by tilting the brass tube at an acute angle while still embedded in the agar plate and exerting a very slight negative pressure through the mouth tube. The plug may then be transferred to another Petri plate and discharged by a slight increase in pressure on the mouth tube. The humidity is maintained by a moist piece of filter paper covering about one-half of the bottom of the plate.

The isotope-labeled pseudoplasmodia may be harvested by any of the methods described for nonlabeled slime molds. There are special methods utilized, however, to obtain individual pseudoplasmodia as free from bacteria or isotope contamination as possible without actually subjecting them to a washing procedure. The first of these methods involves transferring approximately 18-mm discs of isotope agar bearing 24- to 36-hour-old myxamoebae to identical-sized holes prepared in nonnutrient plates (Gregg and Bronsweig, 1956). These discs are cut with a brass tool or a test tube. The slime molds are then replaced in the incubator. The pseudoplasmodia which subsequently migrate onto the nonnutrient agar may be removed from the relatively uncontaminated surface with the smaller brass tool. This method is of particular advantage with *D. discoideum* which does not rise above the surface of the agar prior to culmination as opposed to the tendency of *D. mucoroides* or *P. violaceum* to soar during the later stages of migration. The tendency of *D. mucoroides* to rise above the agar surface enables one to harvest relatively uncontaminated pseudoplasmodia with a pair of fine-tipped forceps which are used to grab and break the stalk several millimeters from the cell mass (Fig. 2). This type of transfer is preferably made by pouring the isotope agar in one compartment of a divided 15-mm × 90-mm plastic Petri plate. In order to harvest the pseudoplasmodia the bottom half of a 10-mm × 35-mm plastic Petri plate containing nonnutrient agar is placed in the other compartment. The pseudoplas-

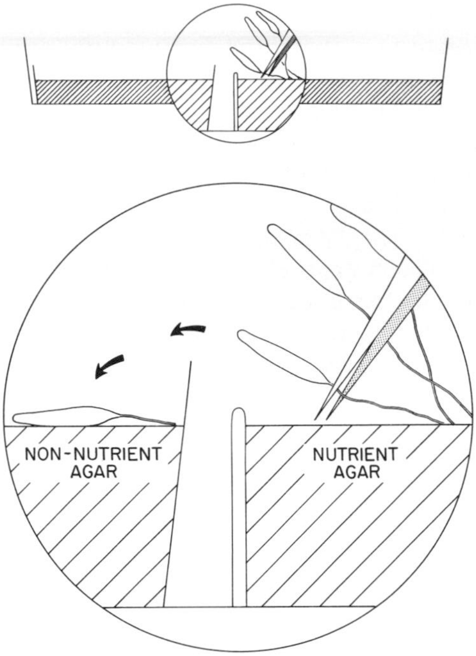

FIG. 2. The technique of transferring *D. mucoroides* migrating pseudoplasmodia from the culture media to a nonnutrient agar surface.

modia may then be transferred with the forceps directly to the nonnutrient agar. The compartmented plate alleviates the necessity of transferring the slime molds from one large Petri plate to another with attendant problems of drying and focusing. The labeled pseudoplasmodia are transferred a second time if necessary by the small brass tool. The entire operation is facilitated by pouring all agar plates to the same depth if possible which eliminates subsequent problems of focusing the microscope.

Culminating or Mature Sorocarp Stages

Slime molds at these stages may be harvested in mass as described for the previous stages. The spores and stalks may be harvested separately by the following technique:

1. The mature spores are collected by carefully sweeping a bent glass rod across the culture dish on a level with the spore masses but sufficiently high to avoid contact with the surface of the plate (Fig. 3). The spores readily adhere to the rod and may be transferred to a centrifuge tube filled with buffer for subsequent concentration.

2. The stalks which remain are washed from the plates with buffer and placed in a beaker. At this point a propeller-shaped beater approximately 20 mm in diameter constructed from a nichrome wire and driven by a stirring motor is used to agitate the stalk masses to dislodge any remaining spores or clumps of bacteria. The mixture is then poured into a 25-mm diameter glass tube the opposite end of which is covered with 93 μ Nitex. The spores and bacteria are eliminated through the filter but the stalks are retained on the nylon mesh. They may be cleaned further by a jet of buffer from a wash bottle or agitated in a beaker of buffer. The contamination from spores or bacteria in such preparations is very low. The stalks may then be conveniently transferred to a desired container by carefully removing the Nitex which is held in place by rubber bands.

TRANSECTING AND GRAFTING PSEUDOPLASMODIA

The cellular slime molds have an unusual capacity to regulate (Raper, 1940; Gregg, 1965). Consequently isolated masses of prestalk cells or prespore cells will reorganize within a few hours and subsequently form fruiting bodies. Under these circumstances each isolate must differentiate the missing cell type in order to complete development. Thus, the opportunity arises to study cell differentiation at intervals during regulation of the isolates. Reciprocal grafting may also be effected between isotope-labeled and normal migrating pseudoplasmodia or between two different species (Bonner and Adams, 1958).

Microknives for transecting purposes are constructed from stainless steel insect pins or wire by grinding the blade with a small hand grinder under the stereomicroscope. The dimensions of the knives may be determined by reference to Fig. 4.

Individual migrating pseudoplasmodia either labeled with isotope or unlabeled are transferred with the small brass tool to a humid Petri plate. An important step in achieving clean cuts and discrete masses of tissue depends upon having the slime molds at a temperature of not more than 23°C. They also may be chilled for a few minutes in a refrigerator before transection. When a transection is made the fragment

FIG. 3. The techniques of harvesting stalks and spores separately.

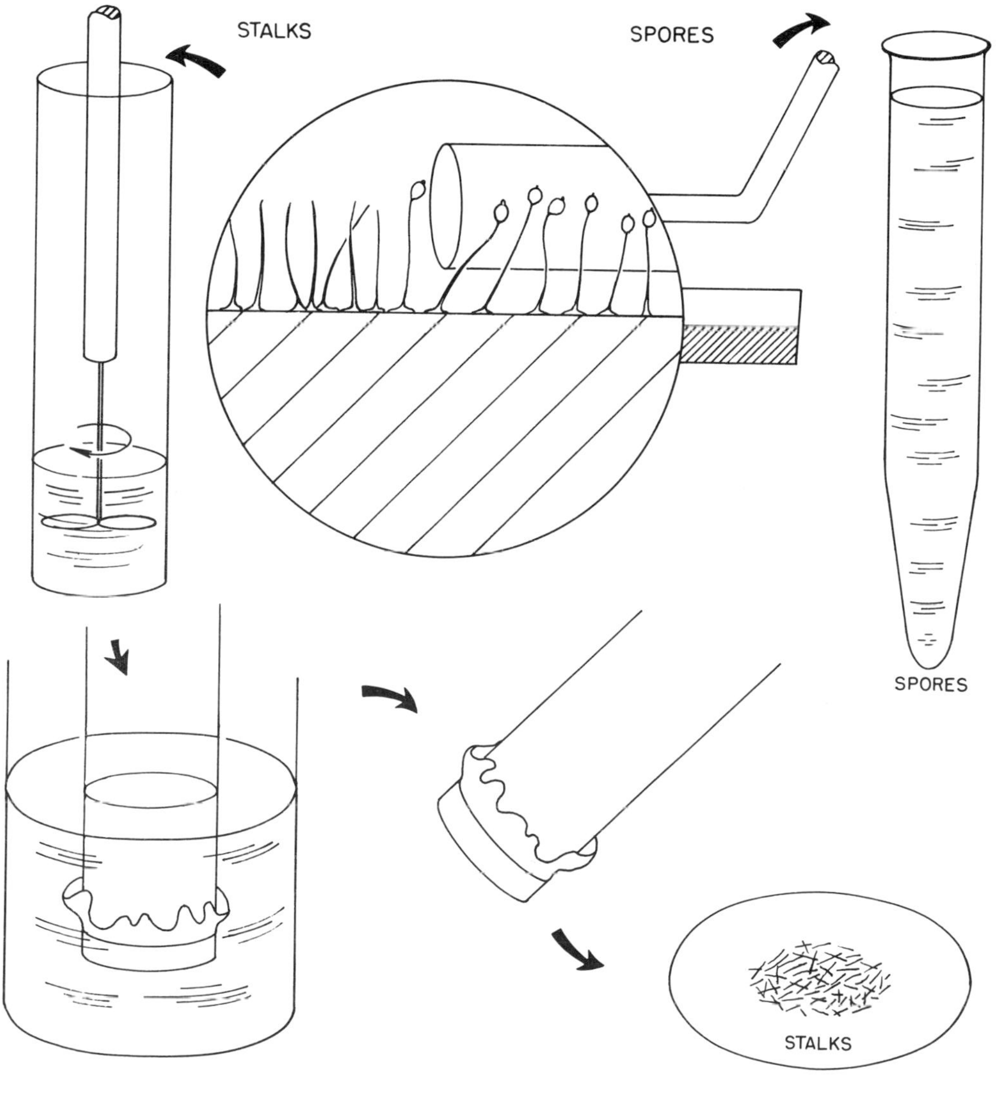

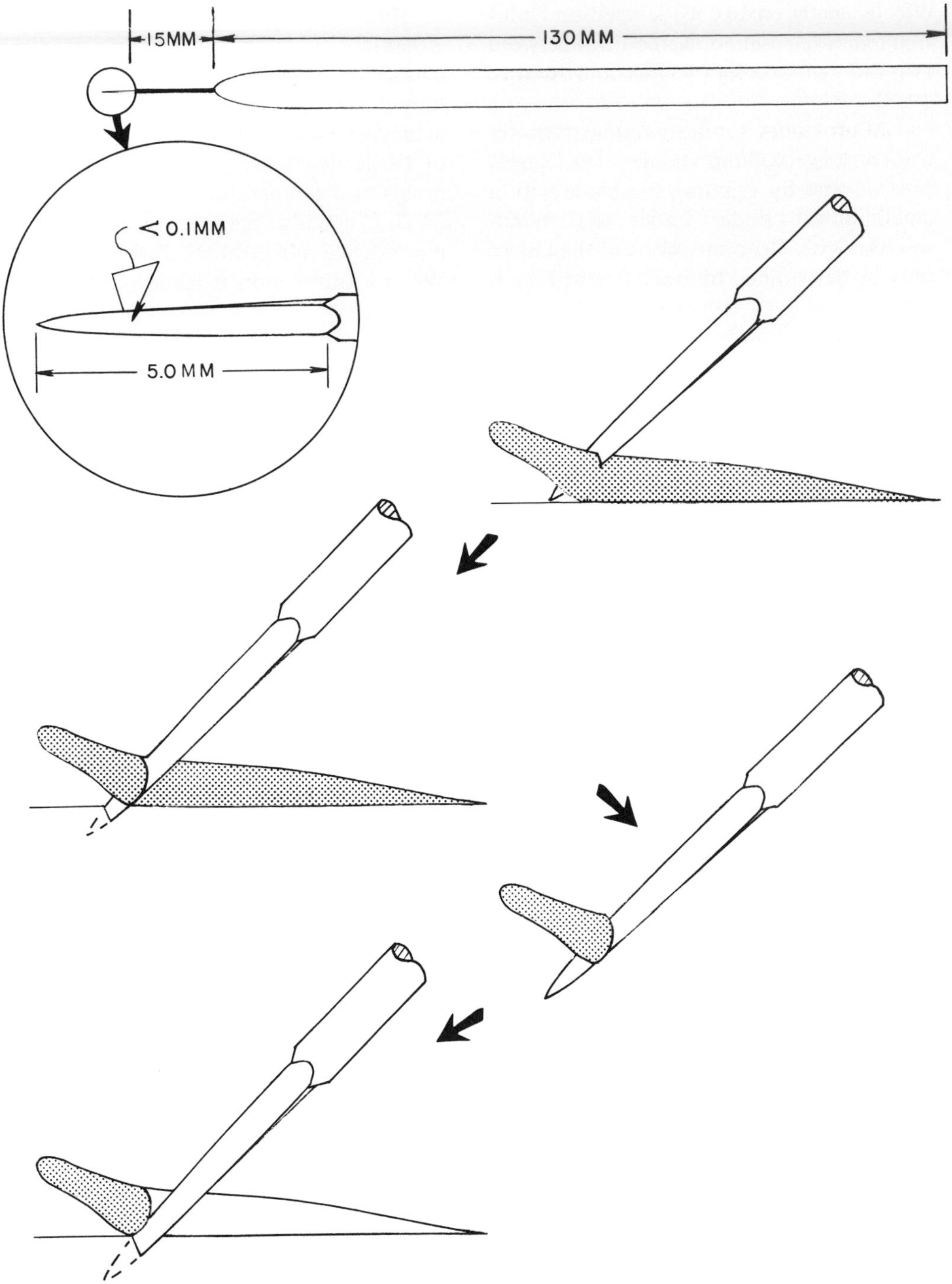

FIG. 4. The technique of transecting and grafting fragments of migrating pseudoplasmodia.

may be gently pushed aside with the broad edge of the blade to remove it from the proximity of the other portion. By proper manual manipulations a fragment may be picked up on the knife in order to transfer it to another region (Fig. 4). The release of the fragment is effected by continuing the knife downward into the agar which results in the fragment remaining on the agar surface. The knife is then withdrawn beneath the agar surface and does not come into contact with the cells again.

When making reciprocal grafts it is of importance to have the pairs of pseudoplasmodia within one Petri plate and adjacent to each other to avoid unnecessary adjustments during the course of the transfer. Reciprocal grafting is carried out by removing a fragment from pseudoplasmodium A and transferring it to the agar a few millimeters from pseudoplasmodium B (Fig. 5). The fragment transected from pseudoplasmodium B is then transferred and grafted to A. In this instance the empty side of the knife is brought to bear on the cut surface of A and the knife again manipulated through the agar to release the fragment (Fig. 4). The fragment resting near pseudoplasmodium B is pushed gently into place. It is also important to avoid excessive trauma or disturbance of the graft or host as this will tend to effect multiple fruiting body formation rather than the single unit desired.

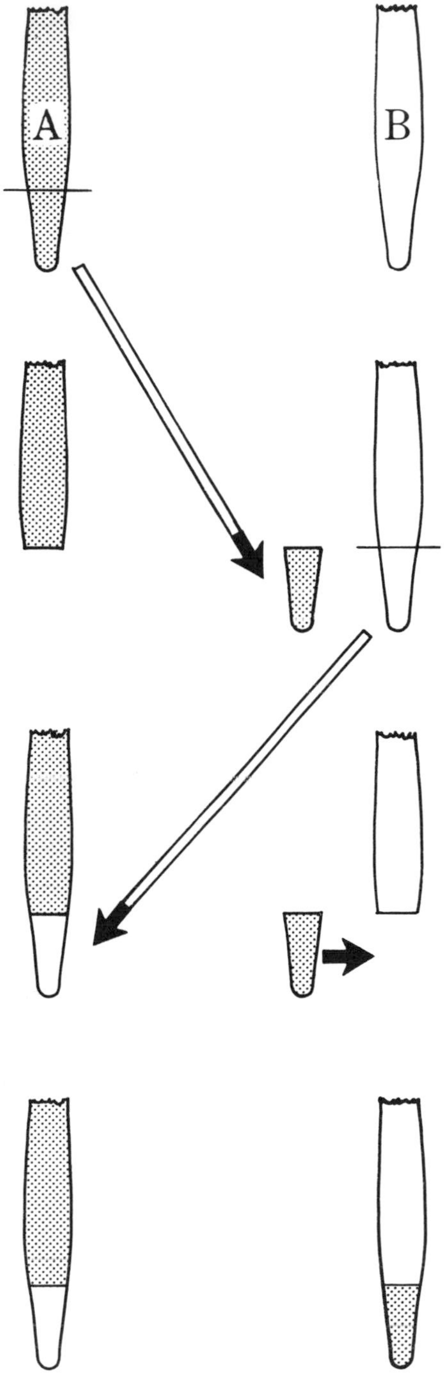

FIG. 5. The procedure followed in effecting reciprocal grafts between two migrating pseudoplasmodia (see text).

DETERMINING THE SIZE OF TISSUE SAMPLES

The slime mold pseudoplasmodia have a very wide range in size. Consequently it is impossible to analyze individual or small numbers of pseudoplasmodia with the assurance that the tissue sample sizes are identical. There are several methods by which the sizes of samples of vegetative myxamoebae or pseudoplasmodia may be determined.

Ultramicrobalances

Commercial ultramicrobalances[2] are available having capacities to 10.0 gm with accuracies of ± 0.1–$0.2\ \mu g$. Individual *Dictyostelium* pseudoplasmodia range up to 9.0 μg dry weight (Bonner, 1952). Thus, they may easily be weighed with such balances. Tared platinum or aluminum pans are used to hold the samples for drying and subsequent weighing.

A relatively economical ultramicrobalance may also be fabricated using commercially available quartz helices. These quartz helices must be selected according to the expected range of weights of samples; for example one helix is prepared to weigh in the range 1.0 to 1,000 μg. The helices must be enclosed within a glass tube or other similar housing and the extension of the loaded balance may be determined with a reading microscope or cathetometer. An elaborate discussion of ultramicrobalances is beyond the scope of this article; however, the reader may refer to Kirk and Schaffer (1948) and Kirk (1950) for descriptions of various types of quartz balances and their manipulation.

It is of obvious advantage to utilize very light-weight pans regardless of the type of balance which is utilized. Pans may be made from aluminum foil or cellophane or with extremely thin films obtained by pouring a small quantity of diluted collodion or nylon solution onto distilled water in a large shallow tray. The film may then be picked up on a flat piece of glass and cut with a cork borer into desired sizes. Aluminum pans may be conveniently cut with a compass equipped with a fragment of razor blade to cut the discs.

[2] Cahn Electrobalance, Mettler Ultra-microbalance, and Worden Fused Quartz Microbalance.

Total Kjeldahl Nitrogen

The ultramicromethod described originally by Brüel *et al.* (1946), and modified by Gregg (1950) is designed to determine total nitrogen (N) in the microgram range with an accuracy of 0.005 μg N. The reagents necessary in conducting these analyses are listed below but the details of the procedure must be obtained by reference to the above articles and from Fig. 6.

REAGENTS

1. Digestion fluid	
$CuSO_4 \cdot 5H_2O$	1.0 gm
K_2SO_4	10.0 gm
Sucrose	0.2 gm
Conc. H_2SO_4	5.0 ml
Distilled H_2O	100.0 ml final volume
2. Catalyst	
Conc. H_2SO_4	1.0 ml
Selenium	10.0 mg
3. H_2SO_4	0.01 *N*
4. NaOH	0.01 *N*
5. NaOH	9.00 *N*

Individual *D. discoideum* migrating pseudoplasmodia have been analyzed which ranged from 0.4 to 1.5 μg total nitrogen. Thus, the sizes of pseudoplasmodia permit analysis by this procedure. Protein nitrogen may also be determined provided the sample is large enough to fall within the range of the method. This, of course, necessitates the precipitation of protein from homogenized slime molds by the usual techniques and reagents. In addition a method which has not been tried in this laboratory on slime molds but which appears to be ideal for determining total protein in the millimicrogram range has been described by Nayyar and Glick (1954).

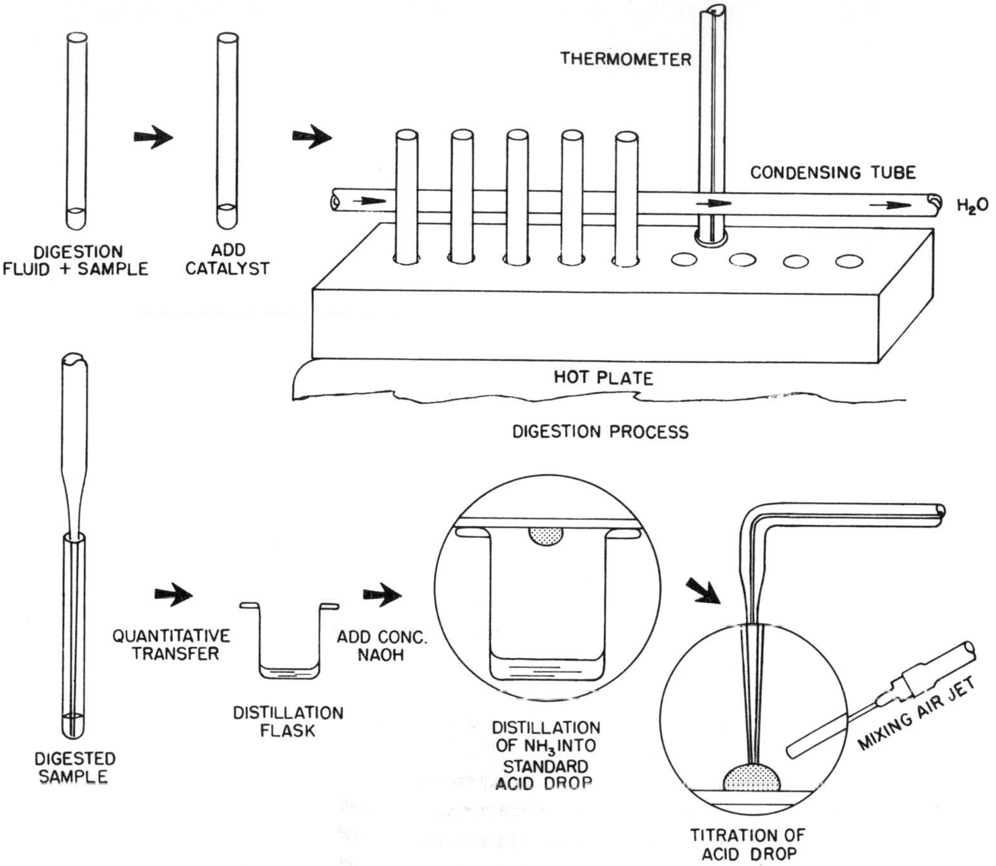

FIG. 6. The major steps in the micro-Kjeldahl analysis for total nitrogen in single pseudoplasmodia.

The Aliquot Method

It is possible to take aliquots of vegetative myxamoebae and plate them out on nonnutrient agar. The dry weight, total nitrogen, etc. of an aliquot may be determined or the cells may be counted with a hemocytometer. The slime molds are allowed to continue development. Consequently, if one establishes that reasonably synchronous development has occurred, the aliquots may be harvested as each desired stage is reached for specific analyses.

IMMUNOLOGICAL TECHNIQUES

Immunological techniques have been brought to bear on a variety of developmental problems in cellular slime molds (Gregg, 1964). The following procedures are utilized in this laboratory in preparing injection antigens and antisera.

Antigen Preparation and Antisera Production

The cells may be harvested by the techniques previously described. Each developmental stage is collected separately, lyophilized, and homogenized with a mortar and pestle in 0.5 percent NaCl or phosphate buffer. The homogenate is maintained in a relatively concentrated state by utilizing the least amount of buffer necessary in homogenization. An aliquot of the homogenate is used to determine the total N of the entire volume of antigen. The total N may also be calculated satisfactorily for these purposes by determining the dry weight of the aliquot. The total N of *D. discoideum* migrating pseudoplasmodia may be determined by the following calculation:

Total N in aliquot
  = μg dry weight of aliquot × 0.094[3]

When each stage of development has been harvested, homogenized, etc., the antigens may be diluted so that they now contain equal amounts of total N per milliliter. The antigens may be combined into one injection antigen if desired and stored in small ampules at −15°C. It is convenient to dilute the antigens so that 0.5–1.0 ml is given per injection to an adult male rabbit. Each rabbit is given nine or ten injections. The total antigen injected per rabbit may range from 1.0 to 20.0 mg total N (Gregg, 1960, 1961). The necessary amounts are injected alternating intravenous with subcutaneous routes. Other injection schedules utilizing Freund's adjuvant are equally satisfactory (Sonneborn *et al.*, 1964).

Preinjection serum and antiserum are obtained by heart puncture. The antiserum is collected 5 days after the final injections. All sera are allowed to stand for an hour at room temperature, the clots ringed, refrigerated overnight, and centrifuged to separate the sera from the red cells. The sera are usually heated at 56°C for 30 minutes to destroy complement before storing in a deep freeze at −15°C.

[3] 0.094 = μg N per microgram dry weight of migrating pseudoplasmodia (Gregg *et al.*, 1954).

Fluorescent Antibody Preparation

In conducting research on the cellular slime molds it is often necessary to distinguish one cell type from another. One of the techniques which effect a sharp distinction between the prestalk and prespore cells in a pseudoplasmodium involves the use of fluorescent antiserum (Takeuchi, 1963; Gregg, 1965).

The process of producing fluorescein isothiocyanate labeled antiserum and normal serum is described in the following paragraphs as it is practiced in this laboratory.

REAGENTS

1. Tampon solution

1.0 *M* sodium carbonate	1.0 volume
1.0 *M* acetic acid	1.0 volume
Distilled water	23.0 volumes

2. Aqueous methanol

99.9 percent methanol	3.0 volumes
Distilled water	4.0 volumes

3. 1.0 *M* carbonate-bicarbonate buffer at pH 9.0

4. Fluorescein isothiocyanate[4]

GLOBULIN PRECIPITATION AND CONJUGATION (DUBERT *et al.*, 1953)

1. Cool all reagents and sera in an ice bath to 0°C or lower and maintain throughout precipitation.

2. Place 2.0 volumes of serum in a 50-ml plastic centrifuge tube (author has found 7.5–8.0 ml serum to be optimal in such tubes). Add 1.0 volume of Tampon solution.

3. Add slowly while stirring 7.0 volumes of aqueous methanol.

4. Cap tubes and wait 30 minutes before centrifuging for 20 minutes at 3,000 *g* in refrigerated centrifuge.

5. Discard supernate; precipitate con-

[4] Baltimore Biological Laboratory.

tains gamma globulin and certain other fractions.

6. Redissolve globulin in 2.0 volumes of 1.0 percent NaCl. (This returns globulin to original concentration in serum.)

7. Adjust pH to 8.0.

8. Precipitate again following steps 1–6.

9. Redissolve globulin in 1.70 volumes of 1.0 percent NaCl.

10. Dry and weigh 100–200 μl globulin solution. Compute dry weight of total globulin available.

11. Add 0.3 volume carbonate-bicarbonate buffer to globulin solution.

12. Weigh out 0.0125–0.025 mg fluorescein isothiocyanate per milligram of globulin (Griffin *et al.*, 1961). The average value (0.0188 mg FITC) is used in this laboratory.

13. Place globulin solution in 250-ml Erlenmeyer flask. Chill in dry ice-methyl cellosolve bath to initiate ice crystal formation (Marshall *et al.*, 1958).

14. Add fluorescein isothiocyanate and magnetic stirring bar. Mount in 5°C refrigerator and slowly stir magnetically for 15–18 hours.

15. Centrifuge for 20 minutes at 3,000 *g* to remove particulate matter resulting from conjugation process.

16. Transfer supernate to a G-25 Fine Sephadex[5] column constructed and utilized as described by Peters (1963). This process separates the conjugated globulin from the nonincorporated fluorescein isothiocyanate. Store the labeled sera in 1- to 5-ml glass ampules in a −15°C freezer.

[5] Pharmacia Fine Chemicals, Inc.

HISTOLOGICAL PROCEDURE

The following procedure has been found to be successful in this laboratory for both fluorescent antibody and autoradiographic studies of pseudoplasmodia.

Fixation

The plugs of agar bearing whole pseudoplasmodia, reorganized fragments, etc. are dropped gently into fixative. The slime molds are teased from the agar with microknives or sharp probes and if necessary small bits of debris, slime track, etc. are removed from the cell masses.

Reagents

Carnoy's fixative (fix for 48–72 hours)

Glacial acetic acid	1.0 volume
Chloroform	3.0 volumes
Absolute ethyl alcohol	6.0 volumes

Dehydration Schedule (Johansen, 1940)

Transferring the pseudoplasmodia from one solution to another is accomplished by placing them in a 10-mm deep × 15-mm wide glass tube one end of which is covered with 93-μ Nitex (Table 1).

TABLE 1. SOLUTIONS IN VOLUMES

	SOLUTION NUMBER					
	1	2	3	4*	5	6
Distilled H_2O	50	30	15	0	0	0
Ethyl alcohol, 95%	40	50	50	45	0	0
Tertiary butyl alcohol	10	20	35	55	75	100
Ethyl alcohol, 100%	0	0	0	0	25	0
Hours dehydration	1.0	20.0	1.0	1.5	1.5	20.0

* Add erythrosin to solution 4 to color slime molds to facilitate paraffin embedding.

Paraffin Embedding

1. Following the final dehydration (solution 6) transfer the pseudoplasmodia to a solution composed of equal volumes of tertiary butyl alcohol and paraffin oil for 2 hours.

2. Transfer pseudoplasmodia to small glass dishes (18-mm deep × 22-mm wide) on to hard (60°–62°C) paraffin. Remove excess tertiary butyl alcohol paraffin oil solution.

3. Place in oven at 63°C. As soon as the paraffin is melted, discard and add fresh paraffin. Four additional changes of paraffin are made over a 24-hour period.

4. Maintain paraffin containing pseudoplasmodia at 63°C by placing in a Petri dish of water warmed over an alcohol lamp. Transfer each pseudoplasmodium to a plastic embedding dish and orient. The paraffin in the upper layer of the embedding dish is melted by standing in the Petri dish bath. The orientation of the pseudoplasmodium is accomplished with the aid of a hot needle and a stereomicroscope on a swinging arm stand.

5. The paraffin blocks are trimmed and the pseudoplasmodia sectioned at 5 μ.

Hydration and Staining

The paraffin sections are prepared for various staining procedures by the steps shown in Table 2 (Davenport, 1960).

The hydrated slides are now ready for staining with fluorescent antiserum, autoradiography, or other staining procedures.

HISTOLOGICAL STUDIES

Staining with Fluorescent Antisera

VEGETATIVE MYXAMOEBAE

Vegetative myxamoebae may be removed directly from a culture dish using a small quantity of Bonner's solution and a fine-tipped pipette. The cells are transferred to a Number one 22-mm × 50-mm cover slip which is then confined to a humid Petri dish for several minutes or until the cells reach the aggregation phase. During this period the myxamoebae make contact with the glass surface. The cover slip-myxamoebae preparation is then fixed for 1–3 minutes in 99.9 percent methyl alcohol which is chilled in a dry ice-methyl cellosolve bath (Takeuchi, 1963; Gregg, 1965). The preparation is dried for a few minutes in air. The following procedure is then used in the fluorescent staining:

1. Using a micropipette place 50–200 μl fluorescent serum on the cells.

2. Transfer into a humid Petri plate and cover plate to obscure light.

3. Wait 10 minutes.

4. Rinse off serum with phosphate buffered NaCl (pH 7.3) and place in Copeland jar in buffer and maintain in darkness for 10 minutes.

TABLE 2.

	SOLUTION NUMBER								
	1	2	3	4	5	6	7	8	9
Xylene	100%	100%							
Ethyl alcohol			100%	100%	95%	95%	70%	70%	
Distilled H_2O									100%
Time in minutes	4	4	2	2	2	2	2	2	

Buffer components:

NaCl	7.6500 gm
Na_2HPO_4	1.2688 gm
NaH_2PO_4	0.1000 gm
KH_2PO_4	0.2113 gm
Distilled H_2O	1,000 ml

5. Mount preparation on microscope in buffer or a solution composed of 9 parts glycerine to 1 part of buffered NaCl.

6. Examine with microscope equipped for fluorescent microscopy.

PSEUDOPLASMODIA

The histological sections of pseudoplasmodia are transferred to buffered NaCl following the terminal step in the rehydration process described previously. The excess buffer is quickly removed from the slides by touching the edges with filter paper. The staining technique with fluorescent sera is identical to that described for the vegetative myxamoebae.

Autoradiography

The slides bearing isotope-labeled sections are treated with 0.2 *N* perchloric acid for 1 minute and then washed in running tap H_2O for 20 hours. The slides are now ready to be subjected to autoradiographic procedures according to conventional methods (Prescott, 1964). In this laboratory Kodak NTB liquid emulsion[6] was employed. An exposure of 2–3 months was required using this emulsion on histological sections of pseudoplasmodia which had been cultured on agar containing 10 μc isotope per milliliter.

SCINTILLATION SPECTROSCOPY

The slime molds may be harvested according to the previous instructions. A sample of tissue is treated with 0.2 *N* perchloric acid for 30 minutes at 2°C to remove the nonincorporated isotope. The samples are washed five times with buffer to remove the perchloric acid. At this point the samples are transferred to small discs of black combustion paper, dried, and weighed on an ultramicrobalance. After weighing they are wrapped in No. 6471-Q25 black sample wrappers.[7] Each sample is transferred to a Thomas-Ogg Oxygen Combustion Flask[7] (Oliverio *et al.*, 1962) and ignited with a Thomas-Ogg Safety Igniter.[7] This process converted the tritiated materials to tritiated H_2O. The water is then frozen to the bottom of the combustion flask by immersing the lower surface into a dry ice-methyl cellosolve bath; 15 ml of dioxane is added to the flask and 5 ml aliquots of the tritiated H_2O-dioxane mixture placed in scintillation vials containing 10 ml scintillation fluid. The scintillation fluid contains dioxane as the solvent. The investigator will, of course, have to establish through adequate controls that the isotope is recovered during the combustion process and that corrections are made for quenching, etc.

Mature spores cultured on agar containing 1.0 μc tritiated uridine and processed as described above averaged 13,000 counts per minute per milligram dry weight; amino acids averaged 82,000 counts per minute per milligram dry weight.

Another simple way to prepare tissue samples for counting is to dissolve the perchloric acid-treated, buffer-washed, weighed samples in base without combustion. The organic base, Hyamine,[8] is commonly used. The dissolved sample is then mixed with 10 volumes of a toluene-

[6] Rochester, New York.

[7] Arthur H. Thomas Company.

[8] Packard Instrument Corporation.

based scintillation fluid and counted by conventional methods.

OPTICAL PREPARATIONS WITH LIVING CELLS AND PHOTOGRAPHIC TECHNIQUES

It has been found advantageous in examining living vegetative or aggregating myxamoebae to transfer them in Bonner's solution to Number one cover slips and allow them to make contact with the glass while maintained in a humid Petri plate. A few dozen short fragments of glass wool are cut with a pair of scissors and allowed to fall on a microscope slide. The cover slip bearing the myxamoebae is then transferred to the slide for examination with a compound microscope. The fragments of glass wool support the cover slip in such a way that the myxamoebae are free to move.

To photograph pseudoplasmodia of various stages with a stereomicroscope a plastic Petri dish is prepared in the following manner:

1. Drill a 10-mm-diameter hole near the edge of the Petri plate cover.

2. Attach a short glass rod as a handle to a cover slip or to a piece of microscope slide with Pyseal or deKhotinsky cement. This serves as a cover for the hole in the Petri plate cover.

3. Cover 50 percent of the bottom half of the Petri plate with moist filter paper.

4. Pick up the pseudoplasmodium with the small brass tool and transfer it to the Petri dish. The agar plug may be turned on its side and rolled into the desired position for profile photos or stood on its flat surface for birdseye views of the pseudoplasmodium. A combination of substage and overhead illumination may be experimented with to achieve desired effects.

5. Immediately prior to snapping the camera shutter the glass cover is moved aside. Consequently the fogging on the inner surface of the cover does not constitute a problem. The small opening prevents excessive loss of moisture from the pseudoplasmodium when the cover is removed to focus the microscope or to operate the camera shutter.

The film which has been used with success in this laboratory is:

Black and white: Kodak Plus-X pan
Printing paper: Agfa Brovira 2, 3, and 4
Color: Anscochrome 200; used primarily for fluorescent microscopy

REFERENCES

BONNER, J. T., 1944: A descriptive study of the development of the slime mold *Dictyostelium discoideum*. *Am. J. Botany*, 31: 175.

———, 1947: Evidence for the formation of cell aggregates by chemotaxis in the development of the slime mold *Dictyostelium discoideum*. *J. Exp. Zool.*, 106: 1.

———, 1952: The pattern of differentiation in amoeboid slime molds. *Amer. Nat.*, 86: 79.

———, and M. S. ADAMS, 1958: Cell mixtures of different species and strains of cellular slime moulds. *J. Embryol. Exp. Morph.*, 6: 346.

———, A. P. KELSO, and R. G. GILLMOR, 1966: A new approach to the problem of aggregation in the cellular slime molds. *Biol. Bull.*, 130: 28.

BRÜEL, D., H. HOLTER, K. LINDERSTRØM-LANG, and K. ROZĪTS, 1946: A micromethod for the determination of total nitrogen (accuracy 0.005 μg N). *Compt. rend. Lab. Carlsberg. Serie Chim.*, 25: 289.

DAVENPORT, H. A., 1960: *Histological and Histochemical Techniques.* 401 pp. Saunders Co., Philadelphia, Pa.

DUBERT, J. M., P. SLIZEWCZ, P. REBEYROTTE, and M. MACHEBOEUF, 1953: Nouvelle méthode de séparation des protéines sériques par le méthanol. Application aux serums de lapin et de cheval. *Ann. Inst. Pasteur*, 84: 370.

GERISCH, G., 1959: Ein Submerskulturverfahren für entwicklungsphysiologische Untersuchungen an *Dictyostelium discoideum. Naturwiss.*, 46: 654.

GLICK, D., 1961: *Quantitative Chemical Techniques of Histo- and Cytochemistry.* Vol. I, 470 pp. Interscience Publishers, New York.

———, 1963: *Quantitative Chemical Techniques of Histo- and Cytochemistry.* Vol. II, 513 pp. Interscience Publishers, New York.

GREGG, J. H., 1950: Oxygen utilization in relation to growth and morphogenesis of the slime mold *Dictyostelium discoideum. J. Exp. Zool.*, 114: 173.

———, 1960: Surface antigen dynamics in the slime mold *Dictyostelium discoideum. Biol. Bull.*, 118: 70.

———, 1961: An immunoelectrophoretic study of the slime mold *Dictyostelium discoideum. Develop. Biol.*, 3: 757.

———, 1964: Developmental processes in cellular slime molds. *Physiol. Rev.*, 44: 631.

———, 1965: Regulation in the cellular slime molds. *Develop. Biol.*, 12: 377.

———, A. L. HACKNEY, and J. O. KRIVANEK, 1954: Nitrogen metabolism of the slime mold *Dictyostelium discoideum* during growth and morphogenesis. *Biol. Bull.*, 107: 226.

———, and R. D. BRONSWEIG, 1956: Biochemical events accompanying stalk formation in the slime mold *Dictyostelium discoideum. J. Cellular Comp. Physiol.*, 48: 293.

GRIFFIN, C. W., T. R. CARSKI, and G. S. WARNER, 1961: Labeling procedures employing crystalline fluorescein isothiocyanate. *J. Bact.*, 82: 534.

HOHL, H. R., and K. B. RAPER, 1963: Nutrition of cellular slime molds. III. Specific growth requirements of *Polysphondylium pallidum. J. Bact.*, 86: 1314.

JOHANSEN, D. A., 1940: *Plant Microtechnique.* 1st ed., 523 pp. McGraw-Hill Co., Inc., New York.

KIRK, P. L., 1950: *Quantitative Ultramicroanalysis.* 310 pp. John Wiley & Sons, Inc., New York.

———, and F. L. SCHAFFER, 1948: Construction and special uses of quartz helix balances. *Rev. Sci. Instruments*, 19: 785.

MARSHALL, J. D., W. C. EVELAND, and C. W. SMITH, 1958: Superiority of fluorescein isothiocyanate (Riggs) for fluorescent antibody technic with a modification of its application. *Proc. Soc. Exp. Biol. Med.*, 98: 898.

NAYYAR, S. N., and D. GLICK, 1954: Studies in histochemistry XXXI. A method for the determination of protein in millimicrogram quantities. *J. Histochem. Cytochem.*, 2: 282.

OLIVERIO, V. T., C. DENHAM, and J. D. DAVIDSON, 1962: Oxygen flask combustion in determination of C^{14} and H^3 in biological materials. *Analytical Biochemistry*, 4: 188.

PETERS, H., 1963: Construction and use of a small sephadex column for the separation of fluorescent antibodies. *Stain Tech.*, 38: 260.

PRESCOTT, D. M., 1964: Autoradiography with liquid emulsion. In D. M. Prescott (ed.), *Methods in Cell Physiology*, Vol. I, Academic Press, New York.

RAPER, K. B., 1937: Growth and development of *Dictyostelium discoideum* with different bacterial associates. *J. Agri. Res.*, 55: 289.

———, 1940: Pseudoplasmodium formation and organization in *Dictyostelium discoideum. J. Elisha Mitchell Sci. Soc.*, 56: 241.

SHAFFER, B. M., 1957: Properties of slime-mould amoebae of significance for aggregation. *Quart. J. Micro. Sci.*, 98: 377.

SONNEBORN, D. R., M. SUSSMAN, and L. LEVINE, 1964: Serological analyses of cellular slime-mold development. I. Changes in antigenic activity during cell aggregation. *J. Bact.*, 87: 1321.

SUSSMAN, R. R., and M. SUSSMAN, 1953: Cellular differentiation in Dictyosteliaceae: heritable modifications of the developmental pattern. *Ann. N.Y. Acad. Sci.*, 56: 949.

TAKEUCHI, I., 1963: Immunochemical and immunohistochemical studies on the development of the cellular slime mold *Dictyostelium mucoroides*. *Develop. Biol.*, 8: 1.

Part II

CULTURE METHODS

Mammalian Embryo Culture*

By Beatrice Mintz

INTRODUCTION

Mammalian embryos, as integral organisms, have been virtually ignored in earlier handbooks of investigative methodology. This is scarcely surprising, since, for some time, little success had been achieved in maintaining the embryos outside their maternal environment. The low rate of egg production in mammals was itself a deterrent in any technical explorations.

In recent years, however, the stalemate has come to an end. Short-term "organism culture" of early stages has become a practical reality; as a result, increasingly revealing experimentation under controlled conditions can be anticipated. Novel techniques have in fact already been introduced for the manipulation of development *in vitro*, and some of them now make problems of fundamental significance more accessible to us. If the mammalian embryo has not been a prime object of experimental inquiry in the past, it will surely be one in the future.

It carries, to be sure, an intrinsic interest for us, *qua* mammal. Apart from this, what are the general kinds of investigations for which the embryos of mammals might become peculiarly useful?

Perhaps the area of greatest promise lies in the genetic control of differentiation —both "normal" and "abnormal." The problem of how a single genome can mediate progressive divergence of cell types within an individual is most cogently examined in terms of specific genes and their expressions. And, while interesting mutations are increasingly coming to light in a number of vertebrate species, the mouse at present far outranks all other vertebrates in the total potentialities which it offers for genetic analysis. Not only are there a number of standard inbred strains of mice in existence, but a great many specific mutations are also known, and some of these are available on inbred-strain backgrounds (see Kallman, this volume, pp. 3–12).

A further feature of placental mammalian embryos which renders them especially favorable for experimental dissection of developmental processes is their great dependence on and interaction with their environment. Such a situation basically affords the sorts of analytical opportunities which cannot very well exist in embryos that are largely self-sufficient.

Among laboratory mammals, the mouse combines the largest number of advantages for the study of development.

* The investigations carried on in this laboratory were supported by U.S. Public Health Service Research Grants No. HD 01646 and CA 06927 from the National Cancer Institute.

It is, as already indicated, excellent material from a genetic point of view; it is easily maintained and bred; and its embryos can now be grown *in vitro* from two-cell stage to blastocyst, and during part of the postimplantation period. This chapter will therefore be largely restricted to procedures found applicable to the mouse.

Rabbit eggs can also be cultivated during cleavage, and have served in a number of interesting investigations. Rat and hamster eggs cannot yet be cultured. References to studies with other mammals, along with further references on mice, can be located through Austin's book on mammalian eggs (1961), and the recent Ciba Symposium volume (Wolstenholme and O'Connor, 1965). The earlier book by Pincus (1936) is also of interest.

Methods chosen for detailed presentation here are intended primarily for the student or investigator who is new to the field, so that the basic procedures for obtaining, handling, cultivating, and surgically transferring mouse embryos are emphasized. In addition, some of the special techniques designed for experimental use are outlined; for more detailed descriptions of these, the original publications should be consulted.

It would be impractical to review here all methods which may fulfill a common purpose. Therefore, when alternatives are known, a choice has been made, based on experience and evaluation in this laboratory. Alternatives will be presented only when they offer special conveniences or unique experimental possibilities. References are given only to the most up-to-date version of a technique, if it has been modified by its author.

OBTAINING MOUSE EGGS

Eggs can be obtained in several ways: (1) from sexually mature females, which normally ovulate spontaneously at estrus even when mating does not occur; (2) from immature females that can be induced by hormone treatment to ovulate precociously; (3) from mature females in which ovulation can also be induced by hormone treatment, irrespective of phase of the estrous cycle and of diurnal light-dark rhythms.

Eggs from Spontaneous Ovulation

Spontaneous ovulation and mating take place around the period of estrus and generally occur at night, under ordinary conditions of illumination. On the whole, it is preferable to exclude outdoor light from the animal room and to maintain a constant 24-hour ratio of light to dark by means of an automatic time switch. The two periods may be equal in length, but with a shorter dark period (down to as little as 4 hours), there is less variation in time of spontaneous ovulation among the individuals in a given strain. The midpoint of the ovulation period (i.e., when half the mice have ovulated) seems to be related more to the midpoint of the dark phase than to time of onset of darkness (Braden, 1957).

The estrous cycle of the mouse is approximately 5 days long (Allen, 1922) and is easily modified or even suspended under adverse environmental conditions. In addition, if females are stored together in groups, regular cycles may fail to recur, whereas when they are caged individually, normal cyclic activity is displayed (Whitten, 1959).

Identification of the estrous females is possible by means of the vaginal smear method, in which cornified and nucleated epithelial cells are an indication of estrus. Illustrations of cell types in different parts of the cycle are given by Allen (1922) and Snell (1941). It may be less time-consuming, in setting up matings, simply to use all females without first checking for estrus, though the total percentage of mated females will of course be lower. Females are transferred to the male's cage near the end of the light period (with controlled illumination) or in the late afternoon (with ordinary illumination). Ideally they are individually paired, but when phase of estrus is random and hormone priming is not involved, 3 or 4 females can be housed overnight with a male. The presence of a vaginal plug the next morning signifies that mating has occurred. The plug is formed from secretions of male accessory glands and is more or less superficially situated so that it can be detected with a dissecting probe. Plugs are progressively lost during the day as a result of leucocytic infiltration.

When space is not available to maintain females in individual cages, storage in groups may be a practical alternative and still yield a substantial number of matings, if matings are repeated on successive nights. According to observations by Whitten (1959), females kept in groups of 30 and then paired singly with males came into estrus synchronously and rapidly, so that few matings occurred on the first two nights but about 50 percent mated on the third night, and about 25 percent on the fourth night.

After the birth of a litter, an estrous period recurs and mating may take place, usually the night following parturition. In some strains, mating is more common if the new litter is temporarily removed (i.e., given to a foster mother that has just had a litter of her own). When gestation and lactation accompany each other, the young embryos undergo a developmental lag after reaching the blastocyst stage and are delayed in the uterine lumen for periods ranging from a few days to approximately 2 weeks, before implanting and resuming their development. Therefore, postpartum matings should not be used as a source of postimplantation embryos if definite stages are required.

Eggs from Hormone-Induced Ovulation of Prepuberal Females

Follicular maturation and ovulation are normally under endogenous gonadotropic hormone influence and can be brought under experimental control by means of exogenous hormone administration. Very young females prior to sexual maturity have proved to be an excellent source of ovulated eggs after hormone priming (Runner and Palm, 1953). Such females are also capable of mating and of sustaining normal development of their fertilized ova to the blastocyst stage (Runner and Gates, 1954). The blastocysts may subsequently remain in the uterine lumen, sometimes for several weeks, without implanting (Smithberg and Runner, 1960).

The "superovulation" procedure in prepuberal mice, as more recently described (Gates, 1965), consists of an injection of 2.5–5 International Units (I.U.) of pregnant mare serum (PMS), which has a follicle-stimulating effect, followed 45–48 hours later by an ovulatory injection of 2.5 I.U. of human chorionic gonadotropin (HCG). Both are administered intraperitoneally. Females should be individually paired with mature, untreated males, and can be paired at the time HCG is given. The check for vaginal plugs is made the next day. Three-to-four-week-old females generally yield a high plug incidence and an average egg number several times that of untreated adults. Other investigators have also superovulated females at 1–2 months of age (i.e., between weaning and sexual maturity).

Dosage optima vary with genetic strain and with age. Influence of relative amounts of PMS and HCG on egg number has been examined (Wilson and Zarrow,

1962). There is a tendency for abnormal eggs to be produced in larger numbers as the amount of PMS is increased, and the level can be adjusted to maximize total number and minimize the incidence of anomalies. The interval between PMS and HCG may also be modified; a span of 40–48 hours is most frequently employed. According to one study on a random bred strain, afternoon injections of PMS and HCG resulted in larger numbers of eggs than did morning injections (Lang and Lamond, 1966).

Eggs from Hormone-Induced Ovulation of Mature Females

Hormone-induced superovulation is also applicable to mature females (Fowler and Edwards, 1957). Here the normal estrous and diurnal cycling are conveniently overridden, and egg number is increased as compared with spontaneous matings.

The procedure is similar to the one for immature females: an intraperitoneal injection of PMS is followed by one of HCG, females are individually paired with males, and plugs are checked the next day. Dosages ranging from 2.5 I.U. up to 15 I.U. of each hormone have been reported; most investigators have used low doses (e.g., 3 I.U. of each, by Fowler and Edwards, 1957). Again, however, generalizations are impossible because of significant strain and subline differences, and exploratory tests are desirable. The time interval between PMS and HCG has ranged between 30 and 59 hours, in various reports, and has more often been between 40 and 48 hours.

Injected females which do not mate may be reinjected at a later time. In a systematic comparison of adult females from two inbred strains, repeated courses of treatment were separated by intervals of 4 days to 2 weeks (Lin and Bailey, 1965). Though refractoriness eventually resulted, the yield was still favorable for at least three rounds and sometimes more.

TIMETABLE AND GENERAL CHARACTERISTICS OF EARLY DEVELOPMENT IN THE MOUSE

All germ cells, in both male and female, arise exclusively as direct mitotic descendants of a very small number first distinguishable in and near the yolk sac of the early embryo (Mintz, 1960). In the male, mitosis continues into adult life. In the female, oogonial divisions cease in the embryo, and oocytes enter a prolonged meiotic prophase.

The mature dictyate primary oocyte undergoes its first maturation division just before ovulation, forming a secondary oocyte and a polar body. The second maturation division begins immediately, and the oocyte remains in metaphase until sperm penetration. Approximately eight eggs are ovulated at a time under spontaneous conditions, but different strains of mice produce characteristic average numbers.

If mating takes place, it usually precedes ovulation by 1–5 hours, in strains studied. Ovulation itself is rapid, occupying less than 1 hour in a given female (Braden, 1957). Sperm penetration of eggs occurs in the upper oviduct. When mating and ovulation times were close (in the absence of hormone treatment), sperm penetration was found to begin after $2\frac{1}{2}$–3 hours and to require 4 more hours for completion in all eggs of a given female (Braden and Austin, 1954). Excessive "aging" of mammalian eggs prior to fertilization, by delay in mating until the end of estrus, may possibly lead to nuclear anomalies such as triploidy in embryos, by means of polar body suppression or polyspermy (Braden and Austin, 1954; Austin, 1960).

When females receive gonadotropin

injections, ovulation usually follows HCG by 11–14 hours. Observations of hormone-treated adults showed that sperm penetration through egg membranes started about 1 hour after ovulation and sperm entry into the egg cytoplasm was completed in less than an additional hour. Both these intervals are shorter than when hormones are not given (Edwards and Gates, 1959).

The ovulated secondary oocyte is surrounded by a complex which includes somatic cells from the original ovarian follicle. The oocyte proper measures some 72 μ across (Lewis and Wright, 1935). Its cytoplasm is translucent and granular, and strain-specific differences in cytoplasmic appearance can easily be distinguished in the living state (Braden, 1959). A clear elastic membrane, the zona pellucida, about 11 μ thick, envelops the egg and becomes increasingly separated from the latter by a small fluid-filled (perivitelline) space, in unfertilized as well as fertilized eggs. Peripheral to the zona is a large cloud of follicle cells (cumulus oophorus), embedded in a sticky, gelatinous (hyaluronidase-digestible) matrix; those cells hugging the zona form an even layer, the corona radiata. The entire ovulated complex measures 100–200 μ across. (In the rabbit, unlike the mouse, a thick mucin coat is deposited on the egg in the oviduct.)

The second polar body is expelled by the penetrated ovum, and male and female pronuclei are organized. Replication of DNA (deoxyribonucleic acid) for the first cleavage occurs in the pronuclei before they fuse (Mintz, 1965b).

The timing of some of these events was observed in adults after hormone treatment (Edwards and Gates, 1959). Pronuclear formation occurred at 4 hours after completion of sperm penetration into the egg. Pronuclear fusion, or syngamy, followed after an additional 20½ hours. About a half-hour later, the first cleavage was complete. Under these conditions, therefore, 25 hours elapsed between the end of sperm penetration and the 2-cell stage. An approximately similar period is required after spontaneous ovulation and mating. The first polar body occasionally divides; it more commonly degenerates before or during early cleavage. The second polar body frequently persists into the blastocyst stage.

The cells of the corona and cumulus disperse before the 2-cell stage is reached. They are discarded in the upper oviduct even when the egg remains unfertilized. When uncleaved ova are explanted *in vitro*, the cumulus persists, though individual cells may emigrate and establish colonies on the floor of the dish.

Roughly 12 hours elapse between succeeding cleavages, after the first one. This is subject to considerable interstrain variation. Cleavages within a single egg are not synchronous and all possible numbers of blastomeres are observed during early development. Blastomeres at first are rather rounded, but become more tightly packed against each other in midcleavage (8–16 cells), independently of pressure from the enveloping zona.

The eggs move slowly down the oviducts, and begin to enter the uterine horns around midday or later on day 2 (counting the day of plug detection as day 0), at 8–16 cells. In the morning of day 3, all are usually in the uteri and have reached at least the morula stage. These are solid balls of 16–32 cells. Small fluid-filled vacuoles then appear in some of the cells, and discharge their contents extracellularly, toward the center of the mass. A fluid-filled cavity is thus formed, marking the beginning of the blastocyst stage, which is found with increasing frequency during the day. Multiple small cavities are actually quite common at first in blastocysts, but they quickly coalesce (Mintz, 1965c), and the single cavity with fluid enlarges. The cell layer surrounding the blastocyst is the trophoblast; to one side of the cavity is a cushion of cells, the inner cell mass. The embryo splits its zonal jacket, possibly after fluid uptake in the cavity, and emerges before implantation. (The process of "hatching" has been observed *in vitro* by a number of investigators, and can be seen in the culture media described in the section on Culture Media for Preimplantation Stages.) On day 4, the blastocyst elongates slightly. At this time, it becomes more difficult to recover from the uterine lumen because the process of implantation is beginning. For further details of developmental stages after implantation, Snell (1941), Snell and Stevens (1966), Grüneberg (1943), and comparative embryology texts should be consulted. The length of the gestation period in the mouse varies around 20 days, and shows strain differences.

PROCEDURES FOR HANDLING AND EXAMINING EMBRYOS

General Preparations

If the work area is relatively free of strong air currents, it is possible to maintain complete sterility without resorting to the use of antibiotics in the culture fluids. Vertical drop of contaminants into the cultures can be prevented by the use of a horizontal shield attached to a dissecting microscope having internal (rather than projecting) objectives. A transparent Lucite plate approximately 20 cm square, with a central hole for the lens, is supported from below in the plane of the objectives by means of the threaded lens shield, or by a Lucite ring (with set screws) encircling the objective housing. The shield then rides up and down with the microscope body without impairing visibility or reducing working distance; magnification changes can be dialed above it without passing the hand across the exposed culture. In the event that air movement in the room is rapid, it is preferable to install the microscope in a hood. The slant front panel should be of Lucite or glass. An area across the bottom may be left open for introducing the hands, or can be partly covered with a flexible plastic flap. A burner with an adjustable micropilot flame is essential in order to keep from overheating the interior of the hood during prolonged use.

For initial dissection of the embryo donor, reflected light is used. During all further routine handling of preimplantation embryos, transmitted light is preferable, and total magnifications ranging from 20 × to 80 × are adequate. A foot focus attachment to the microscope is a considerable convenience. Many delicate manipulations, including handling of individual blastomeres, can easily be done free-hand after some practice, and a micromanipulator is therefore unnecessary, unless special techniques such as microinjection are employed.

Instruments do not require presterilizing. They can be repeatedly cleaned, dipped in alcohol, and flamed, during use. All dishes for dissection or culture are sterilized inside Petri dishes and the lid of the latter is used to guard against contamination whenever feasible in the course of explantation.

Removal of Embryos from the Donor

The female is killed by dislocating the cervical vertebrae or stretching the spinal cord, and is then briefly immersed in 95 percent alcohol. The animal need not be pinned out on a dissecting board but can simply be laid out on a small sheet of aluminum foil with edges bent up to form a shallow pan. The ventral body wall is opened with a wide V-shaped incision. Whether oviducts, uterine horns, or both, are removed is determined by the developmental stage sought. For uncleaved eggs, only the anterior part of the oviduct is cut out; for cleavage stages, each oviduct is severed from its uterine horn just below the uterotubal junction. Ovaries, fat, and most of the mesentery are left behind. The ducts are immediately immersed in medium. For preimplantation stages, a dish with a depression (e.g., a triple-well clear Pyrex spot plate with a capacity of about 0.4 ml per well, or a Maximow slide) helps to collect the eggs, which can be swirled into the bottom of the well. Since dissection of postimplantation embryos requires a larger quantity of medium, small Petri dishes are used.

Uncleaved eggs still in the cumulus are visible through the distended wall of the oviduct ampulla as large pale masses. They can be eased out either by nicking the wall with a sharp knife and applying light pressure, or by tearing it outward from one end with two pairs of fine watchmaker's forceps. For all later preimplantation stages, the flushing technique is the most efficient for removal of embryos. A minimal amount of culture medium (usually less than 0.1 ml) is introduced into the anterior end of the submerged duct, from a short (1 or 2 ml) syringe with a truncated, smoothed-tip 30-gauge needle. When morulae or blastocysts are present in the uterus, there are fewer losses if the oviduct remains attached and the entire tube is flushed from the infundibular end. The infundibulum is held in place around the needle with fine forceps.

Postimplantation embryos are found on the antimesometrial side of the uterine wall and the early ones can be seen with reflected light after the tube has been cut open near the mesometrial border and spread flat. For still later stages, the excised horn is cut transversely between the enlarged implantation sites and one of the end openings of each site is carefully torn wide to expose the embryo in its membranes (see section on Culture Media for Postimplantation Stages for further details).

Handling of Embryos

All eggs or embryos need to be rinsed in at least one change of fresh medium, or in several if they are to be grown in a solution with restricted and defined components. The use of simple saline or even balanced salt solutions for either flushing or rinsing embryos is to be avoided; the final type of protein-containing culture medium should be employed or approximated whenever possible in all initial handling of the material.

The eggs or embryos are picked up in a short, finely drawn Pyrex pipette, operated either by a soft amber rubber bulb or a mouth-held rubber tube. The former is generally less cumbersome. If eggs are still in the sticky cumulus mass, it may be helpful to silicone the pipettes. For later stages, with or without the zona, this is unnecessary.

The rapid transfer of cleaving embryos and blastocysts in a minimal amount of fluid depends upon a proper pipette with a thin-walled uniformly narrow tip. The tip should be 2–2.5 cm long and of internal diameter only slightly larger than that of the embryo. The pipette is made by pulling tubing in a hot flame and re-pulling once or twice more in an ordinary flame in the region of gradual taper of the glass. The tip is broken off so as to yield a slant bevel, by holding the capillary under slight finger pressure against the edge of a hard Arkansas stone, scratching one side lightly, and increasing the pressure toward that side. The bevel is fire-polished by brief passage in a microburner flame. Such a pipette, of about 7 cm total length, can be delicately controlled and conveniently held at an angle, with the oval opening cupped

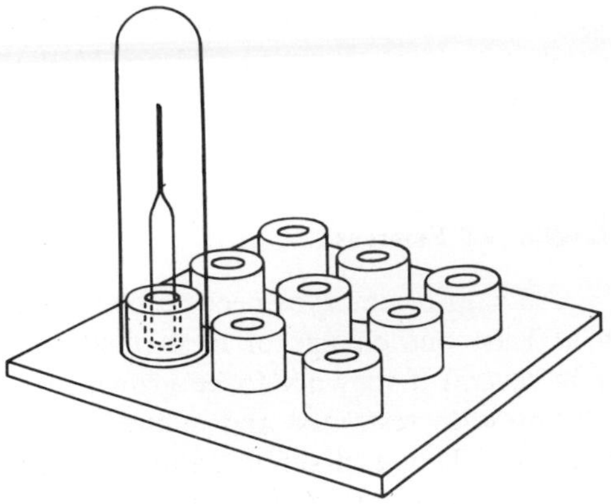

FIG. 1. Sterilizing rack for fine pipettes.

over an egg so that a series of eggs can be quickly picked up like a string of beads. A cotton filter can be omitted from the pipette, as fibers tend to be deposited in the medium and entrap eggs.

Fine pipettes are sterilized in a rack designed in this laboratory, to minimize breakage and ensure continued sterility (Fig. 1). The rack is constructed of stainless steel or aluminum. Each of nine pipettes stands in a hollow plug support affixed to a solid base, and is covered by its individual test-tube sheath, so that only one at a time is exposed.

We also employ a drying rack of our own design for pipettes of fine bore. A small hole is drilled from the floor of each

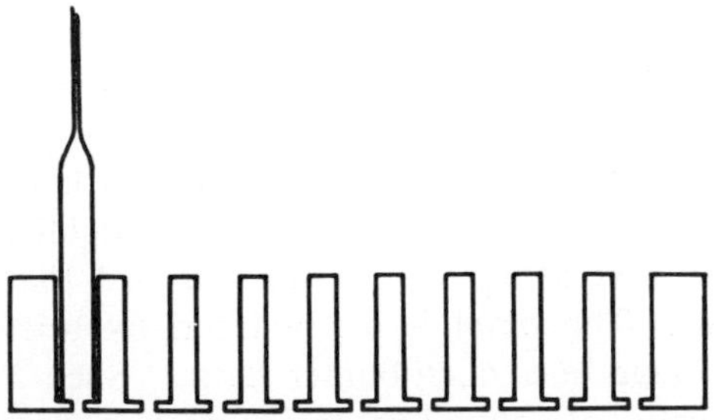

FIG. 2. Drying rack for fine pipettes; shown in cut-out side view.

well down through the base of a metal block. The stand holds eighteen pipettes in two rows of nine each, and is shown in side view in Fig. 2. When it is placed on an open-screen shelf in the oven, warm air can circulate through the full length of each pipette.

Microscopic Examination

For study of structural details, or for photography, eggs or young embryos must be examined with the compound microscope, preferably with apochromatic objectives. If later reincubation is planned, it should be borne in mind that prolonged exposure to light may impair development (Daniel, 1964). Incubator temperatures are not obligatory during any phase of handling, and cleavage-stage embryos may in fact be left at room temperature for days and still resume development when returned to 37°C. Nevertheless, there is a lag in resumption of normal developmental rate, and this is particularly pronounced in younger stages after cooling. Therefore, for frequent inspection or photography, the microscope must be enclosed within a warmed chamber or installed in a walk-in incubator.

For ordinary examination, eggs can be placed on a thin flat glass slide in a small drop of medium, in the center of an incomplete circle of silicone grease. A cover slip is then rested on the wall of grease and lowered so as to allow air bubbles to escape through the opening in the circle before self-sealing occurs. The cover slip may be gently lowered further to compress the egg slightly, and then slid forward in order to roll the egg, to permit observation of various parts. Phase-contrast examination serves to reveal many nuclear details at the time of fertilization (Austin and Smiles, 1948). As cleavage progresses, phase-contrast illumination is less satisfactory than regular illumination for resolving details within the thick mass.

Some media require a precise gas phase for development to progress satisfactorily. Sustained time-lapse cinematography under these circumstances may necessitate provision for introducing a gas atmosphere into the culture chamber (Cole and Paul, 1965).

SURGICAL TRANSFER OF PREIMPLANTATION EMBRYOS TO A FOSTER MOTHER

General Applicability

At the present time, it is not yet possible to culture mammalian embryos continuously during long periods of their development. Many experiments can of course be entirely encompassed within the allowable culture span. For others, the final results of a treatment or manipulation imposed *in vitro* must be read at some later stage. Here the return of the embryo to an *in vivo* environment becomes an indispensable adjunct to the investigation.

Surgical transfer of preimplantation embryos from a natural to a foster mother, resulting in birth of live young, has been successfully practiced since the end of the last century in many species of mammals. The transfer itself inevitably necessitates some minimal exposure to culture conditions which differ in varying degree from the endogenous ones. Just how far this exposure can be safely attenuated, between the embryo's residence in its original and in its adoptive mother, is empirically reflected in the developmental capacity *in vitro* of the stage in question. Thus the mouse zygote, which at best undergoes little development after explantation, must be returned within approximately a day or even sooner to an *in vivo* situation. Embryos explanted at the stage of 2-cells or later, on the other hand, are capable of reaching the blastocyst stage in culture; when their sojourn *in vitro* is prolonged until that time, there is no appreciable diminution in their subsequent survival to birth after transfer, as compared with that of blastocysts which are directly transferred from a donor to a recipient female. In the mouse, the level of survival past birth, for embryos cultured before transfer, has now reached 50 percent (Mintz, 1967, and unpublished data). The high viability has been obtained despite considerable manipulation of the embryos, in these experiments, during a 1- to 2-day culture period following explantation in early or mid-cleavage.

Preparation of the Recipient

In order that transferred embryos implant and continue their development, the recipient female must be either pregnant or pseudopregnant. The former poses the inconvenience that alien offspring must always be distinguishable from native ones by means of genetic markers. A state of pseudopregnancy is therefore preferable, and follows a sterile mating with a vasectomized male. During pseudopregnancy, the next estrus is delayed and the uterine changes necessary for implantation occur at the appropriate time.

Spontaneous sterile matings, rather than sterile matings after hormone priming of the female, appear more favorable for embryo survival in the mouse. Females which have previously had at least one litter tend to make superior hosts.

The male is vasectomized through a small incision on each side. Two silk ligatures are placed around each vas deferens, one near the cranial and one near the caudal level of the adjacent epididymis. A section of the vas is then excised between the ligatures and the cut ends are turned slightly away from each other. The body wall is closed with sutures and the skin with wound clips. The males may be test-mated to verify sterility. In extensive retesting of many operated males, we have not encountered any instances of functional regeneration of ducts.

Recipient Stage in Relation to Embryo Stage

The reproductive tract, as well as the embryo, undergoes a progressive differentiation during gestation and it is therefore not surprising that the results of egg transfer are greatly influenced by the post-ovulatory stage of the recipient in relation to that of the embryo. The observations of Chang (1950) on the rabbit were important in demonstrating that the 2-cell egg actually degenerates when it is introduced into a uterine environment considerably more advanced than its own developmental stage.

Ideally, the host for transferred eggs should be precisely synchronous with the donor, provided that the two are identical in genotype and that *in vitro* conditions have permitted embryo development to continue at its normal pace. These requirements, however, are frequently not met. Empirical examination must therefore determine the optimal time relations under actual conditions. Such investigations have been undertaken with mouse, rat, and rabbit eggs, and the general consensus clearly is that the embryo at the time of transfer should be a day older than, or the same postovulatory age as, the recipient, but not younger.

The question of which of these allowable alternatives is the more desirable has led to many comparisons between results obtained in separate studies. These studies are not comparable, however, for the following reasons: (1) Genotypes of egg and host have usually differed from each other, even within single investigations. Fekete (1947) noted that reciprocal transfers between two strains did not prove equally favorable. And recent observations on preimplantation uterine changes have revealed marked strain differences in timing of these changes (Mintz, unpublished data). (2) Developmental retardation due to handling must differ greatly in the various published experiments, since departures from body temperature occur for varying periods. (3) Culture media employed in transfers have also differed widely. (4) Gross morphological criteria are inadequate for exact determination of embryo stage, and differences in rate of development may be more significant (Whitten and Dagg, 1961; Gates, 1965).

Therefore, studies on this subject should be considered individually, within the framework of the conditions employed. Thus, for mouse embryos removed on day 3 and transferred directly to the uterus, a day 2 host proved to be superior to a day 3 host in one extensive investigation (McLaren and Michie, 1956). Under other conditions, day 3 embryos fared slightly better in a day 3 than in a day 2 uterus (employing here, for uniformity, our chronology based on a day 0 plug date) (Doyle, Gates, and Noyes, 1963). If a culture period were interposed before transfer, the synchronous combination might possibly lose its superiority.

Transfer Sites in Relation to Embryo Stage

As indicated in the preceding discussion, an embryo at any given stage does not find all parts of the tract equally compatible with its developmental needs (e.g., Chang, 1950). Again, the ideal arrangement, in which the embryo would be restored to its normal geographical location, may not be the best one in actual practice.

The sites which have been utilized in transplantation of eggs include the ovarian bursa, the oviduct, and the uterus. The most exhaustive comparison of these sites has been carried out in the rat, in which preimplantation development is a day

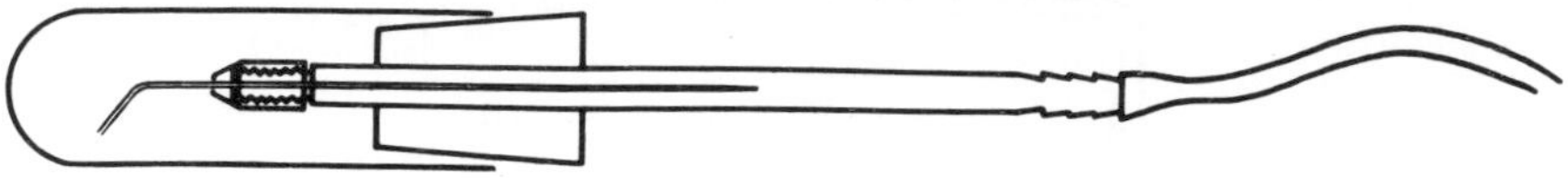

FIG. 3. Pipette for surgical transfer of eggs.

longer than in the mouse. Donors and hosts were of different strains, and eggs were only briefly *in vitro* at 37°C (Noyes and Dickmann, 1961). The results indicated that fertilized eggs on day 0 (again using our chronology) were best transferred to the bursa or oviduct (on day 0 of the host); eggs on day 1 survived best in the oviduct (on day 0 of the host); day 2 eggs fared best in the oviduct (on day 1 of the host). Older stages did better in the uterus. Under the conditions used, if there is a choice of stage when eggs are to be transferred, it appears best to wait until they can be introduced into the uterus, since uterine transfers were on the whole more successful. Our own trials with the mouse have led to a similar conclusion.

Transfer Methods

Though ether or Nembutal is acceptable for anesthesia of the recipient, Avertin (Winthrop Labs.) has been more satisfactory in our hands, in that it has produced no fatalities, yet it acts rapidly. The animal need not be tied down to an operating board. Shaving of the operative area is also unnecessary; the fur can simply be parted after local swabbing with alcohol.

A short incision is made longitudinally through the skin over one ovary at a time; the ovary can be seen through the muscle wall. The latter is then cut. The fat pad attached to the ovary can be grasped with blunt forceps and the anterior end of the tract drawn out to the surface.

For transfer into the ovarian bursa, the pipette is used to penetrate the ovarian fat pad and is passed directly through it into the interior of the capsule. The eggs are expelled and the pipette withdrawn (Runner, 1951). In oviduct transfers, the capsular wall can be cut open (Tarkowski, 1959), but if an electro-scalpel is available, bleeding into the working area is minimized (Noyes and Dickmann, 1961). The pipette is introduced into the infundibular opening. When eggs are to be transferred to the uterus, the thicker part of the mesentery at the uterotubal junction is held with fine forceps, a small hole is made with a sharply pointed needle near the anterior end of the uterine horn, and the pipette is introduced into the hole, pointing posteriorly. After eggs are transferred, the tract is gently eased back in position by gripping the two edges of the muscle wall incision and lifting them slightly. The wall is closed with sutures and the skin with wound clips.

The design of our transfer pipette is based on the braking pipette devised by Holter (1943; see also the drawing of Runner's pipette shown by Noyes *et al.*, 1961). A glass capillary tube is housed inside a wider-bore holder. A gradual inward taper or constriction near the upper end of the capillary serves as a braking mechanism during use (Fig. 3). It permits the operator to produce very small changes in fluid volume by suction or pressure through the mouthpiece. Effective diameter of the braking tip can be found by trial, in relation to length of the channel. The Pyrex capillary here has an over-all length of approximately 9 cm and the internal diameter of the wide end is slightly

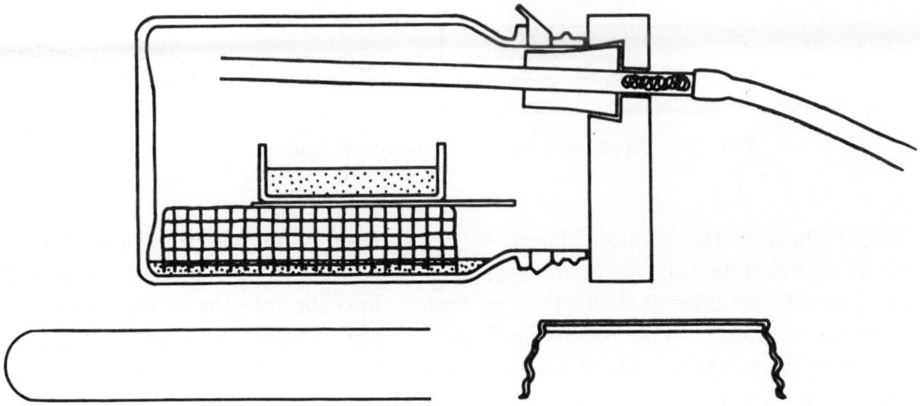

FIG. 4. Large-size culture chamber (1-pint container) for eggs, older embryos, or organ rudiments. The cap (lower right) is off while the gassing apparatus is shown in operation.

larger than the egg. The wide end is broken straight across and fire-polished, and an angle bend is then introduced. The housing is metal or plastic and a small one-hole rubber ring is inserted in the conical threaded nut to hold the capillary in place with an airtight seal. The rubber stopper fits into a test tube to form a storage case.

Eggs should be transferred with a minimum of fluid; in oviduct and uterine transfers, introduction of air bubbles should be avoided. Media are described in the section on culture. The total number of eggs that can be transplanted to a single individual without impairing the embryos' chances of success may depend upon strain-specific factors. A generally sound choice is a number equal to or slightly greater than the mean litter size of the host strain.

CULTIVATION *IN VITRO*

Culture Chambers

The culture medium in which embryos are explanted must maintain its osmotic pressure and its hydrogen ion concentration. An atmosphere of high humidity should therefore be provided, to prevent water loss; the use of balanced salt solution for this purpose is preferable to water. Since mammalian embryos require carbon dioxide and are grown in media containing a bicarbonate buffer at a pH close to 7.0, the medium can be kept in equilibrium with a gas atmosphere of 5 percent CO_2 in air. Continuous gassing during culture is unnecessary, with the small quantities of tissue usually involved.

Humidified incubators flushed with CO_2 in air can be employed, with Petri dish cultures (see Wessells, this volume, pp. 445–456). When the incubator is frequently opened for introduction or examination of cultures, however, the resultant fluctuations in pH, even though transitory, can be an appreciable handicap to mammalian embryos. This difficulty may be partly circumvented by employing isolation units in the incubator, such as plastic culture boxes, so-called anaerobic jars, or sealable desiccators. However these require relatively long periods for gas equilibration after each inspection and are too large to be practical for single cultures.

We have therefore introduced exclusive reliance upon small, self-contained, single-culture chambers (Mintz, 1964), and have designed a series of these which are variously adapted for culture of eggs, of older embryos, or of organ rudiments or small organs. All are simple to manipulate, gas, and humidify. They occupy little space and can quickly be made from inexpensive, readily available materials.

The most versatile of these chambers is shown in Fig. 4. It consists of an ordinary 1-pint Mason jar with flattened sides and a glass-lined screw cap (lower right) which, with the rubber ring supplied with the jar, forms a gas-tight seal. Balanced salt solution containing sodium bicarbonate (plus penicillin and streptomycin), on the floor of the bottle, humidifies the interior; phenol red is included for colorimetric monitoring of pH. The culture itself is placed in a 55-mm outside diameter (or smaller) Petri dish bottom (or watch glass) which sits on a table made by bending stainless steel screening. Interposed between dish and table is a 75- × 25-mm glass slide which serves as a carrier to convey the dish into and out of the bottle. The dish holds sufficient medium (up to 15 ml) so that it can be used for organ cultures as well as postimplantation or preimplantation embryos. Into the dish can be inserted any of the numerous kinds of rafts and supports frequently required in organ culture work (e.g., lens paper or millipore rafts on glass rings, etc.). The culture can also easily be fed with fresh medium and the gas atmosphere renewed if necessary.

The gassing apparatus, demonstrated in use in Fig. 4, is a glass tube with sterile cotton plug, attached to the gas-washing bottle. The one-hole rubber stopper around the tube keeps it sterile when it is stored in a test tube (lower left). During gassing of a wide-mouthed container, the mouth must be partly shielded to prevent excessive loss of the newly introduced gas phase. This is accomplished by lodging the nonsterile end of the stopper firmly at a slight angle in a cut-out (or tapered hole) passing through a block of Lucite. The shielding block is free-standing and permits gas phase replacement to be completed quickly.

With smaller working volumes (1 ml or less), as in cultures of preimplantation stages, it is more convenient to use a smaller chamber, such as the two shown in Figs. 5 and 6. Both are flat-sided French square bottles with gas-tight rubber-lined screw caps. In both, the indicator-colored balanced saline with bicarbonate is pipetted onto the floor and the chamber is gassed with the gassing apparatus. The larger bottle (8 ounces) was described in an earlier paper (Mintz, 1964), and accommodates a low-walled flat Pyrex dish on a stainless steel open-hole rack with handle, so that the culture can be examined with transmitted illumination. The smaller bottle (4 ounces) requires still less gas phase; it has a Pyrex "micro-dish" with attached handle, on a stainless steel screen

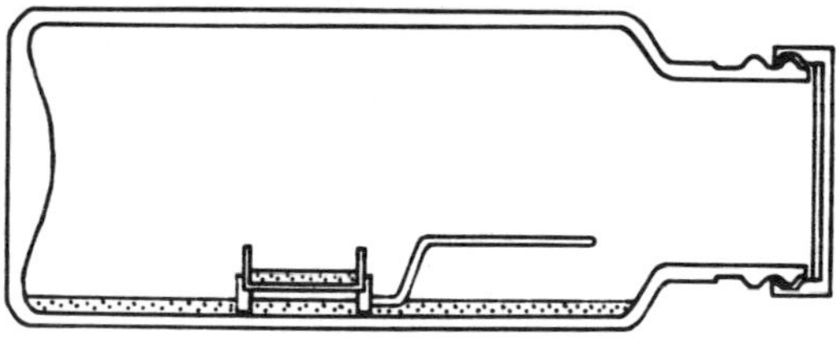

FIG. 5. Intermediate-size culture chamber (8-ounce container) for eggs, with culture dish on separate rack.

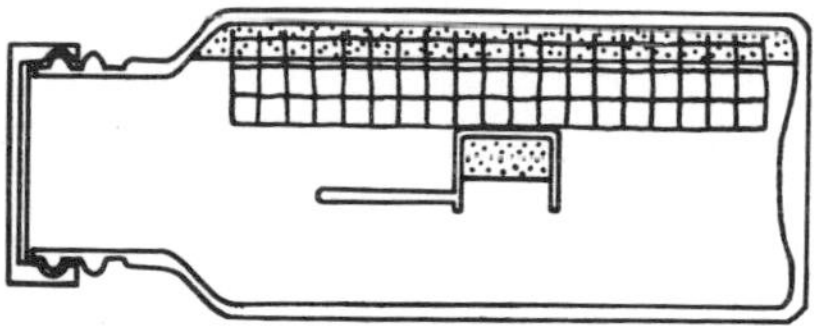

FIG. 6. Small-size culture chamber (4-ounce container) for eggs, with culture dish including handle.

platform. Because of the steeper walls and small diameter of this dish (12 mm high, 17 mm outside diameter), an angle bend at the tip of the pipette is helpful. (Microdish and French square bottles are obtainable from A. H. Thomas Co., Philadelphia.)

Stage-Specific Capacities for *in Vitro* Development

Successful cultivation of mammalian embryos can be carried out during a series of somewhat discrete periods. Although these periods partially overlap, a *given* embryo cannot now be continuously cultured through more than one such phase. This restriction presumably reflects the fact that an embryo in general is, by definition, a changing system, and that the mammalian embryo in particular is exceedingly dependent upon its environment. Its metabolic characteristics and its exogenous requirements must inevitably change. Many transitions are likely to be gradual ones, and a sharp separation of stage-specific requirements would therefore be artificial. Culture conditions can be provided which satisfy some kinds of transient needs; at certain times, however (e.g., in earliest cleavage), the conditions are apparently too marginal to be compatible with further development.

In the mouse, the explanted fertilized egg can undergo one cleavage *in vitro*, but rarely progresses beyond this. The rabbit zygote may more often go as far as the morula stage, but development to blastocyst remains exceptional. In both species, embryos explanted at the 2-cell stage commonly develop into blastocysts. The gradual character of embryonic change is well illustrated within this 2-cell period: mouse eggs placed in culture soon after reaching the 2-cell stage have considerably less chance of becoming blastocysts than those explanted progressively later. If hormone priming has been used, 2-cell eggs timed at more than approximately 40 hours after the HCG injection show high survival in culture. Different strains differ in the rates at which they reach a time favorable for explantation (Mintz, unpublished data). The range of nutritional substrates which the egg can utilize effectively at this point is very limited; by the time the embryo has ±8 cells, it exhibits increasing latitude in its ability to employ different energy sources (Whitten, 1957; Brinster, 1965a), and can also dispense with either the energy source or the fixed nitrogen source (Brinster and Thomson, 1966). Cultivation to blastocyst in a much larger variety of media is easily as successful as development *in vivo*.

The types of "preimplantation" culture media which are favorable for 2-cell explants can also be used for limited *in vitro* work with uncleaved eggs (fertilized or unfertilized). Other handling media designed entirely for brief exposure *in vitro* of uncleaved eggs, and compatible with their survival after surgical transfer, may be found in publications on egg transfer (cited in the section on Surgical Transfer) or on *in vitro* fertilization or microinjection (see the section on Special Experimental Techniques).

In the late blastocyst stage, just before implantation, enriched media are needed for any substantial continuation of cell proliferation. The presence of an irradiated feeder layer (Cole and Paul, 1965) or other co-cultured tissue (Mintz, unpublished data) in a complex medium can result in appreciable increase of inner cell mass and of trophoblast cells. Growth is limited and generally disorganized. Nevertheless, some progress has been made with freshly isolated rabbit blastocysts which, after zona removal, may pass through the egg cylinder stage and begin early organogenesis (Cole and Paul, 1965).

Postimplantation embryos removed before yolk-sac expansion exhibit little development outside the mother. But embryos explanted after yolk sac formation are capable of undergoing a good deal of development *in vitro*, when a rich medium is supplied.

In the following sections, media will be described. Preparative details covered in standard tissue culture manuals are omitted here (e.g., preparation of a plasma clot, embryo extract, an agar medium, a feeder layer; see Wessells, pp. 445–456, or Cahn, Coon, and Cahn, pp. 493–530). Components in widely used solutions can also be located through texts (Paul, 1960; Parker, 1961).

Millipore filtration is recommended for solutions requiring sterilization, with the use of pressure rather than suction, if protein is present, to avoid denaturation.

All media are employed with a humid atmosphere of 5 percent CO_2 in air, at 37°C, unless otherwise stipulated.

We have found it desirable, for retention of proper pH, to store all bicarbonate-containing liquid media in sealed, presterilized, and pregassed serum bottles. The apparatus devised by us for gassing the bottles consists of the barrel of a 1-ml syringe, its head having first been cut off to allow attachment of tubing from the gas line; a sterile cotton plug inside the barrel; and an attached hypodermic needle. During gassing, the needle is introduced through the rubber cap of the bottle. A separate hypodermic needle, inserted by itself into the cap, serves as a vent while the gas phase is being replaced. The medium is later withdrawn, and temporarily stored, entirely in syringes. Carbon dioxide retention is excellent in this closed system, and small quantities of liquid can be quickly dispensed at the last minute, as needed.

Culture Media for Preimplantation Stages

For culture of mouse eggs from ±8 cells to blastocyst, one of the useful defined media, from the early work of Whitten (1956), contains Krebs-Ringer bicarbonate at pH 7.4, glucose (0.1 percent), and crystalline bovine serum albumin (0.1–0.3 percent). To this can be added phenol red indicator (0.002 percent), penicillin G (potassium, 100 units per milliliter), and streptomycin sulfate (50 μg per milliliter). The CO_2-air gas mixture is bubbled through the liquid before adding albumin. A more recent modification (Brinster and Thomson, 1966) allows glucose or albumin alone, or other specified single energy sources, to be used.

Although such a medium will not support development of 2-cell eggs, Whitten observed, in 1957, that lactate enabled a large proportion of late 2-cell eggs to develop. This has been an especially important contribution, since it has provided a basis for all subsequent work in which a single medium has been employed to carry eggs in culture through most of their preimplantation development.

One such medium for 2-cell mouse eggs (Mintz, 1964) is composed of equal parts of fetal calf serum and Earle's balanced salt solution, plus 0.1 percent added lactic acid (which can be added from a 40 percent solution of L (+)-lactic acid), and 0.002 percent phenol red; the pH is then adjusted with sodium bicarbonate (7.5 percent) to 7.0 under 5 percent CO_2 in air, at 37°C. (Eggs need not be grown in microdrops under paraffin oil). This medium has the advantage that it is well buffered and retains a physiologically favorable pH during relatively long periods while eggs are being handled in it for experimental purposes, within open dishes. No antibiotics are included. If uncleaved eggs are to be handled, however, penicillin and streptomycin should be added, as the oviduct normally contains microbial contaminants on day 0 (see Wolstenholme and O'Connor, 1965, p. 402).

A still more complex medium for early eggs has been introduced by Cole and Paul (1965), to improve development during the late blastocyst and implantation periods, when requirements change and simple media become inadequate. Waymouth's MB 752/1 medium is supplemented with 5 percent calf serum and 2 percent human serum; ATP (0.001 percent); deoxyadenosine, deoxyguanosine, deoxycytidine, and thymidine (each at 0.001 percent); 5-methylcytosine (0.0001 percent); and a feeder layer of irradiated HeLa cells. The embryos are grown in groups of 10 in small drops of medium under paraffin oil previously equilibrated by shaking with medium. The authors suggest that the beneficial aspect of the small-volume arrangement may result from counteracting a loss of diffusible substances.

Analysis of the changing requirements of the developing egg necessitates the use of defined, rather than complex, media, for which the type of medium described by Whitten (1956, 1957) is an appropriate point of departure. In a series of studies by Brinster, several parameters have been investigated and characterized, notably the utilizable energy source. The explanted 2-cell egg was found to be capable of relying upon either lactate, pyruvate, oxaloacetate, or phosphoenolpyruvate as its sole energy source (Brinster, 1965a). The best combination of conditions for development to blastocyst proved to be the inclusion of both lactate (at $2.5–5.0 \times 10^{-2}$ *M*) and pyruvate ($2.5–5.0 \times 10^{-4}$ *M*), at pH 7.38 (Brinster, 1965b). This medium is of course the most favorable one to serve as a baseline for testing effects of a variety of added substances. Its composition is given in Table 1.

The sodium lactate is prepared by adding 1.82 ml of concentrated DL-lactic acid (85–90 percent) to 200 ml of double distilled water, and then adjusting to pH 7.4 (with about 15–20 ml of 1 *N* NaOH). The sodium pyruvate stock is 0.00154 *M* pyruvate in 0.154 *M* NaCl (17 mg per 100 ml). The calcium chloride stock is 0.11 *M*. Most consistent results were obtained when eggs were grown in microdrops (approximately 0.1 ml) in groups of about 12 per drop, under light-weight grade paraffin oil (viscosity 125/135). The paraffin oil is first equilibrated by shaking 10 ml of sterile salt solution (without albumin) with 490 ml oil, bubbling the gas mixture through for 15 minutes, and storing the oil at 37°C until it clears.

Culture Media for Postimplantation Stages

Mouse embryos explanted on days 7–10 can undergo considerable development in culture. Maximal progress is made if the yolk sac remains intact and the embryo is contained within the yolk sac sphere (New and Stein, 1964). For some kinds of experimental work, however, it is necessary to have direct access to the embryo, and therefore the yolk sac must be opened (Smith, 1964).

According to the method of New and Stein (1964), the entire muscular uterine wall is torn open around each decidual swelling from a pregnant female on day 7–10, and the pear-shaped decidua is dissected out. It is incised starting at the broad end and going along the meridional groove, so that the decidua can be torn into two halves; the embryo usually remains embedded in one half. Though balanced salt solution (e.g., Tyrode's) may be used up to this point, the decidua should now be transferred to protein-

TABLE 1. BRINSTER'S (1965b) MEDIUM

SUBSTANCE	MILLIMOLES	GRAMS PER LITER	MILLILITERS OF 0.154 *M* STOCK IN 13 ml
NaCl	94.88	5.546	5.90
Sodium lactate	25.00	2.253	2.10
Sodium pyruvate	0.25	0.028	2.10
KCl	4.78	0.356	0.40
$CaCl_2$	1.71	0.189	0.20
KH_2PO_4	1.19	0.162	0.10
$MgSO_4 \cdot 7H_2O$	1.19	0.294	0.10
$NaHCO_3$	25.00	2.106	2.10
Penicillin G (potassium)	100 units per milliliter		
Streptomycin sulfate	50 μg per milliliter		
Crystalline bovine serum albumin	1 mg per milliliter		

containing medium, such as dilute embryo extract (2–3 parts of Tyrode's with 1 percent glucose + 1 part of ground chick or mouse embryos as described below, under composition of the medium). Reichert's membrane surrounding the embryo is torn open with fine forceps and discarded (see Snell, 1941, or Snell and Stevens, 1966). The final explant consists of the embryo, amnion, and allantois within the yolk sac sphere, and the ectoplacental cone. The medium is a plasma clot made from 15 drops of fowl plasma and 5 drops of embryo extract. The latter is prepared either from 13-day chick embryos, or from whole uteri and contained fetuses of 17- to 19-day pregnant mice. The tissue is ground, diluted with an equal volume of Tyrode's solution containing 1 percent glucose, and centrifuged. This diluted embryo extract is used to transfer the explant to the surface of the plasma clot (in a watch glass or small Petri dish), and is spread so as to just cover the explant with a flat liquid surface. The ectoplacental cone is placed on one side. The culture chamber is gassed with 5 percent CO_2 in air for the presomite embryos, or with 5 percent CO_2 + air containing 60 percent oxygen for the somite stages. The authors employed a buffer solution devised by Pardee (1949) as a method for maintaining CO_2 in the atmosphere. During incubation, the yolk sac enlarges considerably and digests some of the underlying clot, so that the explant sinks into a liquid-filled cavity.

Explants taken on day 7 at the primitive streak stage form only a few somites. If 1–7 somites are present at explantation (on days 8–9), over half go as far as 16–24 somites; the developmental rate is comparable to that *in vivo*, in the most favorable cases. The most advanced development, attained by only a few, was 24–32 somites. When the embryo has more than 7 somites at explantation (on day 9), well over half can progress to the 24- to 32-somite stage in culture. For still later explants (15–20 somites, on days 9–10), sufficient diluted embryo extract is required so as to cover the clot to a depth of about 2 mm. These go up to 30 somites, with blood circulation continuing for a day.

Modifications concerning rat embryos are given in the same paper and a subsequent one (New and Stein, 1964; New, 1966).

If the embryo must be exposed, a plasma clot medium is unfavorable because it promotes cell outgrowth and leads to loss of embryo structure and organization. A semisolid medium stiffened with agar tends to minimize such disorganized outgrowth. Smith (1964) has employed such a medium for cultivation of mouse embryos explanted on day 8 (at 0–10 somites). The composition is: 2 parts of Hanks' BSS containing 0.35 gm per 100 ml purified agar; 2 parts of horse serum; 1 part of 10-day-old chick embryo extract made up 1:1 in Hanks' BSS. To this mixture is added 0.2 ml per milliliter of a 10 × stock of vitamins, as found in Eagle's Minimal Essential Medium. Dissection is performed in a 1:1 mixture of Hanks' BSS and horse serum (pregassed with 5 percent CO_2 in air). The yolk sac and amnion are torn open, so that the embryos can flatten out, but are allowed to remain attached. The embryo can be cultured for 18–20 hours on the surface of the agar before degenerating. During this time, embryos add up to about 8 somites, with earlier-stage explants adding fewer somites.

SPECIAL EXPERIMENTAL TECHNIQUES

Experimental approaches to a number of basic developmental problems are being undertaken with mammalian embryos. While the procedures already presented in this chapter have served as a broad technical foundation in recent investigations, some additional techniques have been devised to satisfy special experimental requirements. In the brief summaries below, some of the more interesting lines of current experimentation will be indicated; the original publications should be consulted for fuller procedural details.

Fertilization *in Vitro*

In a few mammalian species, especially the rabbit, attempts to obtain fertilization of oocytes directly *in vitro* have met with some success and a number of questions concerning the nature of the fertilization process are under examination. Among them is the possible influence of the uterine environment upon sperms, in affecting their capacity for fertilization (Chang, 1959; Thibault, 1961; Austin, 1963; Brackett and Williams, 1965). In the mouse, the explanted oviduct containing ovulated eggs has been used as a means of studying fertilization outside the organism (Brinster and Biggers, 1965; see also the section on Combined Organ Culture and Embryo Culture, below).

Microinjection of Eggs

Macromolecules can be introduced directly into the mammalian egg, according to the techniques employed in the mouse by Lin (1966). The egg, in a microdrop of bovine gamma globulin in a citrate-Locke's solution under mineral oil, is held on the tip of an "egg-holder" pipette and is penetrated by a micromanipulator-controlled injection pipette. In a test of this system, Lin has found that fertilized (pronuclear) mouse eggs which were microinjected *in vitro* with the globulin-containing medium and then transferred to oviducts of synchronous recipients were, in some cases, capable of surviving at least to late fetal life.

Formation of Genetic Mosaic Mice from Aggregated Blastomeres

It is possible to produce adult mice made up of cells of two (or more) distinctive genotypes, chosen at will, with no immunological restrictions (Mintz, 1964, 1965a, 1965c, 1967; Mintz and Palm, 1965). The separate genotypes are present in the same individual from early cleavage onward, and any cell type in the adult may be represented by different genetic populations. The wide range of genetic markers available for introduction into a mosaic situation creates many new avenues along which problems of gene control of differentiation, regulation of physiological events, and etiology of disease can now be explored with precision.

The techniques introduced by Mintz (1964, 1965a) have yielded approximately 95 percent success in formation of mosaic embryos *in vitro* from aggregated blastomeres, and up to 50 percent survival of these embryos past birth (Mintz, 1967 and unpublished data), after their transfer to a recipient female.

Two (or more) eggs are first stripped of their zona pellucida with 0.5 percent pronase (Mintz, 1962) during cleavage, in order to bring their blastomeres into direct contact in a single mass. The cells are apposed in a siliconed dish at 37°C, since aggregation was found to be temperature-dependent. Each of the developing aggregates usually forms a normal embryo in culture, and they are transferred at morula or blastocyst to the uterus of a recipient which is at a stage a day earlier in pseudopregnancy.

We have recently found variation in quality of enzyme lots, and have modified our procedure for preparation of pronase (Mintz, 1962). The filtered non-sterile solution is first incubated for 2 hours at 37°C, as recommended by Gillespie and Spiegelman (1965) for digestion of contaminating ribonuclease, and then dialyzed against Hanks' BSS overnight before sterile filtration.

Development of Isolated Blastomeres

The marked lability in developmental capacity of the preimplantation mammalian egg can be demonstrated not only by the normalcy of mice from aggregated eggs, but also by observing development of isolated blastomeres. Single cells can be separated at the 2- to 8-cell period by pronase treatment and pipetting (Mintz, 1964); some will become miniature but normal embryos.

Alternatively, one or more individual blastomeres can be destroyed with a glass needle, within the intact zona, as shown in the rabbit by Seidel (1960) and in the mouse by Tarkowski (1959b). The normal embryos which are obtained furnish clear positive evidence of full development from only part of the original egg. In all such injury experiments, however, the abnormal cases cannot provide an unambiguous basis for any contrary conclusion.

Combined Organ Culture and Embryo Culture

The fertilized mouse egg may be allowed to develop within its normal environment, the oviduct, after the latter is explanted and maintained as an organ culture. This method lends itself to studies of tubal influences on eggs, and of effects of maternal pretreatment prior to explantation; it has also been used to produce fertilization within the cultured tube following incubation with sperms (Brinster and Biggers, 1965). The culture medium of Brinster (1965a), with pyruvate and glucose, was employed. The ampullary region alone could be cultivated, and was placed on a tea-bag-paper surface in the medium.

Implantation *in Vitro*

The process of implantation involves complex and little understood interrelationships between blastocyst and uterus, along with possible indirect systemic influences. Glenister (1961) has introduced co-culture of apposed rabbit blastocyst and endometrium as a means of manipulating some of the variables experimentally (e.g., hormonal state of the endometrial donor). The embryo is explanted in the blastocyst stage, after removal of the zona pellucida, onto endometrial strips supported on cellulose acetate fabric on top of a semisolid agar medium. Though embryogenesis is not appreciably sustained, invasion of endometrium by trophoblast takes place.

Surgery on Postimplantation Embryos

As indicated earlier (section on Culture Media for Postimplantation Stages), the postimplantation embryo can be directly exposed and grown in culture on an agar medium for limited periods (18–20 hours), during which the effects of surgical intervention can be observed (Smith, 1964). Under these conditions, 4- to 8-somite mouse embryos (day 8) were subjected to one or more transections at various axial levels, or to extirpations, for analysis of somite, notochord, and neural tube morphogenesis.

Cell Cultures from Early Stages

Interesting possibilities exist for the study of differentiation if cells from early embryos could be made to proliferate *in vitro* as cell cultures, rather than as organized embryos. No success has been achieved, however, in obtaining long-term cultures from stages prior to blastocyst. Even at blastocyst, trophoblast cells can attach to the substrate and migrate out as sheets, with overlying embryonic mass cells, but survival is limited in both mouse and rabbit (Cole and Paul, 1965; Cole, Edwards, and Paul, 1966). Better results were obtained from rabbit embryos just before primitive streak formation. The entire embryonic disc was excised and explanted, or its cells were dissociated and then plated onto a collagen substrate (using medium discussed above in the section on Culture Media for Preimplantation Stages, without the feeder layer). Some primary cultures survived. Of special interest are several, derived from dissociated discs, which persisted as cell lines. It must of course be borne in mind that the extent of (inapparent) differentiation of cells at the time of dissociation is not yet known.

REFERENCES

ALLEN, E., 1922: The oestrous cycle in the mouse. *Amer. J. Anat.*, 30: 297.

AUSTIN, C. R., 1960: Anomalies of fertilization leading to triploidy. *J. Cell. Comp. Physiol.*, 56 (Suppl. 1): 1.

———, 1961: *The Mammalian Egg.* 183 pp. Blackwell, Oxford, Eng.

———, 1963: Fertilization and transport of the ovum. In Carl G. Hartman (ed.), *Conference on Physiological Mechanisms Concerned with Conception*, Pergamon Press, New York, p. 285.

———, and J. SMILES, 1948: Phase-contrast microscopy in the study of fertilization and early development of the rat egg. *J. Roy. Micros. Soc.*, 68: 13.

BRACKETT, B. G., and W. L. WILLIAMS, 1965: *In vitro* fertilization of rabbit ova. *J. Exp. Zool.*, 160: 271.

BRADEN, A. W. H., 1957: The relationship between the diurnal light cycle and the time of ovulation in mice. *J. Exp. Biol.*, 34: 177.

———, 1959: Strain differences in the morphology of the gametes of the mouse. *Austral. J. Biol. Sci.*, 12: 65.

———, and C. R. AUSTIN, 1954: Fertilization of the mouse egg and the effect of delayed coitus and of hot-shock treatment. *Austral. J. Sci.*, 7: 552.

BRINSTER, R. L., 1965a: Studies on the development of mouse embryos *in vitro*. II. The effect of energy source. *J. Exp. Zool.*, 158: 59.

———, 1965b: Studies on the development of mouse embryos *in vitro*. IV. Interaction of energy sources. *J. Reprod. Fertil.*, 10: 227.

———, and J. D. BIGGERS, 1965: *In-vitro* fertilization of mouse ova within the explanted fallopian tube. *J. Reprod. Fertil.*, 10: 277.

———, and J. L. THOMSON, 1966: Development of eight-cell mouse embryos *in vitro*. *Exp. Cell. Res.*, 42: 308.

CHANG, M. C., 1950: Development and fate of transferred rabbit ova or blastocyst in relation to the ovulation time of recipients. *J. Exp. Zool.*, 114: 197.

———, 1959: Fertilization of rabbit ova *in vitro*. *Nature*, 184: 466.

COLE, R. J., R. G. EDWARDS, and J. PAUL, 1966: Cytodifferentiation and embryogenesis in cell colonies and tissue cultures derived from ova and blastocysts of the rabbit. *Devel. Biol.*, 13: 385.

———, and J. PAUL, 1965: Properties of cultured preimplantation mouse and rabbit embryos, and cell strains derived from them. In G. E. W. Wolstenholme and M. O'Connor (eds.), *Ciba Foundation Symposium on Preimplantation Stages of Pregnancy*, Churchill, London, Eng., p. 82.

DANIEL, J. C., 1964: Cleavage of mammalian ova inhibited by visible light. *Nature*, 201: 316.

DOYLE, L. L., A. H. GATES, and R. W. NOYES, 1963: Asynchronous transfer of mouse ova. *Fertil. and Steril.*, 14: 215.

EDWARDS, R. G., and A. H. GATES, 1959: Timing of the stages of the maturation divisions, ovulation, fertilization and the first cleavage of eggs of adult mice treated with gonadotrophins. *J. Endocr.*, 18: 292.

FEKETE, E., 1947: Differences in the effects of uterine environment upon development in the DBA and C57 Black strains of mice. *Anat. Rec.*, 98: 409.

FOWLER, R. E., and R. G. EDWARDS, 1957: Induction of superovulation and pregnancy in mature mice by gonadotropins. *J. Endocr.*, 15: 374.

GATES, A. H., 1965: Rate of ovular development as a factor in embryonic survival. In G. E. W. Wolstenholme and M. O'Connor (eds.), *Ciba Foundation Symposium on Preimplantation Stages of Pregnancy*, Churchill, London, Eng., p. 270.

GILLESPIE, D., and S. SPIEGELMAN, 1965: A quantitative assay for DNA-RNA hybrids with DNA immobilized on a membrane. *J. Molec. Biol.*, 12: 829.

GLENISTER, T. W., 1961: Organ culture as a new method for studying implantation of mammalian blastocysts. *Proc. Roy. Soc., Ser. B*, 154: 428.

GRÜNEBERG, H., 1943: The development of some external features in mouse embryos. *J. Hered.*, 34: 89.

HOLTER, H., 1943: Technique of the Cartesian diver. *C. R. Trav. Lab. Carlsberg, Sér. Chim.*, 24: 399.

LANG, D. R., and D. R. LAMOND, 1966: Some factors affecting the response of the immature mouse to pregnant mare serum gonadotrophin and human chorionic gonadotrophin. *J. Endocr.*, 34: 41.

LEWIS, W. H., and E. S. WRIGHT, 1935: On the early development of the mouse egg. *Carneg. Inst. Contrib. to Embryol.*, 25: 115.

LIN, T. P., 1966: Microinjection of mouse eggs. *Science*, 151: 333.

———, and D. W. BAILEY, 1965: Difference between two inbred strains of mice in ovulatory response to repeated administration of gonadotropins. *J. Reprod. Fertil.*, 10: 253.

MC LAREN, A., and D. MICHIE, 1956: Studies on the transfer of fertilized mouse eggs to uterine foster-mothers. I. Factors affecting the implantation and survival of native and transferred eggs. *J. Exp. Biol.*, 33: 394.

MINTZ, B., 1960: Embryological phases of mammalian gametogenesis. *J. Cell. Comp. Physiol.*, 56 (Suppl. 1): 31.

———, 1962: Experimental study of the developing mammalian egg: removal of the zona pellucida. *Science*, 138: 594.

———, 1964: Formation of genetically mosaic mouse embryos, and early development of "lethal (t^{12}/t^{12})-normal" mosaics. *J. Exp. Zool.*, 157: 273.

———, 1965a: Genetic mosaicism in adult mice of quadriparental lineage. *Science*, 148: 1232.

———, 1965b: Nucleic acid and protein synthesis in the developing mouse embryo. In G. E. W. Wolstenholme and M. O'Connor (eds.), *Ciba Foundation Symposium on Preimplantation Stages of Pregnancy*, Churchill, London, Eng., p. 145.

———, 1965c: Experimental genetic mosaicism in the mouse. In G. E. W. Wolstenholme and M. O'Connor (eds.), *Ciba Foundation Symposium on Preimplantation Stages of Pregnancy*, Churchill, London, Eng., p. 194.

———, 1967: Gene control of mammalian pigmentary differentiation. I. Clonal origin of melanocytes. Proc. Nat. Acad. Sci., 58: 344.

———, and J. PALM, 1965: Erythrocyte mosaicism and immunological tolerance in mice from aggregated eggs. *J. Cell. Biol.*, 27: 66A.

NEW, D. A. T., 1966: Development of rat embryos cultured in blood sera. *J. Reprod. Fertil.*, 12: 509.

———, and K. F. STEIN, 1964: Cultivation of post-implantation mouse and rat embryos on plasma clots. *J. Embryol. Exp. Morphol.*, 12: 101.

NOYES, R. W., and Z. DICKMANN, 1961: Survival of ova transferred into the oviduct of the rat. *Fertil. and Steril.*, 12: 67.

———, L. L. DOYLE, A. H. GATES, and D. L. BENTLEY, 1961: Ovular maturation and fetal development. *Fertil. and Steril.*, 12: 405.

PARDEE, A. B., 1949: Measurement of oxygen uptake under controlled pressures of carbon dioxide. *J. Biol. Chem.*, 179: 1085.

PARKER, R. C., 1961: *Methods of Tissue Culture*. 358 pp. Paul B. Hoeber, New York.

PAUL, J., 1960: *Cell and Tissue Culture*. 312 pp. Williams and Wilkins, Baltimore, Md.

PINCUS, G., 1936: *The Eggs of Mammals*. 160 pp. Macmillan, New York.

RUNNER, M. N., 1951: Differentiation of intrinsic and maternal factors governing intrauterine survival of mammalian young. *J. Exp. Zool.*, 116: 1.

———, and A. GATES, 1954: Conception in prepuberal mice following artificially induced ovulation and mating. *Nature*, 174: 222.

———, and J. PALM, 1953: Transplantation and survival of unfertilized ova of the mouse in relation to postovulatory age. *J. Exp. Zool.*, 124: 303.

SEIDEL, F., 1960: Die Entwicklungsfähigkeiten isolierter Furchungszellen aus dem Ei des Kaninchens *Oryctolagus cuniculus*. *Roux' Arch. f. Entwmech.*, 152: 43.

SMITH, L. J., 1964: The effects of transection and extirpation on axis formation and elongation in the young mouse embryo. *J. Embryol. Exp. Morphol.*, 12: 787.

SMITHBERG, M., and M. N. RUNNER, 1960: Retention of blastocysts in nonprogestational uteri of mice. *J. Exp. Zool.*, 143: 21.

SNELL, G. D. (ed.), 1941: *Biology of the Laboratory Mouse*. First ed., 497 pp. Dover, New York.

———, and L. C. STEVENS, 1966: Early embryology. In E. L. Green (ed.), *Biology of the Laboratory Mouse*, 2nd ed., McGraw-Hill, New York.

TARKOWSKI, A., 1959a: Experiments on the transplantation of ova in mice. *Acta Theriol.*, 2: 251.

———, 1959b: Experimental studies on regulation in the development of isolated blastomeres of mouse eggs. *Acta Theriol.*, 3: 191.

THIBAULT, C., 1961: Analyse des conditions de la fécondation *in vitro* de l'oeuf de la Lapine. *Ann. Biol. Anim. Biochim. Biophys.*, 1: 277.

WHITTEN, W. K., 1956: Culture of tubal mouse ova. *Nature*, 176: 96.

———, 1957: Culture of tubal ova. *Nature*, 179: 1081.

———, 1959: Occurrence of anoestrus in mice caged in groups. *J. Endocr.*, 18: 102.

———, and C. P. DAGG, 1961: Influence of spermatozoa on the cleavage rate of mouse eggs. *J. Exp. Zool.*, 148: 173.

WILSON, E. D., and M. X. ZARROW, 1962: Comparison of superovulation in the immature mouse and rat. *J. Reprod. Fertil.*, 3: 148.

WOLSTENHOLME, G. E. W., and M. O'CONNOR (eds.), 1965: *Ciba Foundation Symposium on Preimplantation Stages of Pregnancy*. 430 pp. Churchill, London, Eng.

Avian Embryo Culture

By Robert L. DeHaan

INTRODUCTION

The hen's egg clearly establishes the ultimate in a culture system designed to support the chick embryo outside the body of its mother. It may be viewed as an idealized model which any laboratory culture technique must emulate. The egg provides the essential elements: physical support and protection, immunity from microorganisms, an ideally suited nutrient medium, an efficient mechanism for gas exchange, and a means for disposing of metabolic waste products. It is deficient only in its inability to maintain the required incubation temperature.

Yet this superbly fashioned little culture chamber is universally available in any barnyard. It is undoubtedly because of this ready accessibility that the chick embryo is among the most time-honored of subjects for the study of developmental processes (see Oppenheimer, 1955; New, 1966).

In Ovo Studies

While the first detailed description of the chick embryo is credited to Aristotle in the 4th century B.C., it was Bequelin (1751) who took the first small step toward laboratory cultivation by keeping the living embryo under observation for a protracted period after opening the shell. In the transition of embryology from a purely descriptive to an experimental science, with the works of His, Roux, Spemann, and others, operative techniques became of paramount importance. From the middle of the last century, experimental attacks have been made on the embryo *in ovo* (Valentin, 1851). In fact, much of the fundamental information we have on the causal mechanisms of bird embryogenesis derives from experiments performed on embryos in their natural situation—from the early marking studies of Peebles (1898) and Wetzel (1929) to the recent elegant microsurgical experiments of Lutz *et al.* (1963) on duck embryos—to choose a few examples which span the period. The now routine "window technique" for observing and manipulating the embryo in the egg has been described in standard manuals of experimental embryology (Hamburger, 1960; Rugh, 1962). Recently, Schlesinger (1966) has introduced a wholly new method for observing the embryo, replacing the egg shell with a plastic bag. Because of its simplicity (an ordinary polyethylene sandwich bag can be used) and the remarkably good observational accessibility of the embryo, this technique promises to have special use in the classroom.

However, the technical difficulties of operating on the embryo *in ovo*, especially at early stages (Wolff, 1936), have led to the search for methods of keeping embryos alive after they have been removed from the shell and operated on in more favorable circumstances. Early workers attempted to graft blastoderms, or fragments of them, into subcutaneous sites in adult birds (Fére, 1895; Fére and Elias, 1897) or into newly hatched chicks (Strangeways and Fell, 1926). Much more extensive, and successful, use has been made of grafts to the chorioallantoic membrane (CAM) of host embryos of 7–9 days of incubation. This method was introduced by Rous and Murphy (1911) for studying the growth of tumors, and was first used in connection with embryology by Danchakoff (1916), Hoadley (1924), and Willier (1924). Since that time, the technique has been perfected and used most extensively by Willier and his colleagues. (For reviews, see Rawles, 1952; Coulombre, this volume, pp. 457–469). Grafts have also been transplanted to other sites within an embryonic host. An especially favorable technique, that of intracoelomic grafting, was introduced by Hamburger (1938). Again, descriptions of this technique, in several variations, are already available (Hamburger, 1960; Rugh, 1962; Coulombre, this volume).

In Vitro Cultivation

The first attempts to cultivate the chick embryo *in vitro* were surprisingly successful, considering the primitive methods used. McWhorter and Whipple (1912), who used a hanging drop technique, explanted 9- to 10-somite embryos, and were able to keep them alive in culture up to 31 hours. They had no success with earlier stages. Sabin (1920) used a similar method to observe the formation of blood vessels. Her cultures of presomite and early somite stage embryos survived an average of about 5 hours. However, it was not until the "watch glass technique" was developed for the culture of large explants at the Strangeways Laboratory (Fell and Robison, 1929) that greater success was attained. Waddington (1932) adapted this technique to the whole blastoderm, with the result that the embryo survived and continued nearly normal development for periods of 2 to 3 days. In its essentials, the technique consisted of nothing more than the explantation of the blastoderm to the surface of a plasma clot (composed of equal parts of chicken plasma and embryo extract) contained in a watch glass enclosed in a humidified chamber—the latter provided by a Petri dish containing a ring of moist cotton. The essential point of the method is that the preparation is never allowed to dry, yet it is not submerged under a layer of fluid.

Numerous modifications of this technique have since been introduced. Spratt (1947a) greatly simplified the method by replacing the plasma clot with an agar-albumen base. The latter is not only much simpler to prepare, but, because of the bacteriostatic properties of albumen, eliminates the need for elaborate aseptic precautions. Wolff and Haffen (1952) and later Simon (1956), in Wolff's laboratory, used an agar and embryo-extract base. More recently Britt and Hermann (1959) and Spratt and Haas (1960) have used an agar and egg-extract base (see Table 1). On the other hand, New (1955) recognized the advantage, to the embryo, of remaining in its natural position attached to the vitelline membrane. He employed that membrane, stretched over a pool of albumen, as the substratum upon which the embryo grows. This technique has, in turn, been refined by Nicolet and Gallera (1963) and by DeHaan (1958; 1963a) for particular experimental designs. For a review of the literature on the *in vitro* culture of the chick embryo, see New (1966).

TABLE 1. SUMMARY OF COMPONENTS USED IN SEMISOLID MEDIA FOR EMBRYO CULTURE

MEDIUM	SALT SOLUTION	AGAR FINAL CONC. (%)	EGG ALBUMEN (FINAL VOL. %)	OTHER COMPONENTS (FINAL VOL. %)
Britt and Hermann (1959)	HR*	0.75	Approx. 33†	Whole egg extract 50
DeHaan (1963a)	GHR‡	1.0	50	..
Simon (1956)	Tyrode	0.57	..	Embryo extract§ 24
Spratt (1947)	Chick Ringer**	0.2	Approx. 16†	..
Spratt and Haas (1960)	HR*	1.3	Approx. 33†	Whole egg extract†† 50
Wolff and Haffen (1952)	Tyrode	0.5	..	Embryo extract§ 25

* Howard Ringer: see p. 404.
† An "average" large egg = 35 ml albumen and 17 ml yolk.
‡ Glucose Howard Ringer: see p. 404.
§ Embryonic extract: homogenize 7-day embryos; dilute 1:1 in Tyrode's.
** Chick Ringer: NaCl, 0.9%; KCl, 0.042%; $CaCl_2$, 0.024%.
†† Whole egg extract: shake contents of two unincubated eggs vigorously; centrifuge mixed yolk-albumen at 4,000 rpm for 30 minutes; combine supernatant 1:1 with 2.6% agar in Ringer.

METHODS FOR *IN VITRO* CULTIVATION

The two methods now most commonly employed for making whole embryo explants are the one introduced by Waddington (1932) and later refined by Spratt (1947a, b,) and the other designed by Dennis New (1955). Either of these is sufficiently simple to be used as a laboratory exercise for undergraduate students. No elaborate equipment is needed, nor is it necessary to observe scrupulous sterile precautions, unless nutrient media are used without egg albumen.

The handling of eggs used for cultivation purposes is of some importance. Eggs should be obtained from a reliable supplier and should be free of bacterial or viral contaminants. Ninety percent fertility is common for good eggs throughout the year, with only slight decreases in fertility (to 75 percent) during the hottest summer months. Fertile eggs should be stored in a cool dry location before incubation; 10°–15°C appears to be the optimal temperature. At this temperature, viability does not begin to decrease until after 6–7 days of storage. At lower temperatures, or at temperatures above 18°–20°C, eggs are more perishable.

Numerous balanced salt solutions have been devised for working with chick embryos. The two most commonly employed are those of Pannett and Compton (1924) and Howard (1953). Howard Ringer (HR) is simple to prepare and can be autoclaved if desired without fear of precipitating calcium. It may also be modified by adding phosphate buffer (final concentration: 40 mM), or converted to a nutrient solution by addition of glucose to a final concentration of 1 percent (GHR).

Culture of the Embryo on Semisolid Media

"SPRATT" TECHNIQUE

The original technique (Spratt, 1947a) called for a very soft, dilute agar-albumen medium, in a watch glass-humid chamber preparation. In our own hands, better development and a more reliable and convenient preparation has been obtained using a firmer gel and more concentrated albumen. In addition the watch crystal and Petri dish may be replaced by a 35-mm-diameter plastic tissue culture dish (Falcon Plastic Division, Becton-Dickinson Co.).

A step-by-step outline of the technique and required materials is given below.

1. Howard Ringer solution (HR)

NaCl	7.2 gm
$CaCl_2$ (2 H_2O)	0.17 gm (0.23 gm)
KCl	0.37 gm
Distilled water	1,000 ml

2. Egg Incubation

This technique is most suitable for embryos incubated *in ovo* for 12 to 24 hours at 37.5°C, to stages between three and seven (Hamburger and Hamilton, 1951).

3. Preparation of culture medium

The final medium consists of two components which are prepared separately and combined warm, just before the medium is placed in the culture dishes and allowed to gel.

Part A: (2 percent GHR-agar)—Weigh 2 gm of agar and 1 gm of glucose into a 200-ml flask. Add 100 ml Howard Ringer. Cover flask with aluminum foil and autoclave. After removing from the autoclave, wait a few minutes to be sure the temperature has fallen below the boiling point but is still hot, and then stir the melted agar to produce an even solution.

Part B: Thin albumen obtained from an egg incubated up to 24 hours.

4. To prepare culture cups
   a. Melt Ringer-agar (Part A) in an autoclave. Allow it to cool to 50°C (hot to the touch).
   b. Collect 10 ml thin albumen (Part B) in a graduated cylinder and warm it in a water bath to 45°C. Add 10 ml of Ringer-agar to the albumen, stir quickly, and replace in warm bath at 45–50°C.
   c. Working quickly, pour 1.5–2 ml of the agar-albumen mixture into each of twelve 32-mm culture dishes (or watch glasses), making a layer 1–2 mm deep. Gently swirl the cups and allow to gel. These cups may be stored at 4°C for up to 1 week before use.
5. Operative procedure
   a. Crack an egg into a finger bowl containing about 200 ml HR solution. Hold the yolk steady with a pair of forceps while making a cut through the vitelline membrane all around the blastoderm, about $\frac{1}{4}$ inch from its border.
   b. Suck the disc of vitelline membrane, with attached blastoderm, into a wide-mouth pipette, and transfer it to a Petri dish containing HR solution.
   c. Under a dissecting microscope, clean the blastoderm by swirling it gently through the solution. Free the blastoderm from the vitelline membrane by working jeweler's forceps around its border. Transfer the embryo, or parts of it to be cultured, to the surface of the culture medium with a wide-mouth pipette (3–4 mm, inside diameter). The pipette is best controlled with a soft rubber bulb.
   d. Orient the explant as desired, and flatten it by slowly sucking off excess saline with a fine pipette. With this method the

embryo may be oriented with its dorsal surface (epiblast) up or down.

e. Cover the dish and incubate it at 37.5°C in humidified air. Somewhat better development can be obtained using an atmosphere of 40 percent oxygen, 5 percent carbon dioxide, and 55 percent nitrogen.

REFINEMENTS AND SPECIAL APPLICATIONS

Cultivation of embryos on a semisolid medium is a method especially suited to nutritional and metabolic studies. Most or all of the yolky opaque area can be trimmed away, leaving the embryo dependent for its nutrients upon substances dissolved in the underlying medium (Spratt, 1950b; Harrison, 1960; Klein *et al.*, 1962; Hermann, 1963). In addition, the effects of specific inhibitors and antimetabolites on a wide variety of metabolic and synthetic systems in the embryo can readily be tested (Spratt, 1950a; Klein *et al.*, 1962; Reporter and Ebert, 1965; Wilt, 1965).

The embryo, so cultured, is also accessible to an amazing array of microsurgical interventions, including disarrangement of parts of the blastoderm (Spratt and Haas, 1961a), synthesis of blastoderms larger than normal (Spratt and Haas, 1961b), and parabiotic techniques (Simon, 1956)—to give just a few examples.

To obtain adequate development of unincubated embryos, the standard agar-albumen medium is not satisfactory. For this purpose Spratt and Haas (1960) devised a concentrated agar and egg-extract medium, which has since been used to study the morphogenetic cell movements occurring during gastrulation (Spratt, 1963; Spratt and Haas, 1965) and the degree of determination of the early embryo (Eyal-Giladi and Spratt, 1965).

Morphogenetic movements in prestreak and early somite stages have also been investigated in embryos on semisolid media, using cell-marking techniques. Carbon or carmine particles placed on the epiblast or ectoderm layer (Spratt, 1952; Fraser, 1954), or on the hypoblast (Bellairs, 1953; Spratt and Haas, 1960; LeDouarin, 1964) permit the investigator to trace the movements of these layers with some precision. Moreover, surprisingly normal cell movements can occur even in fragments of embryos cultured on such media (DeHaan, 1964).

Culture of the Embryo on the Vitelline Membrane

THE "NEW" TECHNIQUE (NEW, 1955)

OPERATIVE PROCEDURE. Open an egg by tapping it at the broad end with the handle of a pair of large forceps. Remove pieces of the shell and thick albumen. Pour the thin albumen into a container for later use. Free the yolk of adherent thick albumen as well as possible by teasing it away with forceps, while the yolk is still in the shell; discard this albumen. Pour the yolk into a finger bowl containing about 200 ml of HR solution, taking care not to tear the vitelline membrane (VM) on a sharp edge of broken shell.

Remove any viscous albumen still adhering to the VM with two pairs of forceps. Turn the yolk so that the embryo is uppermost. Grasp the VM with a pair of fine forceps at about the equator of the yolk. With a fine scissors make a cut around the yolk along a line passing through the equator (Fig. 1A). Then grasp the edge of the upper hemisphere of VM with a pair of fine forceps in each hand, and gently peel it off the surface of the yolk. If this peeling operation is performed correctly, the yolk is relatively undisturbed, and the blastoderm comes off

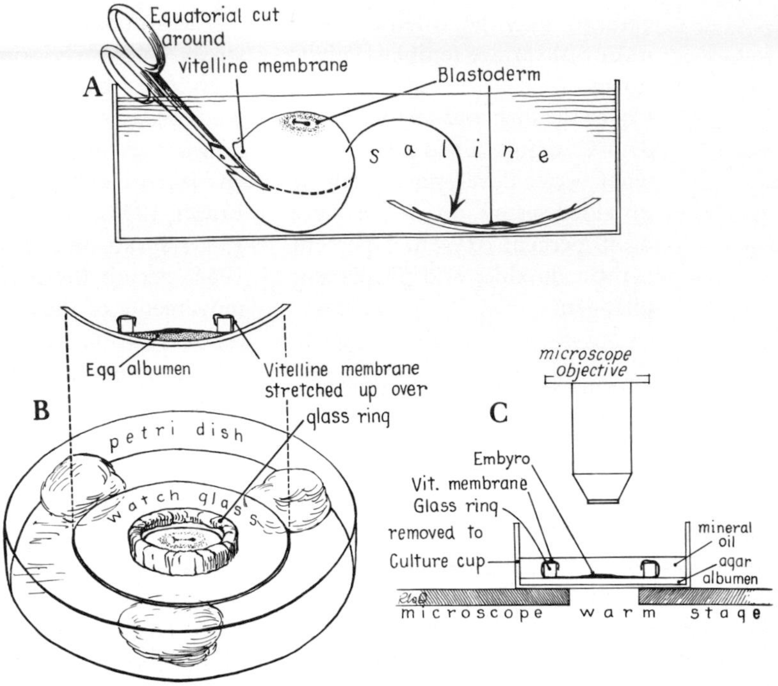

FIG. 1. Embryo culture technique. (A) Embryo being removed from yolk on vitelline membrane; equatorial cut for New culture. (B) Embryo ready for cultivation according to the method of New. (C) Embryo removed to culture dish and covered with oil; ready for time-lapse cinematography. SOURCE: DeHaan, 1963a; courtesy of *Acta Embryologiae Morphologiae Experimentalis.*

attached to the vitelline membrane. It is often possible to obtain the circle of VM almost completely free of yolk. During the peeling process, it is convenient to use one pair of forceps to pull adhering yolk particles away from the VM.

CULTURE PROCEDURE. Pull the VM (with attached blastoderm) through the saline to a watch glass which has been submerged in the finger bowl. Take care that the membrane slides on the watch glass with the blastoderm up. Transfer the watch glass to a paper towel on the work surface. Using two pairs of forceps, straighten and extend the VM. Dip a glass ring[1] in saline, and place it on top of the VM, encircling the blastoderm. Grasp the edges of the membrane which extend beyond the ring and pull gently until the surface within the circle is relatively flat. Then fold the edges of the VM up over the ring. Any small wrinkles left in the membrane at this stage can be ignored, as they

[1] Glass rings 25 mm inside diameter × 30 mm outside diameter × 3 mm thick may be cut from 25-mm tubing. They should be fire-polished to remove sharp edges. For student use split steel key rings are excellent and inexpensive. (C. T. Williamson Co., 1 Montgomery St., Bellville, N.J., Size #48.) One-inch cardboard rings are also suitable.

tend to disappear after the preparation has been returned to the incubator.

Suck off excess saline on the surface of the preparation, and under it, using a fine pipette. It is convenient at this point to transfer the preparation to the stage of a dissecting microscope to determine the stage and condition of the embryo. If particles of yolk still adhere to the surface of the vitelline membrane, they may be loosened by a stream of Ringer solution from an eye dropper and then pipetted off. However, care must be exercised to avoid loosening the edges of the blastoderm in the process. Next, a dropper full of the thin albumen, which was previously reserved, is squirted under the vitelline membrane by lifting one edge of the glass ring; avoid introducing air bubbles under the preparation during the process. The final preparation thus consists of a circle of vitelline membrane with the blastoderm attached, stretched across the bottom of a glass ring, endoderm side up. The watch glass containing this preparation is placed on a ring of moist cotton in a Petri dish containing 3–4 ml HR solution, covered, labeled, and incubated until used for observation or treatment (Fig. 1B). For prolonged culture, the embryo should be incubated in an atmosphere of 40 percent oxygen, 5 percent carbon dioxide, and 55 percent nitrogen; and the thin albumen should be refreshed daily.

REFINEMENTS AND SPECIAL APPLICATIONS

With the New technique, the embryo generally forms an excellent extraembryonic circulation, grows and expands normally and, with care, may develop well for 3 days in culture. It is therefore well adapted to studies of normal development and morphogenesis with marking techniques or time-lapse cinematography (see below). New (1956) has used the technique to investigate the formation of subblastodermic fluid, and also (1959) to study the adhesive and expansive relationships of the blastoderm on the vitelline membrane. He showed experimentally that the blastoderm adheres to the VM at its peripheral edge by means of specialized adhesive cells which form a fringelike border around the entire blastoderm. Expansion of the blastoderm results from outward migration of these ameboid cells (see Bellairs, 1964).

In position on the membrane, the embryo lies with its endoderm surface uppermost. It is thus especially suitable for studies of the hypoblast and endoderm layer, and of structures which develop ventrally such as the foregut and heart. DeHaan has taken advantage of this situation to study the relative movements of the endoderm and precardiac mesoderm (1963a, b, c) and has applied chemical and surgical treatments to the endoderm in order to modify cardiac development (1958, 1959; for review, see DeHaan, 1965). With the embryo in this position, Rosenquist (1966) and Rosenquist and DeHaan (1966) have replaced small fragments of the blastoderm with homologous tissue taken from a donor labeled with tritiated thymidine. They have found that such implants heal in rapidly, participate normally in the development of the host embryo, and can later be identified by autoradiographic methods.

To gain access to the dorsal surface without removing the embryo from its vitelline membrane, Rosenquist (1966) cut and folded back a flap of endoderm-mesoderm, exposing the epiblast to receive his implants. Nicolet and Gallera (1963) solved the problem differently. They simply turned the entire ring preparation over, allowing the embryo to hang suspended from the VM (as it normally does *in ovo*) in a pool of albumen. This refinement yields excellent development of the embryo and also permits the formation of a normal amnion—unlike all other culture methods.

RELATED TECHNIQUES

Methods for Long-Term or Continuous Observation

To observe the embryo during its development *in vitro*, certain precautions must be taken. If the Petri dish containing the embryo is removed from the incubator and opened repeatedly, it will cool and lose moisture. Observation of the embryo on a warm stage or in an incubator through a glass cover, is generally unsatisfactory because of the condensation of moisture on the underside of the cover, which obscures the view. In a time-lapse cinematographic study of the early morphogenesis of the heart, DeHaan (1963a, b) avoided these difficulties by submerging the embryo under a layer of mineral oil. Embryos were explanted according to the New technique. After about an hour of incubation at 37°C, to allow the vitelline membrane to stretch smooth and adhere firmly to the glass ring, the entire preparation—ring, membrane, and blastoderm—was transferred to a small tissue culture cup containing a layer 1 mm deep of agar-albumen medium (Table 1). Mineral oil was then pipetted carefully into the cup until the embryo and glass ring were submerged. Under these conditions (Fig. 1C) the embryo grows and develops normally on a microscope warm stage. Since mineral oil is nonvolatile, and immiscible with water or aqueous solutions, it remains optically clear and completely prevents evaporation from the preparation beneath it. It does not interfere with gas exchange, however, since both oxygen and carbon dioxide diffuse freely through it.

Unfortunately, most commercially available mineral oils are toxic to cells and embryonic tissues. One which is especially light and nontoxic is obtainable, however, under the name of "Klearol."[2] In the author's laboratory, mineral oil has proved to be a convenient method of observing a wide variety of live preparations. It is used routinely with chick embryo explants, organ cultures, and tissue cultures of dissociated heart cells growing as monolayers on glass or plastic, permitting repeated or continuous observation and photography. (For details of cinematographic techniques, see DeHaan, 1963a, b, and Rose, 1963.)

Preparation of Whole Mounts of Embryos Cultivated *in Vitro*

PROCEDURE FOR FIXING EMBRYOS THAT HAVE BEEN CULTURED BY THE "NEW" TECHNIQUE

Secure or make up the desired fixative. For routine fixation of young chick embryos to be used for whole mounts or sectioning, 10 percent neutral Formol (i.e., 4 percent formaldehyde) made up in Howard Ringer solution, has proved quite satisfactory. Pour some of the fixative into a small specimen jar. Include in this jar a paper tag with the number of the embryo. Remove the chick culture from the incubator and clean it if necessary with Ringer solution. Squirt a dropper full of fixative on the surface of the blastoderm. After 2–3 minutes (no more) tear a small hole in the vitelline membrane near the glass ring. Lift the ring with adhering VM and blastoderm from the watch glass, allowing fluids to drain through the tear. Transfer to a Petri dish containing enough Howard Ringer solution to cover the ring. Now loosen the blastoderm from the VM by a

[2] White mineral oil #7617; Sonneborn Division, Witco Chemical Co., Inc,. 277 Park Ave., New York, N.Y. 10017.

gentle pulling action with two pairs of fine forceps. When the blastoderm is completely free of the VM, it can be floated away from the glass ring. Transfer the embryo, with the aid of a section lifter, to a labeled jar of fixative. After a few minutes, see that the blastoderm is resting flat against the bottom of the specimen jar, and is not folded or floating. The embryo should remain in 10 percent Formol overnight (it may stay in 2–3 days if necessary).

After the embryos are properly fixed, they should be transferred to 70 percent ethanol. For whole mount preparations, stepwise dehydration through intermediate concentrations of alcohol is not necessary.

STAINING WITH ALCOHOLIC COCHINEAL

To make up alcoholic cochineal stain: dissolve 10 gm cochineal powder in 90 ml 70 percent ethanol. Shake the bottle well, and let it stand for 2–3 days, with occasional shaking. Filter through Whatman No. 4 paper. Dilute 1:10 in 70 percent ethanol. If necessary, filter again. Once made up in this fashion, the stain keeps indefinitely.

To stain embryos intended for whole mounts, drain the 70 percent ethanol off them and cover them with the filtered stain. They should remain overnight. (They can be left in the stain for longer periods, but best results are obtained if the staining period is not more than 24 hours.)

At the end of the staining period, the stain should be poured off. (It can be refiltered and reused many times.) The embryo is then rinsed in 70 percent ethanol. Occasionally, with very fresh staining solutions the embryo may be slightly overstained. In this event it can be destained in a saturated solution of Li_2CO_3 in 70 percent ethanol. During this destaining, the embryos should be checked frequently under a dissecting microscope until properly differentiated. As a general criterion, the destaining can be stopped when the somites of the embryo are clearly visible. At this stage, the central nervous system and the heart area may remain relatively opaque, but these should become distinct during the subsequent dehydration and clearing. Therefore, when the somites are distinct, the Li_2CO_3 solution may be poured off and replaced by 80 percent ethanol. The embryo should remain in the 80 percent for a minimum of 10 minutes, followed by 90 percent and 95 percent ethanol, also for a minimum of 10 minutes each. Following this dehydration, the embryo is transferred to Pine Oil I, and then to Pine Oil II, for clearing. It should remain in each change of pine oil for at least 30 minutes (upper time limit not critical). Then transfer the embryo to a Syracuse dish containing microscopic mounting medium (at the viscosity as it comes from the bottle). Cover to prevent evaporation (and hardening) and leave in the mounting medium at least half an hour. (Again, the upper time limit is not critical.)

TO MOUNT THE EMBRYO ON A SLIDE

Trim the embryo to the desired proportions while it is still in the Syracuse dish of mounting medium. Using a diamond marking pencil, write the number of the embryo on one end of a 1- × 3-inch slide. Place a polyethylene ring[3] in the center of the slide and cover the area within the ring with mounting medium. Transfer the trimmed embryo to the center of the ring, using a small spatula. Spread a thin coat of dilute mounting medium on a 22- × 22-mm cover slip and lower this slip onto the ring enclosing the embryo. Press the cover slip lightly with the blunt

[3] Rings 18 mm outside diameter × 14 mm inside diameter are punched from polyethylene sheet 0.4 mm thick.

end of a pair of forceps (or similar object) to cause any trapped air bubbles to escape. Place the entire slide on a warm slide bar and put a small weight in the center of the cover slip. Leave on the warm bar overnight to promote hardening of the mounting medium. Excess medium may then be removed from around the edges of the cover slip with a xylene-moistened cloth or tissue. The slide may then be labeled as desired.

REFERENCES

BELLAIRS, R., 1953: Studies on the development of the foregut in the chick blastoderm. 2. The morphogenetic movements. *J. Embryol. Exptl. Morphol.*, 1: 369.

———, 1964: Biological aspects of the yolk of the hen's egg. *Adv. Morph.*, 4: 217.

BEQUELIN, M., 1751: Mémoire sur l'art de couver les oeufs ouverts. *K. Akad. der Wissenschaften, Berlin*, 5: 71.

BRITT, G. L. and H. HERMANN, 1959: Protein accumulation in early chick embryos, grown under different conditions of explantation. *J. Emb. Exptl. Morphol.*, 7: 66.

DANCHAKOFF, V., 1916: Equivalence of different hematopoietic anlages. *Am. J. Anat.*, 20: 255.

DE HAAN, R. L., 1958: Cell migration and morphogenetic movements. In W. D. McElroy and B. Glass (eds.), *A Symposium on the Chemical Basis of Development*, Johns Hopkins Press, Baltimore, p. 339.

———, 1959: Cardia bifida and the development of pacemaker function in the early chick heart. *Devel. Biol.*, 1: 586.

———, 1963a: Organization of the cardiogenic plate in the early chick embryo. *Acta Embryol. Morph. Exp.*, 6: 26.

———, 1963b: Migration patterns of the precardiac mesoderm in the early chick embryo. *Exptl. Cell Research*, 29: 544.

———, 1963c: Oriented cell movements in embryogenesis. In R. J. C. Harris (ed.), *Biological Organization at the Cellular and Supracellular Level*, Academic Press, New York and London, p. 147.

———, 1964: Cell interactions and oriented movements during development. *J. Exptl. Zool.*, 157: 127.

———, 1965: Morphogenesis of the vertebrate heart. In R. L. DeHaan and H. Ursprung (eds.), *Organogenesis*, Holt, Rinehart and Winston, New York, p. 377.

EYAL-GILADI, H., and N. T. SPRATT, 1965: Embryo-forming potencies of the young chick blastoderm. *J. Embryol. Exptl. Morphol.*, 13: 267.

FELL, H. B., and R. ROBISON, 1929: The growth, development, and phosphatase activity of embryonic avian femora and limb buds cultivated *in vitro*. *Biochem. J.*, 23: 767.

FÉRE, C., 1895: Note sur le sort de blastodermes de poulet implantés dans les tissus d'animaux de la même espèce. *Compt. Rend. Soc. Biol.*, 47: 331.

———, and N. ELIAS, 1897: Note sur l'évolution d'organes d'embryos de poulet greffés sous la peau d'oiseaux adultes. *Arch. Anat. Micr.*, 1: 417.

FRASER, R., 1954: Studies on the hypoblast of the young chick embryo. *J. Exptl. Zool.*, 126: 349.

HAMBURGER, V., 1938: Morphogenetic and axial self-differentiation of transplanted limb primordia of 2-day chick embryos. *J. Exptl. Zool.*, 77: 379.

———, 1960: *A Manual of Experimental Embryology*. University of Chicago Press, Chicago.

———, and H. L. HAMILTON, 1951: A series of normal stages in the development of the chick embryo. *J. Morphol.*, 88: 49.

HARRISON, J. R., 1960: *In vitro* utilization of

glucose by the chick embryo at early stages. *Physiol. Zool.*, 33: 68.

HERMANN, H., 1963: Quantitative studies of protein synthesis in some embryonic tissues. In M. Locke (ed.), *Cytodifferentiation and Macromolecular Synthesis.* Twenty-First Growth Symposium, Academic Press, New York, p. 85.

HOADLEY, L., 1924: The independent differentiation of isolated chick primordia in chorio-allantoic grafts. I. The eye, nasal region and mesencephalon. *Biol. Bull.*, 46: 281.

HOWARD, E., 1953: Some effects of sodium chloride concentration on the development of early chick blastoderms in culture. *J. Cell. Comp. Physiol.*, 41: 237.

KLEIN, N. W., E. MC CONNELL, and B. J. BUCKINGHAM, 1962: Growth of explanted chick embryos on a chemically defined medium and effects of specific amino acid deficiencies. *Devel. Biol.*, 5: 296.

LE DOUARIN, N., 1964: Études expérimentales de l'organogenèse du tube digestif et du foie chez l'embryon de poulet. *Bull. Biol. France Belg.*, 98: 543.

LUTZ, H., M. DEPARTOUT, J. HUBERT, and C. PIEAU, 1963: Contribution a l'étude de la potentialité du blastoderme non incubé chez les oiseaux. *Devel. Biol.*, 6: 23.

MC WHORTER, J. E., and H. O. WHIPPLE, 1912: The development of the blastoderm of the chick *in vitro*. *Anat. Rec.*, 6: 121.

NEW, D. A. T., 1955: A new technique for the cultivation of the chick embryo *in vitro*. *J. Emb. Exptl. Morphol.*, 3: 320.

———, 1956: The formation of sub-blastodermic fluid in hen's eggs. *J. Emb. Exptl. Morph.*, 4: 221.

———, 1959: The adhesive properties and expansion of the chick blastoderm. *J. Emb. Exptl. Morph.*, 7: 146.

———, 1966: *The Culture of Vertebrate Embryos*, 245 pp, Logos Press, London.

NICOLET, G., and J. GALLERA, 1963: Dans quelles conditions l'amnios de l'embryon de poulet peut-il se former en culture *in vitro?* *Experientia*, 19: 165.

OPPENHEIMER, J. M., 1955: Problems, concepts, and their history. In B. H. Willicr, P. Weiss, and V. Hamburger (eds.), *Analysis of Development*, W. B. Saunders Co., Philadelphia, p. 1.

PANNETT, C. A., and A. COMPTON, 1924: The cultivation of tissues in saline embryonic juice. *Lancet*, 206: 381.

PEEBLES, F., 1898: Some experiments on the primitive streak of the chick. *Roux' Arch. Entwmech. Organ.*, 7: 405.

RAWLES, M. E., 1952: Transplantation of normal embryonic tissues. *Ann. N.Y. Acad. Sci.*, 55: 302.

REPORTER, M. C., and J. D. EBERT, 1965: A mitochondrial factor that prevents the effects of Antimycin A on myogenesis. *Devel. Biol.*, 12: 154.

ROSE, G. G. (ed.), 1963: *Cinemicrography in Cell Biology*. Academic Press, New York.

ROSENQUIST, G. C., 1966: A radioautographic study of labeled grafts in the chick blastoderm. Development from primitive streak stages to stage 12. *Carnegie Inst. of Washington, Contrib. to Embryology*, 38: 71.

———, and R. L. DE HAAN, 1966: Migration of precardiac cells in the chick embryo: a radioautographic study. *Carnegie Inst. of Washington, Contrib. to Embryology*, 38: 111.

ROUS, P., and J. B. MURPHY, 1911: Tumor implantations in the developing embryo. *J. Amer. Med. Assoc.*, 56: 741.

RUGH, R., 1962: *Experimental Embryology*. Burgess Press, Minneapolis.

SABIN, F. R., 1920: Studies on the origin of blood-vessels and of red blood-corpuscles as seen in the living blastoderm of chicks during the second day of incubation. *Carnegie Inst. of Washington, Contrib. to Embryology*, 9: 213.

SCHLESINGER, A. B., 1966: Plastic bag culture method for chick embryos. CUEBS *News* (Feb.), 2: 10.

SIMON, D., 1956: Sur une technique de culture *in vitro* de blastodermes entiers d'embryons de poulets et sur les interventions expérimentales qu'elle rend possibles. *Arch. d'Anat. Micr. Morphol. Exper.*, 45: 290.

SPRATT, N. T., 1947a: A simple method for explanting and cultivating early chick embryos *in vitro*. *Science*, 106: 452.

———, 1947b: Development *in vitro* of the early chick blastoderm explanted on yolk and albumin extract saline-agar substrate. *J. Exptl. Zool.*, 106: 345.

———, 1950a: Nutritional requirements of the early chick embryo. II. Differential nutritional requirements for morphogenesis and differentiation of the heart and brain. *J. Exptl. Zool.*, 114: 375.

———, 1950b: Nutritional requirements of the early chick embryo. III. Metabolic basis of morphogenesis and differentiation as revealed by the use of inhibitors. *Biol. Bull.*, 99: 120.

———, 1952: Localization of the prospective neural plate in the early chick blastoderm. *J. Exptl. Zool.*, 120: 109.

———, 1963: Role of the substratum, supracellular continuity and differential growth in morphogenetic cell movements. *Devel. Biol.*, 7: 51.

———, and H. HAAS, 1960: Morphogenetic movements in the lower surface of the unincubated and early chick blastoderm. *J. Exptl. Zool.*, 144: 139.

———, and ———, 1961a: Integrative mechanisms in development of the early chick blastoderm. II. Role of morphogenetic movements and regenerative growth in synthetic and topographically disarranged blastoderms. *J. Exptl. Zool.*, 147: 57.

———, and ———, 1961b: Integrative mechanisms in development of the early chick blastoderm. III. Role of cell population size and growth potentiality in synthetic systems larger than normal. *J. Exptl. Zool.*, 147: 271.

———, and ———, 1965: Germ layer formation and the role of the primitive streak in the chick. I. Basic architecture and morphogenetic tissue movements. *J. Exptl. Zool.*, 158: 9.

STRANGEWAYS, T. S. P., and H. B. FELL, 1926: Experimental studies on the differentiation of embryonic tissues growing *in vivo* and *in vitro*. II. The development of the isolated early embryonic eye of the fowl when cultivated *in vitro*. *Proc. Roy. Soc.*, B100: 273.

VALENTIN, G., 1851: Ein Beitrag zur Entwicklungsgeschichte der Doppelmissbildungen. *Vierordt's Arch. f. Phys. Heilk*, 10: 1.

WADDINGTON, C. H., 1932: Experiments on the development of chick and duck embryos cultivated *in vitro*. *Phil. Trans. Roy. Soc.*, B221: 179.

WETZEL, R., 1929: Untersuchungen am Hünchen. Die Entwicklung des Keims während der ersten beiden Bruttage. *Roux' Arch. Entwmech.*, 119: 118.

WILLIER, B. H., 1924: The endocrine glands and the development of the chick. *Amer. J. Anat.*, 33: 67.

WILT, F. H., 1965: Regulation of the initiation of chick embryo hemoglobin synthesis. *J. Mol. Biol.*, 12: 331.

WOLFF, ET., 1936: Les bases de la tératogenèse expérimentale des vertébrés amniotes, d'après les resultats de méthodes directes. *Arch. Anat. Hist. Embryol.*, 22: 1.

———, and K. HAFFEN, 1952: Sur une méthode de culture d'organes embryonnaires *in vitro*. *Texas Rept. Biol. Med.*, 10: 463.

Plant Embryo Culture*

By V. Raghavan

INTRODUCTION

Excised plant embryos have been used in experimental embryology since 1904, when Hännig cultured aseptically embryos of *Raphanus* and *Cochlearia* in media of known composition. The development of new techniques, particularly those relating to the culture of isolated plant organs, and the discovery and characterization of plant growth substances have enormously broadened the horizon of embryo culture. By growing embryos outside the environment of the ovule it is possible to study the factors which influence their metabolism, growth, differentiation, and morphogenesis, as they vary in their functional capacity and proceed from stage to stage during progressive embryogenesis. The seeds of certain hybrid plants which were traditionally condemned as being incapable of germination have attained new importance by the ability of embryos excised from such seeds to resume normal growth when cultured in a nutrient medium. In several species dormancy of seeds has been overcome by excising and culturing the embryos. Thus embryo culture offers a new and refined parameter with which to characterize embryogenesis and related problems in plants.

This manifold application of embryo culture makes it impossible within the space of this chapter to consider in detail the methods used by different workers in culturing embryos. Rather, the treatment will be limited to salient features in the culture of plant embryos as they relate to the choice of materials, nutritional requirements, and other conditions for successful growth of the embryos. In regard to discussion of results, where possible, key references will be cited from which detailed information may be obtained.

EMBRYO FORMATION IN ANGIOSPERMS

For an understanding of the problems in embryo culture, it will be necessary to describe briefly the stages in the normal development of an embryo within the ovule. Although the following description applies to the embryogenesis in Shepherd's Purse (*Capsella bursa-pastoris*, Cruciferae), the pattern of embryo formation observed here is typical of a wide variety of dicotyledonous plants. The zygote undergoes the first division by formation of a transverse wall. In the two-celled embryo, the

* The author wishes to express appreciation for the suggestions made by Dr. B. C. Stone and Dr. G. B. Evans for improvement of the manuscript.

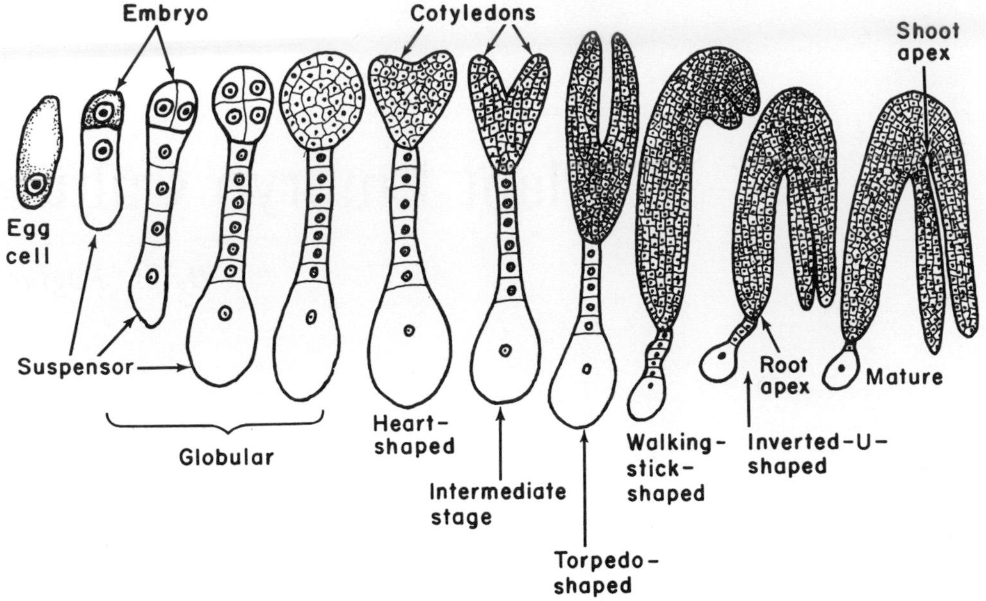

FIG. 1. Stages in the normal development of embryos of *Capsella bursa-pastoris*.

cell nearest to the base of the embryo sac forms a multicellular haustorial structure, called the suspensor, and the apical cell forms the embryo proper. The apical cell divides by both transverse and longitudinal divisions. The developing embryo passes successively through "globular" (less than 80 μ long), "heart-shaped" (81–250 μ long), "intermediate-stage" (251–450 μ long), "torpedo-shaped" (451–700 μ long), "walking-stick-shaped" (701–1,000 μ long), "inverted-U-shaped" (1,001–1,700 μ long) and "mature" (more than 1,700 μ long) stages (Rijven, 1952; Raghavan and Torrey, 1963). The globular embryo has a radial symmetry which it acquires from the egg and which is maintained until the beginning of the heart-shaped stage. At the end of the globular stage, the cotyledons appear at the free end and the spherical embryo becomes more or less heart-shaped. During further development the cotyledons and the future stalk (hypocotyl) elongate (intermediate and torpedo-shaped stages) and a mound of rapidly dividing cells from which the leaves subsequently arise develops in the depression between the cotyledons. Owing to spatial restrictions inside the ovule, the embryo becomes curved at the tip (walking-stick-shaped) and finally assumes the shape of a horseshoe (inverted-U-shaped and mature embryos). For convenience, embryos of different ages are grouped into three morphological stages. They are: proembryos (globular and smaller embryos), immature embryos (heart-shaped, intermediate, and torpedo-shaped), and differentiated embryos (walking-stick-shaped, inverted-U-shaped, and mature); these are shown in Fig. 1.

CULTURE TECHNIQUES

General

A beginner in embryo culture seldom needs to know any special culture techniques other than those routinely used in microbiology. However, there are certain features that are unique to culture of plant embryos which will be emphasized in this article. In the following description it is assumed that excision and transfer of embryos to nutrient media will be done under aseptic conditions in a transfer room using sterilized instruments. The choice of dissecting instruments and the type of containers to be used to grow embryos should be dictated by the nature of the material and the purposes of the experiment, and no generalizations can be made. The nutrient media and glassware should be suitably sterilized. The usual procedure for sterilization of culture media and glassware is by autoclaving at 15 pounds per square inch for 15 minutes; glassware can also be sterilized by dry heat (about 250°C) for 2–3 hours. Organic supplements such as vitamins, amino acids, and growth substances should preferably be sterilized by passage through membrane filters, and then added to the autoclaved mixture in suitable amounts to give the desired final concentrations. Growth of plant tissues in culture is now a well established practice, and one need only refer to the book by White (1963) for ample instructions.

Plant Materials

Embryos excised from moderately large seeds such as those of various legumes and cereals are good starting materials for culture. Seeds have the advantage of providing a large number of embryos of the same genetic strain and of more or less the same stage of development. The embryo contained in the seed is a miniature plant in itself, consisting of embryonic leaves, stem-bearing shoot tip, and a root tip at the basal end. The ease with which the embryos from seeds grow in relatively simple media offers a good introduction to embryo culture work and will enable the investigator to appreciate clearly the problems, as they unfold, in culturing progressively smaller embryos.

When embryos of specific stages of development are required to start cultures, it is best to select plants which flower and fruit regularly in order to ensure a sufficient supply of material in the desired stage. Shepherd's Purse is particularly suited for this type of study: the inflorescence in this plant is a raceme and in a single raceme fertilized ovules in varying stages of maturity as well as unopened flowers are abundantly found. Each capsule contains about 20–25 ovules which are more or less uniform in their development. With a little practice, excision of the embryo is relatively easy. Several other species of Cruciferae, and members belonging to Gramineae have some of the advantages of *Capsella* and have been utilized in embryo culture studies for many years.

With certain plants it is necessary to hand-pollinate the flowers as soon as they open in order to obtain embryos of specific developmental stages. When extensive work on a species is planned, it is informative to obtain growth data on the embryos from hand-pollinated ovaries. One is then able to predict the size of the embryo inside the ovule from the number of days after pollination.

Of particular interest are orchid seeds, which contain undifferentiated embryos surrounded by a thin and membranous testa (Withner, 1959). There are no storage tissues such as cotyledons or endosperm to interfere in nutritional studies, and the relatively small size of the embryos makes possible cultivation of large samples.

Fern embryos are suitable objects for experimental embryology but have been little investigated. Fern gametophytes bearing sex organs can be easily grown from spores and maintained in sterile culture in a simple medium. Fertilization and subsequent growth of the embryos can be controlled in the culture dish. Each gametophyte produces one to several functional embryos, which are available for culture over a long period of time.

In principle, embryos from any plant can be cultivated *in vitro*, but the choice of species is determined largely by the problem at hand. According to a recent survey (Narayanaswami and Norstog, 1964) embryos from 103 species distributed within 39 families of vascular plants have been cultured.

Sterilization

Inasmuch as the embryos are lodged within the sterile environment of the ovule, surface sterilization of the embryos as such is not often necessary. Instead, the entire ovules, seeds, or capsules containing ovules are sterilized and the embryos excised aseptically. Any commercial hypochlorite bleach is recommended for this purpose. In our laboratory we have obtained good results by surface sterilizing the material in 5 percent filtered solution of "Pittchlor" (Pittsburgh Plate Glass Co.) for about 5 minutes, followed by several rinses in sterile water. When the material is small and light, it is supported on paper gauze during sterilization and subsequent washings.

Excision of the Embryos

Since embryos are generally small and often inaccessible, it is necessary to free them from the surrounding tissues before transfer to the nutrient medium. With hard-coated seeds, isolation procedures begin with soaking them in water for periods varying from a few hours to a few days so that the embryos can be removed with ease. Seeds are generally surface sterilized before soaking, although after prolonged periods of soaking they may need to undergo a second sterilization.

Splitting open the seeds and transferring the embryos to the nutrient medium is the simplest technique that can be used with seeds. Procedures for the isolation of comparatively small embryos require that they be removed from the ovule intact and without damage. This aim can be best achieved by carrying out the operations under a dissecting microscope. The following procedure has been used in removing embryos of varying stages of development from the ovules of *Capsella* (Raghavan and Torrey, 1963). All operations on the sterilized capsules were done under a dissecting microscope at a magnification of 90 ×, keeping the tissues in a depression slide containing a few drops of the sterile culture medium. The outer wall of the capsule was removed by a cut in the region of the placenta, and the halves were pulled apart to expose the ovules (Fig. 2a, b). A single ovule was positioned in the depression of a fresh slide with a drop of the medium. In this situation, a small incision in the ovule (Fig. 2c) followed by slight pressure with a blunt needle was sufficient to free walking-stick-shaped and older embryos from the ovules; these embryos without any suspensor cells floated freely in the medium. Torpedo-shaped and younger embryos were confined to one longitudinal half of the ovule and were clearly visible through the chalaza. With the help of a sharp mounted blade the ovule was split longitudinally to isolate the embryo-containing half (Fig. 2d). This operation, if carefully done, rips the embryo sac down the center, exposing the tiny embryo with its attached suspensor. By carefully teasing apart the tissues of the ovules at this stage with #11 surgeons' blades (Clay-Adams), the

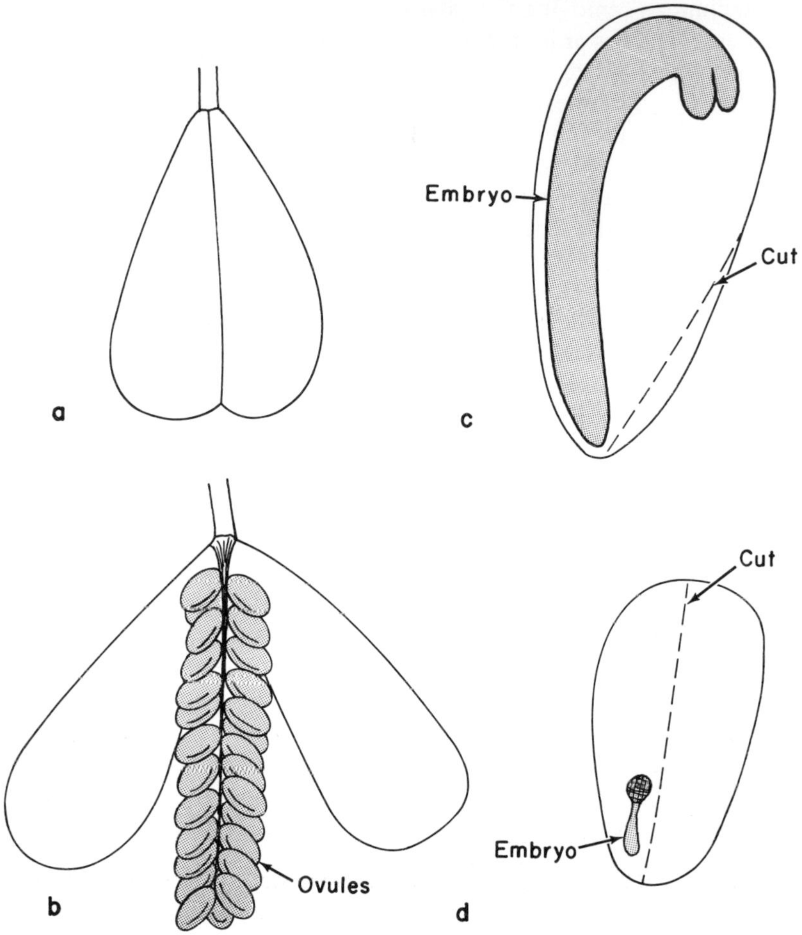

FIG. 2. Isolation of the embryos of *Capsella*. (a) A capsule. (b) The capsule has been opened to expose the ovules. (c) An ovule with walking-stick-shaped embryo inside. The dotted lines show the region of incision of the ovule to release the embryo. (d) An ovule with globular embryo. A cut shown by the dotted lines exposes the embryo.

entire complement of the embryo including suspensor cells could be removed without any apparent injury to them. Embryos only 40 μ long were isolated by this method. Extreme caution must be taken here to see that the operating instruments do not come in contact with the embryo proper; otherwise there is danger that the embryo may break away from the suspensor. Although we have not obtained any evidence on the role of suspensor cells in the growth of cultured embryos, the presence of suspensor cells along with the embryo proper helped in locating them in the dissecting medium after isolation.

For isolation of embryos of the fern *Todea barbara*, the gametophytes were positioned by insect pins in a depression slide coated with a layer of paraffin. Once the embryo is located by cutting the neck of the archegonium, it can be released into the medium by removing the calyptra and surrounding tissues or by applying pressure on the gametophyte by the end of a needle. By this means even fertilized zygotes were removed and cultured (De-Maggio, 1961).

By discriminating selection of dissecting instruments, these procedures may be modified for other plant materials. It must be emphasized that isolation of very small embryos is a delicate operation and survival following culture is often low. As media for growth of embryos in the very early division phases (2- to 32-celled stages) and for unsegmented zygotes are perfected, use of sophisticated instruments like micromanipulators or similar precision mechanical devices for isolation of early stages may prove necessary.

After isolation, the actual transfer of embryos to the nutrient medium presents no difficulty. They are gently sucked along with a drop of dissecting medium into micropipettes with smooth polished tips and deposited on the surface of solidified nutrient medium contained in test tubes or Petri dishes. For making hanging drop cultures the embryo is gently expelled in the middle of a small drop of medium on a clean #1 cover glass. The cover glass is inverted and placed over the depression of a slide. The sides of the cover glass are sealed with a melted 1:1 paraffin-petrolatum mixture to prevent evaporation of the nutrient medium, and incubated at a suitable temperature. The important precaution is to prevent desiccation of the embryos during and after dissection; this is achieved by keeping the tissues in a drop of liquid medium or in paraffin oil during the operations.

NUTRIENT MEDIA

Perhaps the most vexing problem in the culture of plant embryos is to discover what sort of nutrients are to be provided to sustain their growth. The nutrient media employed, although as varied as the number of species investigated, usually fall into two categories: (1) medium for growth of immature and differentiated embryos and (2) medium for growth of proembryos.

Immature and Differentiated Embryos

Since immature and differentiated embryos are autotrophic in nature, their nutritional requirements are simple. They can be best grown in media which contain a few mineral salts and a source of carbon energy. Often a medium successful with one species may prove useful for another species.

Composition of media used for embryo culture has been summarized recently (Rappaport, 1954; Randolph and Khan, 1960; Sanders and Ziebur, 1963; Wardlaw, 1965). The media used differ in many ways, the most important of the variables being the presence or absence of divalent ions, trace elements, and the source of iron. While nitrate is the most common nitrogen source used in macro-concentrations, embryos of the orchid *Cattleya* have been found to grow best on ammonium salts as a nitrogen source, almost to the exclusion of nitrates, nitrites, and amino acids (Spoerl, 1948; Raghavan, 1964; Raghavan and Torrey, 1964). The choice of carbohydrate, although potentially a broad one, has been limited to sucrose. It is however important to determine for each species the optimal concentration of sucrose. For long-term cultures, medium solidified with agar is suited; transfer of the embryos to fresh medium may be made at intervals of 3–4 weeks. In short-term experiments embryos in hanging drop cultures show measurable growth. The rate of growth and morphogenesis of the embryos can be modified by varying the conditions of illumination, pH of the medium, and temperature, and by addition of activating substances such as growth hormones, vitamins, amino acids, and various plant extracts.

Proembryos

In their normal development proembryos are heterotrophic in nature depending not only on their own metabolites, but also on the metabolites of the nutritive tissue of the endosperm in which they are constantly bathed. In terms of cultural requirements, a medium which supports growth of immature and differentiated embryos is virtually unable to nurture proembryos. The following supplements to the basal medium have partially alleviated the difficulties attendant in culturing proembryos of several species; for a full discussion on the culture of proembryos, see Raghavan (1966).

AMINO ACIDS

Rijven (1952) was able to grow proembryos of *Capsella* by supplementing a medium containing mineral salts, growth factors, and sucrose with a complex mixture of amino acids of the composition of the plant globulin, edestin. Interestingly enough, glutamine proved superior to the amino acid mixture in promoting growth of the embryos of the same age. The complement of amino acids and other active components present in casein hydrolyzate (milk protein), malt extract (an endosperm derivative), and yeast extract markedly promoted growth of embryos of several species (Sanders and Ziebur, 1963).

COCONUT MILK

The demonstration by Van Overbeek, Conklin, and Blakeslee (1942) of a dramatic improvement in the culturability of proembryos of *Datura stramonium* by the addition of nonautoclaved liquid endosperm of coconut (coconut milk) to the basal medium was the forerunner of many successful attempts to culture proembryos and other excised plant organs by the use of this substance. The effects of the growth induction stimulus of coconut milk depend on a delicately balanced complex of interacting substances, including amino acids, vitamins, growth substances, and sugar alcohols (Pollard, Shantz, and Steward, 1961; Tulecke, Weinstein, Rutner, and Laurencot, 1961).

GROWTH SUBSTANCES

Another experimental approach in inducing growth of proembryos utilized plant growth substances. Addition of kinetin (Veen, 1963) increased the survival chances of proembryos of *Capsella*, while a balanced mixture of indoleacetic acid, kinetin, and adenine sulfate supported their continued growth and differentiation (Raghavan and Torrey, 1963).

OSMOTIC PRESSURE

It has been demonstrated that proembryos are embedded in the ovular sap under considerable osmotic pressure (Ryczkowski, 1960). In apparent agreement with this finding, proembryos of several species have been successfully cultured in media which are in approximate osmotic balance with the ovular sap. This desirable feature of maintaining high osmotic pressure in the medium is accomplished by the use of appropriate concentrations of sucrose or mannitol.

In Table 1 are summarized the optimal growth conditions for proembryos of several species derived from the above considerations. The foregoing discussion and the data presented in the table should make clear that proembryos are very sensitive to composition of the nutrient

TABLE 1. NUTRIENT MEDIA FOR GROWTH OF PROEMBRYOS OF DIFFERENT SPECIES

		NUTRIENT MEDIA			
SPECIES	LENGTH OF EMBRYO AT EXCISION	CARBON ENERGY SOURCE	MINERAL SALTS	ORGANIC SUPPLEMENTS	REFERENCE
Capsella bursa-pastoris	140–170 μ	Sucrose, 18%	Olsen's mineral salts in phosphate buffer	(mg/liter): thiamine, 0.15; nicotinic acid, 1.0; pyridoxin, 0.2; calcium pantothenate, 0.2; inositol, 0.5; *p*-aminobenzoic acid, 0.5; riboflavin, 0.1; folic acid, 0.01; biotin, 0.0004; alanine, 43.1; valine, 57.0; leucine, 47.0; isoleucine, 75.0; proline, 42.5; phenylalanine, 54.5; cystine, 9.3; cysteine, 5.0; arginine, 167; histidine, 29.0; lysine, 2.4; aspartic acid, 120; glutamic acid, 207; amide-NH_3, 21.5; serine, 63.0; threonine, 38.5; tyrosine, 43.4; tryptophan, 14.8; and methionine, 24.0 (or glutamine 600, instead of the mixture of amino acids)	Rijven (1952)
	40.5–67.5 μ	Sucrose, 2%	Modified Robbins and Schmidt's medium	(mg/liter): thiamine hydrochloride, 0.1; pyridoxin hydrochloride, 0.1; niacin, 0.5; indoleacetic acid, 0.1; kinetin, 0.001; and adenine sulfate, 0.001	Raghavan and Torrey (1963)
Citrus microcarpa	0.14–0.28 mm	Sucrose, 5 or 10%	Modified White's medium	(mg/liter): glycine, 7.5; niacin, 1.25; thiamine hydrochloride, 0.25; calcium pantothenate, 0.025; pyridoxin hydrochloride, 0.025; indoleacetic acid, 1.0; and casein hydrolyzate, 400	Rangaswamy (1961)
Cucumis sativus	0.1–0.2 mm	Sucrose, 5%	White's medium	(mg/liter): indoleacetic acid, 2.0; diphenylurea, 2.5; and casein hydrolyzate	Nakajima (1962)

SPECIES	LENGTH OF EMBRYO AT EXCISION	NUTRIENT MEDIA: CARBON ENERGY SOURCE	NUTRIENT MEDIA: MINERAL SALTS	NUTRIENT MEDIA: ORGANIC SUPPLEMENTS	REFERENCE
Datura stramonium	0.15 mm	Dextrose, 1%	Tukey's medium	(mg/liter): glycine, 3.0; thiamine, 0.15; ascorbic acid, 20.0; nicotinic acid, 1.0; vitamin B_6, 0.2; adenine, 0.2; succinic acid, 25.0; pantothenic acid, 0.5; and nonautoclaved coconut milk about 21% by volume	Van Overbeek, Conklin, and Blakeslee (1942)
	0.10–0.15 mm	Sucrose, 8–12%	Modified Randolph and Cox's medium	400 mg/liter casein hydrolyzate	Rietsema, Satina, and Blakeslee (1953)
Datura tatula	0.11–0.27 mm	Sucrose, 6%	Modified White's medium	Alcohol diffusates from young seeds of *Datura stramonium*, *Lupinus luteus*, and *Sechium edule*	
	0.13–0.28 mm	Sucrose, 8%	As above	50.0 mg/liter casein hydrolyzate	Matsubara (1962)
	0.11–0.48 mm	Sucrose, 8%	As above	10% (by volume) nonautoclaved coconut milk	
Gossypium hirsutum	0.1–0.2 mm	Sucrose, 2%	White's medium 5 times concentrated; 7.0 gm/liter sodium chloride	(mg/liter): glycine, 10.0; pyridoxin hydrochloride, 2.5; nicotinic acid, 2.5; thiamine, 0.5; casein hydrolyzate, 250; adenine, 40.0; and nonautoclaved coconut milk 150 ml/liter	Mauney (1961)
Hordeum vulgare	0.3–1.1 mm	Sucrose, 12.5%	Randolph and Cox's medium	0.1% casein hydrolyzate, and surrounding the embryos with aseptically excised endosperm of *Hordeum*	Ziebur and Brink (1951)
	60–1,500 μ	Sucrose, 12%	White's medium	20% (by volume) nonautoclaved coconut milk; glutamine, 400 mg/liter	Norstog (1961)
	90–100 μ	Sucrose, 9%	Phosphate-enriched White's medium	(mg/liter): niacin, 1.25; thiamine, 0.25; pyridoxin, 0.25; calcium pantothenate, 0.25;	Norstog and Smith (1963)

TABLE 1 (*continued*)

		NUTRIENT MEDIA			
SPECIES	LENGTH OF EMBRYO AT EXCISION	CARBON ENERGY SOURCE	MINERAL SALTS	ORGANIC SUPPLEMENTS	REFERENCE
				malic acid, 100; glutamine, 400; alanine, 400; leucine, 20.0; tyrosine, 10.0; phenylalanine, 10.0; cysteine, 10.0; and tryptophan, 10.0	
Keteleeria davidiana	One to few-celled	Sucrose, 2%	Pfeffer's medium	(mg/liter): indoleacetic acid, 10.0; and thiamine, 0.1	Loo and Wang (1943)
Pinus yunnanensis	One to few-celled	Sucrose, 2%	Pfeffer's medium	(mg/liter): indoleacetic acid, 10.0; or thiamine, 0.1	Loo and Wang (1943)
Todea barbara	160 μ	Sucrose, 1%	Knudson's medium with Nitsch's trace element mixture	5% or 10% nonautoclaved coconut milk or 50.0 mg/liter each of sorbitol and inositol	DeMaggio and Wetmore (1961)
	35–55 μ	Sucrose, 3%	As above	50.0 mg/liter each of sorbitol and inositol	
Zea mays	0.3–3.0 mm	Sucrose, 5%	Tukey's medium	(mg/liter): glycine, 3.0; thiamine, 0.15; ascorbic acid, 20.0; nicotinic acid, 1.0; vitamin B_6, 0.2; adenine, 0.2; succinic acid, 25.0; pantothenic acid, 0.5; biotin, 0.001; and asparagine, 1500	Haagen-Smit, Siu, and Wilson (1945)

media. In the more exacting experiments media should be prepared with double-distilled water, and only chemically cleaned glassware and specially purified salts (Reagent grade) should be used. In view of the small size of the embryos it is desirable to start cultures in hanging drops.

EXPRESSION OF RESULTS

Certain aspects of growth of the embryos may be recorded by direct observation. The cultured embryo is examined microscopically and measurements of increases in length of the root, hypocotyl, and shoot are made. Although this method provides accurate data of the linear dimensions, it can be reliable only when measurements are completed in short-term experiments and the embryo's growth is straight. Under constant conditions of culture, reproducible rates of growth are obtained; if suitably replicated the data can be analyzed statistically. In some cases fresh and dry weights can provide meaningful measure of growth; the dried material can be used to determine the nitrogen constituents by Kjeldahl's method, and growth can be expressed in terms of total nitrogen. Norstog (1965) has used a method in which the same embryos were photographed at intervals over a period of several days; this method allows precise analysis of the morphogenesis of the embryos in culture.

CONCLUSIONS

Embryo culture is subject to the criticism that the cultured embryos do not faithfully reproduce the stages in normal embryogenesis, but "germinate" skipping the normal pattern of embryonic growth. This is evidently due to the absence of any spatial restrictions in culture. The rate of growth of cultured embryos is slow in comparison to those growing *in situ* inside the ovule. These objections need not invalidate the fact that most of the information on the rapidly changing nutritional requirements of developing plant embryos has accrued by culture methods. No doubt, the ultimate value of the method will be judged by the light it sheds on embryonic differentiation.

REFERENCES

DE MAGGIO, A. E., 1961: Morphogenetic studies on the fern *Todea barbara* (L.) Moore—I. Life history. *Phytomorphology*, 11: 46.

——, and R. H. WETMORE, 1961: Morphogenetic studies on the fern *Todea barbara.* III. Experimental embryology. *Amer. J. Bot.*, 48: 551.

HAAGEN-SMIT, A. J., R. SIU, and G. WILSON, 1945: A method for the culturing of excised, immature corn embryos *in vitro. Science*, 101: 234.

LOO, S. W., and F. H. WANG, 1943: The culture of young conifer embryos *in vitro. Science*, 98: 544.

MATSUBARA, S., 1962: Studies on a growth promoting substance, "embryo factor," necessary for the culture of young embryos of *Datura tatula in vitro. Bot. Mag.*, 75: 10.

MAUNEY, J. R., 1961: The culture *in vitro* of immature cotton embryos. *Bot. Gaz.*, 122: 205.

NAKAJIMA, T., 1962: Physiological studies of seed development, especially embryonic growth and endosperm development. *Bull. Univ. Osaka Prefect. Ser. B*, 13: 13.

NARAYANASWAMI, S., and K. NORSTOG, 1964: Plant embryo culture. *Bot. Rev.*, 30: 587.

NORSTOG, K., 1961: The growth and differentiation of cultured barley embryos. *Amer. J. Bot.*, 48: 876.

——, 1965: Development of cultured barley embryos I. Growth of 0.1–0.4-mm embryos. *Amer. J. Bot.*, 52: 538.

——, and J. E. SMITH, 1963: Culture of small barley embryos on defined media. *Science*, 142: 1655.

POLLARD, J. K., E. M. SHANTZ, and F. C. STEWARD, 1961: Hexitols in coconut milk: their role in nurture of dividing cells. *Plant. Physiol.*, 36: 492.

RAGHAVAN, V., 1964: Effects of certain organic nitrogen compounds on growth *in vitro* of seedlings of *Cattleya. Bot. Gaz.*, 125: 260.

——, 1966: Nutrition, growth, and morphogenesis of plant embryos. *Biol. Rev.*, 41: 1.

——, and J. G. TORREY, 1963: Growth and morphogenesis of globular and older embryos of *Capsella* in culture. *Amer. J. Bot.*, 50: 540.

——, and ——, 1964: Inorganic nitrogen nutrition of the seedlings of the orchid, *Cattleya. Amer. J. Bot.*, 51: 264.

RANDOLPH, L. F., and R. KHAN, 1960: Growth response of excised mature embryos of *Iris* and wheat to different culture media. *Phytomorphology*, 10: 43.

RANGASWAMY, N. S., 1961: Experimental studies on female reproductive structures of *Citrus microcarpa* Bunge. *Phytomorphology*, 11: 109.

RAPPAPORT, J., 1954: *In vitro* culture of plant embryos and factors controlling their growth. *Bot. Rev.*, 20: 201.

RIETSEMA, J., S. SATINA, and A. F. BLAKESLEE, 1953: The effect of sucrose on the growth of *Datura stramonium* embryos *in vitro*. *Amer. J. Bot.*, 40: 538.

RIJVEN, A. H. G. C., 1952: *In vitro* studies on the embryo of *Capsella bursa-pastoris*. *Acta Bot. Neerland.*, 1: 157.

RYCZKOWSKI, M., 1960: Changes of the osmotic value during the development of the ovule. *Planta*, 55: 343.

SANDERS, M. E., and N. K. ZIEBUR, 1963: Artificial culture of embryos. In P. Maheshwari (ed.), *Recent Advances in the Embryology of Angiosperms*, International Society of Plant Morphologists, Delhi, India, p. 297.

SPOERL, E., 1948: Amino acids as sources of nitrogen for orchid embryos. *Amer. J. Bot.*, 35: 88.

TULECKE, W., L. H. WEINSTEIN, A. RUTNER, and H. J. LAURENCOT, JR., 1961: The biochemical composition of coconut water (coconut milk) as related to its use in plant tissue culture. *Contrib. Boyce Thompson Inst.*, 21: 115.

VAN OVERBEEK, J., M. E. CONKLIN, and A. F. BLAKESLEE, 1942: Cultivation *in vitro* of small *Datura* embryos. *Amer. J. Bot.*, 29: 472.

VEEN, H., 1963: The effect of various growth-regulators on embryos of *Capsella bursa-pastoris* growing *in vitro*. *Acta Bot. Neerland.*, 12: 129.

WARDLAW, C. W., 1965: Physiology of embryonic development in Cormophytes. In W. Ruhland (ed.), *Handbuch der Pflanzenphysiologie*, Vol. 15(1), Springer-Verlag, Berlin, Germany, p. 844.

WHITE, P. R., 1963: *The Cultivation of Animal and Plant Cells*, 2nd ed. Ronald Press Co., New York.

WITHNER, C. L., 1959: Orchid physiology. In C. L. Withner (ed.), *The Orchids*, Ronald Press Co., New York, p. 315.

ZIEBUR, N. K., and R. A. BRINK, 1951: The stimulative effect of *Hordeum* endosperms on the growth of immature plant embryos *in vitro*. *Amer. J. Bot.*, 38: 253.

Excised Root Culture

By H. E. Street

INTRODUCTION

Clones of isolated cultured roots of the following species of higher plants have been successfully established in continuous culture: *Senecio vulgaris* L.; *Medicago sativa* L.; *Trifolium repens* L.; *Datura stramonium* L.; *Lycopersicum esculentum* Mill.; *L. pimpinellifolium* Mill.; *Solanum tuberosum* L.; *Secale cereale* L.; *Triticum vulgare* L. (var. Hilgerdorf); *Androcymbium gramineum* Cav.; *Pinus* spp. including *P. ponderosa* Dougl. and *P. serotina* Michx. Roots of the following species have been maintained in culture for prolonged periods although due to poor lateral root development, multiplication of clones from individual roots has not been achieved: *Callistephus hortensis* Cass; *Helianthus annuus* L.; *Raphanus sativus* L.; *Brassica nigra* Koch; *Convolvulus arvensis* L.; *Isatis tinctoria* L.; *Acer melanoxylon* R.Br.; *Melilotus alba* Destr.; *Pisum sativum* L.; *Linum usitatissimum* L.; *Fagopyrum esculentum* Monch.; *Petunia violacea* Lindl. The roots of a number of other species have been cultured for limited periods. The data on the culturability of excised roots is summarized in tabular form in a recent review (Butcher and Street, 1964). The difficulties encountered in attempting to culture the isolated roots of many species and the differences in culturability between varieties or strains within species have been discussed in some detail (Street, 1957).

Excised root cultures have a number of attractive features for research and teaching in plant physiology. They are clonal material of high growth rate and metabolic activity; for several species there are no difficulties in multiplying up the clone to any desired size; the cultures show a low level of variability so that by suitable and not excessive replication relatively small differences in response to physiological treatments can be shown to be significant; the sterility of the cultures permits the feeding of organic substances without fear of their modification by microorganisms; the aseptic conditions, by excluding dust, and the small transplants required to effect successful subculture permit rapid development of microelement and growth factor deficiencies; the size and ease of handling of the cultures permit them to be grown under a wide range of strictly controlled environmental conditions; the ease of observation permits continuous records to be made of their growth and development.

Work with root cultures has made, in the field of plant metabolism, contributions to knowledge particularly in relation to carbohydrate metabolism, respiration, mineral nutrient requirements and the role of such nutrients in metabolism, the essentiality and role of vitamins and other growth factors including auxins, gibberellins, and cytokinins, and the release of metabolites including alkaloids, nucleotides, and amino acids by roots. In the field of developmental physiology, root cultures have been used in studies on the control of cell division, expansion and differentiation in the root apex, the initiation of lateral roots, and the initiation and functioning of the vascular cambium. Definition of the cultural requirements and synthetic potentialities of isolated roots also provides valuable data for interpretation of the shoot-root relationship (Street, 1959). Root cultures are very attractive experimental material for undergraduate experiments in all these aspects of plant physiology.

BASIC TECHNIQUE

Sterilization and Germination of Seed

Immersion of dry seed for 5 minutes in a 1 percent (w/v) solution of bromine is the most effective sterilizing procedure. If this treatment injures the embryo then the following alternative treatments should be tried: immersion for not more than 8 hours in a bleaching powder filtrate containing 1 percent chlorine or treatment with an aqueous detergent followed by immersion for not more than 20 minutes in 0.1 percent aqueous mercuric chloride. The sterilized seed is then thoroughly washed with sterile distilled water and set to germinate in sterile Petri dishes containing filter papers moistened with sterile distilled water. Germination is allowed to proceed in the dark at a suitable temperature (25°C is a suitable temperature for many seeds) until the radicle or seminal roots are 20–40 mm long.

Initiation of Root Cultures: Establishment of a Clone

Ten-millimeter apical tips of such sterile seedling roots are excised with a sterile scalpel and transferred with a platinum loop singly to the surface of sterile culture medium. One hundred milliliter Pyrex wide-mouthed Erlenmeyer flasks containing 50 ml of culture medium are most suitable for stock root cultures. The cultures are then incubated at 25°–27°C for a suitable period. With clones of tomato (*Lycopersicum esculentum*) this period is 7 days at 27°C. The root grows in length, and lateral roots emerge from the main axis. A clone can be established from a single root culture of this kind by now setting up from it one or more "sector" cultures. Using a pair of fine iridectomy scissors, portions of the main root axis are cut out, each of which bears four or five young lateral roots (with tomato these laterals should be 3–8 mm long). These sectors are then transferred singly to new flasks of culture medium and again incubated. During incubation the laterals grow in length and in turn come to bear laterals. From such a developed "sector" culture one can excise the 10-mm apical tips of the primary laterals and new sector pieces. The main lateral tips when cultured give roots similar to those developed from the initial seedling root tip; such cultures are often referred to as "tip" cultures and are the kind used in experiments. The sector pieces serve to propagate the clone and to yield further root apices from which to initiate experimental tip cultures. This procedure of clonal maintenance and multiplication is illustrated in Fig. 1.

This general technique is applicable when the root cultures develop a regular sequence of laterals and when such laterals are capable of rapid growth from sector initials. To maintain a high and uniform growth rate of any new clone certain aspects of this basic technique must be approached experimentally. Aspects of the technique which should be varied toward this end are: length of root tips excised for tip cultures, size of laterals on the sector pieces, duration of the incubation periods (passage lengths) for both tip and sector cultures, incubation temperature, composition of culture medium (particularly sugar concentration). There is no evidence that solidified media are preferable to liquid media or that aeration is likely to be a critical factor in the growth of cultures in the standard vessels described. Roots from the first list of species given in the Introduction have been cultured as clones by this general technique.

When an actively growing clone cannot be established by the above technique, it may be possible, using an appropriate passage length and culture medium, to grow each individual root continuously by repeated excision and transfer to fresh culture medium of the apex of the main root axis. Roots from the second list of species given in the Introduction have been maintained in continuous culture by this technique.

The manipulations outlined above should be carried out under aseptic conditions. When large numbers of cultures are being set up, the maintenance of asepsis is greatly assisted by the use of a walk-in inoculating cabinet fitted with facilities for keeping instruments in boiling water and a bactericidal ultraviolet (UV) lamp and in which there is maintained a positive pressure of cotton-wool-filtered air. The operator should wear a special overall and cap, should "scrub-up" as for surgery, and should expose his hands to the UV radiation for the permitted time before commencing work. Cultures should be regularly inspected for the appearance of microbial infection and all contaminated cultures immediately autoclaved and then rejected. Since many organisms grow only

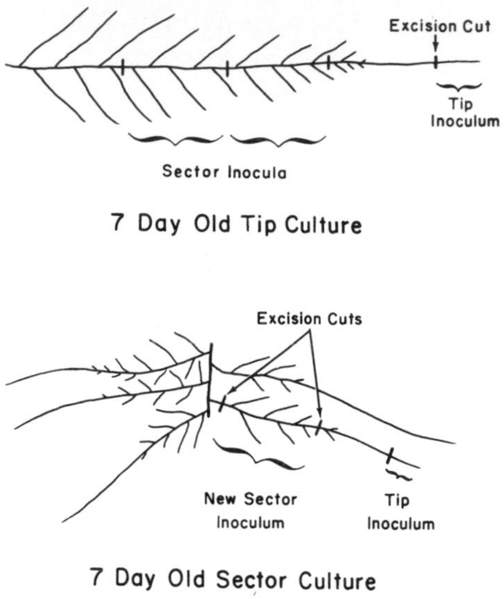

FIG. 1. "Tip" and "sector" cultures showing portions excised to initiate both sector and tip cultures again.

sluggishly in standard root culture media it is important to carry out periodically a sterility test. A simple sterility test is to enrich the standard root culture medium (Table 1) by incorporating 200 mg per liter acid-hydrolyzed casein. This medium is not inhibitory to the growth of most root cultures but promotes the growth of many microorganisms. The whole clone can periodically be screened by a passage in this enriched medium.

Standard Root Culture Media

A medium which has been very widely used in root culture is a modified White's medium. This medium has the composition shown in Table 1. The medium is prepared by using a stock solution of the inorganic salts (minus the ferric chloride) at 10 times the strength required in the culture medium. This stock solution is stored at 4°C and replaced at monthly intervals. The "vitamin solution" (containing the three B vitamins plus

TABLE 1. MODIFIED WHITE'S ROOT CULTURE MEDIUM

	CONTENT PER LITER OF MEDIUM EXPRESSED AS WEIGHT OF ANHYDROUS COMPOUND
Calcium nitrate, $Ca(NO_3)\cdot 4H_2O$	200 mg
Potassium nitrate, KNO_3	80 mg
Potassium chloride, KCl	65 mg
Sodium dihydrogen phosphate, $NaH_2PO_4\cdot 4H_2O$	16.5 mg
Manganese chloride, $MnCl_2\cdot 4H_2O$	4.5 mg
Zinc sulfate, $ZnSO_4\cdot 7H_2O$	1.5 mg
Potassium iodide, KI	0.75 mg
Sodium sulfate, $NaSO_4\cdot 10H_2O$	200 mg
Magnesium sulfate, $MgSO_4\cdot 7H_2O$	360 mg
Boric acid, H_3BO_3	1.5 mg
Molybdic acid, H_2MoO_4	0.0017 mg
Copper sulfate, $CuSO_4\cdot 5H_2O$	0.013 mg
Ferric chloride, $FeCl_3$	2.5 mg
Aneurin hydrochloride	0.1 mg
Pyridoxine hydrochloride	0.1 mg
Nicotinic acid	0.5 mg
Glycine	3.0 mg
Sucrose	20 gm

NOTE: White, 1943; Street and McGregor, 1952.

glycine) is prepared as a second stock solution at 100 times the final concentration and stored in measured aliquots in Pyrex tubes at −20°C. The ferric chloride is available as a concentrated "Specpure" solution (Johnson Matthey Ltd., Covent Garden, U.K.). To prepare a batch of medium the sugar is dissolved in distilled water. To this is added in turn the solution of ferric chloride, the vitamin solution, and the inorganic solution. The mixed solution is diluted almost to volume with distilled water and then its pH adjusted to 4.9–5.0 with the aid of a small volume of NaOH or HCl, the medium adjusted to final volume and distributed to the culture vessels for sterilization by autoclaving at 15 pounds per square inch for 5–15 minutes.

All glassware should be very carefully cleaned and there should be a final rinse with distilled water. Traditionally, chromic acid-sulfuric acid has been used but probably detergents are a satisfactory alternative provided they are very thoroughly removed by rinsing. All glassware should be of borosilicate glass (Pyrex) and the distilled water should be prepared from stills of this glass. "Analar" grade chemicals should be used to prepare culture media. Clean glassware should be protected from dust contamination. Culture vessels should be closed with nonabsorbent cotton plugs wrapped in dressing-free gauze or wide-open-wove bandage and these plugs protected from drip in the autoclave by inverted glass or aluminum beakers.

The standard medium contains 2 percent sucrose but this may not be the optimal concentration for a particular clone, and for roots of monocotyledons the sucrose should be replaced with an appropriate concentration of glucose. For some clones the glycine of the standard medium can, with advantage, be omitted.

Various workers have used different solutions of inorganic salts in preparing their root culture media and one or another of these may be superior, for a particular clone, to the inorganic salt mixture detailed in Table 1. Alternative formulas are detailed in papers by Robbins, 1922; Bonner and Devirian, 1939; Almestrand, 1949; and Heller, 1953.

Measurements of Growth

Linear growth of the cultures is expressed by the following criteria: increase in length of main axis (millimeters);

number of emergent laterals (lateral number); total length of laterals per root (millimeters). Fresh and dry weights are usually recorded by bulking five or ten roots. Reproducible fresh weights can be obtained by adopting a precise blotting technique and dry weights by gentle washing of the roots followed by drying to constant weight in small metal boats at 80°C. Measurements of cell expansion can be based upon the length and transverse diameter of exodermal cells in roots fixed in 70 percent ethanol and cleared with lactophenol. Usually ten cells are measured in each of five replicate roots at a point (5 mm or more from the extreme tip) where cell expansion is complete.

Measurement of the rate of production of new cells per culture per 24 hours can be carried out by the method of Brown and Rickless (1949), modified by Butcher and Street (1960).

USEFUL ADDITIONAL TECHNIQUES

Alternative Culture Vessels

The 100-ml Erlenmeyer flasks containing 50 ml of culture medium are suitable for the growth of single root tips or sectors over short periods (not more than 7 days with vigorously growing clones). As an alternative to such Erlenmeyer flasks, deep Petri dishes have been used by some workers on the grounds that they permit easier inspection and measurement of the cultures growing in a uniform layer of medium with a large surface area visible from above. Such dishes are, however, difficult to handle and transport without spilling, are more liable to infection, and suffer from the disadvantage that condensation on the lid interferes with visibility.

For growth of root cultures over longer periods, penicillin flasks containing 500 or 1,000 ml of medium have proved very suitable. Where root material or "staled" culture medium is required for analysis such flasks can be used to grow a number (ten to twenty) of root tips together. When tomato roots are cultured in this way they form, after about 21 days' incubation, a surface mat of roots from under which the culture medium can be withdrawn and replaced by new medium. This has proved useful in studying, over periods up to 48 hours, the release of metabolites and uptake of nutrients by growing cultured roots.

Where it is desired to eliminate the effects on growth of changes in the composition of the culture medium, a system which allows a continuous flow of sterile culture medium over the growing root culture must be used. An apparatus of this type was developed for studying the daily growth of individual cultured tomato roots over periods up to 28 days (Street and Roberts, 1952) and is illustrated in Fig. 2.

A technique permitting some nutrients to be supplied to the basal end of the root and others to the apical end has been described by Raggio and Raggio (1956). The basal end of the root is inserted in an open-ended tube containing medium solidified with agar. This tube passes down through the neck of the culture vessel and terminates above the liquid medium. The apical end of the root crosses the short air gap between the end of the tube and the liquid medium. The organic constituents (sugar and organic growth factors) can be supplied via the basal mature tissues while the growing root projects into the inorganic salt solution. This arrangement has permitted the experimental nodulation by *Rhizobium phaseoli* of cultured roots of *Phaseolus vulgaris* (black wax bean) and *Glycine soja* var. *Biloxi* (Raggio, Raggio, and Torrey, 1957). Modifications of this technique have recently been described by Torrey (1963),

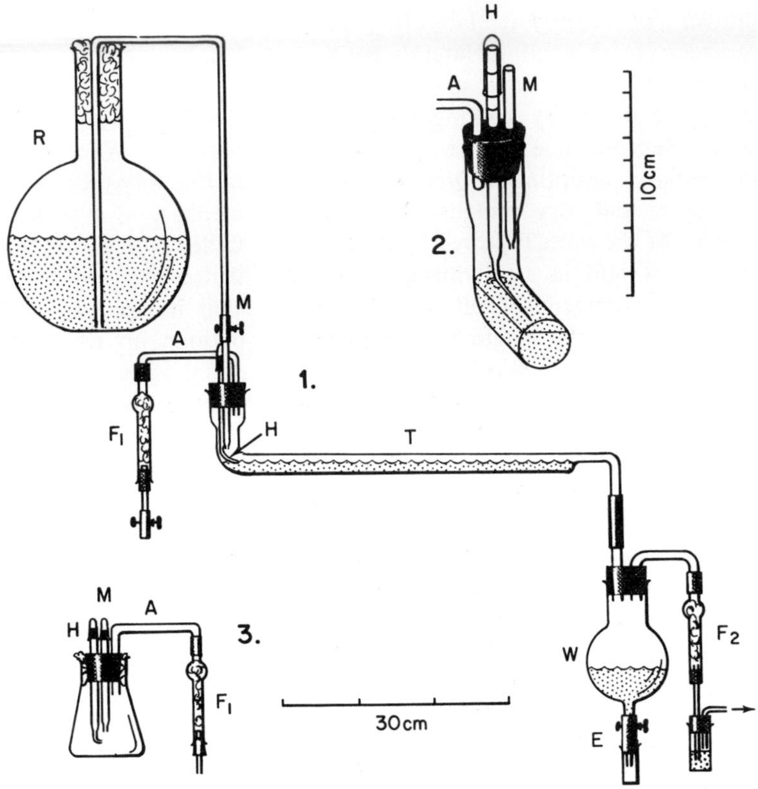

Loomis and Torrey (1964), and Bunting and Horrocks (1964).

The use of borosilicate glass is clearly precluded when it is desired to study boron deficiency. Boron deficiency has been induced in cultured roots by using polythene storage containers and measures, plastic, stainless steel, or aluminum culture vessels, and water distilled from a quartz still or a heavily tinned still fitted with a soda-glass condenser tube (Neales, 1964).

Culture Media for Special Purposes

Growth of roots in modified White's medium (Table 1) results in a rise in pH; a single excised tomato root tip growing in 50 ml of this medium causes the pH to rise from the initial value of 4.8–4.9 to 5.8–6.0 during a 7-day incubation. Above pH 5.2 iron is rendered insoluble to the extent that a deficiency of this element supervenes to limit further growth. The simplest way to prevent this is to replace the ferric chloride of the standard medium by ferric sodium ethylenediaminetetraacetate (Fe-EDTA) and a suitable Fe-EDTA preparation is compounded as follows: 0.8 gm disodium ethylenediaminetetraacetate is dissolved in water, 3.0 ml of a 10 percent w/v solution of ferric chloride added, and the volume adjusted to 1 liter; 6.5 ml of this solution per liter of medium gives the standard iron concentration. Fe-EDTA should always be used when culture is to be prolonged or the effect of pH on root growth is being examined. We have found it slightly inferior to ferric chloride for normal clonal maintenance and multiplication.

The modified White's medium is very

FIG. 2. Apparatus for growth of excised roots in flowing culture medium. (1) Complete apparatus for growth of excised roots in flowing medium. (2) Part of the growth tube showing attachment of the root in its holder. (3) Rubber bung carrying root holder, medium feed tube, and air inlet tube shown in the carrier conical flask ready for autoclaving. (4) Culture tube in which the culture medium flows counter to the growth of the root.

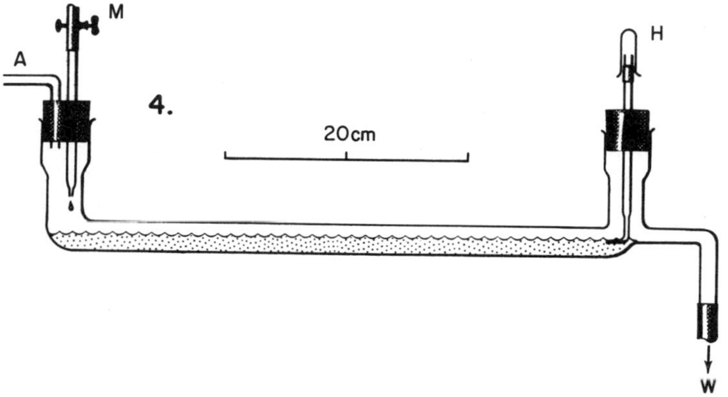

weakly buffered. No satisfactory method of increasing significantly the buffer capacity by adding soluble salts has been discovered. Sodium phosphates, for instance, have to be added in amounts which are markedly inhibitory to the growth of all root cultures examined. Studies of the relationship between pH and the growth of cultured roots have, however, been carried out by using as "solid buffers" the sparingly soluble salts, amorphous calcium dihydrogen orthophosphate $Ca(H_2PO_4)_2$, precipitated calcium phosphate prepared according to the British Pharmaceutical Codex, and calcium carbonate (Sheat, Fletcher, and Street, 1959). Appropriate mixtures of these compounds can be used to stabilize pH at any desired value within the range 4.2–7.5.

Root cultures are relatively insensitive to sodium and chloride ions, and culture media lacking particular mineral elements can be prepared by using purified salts (for general methods of purifying salts see Hewitt, 1952) and substituting the corresponding sodium salts or chlorides. In view of the high sugar content of root culture media, purification of the sugar by suitable exchange resins may be essential to induce deficiency. Root cultures are very sensitive to residues from the reagents used in salt purifications, and it is essential to test for full restoration of the growth-promoting activity of the purified medium by addition of an effective concentration of the omitted element.

Many organic substances, including most natural sugars, suffer chemical change during autoclaving, particularly in the presence of the mixed salt solution of root culture medium. The extent of hydrolysis or oxidation of sugars can be very greatly reduced by autoclaving the sugar separately in aqueous solution and then adding this aseptically to the remainder of the medium which has been autoclaved separately. Heating of substances can be avoided in the preparation of sterile root culture media by two alternative approaches: (1) the whole medium or a solution of the thermolabile constituent can be rendered sterile by passage through a Pyrex sintered-glass sterilizing filter (porosity H 5) or an appropriate Millipore filter (Millipore Filter Corporation, Bedford, Mass.). Seitz, Berkfeld, and Pasteur filters are unsuitable both because they adsorb constituents of the medium and because they release alkaline material; (2) the dry substance can be treated with pure ethyl ether, the ether removed at a temperature below 30°C, and the substance dissolved aseptically in sterile water. Solid chemicals are often sterile or almost sterile as purchased and hence when this technique is used the substances should be handled aseptically throughout.

Culture media can be solidified by incorporation of agar (0.7–1.0 percent), but except in the technique of Raggio and Raggio, this is not to be recommended. The growth of cultured roots is generally markedly reduced on solidified media as compared to liquid media.

Techniques for the Study of Various Aspects of Metabolism

Where the metabolism, uptake, or requirement for a natural substance is to be studied, it is often advantageous to induce, by an appropriate pretreatment, a partial deficiency in the root tissues. Thus, in studies on the uptake and metabolism of sugars, the soluble sugar content of the root cells can be markedly reduced without impairing subsequent growth potentiality by a preincubation of up to 72 hours in sugar-free medium. Similarly, a 7-day passage in a medium lacking a particular B vitamin will usually induce a marked but noninjurious deficiency.

The action of a number of physiologically active substances, such as auxins, can with advantage be studied not only when the substance is present in the culture medium but in a subsequent period following transfer to a medium lacking the substance under test (Charles, 1959; Charles and Street, 1959). This technique has been used, for instance, first to induce lateral initiation, and then subsequently to permit active extension growth of the laterals. Two media, one containing adenine and the other an auxin, were used in alternate passages to maintain the roots of *Androcymbium gramineum* in continuous culture (Bausa Alcalde, 1961).

Root cultures are particularly suitable for work with metabolites labeled with radioactive isotopes, and this is well illustrated by studies on the uptake, transport, and metabolism of C^{14}-labeled sugars by cultured tomato roots (Thomas, Craigie, and Street, 1963; Goldsworthy and Street, 1965).

Root cultures are metabolically very active as illustrated by their high rate of oxygen uptake (Morgan and Street, 1959), and since root cultures lack woody tissues, they lend themselves to the isolation of enzymes and cellular particles. As an example, root cultures have been successfully used in studies on enzymatic adaptation (Vaidyanathan and Street, 1959a, 1959b).

FURTHER READING

The above account has been confined to an outline of the techniques used in culturing excised roots. For a fuller discussion of certain aspects of technique and for a critical assessment of the contributions to our knowledge of root growth and metabolism which have resulted from work with root cultures the reader is referred to three chapters (Chapters 8, 9, and 10) by the author in *The Biology of Cells and Tissues in Culture: Methods, Biology and Physiology*, Vol. 3, edited by E. N. Willmer (1966).

REFERENCES

ALMESTRAND, A., 1949: Studies on the growth of isolated roots of barley and oats. *Physiol. Plantarum*, 2: 372.

BAUSA ALCALDE, M., 1961: Sobre el cultivo *in vitro* de raices aisladas de *Androcymbium gramineum* (Cav.) McBride. *Farmacognosia*, 21: 71.

BONNER, J., and P. S. DEVIRIAN, 1939: Growth factor requirements of four species of isolated roots. *Am. J. Botany*, 26: 661.

BROWN, R., and P. RICKLESS, 1949: A new method for the study of cell division and cell extension with some preliminary observations on the effect of temperature and of nutrients. *Proc. Roy. Soc. (London) Ser. B*, 136: 110.

BUNTING, A. H., and J. HORROCKS, 1964: An improvement in the Raggio technique for obtaining nodules on excised roots of *Phaseolus vulgaris* L. in culture. *Ann. Botany (London)*, 28: 229.

BUTCHER, D. N., and H. E. STREET, 1964: Excised root culture. *Botan. Rev.*, 30: 513.

———, and ———, 1960: The effects of gibberellins on the growth of excised tomato roots. *J. Exptl. Botany*, 11: 206.

CHARLES, H. P., 1959: Studies on the growth of excised roots. VII. *New Phytologist*, 58: 81.

———, and H. E. STREET, 1959: Studies on the growth of excised roots. VI. *New Phytologist*, 58: 75.

GOLDSWORTHY, A., and H. E. STREET, 1965: The carbohydrate nutrition of tomato roots. VIII. The mechanism of the inhibition by D-mannose of the respiration of excised roots. *Ann. Botany*, 29: 45.

HELLER, R., 1953: Recherches sur la nutrition minérale des tissus végétaux cultivés *in vitro*. *Ann. Sci. Nat. Botan. Biol. Végétale*, Series II, 1.

HEWITT, E. J., 1952: *Sand and Water Culture Methods Used in the Study of Plant Nutrition.* Commonwealth Agricultural Bureau, Farnham Royal, U.K.

LOOMIS, R. S., and J. G. TORREY, 1964: Chemical control of vascular cambium initiation in isolated radish roots. *Proc. Nat. Acad. Sci. U.S.*, Washington, D.C., 52: 3.

MORGAN, D. R., and H. E. STREET, 1959: The carbohydrate nutrition of tomato roots, VII. *Ann. Botany (London)*, 23: 89.

NEALES, T. F., 1959: The boron requirement of flax roots grown in sterile culture. *J. Exptl. Botany*, 10: 426.

———, 1964: A comparison of the boron requirements of intact tomato plants and excised tomato roots grown in sterile culture. *J. Exptl. Botany*, 15: 647.

RAGGIO, M., and N. RAGGIO, 1956: A new method for the cultivation of isolated roots. *Physiol. Plantarum*, 9: 466.

———, ———, and J. G. TORREY, 1957: The nodulation of isolated leguminous roots. *Am. J. Botany*, 44: 325.

SHEAT, D. E. G., B. H. FLETCHER, and H. E. STREET, 1959: Studies on the growth of excised roots. VIII. *New Phytologist*, 58: 128.

STREET, H. E., 1957: Excised root culture. *Biol. Rev. Cambridge Phil. Soc.*, 32: 117.

———, 1959: Special problems raised by organ and tissue culture. Correlation between organs of higher plants as a consequence of specific metabolic requirements. In W. Ruhland (ed.), *Encyclopaedia of Plant Physiology*, Springer-Verlag,

Berlin. Vol. XI: 153.

———, and E. H. ROBERTS, 1952: Factors controlling meristematic activity in excised roots. I. *Physiol. Plantarum*, 5: 498.

———, and S. M. MC GREGOR, 1952: The carbohydrate nutrition of tomato roots. III. *Ann. Botany* (*London*), 16: 185.

THOMAS, D. R., J. S. CRAIGIE, and H. E. STREET, 1963: Carbohydrate nutrition of the excised root. In *Plant Tissue and Organ Culture—A Symposium*, International Society of Plant Morphologists, Delhi, p. 26.

TORREY, J. G., 1963: *Cellular Patterns in Developing Roots. Symposium of the Society for Experimental Biology.* University of Cambridge Press, Cambridge, Eng., 17: 285.

VAIDYANATHAN, C. S., and H. E. STREET, 1959a: A non-dialysable inhibitor of glutamotransferase present in excised tomato roots. *Nature*, London, 184: 347.

———, and ———, 1959b: Nitrate reduction by aqueous extracts of excised tomato roots. *Nature*, London, 184: 531.

WHITE, P. R., 1943: *A Handbook of Plant Tissue Culture.* Cattell & Co., Lancaster, Pa.

WILLMER, E. N. (ed.), 1966: *The Biology of Cells and Tissues in Culture: Methods, Biology and Physiology*, Vol. III, Academic Press, New York.

Shoot and Leaf Organ Culture

By Mary E. Clutter and Ian M. Sussex

INTRODUCTION

The shoot system of higher vascular plants consists of two components: the stem and the leaf. Both kinds of organs originate from the shoot apical meristem but differ greatly in their pattern of development. The stem is typically radially symmetrical and indeterminate in the duration of its growth; the leaf is typically dorsiventral and determinate in growth. The responses of these two organs to many exogenous stimuli also differ. Whereas the elongation of stems is generally stimulated by darkness, leaf expansion is inhibited; auxins which stimulate stem growth frequently are without effect on leaves. The different developmental patterns and physiological responses of the two kinds of organs are presumably manifestations of underlying biochemical differentiation. Although this might suggest different requirements for growth *in vitro*, it has been found that conditions which are suitable for the growth of one will often permit growth of the other.

In analyzing factors which regulate growth and development of stems and leaves many investigators have employed organ culture techniques in which a specific region is excised and cultured in isolation from the remainder of the plant. The following are the principal kinds of experimental organ culture systems:

1. Shoot culture—in which various lengths of the shoot including stem, leaves, and apical meristem are excised from the rest of the plant and grown in culture.
2. Apical meristem culture—in which the apical meristem is isolated from all the other tissues of the shoot and grown separately.
3. Leaf culture—in which leaf primordia in different developmental stages are excised from the plant and grown separately.
4. Stem section culture—in which sections cut from the stem to include only internodal or nodal tissue are grown in isolation to examine growth responses of specific regions of the stem.
5. Leaf disc culture—in which discs removed from mesophyll or vein regions of developing leaves are grown in culture to examine responses of different components of the leaf.

Stem section culture and leaf disc culture studies have usually been concerned with examination of the cell expansion phase of organ growth. Experiments have typically been of short duration (from several to 48 hours), and preservation of aseptic conditions has not usually been a major concern. Either no precautions have been taken to avoid contamination by microorganisms, or the culture medium has been renewed at intervals, or antibiotics have been added to the system (Sorokin, Mathur, and Thimann, 1962). Experimental design for these organ culture systems is covered by other articles in this volume (Morré and Key, pp. 575–593, and Johri and Varner, pp. 595–611), and will not be further discussed here.

The culture of isolated shoots, apical meristems, or leaves may require periods of time from a few weeks to several months for completion, during which time considerable development, involving the initiation and expansion of new structures by cell division and enlargement, may take place. In these experiments, therefore, it is essential that aseptic conditions be established and preserved throughout the culture period.

The usual procedure for obtaining aseptic plant material has been either to use organs which are not contaminated in their natural state, or to sterilize the plant material in a way which will kill all adhering microorganisms while leaving the plant tissue unharmed. Once sterility of the plant material is obtained it is preserved by the use of instruments, culture medium, and containers which have themselves been sterilized, and by using procedures which will avoid contamination by microorganisms during the subsequent growth period.

SHOOT CULTURE

The culture of shoots removed from naturally growing plants presents numerous technical difficulties because of the presence of microorganisms on all the exposed surfaces. Since these surfaces are frequently pubescent or fissured they have often been found difficult to sterilize. However, if some of the outer leaves of the terminal bud are first removed the remainder can sometimes be satisfactorily sterilized by following the schedule outlined in the next paragraph.

A more satisfactory source of material is the vegetative shoot from seedlings which have been grown aseptically from sterilized seeds, or from embryos grown in culture. The latter technique is covered in the article by Raghavan in this book. Seeds may be sterilized by immersion in a solution of calcium hypochlorite. An easily handled and readily available source of this solution is a liquid laundry bleach such as Clorox. Because the seed coat is relatively impermeable to aqueous solutions, rigorous sterilization procedures may usually be employed, and solutions of 15 to 20 percent Clorox applied for 15 minutes are not usually damaging to seeds. During sterilization the container of seeds should be shaken continuously to ensure that all seed surfaces come in contact with the disinfectant. The seeds are then washed once or twice in sterile distilled water. From this point on, all instruments, containers, and solutions with which the plant material comes in contact must be sterile. Small flasks of water and culture medium are most easily sterilized by autoclaving at 15 pounds pressure (121°C) for 15 minutes. Petri dishes and other items can be autoclaved for comparable times, or if the stacks are bulky for longer periods. Sterilization of the instruments, which are normally used repeatedly, is best achieved by dipping in ethanol and flaming them. The instruments should then be placed between sheets of sterilized paper until they are sufficiently cool to handle the plant material without damaging it. After being used the instruments are returned to the ethanol and the sterilization is repeated.

The sterilized seeds are transferred aseptically to Petri dishes containing water-moistened filter paper. While it is best to perform this and all subsequent manipulation of the material in a sterile transfer room equipped with ultraviolet lights, or some other method of air sterilization, it can be performed satisfactorily in an open room if the windows and doors are kept closed to reduce air circulation as much as possible. Wiping the surface of the work area frequently with ethanol-soaked cloth or cotton will further reduce the possibility of contamination. After the seeds have germinated the shoot may be excised with a scalpel or scissors and planted in culture medium. The preparation of a suitable culture medium is described in the Appendix of this chapter. Additional information on media and on aseptic techniques has been given by White (1954) and by Gautheret (1959), and several other culture media are listed in articles referred to in the bibliography at the end of this article. It is possible to grow shoots *in vitro* in total darkness or to use natural or artificial light for illumination. The best conditions can be obtained in a culture room where light intensities can be regulated and where a constant temperature can be maintained. Light intensities of 50 to 500 ft-c, which can be obtained from fluorescent lights, and temperatures of about 25°C provide near-optimal growth conditions.

The culture of excised vegetative shoots has not been used extensively in studies of shoot morphogenesis, although it has been employed successfully for many years beginning with experiments by Robbins (1922) to determine nutritional requirements of the shoot system. More recently this technique has been used to study the source of shoot growth stimulating substances (Loo, 1945), the physiology of adventitious root initiation (Galston, 1948), and developmental potentialities of the shoot (Marsden and Wetmore, 1954). Shoot culture has recently come into prominence in several European countries where it has been used to decontaminate species of crop plants such as potatoes and strawberries from systemic viral infections. The viruses multiply in mature tissues, and excised shoot tips grown in sterile culture until they rooted and were large enough to be transferred to soil, were found to produce plants which were virus free (Belkengren and Miller, 1962; Morel and Martin, 1955).

Shoot culture methods have also been applied in the study of ontogenetic modifications of development, and it is in this area that the technique may find its greatest use. Developmental modification of a shoot during its ontogeny may lead to maturation as a flower, spine, tuber, or some other structure. These are all recognized as modified shoots, but knowledge of the underlying causes is in many cases fragmentary. The development of a reproductive shoot has been the most thoroughly investigated modification. During this process the apical meristem of a previously vegetative shoot continues to produce lateral primordia which, however, instead of developing as leaves, develop as the organs of the flower. The initiation of floral development in excised shoots has been studied by Raghavan and Jacobs (1961); and the development of flowers and the specific growth requirements of the various floral organs in sterile culture have been studied by Tepfer, Greyson, Craig, and Hindman (1963).

APICAL MERISTEM CULTURE

The shoot apical meristem, which gives rise to both the stem and the leaves, is located at the distal extremity of the stem and is surrounded by the youngest leaves of the terminal bud. It is a region of great significance in the development of the shoot, and it is of importance in the analysis of development to know to what extent it is an organizer region and to what extent it is a plastic region responding to formative stimuli coming from other parts of the plant. However, because of its intimate association with the tissues and organs to which it gives rise it is difficult to answer questions of this sort in the intact plant, and separate culture of the apical meristem has provided a method by which these problems may be attacked.

The leaves comprising the terminal bud must be removed before the apical meristem can be excised. However, since the smallest leaf primordia are of microscopic size, and since the apical meristem is not usually over 0.25 mm in diameter, this is a technique requiring reasonable manipulative skill and fine instruments, and, in the final stages, it is best done under a dissecting stereomicroscope.

A plant which has been frequently used in studies of this type is the white lupin (*Lupinus albus* L.). Seeds of this species are not usually available from seed companies, but they can be obtained from many Italian grocery stores under the name "lupini beans." Three-week-old soil-grown plants are sufficiently well developed that they can be easily handled during apical meristem excision. It is unnecessary to sterilize the plant because the apical meristem and its immediate surroundings are free from microorganisms and, providing that the outer leaves are removed carefully with frequent changes of sterile instruments, no contaminants will be carried into the apical meristem.

The surgical instruments which serve best are scalpels and forceps which are finer than those usually available. Suitably fine forceps are numbers 4 and 5 watchmaker's forceps which are available from watchmaker supply companies (for instance: Levenson, 42 Asylum St., Hartford, Conn., U.S.A.). Microscalpels can be made by breaking pieces from the sharp edge of razor blades with pliers. The razor blade fragments may then be held in chuck-type needle holders, or in pin slides, the latter also obtainable from watchmaker's suppliers. Microscalpels made in this way are suitable for the excision of most apices, but they may be further improved by grinding the sides of the blade. This can be done on a flat stone or, more reliably, on a small power-driven, coarse grinding wheel. In the latter case a stereomicroscope can be set over the wheel so that the grinding process can be controlled. Additional information on microinstruments and their preparation can be found in the article by Cutter, pp. 623–634, in this volume. All the instruments can be sterilized by dipping in ethanol and flaming. However, the fine points and edges are better preserved if they are not flamed, but are rinsed in sterile water after the ethanol dip and are then dried between sheets of sterile paper.

When dissecting the plant to expose the apical meristem the large outer leaves of the bud can be stripped away by hand. Smaller ones can be removed by forceps, each pair of forceps being used to remove one or two leaves only before being resterilized. When leaves too small to be distinguished readily by eye are reached, the tip of the shoot may be held erect under a stereomicroscope at about 30 × magnification. The remaining leaf primordia can then be removed. The apical meristem of lupin is a hemispherical, glistening, dark green dome of tissue approximately 0.25 mm in diameter, and it can be readily distinguished from any leaf primordia which remain. The morphology of the shoot apical meristem differs in different species. In many it is pale green or colorless, smaller, and less conspicuously mounded than the meristem of lupin. However, the apical meristem of all vascular plants can be exposed by carefully removing the surrounding leaf primordia. The meristem can be excised by making three or four deep vertical cuts with a microscalpel around its margin, and undercutting the central column of tissue with a horizontal incision. It can then be lifted out on the tip of the scalpel and transferred directly to the surface of an agar-solidified or a liquid culture medium.

Growth of the cultured apical meristem is initially quite slow, and it is usually more than a week before microscopically visible evidence of growth is obtained. However, examination of the apical meristem within its culture tube with a stereomicroscope may reveal early developmental changes. The overall growth rate increases when leaf primordia are initiated and stem elongation commences.

Excised apical meristems of ferns and fern allies have been grown in culture to test the effect of different levels of nutrient supply on the development of the meristem, and particularly to examine the effect of carbohydrates on the shape of developing leaves (Wetmore, 1954). Excised portions of the apical meristem of several flowering plants have been grown in culture to test the growth potential of different regions within the apical meristem (Wetmore, Gifford, and Green, 1959). Other investigators have compared the growth of apices from vernalized and unvernalized plants (Morel, 1963), or the influence of young leaf primordia on the growth of the apical meristem (Ball, 1946, 1960). In some of these investigations the apical meristem was excised in a way which excluded all leaf primordia, in others one to several of the youngest leaf primordia were excised with the meristem. These latter should more correctly be considered as extreme cases of shoot culture. However, in their growth requirements these small terminal portions of the shoot are more like the isolated apical meristem than they are like the shoot, and they form a bridge between shoot culture and apical meristem culture.

LEAF CULTURE

The terminal cells of a leaf, which are initially meristematic, become differentiated, and a fully developed leaf consists of mature cells only. The differentiation of the meristematic cells occurs at different times in the leaves of different groups of vascular plants. In flowering plants they usually cease division by the time the leaf is a millimeter in height, but in some ferns they continue to function meristematically until the leaf is several centimeters or more in height. Culture experiments have been directed at the control of the duration of the cell division phase in the leaf tip. These experiments provide information on the developmental differences between leaf and stem, the former having a limited period of terminal meristematic activity, the latter an unlimited period.

Leaf cultures of ferns have been made almost exclusively on members of the family Osmundaceae.[1] The terminal bud in these plants is very large. It contains leaf primordia which develop in the bud over a period of several years before maturation, and it is completely surrounded by protective bud scales which do much to reduce microorganism infection of the inner bud members. Thus, it is possible to obtain a large number of leaf primordia of different developmental stages which are devoid of contaminating microorganisms. A detailed description of the bud of one species from this family has been given by Steeves and Wetmore (1953).

After the roots which cover the stem of a fern such as *Osmunda cinnamomea* L. have been removed, and the old leaf bases and expanded fronds have been cut away to expose the scale leaves surrounding the bud, the whole shoot can be sterilized in

[1] Several species of *Osmunda* may be purchased in quantity from I. L. Williams, Exeter Wild Flower Gardens, P.O. Box 352, Exeter, New Hampshire distributors of American native plants.

20 percent Clorox for 30 minutes, then rinsed in sterile distilled water and placed between sheets of sterile paper. Further dissection must be carried out with forceps, using coarse forceps to remove the outer leaves and finer ones for the small, inner leaves. The younger primordia respond more extensively to experimental treatment, and for many morphogenetic studies it is preferable to use leaves which are not more than 5 mm in length at the time of excision. If the smallest leaf primordia which surround the apical meristem are to be excised the final stages of the dissection should be carried out while viewing the shoot tip through a stereomicroscope. In order to examine the later stages of leaf growth such as the uncoiling and expansion of the frond, larger leaves located near the periphery of the bud can be cultured. Leaf primordia can be cultured either on agar-solidified media or in liquid media. Since experiments of this type are of long duration, the leaves requiring 2 to 3 months in culture to reach maturity, it may be necessary to transfer them to fresh culture media at monthly intervals.

Investigations of fern leaf development have been concerned principally with the effects of nutrients in the control of leaf shape. On media containing low concentrations of sugar, leaves resembling juvenile fronds developed. As the sugar concentration of the medium was raised leaves developed shapes progressively more like that of the adult frond (Sussex and Clutter, 1960). When the youngest leaf primordia of *Osmunda* were grown in culture they developed not as leaves but as shoots (Steeves, 1962), and analyses of results of this kind have contributed to an understanding of the developmental control mechanisms which underlie the differentiation of leaf and stem. Other studies have been concerned with the initiation of sporangia on excised fern leaves (Steeves and Sussex, 1957), or the initiation of meiosis and spore development in cultured fertile leaves (Clutter and Sussex, 1965), and the developmental potentialities of cultured fern leaf fragments (Kuehnert and Steeves, 1962). Excised leaves of flowering plants have been grown only occasionally in culture (Steeves, Gabriel, and Steeves, 1957). However, leaves of *Helianthus annuus* (sunflower) and *Nicotiana tabacum* (tobacco) grew to quite large size in culture, and the method of leaf culture may in the future be used in studies to analyze the development of angiosperm leaves.

Of the various lateral organs of the flower which could be excised and grown separately in culture only anthers have been studied intensively. Studies utilizing anther cultures have been concerned with the control of meiosis and the development of microspores (Vasil, 1963). However, in contrast to work on the initiation of meiosis in fern leaves, no method has yet been found to initiate meiosis in excised anthers of any species of flowering plant.

CONCLUSION

In comparison with the extensive contribution which root culture has made to the analysis of root growth (Street, this volume, pp. 425–434) organ culture methods appear to have provided much less toward the understanding of shoot growth. This difference is probably a reflection of the relative difficulty of measuring growth and development in roots and shoots. It is fairly simple to measure growth of a root, which is a cylindrical organ, perhaps devoid of lateral organs, at least near the tip, and with differentiation linearly related to the terminal meristem, but the analysis of shoot growth is far more difficult. Not only are numerous lateral organs formed sequentially in proximity to the apical meristem, but these undergo marked shape changes during development and also influence the differentiation of adjacent tissues in the stem. In many cases it has only been possible to describe these events in general terms, and quantitative methods for dealing with many of them have not yet been perfected. When quantitative methods are available organ cultures of the shoot system will be far more productive. However, in providing comparative information on the relative dependence on other parts of the plant of the leaf meristem and the shoot meristem, organ cultures have already provided data which would not have been obtainable by any other procedure (Sussex, 1963), and the shoot tip cultures of virus-infected plants have demonstrated the practical value of the method.

Some of the techniques described here have been developed in the authors' laboratory as part of a research program supported by the National Science Foundation.

APPENDIX

There is a wide variety of formulas for nutrient media on which plant organ cultures can be grown. Most of these are modifications of a medium formulated by White (1954). Basically, they consist of an inorganic salt solution, a carbohydrate source and, sometimes, a vitamin supplement. Most plant organs will grow on a very simple medium, but alterations in the carbohydrate level may be necessary depending on the species of plant used. For example, most fern organs have a very low sugar requirement (0.25–1 percent sucrose) while angiosperms usually require higher concentrations (2–3 percent). Auxins, kinetin, gibberellin, coconut milk, and other growth-regulating substances may be added to the medium in a range of concentrations and combinations within physiological limits (auxins, kinetin, and gibberellin at about 1 mg per liter and coconut milk at about 15 percent).

The following is a basal medium used in our laboratory for organ culture. It can easily be supplemented with other growth-regulating substances. For convenience, the stock solutions can be made in advance and stored in a refrigerator. All solutions should be made with double-glass-distilled water.

Basal Medium for Shoot and Leaf Cultures

Modified Knop's stock	250 ml
Trace elements stock	1 ml
Phosphate stock	1 ml
Ferric chloride	1 ml
Sucrose (2.0 percent)	20 gm
pH	5.5
Agar (purified Bacto-agar 0.8 percent)	8 gm
Double-distilled water	to 1,000 ml

The stock solutions for this medium are as follows:

Modified Knop's Stock—1 liter

$Ca(NO_3)_2 \cdot 4H_2O$	1.0 gm
KNO_3	0.25 gm
$MgSO_4 \cdot 7H_2O$	0.25 gm
Double-distilled water	to 1.0 liter

NOTE: Use 250 ml per liter of medium.

Trace Elements Stock—50 ml

H_2SO_4, sp. gr. 1.83	0.1 ml
$MnSO_4 \cdot 4H_2O$	150 mg
$ZnSO_4 \cdot 7H_2O$	25 mg
H_3BO_3	25 mg
$CuSO_4 \cdot 5H_2O$	1.25 mg
$Na_2MoO_4 \cdot 2H_2O$	1.25 mg
$CoCl_2$	1.25 mg
Double-distilled water	to 50 ml

NOTE: Use 1 ml per liter of medium.

Phosphate Stock—50 ml

KH_2PO_4	3.125 gm
Double-distilled water	50 ml

NOTE: Use 1 ml per liter of medium.

Ferric Chloride Stock—50 ml

$FeCl_3 \cdot 6H_2O$	0.5 gm
Double-distilled water	to 50 ml

NOTE: Use 1 ml per liter of medium.

When all constituents of the medium except agar have been dissolved, and most of the water has been added, the solution is adjusted to a pH of 5.5 with dilute KOH or NaOH or HCL. Then the medium is heated to the boiling point, the agar is added and, finally, enough water is added to make it to volume. It can then be dispensed into culture tubes or flasks. In our laboratory the tubes are covered with stainless steel caps, then autoclaved at 15 pounds per square inch pressure for 15 minutes. Aluminum foil caps can be substituted for the steel ones. After autoclaving and cooling the medium is ready for use. Cultures are set up as described in the text. When ready, the tubes are capped with polyethylene film 0.0015 inch thick which has been sterilized in 70 percent ethanol and dried between sheets of sterile paper. The caps are held in place by rubber bands.

The foregoing medium is one devised by Steeves and Sussex (1957) for excised *Osmunda cinnamomea* leaf primordia. A more complete description of this medium and supplementation of it can be found in the original publication.

REFERENCES

BALL, E., 1946: Development in sterile culture of stem tips and subjacent regions of *Tropeolum majus* L. and *Lupinus albus* L. *Amer. Jour. Bot.*, 33: 301.

———, 1960: Sterile culture of the shoot apex of *Lupinus albus*. *Growth*, 24: 91.

BELKENGREN, R. O., and P. W. MILLER, 1962: Culture of apical meristems of *Fragaria vesca* strawberry plants as a method of excluding latent A virus. *Plant Disease Reporter*, 46: 119.

CLUTTER, M. E., and I. M. SUSSEX, 1965: Meiosis and sporogenesis in excised fern leaves grown in sterile culture. *Bot. Gaz.*, 126: 72.

GALSTON, A. W., 1948: On the physiology of root initiation in excised asparagus stem tips. *Amer. Jour. Bot.*, 35: 281.

GAUTHERET, R. J., 1959: *La culture des tissus végétaux; techniques et réalisations.* Masson, Paris.

KUEHNERT, C. C., and T. A. STEEVES, 1962. Capacity of fragments of leaf primordia to produce whole leaves. *Nature*, 196: 187.

LOO, S. W., 1945: Cultivation of excised stem tips of asparagus *in vitro*. *Amer. Jour. Bot.*, 32: 13.

MARSDEN, M. P. F., and R. H. WETMORE, 1954: *In vitro* culture of the shoot tips of *Psilotum nudum*. *Amer. Jour. Bot.*, 41: 640.

MOREL, G., 1963: Discussion at Brookhaven Symposium in Biology: Meristems and Differentiation. *Brookhaven Symp. Biol.*, 16: 11.

———, and C. MARTIN, 1955: Guérison de plantes atteintes de maladies à virus. *14th Intern. Hort. Congr.*, 1: 303.

RAGHAVAN, V., and W. P. JACOBS, 1961: Studies on the floral histogenesis and physiology of Perilla. II. Floral induction in cultured apical buds of *P. frutescens*. *Amer. Jour. Bot.*, 48: 751.

ROBBINS, W. J., 1922: Cultivation of excised root tips and stem tips under sterile conditions. *Bot. Gaz.*, 73: 376.

SOROKIN, H. P., S. N. MATHUR, and K. V. THIMANN, 1962: The effects of auxins and kinetin on xylem differentiation in the pea epicotyl. *Amer. Jour. Bot.*, 49: 444.

STEEVES, T. A., 1962: Morphogenesis in isolated fern leaves. In D. Rudnick (ed.), *Regeneration. 20th Symp. Soc. Study Dev. & Growth*, Ronald Press, New York, p. 117.

———, H. P. GABRIEL, and M. W. STEEVES, 1957: Growth in sterile culture of excised leaves of flowering plants. *Science*,

126: 350.

———, and I. M. SUSSEX, 1957: Studies on the development of excised leaves in sterile culture. *Amer. Jour. Bot.*, 44: 665.

———, and R. H. WETMORE, 1953: Morphogenetic studies on *Osmunda cinnamomea* L.: some aspects of the general morphology. *Phytomorphology*, 3: 339.

SUSSEX, I. M., 1963: The permanence of meristems: developmental organizers or reactors to exogenous stimuli? *Brookhaven Symp. Biol.*, 16: 1.

———, and M. E. CLUTTER, 1960: A study of the effect of externally supplied sucrose on the morphology of excised fern leaves *in vitro*. *Phytomorphology*, 10: 87.

TEPFER, S. S., R. I. GREYSON, W. R. CRAIG, and J. L. HINDMAN, 1963: *In vitro* culture of floral buds of *Aquilegia*. *Amer. Jour. Bot.* 50: 1035.

VASIL, I. K., 1963: Some new experiments with excised anthers. In P. Maheshwari and N. S. Rangaswamy (eds.), *Plant Tissue and Organ Culture—a Symposium*, Catholic Press, Ranchi, India, p. 230.

WETMORE, R. H., 1954: The use of "in vitro" cultures in the investigation of growth and differentiation in vascular plants. *Brookhaven Symp. Biol.*, 6: 22.

———, E. M. GIFFORD, JR., and M. C. GREEN, 1959: Development of vegetative and floral buds. In R. B. Withrow (ed.), *Photoperiodism and Related Phenomena in Plants and Animals*, Am. Assoc. Advan. Sci., Washington, D.C., p. 255.

WHITE, P. R., 1954: *The Cultivation of Animal and Plant Cells*. Ronald Press, New York.

Avian and Mammalian Organ Culture*

By Norman K. Wessells

INTRODUCTION

One of the most powerful techniques for analyzing organ morphogenesis and factors controlling cytodifferentiation is organ culture *in vitro*. Many organ rudiments from embryos of the homeothermic vertebrates survive and continue development in simplified conditions *in vitro*, so that it is possible to analyze maturational processes in the absence of the complexities of the normal *milieu intérieur*.

The degree of success in obtaining continued development *in vitro* is dependent upon age (developmental stage) and size of the explant, nutrients, and physical parameters of the environment (substrate, gases, humidity, etc.). In some cases ontogeny *in vitro* resembles maturation *in vivo*. However, it may differ in important details. Consequently, a comparative series of *in vivo* and *in vitro* material should always be prepared in order to establish characteristics of the particular experimental system under investigation.

The purpose of this chapter is to outline some simple techniques that will allow successful organ culture in the research or classroom laboratory. Brief consideration is given to culture apparatus, media, environmental conditions, and a few sample experimental procedures. Most specific points touched upon here are treated exhaustively in books by Parker (1961), White (1963), Paul (1965), Merchant, Kahn, and Murphy (1960), and Willmer (1965), and in the article by New (1965). For examples of experimental programs using organ culture extensively, see: Borghese (1958, 1965), Fell (1951), Grobstein (1965), or Wolff (1965).

BASIC CULTURE APPARATUS

The type of culture chamber to be used, as well as the actual physical support for organs cultured *in vitro*, is largely determined by the nutrient supply employed. A simple vessel that adapts to a variety of media is a Petri plate (100 mm × 20 mm) containing a depression slide. Either thick (13 mm), borosilicate glass slides with three depressions (commonly called spot plates in catalogues) or sets of three to six depressions cut from large plastic sheets of spot depressions prove satisfactory, particularly if solid medium substrates are employed. Combination of presterilized plastic Petri plates with the plastic de-

* Test of various procedures outlined in this paper was carried out with the support of United States Public Health Service Research Grant GM-10060.

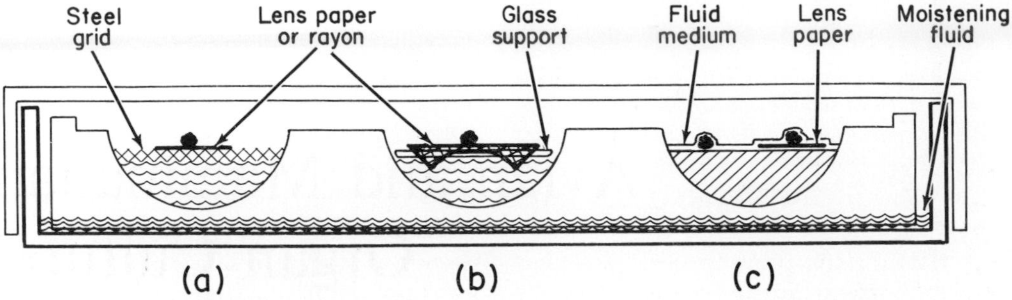

FIG. 1. Petri plate culture chamber containing glass "spot-plate" depression slide. (a) Fluid medium. Tissue on lens paper or rayon raft supported by metal grid. (b) Fluid medium. Tissue on lens paper or rayon raft supported by borosilicate glass triangle. (c) Solid medium; agar or plasma clot. Tissue directly on medium or on raft resting on medium. Thin layer of fluid over solid substrate is optional.

pressions yields an inexpensive, disposable unit. Glass Petri plates and slides should be assembled and then sterilized by heating at 180°C for several hours, whereas plastic slides should be sterilized in 70–80 percent ethyl alcohol (15–30 minutes), rinsed thoroughly with sterile water, and then inserted in sterile Petri plates. When such plastic depression slides are used, a mat of sterile absorbent cotton should be arranged around the base of the slide to prevent tipping. Fluid may be added to the cotton for moist chamber culturing (see p. 451). In the use of glass plates and slides no cotton is needed; hence, the fluid can be placed directly in the Petri plate. These techniques are a modification of the watch glass-Petri plate method perfected years ago by Fell.

In addition to Petri plates and depression slides, specially designed organ culture dishes are available commercially. The glass Grobstein dish (Microchemical Specialties, Berkeley, California, U.S.A.) contains a small depression (about 1.0 ml volume), surrounded by a wide shelf upon which preparative procedures may be performed. A presterilized, disposable modification of the Grobstein dish (Falcon Plastics, Los Angeles, California, U.S.A.) contains a similar central depression surrounded by a narrow shelf, and a moist chamber perimeter. If desired, the latter dishes may be reused after washing and resterilization in alcohol.

Solid substrates for organ cultures may be prepared directly in the slide depression. Agar (final concentration about 0.5 to 1 percent) may be mixed with a complex nutrient broth (see Fig. 1), with whole egg or egg white extracts (for early blastoderm culture), or with defined nutrients. The agar is usually prepared at appropriate higher concentrations in a salt solution, such as 0.7 percent NaCl [buffering with tris(hydroxymethyl)-aminomethane at pH 7.4 may be desirable], autoclaved, cooled to 45°C, and mixed with the warmed nutrient solution. The depressions are filled to two-thirds capacity with the agar-medium solution by using a warm (not hot) pipette. The agar gels after several minutes at room temperature. Another type of solid substrate is prepared by mixing approximately equal quantities of blood plasma with embryo extract (see below). A solid substrate may also be prepared from solutions of solubilized collagen. Collagen (as prepared by Parker, 1961) is dissolved in salt solution or distilled water and sterilized. If exposed to ammonia vapors or incubated in the depressions for several hours at 37°C a firm gel results.

If fluid media are employed, explanted organ fragments should be placed on solid or semisolid platforms. Small pieces of lens paper (Chen, 1954), rayon cellulose-acetate cloth (Shaffer, 1956), and thin porous filters (as Millipore) have all been used successfully. These substrates must be supported at the air-fluid interface by titanium or stainless steel grids (Trowell, 1954; about 0.5-mm-square mesh, Falcon), by glass rods pulled thin (about 0.5 mm) and shaped in the form of equilateral triangles that rest in the depressions, or by specially constructed plastic assemblies (for filters). Lens paper can be treated with silicone so that it will tend to float; for safety, however, a solid support is still desirable. Pieces of Millipore filter may be placed over a hole (about 3 mm diameter) punched in a lens paper raft (Lash, Holtzer, and Holtzer, 1957), or it may be glued over a hole (about 3 mm diameter) drilled in a rectangular sheet of plastic (18 × 6 × 1 mm) which fits in the culture slide depressions (Auerbach, 1960; or see Grobstein, 1965). The "glue" is prepared by dissolving scraps of filters in acetone to yield a viscous solution. Lens paper cut to desired size should be washed in ether, absolute alcohol, detergent, and water, and then sterilized in alcohol or in dry heat (125°C) for 3 hours. Steel grids may be cleaned and sterilized in routine fashion. Millipore filters mounted on plastic or lens paper may be sterilized in 70–80 percent ethyl alcohol for 10–15 minutes, followed by washing several times in large volumes of sterile salt solution. It is best to use glass slide depressions for those techniques requiring support structures, since the walls of most commercial plastic spot-plate depressions are too steep.

Choice of raft materials for use with fluid media may be dictated by histological requirements. Lens paper cannot be sectioned during histological processing, whereas rayon acetate cloth can be dissolved by treatment with acetone. Millipore filters may be embedded directly in paraffin or plastic and sectioned.

It should be noted that when either solid substrates or liquid media are employed as described above, it is essential that explanted tissues remain near the gas-liquid interface. Most developing tissues tend to preserve reasonably normal histological organization there. Beneath fluid or at a glass-clot interface, cell migration is often marked, necrosis is more prevalent in central regions of thick tissues, and tissue architecture tends to become abnormal.

MEDIA

Media used for organ culture must provide nutrients, suitable osmotic pressure and ion balance, and buffering. Discussions of the latter two problems are available in many reviews (for instance, see Parker, 1961). Numerous treatments of essential nutrients, roles of proteins, embryo extracts, etc., are available also (for references, see Eagle, 1964; or Waymouth, 1954, 1965). Most studies on nutrient effects *in vitro* have been performed with cells of established tissue culture lines (derived some years previously from normal or neoplastic adult tissues) growing in monolayer culture. It would be incorrect, therefore, to try to apply results from such studies directly to the embryonic organ culture system, where considerable conditioning of media may occur in limited intercellular tissue spaces. Consequently, empiricism remains the method for choosing a medium for most organ culture situations.

Complex Media

A plasma clot-embryo extract mixture is a commonly used solid medium. Fell's method calls for fresh extract prepared from 13- or 14-day chicken embryos and diluted 1:1 with balanced salt solution. For preparation, the embryos are removed from the shell and membranes, minced in a sterile Petri plate or beaker with sterile scissors, poured into a syringe, and pushed through a stainless steel or monel grid (about 1.0-mm holes) placed at the base of the syringe barrel. After adding an equal volume of sterile salt solution (Tyrode's or others), the resultant mixture can be incubated for 10–15 minutes at room temperature. Cells and debris are removed by centrifugation at about 3,000 *g* (0°C, 10 minutes) and the supernatant is used fresh or is stored in a dry ice chest or, less desirably, in a normal freezer. If stored on dry ice, the containers must remain gastight even when chilled. Recentrifugation is necessary upon thawing. Embryos of 9 or 10 days also yield an active extract. Moreover, they contain less calcified material and are much easier to handle than older embryos. Gaillard (1953) has claimed optimal results by employing a graded series of extracts obtained from embryos of increasing age. In any situation where hormones could affect maturation of a particular organ, it is worth investigating the use of such series of extracts.

Blood plasma (usually adult chicken) that meets most organ-culture requirements can be obtained commercially (that from Grand Island Biologicals, Grand Island, New York, U.S.A., works in our laboratory for mouse and chick tissues; other sources may be equally useful). Little evidence is available on the relative merits of homologous or heterologous plasmas. Some organ systems do not develop well in commercial plasmas and, in fact, if difficulties are encountered when culturing in the presence of clots, the first place to look for deficiencies is in the plasma. Fresh plasma may overcome difficulties, particularly if subjected to special treatments such as dialysis against balanced salt solution (at 0°C) or concentration by forced evaporation at low temperatures (place plasma in sterile dialysis membrane; blow dry, cold air over the membrane). See Parker (1961) for methods of bleeding and preparation of normal plasma. One should not be repelled by the seeming complexities of bleeding. Wing vein puncture of 48-hour starved chickens is exceedingly simple when plastic disposable syringes, centrifuge tubes, etc., are used. The only precautions involve use of siliconized needles, and disposal of the first few milliliters of blood and of the 1-ml syringe used during entry of the vein (i.e., the needle is left in place and a large syringe is affixed to it).

To prepare a clot for culture, mix approximately equal quantities of blood plasma (kept chilled on ice until actually mixed) and embryo extract (as prepared above or diluted to as low as 20 percent by volume with salt solution) together thoroughly in a separate dish or in the final culture depression. An orally controlled micropipette is a convenient mixing tool. A firm clot should form in a few minutes and the rudiment to be explanted can be transferred to its upper surface. Normally, explants are transferred to fresh clots every other day. To do this, the rudiment is cut from the clot surface with sharpened iridectomy knives, leaving behind any unneeded fibroblast outgrowth zone, transferred to an embryo extract or salt solution for rinsing, and then placed on the surface of a fresh clot. The frequency of transfer must be determined empirically for each organ system. Organ rudiment development is often improved, and transfer procedures are certainly simplified, if cultures are placed on lens paper or other porous supports that rest on the clot. The raft and tissue can be lifted from a spent clot, rinsed, and arranged on a fresh clot with facility and less loss of cells.

Many complex liquid media prove satisfactory for organ culture. Most involve mixing a saline-glucose base containing small molecular nutrients (amino acids, vitamins, nucleic acid precursors), with a macromolecular component such as serum and an embryo extract. For example, we find the following to be optimal for a number of mouse and chick embryo organs: Waymouth's MB 752/1, 87 percent; horse serum (Colorado Serum Co., Denver, Colorado, U.S.A.), 10 percent; 9-day chick embryo extract (1:1 dilution as above), 3 percent (10 percent is sometimes better); and traces of antibiotics (see below). Other defined mixtures might be substituted for Waymouth's and other sera may be used. For each organ system, a preliminary screening is probably best; in the case of mouse pancreatic epithelia cultured on Millipore filters, for instance, horse serum is satisfactory, while fetal calf serum is unsatisfactory and few exocrine cells mature. Sera from different commercial sources also vary—this is obvious in terms of degree of contamination with hemoglobin or fats. It is less obvious in terms of supporting normal development and once a satisfactory source of serum has been found, it is usually best to use only that supplier. The level of embryo extract employed in medium should also be checked, since different growth rates may occur at different concentrations.

For optimal results it is best to replace the nutrient medium on organ cultures every day. A convenient way to do this is to aspirate the used medium into a small pressure flask via a large bore hypodermic needle (sterilized by passage through a flame prior to draining each culture) and then add fresh medium (at room temperature) using sterile technique.

If a solid substrate is desired, complex liquid media may be mixed directly with agar (see above). In such cases, or even with plasma clots as substrate, a small quantity of the fluid medium (about 0.05–0.1 ml per depression) may be layered over the firm substrate to supplement the nutrient supply. Every day the fluid should be drained off the surface completely, and a fresh aliquot added. Alternatively, the explant can be transferred to a fresh nutrient-agar depression. Care must be taken not to add too large a volume of fluid above a solid substrate, since some rudiments do not develop optimally if even partially submerged. For that reason, it may be desirable to place tissues upon a piece of lens paper or other thin, porous support that in turn lies upon the substrate.

Protein-Free Media

Many protein-free, defined nutrient mixtures are of potential use in organ culturing (see Waymouth, 1965). They permit one to test the effects of known nutrients, subject of course to the qualification that they cannot be considered completely "defined" or "protein-free" after tissues have metabolized in them for even brief periods. Whether they are of use for any particular system can only be determined by test. For example, shank skin from an 11-day chick embryo undergoes normal histodifferentiation in freshly prepared Waymouth's MB 752/1 and essentially duplicates development *in vivo*, whereas the same tissues behave in quite a different manner if cultured on the same medium supplemented with 10 percent horse serum, or on a plasma-embryo extract clot.

If protein-free media are employed, care must be taken to rinse all equipment that will contact the medium, its components, and the tissues with water of the highest purity (<0.01 ppm NaCl). Several relatively inexpensive high-yield borosilicate glass stills are available to produce such water from normal distilled water (as, Bellco, Vineland, New Jersey, U.S.A.). Similarly, if defined media are made from separate chemicals or from the prepackaged dry mixtures now available, only high-purity water should be used.

If commercial sources of sterile defined liquid media are used, several sources should be checked. One large supplier, for instance, keeps stocks on hand for as long as 12 months; such media apparently meet the industry's standards for cell culture, but the chick skin described above fails to develop normally in it, although it does so perfectly in the same medium from some other manufacturers, or in that prepared fresh in the laboratory. Finally, if commercial liquid defined media are to be stored for extended periods, the medium should be transferred to sterile borosilicate vessels, since most suppliers package fluid medium in soft glass of some type.

Antibiotics

Normally all equipment, dissecting instruments, solutions, and media are sterilized before explantation *in vitro* is attempted. Because of lengthy surgical procedures during tissue preparation, presence of extraordinary quantities of dust and microorganisms in the air, or other reasons, it may be desirable to ensure sterility during incubation by including antibiotics in the media. Mixtures of penicillin and streptomycin (available from several manufacturers as a sterile aqueous solution) provide a commonly used broad range of protection. Levels of 50–100 units penicillin and 50–100 μg streptomycin per milliliter seem to produce no apparent effect upon most organ cultures while serving to protect adequately from contamination. In some situations, a fungicide such as Mycostatin (Squibb; about 100 units per milliliter) may be required. Before conducting any complex series of organ culture experiments, sample runs should be performed in the presence and absence of the antibiotics to be used, in order to ensure absence of deleterious effect. Furthermore, it should constantly be borne in mind that antibiotics are not infallible. Careful sterile technique is the only sure way that antibiotic-resistant microorganisms can be permanently excluded from one's laboratory.

USE OF SPECIAL CHEMICALS

Difficulties in interpretation always accompany attempted test of a specific agent against the background of complex nutrient media. Levels of vitamins, hormones, or other agents with synergistic or antagonistic effects to the substance being tested should be determined if such information is pertinent to interpretation of results. If special procedures must be used when a specific agent is tested (as when vitamin A alcohol is dissolved in 100 percent ethyl alcohol), experimental design should include appropriate control series.

A medium of protein-free, defined nutrients is ideal for testing the effects of specific agents upon development. For example, when labeling with radioisotope-labeled metabolic precursors, media may be prepared lacking the normal unlabeled precursor. In special circumstances, such as labeling with carrier-free [P^{32}]-phosphate in a medium containing phosphates as buffers, the levels of Na_2HPO_4 or NaH_2PO_4 can be lowered, or a different buffer system may be substituted such as tris-(hydroxymethyl)-aminomethane.

Addition of specific agents to organ cultures presents certain problems not encountered with cell cultures or monolayer cultures. Penetration may be impeded by various barriers not present in a simpler system (peripheral tissue cell membranes, basement membranes, intercellular spaces, tissue thickness, etc.). Gradients of decreasing isotope incorporation from the periphery to the inside of a thick (0.5–1.0 mm) organ culture are often seen on autoradiograms. It is not known whether such gradients reflect limited penetration, larger unlabeled precursor pools in internal cells, or lower rates of metabolic activity and incorporation in internal regions. These same problems are encountered in reverse form if organ cultures are treated for intervals with an agent and then cultured (i.e., chased). For radioisotopes, excess unlabeled precursor (100 to 1,000 times by weight) may be added to the medium to decrease continued incorporation during the "chase" period. A possible lag in effectiveness of the chase must also be considered, particularly when thick tissue masses are involved. For agents such as vitamins and hormones, effective chase may be more difficult and only specific measurements of residual levels in free or bound state can aid in interpretation of the experiment. In all cases washing in several large volumes (5–10 ml) of salt solution or medium is essential prior to reincubation in the chasing medium.

PHYSICAL CONDITIONS

Humidity

Evaporation from the small volumes of medium commonly employed for organ cultures can lead to increase in osmotic pressure of the medium and eventually to drying of the cultures. Evaporation can be minimized by saturating the atmosphere of the whole incubator or of the culture dish itself. It is probably best to humidify the incubator if unsealed culture vessels are employed or if the volume of nutrient medium per culture is small (0.5 ml or less). Several commercial incubators are available in which 85–95 percent relative humidity can be achieved. A similar setup can be prepared easily by inserting a controllable immersion heater in a pan of water placed on the floor of the incubator. Adjustment of the incubator thermostat is usually necessary. The water pan may be fed from a reservoir through a float valve. If continuous gas flow into the incubator is used in a humidified incubator, it may be best to pass the gas through a gas diffusion tube into the water pans in the incubator in order to warm and humidify it. If high humidity is maintained in an incubator for long periods, periodic cleaning of the whole interior with detergent is necessary to check growth of molds. Humidification of the whole incubator is not essential if moist chamber culture vessels are employed. The chamber should contain enough sterile water so that evaporation of the medium is checked and care must be taken that no liquid is splashed into culture compartments during handling of the culture dishes. If small volumes of nutrient medium are used, it is best to use a salt solution with equal tonicity as a moistening agent and add antibiotics to it for safety.

Gas Phase

The successful culture, by Fell's group, of bones, skin, and other organs on plasma clots in air in unsealed dishes is proof that special gas conditions are not always requisite for organogenesis *in vitro*.

If tris or phosphate buffers can be used for the system being studied, normal air should prove satisfactory. Whenever the bicarbonate-CO_2 buffer system is used, however, control of the gas phase is important (see Loomis, 1959, for general treatment). This applies to most complex or defined media. Mixtures of 5 percent CO_2 in air or oxygen are available commercially, or tanks or pure CO_2 may be obtained for mixture with air in the laboratory. Pressure-reducing valves, flow valves, and flow gauges (obtainable from standard supply houses) are all that are required to construct a dependable mixing system. The precise proportions of CO_2 to other gases (generally 5–8 percent CO_2) and the rate of flow (generally quite low) are best determined empirically for a particular medium and culture situation. This process is not difficult if the medium used contains about 10 mg per liter of phenol red and the color corresponding to pH 7.4 is maintained. For sterilization, the final gas mixture should be passed through nonwettable cotton packed in a drying tube which has been autoclaved.

Depending on the number of cultures and the frequency with which they must be handled, either continuous flow or daily renewal of the gas phase may be used. Daily renewal of gas is adequate when smaller numbers of culture dishes are employed. A heavy-walled vacuum desiccator fitted with a stopcock or rotating sleeve hose connection may serve for this purpose. Water for humidification may be placed in the bottom below the removal shelf. Gas should be passed into the desiccator via a long, sterile, cotton-plugged pipette. The pipette is inserted with the desiccator top ajar, so that the gas flows out near the bottom of the chamber. When sufficient exchange has occurred (about 1–2 minutes; 60 bubbles per minute) the top is sealed in place. An excellent substitute for a desiccator is a heavy-walled plastic CO_2 chamber (Labtool Specialties, Ypsilanti, Michigan, U.S.A.), with a gas-tight door, entrance and exit gas ports, and large shelf space. Either of these sealable culture chambers may be incubated in a Biological Oxygen Demand (B.O.D.) incubator or a constant temperature room (or other less expensive incubators, if some temperature fluctuation is not critical to experimental results).

Temperature

Avian and mammalian organ cultures continue developing if maintained at 35°–38°C. If very long survival times are required, lower temperatures (33°–35°C) may be beneficial (Martinovitch, 1939).

Tissue Size

As a rule of thumb, initial explant size should not exceed 0.5 to 1 mm in shortest dimension. Necrosis often occurs relatively rapidly in the center of organ cultures that exceed 2–3 mm in diameter. Large thin sheets of skin and pieces of a variety of organs with relatively loose architecture can survive *in vitro* as long as they remain thin in one dimension, and as long as peripheral exchange is not impeded by keratinization or analogous phenomena.

TYPICAL PROCEDURES

Two examples of organ culture will be outlined. Each experiment is simple to carry out and yields measurable results, so that techniques can be evaluated promptly as organ culture procedures are being learned.

Bone Development

1. Prepare Petri plates and depression slides with sterile water in the dishes around the slides and stainless steel or glass

triangle supports in each depression. Prepare and store fluid medium or mix medium with agar and place in the depressions. Fill Petri plates to be used for dissection with sterile dissecting fluid (1:1, horse serum:Tyrode's solution) if undefined nutrients are to be used, or with Tyrode's if protein-free, defined nutrients will subsequently be employed.

2. Wash the surface of a chicken egg incubated for 5–6 days with 0.5 percent sodium hypochlorite solution followed by 70–80 percent ethyl alcohol or another sterilizing agent. Using heavy, curved tip forceps that have been immersed in alcohol and flamed dry, pierce the shell on one side and remove a circular piece of shell about 3 cm in diameter. Using a second pair of sterile forceps, locate the embryo and grasp it gently around the neck (decantation of part of the fluid contents of the egg may aid this procedure), and transfer the embryo to a dissecting dish. Determine the stage of the embryo.

3. Using two pairs of alcohol-sterilized watchmaker's forceps (Dumont No. 5), sharpened and polished to very fine points with fine polishing cloth, remove and discard the head. Then remove the hind limbs by cutting the pelvic girdle from the vertebral column and the thigh musculature and skin from adjacent trunk tissues. Transfer the limbs to a fresh dissecting dish, and clean the skin and muscle from the skeletal elements. Be careful not to dislodge the ends of the femur. Finally, cut the femur free of pelvic girdle and lower leg bones. Submerge a piece of sterile lens paper or rayon acetate cloth in the dish, and place the bone upon it. Lift the lens paper by one edge and pass it through the surface film of the solution at a 45-degree angle, guiding the bone and lens paper with the other forceps. Touch the lowest corner of the paper to the upper edge of the plate so that any adhering drop of dissecting fluid is removed, and then transfer the paper to the upper surface of the stainless steel support or the agar substrate.

4. If fluid medium is used, immediately pipette medium into the depression so that the lens paper is wetted from below but does not float. If agar is used add a small volume of fluid nutrient medium over the surface.

5. Just before incubating, measure the length and width of the explanted bone with an ocular micrometer and sketch the shape in scale on graph paper (a camera lucida attachment is useful).

6. Feed the cultures daily by withdrawing old medium and adding freshly prepared medium. Record changes in bone length and shape (see Fell, 1951a, b; and Biggers, 1965, for summary, variations, etc.).

Salivary Gland Development

1. Prepare the culture vessels. Use a solid substrate (agar) mixed with complex medium, or Millipore filter platforms and complex liquid medium.

2. Kill a 13-day pregnant mouse by cervical dislocation (the morning of discovering the vaginal plug = day "0"). Remove the uterus and place it in Tyrode's solution. Tear open the uterine wall and extraembryonic membranes with fine-tipped forceps, and remove the head of an embryo by cutting through the neck, using care to leave the lower jaw uninjured. Transfer the head to a sterile Petri plate of dissecting fluid (1:1, horse serum:Tyrode's). With finely sharpened iridectomy or cataract knives, remove the lower jaw from the head and dissect out the submandibular glands located below and slightly lateral to the base of the tongue. Transfer the glands to a fresh dish of dissecting fluid and clean any loose jaw mesenchyme from the dense capsular mesenchyme that surrounds the tip of the

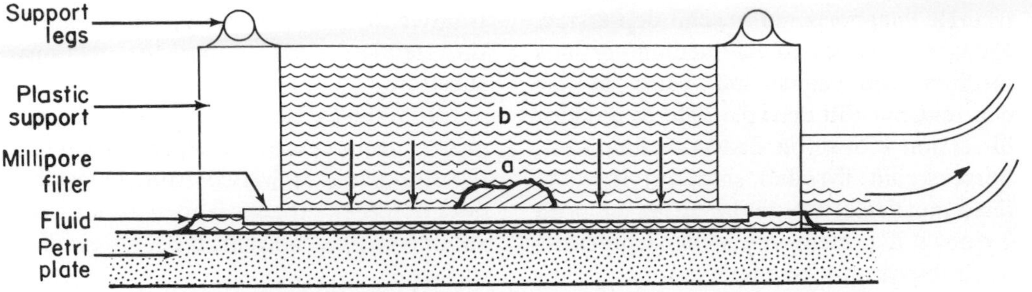

FIG. 2. Stranding procedure (after Grobstein). Fluid (b) is sucked downward through the filter by applying slight suction to the pipette on the right. Capillarity carries the fluid between the filter and the dry plastic Petri plate to the pipette. The tissue (a) is stranded firmly in place by withdrawing all possible fluid.

epithelial bulb. Remove and discard the small sublingual gland epithelium that grows into the same capsular mesenchyme. A whole submandibular gland may be explanted, or for a more spectacular demonstration, cut through the dense capsular mesenchyme and the salivary epithelium as near as possible to the tip of one of the peripheral epithelial expansions—a tiny epithelial fragment, barely visible against the mesenchyme at time zero will yield a large branched organ in a week of culturing. If a solid substrate is used, transfer the rudiment to its surface, drain excess fluid, add a small aliquot of medium, and incubate. If a filter is used, transfer the rudiment to the side of the filter that makes up the floor of the depression drilled in the plastic support piece. With an orally controlled micropipette, position the rudiment at the center of the filter.

3. Place equal-sized drops of chilled blood plasma and dilute embryo extract (about 30 percent in Tyrode's) next to one another in the bottom of a dry, sterile plastic Petri plate.

4. Move the Millipore filter assembly to the "ledge" of a Grobstein organ-culture dish or to a flat, dry, sterile surface (as on the floor of a plastic Petri plate). Place the tip of a micropipette (about 0.3-mm pore diameter whose terminal 5 mm is bent at 45 degrees) flush against the side of the plastic filter support and also against the ledge surface—suck the fluid around the tissues down through the filter and between the plastic assembly and ledge (Fig. 2). Drain completely so that no fluid reenters the filter cavity when the assembly and filter is moved or picked up. By this process the tissue is pulled down against the filter and effectively stuck to it.

5. Rapidly place the assembly over the depression in an organ culture dish. Mix the clot components (about 2:1, plasma: embryo extract) with a micropipette and immediately place a large drop of the mixture in the filter depression so as to fill it even with the top. Let stand for about 5 minutes or until the clot is quite firm.

6. Invert the filter in the final culture depression or dish and add fluid medium. The tissue is held on the lower surface of the filter by the clot.

7. Change medium daily. The organ will show progressive branching and adenomere formation at the branch tips.

8. For a variation, transfilter interaction of salivary mesenchyme and epi-

thelium may be demonstrated as follows. Place the dissected glands in trypsin solution [2.25 percent crude trypsin plus 0.75 percent pancreatin (Difco, Detroit, Michigan, U.S.A.) in CaMg-free Tyrode's solution, filtered and stored frozen in convenient aliquots] at room temperature for about 5 minutes. Using a micropipette with tip lumen diameter the same dimension as the salivary epithelium, flush the gland in and out of the pipette. As soon as the large end of the capsular mesenchyme comes free, transfer it to horse serum—Tyrode's. Continue flushing the epithelium until all adherent mesodermal cells have been removed; then, transfer it to the horse serum solution. Clot the epithelium on the lower surface of a filter as described above. After medium is added below the filter assembly, transfer the mesenchyme to the upper surface of the filter directly above the epithelium. Keep the tissue near the tip of the pipette and add a minimum of fluid to the filter top during positioning. Culture as above.

9. See Borghese (1958, 1965) or Grobstein (1965) for information on salivary gland cultures.

REFERENCES

AUERBACH, R., 1960: Morphogenetic interactions in the development of the mouse thymus gland. *Develop. Biol.*, 2: 271.

BIGGERS, J. D., 1965: Cartilage and bone. In E. N. Willmer (ed.), *Cells and Tissues in Culture*, Academic Press, New York, Vol. II, p. 197.

BORGHESE, E., 1958: Organ differentiation in culture. In W. McElroy and B. Glass (eds.), *The Chemical Basis of Development*, The Johns Hopkins University Press, Baltimore, Md., p. 704.

———, 1965: Salivary glands, intestinal tract, pancreas. In E. N. Willmer (ed.), *Cells and Tissues in Culture*, Academic Press, New York, Vol. II, p. 591.

CHEN, J. M., 1954: The cultivation in fluid medium of organised liver, pancreas, and other tissues from foetal rats. *Exper. Cell. Research*, 7: 518.

EAGLE, H., 1964: Population density and the nutrition of cultured mammalian cells. In D. Mazia and A. Tyler (eds.), *The General Physiology of Cell Specialization*, McGraw-Hill, New York, p. 151.

FELL, H. B., 1951: Histogenesis in tissue culture. In G. H. Bourne (ed.), *Cytology and Cell Physiology*, 2nd ed., Clarendon Press, Oxford, Eng., p. 419.

———, 1951: Techniques of bone cultivation. In M. B. Visscher (ed.), *Methods in Medical Research*, Year Book Publishers, Inc., Chicago, Ill., Vol. IV, p. 234.

GAILLARD, P. J., 1953: Growth and differentiation of explanted tissues. *Intern. Rev. Cytol.*, 2: 331.

GROBSTEIN, C., 1965: Differentiation: environmental factors, chemical and cellular. In E. N. Willmer (ed.), *Cells and Tissues in Culture*, Academic Press, New York, Vol. I, p. 463.

LASH, J., S. HOLTZER, and H. HOLTZER, 1957: An experimental analysis of the development of the spinal column. VI. Aspects of cartilage induction. *Exper. Cell Research*, 13: 292.

LOOMIS, W. F., 1959: Feedback control of growth and differentiation by carbon dioxide tension and related metabolic variables. *Symp. Soc. Study Development and Growth*, 17: 253. Ronald Press, Philadelphia, Pa.

MARTINOVITCH, P. N., 1939: The effect of subnormal temperature on the differentiation and survival of cultivated *in vitro* embryonic and infantile rat and mouse ovaries. *Proc. Roy. Soc. Ser. B.*, 128: 138.

MERCHANT, D. J., R. H. KAHN, and W. H. MURPHY, JR., 1960: *Handbook of Cell and Organ Culture*. Burgess Publishing Co., Minneapolis, Minn.

NEW, D. A. T., 1965: Organ culture *in vitro*. In V. M. Emmel and E. V. Cowdry (eds.), *Laboratory Technique in Biology and Medicine*, Williams and Wilkins, Baltimore, Md., p. 319.

PARKER, R. C., 1961: *Methods of Tissue Culture*. Harper and Row, New York.

PAUL, J., 1965: *Cell and Tissue Culture*. Williams and Wilkins, Baltimore, Md.

SHAFFER, B. M., 1956: The culture of organs from the embryonic chick on cellulose acetate fabric. *Exper. Cell Research*, 11: 244.

TROWELL, O. A., 1954: A modified technique for organ culture *in vitro*. *Exper. Cell Research*, 6: 246.

WAYMOUTH, C., 1954: The nutrition of animal cells. *Intern. Rev. Cytol.*, 3: 1.

———, 1965: Construction and use of synthetic media. In E. N. Willmer (ed.), *Cells and Tissues in Culture*, Academic Press, New York, Vol. I, p. 99.

WHITE, P., 1963: *The Cultivation of Animal and Plant Cells*. 2nd ed. Ronald Press, New York.

WILLMER, E. N. (ed.), 1965: *Cells and Tissues in Culture*. Academic Press, New York.

WOLFF, E. T., and K. HAFFEN, 1965: Germ cells and gonads. In E. N. Willmer (ed.), *Cells and Tissues in Culture*, Academic Press, New York, Vol. II, p. 697.

Grafting of Embryonic Rudiments*

By Alfred J. Coulombre

The embryo of the domestic fowl is widely used as a host for grafts of embryonic tissues or organ rudiments. Grafts have been placed within the embryo (e.g., brain ventricles, coelom, eye), on its surface (e.g., head, flank), or on its extra-embryonic membranes (chorioallantoic grafts). The avian embryo can be used as a host for one type of graft as soon as the primitive streak stage has been attained (Abercrombie, 1937, 1939; Abercrombie and Waddington, 1937; Cairns, 1937; Abercrombie, 1939), and most types of grafts can be made throughout the greater part of prehatching development (see below for limitations).

CHORIOALLANTOIC GRAFTING

Chorioallantoic grafting involves the establishment of vascular connections between the chorioallantoic circulation and the graft tissue or organ. The embryo of the domestic fowl usually serves as host, and the white Leghorn strain is most commonly employed.

History

Rous and Murphy (1911) modified methods developed by earlier workers for injecting cells of mammalian and avian sarcoma into chick embryos. They noted that at the point where the hypodermic needle had punctured the chorioallantoic membrane (CAM) a well vascularized sarcoma developed which was serially transplantable from host to host (Murphy, 1912). The ability of the CAM to vascularize and support exogenous tissues was adapted to embryological investigations by Danchakoff (1916, 1918, 1924, 1926, 1929), Hoadly (1924), and Willier (1924). The history of the subsequent development of the technique is reviewed by Rudnick (1944) and by Rawles (1952), who played an important role in its perfection.

Viruses (Keogh, 1938), microorganisms (Goodpasture, 1938; Hamilton, 1946), and metazoan tissues have all been cultivated on the CAM. Tumors grow well on this membrane (Rous and Murphy, 1911; Campbell, 1949). Among normal metazoan tissues almost any chick tissue, or grouping of tissues, at least a part of which is normally vascular, will graft successfully to the CAM, e.g.: early blastoderms (Murray and Selby, 1930b; Rudnick, 1932; Hunt, 1934; Butler, 1935; Dalton, 1935; Rudnick and Rawles, 1937; Rawles, 1940); limb bud (Murray and

* This selection was prepared while the author was on the staff of the National Institutes of Health, Department of Health, Education, and Welfare.

Huxley, 1925; Murray, 1926); intestine and skin (Murray, 1928); skeleton (Murray and Selby, 1930; Stephenson and Tomkins, 1964); muscle (Hunt, 1932); hypophysis (Stein, 1933); eye (Alexander, 1937). The tissues of other avian forms also do well (Sandstrom and Kauer, 1933). Donor tissues from other classes of vertebrates can also be grafted successfully: mammal (Hiraiwa, 1927; Danchakoff and Gagarin, 1929; Nicholas and Rudnick, 1933; Watterman, 1936); fish (Oka, 1938); reptile (Nakao, 1939). Grafts from foreign species do poorly when the host erythrocytes are too large for the graft vascular channels or when immunological incompatibilities develop.

Purposes

Chorioallantoic grafting has a number of uses. It has been used to determine the fate (direction of differentiation) of small pieces of tissue isolated from early embryos (Danchakoff, 1916, 1918; Hoadley, 1924; Murray and Huxley, 1925; Murray, 1926, 1928; Murray and Selby, 1930a; Butler, 1935; Willier and Rawles, 1935; Clarke, 1936; Rawles, 1936, 1943). Grafting to the CAM reveals the interactions between the host and graft when tissues are supplied in larger than normal quantity, or when the host is confronted by graft tissues of a younger or older age (Willier, 1924; Simonsen, 1957; Solomon, 1961; Coulombre and Coulombre, 1964). The CAM is a convenient environment for studying the interaction of graft tissues which do not normally confront one another (e.g., tissues of different ages, from different organs, or from different species; Rawles, 1952). The CAM itself may be studied for its reaction to grafts or to other treatments (Moscona, 1958, 1959; Huxley and Murray, 1924; Fell, 1954). The long list of possible applications of this technique includes: the study of the manner in which specific vascular patterns become established in different organs; the direct observation of the time at which and the manner in which muscular contractions appear in different embryonic organs; the immune interactions which occur between host and graft (Simonsen, 1957).

Method of Grafting to the CAM

Previous summaries of this technique can be found in works by Hamburger (1960), Rugh (1962), and Zwilling (1959).

PREPARATION OF THE HOST

1. The host can be any age from 6 days of incubation (when the CAM is just well enough established to begin to receive a graft) to about the seventeenth day, just before the vasculature of the CAM stops functioning. Hosts between 7 and 10 days of incubation are most usually chosen to maximize the time for graft maintenance before the CAM dries out.

2. "Candle" the egg in a darkened room by shining a beam of light through one end. A microscope illuminator with an iris diaphragm may be used for this purpose. The major vessels of the CAM can thus be seen through the egg shell. Locate the chorioallantoic vein (CAV). It is short, of light red hue (in contrast to the dark red arteries), and is forked at *both* extremities. At one end it is confluent with the common CAV which leaves the CAM and enters the embryo. On the shell overlying one of the bifurcations of this vessel pencil the location for a *small* window (1 centimeter square, maximum).

3. Place the egg in a nest of cotton in a small shallow dish, or in any other suitable holder, in such a way that it will not roll.

4. Swab the egg with sterile absorbent cotton soaked in 70 percent ethanol.

5. Use blunt watchmaker's forceps, a

dissecting needle, or any thin, pointed object to puncture the shell and outer shell membrane overlying the air chamber at the blunt end of the egg.

6. Score the margins of the window through the egg shell down to the level of the egg shell membrane. For this purpose a small saw blade with very fine teeth may be used (e.g., a fine toothed hacksaw blade or an ampule file). Alternatively a carborundum or diamond grinding wheel can be used in conjunction with a dental drill. The grinding wheel must not be held long at any one spot since any heating of the adjacent shell by friction will damage the underlying tissues.

7. Use blunt watchmaker's forceps to remove the egg shell either in one piece or by chipping it away in fragments.

8. Place a drop of sterile saline (0.9 percent NaCl in water) in the center of the exposed shell membrane.

9. Insert the tips of watchmaker's forceps into the center of the drop of saline and place the shell membrane under tension until a small rent appears, allowing the saline to flow between the shell membrane and the CAM. By applying lateral tension with the forceps extend the rent to the edge of the window in the egg shell. Rock the egg gently until the CAM drops leaving an air space between it and the shell surrounding the window. Take care not to puncture the CAM since air will then enter the allantoic cavity and the CAM will not drop away from the shell.

GRAFT

SOURCE OF THE GRAFT. Grafts of avian embryonic tissues to the chick CAM vascularize well. Donors from other vertebrate classes may be used, but some combinations fail to vascularize, or do so for only a brief period. Tissues from earlier embryonic stages (especially just after they develop a vascular bed) form successful grafts in a higher percentage of cases than do older tissues.

ISOLATION OF THE GRAFT. Use sterile technique. It is helpful to clean the dissecting microscope with absorbent cotton soaked in 70 percent ethanol. Remove the organ or tissue to be grafted to a small sterile Petri dish which may be half filled with sterile saline (0.9 percent NaCl). Dissect the donor tissue under a dissecting microscope. Use iridectomy scissors or glass or tungsten needles (Dossel, 1958) to cut the graft to a size usually not larger than 1.0 mm^3.

PLACING THE GRAFT. To transfer the donor tissue from the Petri dish to the surface of the CAM use a sterile, thin-walled pipette (e.g., Pasteur pipette), drawn out in such a way that its fire-polished orifice is slightly larger than the graft. Orient the graft at one of the bifurcations of the CAV with watchmaker's forceps or with glass or tungsten needles. Use a fine sterile pipette to remove excess fluid from the surface of the CAM. Avoid sucking up the graft or the surface of the CAM.

SEALING THE EGG. Use cellophane tape to seal the hole in the shell over the air sac, as well as the window over the graft. Rub the tape repeatedly with a blunt object (e.g., the thumb nail) to bond it thoroughly to the egg shell. Work rapidly so that moisture from the interior of the egg does not condense on the tape and prevent it from adhering to the shell. Alternatively, some prefer to replace the rectangle of shell which was removed from the window by affixing its edges to the window margins with molten paraffin applied with a fine brush. For this purpose it is necessary to have at hand a reservoir of molten paraffin thermostatically regulated a degree or two above the melting point. Replace the egg in the incubator with the window uppermost. Do not rotate the egg or otherwise disturb it for at least 24 hours. By then vascularization of the graft should have begun, and the host egg can be rotated as usual if this is desired. At this juncture any failure to seal the egg properly will become apparent in leakage of fluid between the shell and the tape or paraffin.

RETRIEVAL OF THE GRAFT

1. Since the vessels of the CAM of the chick embryo normally begin to occlude at about 18 or 19 days of incubation, grafts should be harvested at or before this time.

2. Remove the cellophane tape and break away the shell and shell membrane to enlarge the window. Systematically explore the CAM for the graft using the extraembryonic vessels as guides. Excise the graft and a small ring of adjacent CAM with iridectomy scissors and watchmaker's forceps.

3. Fix the graft and process it for histologic examination as with any tissue.

PREVENTING DRYING OF THE GRAFT

In some cases, especially when periodic observation of the graft is contemplated, it is undesirable to roll the host egg. Since under these circumstances one surface of the graft is exposed to an air reservoir there is a tendency for the graft to dry out. Rawles (1963) avoided drying of the graft by adding fresh egg albumen (15 parts albumen plus 1 part of 0.9 percent NaCl, shaken thoroughly and decanted) daily in amounts just sufficient to keep the graft submerged. Because the CAM rises each day provision is made for its expansion by fitting a paraffin chimney around the shell window. The chimney is fashioned by paraffin-coating an appropriately shaped cylinder of twine, sterilized by overnight immersion in 70 percent ethanol, sealed to the egg surface with molten paraffin, and closed by a sterile cover slip affixed with molten paraffin. No supplemental albumen should be added until the graft has vascularized (12–18 hours at the earliest).

INTRACOELOMIC GRAFTING

Intracoelomic grafts are introduced into the body cavity of the embryo where they usually adhere to a viscus or to the body wall and become vascularized. The chick embryo is the usual host.

History

The method was introduced by Hamburger (1938). Initially hosts of $2\frac{1}{2}$ days of incubation were employed. Coelomic grafting of chick tissues from donors of different ages to chick hosts at this stage has been exploited for a wide range of studies (Rawles, 1944, 1945; Rudnick, 1945). In addition, Rawles (1940) demonstrated that mouse embryonic tissues grow and differentiate in the chick coelomic cavity, thus opening the way for the grafting of mammalian tissues to the chick coelom. Dossel (1954) modified the technique so that it can be employed up to stage 23 (about 4 days of incubation), thus allowing larger pieces of tissue to be grafted. Dossel's procedure was later adapted to host embryos as old as 5 days of incubation (Philpott and Coulombre, 1965).

Purpose

Coelomic grafting is used for most of the reasons that grafts are made to the CAM. It has the added advantage of allowing the graft to be maintained after the host has hatched. It has two disadvantages: the graft cannot easily be observed until the experiment is terminated; and the younger hosts cannot accommodate grafts as large as are possible on the CAM.

The coelom will maintain tissues which are normally vascularized as well as those such as lens which do not normally contain blood vessels (McKeehan, 1954; Philpott and Coulombre, 1965). Young tissues from donors taxonomically close to the host do better than older tissues or those from distantly related species.

Method

Two procedures have been developed for coelomic grafting. The technique of Hamburger (1938) is more appropriate for hosts of 60 70 hours of incubation. It is outlined by Hamburger (1960) and Rugh (1962). The technique of Dossel (1954) can be used up to 5 days of incubation. Beyond 5 days of incubation the allantois has enlarged to such an extent that coelomic grafting, while possible (author's laboratory), is difficult and is rarely done.

PRELIMINARY STEPS

1. "Candle" the egg in a darkened room by shining a beam of light through one end. Locate the embryo and mark its location in pencil on the egg shell by outlining a small window over it (1 square centimeter maximum).

2. To open a window in the egg follow the steps outlined for chorioallantoic grafting.

3. Use sterile technique to isolate the graft tissue in a small Petri dish filled with sterile saline (0.9 percent NaCl in water). Use iridectomy scissors and watchmaker's forceps, or tungsten needles (Dossel, 1958) to cut the graft to a size appropriate to the age of the host. At $2\frac{1}{2}$ days of incubation (Hamburger and Hamilton, 1951; stages 17, 18, and 19) the graft should be less than 0.25 mm on a side. At older ages a cube 1 mm^3 can be inserted into the coelom. Larger pieces are rarely used.

4. Use a sterile Pasteur pipette to transfer the graft onto the surface of vitelline membrane of the host (stages 17 and 18) or onto the surface of the chorion (stage 19 and beyond) in the region just behind the developing right forelimb.

YOUNG HOSTS

Use a sterile pipette to transfer the graft over the embryo (stages 17 and 18) in the region just behind the site of the developing right forelimb. Use glass or tungsten needles to make a small incision in the vitelline membrane over this site. Make a short longitudinal incision in the flank somatopleure anterior to the vitelline veins and ventrolateral to the posterior cardinal veins. With glass or tungsten needles, or with a fine, blunt-tipped glass probe, introduce the graft through these incisions and cephalad into the coelom. Throughout the procedure avoid damage to the major blood vessels.

HOSTS AT AND BEYOND STAGE 19

To gain access to the coelom in hosts between stages 20 and 25 ($3\frac{1}{2}$ to 5 days of incubation) the method of Dossel (1954) is used. At these stages the allantois has begun to expand. The incision in the chorion is made just outside its zone of junction with the allantois. A fine, blunt-tipped glass probe is then inserted between the amnion and the wall of the allantois in the umbilical region to gain access to the coelom. The graft is transferred to the surface of the host chorion with a sterile Pasteur pipette, inserted into the extraembryonic body cavity through the

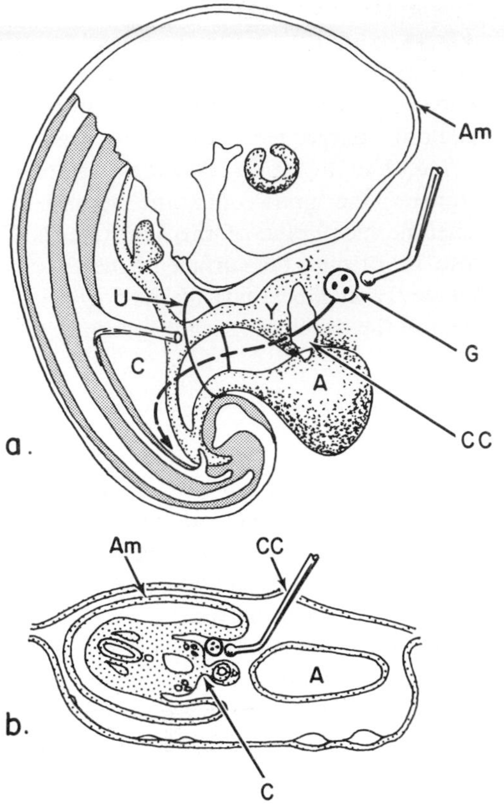

FIG. 1. (a) Diagram of 4-day-old chick embryo with right body wall removed; the arrow shows the path along which the graft moves during implantation. (b) Diagrammatic cross section through 4-day-old chick embryo showing membranes and the path followed by the graft during the first phase of implantation. Symbols: A, allantois; Am, Ammion; C, coelom; CC, cut edge of chorion; U, umbilical ring; G, carbon-marked graft; Y, yolk stalk. SOURCE: W. Dossel, "New Method of Intracoelomic Grafting," *Science* (Aug., 1954), 120:262-63. Both diagrams modified after Patten, 1927. Reprinted by permission of author and publisher.

opening in the chorion and forced into the embryonic coelom through the umbilical opening with a blunt-tipped glass rod (Fig. 1).

Seal the egg with cellophane tape.

Retrieving the Graft

1. The graft may be retrieved at any time during the life of the host. Chances of successful retrieval are better at younger ages. For genetically dissimilar graft and host combinations immunological incompatibilities become evident at older ages.

2. The graft may attach to any coelomic viscus or to the body wall. A systematic search of the coelomic surface is necessary. Make a midline incision and examine each of the viscera in turn until the graft is located. Excise the graft and fix it for routine histological processing.

INTRAOCULAR GRAFTING

Small pieces of tissue can be grafted to either the embryonic or the adult vertebrate eye.

History

Markee (1940) relates that the procedure for grafting to the adult vertebrate eye was initiated by Cohnheim in 1877 and subsequently exploited by Salomonsen in 1879, Baumgarten in 1880, and Kleps in 1883. The technique was revived by S. F. Schoshet of the University of Chicago who introduced it to Markee (1940). A wide variety of tissues has been grafted in this way: endometrium (Markee, 1940); mammalian tumors (Green, 1941); mouse ova (Fawcett, Wislocki, and Waldo, 1947; Runner, 1947; Levak-Svajger and Skreb, 1965); embryonic shield (Grobstein, 1951); mesonephros (Runner, 1946); trophoblast (Grobstein, 1950). A variety of mammals have been used as hosts (guinea pig, mouse, goat, sheep, etc.).

Stone (1959) and Reyer (1962) have reviewed extensive work by themselves and others using the amphibian eye as a graft site. Techniques have recently been developed for using the eye of the chick embryo as a graft site (Coulombre and

Coulombre, 1964, 1965). The procedures for grafting to the adult eye and to the eye of the chick embryo will both be described.

Intraocular Grafts to Adult Hosts

1. Purpose: Tissues which are introduced into the aqueous compartment of the vertebrate eye usually adhere to the anterior surface of the iris and become vascularized. Since they lie between the anterior surface of the iris and the transparent cornea they can readily be observed in the living condition at any subsequent stage. It is, possible, for example, to follow the changes in an endocrine target tissue which are brought about by modifying the endocrine environment of the host (Markee, 1940; Grobstein, 1950).

2. Anesthetize the host by a suitable method.

3. The tissue to be grafted is removed from the donor, placed in a sterile Petri dish, and pieces for grafting are trimmed to a millimeter or less on a side. The Petri dish is covered and set aside.

4. Gently retract the lids or place the circumocular skin under tension. With a fine, sharply pointed, broadly tapering iridectomy knife make a small radial incision in the cornea near the corneal-scleral junction.

5. Pick up the graft in a sterile Pasteur pipette, the tip of which has been bent at a 45-degree angle about 3 or 4 mm back from the end, and whose tip has an internal diameter of 0.3 mm or larger as necessary to accommodate the graft. The tip should be fire polished.

6. Move the graft to the tip of the Pasteur pipette. Insert the end of the pipette into the incision in the cornea and discharge the graft and a small amount of saline into the aqueous chamber.

7. Wedge the graft into the drainage angle between the cornea and the anterior surface of the iris. It should be placed well away from the incision in the cornea.

8. The graft will usually vascularize within 24 hours. Those tissues which tend to vascularize slowly will tend to be replaced by a predominance of fibrous tissue. The graft is usually recovered by killing the animal, enucleating the eye, removing the cornea by an incision at the limbus, and, finally, excising the graft together with a patch of adhering iris. Fixation and histologic processing follow the usual procedures.

Intraocular Grafts to Embryonic Hosts

1. Grafts may be made to the eye of the chick embryo at any time during incubation. The procedure varies considerably from age to age. The procedure for the 5-day chick embryo will be described here, since it is the most useful.

2. The host embryo is located by candling the egg and a window is placed through the shell over the embryo in the manner described previously.

3. Under a dissecting microscope watchmaker's forceps (e.g., DuMont et fils #5) are used to make a small rent in the chorion just outside the margin of its junction with the allantois. Through this opening the amnion can be grasped with the forceps and pulled "hand over hand" with the two pair of forceps until the right eye of the embryo is clearly in view.

4. The right-hand forceps are used to make a small rent in the amnion immediately over the embryonic eye. The edge of this incision is grasped with the left-hand forceps while the apposed tips of the right-hand forceps are introduced through the incision and placed against the dorsal limbus of the cornea so that the forceps are about 45 degrees from the axis of the eye. A short, quick thrust of the right-hand forceps will drive the closed tips through a natural abscission plane at the corneal limbus and between the equator of the lens and the margin of the optic cup. By allowing the tips of the forceps to spring

apart slightly this incision can be extended for approximately one-third the circumference of the limbus. The tips of the forceps are now brought against the posterior capsule of the lens and brought together again in such a way that the small fold of capsule is caught between them. The lens is gently rocked, removed through the incision, and discarded.

5. Use a Pasteur pipette filled with saline (0.9 *M* NaCl) to transfer the graft ($1.0\ mm^3$ maximum dimensions) tissue to the surface of the chorion in the region where it has begun to fuse with the allantois.

6. Use the right-hand pair of forceps to guide the graft through the incisions in the chorion and in the limbus of the cornea and into the position formerly occupied by the lens of the embryonic eye.

7. Withdraw both pairs of forceps from the egg, seal it with cellophane tape as described above, and return it to the incubator.

8. The graft is usually recovered by killing the host and dissecting the right eye.

CONTINUOUS OR PROGRAMMED INFUSION INTO THE EXTRA-EMBRYONIC CIRCULATION OF THE CHICK EMBRYO

History

This technique (Drachman and Coulombre, 1962) combines procedures for acute injection into the vascular compartment of the chick embryo (Goldwasser and Shelesnyak, 1953) with a technique of continuous infusion of water-soluble substances into tissues (Singer, 1953, 1954). It permits continuous, long-term infusion into the embryonic blood stream.

Purposes

The procedure has been used to assess the effects upon the embryo of pharmacologic agents (Drachman and Coulombre, 1962; Drachman, 1963, 1965). Botulinum toxin has also been infused into the chick embryo (Drachman, 1964). Any water-soluble, relatively heat-stable substance can be infused.

Method

The apparatus includes a special polyethylene catheter, a hypodermic syringe, and a syringe drive for depressing the syringe plunger at a constant rate.

1. In one type of syringe drive (Fig. 2) a constant speed motor (a) is coupled to a lead screw (b) by a clutching device (c). The lead screw is threaded through a gate (d) whose forward movement depresses the syringe plunger (e) of a syringe whose barrel is clamped in place by a pressure plate (f). If the syringe drive accommodates more than one syringe some provision should be made to adjust for differences in plunger length among the syringes. Adjustable thumb screws in the gate (g in Fig. 2) are one way of meeting this requirement. Today syringe drives are commercially available in a variety of designs. Two suppliers are:

The Sage Instrument Co., Inc.
2 Spring Street
White Plains, New York 10601

The Harvard Apparatus Co.
Dover, Massachusetts 02030

The following considerations govern the choice of a syringe drive (sometimes called an infusion pump):

a. It should be compact enough to fit easily into the forced draft incubator that is to be used for incubating the eggs.

b. It should be capable of rates of delivery in the neighborhood of 0.01 ml per hour when 0.25 or 0.5 capacity tuberculin type syringes are used. A rate of infusion of 0.01 ml per hour is suitable for all ages between 6 and 17 days of incubation.

c. It should be capable of operating

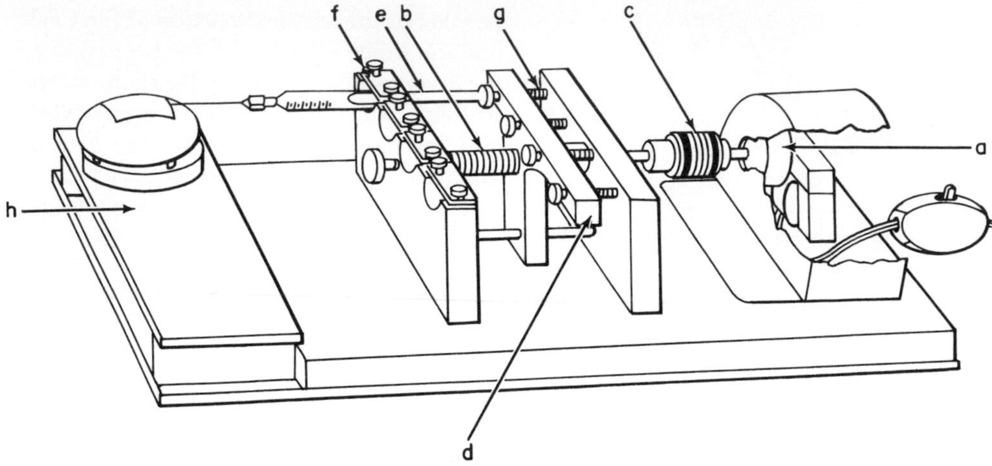

FIG. 2. Infusion pump. See text for description. SOURCE: D. Drachman and A. Coulombre, "Method for Continuous Infusion of Fluids into the Chorioallantoic Circulation of the Chick Embryo," *Science* (Oct., 1962), 138:144-45. Reprinted by permission of authors and publisher.

safely and without damage in high humidity and at temperatures of up to at least 40°C.

d. It should be equipped with a device (usually a microswitch) that can automatically turn off the pump before the syringe plungers have been depressed all the way.

e. It should be equipped with a platform (h in Fig. 2) capable of holding the dishes containing the eggs attached to the pump.

2. The hypodermic syringe should have a relatively narrow bore (e.g., the 0.25- and 0.5-ml capacity tuberculin types) to increase the accuracy of delivery. At the slow rate at which the plunger is depressed leakage will occur unless special precautions are taken. The application of silicone grease (Dow Chemical Company) or high vacuum grease (Fisher and Company) to the plunger and to the junction between the syringe barrel and the hypodermic needle will prevent leakage. A number 27 hypodermic needle of 0.5 inch length is used.

3. The catheter is made from number 20 polyethylene (PE) tubing. The length of the catheter should be as short as is compatible with the geometry of the pump. The end of the catheter which is to be attached to the hypodermic needle is flared by holding it close to (but not in) a small flame. The end to be inserted into the CAV is heated over (but not in) a microflame and drawn out to a suitable attenuation (200 μ outside diameter for younger ages; 325 μ outside diameter for older ages). The attenuated tip is then bent (Fig. 3) over an electrically heated high resistance wire (e.g., nichrome wire) whose temperature is regulated by experience with a variable transformer (Powerstat). The lengths of the shank (4 to 8 mm) and the tip (2.5 to 4 mm) must be larger for older ages. The tip is beveled (Fig. 3) with a razor blade to provide a sharp point for penetrating the wall of the CAV. The catheters can be sterilized either by filling them with a disinfectant (e.g., 70 percent ethanol) and immersing them in it for 1 hour, or by exposure to ethylene oxide in a gas sterilizer.

4. A window is made in the egg shell over the terminal portion of the chorio-

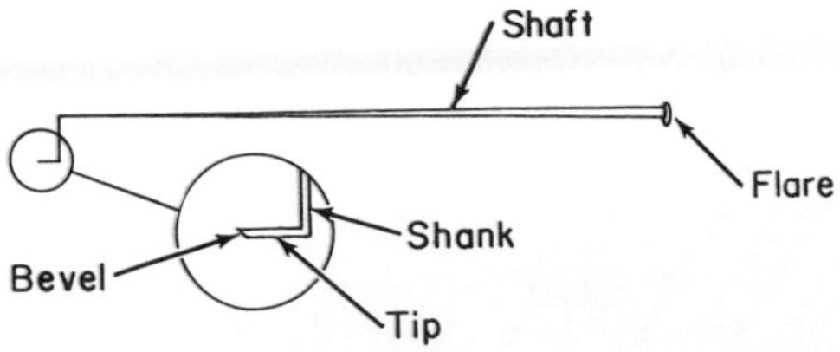

FIG. 3. Microcatheter drawn out from PE-20. SOURCE: D. Drachman and A. Coulombre, "Method for Continuous Infusion of Fluids into the Chorioallantoic Circulation of the Chick Embryo," *Science* (Oct., 1962), 138:144-45. Reprinted by permission of authors and publisher.

allantoic vein (CAV) (see section on method of grafting to the CAM). Under a dissecting microscope the catheter is taped to the egg shell so that its tip lies parallel to the terminal portion of the CAV and its orifice is level with the beginning of the common CAV. Grasp the shank of the catheter with one pair of forceps while another pair is used to grasp the chorio-allantoic membrane next to the CAV. The tip of the catheter is drawn back and pushed through the wall of the CAV which is steadied by the other pair of forceps.

5. The window is closed with cellophane tape and the egg is transferred to the pump where the syringe is clamped in place. When all positions on the pump have been filled transfer it to the egg incubator.

6. If programmed infusion is desired any suitable programming device can be interposed between the power input of the infusion pump and the power line.

REFERENCES

ABERCROMBIE, M., 1937: The behavior of epiblast grafts beneath the primitive streak of the chick. *J. Exp. Biol.*, 14: 302.

———, 1939: Evocation in the chick. *Nature*, 144: 1091.

———, and C. H. WADDINGTON, 1937: The behavior of grafts of primitive streak beneath the primitive streak of the chick. *J. Exp. Biol.*, 14: 319.

ALEXANDER, L. E., 1937: An experimental study of the role of optic cup and overlying ectoderm in lens formation in the chick embryo. *J. Exp. Zool.*, 75: 41.

BUTLER, ELIZABETH, 1935: The developmental capacity of regions of the unincubated chick blastoderm as tested in chorio-allantoic grafts. *J. Exp. Zool.*, 70: 357.

CAIRNS, J. M., 1937: *The Development of Hensen's Node when Grafted Directly to the Chick Blastoderm.* M.S. thesis, University of Rochester, Rochester, N.Y.

CAMPBELL, J. G., 1949: The cultivation of tumors in the fertile egg, with special reference to associated ectodermal lesions of the chorio-allantoic membrane. *Brit. J. Cancer*, 3: 72.

CLARKE, L. F., 1936: Regional differences in eye-forming capacity of the early chick blastoderm as studied in chorio-allantoic grafts. *Physiol. Zool.*, 9: 102.

COULOMBRE, A., and J. COULOMBRE, 1964: Lens development. I. Role of the lens in eye growth. *J. Exp. Zool.*, 156: 39.

———, and ———, 1964: Corneal development. III. The role of the thyroid in dehydration and the development of transparency. *Exp. Eye Research*, 3: 105.

COULOMBRE, J., and A. COULOMBRE, 1965: Regeneration of neural retina from the pigmented epithelium in the chick embryo. *Dev. Biol.*, 12: 79.

DALTON, A. J., 1935: The potencies of portions of young chick blastoderms as tested in chorioallantoic grafts. *J. Exp. Zool.*, 71: 17.

DANCHAKOFF, V., 1916: The wandering cells in loose connective tissue of the bird and their origin. *Anat. Rec.*, 10: 483.

———, 1916: Concerning the conception of potentialities in embryonic cells. *Anat. Rec.*, 10: 415.

———, 1916: Equivalence of different hematopoietic anlages (by method of stimulation of their stem cells). I. Spleen. *Amer. J. Anat.*, 20: 255.

———, 1918: Equivalence of different hematopoietic anlages II. Grafts of adult spleen on the allantois and response of the allantoic tissues. *Amer. J. Anat.*, 24: 127.

———, 1924: Wachstum transplantierten embryonaler Gewebe in der Allantois. *Z. Ges. Anat., Abt. I*, 74: 401.

———, 1926: Lens ectoderm and optic vesicles in allantois grafts. *Carnegie Inst. Wash. Contrib. Embryol.*, No. 94, p. 63.

———, and A. GAGARIN, 1929: Embryoherz in der Chorio-allantois des Hühnchens. *Z. Ges. Anat., Abt. I*, 89: 754.

DOSSEL, W. E., 1954: New method of intracoelomic grafting. *Science*, 120: 262.

———, 1958: Preparation of tungsten microneedles for use in embryological research. *Lab. Invest.*, 7: 171.

DRACHMAN, D., 1963: The developing motor end-plate: pharmacological studies in the chick embryo. *J. Physiol.*, 169: 707.

———, 1964: Atrophy of skeletal muscle in chick embryos treated with botulinum toxin. *Science*, 145: 719.

———, 1965: The developing motor end plate: curare tolerance in the chick embryo. *J. Physiol.*, 180: 735.

———, and A. COULOMBRE, 1962: Method for continuous infusion of fluids into the chorioallantoic circulation of the chick embryo. *Science*, 138: 144.

———, and ———, 1962: Experimental clubfoot and arthrogryposis multiplex congenita. *The Lancet*, Sept. 15, 523.

FAWCETT, D., G. WISLOCKI, and C. WALDO, 1947: The development of mouse ova in the anterior chamber of the eye and in the abdominal cavity. *Amer. J. Anat.*, 81: 413.

FELL, H. B., 1954: The effect of environmental factors on the differentiation of allantoic endoderm in organ culture. *J. Embryol. Exp. Morphol.*, 2: 348.

GOLDWASSER, R., and M. C. SHELESNYAK, 1953: A syringe carrier and egg clamp for intravenous inoculation of chick embryo. *Science*, 118: 47.

GOODPASTURE, E. W., 1938: Some uses of the chick embryo for the study of infection and immunity. *Amer. J. Hyg.*, 28: 111.

GREEN, H., 1941: Heterologous transplantations of mammalian tumors. *J. Exp. Med.*, 73: 461.

GROBSTEIN, C., 1950: Production of intraocular hemorrhage by mouse trophoblast. *J. Exp. Zool.*, 114: 359.

———, 1951: Intra-ocular growth and differentiation of the mouse embryonic shield implanted directly and following *in vitro* cultivation. *J. Exp. Zool.*, 116: 501.

HAMBURGER, V., 1938: Morphogenetic and axial self-differentiation of transplanted limb primordia of 2-day chick embryos. *J. Exp. Zool.*, 77: 379.

———, 1960: *A Manual of Experimental Embryology.* University of Chicago Press, Chicago, Ill.

———, and H. HAMILTON, 1951: A series of normal stages in the development of the chick embryo. *J. Morphol.*, 88: 49.

HAMILTON, H. L., 1946: Growth of the rickettsia of Tsutsugamushi fever on the chorio-allantoic membrane of the developing chick embryo. *Amer. J. Pathol.*, 22: 89.

HIRAIWA, Y. K., 1927: Studies on grafts of embryonic tissues of the rat on the chorioallantoic membrane of the chick. I. Differentiation of ectodermal derivatives. *J. Exp. Zool.*, 49: 441.

HOADLEY, L., 1924: The independent differentiation of isolated chick primordia in chorio-allantoic grafts. I. The eye, nasal region and mesencephalon. *Biol. Bull.*, 46: 281.

HUNT, E. A., 1932: The differentiation of chick limb buds in chorioallantoic grafts, with special reference to the muscles. *J. Exp. Zool.*, 62: 57.

HUNT, T. E., 1934: The differentiation in chorio-allantoic grafts of gut and liver from the mesectoderm of early chick blastoderms. *Anat. Rec.*, 58 Sup.: 21.

HUXLEY, J. S., and P. D. F. MURRAY, 1924: A

note on the reactions of chick chorio-allantois to grafting. *Anat. Rec.*, 28: 385.

KEOGH, E. V., 1938: Ectodermal lesions produced by the virus of Rous Sarcoma. *Brit. J. Exp. Pathol.*, 19: 1.

LEVAK-SVAJGER, B., and N. SKREB, 1965: Intraocular differentiation of rat egg cylinders. *J. Exp. Embryol. Morphol.*, 13: 243.

MARKEE, J., 1940: Menstruation in intraocular transplants in the Rhesus monkey. *Carnegie Inst. Wash. Contrib. Embryol.*, 28: 219.

MC KEEHAN, M., 1954: A quantitative study of self-differentiation of transplanted lens primordia in the chick. *J. Exp. Zool.*, 126: 157.

MOSCONA, A., 1958: Keratinization *in vitro* of chorionic epithelium of the chick embryo. *Proc. Soc. Exp. Biol. Med.*, 98: 757.

———, 1959: Squamous metaplasia and keratinization of chorionic epithelium of the chick embryo in egg and in culture. *Dev. Biol.*, 1: 1.

MURPHY, J. B., 1912: Transplantability of malignant tumors to the embryo of a foreign species. *J. Amer. Med. Ass.*, 59: 874.

MURRAY, P. D. F., 1928: Chorioallantoic grafts of fragments of the two-day chick, with special reference to the development of the limbs, intestine, and skin. *Aus. J. Exp. Biol. Med. Sci.*, 5: 237.

———, and J. S. HUXLEY, 1925: Self-differentiation in the grafted limb-bud of the chick. *J. Anat.*, 59: 379.

———, and D. SELBY, 1930a: Intrinsic and extrinsic factors in the primary development of the skeleton. *W. Roux' Arch. Entwicklungsmech. Organ.*, 122: 629.

———, and ———, 1930b: Chorio-allantoic grafts of entire and fragmented blastoderms of the chick. *J. Exp. Biol.*, 7: 404.

NAKAO, Y., 1939: Recherches sur les greffes chorioallantoidiennes des tissus embryonnaires du lézard. *Zool. Mag. Tokyo*, 51: 683.

NICHOLAS, J. S., and D. RUDNICK, 1933: The development of embryonic rat tissues upon the chick chorioallantois. *J. Exp. Zool.*, 66: 193.

OKA, T. B., 1938: Differentiation of the embryonic tissues of the fish *Oryzias latipes*, transplanted on the chorio-allantois of the chick. *Annot. Zool. Jap.*, 17: 636.

PHILPOTT, G., and A. COULOMBRE, 1965: Lens development. II. The differentiation of embryonic chick lens epithelial cells *in vitro* and *in vivo*. *Exp. Cell Res.*, 38: 635.

RAWLES, M. E., 1936: A study in the localization of organ-forming areas in the chick blastoderm of the head-process stage. *J. Exp. Zool.*, 72: 271.

RAWLES, M., 1940a: The pigment-forming potency of early chick blastoderms. *Proc. Nat. Acad. Sci.*, 26: 86.

———, 1940b: The development of melanophores from embryonic mouse tissues grown in the coelom of chick embryos. *Proc. Nat. Acad. Sci.*, 26: 673.

———, 1943: The heart forming areas of the chick blastoderm. *Physiol. Zool.*, 16: 22.

———, 1944: The migration of melanoblasts after hatching into pigment-free skin grafts of the common fowl. *Physiol. Zool.*, 17: 167.

———, 1945: Behavior of melanoblasts derived from the coelomic lining in inherited grafts of wing skin. *Physiol. Zool.*, 18: 1.

———, 1952: Transplantation of normal embryonic tissues. In *The Chick Embryo in Biological Research. Ann. N.Y. Acad. Sci.*, 55: 302.

———, 1963: Tissue interactions in scale and feather development as studied in dermal-epidermal recombinations. *J. Embryol. Exp. Morphol.*, 11: 765.

REYER, R., 1962: Regeneration in the amphibian eye. In D. Rudnick (ed.), *Regeneration*, Ronald Press Co., New York, p. 211.

ROUS, P., and J. B. MURPHY, 1911: Tumor implantations in the developing embryo. *J. Amer. Med. Ass.*, 56: 741.

RUDNICK, D., 1932: Thyroid-forming potencies of the early chick blastoderm. *J. Exp. Zool.*, 62: 287.

———, 1944: Early history and mechanics of the chick blastoderm. *Quart. Rev. Biol.*, 19: 187.

———, 1945: Limb-forming potencies of the chick blastoderm: including notes on associated trunk structures. *Trans. Conn. Acad. Arts and Sci.*, 36: 353.

———, and M. RAWLES, 1937: Differentiation of the gut in chorio-allantoic grafts from chick blastoderms. *Physiol. Zool.*, 10: 381.

RUGH, R., 1962: *Experimental Embryology.* Burgess Press, Minneapolis, Minn.

RUNNER, M., 1946: The development of the mesonephros of the albino rat in intraocular grafts. *J. Exp. Zool.*, 103: 305.

———, 1947: Development of mouse eggs in the anterior chamber of the eye. *Anat. Rec.*, 98: 1.

SANDSTROM, C. J., and G. L. KAUER, 1933: Heteroplastic transplants of duck cartilage to the chorio-allantoic membrane of the chick. *Anat. Rec.*, 57: 119.

SIMONSEN, M., 1957: The impact on the developing embryo and newborn animal of adult homologous cells. *Acta Path. Microbiol. Scand.*, 40: 480.

SINGER, M., 1954: Apparatus for continuous infusion of microvolumes of solution into organs and tissues. *Proc. Soc. Exper. Biol. Med.*, 86: 378.

———, M. SCHEUING, and M. HALL, 1953: A microinfusion apparatus for regeneration studies and its use in the study of the nature of the adult newt. *Anat. Rec.*, 117: 576 (abstract).

SOLOMON, J. B., 1961: The onset and maturation of the graft versus host reaction in chickens. *J. Embryol. Exp. Morphol.*, 9: 355.

STEIN, K., 1933: The location and differentiation of the presumptive ectoderm of the forebrain and hypophysis as shown by chorioallantoic grafts. *Physiol. Zool.*, 61: 205.

STEPHENSON, N. G., and J. K. N. THOMKINS, 1964: Transplantation of embryonic cartilage and bone onto the chorioallantois of the chick. *J. Embryol. Exp. Morphol.*, 12: 825.

STONE, L., 1959: Regeneration of the retina, iris and lens. In C. S. Thornton (ed.), *Regeneration in Vertebrates*, University of Chicago Press, Chicago, Ill., p. 3.

WILLIER, B., 1924: The endocrine glands in the development of the chick. *Amer. J. Anat.*, 33: 67.

———, and M. RAWLES, 1935: Organ-forming areas in the early chick blastoderm. *Proc. Soc. Exper. Biol. Med.*, 32: 1293.

ZWILLING, E., 1959: A modified chorioallantoic procedure. *Transplantation Bulletin*, 6: 115.

In Vivo Chamber Culture Technique*

By Paul Nettesheim and T. Makinodan

INTRODUCTION

To perform quantitative analysis of proliferation and differentiation of complex cell populations, one needs a culture system that fulfills the following requirements:

1. It must be a closed system, unlike tissues and organs *in situ*; i.e., cells must appear and disappear through proliferation, differentiation, and/or death, *but never through migration.*

2. It must support proliferation and differentiation of a cell population of known size equally as well as a tissue or organ *in situ.*

3. It must be accessible at any time during culture for unbiased biochemical and morphological sampling.

4. It must be exposable to physical and chemical agents at any time after culture for various lengths of time.

Investigators have been searching for such a system, since *in vitro* tissue culture usually does not fully support differentiative events. Encouraged by early experiments in which collodion bags had been used to culture bacteria *in vivo,* Rezessi in 1932 and Bisceglie in 1934 tried to use the same techniques to culture mammalian cells *in vivo.* However, it was not until 1954, when Algire, Weaver, and Prehn developed the diffusion chamber culture method, that the above requirements could be met. They first introduced the diffusion chamber culture method as an extension and modification of the transparent chamber technique designed to study tissue changes *in vivo* (Algire, 1954). The same group (e.g., Algire, 1957) then applied the technique to the study of cellular and humoral factors in homograft and heterograft rejection. Since then it has been used in various other fields of biology (Nettesheim, Makinodan, and Chadwick, 1966).

Although several types of diffusion chambers have been constructed with Millipore filters (see review by Brooks and Hill, 1960; Amos, 1961 and 1962), this chapter deals with the diffusion chamber technique adapted for study of the kinetics of antibody response (Capalbo, Albright, and Bennett, 1964; Nettesheim *et al.,* 1966). In antibody response, a lymphoid cell population, stimulated specifically by a chemically defined agent (antigen), undergoes typical proliferative and differentiative changes leading to the appearance of nondividing, terminal cells

* Research jointly sponsored by the National Institutes of Health and by the United States Atomic Energy Commission under contract with the Union Carbide Corporation.

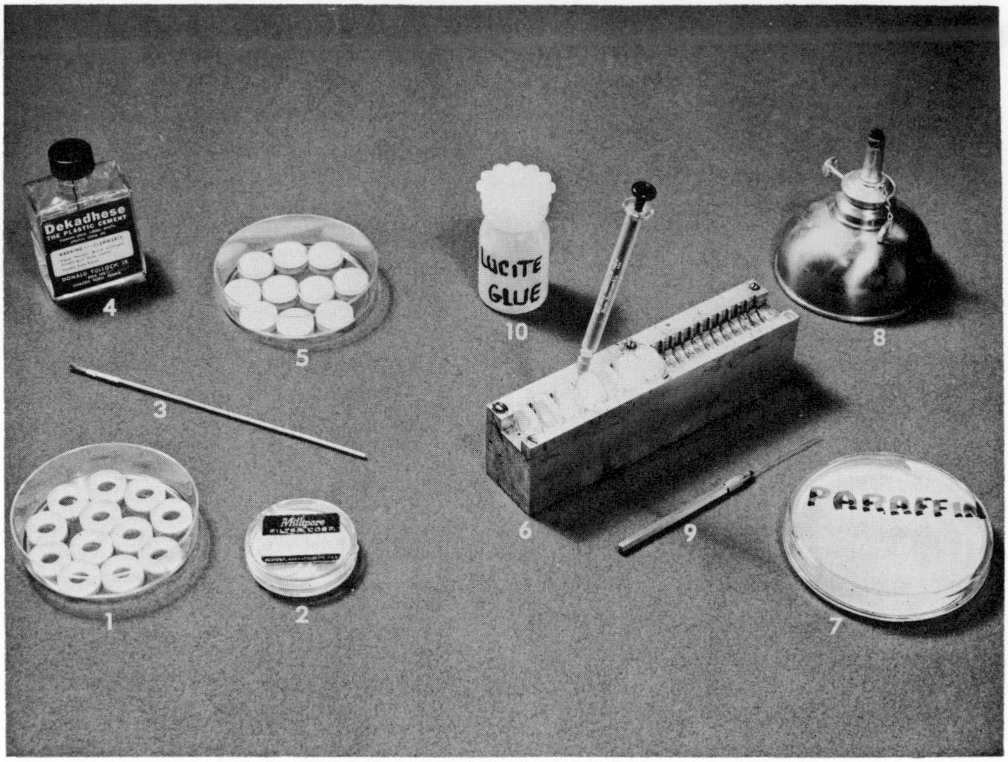

FIG. 1. Equipment routinely used for diffusion chamber technique. (1) Lucite rings. (2) Millipore filters. (3) Brush. (4) Acryloid glue. (5) Chambers ready for use. (6) Rack with chambers and tuberculin syringe. (7) Paraffin. (8) Alcohol burner. (9) Microdissecting needle. (10) Lucite glue.

synthesizing antibody globulins. With diffusion chambers, these events can be assessed quantitatively with a small sample size. The lymphoid cell system, therefore, can be used to demonstrate the potential usefulness of the diffusion chamber culture technique for quantitative analysis of any tissue undergoing proliferation and differentiation.

MATERIALS AND METHODS

Chamber Construction

MATERIALS (SEE FIG. 1)

1. Lucite rings cut from Lucite plates (inner diameter, 10 mm; outer diameter, 20 mm; height, 3 mm) with a 1-mm radially oriented filling hole are soaked in petroleum-ether for 24–48 hours, washed in detergent solution, rinsed in distilled water, and dried at 80°C.

2. Millipore filter discs (Millipore Filter Corporation, Bedford, Mass.), 18 mm diameter, 0.1 μ porosity.

3. Dekadhese plastic cement (D. Tulloch, Jr., Chadds Ford, Pa.), an acryloid glue with ethylenedichloride as solvent.

4. A small brush.

PROCEDURES

Acryloid glue is applied with the brush to the periphery of one side of the ring. This side of the ring is then pressed against one Millipore filter disc lying flat on a smooth surface. To assure "cell-tight" sealing, the glue is applied again after a few minutes to the outer edge of the filter. After several hours of drying the second filter disc is glued to the opposite face of the ring in the same manner. The chambers are sterilized at 80°C for 24–48 hours.

For certain purposes, e.g., culture of tissue fragments, the second filter is glued to the Lucite ring only after the tissue fragment is introduced into the chamber.

Double chambers are made by gluing two rings together with a filter in between and then sealing a filter to the outer side of each ring.

Preparation of Cell Suspension, Inoculation, and Intraperitoneal Implantation of Chambers

MATERIALS (ITEMS 1 THROUGH 5 MUST BE STERILIZED)

1. Syringes, 5 ml and 1 ml (tuberculin type); 19- and 22-gauge needles.
2. Forceps with blunt tips and with "mouse teeth," small scissors, hemostats, razor blades, catgut with needle.
3. Stainless steel sieve (mesh 200) (Buffalo Wire Works, Buffalo, New York).
4. Beakers (25, 50 ml), Petri dishes (100 × 20 mm), pipettes (2, 5, 10 ml), graduated cylinders (25, 50 ml).
5. Chamber rack (see Fig. 1).
6. Hemocytometer, white and red blood cell (WBC, RBC) pipettes and diluents.
7. Alcohol burner, paraffin, microdissecting needle, microdissecting forceps.
8. Lucite acetone glue (made from Lucite shavings dissolved in acetone, 5/100 (w/v), disposable syringe (5 ml).
9. Wooden board, pushpins.
10. Hanks' balanced salt solution with 1 percent normal mouse serum, penicillin (4.5 μg per milliliter), and streptomycin (4.5 μg per milliliter).
11. Mouse restraining cage.
12. Donor and recipient mice (if possible, isologous mice irradiated with 500–600 r). Species other than mice can also be used.

PREPARATION OF CELL SUSPENSIONS

Cell and antigen suspensions are kept at ice temperature throughout the procedure. A cell suspension is prepared from appropriate donors by teasing their spleens or lymph nodes in Hanks' solution containing 1 percent sterile isologous mouse serum with a 19-gauge needle mounted on a syringe. The cell suspension is then strained through a stainless steel sieve. The cell concentration of the suspension is determined by counting a sample in a hemocytometer and adjusting to the desired concentration. For example: A suspension is desired that contains 250×10^6 nucleated cells per milliliter. If 3 ml of spleen cell suspension has been prepared, and hemocytometer count indicates that it contains 320×10^6 nucleated cells per milliliter, 0.84 ml of the diluent must be added to produce the proper concentration.

PREPARATION OF ANTIGEN

The antigen, usually sheep or rat RBC, is obtained in sodium citrate or Alsever's solution. The suspension is washed 3 or 4 times at 1,200 rpm for 5–10 minutes with 10 volumes of 0.15 *M* NaCl to remove the buffy coat, the plasma, and the anticoagulant.

The antigen is finally suspended in the same medium as the spleen or lymph node cells. Hemocytometer counts are made and the suspension adjusted to the needed concentration. Suspensions of spleen or lymph node cells and the antigen are then mixed in an appropriate ratio, and the mixture is constantly stirred using a magnetic stirrer. Soluble antigens, such as albumin or gamma globulins, and bacterial antigens can also be used.

INOCULATION OF CHAMBERS

The sterilized chambers are lined up in the chamber rack and are inoculated with 0.15 to 0.20 ml of the cell-antigen mixture through the filling hole using a 1-ml tuberculin syringe and a 22-gauge needle. The hole is then sealed with liquid paraffin (using a preheated micro-dissecting needle). After the paraffin has solidified a small drop of acetone Lucite glue is applied with a syringe to cover the area of the hole. These chambers are kept in Petri dishes containing Hanks' solution (plus antigen, if soluble antigens are used) until they can be implanted.

IMPLANTATION OF CHAMBERS

Recipient mice are placed in a small restraining cage and are anesthetized by injecting 0.15 to 0.25 ml of sodium barbital (6 mg per milliliter) into the tail vein. To facilitate intravenous injection, recipient mice are warmed under a lamp to dilate their subcutaneous blood vessels. They are then secured abdomen up to a wooden board with pushpins applied to the limbs. The abdomen is shaved with a razor blade, and the chamber is introduced through a midline incision. The wound is closed with a catgut suture.

Sampling of Serum and Chamber Content

MATERIALS

1. Heparinized Pasteur pipettes
2. Graduated centrifuge tubes (12 ml)
3. Scissors, forceps, razor blades
4. Hemocytometer, WBC and RBC pipettes, and diluents
5. Brushes, microscope slides
6. 0.5% Pronase (Cal. Biochem., Los Angeles, Calif.) in Hanks' solution.
7. 2% Versene (disodium ethylenediaminetetraacetate) in PBS, 0.01 *M* phosphate buffered saline, pH 7.0–7.2.
8. Automatic shaker or magnetic stirrer.

SAMPLING OF SERUM AND CHAMBER FLUID

Serum samples are obtained from chamber-bearing recipients by retroorbital bleeding with a Pasteur pipette, in which case the animals can be kept alive for further studies, or by bleeding from the throat. In the latter case chambers are removed from the peritoneal cavity. One filter is punctured with a Pasteur pipette, and the chamber fluid is withdrawn and collected in a test tube. Blood and chamber fluid are centrifuged at 1,500–2,000 rpm for 10 minutes. The supernatant fluid is removed and stored at −20°C until it is titrated for hemagglutinating antibodies by a standard twofold dilution method. Titers are expressed as the reciprocal of the last dilution showing macroscopic hemagglutination. Serum and chamber fluid samples can also be analyzed immunoelectrophoretically. To assess protein or antibody synthesized by the culture, autoradiographic analysis can be made of the immunoelectrophoretic patterns of serum and chamber fluids obtained from pulse-labeled cultures (Onoue, Yagi, and Pressman, 1963).

SAMPLING CELLULAR MATERIAL FROM CHAMBERS

The chambers, after removal from the peritoneal cavity, are immersed for 1 hour in 0.5 percent Pronase at room temperature under constant shaking to dissolve the clot that almost invariably forms within the chamber. The outer chamber surface is then carefully wiped free of host peritoneal cells. One filter is punctured with a Pasteur pipette to collect the chamber fluid. It is then removed by cutting it from the ring with a razor blade, and rinsed with buffer containing 2 percent Versene. The inside of the chamber is also carefully washed. The washings are added to the chamber fluid to make a total volume of 0.5 ml. Hemocytometer counts are made to determine the total number of cells per chamber. The contents of two to four chambers are pooled and centrifuged at 800 rpm for 10 minutes. The supernatant fluid is removed, and a drop of isologous serum is added to the pellet. Brush smears are made, rapidly air-dried, fixed in methanol, and stained with Giemsa. For studies of nucleic acid or protein synthesis, radioactive precursors are injected intraperitoneally into the chamber-bearing recipients at appropriate intervals before sampling (see Makinodan, Hoppe, Sado, Capalbo, and Leonard, 1965).

EVALUATION OF DIFFUSION CHAMBER TECHNIQUE

Cell Impermeability of Diffusion Chambers

If the diffusion chamber technique is used to study the kinetics of an *isolated* cell population under *in vivo* conditions, it is imperative to establish that the chambers to be used are truly cell impermeable. Table 1 summarizes experiments carried out for this purpose, using two different gluing agents and four types of Millipore filters of varying pore size (from Nettesheim *et al.*, 1966). The experiments described were carried out with chambers of one size (10 × 3 mm), because earlier studies revealed that chambers with larger inside diameters (20–25 mm), regardless of filter pore size, very frequently became contaminated with host cells. The chambers were filled only with Tyrode's solution (containing 1 percent normal mouse serum) and were implanted in the peritoneal cavity of 600-r-irradiated mice. From 3 to 10 days later the chambers were removed from the recipients, and 5.4 mm³ of *undiluted* chamber fluid was then examined microscopically in hemocytometers for possible contamination with host cells. Of the filters tested, only 0.1-μ porosity filters regularly prevented host-cell penetration into "empty" chambers, and the acryloid glue was superior to the Lucite glue (Table 1). We have recently found that 0.22-μ porosity filters also are impermeable. The data further suggest that the 0.45-μ porosity filter was just on the borderline, where cell migration may or may not be prevented. Thus the use of 0.45-μ porosity filters resulted in only a slightly greater frequency of contaminated chambers than the use of 0.1-μ porosity filters, but the use of 0.64-μ porosity filters

TABLE 1. CONTAMINATION OF EMPTY CHAMBERS WITH HOST PERITONEAL CELLS AS A FUNCTION OF FILTER POROSITY AND TYPE OF CEMENT

MEMBRANE POROSITY (μ)	TYPE OF CEMENT	NO. OF CONTAMINATED CHAMBERS	TOTAL NO. OF CHAMBERS
0.1	Acryloid*	0	10
0.1	Lucite†	1 (8)‡	11 (12)
0.45	Acryloid	2	19
0.45	Lucite	6	16
0.64	Acryloid	7	9
0.64	Lucite	8	8
1.20	Acryloid	10	10
1.20	Lucite	9	9

SOURCE: Nettesheim, Makinodan, and Chadwick, 1966.
* Acryloid in ethylenedichloride.
† Lucite shavings in acetone (5/100, w/v).
‡ Numbers in parentheses were obtained with a second set of chambers fabricated by an inexperienced investigator.

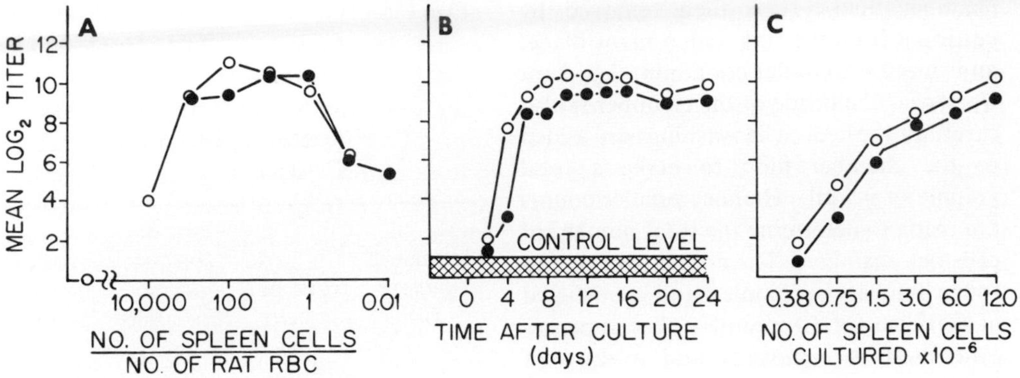

FIG. 2. Secondary antibody response as a function of: (A) *Antigen dose.* ○, 12.0 × 10^6 primed spleen cells stored for 3 months at −180°C; ●, 24 × 10^6 freshly prepared primed spleen cells; test antigen, rat RBC; 5 to 10 samples per point. (B) *Time after culture* of 12.0 × 10^6 primed spleen cells with 1.20 ×10^6 sheep RBC. ○, chamber fluid titer; ●, serum titer. Control chambers contained 12.0 × 10^6 primed spleen cells and 1.20 × 10^6 isologous mouse RBC instead of sheep RBC; 5 samples per point. (C) *Spleen cell dose.* ○, chamber fluid titer; ●, serum titer. Primed spleen cells to sheep RBC ratio, 10:1; 10 samples per point. SOURCE: Nettesheim, Makinodan, and Chadwick, 1966.

produced a very high frequency of contaminated chambers. The varying results obtained in the different laboratories using 0.45-μ porosity filters (Algire and Moore, 1959; Shelton and Rice, 1959; Capalbo *et al.*, 1964) may be explained on these grounds. Another possible method to test cell impermeability of diffusion chambers is to implant chambers containing highly invasive tumors and to assess the frequency of death of chamber-bearing mice (Algire and Moore, 1959; Law, Dunn, Trainin, and Levey, 1964). But since these tumors are not readily available in every laboratory, the penetration of host cells into empty diffusion chambers is the method of choice.

Functional Capacity of Diffusion Chamber Cultures

To demonstrate that this method is most suitable for cytokinetic analysis of cells undergoing proliferation and differentiation, evidence will be presented to show that serum and chamber fluid antibody response is (1) a function of antigen dose and number of immunologically competent cells, and (2) a reflection of an increase in the number of blast cells, reticulum cells, and immature and mature plasma cells.

In the study of antibody production as a function of antigen dose, a fixed number of spleen cells was cultured together with varying amounts of the test antigen, varying the spleen cell to RBC ratio from 1:100 to 10,000:1 and assessing the 8-day serum hemagglutinin titers (Fig. 2A). The optimum spleen cell to RBC ratio was found in the range from 100:1 to 10:1. In contrast, the optimum spleen cell to RBC ratio for the isologous cell transfer (*in vivo* culture) method was 1:10 (Albright and Evans, 1965). Furthermore, the dose of antigen needed to induce intact primed mice to give a comparable 8-day response was 100 times more than that needed in chambers (Makinodan, Friedberg, Tolbert, and Gengozian, 1959). These results show that, in terms of antigen dosage, the diffusion chamber method is at least 100 times more efficient than intact animals or the *in vivo* culture method.

A typical antibody response profile under optimum antigenic stimulation is characterized by a latent phase of approximately 2 days, a log phase of 3 to 4 days, and a stationary phase of at least 3 weeks (Fig. 2B). Antibody output under these conditions is mainly an expression of the number of antibody-producing cells (Makinodan *et al.*, 1965). The 7.6 $\log_2$ unit rise in the level of chamber fluid antibody titer during the log phase therefore indicates that the competent cells are doubling every 9 hours. This agrees well with the experimentally determined cell cycle time of blast cells undergoing antibody response (Sado and Makinodan, 1964). It follows then that the increase in the number of competent cells during the log phase is due mainly to proliferation and not transformation.

In the study of antibody production as a function of spleen cell dose, 0.38×10^6 to 12.0×10^6 spleen cells were cultured with an optimal dose of test antigen. On day 10 after culture, chamber fluid and serum were collected and titrated for hemagglutinins. As illustrated in Fig. 2C, a linear $\log_2$ relationship with a slope of 1.0 existed between spleen cell dose and antibody titers in the range from 1.5×10^6 to 12.0×10^6 spleen cells; i.e., under optimal antigenic stimulation a twofold increase in spleen cell number ranging from 1.5×10^6 to 12.0×10^6 induced a twofold increase in antibody output 10 days after culture. Below 1.5×10^6 the slope was much steeper (approximately 3.0), due to the increasing number of nonresponders with decreasing spleen cell dose. Because other studies (Makinodan *et al.*, 1965) have shown that the plateau titer is directly related to the relative number of functional antibody-producing cells, these results indicate that the relative number of fully differentiated antibody-producing cells is dependent mainly upon the relative number of progenitor cells initially present in the culture. The fact that nonresponders were detected when the spleen cell number was less than 1,000,000 (Fig. 2C) suggests furthermore that the relative number of progenitor cells in the spleen is very low, probably in the range of only 1 in 100,000 to 1,000,000 spleen cells. These results on the relative number of progenitor cells in the spleen are in agreement with those derived from all-or-none assays (Albright and Makinodan, 1965).

Attempts to quantitate cell growth in diffusion chamber cultures have been made at several laboratories. Gabourel and Fox (Gabourel and Fox, 1959; Gabourel, 1961) used the level of the enzyme lactic dehydrogenase to estimate cell number and growth. Others (Holub, 1960; Amos and Wakefield, 1958; Capalbo *et al.*, 1964) determined the number of cells per chamber by sampling the chamber contents and making direct microscopic cell counts. In the latter case it is also possible to perform cytomorphological studies. However, studies of this type were hampered by the fact that only about 50 percent of the cells present at any given time after culture could be recovered. Cells in the gelatinous clot that forms in most instances 2 or 3 days after culture and cells growing on the inner surface of the chamber were recovered only in part, although attempts were made with different enzymes to increase cell yield (Capalbo *et al.*, 1964). This not only decreased the sample size, but also, in the event that the distribution of cell types in the free chamber fluid and

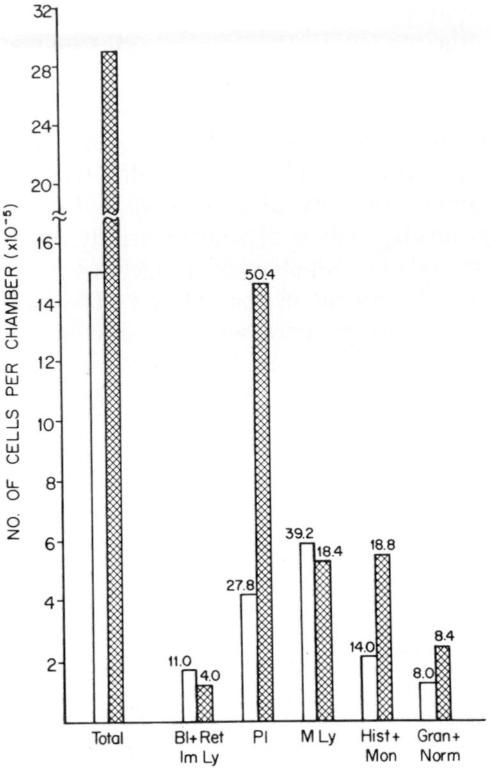

FIG. 3. Effect of Pronase treatment on cell yield, and differential cell count of 8-day chamber cultures. Each chamber was inoculated with 25 $\times$ 10^6 primed spleen cells and 2.5 $\times$ 10^6 rat RBC. Chambers were immersed either in Hanks' solution □ or in Pronase ▩ for 1 hour at room temperature under constant shaking. Bl = blast cells, Ret = reticulum cells, ImLy = immature lymphocytes, Pl = plasma cells, MLy = mature lymphocytes, Hist = histiocytes, Mon = monocytes, Gran = granulocytes, Norm = normoblasts. Numbers on top of columns are percentages. SOURCE: Nettesheim, Makinodan, and Chadwick, 1966.

in the clot were not comparable, could have prevented true random sampling of the chamber contents. Since Pronase has been described as superior to other enzymes in dispersing tissues for tissue culture purposes (e.g., Wilson and Lau, 1963; Gwatkin and Thomson, 1964), we treated our chambers with this enzyme. Maximum recovery of morphologically uninjured cells was obtained when chambers were immersed in Hanks' solution containing 0.5 percent Pronase for 1 hour at room temperature under constant shaking. This dissolved the clot completely. The results of one such experiment are summarized in Fig. 3. Pronase treatment doubled the number of recoverable cells in antigen-stimulated chamber cultures and increased the yield 1.5 times in nonstimulated cultures. Very few cells were detected on the inner surface of chamber membranes after Pronase treatment. The number of blast cells, reticulum cells, and immature and mature lymphocytes was about the same whether cultures had been treated with Pronase or not. On the other hand, Pronase treatment produced twice as many histiocyte-monocytes and granulocyte-normoblasts as PBS treatment, and three times as many plasma cells. This indicates that without Pronase pretreatment cell sampling is biased mainly against plasma cells.

An example of the proliferative and differentiative events taking place in chamber cultures of spleen cells after secondary antigenic stimulation is seen in Fig. 4. The number of blast cells, reticulum cells, and immature lymphocytes reached their peak level on or before day 4 after antigenic stimulation. This was followed by a rise in the number of plasma cells to a peak level on days 6 to 8. The rise in hemagglutinin titer between days 4 and 6 parallels the rise in the number of plasma cells per chamber. These results are very similar to the observation made previously (e.g., Makinodan *et al.*, 1965), except a more pronounced plasmacytopoiesis was observed. It should be emphasized at this time that under optimum culture conditions as many as 10 percent of the total nucleated cells at the height of antibody response are antibody-containing cells (Makinodan *et al.*, 1965). In contrast, antibody-containing cells in the spleen and lymph nodes of hyperimmunized animals constitute less than 1 percent of the total nucleated cells (Vazquez, 1964). This demonstrates that antibody formation in *in vivo* chamber cultures is at least 10 times more effective than that *in situ*.

Figure 5 (from Capalbo and Makinodan, 1964) illustrates how doubling time (T_2) and half-time ($T_{1/2}$) of various cell subpopulations of chamber cultures can be studied with radioactive cell markers. An intraperitoneal injection of H^3-thymidine was given to chamber-bearing mice 4 days after antigenic stimulation. At intervals of 1 to 30 hours after pulse-labeling the number of labeled cells per chamber and of a given cell type per chamber was determined. The rate of production of new cells in the antigen-stimulated group during the early log phase was faster (T_2, 15 hours) than that in the unstimulated control group (T_2, 24 hours). The $T_{1/2}$ of blast cells and the T_2 of plasma cells and lymphocytes were shorter after antigenic stimulation than without antigenic stimulation. Figure 6 shows several immature labeled cells from a chamber culture of primed spleen cells 10 days after antigenic stimulation. A pulse injection of H^3-thymidine was given intraperitoneally to the chamber-bearing mice 1 hour before sacrifice (the chambers

FIG. 4. Differential cell counts of diffusion chamber cultures of 25 × 10^6 primed spleen cells with 2.5 × 10^6 rat RBC (○) and without the test antigen (●). The chambers were treated with Pronase before the chamber content was harvested. Cells of three chambers were pooled for each point. SOURCE: Nettesheim, Makinodan, and Chadwick, 1966.

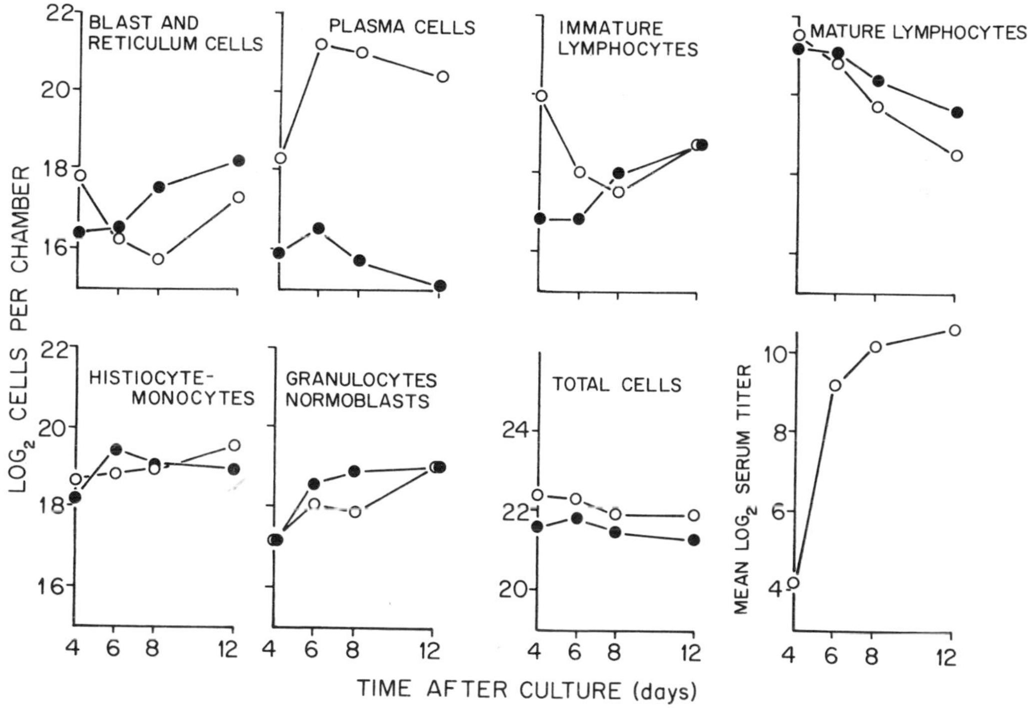

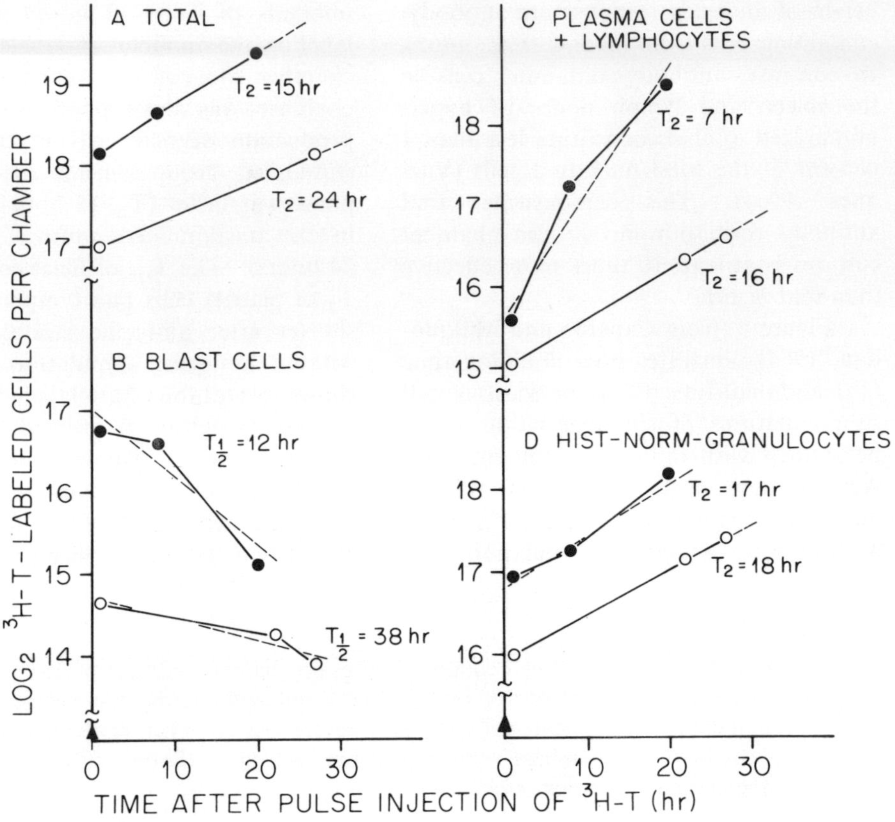

FIG. 5. Estimation of T_2 and $T_{1/2}$ of cells 4 days after culture. ○, control; ●, experimental; ↑, time of H^3-thymidine injection. SOURCE: Capalbo and Makinodan, 1964.

were incubated 1 hour in Pronase as described above). More detailed accounts of the cytokinetics and the nucleic acid and protein metabolism of competent cells after antigenic stimulation have been given elsewhere (Urso and Makinodan, 1963; Capalbo and Makinodan, 1964; Sado and Makinodan, 1964; Makinodan *et al.*, 1965; Nettesheim and Makinodan, 1965.

In Vivo Transfer and *in Vitro* Maintenance of Chambers

It has been reported that the permeability of the chamber for fluid decreases with culture time (Holub, 1960), owing to growth of host peritoneal cells on the outer surface of the chambers. Also, deposition of insoluble materials in the pores of Millipore filters can occur *in vivo* (Grobstein and Dalton, 1957; Bassett and Campbell, 1960). To determine when faulty fluid exchange begins to impair growth and function of immunologically competent cells, we cultured primed spleen cells with and without antigen in diffusion chambers up to 4 months. The number of nucleated cells per culture, chamber fluid titer, and serum antibody titer were determined at intervals. The results revealed that a poor exchange between chamber and circulation occurred 1 month after culture (Nettesheim *et al.*, 1966). This poses a serious problem for any long-term culture studies. To overcome this difficulty we transferred the chambers to other recipient mice at relatively short intervals, wiping host peritoneal cells off the outer chamber surfaces at time of transfer to reestablish fluid permeability. The results showed that antibody production was not hampered by transfer of chambers and could be maintained for more than 3 months. It follows, then, that long-term cultures can be maintained with use of this procedure of transferring chambers serially and wiping the host peritoneal cells off the outer chamber surface. In a subsequent study, chambers containing primed spleen cells stimulated with an optimum dose of antigen were removed from the first set of recipients 0, 2, 4, and 6 days after culture and were kept *in vitro* for up to 6 hours at room temperature. They were then implanted in the second set of isologous, sublethally irradiated recipients. As judged by their 9-day serum and chamber fluid titers, the antibody-forming capacity of the chamber cultures was not reduced. The results of these two types of experiments thus showed that it is possible (1) to remove diffusion chamber cultures from the recipients at varying times after culture, (2) to expose them *in vitro* for a fixed time period to any physical or chemical agent, (3) to implant them in a second set of recipients, and (4) to determine the effect of the agent on the culture. This procedure eliminates any possible indirect effects which could be caused either by the action of an agent on the recipient or by the alteration of fluid permeability of the chambers.

FIG. 6. Primed spleen cells cultured in diffusion chambers 10 days after antigenic stimulation. H^3-thymidine was given intraperitoneally to chamber-bearing recipients 1 hour before removal and Pronase treatment. The radioactive label is incorporated into immature cells only.

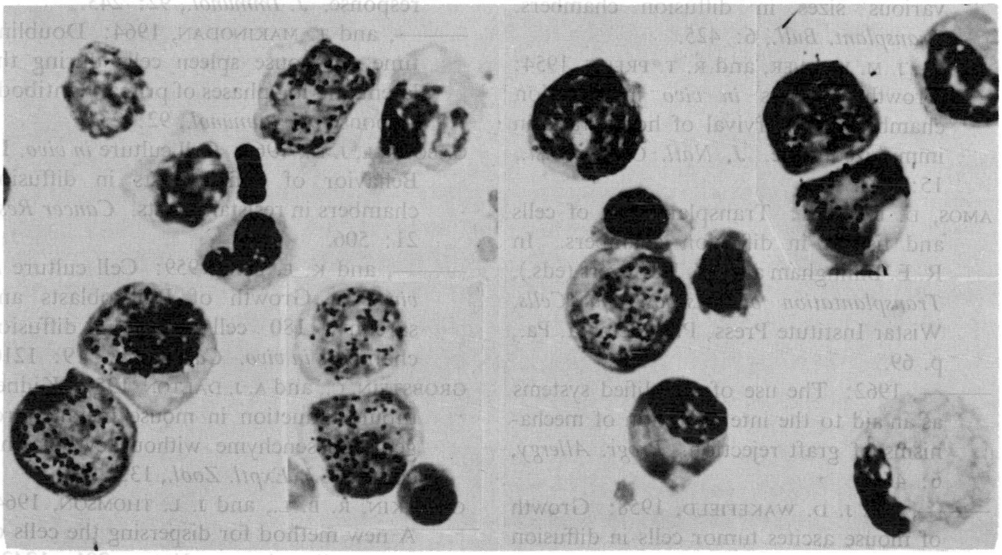

CONCLUSION

The evidence presented here demonstrates that the *in vivo* diffusion chamber culture technique fulfills the four basic requirements stipulated in the Introduction and therefore is one of the most suitable methods for quantitative studies of cell proliferation and differentiation.

REFERENCES

ALBRIGHT, J. F., and T. W. EVANS, 1965: Influence of antigen dosage on kinetics of hemagglutinating antibody production. *J. Immunol.*, 95: 368.

———, and T. MAKINODAN, 1965: Dynamics of expression of competence of antibody-producing cells. In J. Sterzl (ed.), *Molecular and Cellular Basis for Antibody Formation*, Czechoslovak Academy of Science Press, Prague, p. 427.

ALGIRE, G. H., 1954: Vascular reactions of normal and malignant tissues *in vivo*. VII. Observations on vascular reactions in destruction of tumor homografts. *J. Natl. Cancer Inst.*, 15: 483.

———, 1957: Diffusion chamber techniques for studies of cellular immunity. *Ann. N.Y. Acad. Sci.*, 69: 663.

———, and R. O. MOORE, 1959: Passage of mouse leukemia cells through pores of various sizes in diffusion chambers. *Transplant. Bull.*, 6: 425.

———, J. M. WEAVER, and R. T. PREHN, 1954: Growth of cells *in vivo* in diffusion chambers. I. Survival of homografts in immunized mice. *J. Natl. Cancer Inst.*, 15: 493.

AMOS, D. B., 1961: Transplantation of cells and tissues in diffusion chambers. In R. E. Billingham and W. K. Silvers (eds.), *Transplantation of Tissues and Cells*, Wistar Institute Press, Philadelphia, Pa., p. 69.

———, 1962: The use of simplified systems as an aid to the interpretation of mechanisms of graft rejection. *Progr. Allergy*, 6: 468.

———, and J. D. WAKEFIELD, 1958: Growth of mouse ascites tumor cells in diffusion chambers. I. Studies of growth rate of cells and of the rate of entry of antibody. *J. Natl. Cancer Inst.*, 21: 657.

BASSETT, C. A. L., and J. B. CAMPBELL, 1960: Calcification of Millipore *in vivo*. *Transplant. Bull.*, 26: 132.

BISCEGLIE, V., 1934: Über die antineoplastische Immunität. II. Mitteilung. Über die Wachstumsfähigkeit der heterologen Geschwülste in erwachsenen Tieren nach Einpflanzung in Kollodiumsäckchen. *Z. Krebsforsch.*, 40: 141.

BROOKS, J. R., and G. J. HILL, 1960: Current status of endocrine homografts using the Millipore Diffusion Chamber technique. *Am. J. Surg.*, 99: 588.

CAPALBO, E. E., J. F. ALBRIGHT, and W. E. BENNETT, 1964: Evaluation of the diffusion chamber technique for study of the morphological and functional characteristics of lymphoid cells during antibody response. *J. Immunol.*, 92: 243.

———, and T. MAKINODAN, 1964: Doubling time of mouse spleen cells during the latent and log phases of primary antibody response. *J. Immunol.*, 92: 234.

GABOUREL, J. D., 1961: Cell culture *in vivo*. II. Behavior of L-fibroblasts in diffusion chambers in resistant hosts. *Cancer Res.*, 21: 506.

———, and K. E. FOX, 1959: Cell culture *in vivo*. I. Growth of L-fibroblasts and sarcoma 180 cell lines in diffusion chambers *in vivo*. *Cancer Res.*, 19: 1210.

GROBSTEIN, C., and A. J. DALTON, 1957: Kidney tubule induction in mouse metanephrogenic mesenchyme without cytoplasmic contact. *J. Exptl. Zool.*, 135: 57.

GWATKIN, R. B. L., and J. L. THOMSON, 1964: A new method for dispersing the cells of mammalian tissues. *Nature*, 201: 1242.

HOLUB, M., 1960: Morphology of antibody production by different cell systems in diffusion chambers. *Folia Microbiol.*, 5: 347.

LAW, L. W., T. B. DUNN, N. TRAININ, and R. H. LEVEY, 1964: Studies of thymic function. In V. Defendi and D. Metcalf (eds.), *The Thymus*, Wistar Institute Press, Philadelphia, Pa., p. 105.

MAKINODAN, T., B. H. FRIEDBERG, M. G. TOLBERT, and N. GENGOZIAN, 1959: Relation of secondary antigen injection to time of irradiation on antibody production in mice. *J. Immunol.*, 83: 184.

———, J. HOPPE, T. SADO, E. E. CAPALBO, and M. R. LEONARD, 1965: The suppressive effect of supraoptimum doses of antigen on the secondary antibody-forming response of spleen cells cultured in cell-impermeable diffusion chambers. *J. Immunol.*, 95: 466.

NETTESHEIM, PAUL, and T. MAKINODAN, 1965: Differentiation of lymphocytes undergoing an immune response in diffusion chambers. *J. Immunol.*, 94: 868.

———, ———, and C. CHADWICK, 1966: Improved diffusion chamber cultures for cytokinetic analysis of antibody response. *Immunology*, 11: 112.

ONOUE, K., Y. YAGI, and D. PRESSMAN, 1963: Multiplicity of antibody proteins in rabbit anti-*p*-azobenzenearsonate sera. *J. Immunol.*, 92: 173.

REZZESI, F. D., 1932: Eine Methode zur Züchtung der Gewebe *in vivo*. *Arch. Exptl. Zellforsch. Gewebezücht.*, 13: 258.

SADO, T., and T. MAKINODAN, 1964: The cell cycle of blast cells involved in secondary antibody response. *J. Immunol.*, 93: 696.

SHELTON, E., and M. E. RICE, 1959: Growth of normal peritoneal cells in diffusion chambers: A study in cell modulation. *Am. J. Anat.*, 105: 281.

URSO, P., and T. MAKINODAN, 1963: The roles of cellular division and maturation in the formation of precipitating antibody. *J. Immunol.*, 90: 897.

VAZQUEZ, J. J., 1964: Kinetics of proliferation of antibody-forming cells. In R. A. Good and A. E. Gabrielson (eds.), *The Thymus in Immunobiology*, Harper and Row, New York, p. 293.

WILSON, B. W., and T. L. LAU, 1963: Dissociation and cultivation of chick embryo cells with an actinomycete protease. *Proc. Soc. Exptl. Biol. Med.*, 114: 649.

In Vivo Culture of *Drosophila* Imaginal Discs

By Heinrich Ursprung

INTRODUCTION

The techniques described below were originally devised by Ephrussi and Beadle (1936), and have since been modified by a number of workers in the areas of biochemical genetics, developmental genetics, and embryology.

In biochemical genetics, Beadle and Ephrussi's reciprocal transplantation of eye discs of the *Drosophila* mutants *vermilion* and *cinnabar* has become a classic and served as a model for numerous investigations on the genetic control of biochemical pathways in this organism. The question of whether a given biochemical trait is the property of a cell or is brought about by the influence of other cells or tissues in the organism (autonomy or nonautonomy) can be answered readily by transplanting organ primordia from one mutant into another. This is feasible in insects because thus far no adverse immunological effects have been encountered.

Developmental geneticists and embryologists have used the method extensively in studies on the embryological organization of imaginal discs, and in investigations of the genetic control of pattern formation (for reviews see Hadorn, 1965; Ursprung, 1963). Fate maps of imaginal discs were obtained by implanting disc fragments into host larvae, where implants undergo metamorphosis synchronously with the host and can be recovered from the adult for microscopic analysis of the structures formed. Dissociated and reaggregated cells also can be reared in host larvae through metamorphosis, and thus information can be gained on the question of pattern formation.

Whether or not implants develop to the point of terminal differentiation depends on the hormonal milieu provided by the host (see Schneiderman and Gilbert, 1964, for review). When implanted into a larva, larval cells grow, divide, and metamorphose in synchrony with the host. When, on the other hand, an adult is chosen as host for larval tissue, the implant will as a rule only grow and divide, but not differentiate. However, the implanted cells do maintain the capacity to differentiate. When they are recovered from the adult host and transferred to a larval host, they will undergo metamorphosis as soon as their new host does (Bodenstein, 1957).

The technique thus combines the virtues of any transplantation technique with some desirable properties of the organism, such as availability of genetic markers, absence of immune effects, and the possibility of subtle control of cell division and/or differentiation by the hormonal milieu of the host. Its obvious weakness is that the tissues, once implanted, escape direct visual observation until they are recovered again from the host. In this respect culture *in vitro* (see Schneider, this volume, pp. 543–554) is clearly superior. However, to date culture *in vitro* has been successful for only a limited number of imaginal disc types, probably owing to the difficulty of reproducing the hormonal balance required for the development of the various discs. Because of this, the *in vivo* method is still superior.

The method is fundamentally simple, and with proper guidance its essentials can be learned by a half-way dexterous graduate student within an afternoon. It consists of removing imaginal discs from host larvae and then, after the desired experimental treatment, injecting them into the body cavity of a larval or adult host, where they will float freely. The body cavity of the host serves as the culture vessel, its hemolymph as the incubation medium. After metamorphosis, implants are recovered from the host's abdomen by dissection.

TIMING OF DONOR AND HOST LARVAE

Preparation of *Drosophila* Food (see also Doane, this volume, pp. 219–244)

Combine in a 6- to 8-quart pot:

Water	6,258 ml
Corn meal (yellow)	575 gm
Quick cooking oats (Quaker)	287 gm
Dextrose	575 gm
Agar agar	29 gm
Brewer's yeast (dry)	58 gm

Cook over a burner while stirring constantly until the food thickens but is still liquid enough for easy pouring. Then add 28.7 ml of 10 percent Tegosept M (Goldschmidt Chemical Corp., New York, N.Y., U.S.A.) or 28.7 ml of 0.5 percent propionic acid. Mix thoroughly. Pour into glass containers (milk bottles for stocks, Syracuse dishes for "laying" [see below], crystallizing dishes for collecting larvae), and autoclave (15 minutes, 120°C).

There are many other recipes for *Drosophila* food, and it is by no means important that the above formula be used.

Setting Up "Laying Dishes"

A layer about 1 mm thick of a viscous suspension of live yeast (Fleischmann's cake yeast, for example) is spread over the surface of the solidified food in Syracuse dishes, and these dishes are then kept in a closed container for at least 4 hours at room temperature. After that, a supply of dishes may be stored in a refrigerator for weeks.

One of these dishes is placed (after reaching room temperature, if it was stored in the cold) in a tall drinking glass containing 100–200 etherized *Drosophila* of both sexes, the glass is stoppered with a gauze-covered cotton plug, and this arrangement is stored horizontally in a 25°C dark incubator. When the flies awaken they start laying eggs on the yeast surface. The first batch of eggs should not be used for accurate timing of larvae, however, since etherization and possible crowding in the stocks from which the adult flies were taken interfere with continuous laying. It is advisable to let flies lay eggs on the first laying dish for 8–12 hours before actual timing begins.

After the initial period, the glass is held against a strong light source so that the plug can be removed without flies escaping. The laying dish is removed from the glass and replaced by a new laying dish (room temperature, not cold!). The assembly is then returned to the dark incubator, and the time is recorded. After 4 hours, for example, the laying dish is again replaced, and the food, whose surface is now covered with eggs, scooped into a crystallizing dish containing more *Drosophila* food. This dish may now be labeled; the zero time (oviposition) of the larvae developing in it is known with an accuracy of ±2 hours in the example we chose.

Collecting Donors and Hosts

If the ages of donors and hosts are irrelevant for the experiments, it is easiest to use late third instar larvae as donors. At about 100 hours after oviposition, these larvae tend to crawl up the side of the containers and can easily be collected with a wet brush. As hosts, young third instar larvae are best suited. Although they are somewhat smaller than older larvae, their cuticle appears to be softer than that of older stages. In our experience, the survival rate is highest if larvae about 75–80 hours after oviposition are used as hosts.

DISSECTION OF IMAGINAL DISCS

Larvae of the desired stage are washed with tap water, using a soft brush. They are then transferred to a depression slide containing enough insect Ringer's to cover the larvae completely. The Ringer's solution consists of 7.5 gm NaCl, 0.35 gm KCl, and 0.21 gm $CaCl_2$ per liter of water (Ephrussi and Beadle, 1936).

The location and morphology of the various imaginal discs has been described by Bodenstein (1950). For dissection, the larva is first torn into two halves of about equal length with two pairs of sharp watchmaker's forceps. Access to all imaginal discs except the genital discs is gained easily by everting the anterior half-larva entirely ("glove-finger method," Fig. 1). While one pair of forceps gently holds the open end of the anterior part by its spring tension the other, closed pair of forceps, or a blunt needle instead, pushes the anterior tip of the larva toward the open end. In the process, the larva becomes turned inside out and the imaginal discs can be peeled off with sharp dissecting needles. The genital disc may be removed if the same procedure is applied to the posterior half. All these operations are carried out under a dissecting microscope, preferably with incident light against a black background.

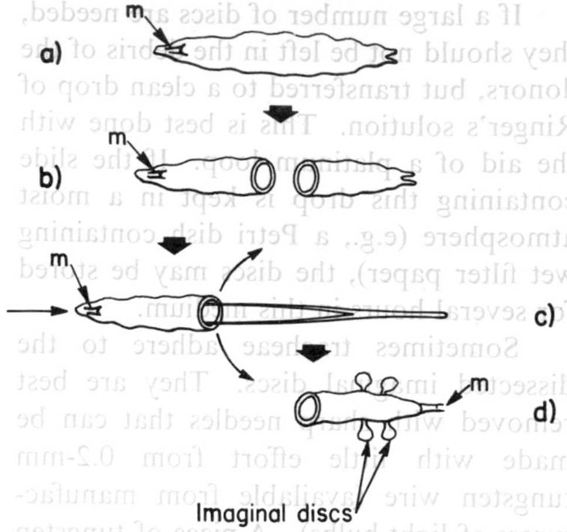

FIG. 1. The glove-finger method for dissecting imaginal discs. The larva, mouth parts (m) on the left side, posterior end pointing to the right (a), is torn into two halves with tweezers (b). A pair of forceps (c), is then inserted a short distance into the open end of the anterior half; this end may be held in position firmly by the spring tension of the forceps (curved arrows in c). Now a blunt needle is pushed against the mouth parts (horizontal arrow at the left) and, in the process, the anterior half is everted inside-out. The imaginal discs are now sticking out into the dissection medium (d) and may be peeled off.

If a large number of discs are needed, they should not be left in the debris of the donors, but transferred to a clean drop of Ringer's solution. This is best done with the aid of a platinum loop. If the slide containing this drop is kept in a moist atmosphere (e.g., a Petri dish containing wet filter paper), the discs may be stored for several hours in this medium.

Sometimes tracheae adhere to the dissected imaginal discs. They are best removed with sharp needles that can be made with little effort from 0.2-mm tungsten wire (available from manufacturers of light bulbs). A piece of tungsten wire is melted into a Pyrex pipette and then sharpened by immersion in $NaNO_2$ heated in a crucible until melted. The needles should be rinsed in water before use.

PREPARATION OF HOSTS FOR IMPLANTATION

Larvae

Larvae of the desired age are washed in tap water and then placed in 70 percent ethanol for a short time. A group of 10–20 larvae is placed on a clean microscope slide and dried carefully and completely with filter paper. The slide with the "dry" larvae is placed in an etherizer. A 50-ml centrifuge tube containing at the bottom a cotton ball soaked with ether works well. At first, the larvae become very excited in the etherizer. Once they have become immobile, they should be left in the etherizer for approximately 30 additional seconds. The slide is then withdrawn from the etherizer, and a drop of Ringer's solution applied over the larvae. Upon addition of the saline, the larvae should become relaxed and elongated. If they retain their crumpled appearance or assume the shape of a spindle, they are overetherized and should be discarded.

The relaxed larvae are lined up on the slide in a row as indicated in Fig. 2, at a slight angle, with their dorsal tracheae pointing up. Most of the Ringer's solution still surrounding the larvae is removed with filter paper. The last traces of Ringer's solution evaporate quickly, and as a result, the larvae become slightly affixed to the slide, which is desirable. They will remain immobile for at least 15 minutes, which is sufficient time to complete between 10 and 20 implantations.

FIG. 2. Injection. Etherized, relaxed larvae are lined up on a microscope slide at an angle, dorsal tracheae up (t), mouth parts (m) pointing toward the operator (a). A dissecting needle, with its tip resting on the slide, is used to stretch the skin gently in the direction of the arrow (b), and the implantation pipette is inserted tangentially into the flank of the host.

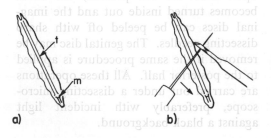

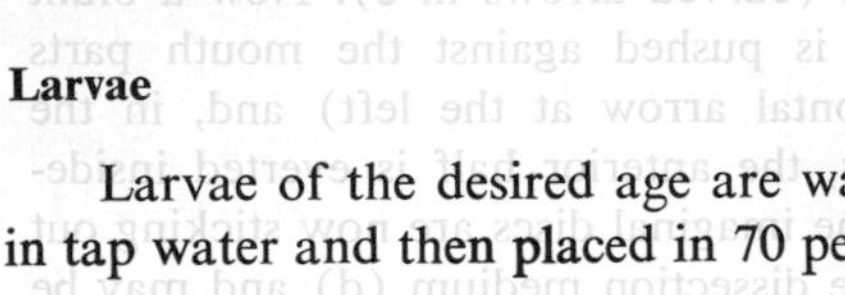

Adults

A microscope slide is covered with a strip of double-faced Scotch tape. Etherized flies are then affixed to the sticky tape, belly up, in a row, by gently tapping their wings against the tape. Forceps or blunt needles are well suited for this manipulation.

IMPLANTATION

Tools

The technique described is not really an implantation, but a microinjection.

Almost any commercial microinjection apparatus can be used, or one can very simply be built. We have been using an all-glass 1-ml "Tuberculin" type syringe with a well-fitting glass plunger. The syringe is mounted on a laboratory stand or a heavy metal base. A 2-foot length of tygon tubing, anywhere from 1 to 4 mm inside diameter is connected to a commercial needle holder (available from Mr. Robert Sulzer, Department of Zoology, University of Zurich, Switzerland; similar holders are sold by manufacturers of micromanipulation apparatus or can be built by a skilled machinist; see Fig. 3). The tubing should be filled with distilled water, avoiding air bubbles.

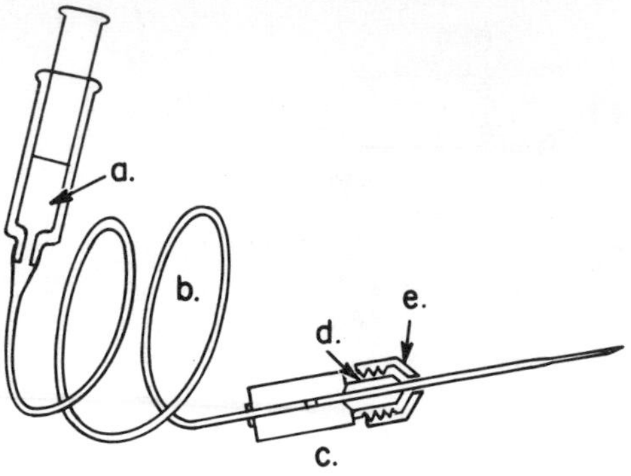

FIG. 3. Injection assembly. (a) Syringe (in use, mounted on a laboratory stand and operated with the left hand); (b) tygon tubing; (c) needle holder assembly; (d) rubber or polyethylene seal; (e) screw cap. When tightened, the seal is pressed against the pipette. In use, the needle holder assembly is mounted on a microdissector or guided directly with the right hand.

Needles (pipettes) for injection are drawn from Pyrex capillaries (outside diameter 1 mm, inside diameter 0.8 mm; available from Drummond Scientific Co., Broomall, Pennsylvania, U.S.A.) either on a commercial pipette puller (e.g., "Livingston" pipette puller available from Mr. Habel, Rutlidge, Pennsylvania, U.S.A.) or on a homemade microburner. A gauge 18 hypodermic needle, with its tip clipped off, mounted on a laboratory stand and connected to a gas line works well; a screw clamp is used to regulate the flame size. In pulling the pipettes, care should be taken to obtain thin walls. The inside diameter of the pulled part of the injection pipette may be as small as about one-half of the diameter of the discs that one wants to inject, because the discs are quite pliable and do not rupture easily. For example, pipettes with an inside diameter of about 150 μ are quite suitable for eye imaginal discs. Some practice is required to pull pipettes of a given diameter reproducibly by hand. Of course a needle-puller will give more reproducible results. It should be pointed out however that the exact diameter of the pipette is not crucial at all. Once the capillaries are pulled to the desired size, their tips must be given the shape of hypodermic needle tips. This step requires some practice. The capillary is held with one hand on the stage of a dissecting microscope, which is focused on the pulled portion of the capillary. A dissecting needle, held almost horizontally in the other hand, is then pushed down onto the pulled portion of the capillary, at right angles to the longitudinal axis of the capillary. A more or less ragged break is produced this way which often is U-shaped (see Fig. 4). Now, one of the spurs, or one of the legs of the U, is gently broken off with the tip of the dissecting needle. As a consequence, a break following the dotted line in Fig. 4 is often obtained, thus producing a sharp hypodermic tip. This procedure may have to be repeated several times. It is important that the entire tip be a smooth rather than serrated break.

Next, the injection pipette must be equipped with a constriction (Fig. 4) at which the implant will come to a halt

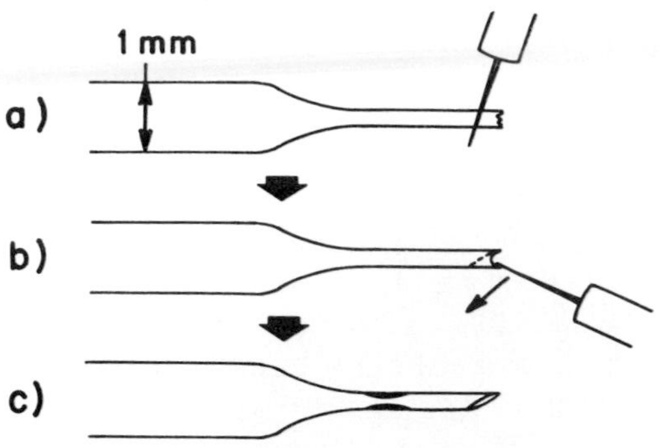

FIG. 4. Injection pipette. After pulling the pipette, pressure is applied from above with a dissection needle (a), crushing the pulled out capillary near its tip. This often results in a U-shaped break (b). Now one of the spurs is pried off gently with a needle in the direction of the arrow in (b). If necessary through repetition of this process, a tip of the shape shown in (c) is obtained. The constriction behind the tip is made with a microflame, as described in the text.

when sucked up into the pipette. If a microforge is not available, the smallest flame obtainable from a gauge 18 hypodermic can be used. The pulled portion of the pipette is held against the flame carefully until it just starts to melt. The pipette is then rotated 180 degrees and held against the flame again until it begins to melt. An inspection under the dissecting microscope may show that the constriction is already good enough. If not, the procedure should be repeated, always rotating the pipette so that the constriction is formed uniformly around its circumference. As a final step, the pipette is bent at a slight angle (see Fig. 4) which will make the desired almost tangential injection easier. Furthermore, it is highly desirable to fire polish the large, open end of the pipette. If this step is omitted, rubber shavings are often scraped off the seal when the pipette is inserted into the needle holder, and these shavings may plug up the constriction from behind during injection and so ruin the pipette.

Injection

The two microscope slides containing hosts and dissected discs, respectively, are placed on the stage of a dissecting microscope. The needle holder with the injection pipette is held in the right hand or mounted on a Singer Microdissector (obtainable through Sobotka Instruments, New York, N.Y., U.S.A.). The left hand operates the plunger of the syringe, which is connected to the needle holder by the tygon tubing. The air contained in the pipette is now displaced by distilled water by pushing the plunger gently inward. The tip of the pipette is then held into the drop containing the imaginal discs, and the pipette is filled with Ringer's solution by gently withdrawing the plunger. (If for any reason it is desirable to avoid mixing the fluid of the injection apparatus with that to be injected, a small droplet of a dividing phase, e.g., paraffin oil, can be sucked into the pipette before it is filled with the experimental liquid. In transplanting discs, this precaution is not necessary so long as the discs do not come into direct contact with the distilled water of the apparatus.)

Before injecting discs, it is advisable to "lubricate" the pipette. The easiest way of doing this is to suck up and eject, repeatedly, a piece of fat body. Sticking of discs to the glass is prevented by this simple step. Now, a disc is taken into the pipette gently until it rests against the constriction. The left hand then leaves the plunger and uses a blunt dissecting needle for holding the host and stretching its body wall tight. The right hand places the tip of the pipette against the tightly stretched body wall, at a point about one-third of a body length from the posterior end of the larva (or about in the middle of the abdomen of an adult). When the tip of the pipette touches the host, it is good to pause for a moment. A minute amount of liquid will leave the pipette and wet the future wound area, which is desirable because it prevents the pipette from sticking to the wound edge and ripping the host open during retraction. After this moment of pause, the pipette is inserted gently, tangentially under the skin from the flank of the animal, avoiding its heart. The left hand now leaves the dissecting needle and operates the plunger again, pushing or rotating it gently so that the disc is injected. The pipette is then withdrawn quickly. Ideally, no host tissue should protrude from the wound. If some fat body sticks out, it may be pushed back in with a blunt needle or clipped off with a thin, sharp needle. If Malpighian tubules protrude, the host should be discarded; it is rather difficult to push those delicate organs back without further injury. As soon as this operation is completed, a new disc is taken into the pipette and injected into the next host. When the animals start to wake up, they are wetted with Ringer's, picked up individually with a wet brush, and transferred to wet filter paper inserted into the food of a vial. They soon start feeding on the live yeast layer covering the food. During the following day, they will crawl back onto the filter paper or the sides of the vial for pupation.

About 10–20 larvae can be injected by a routine worker within the quiet period that follows an etherization. While survival rates may be low initially, they reach 80 percent or 90 percent with some practice.

Trouble Shooting

If larvae do not wake up after the operation (but controls do) or the area on the filter paper around the larva is darkened, heavy loss of hemolymph due to too large a wound is the probable cause. There are two main causes: a serrated or thick-walled and therefore blunt injection pipette; insufficient wetting of wound area followed by sticking of skin to the needle during retraction, causing rupture. A third cause, less frequent, is a wrong angle of injection which may damage the heart.

If the larvae wake up and crawl into food, but soon die and turn black, the same causes are indicated as in the previous case, plus possible infection. Keep glassware and instruments cleaner (note: it is not necessary to work under entirely sterile conditions).

If hosts die as pupae, this may indicate larval damage, mold growing in the food, or dehydration of the food. Use cleaner food (fresh yeast), and wet the filter paper periodically to maintain food and vial moist.

If flies do not hatch from the puparium completely, again this indicates an operation damage. Simply dissect fly free from its puparium.

If hosts do not contain implants in the abdomen, in most cases the implant was pulled out again by the pipette, or pushed out by the host that was about to wake up. Remedies: diagnose this trouble early by searching the environment of the host immediately after injection for ejected discs. Inject with more of a squirt, so that implant is moved away from the wound. Do not withdraw pipette too early.

REFERENCES

BODENSTEIN, D., 1950: The post-embryonic development of *Drosophila*. In M. Demerec (ed.), *Biology of Drosophila*, Wiley, New York, p. 275.

———, 1957: Humoral dependence of growth and differentiation in insects. *Rec. Adv.*

Invert. Physiol. Symp., 1955, 197.

EPHRUSSI, B., and G. W. BEADLE, 1936: A technique of transplantation in *Drosophila. Am. Naturalist*, 70: 218.

HADORN, E., 1965: Problems of determination and transdetermination. *Brookhaven Symposia in Biology*, 18: 148.

SCHNEIDERMAN, H. A., and L. I. GILBERT, 1964: Control of growth and development in insects. *Science*, 143: 325.

URSPRUNG, H., 1963: Development and genetics of patterns. *Am. Zoologist*, 3: 71.

Cell Culture and Cloning Techniques

By Robert D. Cahn, Hayden G. Coon, and Martha B. Cahn

INTRODUCTION

The use of cell culture as a tool for the study of development has increased rapidly in recent years. Methods are now available which allow both the short-term culture of differentiated cells in confluent monolayers, and the long-term culture of differentiated cells as clones.

Mass cultures (i.e., high density monolayer cultures in Petri dishes or bottles) of differentiated cells may be used to study the biochemistry of phenotypic expression (e.g., messenger half-life, control of specific protein synthesis). This type of culture may also be useful in studies of "induction" of function in a given differentiated cell, and in studies of cell-cell interaction leading to expression of differentiation, such as in the muscle cell (Hauschka and Konigsberg, 1966; Konigsberg, 1961, 1963; Konigsberg and Hauschka, 1965). Finally, mass cell cultures have been used for studies of environmental control of enzyme patterns and metabolic pathways (Cahn, 1964b; Eagle, 1959, 1965; Eagle and Piez, 1962; Harary *et al.*, 1963; Harary and Kuramitsu, 1964; Paul, 1961; Paul *et al.*, 1964; Prockop *et al.*, 1964).

Mass cultures have many drawbacks for such studies, however, most of which can be eliminated by the use of cloned populations of cells derived from the organism or from very early primary mass cultures. The use of such cloned cell populations accomplishes the following:

1. It assures purity of cell type. If one starts with cloned populations of single cells, subsequent cultures cannot be overgrown by contaminating "fibroblasts" or other foreign cell types (Sato *et al.*, 1960).

2. Clonal growth of cells at low population densities allows closer control of cell nutrition. Mass cultures utilize some components of the medium so rapidly it is impossible to bathe the cells in a constant adequate nutrient medium for longer than a few hours.

3. Mass cultures may undergo an apparent "dedifferentiation" after several passages at high cell density (Fig. 6; Ephrussi and Temin, 1960; Holtzer *et al.*, 1960; Kuroda, 1964a, 1964b; Whittaker, 1963). This inhibition of phenotypic expression at high cell density can be reversed by growing cells at low densities in appropriate media. Such cells stably exhibit their differentiated phenotypes in clonal culture (Figs. 5, 6; Cahn and Cahn, 1966; Coon, 1964, 1966; Coon and Cahn, 1966).

In addition, clonal culture of differentiated cells may be extremely useful as an assay in studies of "induction" or the cellular basis of acquisition and transmission of differentiated properties. Cells can be freed from heterotypic and some early homotypic interactions by cloning. The cellular microenvironment is very precisely controllable during the early stages of colony formation and can be manipulated in studies of "induction." In essence, cloning represents the ultimate in the classic "isolation-transplantation" approach to the study of development.

Finally, clonal cell culture is required for *in vitro* studies of the genetics and epigenetics of cellular differentiation (Harris, 1964; Puck *et al.*, 1958; Todaro and Green, 1963). It is possible that cell matings can be applied to these problems (Ephrussi, 1964; Ephrussi *et al.*, 1964; Ephrussi and Weiss, 1965; Harris and Watkins, 1965; Harris *et al.*, 1966). The hybrid cells, segregants, and recombinant cell types may be reisolated and tested for recombination or dominance of differentiated functions. Cloning is the only practical tool for attacking these genetic and epigenetic problems.

METHODS

Preparation for Culturing

CHOICE OF ROOM

Contamination with yeasts and molds is a constant problem in cell culture since mycostatic agents are often not included in media. A culture room should preferably have a clean filtered air supply, be dust free, and free of contaminating volatile fumes which often enter through return air duct systems. A nonrecirculating air supply and an electrostatic or 1 μ bag filter designed to keep the room under slight positive pressure will afford adequate protection. In addition to this, cell transfers (passages) should be done under a sterile transfer hood, several models of which are available commercially (LabConCo, Kansas City, Mo.). The hood should be fitted with an ultraviolet lamp which is turned on an hour or so before transferring or feeding. The hood should be big enough to allow two people to work simultaneously using two dissecting microscopes, but need not be elaborate. These simple precautions will save much unnecessary loss of time due to contamination. For comfort the room should be air conditioned, but air conditioners should have oversize vents or should be turned off during cell passage or actual culturing to reduce drafts and cut down on dust movement.

INCUBATORS

Most cloning and much mass cell culture work is done in plastic Petri dishes in a humidified, gas-flow, water-jacketed incubator (National Appliance Co., Portland, Ore.). The humidification of the incubator is often a source of mold contamination and precautions should be taken to minimize this difficulty.

1. Include a mycostatic agent in humidification water (Zephiran Chloride, or cupric sulfate).

2. Filter the input air-CO_2 mixture.

3. As an extra precaution the gas mixture may be bubbled through water in removable glass trays or in comparable devices, which are cleaned and replaced once a week.

4. Use only distilled water in the incubator.

The incubator should be water jacketed over all of its inside surface except for the door to minimize dripping of condensed water on the culture plates. Mold spores and yeasts lodge on the outside of the Petri dishes and are easily dropped into the cultures unless precautions are taken (see section on Sterility Precautions,

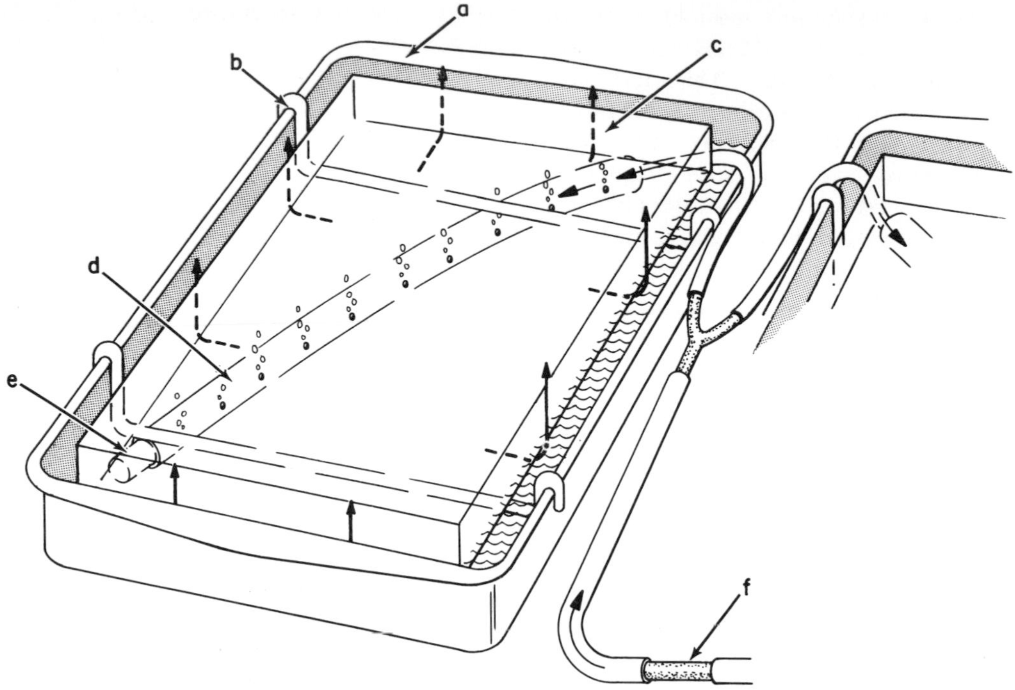

FIG. 1. Bubbling apparatus for controlled atmosphere incubator; 5–7 percent CO_2 in air passes through rubber tubing to the bottom of the incubator chamber, where it is filtered through a length of glass rod containing nonabsorbent cotton or glass wool (f). The mixture then bubbles through a length of tygon tubing (d) which contains holes punched with a hot needle and which is sealed at one end with a glass rod (e). The tygon tubes are anchored with tape to the bottom of a set of two Pyrex baking dishes (a) which contain the water. The inverted plastic trays (c) suspended above the water surface by glass rods (b) prevent splashing. A small amount of copper sulfate is added to the water to prevent contamination.

p. 509). The bubbling device for humidification should be partially covered to eliminate splatter and dispersal of aerosols (see Fig. 1). Sintered glass bubbler nozzles should be avoided since they tend to clog and change the CO_2-air mixture composition. A convenient aerator is a piece of tygon tubing with holes punched along the length with a hot needle.

The CO_2-air calibration meters on many incubators do not indicate the actual percentage of the mixture available to the cells. For a quick check on the gas mixture a Fyrite CO_2 meter can be used (Bacharach Industrial Instrument Co., Pittsburgh, Pa.). Every time the door is opened the CO_2 drops to under 1 percent and may take as long as 90 minutes to reach its former level at the usual rates of gas flow (4–8 liters per minute for a $4\frac{1}{2}$–5 cubic foot incubator). Therefore, it is wise to raise the rate of flow and percent of CO_2 in the gas mixture during periods when the doors will be opened and closed frequently. Recent incubator models allow for preset timed flushing with pure CO_2. This should be done after each time the incubator is opened.

Safety precautions must be taken to ensure that the CO_2 does not run out over a weekend or at night. The most convenient setup is an auxiliary tank, linked in tandem with the operating unit. Good double-valve stainless steel regulators should be used to avoid the valves freezing open or closed. The CO_2 will run only from the tank set at the higher pressure until it runs out.

If a gassing incubator is not available, a suitable incubator can be made from a large desiccator set in a warm room or dry incubator. Alternatively a gassing box can be built or purchased which can be installed in a regular incubator and can be gassed each time it is opened. Desiccators should be set up with distilled water rather than Hanks' or Tyrode's solution in the bottom to allow for adequate humidification. This does not lead to noticeable dilution of media and minimizes contamination. The entire apparatus should be cleaned and autoclaved before use. A solution containing a pH indicator such as phenol red in a beaker or Petri dish should always be in plain sight to check for leaks.

CHOICE OF AND PREPARATION OF MEDIA

Each cell and culture type requires a slightly different medium. Most chick cell cultures do well on media of the following general composition (see Appendix 1 of this chapter for variations to be used with specific cell types):

Cloning

Ham's F-10 (Ham, 1963) with 4 × amino acids and 2 × vitamins	50%
Hanks' saline	40–45%
Embryo extract or EE_{50}[1] fractions (see Appendix 3)	0.1–10%
Fetal calf serum	5–10%
Bovine serum albumin (Armour Fraction V)	5 gm per liter
H_2O	5% excess
[Ham's F_{12} can also be used (Ham, 1965)]	(optional)

Mass cell culture (either the above medium or)

NCI (Pucks N16) (Puck *et al.*, 1958)	40–80%
Hanks' saline	8–48%
Horse serum	10%
Embryo extract	2–10%

For a full discussion of the significance for differentiation of embryo extract (EE) fractions see Cahn and Cahn, 1966; Coon, 1966; Coon and Cahn, 1966. The methods for preparation of these fractions are described in Appendix 3 of this chapter.

Primary cultures of rat and mouse cells do not grow well in these media (on glass or Falcon plastic Petri dishes) and work is still in progress to obtain a relatively defined medium for the growth of differentiated mouse cells. Rabbit cells, however, do grow well in slight modifications of the above media.

Many media can be bought already prepared. In our experience media and sera from Grand Island Biological Co. (Grand Island, N.Y.) and sera from Hyland Labs. (Los Angeles, Calif.) have been reliable, when proper precautions are observed for cold or frozen shipment by air.

It is still recommended that initially the investigator prepare the media stock solutions personally, however, and the following precautions should be taken:

1. Use only grade A reagents obtained from standard suppliers. (If heavy metals are employed, we have found those from Johnson, Matthey and Co., 73/83 Hatton

[1] "EE_{50}" is prepared by adding an equal volume of balanced salt solution to the minced or homogenized embryos (see appendices).

Garden, London, E.C.1, or from Jarrell Ash Co., Waltham, Mass., are reliable.)

2. Water should be double- or triple-glass-distilled or the equivalent. We have successfully used double-distilled deionized water (Caw Engineering, Palo Alto, Calif., specially processed deionizers and organic adsorbents) and double-Pyrex-distilled tap water (Corning Laboratory Glassware, Corning, N.Y.; Brinkman Instrument Co., Westbury, N.Y.).

3. Order of addition and neutralization of components is sometimes critical. Each salt should be dissolved before the next one is added.

4. Care should be taken that the pH of the complete medium does not exceed the range 6.5–7.8. Some of the large molecular weight components (especially in conditioned media and EE_{50}-containing media) may be sensitive to high pH (Rubin, 1966).

Horse serum, bovine, calf, and fetal calf serum are the most often used media supplements for cell culture. They differ with respect to effects on plating efficiency and may show differences in assays of cellular differentiation. Their properties in these systems can be summarized as follows: horse serum has the greatest antitryptic activity (see p. 501), but many lots prove toxic to chick cells; fetal calf serum promotes attachment and stretching activity; calf and bovine sera possess both properties. Most sera are highly variable from batch to batch and must be carefully screened prior to use for each cell type. The best assays for serum reliability are plating efficiency (P.E.) and growth. (Plating efficiency is determined by dividing the number of colonies growing on a plate by the number of cells introduced into the plate at the beginning of the experiment.) Sera can also be tested for effects on clonal differentiation (percent cartilage making colonies seems to be a good test; see Protocol III, this volume, p. 517, and Coon, 1966).

STERILE FILTRATION[2]

We routinely filter-sterilize all media and salt solutions. Some salt solutions (those without glucose or bicarbonate) may be autoclaved.

1. Salt solutions can be filtered by suction on a Millipore, Gelman, or other vacuum filter holder, using an HA (pore size, 0.45 μ) or GS (pore size, 0.22 μ) filter. The pH may rise considerably during filtration; if so, the solution should be well gassed before or after sterilization

[2] It has very recently come to the attention of the authors that Millipore filters and other membrane filters contain 2 to 3 percent of their dry weight as a detergent (Cahn, 1967a). This fact is not immediately obvious when filtering serum-containing media, but becomes immediately recognizable when distilled water or saline solution is filtered through a membrane filter. The resulting filtrate develops persistent foam, whereas the material before filtration does not foam. The content of detergent in eluates of the filter can be high enough to cause damage to cells cultured in these media. Results from a representative experiment have shown that plating efficiency is doubled in 14-day chick sternal chondrocytes grown in media filtered through washed filters as compared with media prepared and filtered through unwashed filters. Similarly, the percent of differentiated colonies is increased by 50 percent in cells grown in media filtered through washed filters as compared with those filtered through unwashed filters. The following filter preparation procedure has now been adopted to combat this problem. It is necessitated because of the fact that removing the detergent from the filters changes their sterilization properties and considerably weakens them. The filters cannot be adequately sterilized after the removal of the bulk of the detergent. Method: Filters are assembled and sterilized as previously and then rinsed with 200 ml of hot distilled water, followed by 100 ml of cold 0.85 percent saline per 47-mm filter. Material and filter are thus cooled down, and all filtration is carried out while the material is cold. The hot distilled water extracts most of the detergent, and filtration in the cold assures that the remaining amount of detergent is very poorly solubilized. Using filters treated in this way, we have obtained plating efficiencies and differentiation superior to those obtained using unwashed filters.

with 5 percent CO_2 in air.

2. Media containing proteins are always filtered under pressure to reduce foaming and pH change. Either a standard stainless steel pressure filter holder (Millipore Corp., Bedford, Mass., or Gelman Instrument Co., Ann Arbor, Mich.) or the large capacity version should be used. Swagelock quick-connectors (Crawford Fitting Co., Solon, Ohio) are very convenient for attaching the gas cylinder to the filter, and for supplying the medium to the filter under pressure. We use either 5 percent CO_2 in air or water-pumped nitrogen for all filtering. Most media are filtered through HA filters (0.45 μ pore size) and we have never experienced contamination from media so filtered. Do not try to force out the last few milliliters of medium, because this may force some small plastic bacteria through the filter. If in doubt about pleuropneumonia-like organisms (PPLO; Whitelock, 1960) or other small contaminants, use GS filters (pore size 0.22 μ). It is possible to pass 2–3 liters or more medium through a 47-mm HA filter, but only 1,200–1,500 ml through a GS. Do not exceed 12–14 psi, because this too may force some bacteria through the filter. Use fiber glass prefilters to reduce plugging of the pores of membrane filters.

POINTERS ON pH CONTROL

Most cell culture media are buffered at pH 7.1–7.4 with a bicarbonate-CO_2 buffer. Phenol red is usually added at a final concentration of 1–5 μg per milliliter as an approximate aid to the estimation of pH. However, the presence of serum proteins and embryo extract alters the color of the phenol red at a given pH. Bovine serum albumin (Armour, Fraction *V*, Armour Pharmaceutical Co., Kankakee, Ill.) is very acid and lowers the pH of media considerably; it also makes the phenol red slightly more yellow than a protein-free standard. Standards should contain the same components as the medium and should be checked on a pH meter (read quickly to avoid CO_2 loss and pH rise). Standards and solutions should be compared in vessels with similar light paths, since large and small volumes of identical pH will appear different in color.

PRESERVATION OF MEDIA AND STOCK SOLUTIONS

Media should be used within 1 to 2 weeks of preparation if stored at 0°–4°C. Prepared media may be stored for much longer periods in liquid nitrogen, or in an electric cold box (Revco, Inc., Deerfield, Mich.) below −80°C. Ordinary freezers are not satisfactory for long-term storage of media because they are rarely below the eutectic point of physiological salt solutions. Thus at ordinary freezer temperatures an equilibrium exists between ice and a very concentrated salt solution. In time this inactivates or dissociates some components, causing the production of turbidity or a precipitate. Dry-ice boxes (−78°C) are inconvenient since everything must be stored in sealed glass ampoules to avoid large pH changes from the gaseous CO_2. Large electric low-temperature boxes may be prone to mechanical difficulties, and to interruption from breaks in electrical service. We have found liquid nitrogen storage of all sensitive materials (complete media, EE, and some sera) to be the least expensive and most reliable of all methods. Media are stored in an LR 35 refrigerator (Union Carbide Corp., Linde Division, New York) in 250-ml Nalgene autoclavable plastic bottles. If bottles are not full it may be necessary to modify the canisters with tops to prevent the bottles from floating.

Sera and media should not be frozen and thawed more than once if possible. This treatment is known to be damaging to lipoproteins, some of which may be essential for successful cell culture and cloning.

WASHING OF GLASSWARE

Although most culturing is done in disposable plastic Petri dishes, both cells and medium come in contact with glass tubes and other containers, and the cleanliness of the glass surface is important for successful cultures. The following precautions should be observed:

1. Prescription bottles ("Moderne Ovals," Foster Forbes Glass Co., Marion, Ind.) are rinsed twice in glass-distilled water and autoclaved or dry heat sterilized. Cells may be grown in several brands of bottles if necessary (Rappaport and Bishop, 1960).

2. Volumetric, measuring, and regular Pyrex glassware is washed by the following procedure:

a. After use, glassware is soaked in plastic buckets containing a 1 percent solution of 7X (Linbro Chemical Co., Inc., New Haven, Conn.). The soaking solution is replaced daily. Before glassware is placed in soaking buckets it is rinsed with water (see section on water) to remove all protein solutions and glucose.

b. Glassware is then soaked overnight at room temperature.

c. The 7X soaking solution is removed and the glassware placed in a large (16-quart) stainless steel bucket of fresh 1 percent 7X, brought to a boil rapidly over a hot gas flame (Model 66382 gas burner, Precision Scientific, Chicago, Ill.) and boiled 5–10 minutes.

d. Cold water is then run into the bottom of the bucket through a rubber hose until the water is just cool enough to touch. The glassware is removed from the 7X, brushed, rinsed several times, and placed in a new bucket containing filtered tap, distilled, or deionized water.

e. Glassware is again boiled 5–10 minutes, rinsed 10 times in distilled water (or 5 times in tap, 5 times in distilled water), and finally rinsed twice in double- or triple-glass-distilled water.

f. Glassware is allowed to drain dry or is dried in an oven (National Appliance Co., Portland, Ore.) at 75°–95°C. It is then covered with aluminum foil and sterilized 4 hours to overnight at 120°–140°C.

3. Pipettes are soaked overnight in a 1 percent 7X solution, and then transferred to a plastic pipette cylinder into which is poured boiling 1 percent 7X. The pipettes soak there for 15 minutes, and are then rinsed *twice* in the same manner in boiling distilled water. They are then rinsed 2 hours in running deionized or filtered tap water and finally rinsed once or twice in glass-distilled water. Automatic pipette washers (The Virtis Co., Gardiner, N.Y.) have sometimes been found to leave an oil slick from the pump on the inside of the pipettes. (Alternatively, the pipettes may be boiled in the regular manner with the glassware, but this is inconvenient and unnecessary.)

Pipettes may be plugged with cotton, but this is not usually necessary. Cells may aggregate around cotton fibers from the plugs and thus ruin an experiment.

Prepulled disposable commercial Pasteur pipettes are plugged without washing and are dry-heat sterilized (120°C overnight).

4. Stainless steel membrane filter holders are disassembled and the filters discarded. The stainless steel parts are rinsed thoroughly with water after use and soaked in 1 percent 7X in a separate plastic bucket to avoid glassware breakage. They are then processed as the glassware. The aluminum connectors and the rubber stoppers are not washed, but are rinsed and dried separately.

5. Sintered glass membrane filter holders are soaked and then heated in distilled water only; they are not boiled in soap. After drying and reassembly, both types of filters are carefully autoclaved at

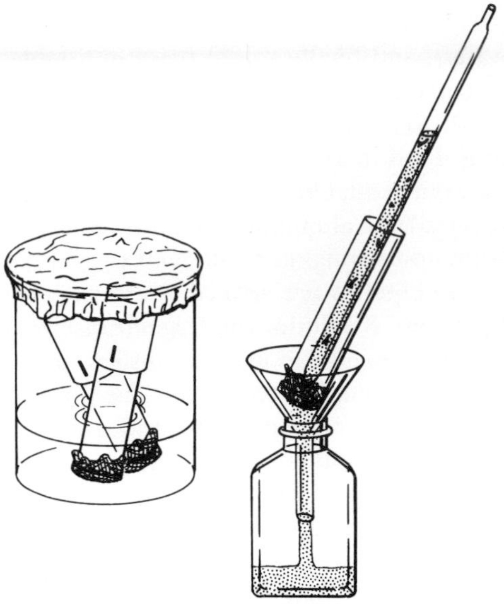

FIG. 2. Cell filtration method. Squares of Nitex monofilament screen cloth are prepared for use as described in text. The desired number of layers is tied to the end of a piece of Pyrex tubing approximately 100 mm x 15 mm inside diameter, 1.5 mm wall thickness. The opposite end of the tubing is protected with an 18-mm Morton culture tube closure. A number of such tubes can be autoclaved together in a beaker containing a small amount of water. Just before use, the cloth end is rinsed in sterile saline or culture medium. The cells are pipetted gently into the open end of the tube and into a bottle, as shown (see p. 503).

14.5–15.0 psi in an autoclave which generates its own steam from glass-distilled water. A good inexpensive automatic autoclave may be obtained from Market Forge Co. (Everett, Mass.). Steam line steam may contain highly toxic "preservatives" such as cyclohexylamine and diethylamine and is not suitable for use in sensitive cell cloning studies. Do not assemble or wrap the apparatus to be sterilized too tightly or the filters may buckle when the pressure is released.

6. Nitex (see Gould, this volume, pp. 163–171) monofilament screen cloth (Tobler, Ernst, and Traber, New York), used for filtering out cell clumps, is prepared for use by boiling in 0.5 percent $NaHCO_3$ followed by glass-distilled water. The string (braided nylon surgical cord) used for fixing the screen cloth to the glass tubes (see Fig. 2) is treated in the same way. Because of their expense the filters are washed as above after thorough back flushing with distilled water. Before use the assembled filters are autoclaved in a beaker containing water or saline to preserve the wettability of the screens (see Fig. 2).

7. Dissecting instruments are washed and cleaned with bars of Bon Ami cleanser to remove debris and corrosion. They are rinsed well, air dried, and sterilized by either dry heat or 70–80 percent alcohol for 20–40 minutes. They are then blotted dry underneath a sterile paper napkin prior to use.

8. Rubber stoppers, plastic caps, and liners are processed apart from the glassware. They are boiled in 7X and then water, autoclaved in glass jars, and air dried overnight or in an oven at 50°–70°C.

9. Nalgene polypropylene plastic bottles are washed with the glassware, but are autoclaved for sterilization. All autoclaving is done in self-generated glass-distilled water steam.

Sources of Cells—Materials for Culturing

Proper incubation of eggs for culture is discussed by Abbott, this volume, pp. 13–52. Mouse material is discussed by Kallman, this volume, pp. 3–12. For most purposes a simple commercial farm incubator is adequate.

Eggs are cleaned with sterile water and wiped with 70 percent ethanol using a sterile paper napkin or cotton balls. Eggs should remain in an incubator at 38.5°C until just before use to avoid pooling of blood in the embryo. Freshly cracked warm eggs leave most of the blood in the chorioallantoic membrane and bleed freely so that red blood cell contamination is kept to a minimum.

Eggs containing very young embryos are cracked and the entire yolk floated into sterile Saline G (Puck *et al.*, 1958) or a simple chick saline (0.85 percent NaCl). The embryonic area is then cut out with a bent scissors. Cutting should start at the lowest point on the yolk. Older eggs are simply cracked and the embryos lifted out with a sterile curved forceps, rinsed in sterile saline, and collected in sterile Saline G.

For obtaining mouse embryonic material, uteri should be dissected from the mother outside the culture area (adult mice should not be brought into the culture area). Embryos are washed in several changes of sterile saline prior to use to remove blood and debris.

Once the tissues under investigation are dissected out they should be washed and stored in Saline G containing 5–10 percent chicken serum, or in Hanks' plus 10 percent chicken serum in a CO_2 box (see below). Horse serum may be acceptable in some instances, but it is highly antitryptic and necessitates longer washing and higher enzyme levels in later steps. Chicken serum is only very weakly antitryptic and does not hinder trypsin-pancreatin dissociation procedures.

PRIMARY CULTURE (SEE APPENDIX FOR SPECIFIC PROTOCOLS ON SEVERAL CELL TYPES)

MASS CULTURES

After dissecting out the material to be cultured, the tissue masses are trimmed of contaminating tissue and prepared for dissociation (see Steinberg, this volume, pp. 565–572). The chunks of tissue are ordinarily cut into pieces no more than 0.5 mm on a face to allow the dissociating agent to penetrate rapidly to all the cells. This is usually done by careful cutting with iridectomy knives or fine curved or bent scissors under the dissecting microscope. If very large amounts of tissue are being used a McIlwain tissue chopper (McIlwain and Buddle, 1953; Paul, 1961) may be used, but this type of chopping usually damages many cells and creates much debris. The tissue pieces are then placed with an appropriate volume of dissociation fluid in a tightly stoppered 25-ml Erlenmeyer flask. Care must be taken that continuity is not established between the portions of the stopper which have been handled and a film of dissociation fluid in the neck of the flask. If too high a concentration of cells per milliliter is used with certain dissociation media [e.g., trypsin-collagenase (T-C) or trypsin alone], many cells may lyse forming skeins of a gel which entrap many remaining cells and complicate filtration (see Steinberg, 1963). A maximum of 10^7 cells per milliliter should be dissociated when agitation is used. In order to minimize the formation of the gel, pancreatin is often added to the final digestion mixture.

Once the tissue pieces are in the dissociating medium they should be monitored at 10-minute intervals under the dissecting microscope to see if they are beginning to separate. Cells which are ready to be mechanically separated (i.e., which are beginning to loosen and fall away from the tissue of their own accord) apparently suffer much less damage during dissociation than those which are forced apart after shorter incubation in the dissociating medium.

Trypsin, pancreatin, viokase, elastase, collagenase, papain, pronase, EDTA (ethylenediaminetetraacetate), and tetraphenyl boron have all been used separately or in different combinations with varying degrees of success for cell dissociation (Cahn, 1964b; Cahn and Cahn, 1966; Coon, 1966; Grobstein and Cohen, 1965; Grover, 1961; Konigsberg, 1961; Moscona, 1961; Parker, 1961; Rappaport and Howze, 1964, 1967; Rinaldini, 1958, 1959; Smith and Berndt, 1964; Steinberg, 1962, 1963; Wilson and Lau, 1963; Zwilling, 1964; also see Steinberg, this volume, pp. 565–572; consult protocols in Appendix 1 of this chapter for details on which reagents to use with different cell types). It should be emphasized, however, that much lower concentrations of these reagents are generally used when dissociating cells to be grown as mass monolayer or clonal cell cultures than those used in cell aggregation studies. It appears that cells recover slowly from enzyme dissociation when grown in monolayer culture, but rapidly and fully if reaggregated immediately.

Different cell types dissociate optimally with different reagents. Epithelial cells are usually insensitive to trypsin, but dissociate well in EDTA and papain (see Zwilling, 1954; Steinberg, this volume pp. 565–572), or in collagenase after a preliminary trypsinization. Cartilage cells can be dissociated with several proteolytic enzymes (trypsin, pancreatin, pronase, viokase, papain, and collagenase) and are quite resistant for long periods to most enzymatic treatments due to the presence of matrix surrounding the cells. Heart and muscle cells, on the other hand, are very sensitive to proteolytic dissociation. Heart cells, dissociated in 0.05 percent trypsin, clone with a primary plating efficiency of 0.01–0.1 percent. In duplicate controls, cells dissociated with collagenase give 10–20 percent plating efficiency (Cahn, unpublished). The total yield of single cells after dissociation is much lower with collagenase, however. Agitation of heart cells during dissociation is usually avoided, since damage (although yield as well) may be increased.

Immediately after the end of the incubation period, cells should be cooled and washed to remove as much of the enzyme or EDTA as possible. The dissociation medium is first removed without disturbing the tissue. Cold medium containing horse or fetal calf serum at pH 7.2–7.4 is then usually added to neutralize the remaining trypsin. Low temperature (5°–15°C) prevents immediate reaggregation. Embryo extract should be omitted at this step because it acts to speed aggregation. Throughout the rest of the procedure, the medium should be maintained at pH 7.0–7.4.

After the cells are suspended in cold medium they must be mechanically agitated to complete the dissociation into single cells. For optimal plating efficiencies cells should *never* be mechanically dissociated while in the EDTA or dissociating enzyme solution. Mechanical dissociation can be effected in one or more of the following ways:

1. Swirling on a Vortex Jr. mixer. Cells are placed in a 12- to 15-ml conical centrifuge tube in 1–5 ml of medium and swirled for 5–30 seconds. Heart cells are very sensitive to the procedure, pigment and cartilage cells less so.

2. Pipetting. Cells are forced through a fairly wide bore pipette (5–10 ml serological blowout) or through a Pasteur pipette. Cells which are more difficult to dissociate may be forced through a very small bore pipette, but this damages many cells and may reduce plating efficiency. Cartilage cells are not damaged by this type of dissociation (Holtzer *et al.*, 1960).

3. Gentle agitation during dissociation on a gyrorotatory shaker (New Brunswick Scientific Co., New Brunswick, N.J.) or with a stirring bar on a magnetic stirrer. This procedure generally gives lower plating efficiencies and lower percentages of viable cells in mass cultures than methods 1 or 2.

Washing is usually accomplished by gentle centrifugation, 2–4 minutes at 100–200 *g* in a clinical centrifuge (International Equipment Co., Needham Heights, Mass.), followed by gentle resuspension with a large bore pipette. Use of an rpm counter (Veeder-Root Speed Counter, Veeder Root, Inc., Hartford, Conn.) is desirable for precise calibration of gravity force. Centrifugation probably damages the cells somewhat, and should be minimized.

No matter how thorough a dissociation procedure is used, clumps of undissociated cells will usually remain. It is not desirable to continue the mechanical dissociation until all the cells are singles since by that time many cells will have been lysed, broken, or damaged. Cell clumps are removed by filtering through cheesecloth, nylon mesh screen (see p. 500), or silk gauze (Dufour, Anchor Brand, Fisher Scientific, New York) or stainless steel bolting cloth (see Fig. 2). Cells are diluted and filtered directly into an equal volume of cool (12°–15°C) medium without embryo extract (pH 7.0–7.4) to prevent rapid reaggregation. Cells may be washed again by centrifugation (2–4 minutes at 100–200 *g*), if necessary, to remove the last traces of dissociating agents.

Cell counts are usually made with a hemocytometer. Proper technique requires separate samples for each side of the hemocytometer (Rinaldini, 1959). Each sample is taken with a clean, dry disposable capillary pipette by dipping into the suspension to a depth of about 10 mm and allowing the suspension to enter the pipette by capillary action. The pipette is then held almost vertical and is touched to the track of the hemocytometer so that the suspension will enter the chamber by capillary action. The chamber is not allowed to overfill. For clonal cultures, dilutions and platings are done on the basis of number of potential colony-forming "centers." Thus, if undissociated aggregates of two or more cells are present in the sample suspension, they must be counted as one center. The number of singles, doubles, etc., is also recorded for each experiment as a measure of the degree of dissociation obtained. Mass cultures, on the other hand, are usually plated out on the basis of actual total numbers of cells. The appearance of the cells in the sample should also be recorded. Healthy cells usually appear round (round to elongate in the case of muscle and heart) with smooth outlines (Fig. 3a) in the hemocytometer, and with no "blebs" or "bubbly" appearance. A fairly reliable estimate of the viability of the cells at this point may be made by the use of the "eosin-exclusion test" (Hanks and Wallace, 1958), described in Appendix 1, Protocol V. A Coulter counter or Celloscope electronic cell counter (Particle Data Co.) may be necessary for accurate counts of cells in individually dissociated clones where concentrations of less than 10^5 cells per milliliter are encountered.

Mass (high density) cultures are usually plated at a density of 2×10^4–10^6 cells per milliliter of medium (or 2×10^3–2×10^5 cells per square centimeter available culture area); 2.5–3.0 ml of medium are used in 60 mm (28.8 cm^2) Petri dishes; 7.5–10 ml of medium in a 100-mm (78.5 cm^2) Petri dish. Plastic Petri dishes with surfaces suitable for culturing are now available (Falcon Plastics, Los Angeles, Calif.). Aliquots of the diluted cell suspension are pipetted slowly into the center of the plate. The cells are distributed evenly over the surface of the plate by swirling the medium gently in the dish, alternately back and forth and around in a circle. Care should be taken that the complete culture medium is at the proper pH (7.0–7.4) before cells are plated into it. This is accomplished by gassing the medium immediately before plating, or by storing prepared dishes preferably in a CO_2 gassing box or in the incubators. *Cells must be fed every second day, or more frequently in high density platings.*

Media containing high concentrations of serum supplement (10–30 percent) as well as those media incorporating whole EE_{50} or the high molecular weight fractions of EE_{50} generally permit longer intervals between feedings. This effect is probably due to the capacity of sera and EE_{50} to generate small molecular weight metabolites which are otherwise exhausted rapidly from the common nutrient formulations (Coon and Cahn, 1966; Eagle, 1959; Eagle and Piez, 1962).

Not all media will support high density platings equally well. In this respect N16 seems to be adequate, while F10 and F12 are not as good. Adequate regimens and media for cartilage, heart, muscle, and pigmented retina are suggested in the Appendix.

High density platings inhibit the expression of differentiation for at least two cell types in the chicken (Cahn and Cahn, 1966; Coon, 1964, 1966). Heart and skeletal muscle cell differentiation is favored by high densities, and by conditioned media (Cahn, 1964a, 1964b; Konigsberg, 1961, 1963; Konigsberg and Hauschka, 1965; see discussion in section on cloning). The conditions optimal for the differentiation *in vitro* of each cell type must be individually determined.

SUBCULTURE OF MASS CULTURES

High densities of cells in mass cultures often exhaust medium so rapidly that thinning is a vital necessity. Figure 7a shows the appearance of some "hungry" cells. It is advisable to divide cultures well in advance of this appearance. Differentiated function may be abolished by failing to feed very dense mass cultures rapidly enough. Clonal cultures, because of their lower density, are often more easily maintained.

Because most media contain either fetal calf serum or horse serum, both of which possess high antitryptic activity, it is necessary to rinse plates to be transferred with saline or growth medium without serum supplement. One rinsing is usually sufficient. Because of the unfavorable concentration gradient between spread cells and the environment, rinsing should be done quickly. For most cells crude trypsin alone suffices to cause them to round up and abandon attachment to glass or plastic.[3] Reduced calcium and magnesium ion concentrations in the dissociation media also appear to favor dissociation. We have found that use of chicken serum (which has a very low trypsin inhibitory activity) protects cells during exposure to the enzyme. Concentrations of 0.1 to 0.01 percent crude trypsin (Difco, Detroit, Mich., 1:250 or Nutritional Biochemicals, Cleveland, Ohio, 1:300) usually suffice.

For cartilage, skeletal, or cardiac muscle, collagenase at from 1 to 5 mg per milliliter has been found useful especially where single cell suspensions are desired. Suspensions of cartilage cells are consistently more uniform with fewer double and triple cell aggregations when collagenase is included in the dissociation medium (Fig. 3a). For harvesting pigmented retina mass cultures, 0.1 percent EDTA (see Protocol I) may be necessary. Incubation with dissociation media should be carried out at room temperature or at 37°C for as short a time as possible. Curiously trypsin does not appear to have a high Q_{10} for dissociation and some trypsinizations are carried out at 0°C (Rawles, 1963). However, for transferring cultures the higher incubation temperatures are recommended. Trypsinization of the cells is always a battle between dissociating

[3] When in doubt about appropriate concentrations for dissociation of mass cultures or established clones, one-tenth the concentration of the same solution used for primary dissociation may be tried.

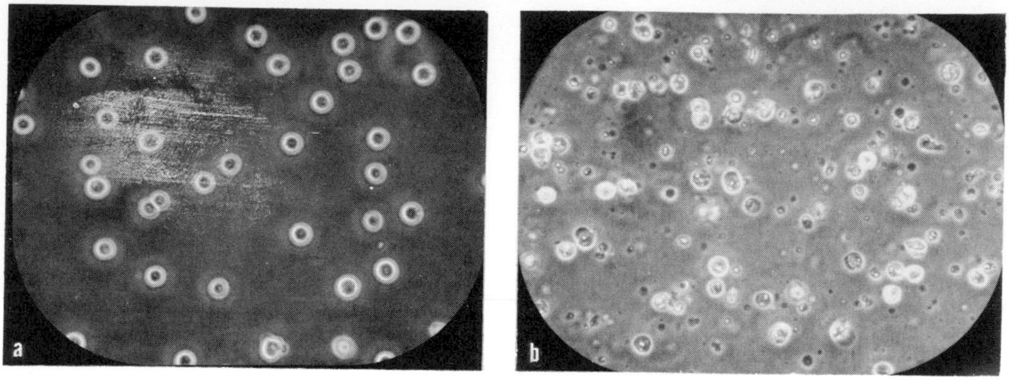

FIG. 3. (a) Healthy cell suspension obtained from cartilage mass cultures growing in H2 medium. One cell shows slight "blebbing." The one "double" present was no doubt interrupted in the last stages of division, judging from the condensed appearance of its nuclei. Phase contrast. All photomicrographs are of chick embryo cells taken at 300 × magnification with a Polaroid camera mounted on a Unitron PH-BMIC phase-contrast binocular microscope. (b) Cellular debris floating in the medium in an unhealthy mass culture of cartilage cells. Such a picture could also be seen after too violent a dissociation procedure.

the cells from one another and from the substrate on the one hand and digestion and consequent lysis on the other. One attempts to strike a balance. If a thick carpet of cells, perhaps several layers thick in places, is to be subcultured, an hour or more at 37°C in trypsin plus collagenase may be required to yield satisfactory single cell suspensions. The total duration of exposure to trypsin may be much reduced by using gentle mechanical agitation, which tends to break up tenuous cell-cell contacts and serves to free cells from the substratum as well. Preliminary incubation with dissociation solution for 15–20 minutes, followed by pipetting solution and cells together (directing the stream from the pipette so that all portions of the floor of the dish are rinsed), followed by a second incubation of 10 or 15 minutes and repipetting usually yields good recovery of viable cells while minimizing trypsinization time. The cells should be washed free of the enzymes or EDTA as soon as possible after the desired degree of dissociation has been obtained.

SPECIAL PROCEDURES FOR CLONING

CLONING FROM *in vivo* TISSUE DIRECTLY. Cells are dissociated as discussed under primary mass cultures. After filtering through Nitex, the cells are plated at 10^2, 10^3, 10^4 cells per plate. Plating efficiencies from primary tissues are usually variable and considerably lower than with the first two methods described, but should fall in the range 0.1–30 percent. Cartilage cells, however, often plate at 50–100 percent P.E. (plating efficiency).

Care should be taken that the medium is gassed and at the proper pH before plating or diluting the cells. All operations prior to final plating should be carried out in cool complete medium without EE. Plates should be placed in a CO_2 gassing box prior to use, and the pH kept below 7.4.

CLONING FROM PRIMARY MASS CULTURE. The easiest methods for cloning differentiated cells involve cloning from a short-term primary mass culture. Cells are grown in mass culture at high densities ($1–5 \times 10^6$ cells per 100 mm dish) for 1–3 days and clonal cultures are derived from these cells. Although this is not technically "primary" cloning (directly from *in vivo* tissue), the cells have a much greater chance of survival and P. E. is often very high. This may be due to the milder dissociation treatments needed to get single cells, as well as to culture adaptation and conditioned medium build-up in mass culture during recovery from primary dissociation. Primary mass cultures do not grow significantly during the first 1–2 days, so that overgrowth by minority cell types is probably minimal. Two methods are available for cloning from these primary cultures, each of which yields clones of differentiated cells.

1. *Cloning from floaters.* After 3–4 days, many floating cells and some debris are observed in high density mass platings. The supernatant from these cultures can be removed, centrifuged gently (100 *g*, 2 minutes) to sediment only the cells, resuspended, and counted (with an electronic cell counter unless several cultures are pooled). These cells are resuspended in fresh medium or one-half fresh, one-half conditioned medium, and plated at a density of 50–400 cells per 60-mm Petri dish in 3 ml medium. Floaters give high plating efficiency and differentiate well. This is the most gentle cloning technique available and is particularly valuable for cloning very young embryonic cells (see Appendix 1, Protocol V, D for chick mesoblasts) and very delicate cells such as heart myoblasts. It selects cells recently in division, as these tend to round up and release their broad attachment to the surface just before metaphase, and cells which have not attached for other reasons. More cells can be obtained by gently agitating the cultures prior to removing the medium. Since the "floater" cell suspension also contains debris and dead cells from the initial mass culture, it is advisable to make a "viable" cell count using a technique such as the "eosin exclusion test" (Hanks and Wallace, 1958; see Protocol V, D, in Appendix 1).

This method can be adapted to cloning from very small amounts of tissue by allowing the cells to grow for several weeks as small lumps of tissue before plating the floaters.

2. *Cloning from short-term mass monolayers.* Mass cultures are prepared as above. After 48–72 hours, the cells are dissociated, washed, and resuspended (see section on cloning from primary mass culture). After counting, the cells are diluted and sown at 10^2–10^4 cells per plate. Because most of the debris from the mass culture is removed during preliminary washing of the culture plates and centrifugation of the cell suspension, it is usually not necessary to do the "viable" cell counts suggested for "floater" cultures.

3. *Subculture from differentiated and undifferentiated colonies.* Crucial to the establishment of clonal strains is the ability to subculture (subclone) individual clones easily and with high efficiency. The original procedure originating in Puck's laboratory (Puck *et al.*, 1956) is to apply a small cylinder of stainless steel (or Pyrex or porcelain) around the colony to be subcultured, and carry out rinsings and trypsinizations within the cylinder as one would with the passage of whole plates of cells. The cylinders are fixed to the bottom of the dish by dipping them in a thin layer of autoclaved and cooled silicone grease (Dow Corning), and pressing them to the surface of the Petri dish around the clone. One must be sure that the cylinders are completely dry before dipping so that a good seal is formed. After the clone has loosened or has fallen apart, it is carefully transferred to a centrifuge tube, washed, mechanically dissociated, filtered, and plated.

This method is especially suitable for "undifferentiated" colonies, which are quite sensitive to dissociation procedures and often do not form a coherent layer which could be easily removed from the dish by the scraping technique (see below) without considerable loss of cells. The cloning cylinder is also ideal for the transfer of very small numbers of cells, (Sanford *et al.*, 1948) such as in passaging the widely scattered cells of a very young colony, or the sub-culture of muscle (myoblast) spindle cells before fusion to form straps. Such colonies may be isolated with a cloning cylinder as described above, making sure that no other cells have inadvertently been included. From 5 to 7 minutes at room temperature in dilute trypsin or T-C (trypsin-collagenase) will often suffice to cause the cells to round up (the progress of the reaction should be monitored under an inverted microscope). As soon as the cells have loosened, they may be removed with a minimum of trypsin by introducing the tip of a pulled (capillary) Pasteur pipette vertically into the cylinder about 0.5 mm directly above the cells, and then venting the pipette. If this is done properly, the cells lying immediately beneath are swept up into the capillary with only 5–10 μl of the enzyme solution. The delivery of this small amount along with the cells into 6–10 ml of serum-containing medium will not prejudice the cloning results. With practice, fine capillary pipettes can be manipulated with mouth tubes so that even individual cells may be transferred in this manner. In order to avoid losses when handling small numbers of cells, it is wise to wet all glass pipettes with medium that contains serum. This prevents the cells from sticking to the walls.

Differentiated or other highly coherent clones can often be scraped intact from the dish with minimal cell damage by using a small tygon policeman (Fig. 4). The thin leading edge of the scraper is inserted at one point along the edge of a colony; with short, gentle scraping motions along the bottom of the dish, the clone is gradually teased off the surface of the dish. If the colony does not lift off easily and all in one piece, a very brief pretreatment with dilute trypsin may be tried. If the colony still does not respond, one must assume that the scraping method would kill many cells, and the cylinder method must be used. Another possible difficulty with the scraping technique is that cells at the edge of the colony may break away or be crushed. If this is the case, trials with both the scraping and the cylinder techniques should be made to be sure that this selection does not alter the results of subsequent experiments. After scraping, each colony is rinsed with saline and transferred carefully to a conical centrifuge tube; 1 ml of dissociation fluid is then added to each tube and incubation is carried out without agitation. The same concentrations of reagents used for primary mass culture transfer are usually successful for dissociation of clones. For

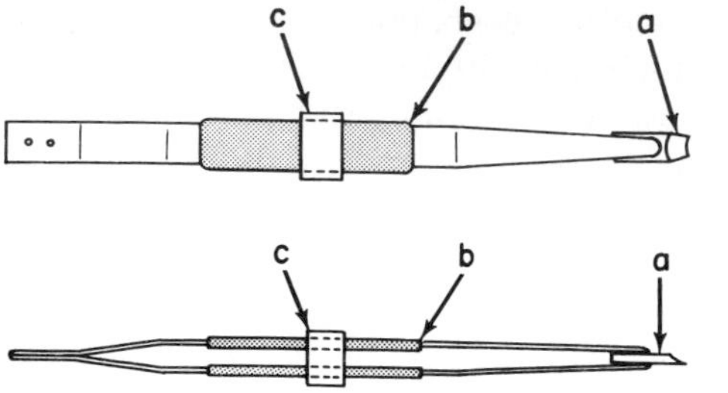

FIG. 4. Tygon policeman for "teasing" clones off Petri dish. A tygon plastic rectangle approximately 10 mm x 5 mm is cut from a short piece of tygon tubing (1/4 inch inside diameter, 1/16 inch wall thickness) and sharpened at one end with a razor blade (a). It is held tightly in place between the tips of a pair of blunt-end forceps (b), with a ring of the same tygon tubing (c), as shown. Forceps from Millipore Filter Corporation, Bedford, Mass.

example, incubation of cartilage cell colonies for 10–15 minutes at 36.5°C in dilute T-C should leave a fine layer of single cells on the bottom of the tube. With differentiated pigment cell clones, much longer incubation (45–60 minutes) in 0.1 percent EDTA is necessary. If great care is taken not to stir up the cells when they are taken from the incubator, nearly all of the dissociation fluid can be removed (leaving less than 20 μl) by gently aspirating the excess with a finely pulled capillary pipette with observation under the low power of a dissecting microscope. Subsequent dilution with 1 ml medium will suffice for washing. If desired, dilution with medium, washing, and filtration may be carried out, but with as few as 1,000 cells per tube losses will be great. If necessary, the cells may be suspended by swirling on a Vortex mixer or by pipetting, and further dilutions may be made before plating.

Counting the number of cells in a small colony is a very difficult task. Estimates may be made by counting sample areas of the clone under a microscope before transferring, but these are accurate only if the colony is a monolayer of cells. Alternatively, large sample clones may be dissociated and the resultant total number of cells in each clone determined from hemocytometer counts; the number of cells then may be correlated with the original diameter of the clone, and the calibration figure so obtained used to estimate the number of cells in a small colony. A third type of estimate may be made by determining the number of cells obtained from many pooled colonies and dividing by the number of colonies.

4. *Preparation and use of conditioned media in clonal culture*. The classic work of Sanford, Earle, and Likely (1948) was the first to take advantage of the conditioned medium technique in achieving the cloning of individual mammalian cells (Sanford *et al.*, 1948). Improvements of technique and medium preparation made possible Konigsberg's first clonal culture work with differentiated skeletal muscle cells (Konigsberg, 1961). Gradually, as we have learned to make efficient and gentle dissociations of embryonic tissue and improve culture media, the use of conditioned medium is being circumvented (Puck, Marcus, and Cieciura, 1956; Konigsberg and Hauschka, 1965; Coon and Cahn, 1966). Conditioning of medium remains the most tried and true formula for success with cloning of any cell, whether cloning is attempted with "feeder layers" (Puck, 1956), from floaters in floater medium (Coon, 1964), or simply by bathing the isolated cells in a medium previously detoxified and enriched by the action of many cells (Konigsberg, 1963).

For the definitive account of the preparation and use of conditioned medium the reader is referred to the paper by Konigsberg (1963). A few remarks may prove useful in attempting to make conditioned media for other cell types.

Three of the five cell types which have been successfully cloned so far in the authors' laboratories have required conditioned medium for expression of their differentiative characteristics as clones: heart, skeletal muscle (but see Konigsberg and Hauschka, 1966, and Appendix 1, Protocol VI), and early limb mesoblasts. Conditioned medium may be prepared in one of the following ways, from initial inocula of 3–5 × 10^6 cells per 100-mm Petri dish in 10 ml culture medium:

1. Cells are fed on day 1 or 2 with 10 ml fresh medium, or medium is replaced completely on day 1 or 2 with 20 ml medium. After 2–3 days incubation, the medium is harvested (2- to 4- or 2- to 5-day "conditioned medium"). For further details of this method, which has been used most frequently in our laboratories, see Appendix 2 and Rubin, 1966.

2. Cells are fed on day 2 by adding 5 ml medium; medium is removed on day 4 and replaced with 10–20 ml fresh medium. The 4- to 6-day "conditioned" medium is harvested on day 6.

3. Cells may be fed regularly for 6 days, and medium collected on day 9 (6- to 9-day conditioned), or on days 9 and 11 (9- to 11-day conditioned) with an intermediate feeding on day 9.

Homologous or heterologous cell types usually can be used for conditioning media (see Rubin, 1966).

Cells (both mass cultures and clones) grow considerably more slowly in conditioned medium than in fresh medium in most systems. However, Rubin has recently (1966) reported the opposite effect at low cell density inocula of "chick embryo fibroblasts" using a medium unlike those recommended here.

The nature of the "conditioning factor(s)" is unknown at present. There may be several different factors involved in promoting the differentiation of different cell types. Rubin (1966) presents evidence that his conditioned medium factor may be derived from the cell membrane or coat. Konigsberg feels (Hauschka and Konigsberg, 1966; Konigsberg and Hauschka, 1965) that collagen or tropocollagen is the conditioning factor for muscle cells. We have presented evidence (Coon and Cahn, 1966) which indicates that conditioning may detoxify the medium. Recently we have also found (Cahn and Cahn, 1966; Cahn and Lasher, 1967; Cahn and Cahn, 1967; Coon and Cahn, 1966) that the need for conditioning media for clonal growth of cartilage and pigmented retina cells may be eliminated with good fetal calf sera, by using very low amounts of EE (0.1%), or by using a low molecular weight fraction of EE. Large concentrations of high molecular weight components of EE speed cell growth but inhibit the expression of differentiation in cartilage and pigmented retina cells (Fig. 6).

Sterility Precautions in Feeding and Transferring Cells

Penicillin and streptomycin in low concentrations (50 and 25 μg per milliliter respectively) are usually sufficient to prevent growth in cultures of normal contaminating bacteria found in laboratories and on the skin. Mycostatin (Squibb) is not included in media in our laboratories as it cannot be filtered terminally, and must be added under sterile conditions to the media just prior to culturing. Furthermore, the toxic level of Mycostatin is quite close to its minimal effective level, so that its use has been avoided unless absolutely necessary. However, Amphotericin B (Fungizone, Grand Island Biological Co.) can be used and filtered terminally; 25–50 units per milliliter are sufficient. At these levels viability and differentiation are not affected.

Since contamination of any sort is virtually nonexistent during primary culturing or fresh platings from transfers, we have concluded that most contamination occurs during routine feeding operations from mold and yeast spores which fall into the cultures from the edges of the Petri dishes. This contamination can be minimized in the following ways:

1. Incubators should be cleaned frequently and humidification water kept as sterile as possible (see section on incubators, p. 494).

2. Tops and edges of moist dishes should be wiped with a sterile napkin and allowed to dry before feeding.

3. Proper feeding techniques involve the following:

a. Lift the edge of the plate slightly and insert pipette at an angle to the edge. Use a 10-ml serological pipette with latex tubing and blood-diluting pipette mouthpiece attached for removing medium.

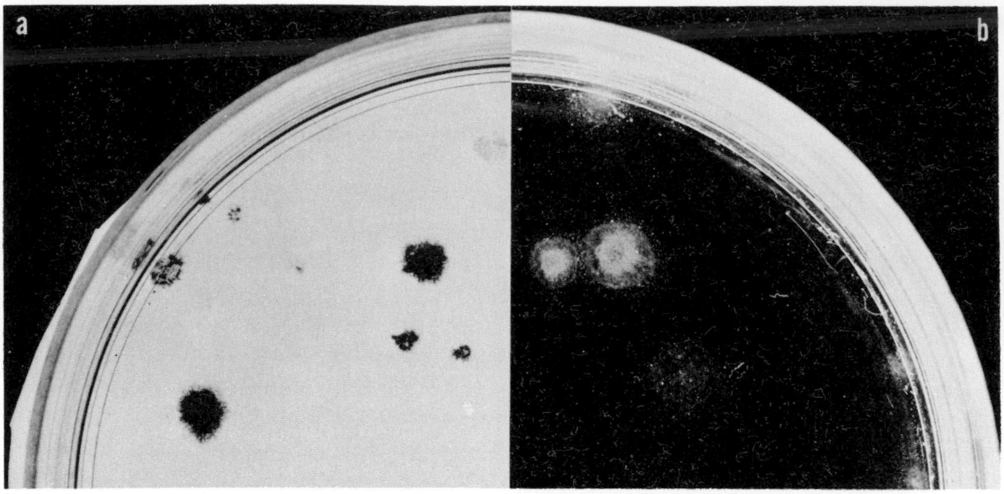

FIG. 5. Portion of 60-mm plastic Petri dish showing general pigmented retina clone morphology after approximately 3 weeks growth in L2. (a) Bright field. (b) Dark field.

b. Do not touch edge of plate or medium with pipette while feeding. This minimizes spread of contamination from one culture to another.

c. Check cultures thoroughly *before* feeding and discard any that are contaminated. If in doubt examine with an inverted microscope.

d. Use each pipette once only (i.e., 5 feedings of 2 ml each) to avoid serial contamination of large numbers of cultures.

e. Do not feed all plates of a single series with same pipette.

f. *Do not flame pipettes.* This does not seem to aid at all in maintaining sterile cultures. It may even cause additional contamination during the turbulence of flaming, and may heat-inactivate components of the medium. Cotton plugs may be used, but the cotton threads tend to get into cultures causing cells to aggregate around them. One of the authors (RDC) never plugs pipettes.

Infection by yeast or bacteria as we have noted above seems to occur most often in connection with feeding. Cultures to be passaged by any of the foregoing techniques should therefore be *very* carefully examined (use inverted phase microscope) for signs of yeast and bacterial aggregates or organisms swimming about. It is possible to overlook an incipient infection and then to transfer infection to each of the subculture plates. In order to minimize the chances of overlooking an incipient infection passage schedules should be arranged so that any contamination has had at least 24 and preferably 36 or 48 hours to grow up and be detected since the last feeding.

Observation of Cells

GENERAL TIPS

An inverted phase-contrast microscope [Unitron (Unitron Instrument Co., Newton Highlands, Mass.); Zeiss (Zeiss Instrument Co., New York); or Wilde (Heerbrugg Instruments, Inc., Port Washington, N.Y.)] is an absolute necessity for meaningful observations on living cells in

Petri dish cultures. (Unitron microscopes are usually unsatisfactory unless objectives are carefully screened and matched with condensors.) Plates should be kept at the proper temperature and proper CO_2 tension if they are to be observed for any length of time. Cells show prominent blebbing and other phenomena if these precautions are not observed. Heat filters (interference or absorption) should always be used on light sources. Tops of Petri dishes will fog unless a heat source is directed at them. For short-term observations this fogging can be remedied by frequent careful exchanges of tops with clean sterile tops.

Routine photographs of cultures can be made conveniently with a Polaroid camera back. Good quality negatives are available from these prints at little cost directly from Polaroid if necessary for publication. Copies obtained from Pola-

FIG. 6. Sibling clones of cartilage (6a and 6b) and pigment cells (6c and 6d) showing varying degrees of differentiation depending on the medium in which they have grown: (a) Small cartilage clone growing in L2. The highly refractile cells indicate matrix production in the formation of a minute clonal cartilage nodule. (b) Cartilage clone in H2. Quite "fibroblastic" in appearance, not producing matrix. (c) Center of pigmented retina clone in L2 medium. Note the regular hexagonal shape of the cells and the density of pigment granules. In culture 11 days. (d) Sister pigmented retina clone of similar size and cell density, but growing in H2 medium. Cells are irregular in shape, and pigment granules are scarce.

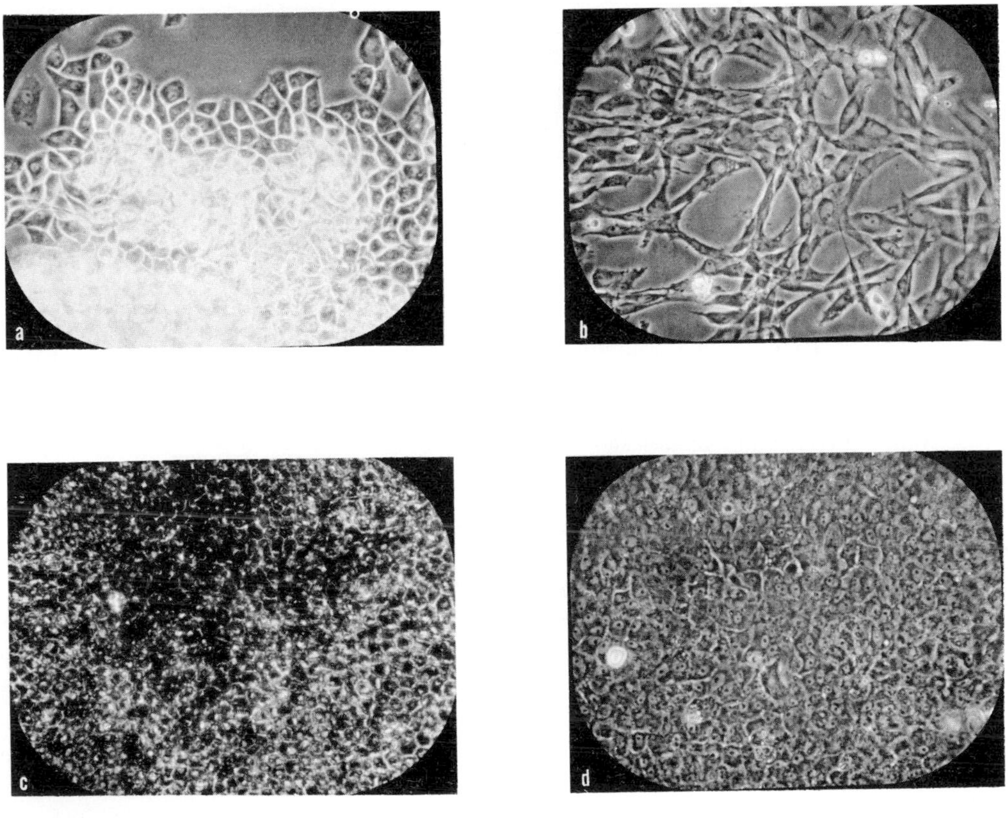

roid will usually serve adequately for publication purposes. More complicated setups are also possible but unnecessary for most phase-contrast observations. For best definition the Petri dish cover should be removed prior to taking the picture as long as the culture is expendable. A water-immersion phase-contrast objective provides optimal resolution when necessary.

DESCRIPTION OF CULTURES: WHAT TO LOOK FOR

Figures 5–7 show some normal and abnormal cells grown as clones from heart, cartilage, and pigmented retina.

The abnormal appearance of cells (Fig. 7) can usually be traced to one or more of the following:

1. Cells are not being fed often enough or are receiving an inadequate nutrient medium.
2. Virus infection, pleuropneumonia-like organisms (PPLO), or other contamination of cultures.
3. Cells are in the decline phase, are aging, and may be heteroploid.
4. Cells are incompatible with the culture surface, stretch too tightly or not at all.
5. Cells have been overtrypsinized or mechanically disrupted too forcefully.
6. Temperature is low or humidity too low in incubator; or medium is hypertonic.
7. Toxic factors have been generated in serum, EE (blebbing, vacuoles).
8. CO_2 has run out in incubator, or air supply has been interrupted for a short or long period of time.

Any of the above may lead to an apparent "dedifferentiation" of the cellular morphology, to transformation of differentiated cells into "fibroblasts," and eventually to cell death.

CONCLUSIONS

Clonal cell culture can provide a tool for the investigation of many of the processes of development. The procedures are relatively straightforward, but demand much patience and care on the part of the student or investigator. We have reviewed the general principles and most common pitfalls of clonal culture of differentiated cells. In the appendices are described in detail the protocols for clonal culture and observation of several types of differentiated embryonic cells. In attempting to reproduce these culturing techniques it is important not to become discouraged by early apparent failure, especially in the first few days of culture. Although the cultures may seem "very sick" initially, never discard a culture until it is several weeks old. These "sick cells" often recover and can be the source of very valuable cultures.

Several factors influence the survival, growth, and normal differentiation of the clonal populations of differentiated embryonic cells. Some of these have been touched on only briefly in this article and are reviewed in greater detail in Hauschka and Konigsberg (1965), Konigsberg and Hauschka (1966), Coon (1966), Cahn and Cahn (1966), Coon and Cahn (1966), Cahn, 1967b, and Cahn and Lasher, 1967. Suffice it to say that the nature of the surface on which the cells grow and the macromolecular constituents of the media profoundly affect *expression* of differentiation in most cell types (Fig. 6). However, these factors have not yet been implicated in control of the *inheritance* or transmission of differentiated properties.

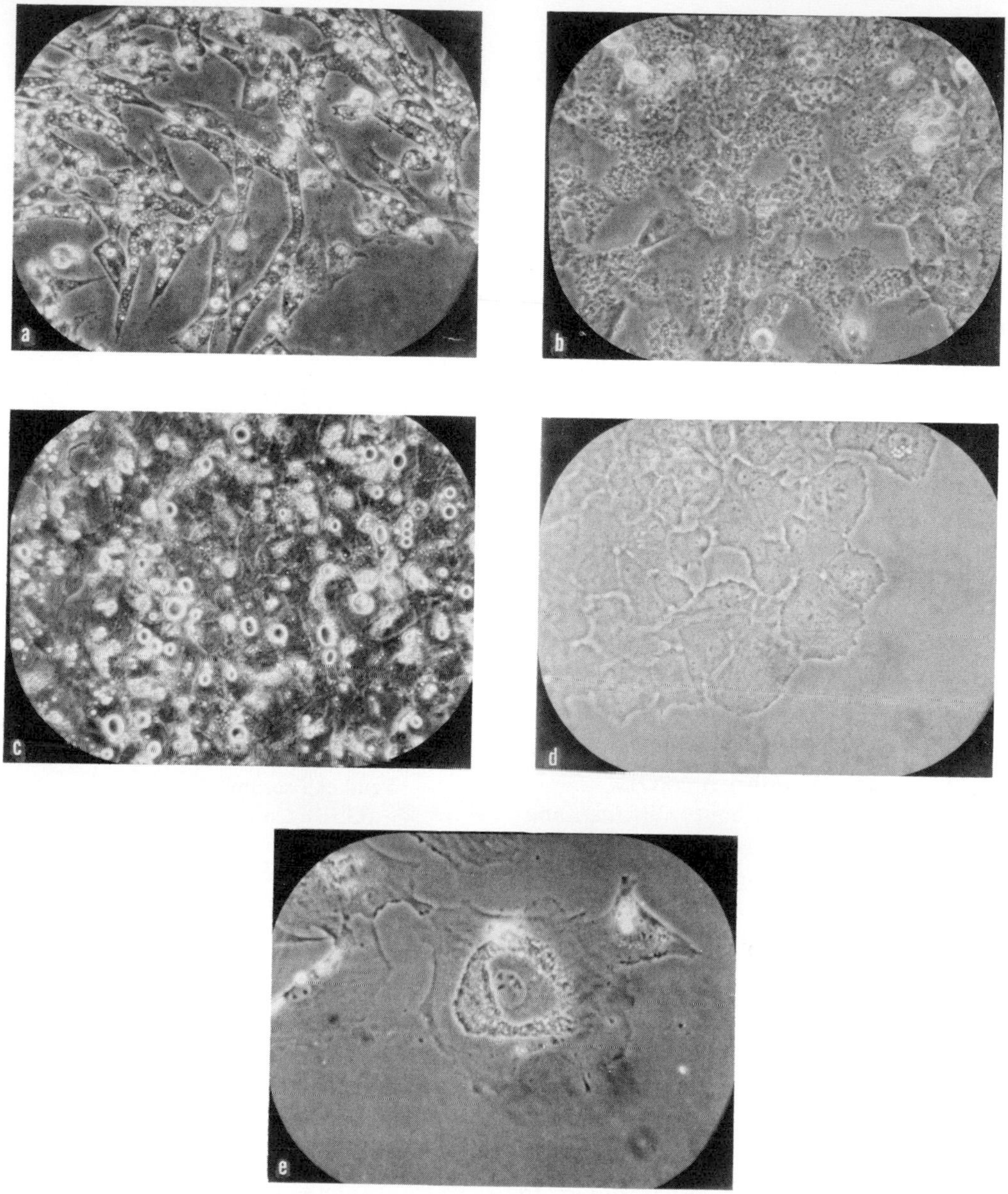

FIG. 7. Appearance of abnormal cultured cells: (a) "Hungry" H2-grown cartilage cells. The lacunae in the cytoplasm disappear within 18 hours after the medium is renewed. (b) Pigmented retina clone growing in L2, showing extreme "bubbling" or "blebbing" of cell surface which may result from damage during prolonged exposure to dissociation solutions or from a tonicity defect in the culture medium. (c) Primary 6-day heart muscle clone showing formation of large refractile cytoplasmic inclusions. These may represent abnormal production of lipids by the cell. (d) Pigmented retina clone showing formation of large, flat, epithelial cells. These result from an exaggerated spreading phenomenon, and probably do not represent true giant cell formation. (e) True giant cell (probably tetraploid) in a primary heart cell culture.

APPENDIX 1

Protocols for Clonal and Mass Culture of Five Chicken Embryo Cell Types

PROTOCOL I. 7-DAY PIGMENTED RETINA

A. Solutions

1. Saline G ("Sal G"; Puck *et al.*, 1958):

INGREDIENT	GRAMS PER LITER
NaCl	8.00
KCl	0.4
$MgSO_4 \cdot 7H_2O$	0.154
$CaCl_2 \cdot 2H_2O$	0.016
$Na_2HPO_4 \cdot 7H_2O$	0.29
KH_2PO_4	0.150
Glucose	1.10
Phenol Red	0.0012

Adjust to pH 7.4 with 1 *N* NaOH.

2. Saline G without calcium and magnesium, containing 6 percent chicken serum (Grand Island Biological Co.): "Ca, Mg-free Sal G + C. S."

3. Trypsin-pancreatin solution (T-P):

Trypsin (Difco, 1:250 or Nutritional Biochemicals, 1:300) 0.5 percent

Pancreatin (Difco, N. F.) 0.25 percent

Make up as a 2 percent T,1 percent P stock solution in Ca, Mg-free Sal G, centrifuge, filter, and store frozen in aliquots. Just before use, thaw, dilute, add 2 percent chicken serum, adjust to pH 7.6, and filter-sterilize.

4. EDTA:

Disodium ethylenediaminetetraacetate, (EDTA), 0.1 percent, in Ca, Mg-free Sal G. Just before use, add 2 percent chicken serum, adjust to pH 7.8, and filter-sterilize.

5. Hanks' balanced salt solution (BSS), modified: for use in culture medium (see next heading, #6):

INGREDIENT	GRAMS PER LITER
NaCl	8.0
KCl	0.2
KH_2PO_4	0.15
$Na_2HPO_4 \cdot 7H_2O$	0.29
$MgSO_4 \cdot 7H_2O$	0.77
$CaCl_2 \cdot 2H_2O$	0.08
$NaHCO_3$	0.75
Glucose	1.00
Phenol red	0.0012

6. Suggested culture medium:

Ham's nutrient mixture F10 with 4 × amino acids and 2 × vitamins (Grand Island Biol. Co.)	50 percent
Hanks' BSS (modified)	38 percent
Fetal calf serum (G.I.B. Co.)	5–10 percent
Penicillin	50 units/ml
Streptomycin	25 units/ml
Fungizone (G.I.B. Co.)	25 units/ml
Bovine serum albumin (Armour)	0.5 gm per 100 ml
Embryo extract (embryo extract or Sephadex fractions of EE replace an equal volume of Hanks')	2 percent
Extra bicarbonate (omit if cultures are grown in 5 percent instead of 6–7 percent CO_2 in air, or if Bovine Serum Albumin is omitted)	0.1 gm per 100 ml

B. Procedure

1. Incubate fertile eggs 6–8 days.
2. Open eggs, take out embryos, and

wash in Saline G, pH 7.4, at room temperature.

3. Transfer heads to fresh Saline G and remove eyes, without trying to remove outer layers of mesenchyme.

4. Place eyes in Ca, Mg-free Saline G plus 6 percent chicken serum.

5. With iridectomy knives, cut around outer border of iris and along edge of pecten, thus isolating the medial portion of the eye containing neutral retina, pigmented retina, and outer mesenchymal layers.

6. Transfer to fresh Ca, Mg-free Saline G plus 6 percent chicken serum. Peel neural retina layer off the underlying pigmented retina. Then gently tease the pigmented retina layer away from the nonpigmented mesenchyme layers beneath. A very thin layer of nonpigmented cells will sometimes adhere to the pigmented layer and be removed along with it. Most of these cells are removed during later enzyme treatment.

7. Transfer isolated pigmented retina pieces to a 15-ml conical centrifuge tube. Allow them to settle, replace saline with trypsin solution (0.5 percent T, 0.25 percent P), stopper tightly, and incubate in 1 ml T-P for 10–15 minutes at 37°C.

8. Swirl tube for 3–5 seconds on a Vortex Jr. mixer. Most of the mesenchyme cells will dissociate, leaving the pigmented retina in small pieces. Allow the pieces to settle for 10 minutes, discard the supernatant of dissociated mesenchyme cells (see heading #6), and wash the pigmented pieces in 10 ml Ca, Mg-free saline G + C. S. Allow pieces to settle out again, discard supernatant, and replace supernatant with 5ml 0.1 percent EDTA plus 2 percent chicken serum (pH 7.8).

9. Stopper tightly and incubate 30 minutes at 37°C. Change solution, swirl tube gently by hand, and return to incubator for 30 minutes longer.

10. Remove as much EDTA as possible without disturbing dissociating pieces, and add 5 ml cool (about 12°–15°C) culture medium without embryo extract. Swirl on a Vortex Jr. mixer 5 seconds or until dissociated (no more than 20 seconds).

11. Dilute with 1–2 ml medium, and filter slowly through 8–10 layers #20 Nitex monofilament screen cloth, thoroughly moistened before use with Saline G. Keep cells cool (about 15°C) to help prevent reaggregation.

12. Count number of cells in a hemocytometer, and make appropriate dilutions in culture medium *without* embryo extract.

13. Plate out into 3 ml complete culture medium in 60-mm plastic tissue culture dishes or 10 ml medium in 100-mm dishes at the following suggested concentrations per dish:

For monolayer mass cultures: 10^5–10^6 cells per 60-mm dish.

For clones: 10^4, 10^3, and 100 cells per 60-mm dish.

The total number of cells should be pipetted into each dish in a total volume of 0.1–0.5 ml medium. Pipette aliquots slowly into dish. Distribute cells evenly over the surface of the plate by gently swirling the dish alternately back and forth and around in a circle.

14. Feed clonal cultures every other day, mass cultures more often. At the first two feedings, add 2 ml fresh medium (5 ml if 100-mm plates are used), and thereafter remove 2 ml (5 ml) and replace with 2 ml (5ml) fresh medium.

15. Plating efficiencies of approximately 1–5 percent can be expected from primary cultures, if one counts only darkly pigmented clones.

C. Modifications for Clonal Subculture

1. Choose clone to be cultured.

2. Tease clone off plate with tygon spatula (see p. 507 and Fig. 3). Clone may be loosened briefly in 0.05 percent trypsin in 2 percent chicken serum before scraping.

Dissociation in "penicylinders" (see p. 506) is not necessary for transfer of very compact black clones, but is recommended for lightly pigmented or nonpigmented clones.

3. Transfer clone gently to 15 ml conical centrifuge tube.

4. Rinse once or twice with Ca, Mg-free Saline G (3–5 ml per rinse). Rinse once with 0.1 percent EDTA + C. S., pH 7.8. Stopper tightly and incubate at 37°C, 45 minutes to 1 hour in 1 ml EDTA solution. After 20–30 minutes incubation replace about half the solution, and mix gently by swirling with finger.

5. Remove as much EDTA as possible, add 1 to 1.5 ml cool culture medium without EE, and swirl 5–10 seconds in centrifuge tube on Vortex Jr. mixer.

6. Make hemocytometer counts if cell concentration is high enough. Filter through Nitex cloth if volume and cell concentration are high enough (see Protocols for primary cultures).

7. Make appropriate dilutions and plate out in fresh medium.

8. For full discussion of general procedures for clonal transfer, see p. 505.

D. General Comments

1. For a full discussion of the results to be expected from such cultures of pigmented retina, see Cahn and Cahn, 1966.

2. The culture medium suggested above will probably not permit maximum differentiation of pigment cell clones. The effect of EE_{50} fractions is dramatic in this respect. For maximum pigmentation in clones, medium F10 L-2 (see Appendix 3) is suggested; for maximum growth rate, medium H-2 (see Appendix 3) is recommended (see Coon and Cahn, 1966).

PROTOCOL II. 6-DAY HEART CELLS

A. Solutions

1. Saline G, Ca, Mg-free Saline G + C. S., and Hanks' (see Protocol I).

2. Trypsin-pancreatin for heart (0.2 percent T, 0.1 percent P). Dilute 2 percent T, 1 percent P (see Protocol I) stock solution 10-fold with Ca, Mg-free Saline G. Just before use, add 2 percent C. S. and readjust pH to 7.6, if necessary.

3. Collagenase stock solution for heart and cartilage dissociation: Dissolve 0.5 gm collagenase (Worthington CLS, Freehold, N.J.) in 100 ml Ca, Mg-free Sal G; dialyze for 2 hours at 4°C against 2 liters Ca, Mg-free Sal G., pH 7.4; adjust to pH 7.4, if necessary; filter-sterilize under pressure; and store in aliquots at liquid nitrogen temperatures. Just before use, add Ca and Mg to the normal Saline G concentrations, and check pH.

4. Culture medium (see Protocol I)
   a. Same as suggested in Protocol I, but with one-fifth the normal amount of KCl in the F10 component, and with no KCl in the Hanks'. This reduction in K^+ concentration supports better maintenance of beating in culture.
   b. Mass cultures are probably better maintained by a medium using Puck's N-16.

B. Procedure

1. Remove embryos from 20 to 30 eggs and immerse in Saline G.

2. Remove ventral aorta and aortic arches, transfer to Ca, Mg-free Saline G + C. S. and cut with iridectomy knives into small pieces 0.5–1 mm in diameter.

3. Wash through several changes of Ca, Mg-free Sal G in a 40-ml centrifuge tube to remove as many blood cells as possible.

4. Transfer washed pieces to a stoppered 25-ml Erlenmeyer flask containing 10 ml dissociation medium (0.2 percent T, 0.1 percent P; or 0.5 percent C) prewarmed to 37°C. Incubate without agitation 10–15 minutes in 0.2 percent T-0.1 percent P

(20–30 minutes if 0.5 percent C is used) at 37°C.

5. Discard supernatant, add fresh 0.2 percent T–0.1 percent P, pipette gently a few times with a 10-ml serological pipette, and return to incubator for an additional 10–15 minutes (20–30 minutes if 0.5 percent C is used).

6. Decant and discard the supernatant, and replace with 5–10 ml cool (15°–18°C) culture medium without embryo extract. Complete the dissociation by pipetting gently up and down 10–20 times with a 10-ml serological pipette.

7. Transfer to a 15-ml conical centrifuge tube and centrifuge at 100–200 *g* (approximately 750 rpm in an International clinical centrifuge) for 4 minutes.

8. Decant and discard the supernatant, and replace with about 5 ml cool culture medium.

9. Resuspend and filter entire suspension through 4–6 layers Nitex monofilament screen cloth No. 53 into a small bottle or tube. Take aliquots for counting, gas the bottle with 5–7 percent CO_2 in air, stopper tightly, and keep cool until ready to plate.

10. Plate according to the general directions in Protocol I.

C. General Comments

1. Using the above procedure for initiation of primary mass cultures, a confluent monolayer of cells can be expected within 2–5 days. This monolayer will include many centers from which rhythmic beating will radiate. This beating may fade out after about 1 week in culture in this growth medium. Other media, containing 20 30 percent serum and no embryo extract (Cahn, 1964a; Harary *et al.*, 1963; Harary and Kuramitsu, 1964; Smith and Berndt, 1964), are employed when higher percentages of beating cells are desired.

2. If a primary cell suspension is plated at cloning concentrations or at intermediate concentrations at which the individual cells do not touch one another until after at least 1 week of growth, about 20–40 percent of the cells can be observed to beat initially; many more appear to be morphologically identical to the beating cells, especially if embryo extract* is excluded from the medium, or if conditioned medium is employed. If such single beating cells are ringed with "penicylinders" and allowed to grow, they are occasionally observed to form a very small clone of beating cells. In this laboratory, such a clone was on one occasion seen to grow into a beating clone of approximately 500–1,000 cells. Work is in progress to determine the variables in the culture medium which may allow prolonged beating by clones. The EE_{50} G-25 fractions seem to have little effect (Cahn, 1964a, b; Harary *et al.*, 1963).

PROTOCOL III. 13- TO 15-DAY STERNUM

The sternum of the 13- to 15-day chick embryo is a particularly convenient source of mature functional chondrocytes. Fifteen-day sterna yield 2–3 × 10^6 viable chondrocytes each. Often primary platings reveal fewer than 0.1 percent fibroblast-like (non-chondrocyte) colonies (see Coon, 1966). Very good single cell suspensions are routinely obtained (0.1–0.01 percent adhering cells—doubles).

A. Solutions

1. Tyrode's solution and Ca, Mg-free Tyrode's solution (or the Saline G equivalents).

2. Culture medium: F10 L-7 (G-25), H-1(G-25), H.I.(G-150), or H 0.1 (see Appendix 3).

* The high K^+ in embryo extract, as well as other (possibly high molecular weight) components, inhibits beating.

3. Chick serum, trypsin, collagenase (T-C):

For dissociations, final concentrations of: 10 percent chicken serum in Ca, Mg-free Tyrode's solution; 0.1–0.2 percent trypsin (NBC 1:300); 2 mg per milliliter collagenase (Worthington: CLS)—dialyzed pH 7.6 (see Protocol I).

B. Procedure

1. Crack 13- to 15-day eggs into sterile Petri dishes. The membranes are removed with sterile forceps and the chick set up on its back (in carving position). The breast is cut free with sterile scissors and transferred to a dish of sterile Tyrode's solution.

2. Using watchmaker's forceps (No. 5) the skin is peeled away leaving the pectoral muscles exposed. The muscle and much of the perichondrial layer will come away very neatly if it is pulled toward the base of the sternum, starting at the posterior (pointed) end. The peritoneum is similarly removed. Any adhering fragments of diffuse tissue at the edges of projections should be removed with the watchmaker's forceps. Particular attention should be paid to cleaning the apex of the keel itself—often a strip of perichondrial material can be removed along its entire length with a single pull. The remaining whole sternum is remarkably clean of adhering "fibroblasts."

3. Whole sterna (cutting into small pieces serves only to kill a great many cells) are transferred with forceps to 25-ml Erlenmeyer flasks (not more than 5 sterna per flask) with about 4 ml of T-C dissociating solution.

4. Incubate the flask in a water bath with a reciprocating or gyrorotatory shaker moving at about 60–80 cycles per minute for 20 minutes at 37°C.

5. The flask is removed and all of the faintly turbid T-C is *discarded*, carrying with it most of the residual perichondrial material.

6. Fresh T-C, 4 ml, is added to the flask and it is returned to the shaker for another 20 minutes.

7. The solution in the flask should be very turbid after this second incubation. The remaining fragments of sternum are allowed to settle to one edge of the flask and the supernatant T-C is aspirated and placed in a 12-ml conical centrifuge tube. Fresh T-C is added to the flask and it is returned to the shaker for a final 10- to 15-minute incubation.

8. Meanwhile, the T-C with the freshly liberated chondrocytes is diluted with 6–8 ml of fresh growth medium and spun for 4 minutes at about 1,000 rpm in a clinical centrifuge. The supernatant mixture is poured off, leaving a white pellet at the bottom of the tube; 1–2 ml fresh growth medium is added and the pellet is dispersed by several 5-second bursts on a Vortex Jr. mixer.

9. Five ml cold medium is added to the contents of the dissociation flask (T-C, cells, and refractory fragments of sterna) which are pipetted vigorously, resulting in a homogeneous cell suspension. The final portion of cells may be pooled with the cells from the earlier run, diluted, centrifuged, and resuspended as described above.

10. After resuspending the washed cells in 1–2 ml of growth medium, the suspension is diluted to 10 ml with growth medium and filtered through 4–6 layers of 20 μ Nitex in order to remove any remaining fragments of undigested matrix.

11. The filtered suspension is counted, diluted, and plated at 500–800 cells per 100-mm dish in 6–10 ml medium.

C. General Comments

1. Clonal platings from primary sternal cell suspensions typically show plating efficiencies of 50–90 percent in media L-7 and H-1(G-25), and H.I. (G-150) (see Appendix 3). Primary platings of sternal chondrocytes usually show a rather

prolonged lag period (2–5 days) in L-media; a rather short lag (1–2 days) in H or H.I. media.

2. The feeding schedules vary with cell density and with inoculum size. For clonal plates (starting with 6 ml medium per 100-mm dish) it usually suffices to add 5 ml fresh medium on day 3 and to remove 5 ml of the spent medium and add 5 ml fresh medium on days 6 and 9; thereafter, it is best to replace the medium entirely every second or third day with 10 ml fresh medium. This feeding schedule is designed to conserve medium; for optimal growth rates, a complete change with 10 ml medium may be made daily. Mass cultures sown at 10^5 or 10^6 cells per 100-mm plate should be fed by effecting a complete change of 10 ml medium on days 2, 4, 6, and then daily up to about $2–5 \times 10^7$ cells per 100-mm plate.

3. Mass cultures of passed chondrocytes (log phase cells) fail to deposit significant amounts of stainable metachromatic matrix or to incorporate autoradiographically detectable quantities of $S^{35}O_4$ greater than that incorporated by choroidal fibroblasts when the cultures are inoculated at densities greater than about 5×10^5 cells per 100-mm plate per 10 ml medium (Cahn and Lasher, 1967). Even cultures sown at clonal densities (10^3 cells per plate) will lose detectable evidence of cartilage cell function in proportion to the concentration of high molecular weight components of chicken embryo extract (Coon, 1966; Coon and Cahn, 1966).

4. Because of the finding (Coon, 1966) that primary cultures of chondrocytes may contain 0.1–2.0 percent nonfunctional (fibroblast-like) colony formers which have an initially much faster growth rate than do the typical chondrocytes, it is best to make a population of pooled cartilage-making colonies after clonal cultures have grown up to about 1,000 cells each, if the presence of up to 50 percent contaminating fibroblast-like cells might adversely affect the experiment in question. Periodic clonal sampling of supposed chondrocyte populations is advisable in order to be sure that a very small proportion of contaminating fibroblast cells has not overgrown the culture. Primary plates sown at $1–5 \times 10^4$ cells per 100-mm plate show very clear evidence of randomly scattered, very rapidly growing, fibroblast-like colonies against a background of minute chondrocyte colonies within 7–9 days' growth. A pooled cartilage-making colony population does not exhibit such evidence of contamination.

D. Modifications for Limb Cartilage (5- to 7-Day Chick)

All procedures and solutions are the same as for 13- to 15-day sternum, except:

1. In order to avoid the centers of ossification which appear after the eighth day of incubation 5- to 7-day leg and wing long bones are used. The long bones may be teased away from the soft tissue with watchmaker's forceps.

2. Because of the complicated shape of the heads of the bone rudiments and because of the adhering tendons (especially at the knee and elbow) these cartilages require more stringent cleaning procedures. Incubate whole rudiments in Ca, Mg-free Tyrode's solution at room temperature for 10–15 minutes. Place the rudiments in a test tube with 1–2 ml of T-C and incubate for 5 minutes (without shaking). Remove the tube and swirl the rudiments in the T-C on a Vortex Jr. mixer. Allow the rudiments to settle, aspirate and discard the supernatant T-C, and replace with fresh T-C. Repeat this cleaning regime until no adhering tendons or perichondrial material are seen, but stop before rudiments themselves start falling apart (two incubations should be enough).

3. Proceed with step 6 in Protocol III.

4. In all other particulars the cartilage

cells from the limb long bone rudiments behave as do the sternal chondrocytes. Usually one may expect higher levels of initial "fibroblast-like" contamination than is found with sternal cell preparations.

PROTOCOL IV. 11-DAY SKELETAL MUSCLE (PREPARED BY I. R. KONIGSBERG)

A. Solutions

1. Saline G (see Protocol I): a phosphate buffered balanced salt solution from which bicarbonate has been omitted so that it may be used in a normal atmosphere.

2. Trypsin: 0.05 percent (NBC 1:300) in Saline G. (Saline G contains calcium and magnesium. The presence of these divalent cations does not interfere with the dissociation of this tissue).

In practice a stock solution of 0.5 percent trypsin adjusted to pH 7.4 in Saline G is kept frozen (at −60°C) in small aliquots. An aliquot is thawed, diluted, and brought to 36°C immediately before use.

3. Growth medium (for use with a collagen substratum; Hauschka and Konigsberg, 1966; Konigsberg and Hauschka, 1965).

79 parts	F-10 (Ham's)
15 parts	Horse serum (pretested; see paragraph 4 below)
5 parts	Embryo extract (H.I. may be substituted)
1 part	Antibiotic stock (10,000 units Penicillin G, Na, and 0.5 mg streptomycin sulfate per milliliter)
0.25 parts	Fungicide stock [0.8 mg Amphotericin B (Grand Island Biological Co.) per milliliter]

4. *Only 1 out of 15–20 horse sera will support myogenesis even on a collagen or gelatin substratum* (*Kaighn* et al., *1966; Cahn, unpublished*). Horse sera must be screened carefully before use to determine their suitability for muscle cell cloning experiments.

5. Embryo extract. Embryos of 12 days of incubation are used. Eyes and forebrains are discarded and body cavity laid open. Embryos are washed free of blood with several changes of Pannett-Compton's solution (Pannett and Compton, 1934) (chilled), and minced in a Latapie mincer (constructed of Lucite except for blades) with an equal volume (per weight of embryos) of Pannett-Compton's solution. Four milligrams of hyaluronidase (Worthington crystalline) is added per 100 gm of embryos and the mince extracted for 1 hour at 5°C. The extract is clarified by centrifugation at 40,000 *g* for 3 hours and passed through a fiber glass prefilter and graded series of Millipore filter membranes, the final filter having a pore size of 0.45 μ. The extract is stored at −60°C.

B. Procedure

1. Seat egg, air chamber up, in egg cup. Wipe with cotton dipped in 70 percent alcohol. (Alcohol cleans but does not thoroughly sterilize the shell when applied for this brief period. *Regard shell and fragments as unsterile.*)

2. Cut a circular hole approximately 1 inch in diameter into the egg and push the cap of shell aside. (Puncture shell with one point of scissors and make small cuts around the circumference of hole.)

3. Cut through the chorioallantoic membrane and grasp embryo (both legs, if possible) below knee joint with forceps. (You may have to search around for the embryo. If so, avoid puncturing the yolk sac.) Lift embryo part way out of egg and cut umbilicus. Decapitate embryo and transfer to a 100-mm Petri plate.

4. Spread the embryo on the dish, dorsal surface up. Cut the skin by drawing the point of the closed scissors along the spinal column. Push back the skin with the edge of the closed scissors. Turn embryo over and cut skin along ventral line of attachment of the leg to the body wall. The skin can now be rolled down below the knee joint. Sever leg as close to the ischial crest as possible, cut joint, and transfer the tibial and thigh portions of the leg to a 5-cm Pyrex Petri plate.

5. After collecting three pairs of legs, remove muscle from bone with a scalpel (Bard-Parker blade No. 10) using the blade to scrape rather than cut. Discard bones. Using a fresh pair of sharp curved scissors mince muscle thoroughly until it is reduced to a homogeneous "soup."

6. Add trypsin (5 cc at a time) and transfer mince to a 50-ml Erlenmeyer flask (use final volume of 20 cc). Pipette mince up and down several times to separate clumps and incubate flask in a water bath at 36°C for 10 minutes. Swirl flask vigorously in water bath. During incubation remove flask once or twice and pipette contents (fairly vigorously) to disperse cells.

7. Pipette tissue once more at the end of the 10-minute incubation period and add an equal volume of chilled (refrigerator temperature) growth medium. Mix with cell suspension by pipetting. Keep suspension cool until final plating to prevent cell aggregation.

8. Transfer cell suspension to gauze filter (1 layer 90–120 mesh cheesecloth). After suspension has filtered through the gauze, remove the filter tube and stopper and cover tube with a piece of sterile aluminum foil.

9. Pack cells by centrifugation at 700 rpm for 5 minutes. Aspirate the supernatant and add about 20 cc of growth medium. With a long spinal tap needle mounted on a 2-cc syringe, slowly suck up the packed cells and transfer to a 12-ml tube. (*If possible*, avoid taking up the erythrocytes which pack separately below the cell pellet.)

10. Resuspend the pelleted cells in about 5–6 cc of growth medium by drawing them up into the syringe and expelling. Repeat several times.

11. Filter suspension through a bolting-silk filter or Nitex (4 layers #53). Wash filter with small amounts of growth medium bringing the total volume to 10 cc. Remove filter tube and cap suspension with foil.

12. Thoroughly mix cell suspension (by swirling tube) before drawing off (with white cell pipette) a sample for counting. Load counting chamber and enumerate cells per milliliter.

13. Make serial dilutions of an appropriate aliquot of the cell suspension to a convenient working concentration and pipette aliquots of this dilute suspension into Petri plates containing 2 ml of growth medium. The serial dilution is performed in tubes containing measured quantities of growth medium set up prior to beginning the dissection and chilled in the refrigerator before use. Petri plates are also labeled, filled, and kept in the incubator for equilibration (approximately 2 hours before use).

14. Work rapidly. Total time (using three embryos) should be about $1\frac{1}{4}$ hours or less.

PROTOCOL V. SOME EARLY EMBRYONIC CELLS

A. General Comments

Methods, still unpublished for the most part, are becoming available for the clonal culture of certain of the "undifferentiated" mesoblast cells of the chick embryo. Limb bud cells from $2\frac{1}{2}$- to $3\frac{1}{2}$-day embryos have been cloned with some success (Coon, 1964). Characteristically, 3 percent of the colonies derived from $3\frac{1}{2}$-day chick wing buds formed cartilage; in muscle-conditioned medium (Konigsberg, 1963) cartilage formation was reduced to less than 1 percent but about 3 percent of the colonies formed multinucleate muscle straps. Most frequently in "floater" conditioned medium (see below) about 7 percent of the colonies became pigmented. Possibly these pigment cell colonies were derived from the neural crest elements which have migrated into the limb buds by the third day of incubation. The remaining 90 percent of the colonies were unrecognizable except as simple "fibroblast-like" colonies.

Techniques for handling the early embryonic cells are still being developed and are far less well worked out than the techniques described above for the clearly differentiated cells from more mature embryonic tissue. Nevertheless, we feel justified in including what little information is available to us now because of the great potential interest students of development may have in clonal culture of cells from the undifferentiated embryonic mesoblasts.

Plating efficiencies of approximately 10 percent for primary clonings of stages 20–22 (Hamburger and Hamilton) limb buds have been made reproducibly both with conditioned medium and with certain of the media supplemented with Sephadex fractions of embryo extract. Unlike the chondrocytes from 5- to 7-day limbs, the limb bud mesoblast cells do not clone with plating efficiencies greater than about 0.1 percent in L-containing media. Substances in the high molecular weight fractions of embryo extract appear to be required. The best results to date have been obtained with the heat-inactivated (65°C for 10 minutes) Sephadex G-100 and G-150 excluded fractions of whole EE_{50} (see Appendix 3). Alternate procedures involving either conditioned medium or a period of culture adaptation in mass cultures before subculture at cloning densities have also been employed successfully. Our experience with each of these techniques has been limited primarily to limb bud mesenchyme; however, some success has also been achieved with somite mesoderm (stages 19–22) and heart muscle (stages 19–23). The procedures described below refer to limb bud tissues specifically; however, other tissues may respond after only slight modifications such as the use of EDTA (50–100 mg per 100 ml T-C) to assist the dissociation of the more epithelial cell types from the somites and the mesonephros.

B. Solutions

1. Solutions listed in the protocol for sternal cartilage cells.
2. Growth media: especially Ham's medium F12 supplemented with 5–7 percent heat-inactivated H from Sephadex G-25 or G-100 and G-150 (see medium H.I. listed in Appendix 3).
3. Modified T-C: 0.4 percent trypsin, 0.75 mg per milliliter collagenase, 5 percent chicken serum in Ca, Mg-free Tyrode's solution.

C. Procedure for Stages 20–23 Limb Bud Mesoblasts (Modified from the Procedure of Zwilling, 1964)

1. Fertile eggs incubated for $3\frac{1}{2}$ days are cracked open into sterile Petri dishes. The embryos are removed from the yolk mass with sterile forceps and placed in dishes of Tyrode's solution. The wing and leg buds are cut free of the body wall with fine iridectomy knives or with iridectomy scissors.
2. It is best to keep the wings separate from the legs because of the curious fact that the cells of the wing buds make better clonal cultures than do those from the leg buds of the same age. In some experiments

the difference in plating efficiency may be as high as a factor of 10. About 24 limb buds are transferred to a 60-mm Petri dish containing Ca, Mg-free Tyrode's solution for 5–10 minutes at room temperature. (Caution: be sure that the pipette has been wetted with saline solution before attempting to transfer tissue.) The limb buds are transferred to a new dish containing T-C and incubated at 37°C for 25–35 minutes (or until the ectodermal jackets have become shrunken and puckered leaving a clear separation between the ectoderm and the apex of the mesoblast).

3. With the dissecting microscope at about 20 ×, a fine iridectomy knife is insinuated between the ectodermal jacket and the coherent mesoblast while a second knife is used to tease the mesoblast and the ectoderm apart.

4. Discard the freed ectodermal jackets and return the nude mesoblasts to the incubator for a second 20- to 30-minute incubation. At the end of the second incubation the mesoblasts should appear somewhat swollen and noticeably more flaccid than when the ectoderms were removed. Ideally, the mesoblasts are coherent enough to be pipetted, without falling apart, with 2- to 3-mm bore Pasteur transfer pipettes.

5. Carefully pipette the mesoblasts (carrying over a minimum of T-C) to a 12-ml conical centrifuge tube already filled with 10 ml of fresh growth medium. Centrifuge the mesoblasts into a pellet (about 2 minutes at 400 rpm) and decant the supernatant medium and T-C.

6. Add 1–2 ml growth medium (preferably without embryo extract in order to discourage rapid reaggregation) and suspend the cells by swirling on a Vortex Jr. mixer using 1 or 2 bursts of about 10 seconds duration.

7. The cells should have formed a good single cell suspension which may be diluted, filtered, counted, and plated as described in Protocol III. (Expect about 2.5×10^5 cells per limb bud.) In the event that there are many large chunks of adhering cells it is probable that longer trypsinization is needed. Generally speaking it is not wise to prolong swirling on the Vortex mixer in order to try to disperse such adherent masses, as prolonged swirling leads to cell lysis. Filter them out or start over again with longer digestions in T-C. If masses of "gel" form it will be necessary to add 0.1–0.2 percent pancreatin to the T-C mixture.

8. Mass cultures are prepared by sowing $1–5 \times 10^6$ cells per 100-mm plate per 10 ml medium. The incubator temperature should be set at 36.5°C. Clonal cultures are initiated by sowing $1–5 \times 10^3$ cells per 100-mm dish per 10 ml conditioned medium or 5 percent H.I. (G-150) medium.

D. Details of a Procedure for "Floater" Cell Cloning of Mesoblast Cells

1. After 24–48 hours' culture at 36.5°C the floaters (see p. 506 in text) are removed aseptically with their conditioned medium. With limb bud mesoblast cultures in these media the floater population consists almost entirely of single cells. The few groups of adhering cells may be removed by filtration through 2–4 layers of 20 μ Nitex filter cloth (see previous protocols). Because the filtered suspension contains the cell debris from the mass culture as well as the floater cells it is usually necessary to perform the "eosin exclusion test" (Hanks and Wallace, 1958) to make a "viable" cell count of samples from the floater medium: 0.5 ml of the filtered floater cell suspension is transferred to a test tube and 0.1 ml of a 0.5 percent solution of Eosin Y in Tyrode's solution is added with mixing. The tube is incubated at room temperature for 2–5 minutes. Samples of the dyed solution are examined

in hemocytometers and only those cells which exclude the dye (they usually appear greenish against a pink background) are counted.

2. Based on the counts of "viable" cells, dilutions are made with fresh or conditioned medium (floater medium from which the debris has been cleared by centrifugation and/or Millipore filtration). If possible the cells are plated at 1–5 × 10^3 per 100 mm plate in 6–10 ml medium with not more than 50 percent fresh growth medium. Each of the media listed above has been used successfully with this procedure. The highest plating efficiencies (10–25 percent) have been achieved in media supplemented with 5 percent whole EE_{50}, 5 percent H (G-25), and 5 percent H.I. (G-150).

3. Feeding schedules are the same as for the sternal cartilage cells listed in Protocol III. However, if undiluted conditioned medium is used, a complete medium change every third day is advisable.

APPENDIX 2

Preparation and Use of Conditioned Medium

The following procedure is outlined for use with limb bud mesenchyme. It has been used with slight modification for cloning of 6-day heart cells (see Protocol II, Appendix 1) and 11-day striated muscle, and probably could be successfully applied to other cell types as well.

With special reference to limb bud mesenchyme, short 2- to 3-day conditioning periods described below appear to be optimal for these early embryonic cells, possibly because they excrete large quantities of ammonia into the medium.

1. Replicate cultures of the desired cell type (e.g., stage 22 limb bud mesoblasts) are set up at 3–5 × 10^6 cells per 100-mm plate per 10 ml fresh growth medium. These plates are cultured for 12–24 hours at 36.5°C and then either all of the medium is removed and 20 ml of fresh growth medium is added, or 10 ml fresh growth medium is added to the original supply resulting in a total of 20 ml in each dish. (Equal plating efficiencies from limb bud mesenchyme result from the two regimens.) The cultures are returned to the incubator for 48–72 hours of growth.

2. The medium is removed aseptically and usually centrifuged free of debris (20 minutes at top speed in a clinical centrifuge) and then filtered by pressure through a GS Millipore filter. This medium may be stored in the refrigerator at 0°–2°C for 2 weeks. Usually it is desirable to use 5 percent CO_2 in air for the pressure filtration, and the bottles of filtered medium should be "gassed" with 5 percent CO_2 in order to prevent the pH from rising above 7.6–7.8 during storage.

Freshly suspended cells or cells removed from existing monolayer cultures may then be sown into 100-mm dishes with 10 ml conditioned medium, or dishes with 5 ml conditioned medium plus 5 ml fresh growth medium. Feeding is accomplished by complete change of the conditioned medium for the first two or three feedings (days 3, 6, 9); thereafter, feeding with fresh medium alone may suffice to support the rapidly growing colonies. Plating efficiencies of 5–25 percent can be anticipated.

4. Especially with media which support slower growth rates (e.g., L-containing media and media without any EE), a

second round of conditioned medium may be obtained from the same mass culture plates. After removing the medium in step 2 above, add 20–25 ml fresh growth medium and return the plates to the incubator for 24–48 hours. Further use of the cells in the original mass culture plates is not advisable because of the very high cell densities reached in the dishes. It is best to subdivide the cultures and start afresh with plates sown at 1–3 × 10^6 cells per plate in 20 ml growth medium. A lower initial inoculum is used because there will be a shorter lag period between passages than occurred with the primary cultures.

5. Pitfalls: Resist the temptation to disregard the Millipore filtration of freshly harvested conditioned medium. Surprisingly, a few cells remain in the supernatant solution after centrifugation (or are stirred up from the pellet when medium is decanted). A few cartilage cells have been found to survive overnight storage in conditioned medium in the refrigerator at 2–4°C. Furthermore, filtration through a GS Millipore should reduce the possibility of carrying PPLO contaminants (Whitelock, 1960) from one culture to another. Since the bacteriostatic action of penicillin and streptomycin decreases even during the first 24 hours of culture with any medium, fresh concentrates of the antibiotics may be added to the conditioned medium prior to sterile filtration.

APPENDIX 3

Preparation of Sephadex Fractions of Embryo Extract

I. PREPARATION OF EMBRYO EXTRACT

1. Whole 9-day embryos are collected aseptically in a glass Osterizer (John Oster Mfg. Co., Milwaukee, Wisc.) homogenizer container at 0°C. Blood which drains out of the embryos during the collection period is removed with a pipette. The embryos are weighed, and an equal volume of modified Hanks' solution (see Appendix 1, Protocol I) containing 10–20 μg of phenol red per milliliter is added to the container. The mixture is then minced in the Osterizer at top speed for 40–60 seconds.

2. The blended mixture is then spun 30 minutes at 34,000 *g* in a Sorvall refrigerated centrifuge. The supernatant is decanted, 0.25 mg hyaluronidase (Nutritional Biochemicals, Type III) per 100 ml is added, and the mixture is stirred for 1 hour at 0°–5°C. It is then centrifuged for 150,000 *g*-hours in a preparative ultracentrifuge.

3. The lipid layer and pellet are discarded, the resulting "whole embryo extract" is stored overnight at 0°–2°C and then fractionated.

II. FRACTIONATION ON SEPHADEX G-25

A. Fractionation

1. A 2.5-cm × 80-cm column packed with Sephadex G-25, coarse, bead form (Pharmacia Fine Chemicals, Piscataway, N.J.), is prepared and washed with Hanks' solution without phenol red, pH 7.4; 80–100 ml whole embryo extract is applied to the column and eluted with modified Hanks' without phenol red at 4°C at a flow rate of 6–10 ml per minute. The excluded fraction (H) which comes off the column first, includes molecules larger

than approximately 10,000 molecular weight, and is tracked on the column by the presence of hemoglobin within it. Fraction L (retarded fraction) immediately follows the H fraction and is collected until phenol red first appears in the eluate. (Phenol red, tyrosine, phenylalanine, and tryptophan lag behind the L front, and are included in the phenol red fraction.)

2. The H and L fractions are filter-sterilized under pressure through a graded series of Millipore filters (minimum pore size 0.45 μ) and are either made up directly into medium or are frozen in aliquots in a liquid nitrogen refrigerator.

B. Preparation of Media

The medium in which H and L fractions are incorporated is described in Protocol I. In calculating appropriate amounts of H and L to be added, the dilution which occurs on the column must be accounted for. If 100 ml whole EE_{50} is fractionated, approximately 200 ml of fraction H and 400 ml of fraction L will usually be collected. Percentages of H and L in culture medium refer to equivalent volumes of whole embryo extract. Thus, 5 percent L medium (L-5) will actually contain 20 ml fraction L. Formulae for 100 ml of two media frequently used in these laboratories are:

	H-2	L-2
F10 (with 4 × amino acids and 2 × vitamins)	50 ml	50 ml
Hanks' (modified)	41 ml	37 ml
Fetal calf serum	5 ml	5 ml
Bovine serum albumin	0.5 gm	0.5 gm
EE_{50} fraction H or L (assuming 1:2 and 1:4 dilution on the column)	4 ml (H)	8 ml (L)
Penicillin G	50 units per ml	50 units per ml
Streptomycin sulfate	25 units per ml	25 units per ml
Extra bicarbonate (if 6–7 percent CO_2 in air is used)	0.1 gm	0.1 gm
Extra water	0.5 ml	0.5 ml

III. FRACTIONATION ON SEPHADEX G-150

A. General Comments

While attempting to characterize the components in the high molecular weight (H) fractions of EE_{50} which are responsible for inhibiting the expression of differentiation in cartilage and pigmented retina cells (Cahn, 1966; Coon, 1966; Coon and Cahn, 1966), it was found that these substances are heat labile. Heat treatment of the Sephadex G-100- and G-150-excluded subfractions of H for 10 minutes at 65°C left material which, when added to media, gave high plating efficiencies and permitted expression of differentiated function equivalent to that seen in media without EE_{50} or including the L (low molecular weight EE_{50}) fractions (Coon and Cahn, 1966). The knowledge that certain cells (mouse cartilage cells, early stages of chick limb bud, and somite cells) required components of EE_{50} not present in L prompted testing of heat-inactivated G-150-excluded EE_{50} fractions as additives to cloning media for the direct clonal plating of these cell types. Our preliminary results have been encouraging, resulting in primary clonal plating efficiencies of 10 percent.

B. Fractionation—Preparation of the Excluded Fraction

1. Add 25 mg of Dextran Blue 2000 and 0.3 ml of a 0.25 percent solution of phenol red to 100 ml whole EE_{50} or to the G-25-excluded H fraction of whole EE_{50}.

2. Place 100 ml of the embryo extract with the dyes on a column 8 × 40 cm of Sephadex G-150 (equilibrated with Hanks' solution without phenol red).

3. After the sample has entered the column, it is eluted with Hanks' solution without phenol red. The columns may be run at 2°–4°C or at room temperature with flow rates of approximately 3 ml per minute. After a distance of 20 cm on the column has been traversed, the sample has separated into three distinct bands. The leading band is weakly bound to the column. By the time the blue fraction is about to emerge from the column, a colorless or faintly blue gap approximately equal to the width of the blue band itself appears between the hemoglobin and the excluded Dextran Blue fraction.

4. The eluate containing the Dextran Blue is collected (the very faint blue tinted trailing material is ignored—the sample usually emerges in approximately 1.5 times the original sample volume).

5. The fraction containing the Dextran Blue-2000 dye marker (which has not been found to be toxic in cloning media) is heat-inactivated by placing it in a prescription bottle and heating the bottle in a beaker of water over a Bunsen flame until the contents of the bottle reach 62°–65°C. The bottle is removed from the boiling water and maintained at 62°–65°C for 10 minutes. At the end of the 10 minutes the bottle is cooled in a low beaker with running tap water.

6. A fine, opalescent precipitate is formed during the heating. This precipitate is largely removed by centrifugation for 40 minutes at 34,000 *g*. The cleared solution is decanted and stored in the refrigerator until it is incorporated into medium.

C. Preparation of Medium

The heat-inactivated G-150-excluded fraction of embryo extract is incorporated at 5 percent (equivalent of whole EE_{50} concentration) into medium with fetal calf serum at 5 percent and bovine serum albumin powder (Armour fraction V) at 0.5 percent. An example of such a medium designated simply "H.I. medium," follows:

5 percent H.I. medium

F10 or F12 (4 × amino acids, 2 × other components except salts)	50 ml
Fetal calf serum	5 ml
Bovine serum albumin (Armour fraction V)	0.5 gm
$NaHCO_3$ (for 6–7% CO_2: air)	0.15 gm
Na-penicillin G (Squibb) (or 30 units per milliliter)	4.0 mg
Heat-inactivated, G-150-excluded EE_{50} (5 percent equivalent—some dilution occurs on the columns)	7.3 ml
Hanks' balanced salt solution	37.7 ml
Total final volume	100 ml

The complete medium is filtered by pressure through a GS Millipore filter with Microweb prefilter. The medium is dispensed in 8-ounce prescription bottles and stored in the refrigerator at 0°–2°C for periods up to 2 weeks.

REFERENCES

CAHN, M. B., and R. D. CAHN, 1967: Manuscript in preparation.

CAHN, R. D., 1964a: Developmental changes in enzyme patterns: The effect of oxidative substrates on lactic dehydrogenase in beating chick embryonic heart cell cultures. *Dev. Biol.*, 9: 327.

———, 1964b: Maintenance of beating and dissociation of biochemical and functional differentiation in clones of chicken embryo heart cells. *J. Cell. Biol.*, 23: 17A.

———, 1967a: Detergents in membrane filters. *Science*, 155: 195.

———, 1967b: Changes in enzyme patterns in functional heart, cartilage, and pigmented retina cells in culture. In R. D. Tanz, J. Kavaler, and J. Roberts (eds.), *Factors Influencing Myocardial Contractility*, Academic Press, New York, p. 293.

———, and M. B. CAHN, 1966: Heritability of cellular differentiation: Clonal growth and expression of differentiation in retinal pigment cells *in vitro. Proc. Nat. Acad. Sci. U.S.*, 55: 106.

———, and R. Lasher, 1967: Simultaneous synthesis of DNA and specialized cellular products by differentiating cartilage cells in *vitro. Proc. Nat. Acad. Sci. U.S.*, Vol. 58, No. 3.

COON, H. G., 1964: The retention of differentiated function among clonal and subclonal progeny of precartilage and cartilage cells from chicken embryos. *J. Cell. Biol.*, 23: 20A.

———, 1966: Clonal stability and phenotypic expression of chick cartilage cells *in vitro. Proc. Nat. Acad. Sci. U.S.*, 55: 66.

———, and R. D. CAHN, 1966: Differentiation *in vitro.* Effects of Sephadex fractions of embryo extract. *Science*, 153: 1116.

EAGLE, H., 1959: Amino acid metabolism in mammalian cell cultures. *Science*, 130: 432.

———, 1965: Metabolic controls in cultured mammalian cells. *Science*, 148: 42.

———, and E. PIEZ, 1962: The population-dependent requirement by cultured mammalian cells for metabolites which they can synthesize. *J. Exp. Med.*, 116: 29.

EPHRUSSI, B., 1964: Observations on the phenotype of somatic cell hybrids. In V. Defendi (ed.), *Retention of Functional Differentiation in Cultured Cells*, Wistar Institute Press, Philadelphia, Symposium Monograph, 1: 99.

———, and H. M. TEMIN, 1960: Infection of chick iris epithelium with the Rous sarcoma virus *in vitro. Virology*, 11: 547.

———, and M. C. WEISS, 1965: Interspecific hybridization of somatic cells. *Proc. Nat. Acad. Sci. U.S.*, 53: 1040.

———, L. J. SCALETTA, M. A. STENCHEVER, and M. C. YOSHIDA, 1964: Hybridization of somatic cells *in vitro*. In R. J. C. Harris (ed.), *Cytogenetics of Cells in Culture*, Academic Press, New York.

GROBSTEIN, C., and J. COHEN, 1965: Collagenase: the effect on the morphogenesis of salivary epithelium *in vitro. Science*, 150: 626.

GROVER, J. W., 1961: The enzymatic dissociation and reproducible reaggregation *in vitro* of 11-day embryonic chick lung. *Dev. Biol.*, 3: 555.

HAM, R. G., 1963: An improved nutrient solution for diploid Chinese hamster and human cell lines. *Exp. Cell Res.*, 29: 515.

———, 1965: Clonal growth of mammalian cells in a chemically defined, synthetic medium. *Proc. Nat. Acad. Sci. U.S.*, 53: 288.

HANKS, J. H., and R. E. WALLACE, 1958: Determination of cell viability. *Proc. Soc. Exp. Biol. Med.*, 98: 188.

HARARY, I., A. FUJIMOTO, and H. KURAMITSU, 1963: Enzyme changes in cultured heart cells. *Nat. Canc. Inst. Monograph*, 13: 257.

———, and H. KURAMITSU, 1964: Studies *in vitro* on single beating rat heart cells: III. Enzyme changes and loss of specific function in culture. *Biochim. Biophys. Acta*, 86: 65.

HARRIS, H., and J. F. WATKINS, 1965: Hybrid cells derived from mouse and man: Artificial heterokaryons of mammalian cells from different species. *Nature*, 205: 640.

———, ———, C. E. FORD, and G. I. SCHOEFL, 1966: Artificial heterokaryons of animal cells from different species. *J. Cell Science*, 1: 1.

HARRIS, M., 1964: *Cell Culture and Somatic Variation.* Holt, Rinehart, and Winston, Inc., New York.

HAUSCHKA, S. D., and I. R. KONIGSBERG, 1966: The influence of collagen on the development of muscle clones. *Proc. Nat. Acad. Sci. U.S.*, 55: 119.

HILFER, S. R., 1962: The stability of embryonic chick thyroid cells *in vitro* as judged by morphological and physiological criteria. *Dev. Biol.*, 4: 1.

HOLTZER, H., J. ABBOTT, J. LASH, and S. HOLTZER, 1960: The loss of phenotypic traits by differentiated cells *in vitro*. I. Dedifferentiation of cartilage cells. *Proc. Nat. Acad. Sci. U.S.*, 46: 1533.

KAIGHN, M. E., J. D. EBERT, and P. M. STOTT, 1966: The susceptibility of differentiating muscle clones to Rous sarcoma virus. *Proc. Nat. Acad. Sci. U.S.*, 56: 133.

KONIGSBERG, I. R., 1961: Cellular differentiation in colonies derived from single cell platings of freshly isolated chick embryo muscle cells. *Proc. Nat. Acad. Sci. U.S.*, 47: 1868.

———, 1963: Clonal analysis of myogenesis. *Science*, 140: 1273.

———, and S. D. HAUSCHKA, 1965: Cell and tissue interactions in the reproduction of cell type. In M. Locke (ed.), *Reproduction: Molecular, Subcellular, and Cellular*, 24th Symposium of the Society for Developmental Biology, Academic Press, New York, p. 243.

KURODA, Y., 1964a: Studies on cartilage cells *in vitro*. I. Morphology and growth of cartilage cells in monolayer cultures. *Exp. Cell Res.*, 35: 326.

———, 1964b: Studies on cartilage cells *in vitro*. II. Changes in aggregation and cartilage-forming activity of cells maintained in monolayer culture. *Exp. Cell Res.*, 35: 337.

MC ILWAIN, H., and H. L. BUDDLE, 1953: Techniques in tissue metabolism. 1. A mechanical chopper. *Biochem. J.*, 53: 412.

MOSCONA, A., 1961: Rotation-mediated histogenetic aggregation of dissociated cells: A quantifiable approach to cell interactions *in vitro*. *Exp. Cell Res.*, 22: 455.

PANNETT, C. A., and A. COMPTON, 1934: The cultivation of tissues in saline embryo juice. *Lancet*, 206: 381.

PARKER, R. C., 1961: *Methods of Tissue Culture*, 3rd ed. Paul B. Hoeber, Inc., New York, p. 115.

PAUL, J., 1961: *Cell and Tissue Culture*, 2nd ed. Williams & Wilkins Co., Baltimore.

———, P. F. FOTTRELL, I. FRESHMAN, W. R. JONDORF, and M. G. STRETHERS, 1964: Regulation of enzyme synthesis in cultured cells. *Nat. Canc. Inst. Monograph*, 13: 219.

PROCKOP, D. V., O. PETTENGILL, and H. HOLTZER, 1964: Incorporation of sulfate and the synthesis of collagen by cultures of embryonic chondrocytes. *Biochim. Biophys. Acta*, 83: 189.

PUCK, T. T., S. J. CIECIURA, and A. ROBINSON, 1958: Genetics of somatic mammalian cells. III. Long-term cultivation of euploid cells from human and animal subjects. *J. Exp. Med.*, 108: 945.

———, P. I. MARCUS, and S. J. CIECIURA, 1956: Clonal growth of mammalian cells *in vitro*. Growth characteristics of colonies from single HeLa cells with and without a "feeder layer." *J. Exp. Med.*, 103: 273.

RAPPAPORT, C., and C. B. BISHOP, 1960: An improved method for treating glass to produce surfaces suitable for the growth of certain mammalian cells in synthetic medium. *Exp. Cell Res.*, 20: 465.

———, and G. B. HOWZE, 1964: Dissociation of adult mouse liver into single cell suspensions with sodium tetraphenyl boron (TPB). *Animal Newsletter*, 5: 4.

———, and ———, 1967: The dissociation of adult mouse liver by sodium tetraphenyl boron—a potassium complexing agent. *Proc. Soc. Biol. Med.*, in press.

RAWLES, M., 1963: Tissue interactions in scale and feather development as studied in dermal-epidermal recombinations. *J. Embryol. Exp. Morphol.*, 11: 765.

RINALDINI, L. M., 1958: The isolation of living cells from animal tissues. *Int. Rev. Cytol.*, 7: 587.

———, 1959: An improved method for the isolation and quantitative cultivation of embryonic cells. *Exp. Cell Res.*, 16: 477.

RUBIN, H., 1966: A substance in conditioned medium which enhances the growth of small numbers of chick embryo cells. *Exp. Cell Res.*, 41: 138.

SANFORD, K. K., W. R. EARLE, and G. D. LIKELY, 1948: The growth *in vitro* of single isolated tissue cells. *J. Nat. Canc. Inst.*, 9: 229.

SATO, G., L. ZAROFF, and S. E. MILLS, 1960: Tissue culture populations and their relation to the tissue of origin. *Proc. Nat. Acad. Sci. U.S.*, 46: 963.

SMITH, T. E., and W. O. BERNDT, 1964: Establishment of beating myocardial cells in long term culture in fluid medium. *Exp. Cell Res.*, 36: 179.

STEINBERG, M. S., 1962: The role of temperature in the control of aggregation of dissociated embryonic cells. *Exp. Cell Res.*, 28: 1.

———, 1963: "ECM": Its nature, origin and function in cell aggregation. *Exp. Cell Res.*, 30: 257.

TODARO, G. J., and H. GREEN, 1963: Quantitative studies of growth of mouse embryo cells in culture and their development into established lines. *J. Cell Biol.*, 17: 299.

WHITELOCK, O. V., St. (ed.), 1960: Biology of the pleuropneumonia-like organisms. *Ann. N.Y. Acad. Sci.*, 79: 305.

WHITTAKER, J. R., 1963: Changes in morphogenesis during the dedifferentiation of chick retinal pigment cells in cell culture. *Dev. Biol.*, 8: 99.

WILSON, B. W., and T. L. LAU, 1963: Dissociation and cultivation of chick embryo cells with an actinomycete protease. *Proc. Soc. Exp. Biol. Med.*, 114: 649.

ZWILLING, E., 1954: Dissociation of chick embryo cells by means of a chelating compound. *Science*, 120: 219.

———, 1964: Development of fragmented and dissociated limb-bud mesoblast. *Dev. Biol.*, 9: 20.

Amphibian Cell Culture, Organ Culture, and Tissue Dissociation

By Antone G. Jacobson

INTRODUCTION

Owing to the special advantages of their embryos, amphibians have been preeminent in vertebrate experimental embryology. Amphibian eggs were used in early experiments by Roux, by Spemann and his followers, and by Ross Harrison when the techniques of tissue culture were developed.

Amphibian embryos are plentiful and easily obtained, free of extraembryonic membranes, and relatively large and easy to work with. Most important, they are hardy. They survive extensive surgical manipulation, are resistant to infection, tolerate a variety of temperatures, and survive variations in ion concentration and pH. Since each cell of the amphibian embryo has an endogenous food source, cell, tissue, and organ cultures are possible in simple, defined media. An aqueous solution of a few simple salts with some minimal buffering makes a tolerable culture medium.

Techniques of amphibian experimental embryology have been developed for many years. They are described in the manuals of Hamburger (1960) and Rugh (1962), which should be consulted by anyone starting work with amphibian material.

This chapter supplements the information in those books with some more recent techniques. It explains in some detail one set of personally preferred methods for preparing amphibian embryos for operations, for excising and culturing cells, tissues, and organs, and for dissociating and reaggregating amphibian embryonic tissues.

PREPARATION OF MATERIALS

Embryos should be handled gently, and kept uncrowded, clean, and cool from the time they are collected until they are used. If laboratory tap water is not contaminated with insecticides and detergents, it can be used as a medium for rearing egg clusters. It should first be sterilized and dechlorinated by boiling for 5 minutes (longer periods may produce a precipitate) and then cooled. "Spring" water or local natural waters are available in some areas and may be suitable for rearing embryos. They should be tested first on a small number of eggs. All natural waters I have tested in central Texas are toxic for amphibian embryos, possibly because of their insecticide content. During some periods, the tap water is also toxic. The safest reproducible method is to run water through an adsorption column that removes organic compounds and then distill it using a glass still. A 10 percent Holtfreter solution made with the distilled water can be used for rearing and washing embryos.

Most amphibian embryos survive and develop best between 10° and 20°C. Bacterial growth will be less at the lower temperatures. To avoid temperature shock, place the embryos in water (or 10 percent Holtfreter solution) that differs no more than 2°C from the water in which the eggs are brought into the laboratory. Warm or cool slowly to the desired temperature. We store all embryos in covered finger bowls in constant temperature boxes kept at 10° or 17°C. With a reasonable volume of water around them, embryos may be transferred between the 10° and 17°C boxes without suffering temperature shock. Do not plunge embryos from water at one temperature into water at another. Avoid overcrowding by storing no more than 30 embryos in a 4-inch finger bowl or 80 embryos in an 8-inch finger bowl. Do not put all your eggs in one finger bowl or they may all rot together.

Batches of freshly collected embryos are often all at the same developmental stage. If they are to be used for more than one experimental session, divide them into groups of a convenient size. Put one group at 17°C and the remaining groups at 10°. By transferring the 10° groups to 17°C at appropriate intervals, the desired stages can be used at separate times. Timing must be worked out for each species.

It is not good practice to operate on embryos taken directly from the 10°C box. They should be incubated at 17°C for a few hours before operating at room temperature. We ensure that none of our embryos ever reaches room temperature by storing all experimental materials at 17°C for several hours before use. This includes washing water, media, racks, all glassware, etc. A 17°C box should be next to the operating table and materials kept out of it for the briefest period possible. It is advantageous to have a cool operating room. Duplicate sets of previously sterilized instruments are preferred to using boiling water or Bunsen burners in the operating room. Instruments can be sterilized by immersion in 70 percent ethanol for 15–30 minutes followed by thorough drying on a sterile rack. Hair loops must be sterilized by this method. Metal or glass instruments and containers may also be sterilized by autoclaving or dry-heat sterilization at 180°C for at least 1 hour. Molds are eliminated best with dry heat.

EQUIPMENT NEEDED FOR ALL OPERATIONS

The following materials are needed to wash and prepare embryos for any operation. All equipment should be prepared in advance, sterilized, and cooled to 17°C. Most glassware can be conveniently sterilized and kept sterile by wrapping in aluminum foil or kept in aluminum foil-covered enamel pans.

The numbers of items needed to process about ten embryos are given. When larger numbers of embryos are to be processed in 1 day, multiple sets of materials are needed.

Materials for Washing Embryos

1. Twelve stender dishes; diameter 26 mm and height 51 mm.

2. One wooden rack to hold stender dishes while washing embryos. The rack should be about 20 inches (51 cm) long, $2\frac{1}{4}$ inches (7 cm) wide and $\frac{3}{4}$ inch (2 cm) thick. Two wooden strips, 20 inches

(51 cm) long, $\frac{1}{2}$ inch (1.2 cm) wide, and $\frac{3}{8}$ inch (1 cm) thick should be tacked on opposite sides and opposite edges of the rack. One strip tilts the rack toward the operator; the other serves as a rim, long enough to hold eight stender dishes in a tilted position.

3. Twelve washing pipettes, 15–17 cm long. These should be made from glass tubing (outside diameter, 8.5 mm; inside diameter, 6.0 mm) with one end drawn to a smaller tip (o.d., 5.2 mm; i.d., 4.0 mm). The tapered portion should be no more than 2 cm long and should extend from the axis of the tubing at an angle of 135 degrees. Before sterilizing, plug the large end with cotton.

4. Twelve transfer pipettes. These differ from the washing pipettes only in the size of the opening at the tapered end. The opening should have an outside diameter of from 3.5 to 4.0 mm and an inside diameter of from 2.5 to 3.0 mm, depending on the size of the eggs being used. The transfer pipettes are designed to move individual embryos; the washing pipettes are for transferring 8 to 10 embryos at a time.

5. Rubber bulbs (33 mm long with a 6-mm opening) to operate the pipettes.

6. An enamel pan covered with aluminum foil as a container for autoclaving pipettes.

Materials for Operating on Embryos

1. Ten operation dishes. The manuals of Hamburger and Rugh describe various ways of making these dishes. We use the following method (Rugh, p. 11):

a. Thoroughly mix four parts of Permoplast (American Art Clay Co.) with one part of low-melting-point paraffin after melting the ingredients in a beaker in a paraffin oven.

b. Fill Syracuse watch glasses (diameter, 200 mm; depth, 10 mm) with the mixture to a depth of 3 mm.

c. When the mixture has cooled slightly, mold it around the edge of each watch glass with your thumb, so that no glass remains exposed in the concavity.

d. Draw out different-sized glass beads onto the ends of solid glass rods. The beads should be the same size and shape as the embryos to be used.

e. Use these beads to form depressions in the Permoplast-paraffin coating when it has cooled. These depressions can be made in advance of the operation and re-used.

f. Sterilize operating dishes by placing them in 70 percent ethanol for a short time (no longer than 10 minutes as the mixture slowly takes up alcohol).

g. Dry the dish upside down on sterile cheesecloth in a clean covered container for at least 10 hours to allow all alcohol to evaporate.

h. An hour or two before operating, place the operation dish upright in a sterile Petri plate and flame the surface with a bunsen burner. This puts a glaze on the surface that I believe must be mostly paraffin.

i. Immediately cover the Petri plate and place the ensemble in the 17°C box to cool before use.

j. Never allow remnants of embryos to rot in an operating dish. Immediately after use, wash the dish under running warm (not hot) water, rinse in 70 percent ethanol and dry. An hour or two in these dishes causes no discernible harm to embryos, but long periods, such as 5 or 10 hours of contact with the Permoplast-paraffin mixture is lethal. We have found all colors of Permoplast to be suitable and we use colors to identify dishes belonging to different people.

2. One pair of iridectomy scissors (two pairs if long series of operations are planned), with one fixed and one shorter movable blade. All necessary cutting can

be done with these scissors, operating the movable blade with the thumb. No iridectomy scissors are suitable as received from the various manufacturers. They must be slowly and carefully sharpened under a dissecting microscope using a fine stone and oil, so as to bring the tips to very fine points without damaging the apposing surfaces or the straight cutting edges. After sharpening, they must be handled very carefully, since properly sharpened points are ruined by contact with a hard surface. The scissors may be sterilized by immersion in 70 percent ethanol (for no more than an hour to prevent rusting). The bottom of the jar containing the alcohol should be covered with a mass of cotton wrapped carefully with cheesecloth. Be certain that all alcohol has evaporated from the scissors, or rinse them in sterile operating medium before insertion into the operating dish.

3. Two pairs of watchmaker's forceps (No. 5, stainless). Before use, these must be sharpened so that the points are very fine and the tips are exactly apposed. Most troubles encountered when removing membranes from eggs come from improperly prepared forceps. Sterilize the forceps in the same manner as the iridectomy scissors.

4. Six hair loops. Hair loops of various sizes are the most useful tools for separating germ layers and moving embryos or pieces of tissue about. Their elasticity prevents cell damage. Prepare hair loops as described by Hamburger (pp. 7–8). Beginners will probably need at least 12. Hair loops are sterilized with alcohol, so care must be taken to close the glass capillary to the tip with wax to prevent the carrying of alcohol into the operating dish. To avoid the possibility of permanently bending the hair loops, use clothes pins or other clamps to suspend them in the alcohol jar. Any sticky cell parts, which may coat the hair during use, must be carefully removed by dipping the loop in alcohol, then rubbing it between a forefinger and the edge of the little finger of the other hand. The loop should be sterilized and dried before its re-use.

5. Two instrument racks. Suitable racks that are easy to sterilize can be made from sheets of metal (20 cm long, 15 cm wide) bent into an elongated "Z" shape. One leg of the "Z" should be 1 cm high, and the other 2 cm with 7 or 8 evenly spaced "V" slots cut 1 cm deep and 1 cm wide at the top. The finished rack would then be 20 cm long and 12 cm wide. Hair loops, forceps, and scissors can be laid flat on the rack with their working ends free in the space beyond the "V" slots.

6. Boiled and cooled tap water (or 10 percent Holtfreter solution), 1,000 ml, in an Erlenmeyer flask capped with an inverted beaker. This is to be used in a small finger bowl when removing embryos from the jelly mass, and in stender dishes when washing embryos.

7. Holtfreter solution (or Niu-Twitty solution), 1,000 ml, for operating medium and for rearing isolates. Other media may be used, some being listed in Hamburger (pp. 35–36) and Rugh (pp. 15–16). The formulas for the Holtfreter and Niu-Twitty solutions are shown on page 535.

The original publication (Flickinger, 1949) and several subsequent publications cite an incorrect formula for calcium nitrate and quote use of anhydrous sodium phosphate. We have always used 110 mg of the dodecahydrate (12 H_2O) with adequate results.

Bring each solution just to a boil to sterilize it, then cool to 17°C. First make solution A in a liter flask, then just before use add solution B, and finally solution C. The $NaHCO_3$ solution should be added last to avoid precipitation of the calcium and magnesium salts. The unmixed stock solutions are good for a day or two if tightly stoppered.

Holtfreter Solution

SOLUTION A
3,500 mg NaCl
50 mg KCl
100 mg $CaCl_2$
500 ml distilled H_2O

SOLUTION B
20 mg $NaHCO_3$
500 ml distilled H_2O

Niu-Twitty Solution

SOLUTION A
3,400 mg NaCl
50 mg KCl
80 mg $Ca(NO_3)_2 \cdot 4H_2O$
100 mg $MgSO_4$
(or 204 mg $MgSO_4 \cdot 7H_2O$)
500 ml dist. H_2O

SOLUTION B
110 mg $Na_2HPO_4 \cdot 12\ H_2O$
20 mg KH_2PO_4
250 ml dist. H_2O

SOLUTION C
200 mg $NaHCO_3$
250 ml dist. H_2O

Materials for Culture

Capillary pipettes for transferring tissues should be available in large numbers since they are best discarded after each use. These pipettes, having a 10-cm handle and a 5-cm capillary drawn from one end, are made from glass tubing with an outside diameter of 5 mm. Plug the handle end with cotton before sterilizing. To ensure a clean break when making these pipettes, score the capillary with a diamond pencil or the sharp edge of a fine stone before breaking it. Capillaries with ragged ends should be rebroken or discarded. Make about 100 capillaries of various sizes at one time, then grade them into about five arbitrary class sizes.

REMOVAL OF EGG JELLY AND WASHING PROCEDURES

Removal of Jelly

Methods for removing embryos from their jelly mass vary with the species. Use two pairs of fine forceps and a pair of fine scissors; do not use operating instruments.

1. *Taricha torosa.* The firm jelly is cut into with scissors and the embryo pipetted out of its cavity with a pipette whose inside diameter is the same size as the egg.

2. *Ambystoma* spp. Individual jelly cells may be removed from the common jelly mass with forceps and scissors. Each one is then opened under water with two pairs of forceps and the embryo removed.

3. Anuran egg masses. Remove one egg with its jelly from the main mass. It can generally be opened with two pairs of forceps. Otherwise, transfer the egg from bowl to bowl of water, dissecting away and leaving some of the jelly in each bowl. In all cases, take care not to transfer pieces of the nearly transparent jelly with the eggs.

Washing Procedures

After removing all jelly coats but not vitelline membranes, the eggs are sterilized by serial washing through eight (optimal for sterilization but minimizing damage) changes of sterile tap water (or 10 percent Holtfreter solution).

Fill the stender dishes no more than half full of washing water (at 17°C) and place in a row on the wash rack. Wash a maximum of ten jelly-free eggs at one time. If hanging-drop cultures are to be made, wash only five or six eggs at a time to ensure better cleansing. Transfer the group of eggs from dish to dish with a washing pipette. The dishes should remain covered except during transfer of eggs into or out of them. Handle the eggs very gently: draw the eggs into the pipette slowly; tilt the pipette so that eggs lie in the angle; move the pipette to the next stender dish; turn the pipette so the eggs can roll out onto the uphill floor of the dish. Some eggs are damaged if dropped even a few millimeters through the water. Allow the eggs to roll to the downhill side of the dish; transfer them to the next dish using a fresh sterile pipette.

If the pipettes are rinsed with 70 percent ethanol immediately after use, no further cleaning is necessary before they are resterilized. Otherwise, mineral deposits form on the inside walls and must be carefully washed out before re-use to avoid cutting the eggs. It is advisable to keep several hundred of these pipettes cycling to avoid their number becoming a limiting factor to further operations.

When the embryos are in the last dish, place them in the 17°C box. Keep them there except when they are removed for operations. Without the jelly, the washed eggs will clump together. If the operations being done are time consuming, the number of embryos per dish should be five or less to ensure adequate oxygenation. Embryos whose vitelline membranes have been injured or removed should be used first. Otherwise, they will become stuck to the dish within an hour.

OPERATING

Choose a sterile operating dish containing depressions that are the correct size for the stage embryo being used. Small depressions near the embryo's depression are useful for temporary placement of tissue pieces. Remove the operating dish from its container and place under the dissecting microscope. The optimal dissecting microscope is the type that is mounted on the end of a long swinging arm; then the operating dish sits directly on the table. It is impractical to operate on a microscope stage. A microscope with a long horizontal arm and a long object-to-lens distance provides the working space that is needed.

Fill the operating dish with Holtfreter or Niu-Twitty solution and transfer the embryo into it. Position the embryo in a depression with a hair loop. Using two pairs of watchmaker's forceps, remove the vitelline membrane as follows: (1) Grasp the membrane with the sides of one pair of forceps. (2) Move the points of the other pair between the forceps and the egg to obtain a second hold on the membrane. (3) Pull gently in opposite directions to tear the membrane off the egg. Lift the membrane out of the dish and discard it. Vitelline membranes can rarely be seen after being released under water and will often float onto the embryo. In preneurula stages, the vitelline membrane is tightly applied to the egg and is difficult to remove without puncturing the surface of the embryo. To get a grip of the membrane, it is often feasible to deliberately puncture the embryo in an area that will not be used in the experiment. The demembranated embryo or its parts will be torn apart if brought into contact with the liquid-air interface.

When motile embryos are used, an anesthetic must be applied. MS-222 (Sandoz Chemical) is the best anesthetic when made up fresh and at the proper concentration. Use a concentration of no more than 1 part MS-222 to 5,000 parts medium for urodele larvae and 1 to 10,000 for anuran tadpoles. High concentrations will kill the larvae or at sublethal dosages completely arrest development so that the embryo remains alive and intact but at the same stage for 2 or 3 weeks before dying. Older larvae and tadpoles are more sensitive to MS-222 and it is safer to use ice water as the anesthetic.

During an operation, do not scratch or nick the glazed surface of the operating dish. Sharp pieces of wax will cut the embryo. Small air bubbles on the floor of the dish will disrupt the epidermis of the embryo. Before putting embryos into the dish, dislodge such bubbles with a stream of fluid expelled from a pipette.

While operating, both forearms from the elbow to the end of the little finger are flat against the table. Instruments are manipulated with the thumb, fore-, and middle fingers. A practiced operator is not aware of his hands, only of the view of the instruments and embryo as seen through the microscope. Desired instrument movements are executed almost automatically. To someone operating for the first time, the idea of what they are attempting may seem impossible. Yet persistence will often prove rewarding even on the first day of effort.

When working on a given organ rudiment at different stages, one soon becomes aware of stage-dependent variation in the degree to which tissues stick one to another. As a result, some stages are better than others for clean removal of a particular rudiment. The most suitable stage for a particular experiment may vary from species to species.

Frequently, the whole embryo will be sticky and difficult to manipulate. The usual causes for this are temperature shock or rough handling while washing or operating. Incorrectly made media or old media of the wrong pH may produce similar results. The less often and more carefully one handles the materials being isolated, the better the cultures will be.

All cuts should be made with iridectomy scissors and all manipulations of embryos and tissues should be performed with hair loops. For example, two hair loops should be used to gently separate the germ layers. Never attempt to cut with the loops and never use the scissors to move the embryos or tissues around. To turn the embryo in the plane of the table, rotate the whole dish.

Use a fresh operating dish for each embryo until the demands of the particular system under investigation are learned. For some operations two to four embryos per dish are permissible. Sterile precautions must be observed throughout the operation. Prior to starting work, the operating area should be cleaned with 70 percent ethanol. The operating area and room must be free of dust and of traffic. Instruments must be resterilized whenever they come into contact with a nonsterile surface. Keep dust out of the operating dish when not actually using it by inverting a sterile bowl over it; also, move the dish out of the light, during these periods, to avoid overheating.

Talking while operating almost guarantees failure. Antibiotics (Hamburger, p. 36) may be used in the operating medium but we have never found this to be necessary.

CULTURE OF TISSUES AND ORGANS

A good knowledge of developmental anatomy is necessary for locating tissues or organ rudiments in the embryo. Many anatomical drawings, photographs, and "fate" maps are to be found in Witschi (1956), Balinsky (1965), Willier, Weiss, and Hamburger (1955), Hamburger (1960), and Rugh (1962). Useful examples of fate mapping not yet in the textbooks are: neural plate (Jacobson, 1959); epidermis and epidermal organs (Schechtman, 1932); endodermal organs (Nakamura, 1961; Tahara and Nakamura, 1961).

Excise the desired tissue or organ and place it in a shallow depression near the embryo. If a single piece of tissue is to be used it can be immediately transferred by pipette to the culture chamber. If two or more tissues are to be combined in an explant, they should be allowed to heal together in a depression in the operating dish for a minimum of 30 minutes before transfer to the culture vessel.

To transfer an excised piece of tissue, choose a capillary pipette with an inside diameter slightly larger than the tissue being transferred. Control the fluid level in the pipette by use of a mouthpiece (commercially available) and a short connecting piece of rubber tubing. To ensure accurate control of fluid in the pipette, dip the end in the medium and allow the fluid to reach an equilibrium level by capillarity only. Work within short distances of this equilibrium level. After equilibrium is reached, close the end of the mouthpiece with the tongue, put the end of the capillary near the excised tissue, and squeeze out a small amount of fluid against the tissue. Do this by holding the pipette with palm and three fingers while applying pressure to the tubing with thumb and forefinger or by mouth control. The small jet of expelled medium will dislodge the tissue from the dish surface. Release of pressure then allows capillarity to draw the tissue into the pipette. Practice will enable one to have the tissue just inside the end of the capillary when the equilibrium level is reached. Without exposing the tissue to surface tension, transfer it to the culture chamber and allow the tissue to drift out into the culture medium, or expel it gently with slight pressure on the tubing. During this period, keep the mouthpiece sealed with your tongue.

If the experiment allows, tissues and organs will do best if cultured encased in epidermis. A sheet of epidermis may be excised and laid, with its outer surface down, on the bottom of the operating dish; the tissue or organs to be investigated are then placed on top of it. Epidermis will heal into a vesicle encasing other tissues in about 30 minutes. The tissues may also be sandwiched in the epidermis by folding the latter or by placing a second piece of epidermis on top of the experimental tissue. Such vesicles are readily cultured in Holtfreter solution diluted with an equal volume of sterile distilled water.

Any small, covered culture dish will be adequate. Glass dishes must be lined with cellophane or agar; otherwise the explant will ultimately attach to and grow over the surface of the glass. Disposable, sterile plastic Petri plates, 35 × 10 mm, are convenient for culturing. They do not need to be lined as the tissues will rarely attach to the plastic. Attachment may occur if the tissues are transferred before healing completely. Plastic dishes are also convenient for observing the explant.

Large pieces of endodermal, mesodermal, or neural tissue may be cultured by the same method without epidermis. For small pieces of these tissues, use the method described below for cell cultures.

Tissues and organ rudiments cultured in epidermal vesicles will survive for long periods and continue to differentiate and function. Using *Taricha torosa*, I have cultured neurula-stage heart rudiments explanted with anterior endoderm inside of epidermal vesicles. At 17°C the hearts begin to beat after 1 week in culture; they continue beating for 90 days. To maintain long-term cultures, it is advisable to change the diluted Holtfreter solution every 10 days. It would be necessary to start feeding cultures if they were to be kept for much more than 90 days.

CULTURE OF CELLS

Small fragments of amphibian embryos may be readily cultured in hanging drops of Holtfreter solution or of Niu-Twitty solution. Cells and tissues adhere to and spread more on the glass substratum in Niu-Twitty solution than they do in Holtfreter solution. The Niu-Twitty medium contains magnesium ions and has a more complex buffer than the Holtfreter solution.

To make hanging-drop cultures, prepare specially cleaned and sterile square cover slips, clean and sterile well slides, and some clean Vaseline. Vaseline from a fresh jar, or from an opened jar from which the surface layer is discarded has always proved to be clean enough. It is important to find a ritual for washing cover slips, the end result of which is to give a surface that holds a well-hung drop. Unfortunately, different brands of cover slips, and the same brand from year to year, require variations in the ritual, and some cover slips just never work. At present, Corning 22 mm square No. 1 cover glasses will hold a drop fairly decently if prepared as follows: separate each cover slip and drop it individually into distilled water in a medium-sized flat enamel pan and bring to a boil over a hot plate. About 100 to 120 slips may be processed at once, but they must be separated initially or they never separate enough to get clean on all surfaces. Spread them out over the entire bottom of the pan. When they come to a boil, remove from the heat, pour off the water, and replace it at once with 95 percent ethanol. Remove each slip individually with a pair of forceps and stand it on edge, leaning against some edge such as the sides of an instrument rack on clean toweling in a dust-free area. When the cover slips are completely dry, place them in batches of from five to ten in Petri dishes and sterilize with dry heat or by autoclaving. Some slips will need more boiling, and some even need detergent. But if too much cleaning is done, the drop will flatten on the glass. Wash and sterilize the well slides. Before excising the cells, prepare as many well slides as will be needed by making a ring of Vaseline around the well to seal on the cover slip. Heated Vaseline becomes toxic so do not attempt to sterilize it with heat. We dispense Vaseline from a 5-cc syringe through a No. 18 needle whose end has been filed flat. The extruded cylinder of Vaseline seems to be about the right amount to seal without squeezing excess Vaseline into the well. Lean the slide well-side down on the edge of an instrument or something similar in a sterile area or container.

Excise the cells and place them near the embryo in the operating dish. Remove a cover slip with forceps from a Petri dish and place it on a clean flat platform such as the lid on a stender dish or small Petri dish. Make a drop out of culture medium. Do not use medium from the operating dish. It is easiest to make a drop with one of the smallest capillary pipettes. It should have no jagged edges on its end. Allow capillarity to fill the capillary to its equilibrium point, then close the rubber tube with your tongue and move the squared end of the capillary into contact with the center of the cover slip and lift. Surface tension ought to draw out a drop of just the right size. Three or four hanging drops may be made on each cover slip, or a single culture drop may be used with several smaller drops to help humidify the well chamber. A single drop will evaporate.

Do not submit to the temptation to make the drop at the same time as transferring the tissue. You are unlikely to get a good drop and may lose the cells in the surface film. Make the drop first and transfer the cells into it. If the transfer pipette is filled with culture medium to its equilibrium point and then the cells are drawn into the very end of the pipette as described before, they can be transferred into the drop where they will slide out with very little transfer of liquid from the operating dish.

As soon as the cells are in place, position the well of the slide over the cover slip and seal the slip onto the slide by pressing down firmly. Even a short delay in covering the drops will lead to evaporation that concentrates the medium. The thinnest hairline opening through the Vaseline seal will result in loss of the culture by evaporation. Leave the slide with cover slip down in the 17°C box for 24 hours before carefully turning so the drops are hanging and can be observed through the cover slip from above. Do not leave the drops in the standing position longer than 24 hours because the shaking of the box is more likely to spread them when they are standing than when they are hanging. The 24-hour period gives the cells time to attach to the glass. If turned immediately the culture will often sink to the inner surface of the drop where spreading of the cells may occur. Wooden racks to support the ends of the slides and leave the center cover slip area open are useful.

Hanging-drop cultures can be easily observed with a dissecting microscope or the low-power optics of a compound microscope. We have been unable to find well slides with optically flat bottoms on both surfaces, and in any event, the rounded air-water interface of the drop spoils observation at high powers or with phase contrast optics. If you wish to observe cultures under high power or phase optics, use the following column-culture method.

Drill a hole $\frac{1}{2}$ inch in diameter through a 1-mm thick plastic slide and sterilize with 70 percent ethanol. Ring both sides of the hole with Vaseline. Seal a prepared cover slip onto one side covering the hole. Make a fairly large drop on another cover slip and transfer in the cells. Now make a drop on the cover slip sealed to the slide and invert the slide over the other cover slip so that the tops of the two drops touch and form a column of fluid between the two cover slips. This column of fluid is a good optical pathway and cells can be readily observed on either glass surface.

The fewer cells being isolated, the more difficult it is to rear them. This is the old problem of "conditioning" the medium. Drops should be made smaller for smaller cell groups. Twitty and Niu (1954) were able to culture single cells using capillary tubes as the culture vessel and coelomic fluid from gravid adult female salamanders as the culture medium. They obtained single cells from neural crest explants in hanging drops by mechanically disengaging a migrating cell and drawing it into the capillary. Capillaries were held by a Vaseline ridge and kept immersed in saline in the bottom of a Petri dish (Twitty and Niu, 1954, for details). Single cells can also be obtained by dissociating tissues as described below.

TISSUE DISSOCIATION

The classic study of tissue affinity in amphibian embryos by Holtfreter (1939), now available in translation in Willier and Oppenheimer (1964), followed by the later studies of Townes and Holtfreter (1955), opened an area and approach that is now very popular. Studies of the dissociation and reaggregation of amphibian embryonic cells have now been performed by several workers. Townes and Holtfreter (1955) placed tissue in calcium-free Holtfreter solution and slowly added potassium hydroxide to a pH of no more than 9.8. Under these conditions the cells disaggregate, after which the pH is returned to 7.8.

Holtfreter (personal communication) has recently revised these methods as follows: disaggregate in a solution of calcium-free Holtfreter solution to which is added 0.005 *M* sodium citrate. For older embryos this solution should be reinforced by the addition of trypsin, varying in concentration with the progressing stage from 0.2 to 2 percent trypsin (Difco). Calcium-free Holtfreter solution with 0.002 *M* ethylenediaminetetraacetate (EDTA or Versene) is also efficient, but Holtfreter believes EDTA has more harmful effects than citrate.

To make the free cells reaggregate, the best method is to replace the disaggregating medium stepwise and gently with Holtfreter solution (pH 7.5) using a pipette. Many cells are lost if one attempts to transfer the disaggregated cells to fresh medium with a pipette.

A smooth-walled hemispherical depression about 1.5 mm in diameter is a good container for the disaggregation and reaggregation procedure. Such a depression can be made with a warmed bead-tipped glass rod in the agar covering the bottom of a culture vessel, or in Permaplast-paraffin in an operating dish.

Boterenbrood (1962, 1958) disaggregated and reaggregated neural plate material using a medium consisting of 0.062 *M* NaCl, 0.0008 *M* KCl, and 0.01 *M* Na-citrate for disaggregation and pipetted the cells to normal Holtfreter solution for reaggregation. She tried several species of urodeles and noted that some are better than others for these procedures. She chose *Triturus alpestris* for her experiments.

Jones and Elsdale (1963) disaggregated and reaggregated various tissues from various stages of *Xenopus* embryos. They used for disaggregation Steinberg's solution (Hamburger, p. 36) made without calcium nitrate or magnesium sulfate, but with 120 mg of EDTA added per liter. Several media were used for reaggregation, all based on complete Steinberg's solution to which was added one of the following: 0.1 percent crystalline Bovine Plasma Albumin (Armour); or 0.1 percent Human Serum Globulin (Bois); or 3.0 percent Horse Serum (Difco). They believed that nonspecific protein in the medium was important for good reaggregation.

CULTURE OF LARVAL AND ADULT AMPHIBIAN CELLS

The main concern of this chapter has been with embryonic and early larval stages when each cell has an endogenous food supply. After this food is exhausted, which varies in time with each species, greatly modified methods of culture are necessary since the cells must be fed. There have been quite a number of methods used to culture older amphibian cells. Usually these methods are modifications of chick and mammalian methods, to the extent, incredibly, of incubating at 37°C in some cases. It is certainly advisable to use cooler temperatures.

A sampling of the literature on the culture of older amphibian cells, by no means complete, follows: Vanable (1965), *Xenopus* larval skin; Wolf and Quimby (1964), *Rana catesbeiana* tongue fibroblasts; Foote and Foote (1962), *Pleurodeles waltlii* urogenital organs; Foote and Foote (1958), *Rana catesbeiana* gonads; Boss (1955, 1954), *Triturus cristatus* fibroblasts; Landau and Marsland (1952), *Rana pipiens* heart.

REFERENCES

BALINSKY, B. I., 1965: *An Introduction to Embryology.* W. B. Saunders Co., Philadelphia, Pa., and London, Eng.

BOSS, J., 1954: Mitosis in cultures of newt tissues. I. A critical study of the methods and material. *Exp. Cell Res.*, 7: 215.

———, 1955: An improved method for cultivating fibroblasts of the newt. *Exp. Cell Res.*, 9: 35.

BOTERENBROOD, E. C., 1958: Organization in aggregates of anterior neural plate cells of *Triturus alpestris. Proc. Kon. Ned. Akad. Wetensch.* (Amsterdam), *Ser. C*, 61: 470.

———, 1962: *On Pattern Formation in the Prosencephalon*: An Investigation on Disaggregated and Reaggregated Presumptive Prosencephalic Material of Neurulae of *Triturus alpestris.* Thesis, University of Utrecht, Netherlands.

FLICKINGER, R. A., 1949: A study of the metabolism of amphibian neural crest cells during their migration and pigmentation *in vitro. J. Exp. Zool.*, 112: 465.

FOOTE, C. L., and F. M. FOOTE, 1958: *In vitro* cultivation of gonads of larval anurans. *Anat. Rec.*, 130: 553.

———, and ———, 1962: The culture *in vitro* of urogenital organs of *Pleurodeles waltlii. J. Embryol. Exp. Morph.*, 10: 465.

HAMBURGER, V., 1960: *A Manual of Experimental Embryology.* Rev. ed. The University of Chicago Press, Chicago, Ill.

HOLTFRETER, J., 1939: Gewebeaffinität, ein Mittel der embryonalen Formbildung. *Arch. f. Exp. Zellf.*, 23: 169.

JACOBSON, C-O., 1959: The localization of the presumptive cerebral regions in the neural plate of the axolotl larva. *J. Embryol. Exp. Morph.*, 7: 1.

JONES, K. W., and T. R. ELSDALE, 1963: The culture of small aggregates of amphibian embryonic cells *in vitro. J. Embryol. Exp. Morph.*, 11: 135.

LANDAU, J., and D. MARSLAND, 1952: Temperature-pressure studies on the cardiac rate in tissue culture explants from the heart of the tadpole (*Rana pipiens*). *J. Cell. Comp. Physiol.*, 40: 367.

NAKAMURA, O., 1961: Presumptive rudiments of the endodermal organs on the surface of the anuran gastrula. *Embryologia*, 6: 99.

RUGH, R., 1962: *Experimental Embryology.* 3rd ed. Burgess Publishing Co., Minneapolis, Minn.

SCHECHTMAN, A. M., 1932: Movement and localization of the presumptive epidermis in *Triturus torosus* (Rathke). *Univ. of Calif. Publ. Zool.*, 36: 325.

TAHARA, Y., and O. NAKAMURA, 1961: Topography of the presumptive rudiments in the endoderm of the anuran neurula. *J. Embryol. Exp. Morph.*, 9: 138.

TOWNES, P. L., and J. HOLTFRETER, 1955: Directed movements and selective adhesion of embryonic amphibian cells. *J. Exp. Zool.*, 128: 53.

TWITTY, V. C., and M. C. NIU, 1954: The motivation of cell migration, studied by isolation of embryonic pigment cells singly and in small groups *in vitro. J. Exp. Zool.*, 125: 541.

VANABLE, J. W., 1965: Organ culture of *Xenopus laevis* larval skin. *Am. Zool.*, 5: 663.

WILLIER, B. H., and J. M. OPPENHEIMER, 1964: *Foundations of Experimental Embryology.* Prentice-Hall, Inc., Englewood Cliffs, N.J.

———, P. A. WEISS, and V. HAMBURGER, 1955: *Analysis of Development.* W. B. Saunders Co., Philadelphia, Pa., and London, Eng.

WITSCHI, E., 1956: *Development of Vertebrates.* W. B. Saunders Co., Philadelphia, Pa., and London, Eng.

WOLF, K., and M. C. QUIMBY, 1964: Amphibian cell culture: permanent cell line from the bullfrog (*Rana catesbeiana*). Science, 144: 1578.

Insect Tissue Culture

By Imogene Schneider

INTRODUCTION

The culture *in vitro* of insect organs, tissues, and cells has proved to be an exceptionally difficult task. Recent reviews have stressed the problems involved and have offered a variety of explanations as to why the successes have been so few and the failures so many. Comforting as these explanations may be, the fact remains that although the field of insect tissue culture is half a century old, it is still, relatively speaking, in its infancy. The potential value of the technique will remain just that until the many problems have been solved. The veritable renaissance of interest in insect tissue culture stems back to the middle 1950's and certainly the number of investigators in the field today attests to the fact that the challenge has served as a stimulant rather than a deterrent.

In general, insect tissues placed in culture have a disconcerting propensity for just "sitting"; extensive cell migration quite often takes place but actual growth just as often does not. Individual organs from immature stages of some species are capable of surviving *in vitro* for protracted periods of time without showing any signs of differentiation, regardless of the supplements, hormonal or otherwise, added to the medium.

Unfortunately, more than a few investigators in the field have confused cell migration with cell division, bleb formation with mitosis, and clumping with aggregation. Consequently, it is rather difficult in many instances to evaluate the worth of a particular technique or culture medium and equally difficult to judge the inherent capacity of a tissue from any one species to adjust to conditions *in vitro*. This situation will doubtless remain until the results are judged by objective quantitation rather than subjective observation. This review has, therefore, been limited to discussing the few techniques which have been more or less standardized. Information on techniques of restricted usage or application may be found in the articles cited at the end of this chapter.

BASIC PROCEDURES AND EQUIPMENT

The methods employed in vertebrate tissue culture for the cleansing and sterilization of glassware and other equipment, filtration of media, and the principles and practices of aseptic technique are equally applicable to insect tissue culture. If necessary, standard reference books should be consulted for the above information (Parker, 1961; Paul, 1960; White, 1963).

The small size of the insect necessitates the use of microinstruments and equipment in addition to those of standard size: jeweler's forceps are usually a "must"; dissecting needles replace dissecting knives and scissors; commercially obtained glass pipettes must often be drawn out into a smaller bore; 5-, 10-, and 25-ml flasks and beakers are probably used more frequently than are the larger sizes; and culture vessels with a capacity of over 30 ml are rarely employed.

Most, if not all, dissections require the use of a dissecting microscope.

CULTURE MEDIA

A cursory survey of the culture media designed for insect tissues reveals great qualitative and quantitative disparities in their composition. Two media designed for the same species may have less in common than do two media designed (or employed) for insects belonging to entirely different orders. Consequently, it is virtually impossible to single out a culture medium which would be representative for any one species, much less for a genus, family, or order.

TABLE 1. MODIFICATION OF WYATT'S MEDIUM BY GRACE (1958, 1962)

COMPONENT	AMOUNT (mg/100 ml)	COMPONENT	AMOUNT (mg/100 ml)
$NaH_2PO_4 \cdot 2H_2O$	114	Sucrose (in gm)	2.668
$NaHCO_3$	35	Fructose	40
KCl	224	Glucose	70
$CaCl_2$	100		
$MgCl_2 \cdot 6H_2O$	228	L-Arginine HCl	70
$MgSO_4 \cdot 7H_2O$	278	L-Aspartic acid	35
		L-Asparagine	35
Malic acid	67	L-Alanine	22.5
α-Ketoglutaric acid	37	β-Alanine	20
Succinic acid	6	L-Cystine HCl	2.5
Fumaric acid	5.5	L-Glutamic acid	60
		L-Glutamine	60
Thiamine HCl	0.002	L-Glycine	65
Riboflavin	0.002	L-Histidine	250
Calcium pantothenate	0.002	L-Isoleucine	5
Pyridoxine HCl	0.002	L-Leucine	7.5
p-Aminobenzoic acid	0.002	L-Lysine HCl	62.5
Folic acid	0.002	L-Methionine	5
Niacin	0.002	L-Proline	35
Isoinositol	0.002	L-Phenylalanine	15
Biotin	0.001	DL-Serine	110
Choline chloride	0.02	L-Tyrosine	5
		L-Tryptophan	10
		L-Threonine	17.5
		L-Valine	10

Supplement: 5% pupal hemolymph pH: 6.5
Antibiotics: Penicillin G (sodium salt), 3 mg/100 ml
Streptomycin sulfate, 10 mg/100 ml

TABLE 2. MODIFICATION OF WYATT'S MEDIUM BY JONES AND CUNNINGHAM (1961)

COMPONENT	AMOUNT (mg/100 ml)	COMPONENT	AMOUNT (mg/100 ml)
NaH_2PO_4	110	Malic acid	60
$MgCl_2 \cdot 6H_2O$	300	α-Ketoglutaric acid	35
$MgSO_4 \cdot 7H_2O$	370	Succinic acid	6
KCl	300	Fumaric acid	5.5
$CaCl_2$	80		
		T. C. Yeastolate	100
Glucose	70	Lactalbumin hydrolysate	1,000
Fructose	40	or	
Sucrose	40	{Lactalbumin hydrolysate	700
		DL-Lysine	100
		L-Histidine	200
		DL-Serine}	100

Supplement: 10% pupal hemolymph pH: 6.35
Antibiotics: Penicillin, 50 I.U. per ml; streptomycin, 100 I.U. per ml

Without question, the medium designed by Wyatt (1956) for the culture of *Bombyx mori* L. ovarian tissue and modified by Grace (1958, 1962) has served as a prototype for the formulation of many of the subsequent media (Table 1). The unprecedented success of the latter investigator in obtaining long-term survival and growth of tissues from numerous lepidopteran species has certainly had much to do with conferring this distinction on the medium. Further modification of this same medium by Jones and Cunningham (1961), which in essence was done to simplify its preparation, has undoubtedly contributed to its appeal as a model (Table 2).

Design of Media for Insect Tissues

The present trend in formulating media, whether wholly advisable or not, seems to be as follows: (1) the concentrations, if known, of the various inorganic ions present in the hemolymph of the particular species in question are duplicated or approximated (a recent review devoted to summarizing our present knowledge of the hemolymph composition of insects is that of Florkin and Jeuniaux, 1964); (2) the concentration of sugar(s) added is determined more or less on a trial and error basis; (3) lactalbumin hydrolyzate in a concentration of 1,000 to 2,000 mg per 100 ml of medium is added in lieu of individual amino acids; (4) a yeast extract in concentrations varying from 100 to 200 mg per 100 ml is added in lieu of the B vitamins; (5) the four organic acids first used by Wyatt (1956) are usually retained in the same or similar concentrations; and (6) an extract from invertebrate or vertebrate sources is usually added to further supplement the medium.

Insect Supplements

When feasible, the supplement added is homologous hemolymph in concentrations ranging from 0.5 to 30 percent.

Heterologous hemolymph has also been employed but it apparently is not as adequate as the former (Grace, personal communication). Before use, the hemolymph must be treated so as to suppress tyrosinase activity. This enzyme catalyzes the production of melanin (readily seen in the visible darkening of hemolymph upon exposure to air) via intermediary quinones, the latter being regarded as toxic to the explanted tissues. The usual treatment is as follows: the hemolymph is expressed from the pupae (occasionally, larvae are used) directly into a chilled centrifuge tube. The tube is then heated for 5 minutes at 60°C, chilled in a deep freeze for 12 to 24 hours, thawed and centrifuged at 6,000 *g* for 10 minutes. The clear supernatant can be used immediately or is stored at −30°C. Wyatt found this incubation time and temperature sufficient to precipitate the enzyme; however, Medvedeva (1959) reported that the hemolymph of certain species may have to be heated for a longer interval (10 to 15 minutes) to suppress the activity of the enzyme adequately. Phenylthiourea has also been used to inhibit tyrosinase; however, it is considered somewhat toxic to insect tissues and consequently, the heat treatment is to be preferred.

Since it is virtually impossible to extract hemolymph in substantial quantity from smaller insects, extracts of whole embryos, larvae, pupae or nymphs, and adults have been used. The general procedure for preparing these extracts is similar to that for the hemolymph except that the material is first ground very lightly in a small amount of saline or culture medium prior to heating, chilling, and centrifugation. In general, the results with these whole insect extracts have not been particularly encouraging.

TABLE 3. ORTHOPTERAN AND HOMOPTERAN TISSUE CULTURE

GENUS AND SPECIES (FAMILY)	SOURCE OF CELLS, TISSUES, OR ORGANS	LENGTH OF TIME IN CULTURE	RESULTS	REFERENCE
Chortophaga viridifasciata (Acrididae)	Ventral nerve cord from embryo	5–6 days	Successive divisions of neuroblasts	Carlson and Gaulden (1964)
Locusta migratoria (Acrididae)	Embryos	20–24 hours	Normal mitotic activity for this limited period	Bergerard and Morio (1963)
Carausius morosus (Phasmatidae)	Embryos of various ages	Up to 9 days	Near-normal development in older embryos; cell migration but no development in younger embryos	Koch (1964)
Blabera fusca (Blattidae)	Embryonic cells	Several weeks	Cell migration and mitoses	Landureau (1965)
Blaberus craniifer (Blattidae)	Embryonic heart fragments	Up to 16 months	Muscular movement "proliferated balls"	Larsen (1964)
Blattella germanica (Blattidae)	Nymphal ovaries, Malpighian tubules, fat bodies	160 days	Extension cell migration; no mitoses seen	Ting and Brooks (1965)
Leucophaea maderae (Blattidae)	Regenerating leg tissue from nymph	Up to 40 days	Maintenance; extensive cell migration	Marks and Reinecke (1964, 1965)
Macrosteles fascifrons, *Agillia constricta*, *Dalbulus maidis* (Cicadellidae)	Embryonic, nymphal, and adult tissues	5 months	Cell division; short-term subcultures	Mitsuhashi and Maramorosch (1964)

Vertebrate Supplements

Vertebrate sera (human, horse, sheep, fetal bovine, newborn calf), coagula (chicken plasma), and tissue extracts (chick embryo) have been used to supplement the media in place of or in addition to insect extracts. The concentrations have ranged from less than 1 percent to more than 20 percent. Peptones and proteoses (0.1 to 2 percent) have also been employed.

Chemically Defined Media

Chemically defined media have been formulated for *Sciara*, *Drosophila*, and *Leucophaea* with results ranging from short-term maintenance (Cannon, 1964) to long-term maintenance with (Schneider, 1964a) or without sporadic growth (Schneider, 1964b; Marks and Reinecke, 1964, 1965). Horikawa and Kuroda (1959) reported survival and multiplication of *Drosophila* larval hemocytes in a chemically defined medium for as long as 5 months. However, some skepticism has been expressed regarding the methodology used in assessing the results (Jones, 1962).

Range and Control of pH; Antibiotics

With few exceptions, the pH range employed for lepidopteran tissues is between 6.35 and 7.1; for dipteran tissues, from 6.5 to 7.2; and for homopteran and orthopteran tissues, from 6.5 to 7.8. Insect tissues appear capable of tolerating fairly wide variations in pH as do vertebrate tissues in culture. The changes in pH are usually monitored with phenol red in a concentration of 0.001 to 0.005 percent. In general, pH control is dependent upon the buffering system of the medium and a tight seal on the culture vessel. Addition of a special gas phase to the vessel is not a common practice.

The antibiotics penicillin (50 to 100 units per milliliter) and streptomycin (50 to 100 μg per milliliter) are routinely added to inhibit bacterial growth.

Survey of Recent Work with Insect Tissues

Tables 3, 4, and 5 list examples of representative organ, tissue, and cell cultures from four orders of insects. Deliberate emphasis has been placed on the work of the past 5 years since reviews by Day and Grace (1959), Jones (1962), and Martignoni (1963) give adequate coverage of the earlier literature. Details of the culture media employed as well as directions for preparation can be obtained by referring to the original articles.

OPERATIVE TECHNIQUES

Sterilization Procedure for the Embryonic Stages

The exochorion of an insect is invariably covered with a microbial flora that must be eliminated prior to culturing. Surface sterilization may be accomplished by immersing the eggs in any one of a number of antiseptic solutions. Among the most common are:

1. 0.05 percent $HgCl_2$ in 70 percent ethanol (15 to 30 minutes)
2. 70 percent ethanol (1 minute) followed by 0.1 to 0.2 percent Hyamine (10 minutes)
3. White's solution (20 minutes). This is composed of 0.25 gm $HgCl_2$, 6.5 gm NaCl, 1.25 ml HCl, 250 ml ethanol, and 750 ml distilled water.
4. 10 percent solution of Benzalkonium chloride (30 to 60 minutes) followed by a distilled water rinse and immersion in 80 percent ethanol (15 to 30 minutes)
5. 2 percent Cetavlon (Cetyltrimethylammonium bromide)[1] for 40 to 60

[1] Calbiochem, Los Angeles, California.

TABLE 4. DIPTERAN TISSUE CULTURE

GENUS AND SPECIES (FAMILY)	SOURCE OF CELLS, TISSUES, OR ORGANS	LENGTH OF TIME IN CULTURE	RESULTS	REFERENCE
Aëdes aegypti (Culicidae)	Imaginal discs of last instar larvae	40 days	Cell migration; proliferation of introduced virus	Peleg and Trager (1963)
Aëdes aegypti (Culicidae)	Newly hatched larvae	5 months	Cell migration and division	Peleg (1965)
Culex pipiens (Culicidae)	Adult ovarian tissue	3 months	Extensive cell migration; some mitoses	Kitamura (1965)
Culex tarsalis (Culicidae)	Adult midgut	5–7 days	Suboptimal maintenance; some development of *Plasmodium relictum* oocysts	Chao and Ball (1964)
Sciara coprophilia (Sciaridae)	Larval salivary glands	24 hours	Maintenance; chromosome puff formation	Cannon (1964)
Miaster sp. (Cecidomyiidae)	Intact embryos	Up to 4 weeks	Limited or fairly extensive differentiation depending on age of embryo	Counce (1966)
Drosophila melanogaster (Drosophilidae)	Eye discs and cephalic ganglia from late third instar larvae	170 hours	Differentiation into adult eye but lacking pigmentation	Gottschewski (1960)
Drosophila melanogaster (Drosophilidae)	Eye-antennal discs and cephalic ganglia from third instar larvae	Up to 36 days	Differentiation into adult antennae; pigmented eyes; minor development of brain lobes	Schneider (1964b, 1966)
Drosophila melanogaster (Drosophilidae)	Embryonic cells	6–7 months	Maintenance and growth; chromosome number constant for 10 days	Horikawa and Fox (1964)
Drosophila melanogaster (Drosophilidae)	Embryonic cells	5–7 days	Aggregation and characteristic positioning of many cell types	Lesseps (1965)
Drosophila melanogaster (Drosophilidae)	Embryonic cells	5 months	Extensive cell migration; limited mitoses	Échalier *et al.* (1965)
Drosophila melanogaster (Drosophilidae)	Embryonic cells	120 hours	Numerous mitoses but number of heteroploid cells increases rapidly as culture ages; polyploid cells rare or absent	Dolfini and Gottardi (1966)
Calliphora erythrocephalia (Calliphoridae)	Prepupal and pupal gonads	Up to 12 days	Moderate amount of differentiation	Leloup (1964)
Glossina palpalis (Muscidae)	Various organs and tissues from pupae and adults	Up to 43 days	Extensive cell migration; mitoses; differentiation of head structures; development of introduced trypanosomes	Trager (1959)

minutes. After the appropriate interval, the eggs are removed from the antiseptic and washed thoroughly in sterile distilled water.

Complete removal of the chorion is a common procedure when working with *Drosophila* embryos. Immersion in a 2.5 to 3 percent sodium hypochlorite solution for 2 to 3 minutes is usually sufficient for this purpose. Following a thorough rinsing with sterile distilled water, the eggs are immersed in an antiseptic solution. Although not advisable, this last step has sometimes been omitted.

Sterilization Procedure for the Postembryonic Stages

Seventy percent ethanol and White's solution are most often used for surface sterilization of larvae, pupae or nymphs, and adults. If care is taken to avoid rupturing the intestinal tract during dissection, microbial contamination can be avoided or held to a reasonable minimum. However, the smaller the insect, the greater the difficulty of making such a dissection.

If the insect is small and/or the nature of the dissection is such that the probability of injuring the intestine is quite high, it is advisable, whenever feasible, to subject the larvae or adults to fasting for 24 to 48 hours prior to dissection.

Axenic Culture of Insects

An obvious method of circumventing the problem of microbial contamination

TABLE 5. LEPIDOPTERAN TISSUE CULTURE

GENUS AND SPECIES (FAMILY)	SOURCE OF CELLS, TISSUES, OR ORGANS	LENGTH OF TIME IN CULTURE	RESULTS	REFERENCE
Anosia plexippus (Danaidae)	Subesophageal ganglion, ovarian tissue, Malpighian tubules from pupae	Up to 28 days	Cell migration and division	Hirumi and Maramorosch (1964)
Antheraea eucalypti (Saturniidae)	Ovarian cells from diapausing pupae	Indefinite	Establishment of cell strains	Grace (1962)
Antheraea pernyi (Saturniidae)	Fifth instar pupal gonads, blood cells	Up to 5 months	Unequal degree of virus infection and multiplication in different tissues	Medvedeva (1959)
Callosamia promethea (Saturniidae)	Ovarian tissue from diapausing pupae	48 weeks	Cell migration and division; subculturing	Grace (1958)
Philosamia advena (Saturniidae)	Ovarian tissue from diapausing pupae	4–6 weeks	Cell migration and division	Jones and Cunningham (1961)
Philosamia cynthia (Saturniidae)	Gonads from diapausing pupae	??	Cell migration; no proliferation of introduced virus	Peleg and Trager (1963)
Peridroma saucia (Phalaenidae)	Larval hemocytes	5–7 days	Multiplication of introduced polyhedrosis virus	Martignoni and Scallion (1961)
Lymantria dispar (Liparidae)	Ovaries of last instar larvae; ovarial sheath of young pupae	Indefinite	Cell migration and division; subculturing	Vago and Flandre (1963)
Bombyx mori (Bombycidae)	Prepupal ovarian tissue	3 weeks	Cell migration and division	Wyatt (1956)
Bombyx mori (Bombycidae)	Diapausing and nondiapausing embryos	7–10 days	Some development in nondiapausing embryos	Takami (1958)
Bombyx mori (Bombycidae)	Embryonic primordium	Up to 7 days	Differentiation to multilayered germ band stage	Krause and Krause (1964)
Galleria mellonella (Pyralidae)	Larval and pupal intestinal, ovarian, and testicular tissues	Up to 28 days	Extensive cell migration; no mitoses recorded	Sen Gupta (1961)
Galleria mellonella (Pyralidae)	Intact gonads from last larval instar	2–7 days	Differentiation of spermatocytes, follicular and nurse cells; increase in oocyte size	Lender and Duveau-Hagege (1963)

would be to use organs, tissues, and cells from insects raised axenically. Unfortunately, synthetic or semisynthetic diets have been formulated for an extremely small number of species and some of these diets appear to be just barely adequate (Trager, 1935; Sang, 1956; Friend, 1958; Dougherty, 1959; Akov, 1962; and Ito and Horie, 1962).

Culture of Intact Embryos

For developmental studies involving intact embryos, the age of the egg must often be ascertained. Usually this is done either by timing the eggs following deposition by the female or by visual examination of the embryo itself. If the chorion of the egg is so dark as to obscure the embryo (e.g., aedine mosquito eggs) the somewhat droll but nonetheless effective method for bleaching eggs devised by Hokama and Judson (1963) may be used. The eggs are placed in a commercial hair bleach preparation (8 parts "Clairoxide," 2 parts "Lightening Booster," and 1 part "Lady Clairol") for approximately 30 minutes followed by alternating rinses of water and 5 percent boric acid solution. It is advisable to stop the action of the bleach before the chorion is completely transparent. If the latter does occur, the embryos from such eggs will not withstand subsequent sterilization very well.

Manipulation of the eggs before they are placed in culture may, in some instances, be facilitated by having the eggs adhere to some surface such as filter paper or glass cover slips. This is usually accomplished by wetting the eggs with a drop or two of saline solution and allowing them to dry on the desired surface.

After the chorion of the egg is carefully slit open with a sharp needle the embryo is removed and transferred to a small amount of saline solution or culture medium. The vitelline membrane is removed and the intact embryo (or any particular part of it) is transferred to a hanging drop.

Methods for short-term culture of neuroblasts from grasshopper embryos, developed primarily for the purpose of studying the mechanism of cell division, is a subject in itself. A detailed description of these techniques may be found in a recent review by Carlson and Gaulden (1964).

Culture of Embryonic Tissues and Cells

Primary cultures of embryonic cells from a few species have been maintained for over 6 months and subculturing is possible, at least for limited periods. However, apparently rather large numbers of embryos must be used. Hirumi and Maramorosch (1964) stated that a minimum of one hundred *Macrosteles* embryos was required to initiate growth whereas the numbers for *Drosophila* have ranged from "several hundred" (Échalier *et al.*, 1965) to as many as three thousand (Horikawa and Fox, 1965). Specific information as to the optimal cell density for initiating such cultures is not yet available.

After chemical or mechanical removal of the chorion and vitelline membrane, the embryos are dissociated into single cells and/or small fragments with trypsin or by gentle homogenizing. The cells are then washed in culture medium and transferred to hanging or sitting drops, test tubes, or culture flasks, depending on the mass of tissue and the volume of culture medium employed.

Culture of Organs, Tissues, and Cells from Postembryonic Stages

Assuming an adequate knowledge of the external and internal anatomy of the insect, dissection and explantation of the various organs and imaginal discs is completely straightforward and poses no major problems other than keeping trauma to a minimum and guarding against microbial contamination.

One technique that can be used to advantage when dissecting the larval stages of small insects such as *Drosophila* is to remove the exoskeleton of the anterior and/or posterior halves without seriously displacing the organs or damaging the intestinal tract. The larva is first "girdled" in the middle by cutting through the body wall with a pair of needles or forceps. The anterior (or posterior) tip of the larva is then held with one forceps while the second forceps is used to progressively separate the body wall from the attached muscles, tracheae, and nerve fibers. Eventually, one entire half of the body wall will be positioned inside-out on the first forceps. The procedure may then be repeated, if desired, on the other half.

For cultures involving discrete organs, the hanging drop technique, with either a single or double cover slip, is usually adequate. The use of plasma clots is not a very common practice although agar-plasma clots have been used for culturing larval gonads of *Galleria* with moderate success (Lender and Duveau-Hagege, 1963). The use of rayon rafts as well as those of nylon monofilament cloth, Millipore filters, and perforated cellophane proved completely unsuitable for the culture of various larval and pupal organs of *Drosophila* (Schneider, 1965). Whether the use of such rafts is inadvisable for insect organs in general remains to be seen.

For primary cell cultures, the organs are usually cut into small pieces 1 to 3 mm^3 in volume and four to six pieces are then placed in an appropriate culture vessel. A "slight" problem arises, of course, when the entire organ is smaller than 1 mm^3 and it may or may not be solved by placing additional tissue from more than one insect in the same culture. In the latter instance, the organs are usually cut in half or their margins are injured to encourage cellular migration.

In general, trypsin is not too effective in dissociating tissues from the post-embryonic stages and, consequently, it is rarely used for this purpose.

The choice of the culture vessel is again dependent on the mass of tissue involved and the volume of medium required for its maintenance. Among the most commonly used are depression and Maximow slides, Carrel flasks 10 × 75 mm, and 12- × 50-mm culture tubes (with or without "flying cover slips"), Leighton tubes, 30-ml culture dishes or flasks, and Rose multipurpose tissue chambers. Renewal of the medium appears to be largely dependent on the whim of the individual investigator. Intervals between 2 and 10 days have been reported.

With few exceptions, cultures are maintained at temperatures ranging from 25° to 30°C. There is no general consensus as to whether or not the cultures should be held stationary.

In the following section of this chapter, a protocol is given which incorporates many of the techniques described in the preceding sections. The procedure, slightly modified, is based on the work of Lesseps (1965).

PROTOCOL FOR THE CULTURE OF DISSOCIATED *DROSOPHILA* EMBRYOS *IN VITRO*

Materials

1. *Drosophila melanogaster* embryos, 10 to 12 hours old; 15 to 20 embryos will be needed for each culture.

2. Ca- and Mg-free *Drosophila* saline containing 0.12 percent ethylenediamine-tetraacetate (EDTA) and 0.15 percent crude trypsin; 2.5 percent NaClO; 0.05 percent $HgCl_2$ in 70 percent ethanol.

3. Sterile depression slides and 22-mm-square cover slips; heated mixture of Vaseline and paraffin (1.5:2).

4. Sterile Swinny hypodermic adapters fitted with Millipore GS filters; 5- or 10-cc syringe, disposable Pasteur pipettes drawn out into a small bore, jeweler's forceps and dissecting needles (preferably of tungsten wire, sharpened by dipping the points in hot $NaNO_2$).

5. Schneider's medium (1964b, 1966) supplemented with 5 or 10 percent fetal bovine serum.

6. FAA fixative (6 ml formalin, 1 ml acetic acid, 15 ml 95 percent ethanol, and 30 ml water).

7. Azan stain (Humanson, 1962).

Procedure

1. Dechorionate embryos by placing them in the NaClO solution for 3 to 5 minutes; rinse thoroughly in sterile distilled water and immerse in the $HgCl_2$ solution for 15 minutes; again rinse thoroughly.

2. Slit the vitelline membrane, remove embryos, and place the appropriate number in a small test tube.

3. Incubate embryos in the saline-EDTA-trypsin solution for 15 minutes; subject the tube to rapid vibrations (on rubber platform of a "Super-Mixer" or similar apparatus) for 15 seconds.

4. Wash the cells three times in culture medium by alternate gentle centrifugation and decanting; transfer cells to hanging drop, 0.005 to 0.008 ml in volume. Invert over depression slide and seal with the Vaseline-paraffin mixture. Maintain the cultures at a temperature of 25°C.

5. After 5 days fix, section, and stain the aggregates. Identify as many cell types as possible.

REFERENCES

AKOV, S., 1962: A qualitative and quantitative study of the nutritional requirements of *Aëdes aegypti* L. larvae. *J. Ins. Physiol.*, 8: 319.

BERGERARD, J., and H. MORIO, 1963: Action de la colchicine sur la mitose chez l'embryon de *Locusta migratoria* en survie *in vitro*. *Ann. Épiphyties*, 14: 55.

CANNON, G., 1964: Culture of insect salivary glands in a chemically defined medium. *Science*, 146: 1063.

CARLSON, J. G., and M. E. GAULDEN, 1964: Grasshopper neuroblast techniques. *Meth. Cell Physiol.*, 1: 229.

CHAO, J., and G. H. BALL, 1964: Cultivation of the insect cycle of Plasmodia. *Am. J. Trop. Med. Hyg.*, 13: 181.

COUNCE, S. J., 1966: Culture of insect embryos *in vitro*. *Ann. N.Y. Acad. Sci.*, 139; 65.

DAY, M. F., and T. D. C. GRACE, 1959: Culture of insect tissues. *Ann. Rev. Entomol.*, 4: 17.

DOLFINI, S., and A. GOTTARDI, 1966: Changes of chromosome number in cells of *Drosophila melanogaster* cultured *in vitro*. *Experientia*, 22: 144.

DOUGHERTY, E. C., 1959: Axenic culture of invertebrate metazoa; A goal. *Ann. N.Y. Acad. Sci.*, 77: 25.

ÉCHALIER, G., A. OHANESSIAN, and M. G. BRUN, 1965: Cultures "primaries" de cellules embryonnaires de *Drosophila melanogaster* (Insecte Diptère). *Compt. Rend. Acad. Sci. (Paris)*, 261: 3211.

FLORKIN, M., and C. JEUNIAUX, 1963: Hemolymph: Composition. In M. Rockstein (ed.), *The Physiology of Insecta*, Academic Press, New York, Vol. III, p. 109.

FRIEND, W. G., 1958: Nutritional requirements of phytophagous insects. *Ann. Rev. Entomol.*, 3: 57.

GOTTSCHEWSKI, G. H. M., 1960: Morphogenetische Untersuchungen an *in vitro* wachsenden Augenanlagen von *Drosophila melanogaster*. *Arch. Entw.-mech. Org.*, 152: 204.

GRACE, T. D. C., 1958: The prolonged growth and survival of ovarian tissue of the promethea moth (*Callosamia promethea*) *in vitro*. *J. Gen. Physiol.*, 41: 1027.

———, 1962: Establishment of four strains of cells from insect tissues grown *in vitro*. *Nature*, 195: 788.

HIRUMI, H., and K. MARAMOROSCH, 1964: Tissue culture of the monarch butterfly, *Anosia plexippus*. *Contrib. Boyce Thompson Inst.*, 22(5): 259.

HOKAMA, Y., and C. L. JUDSON, 1963: A new bleaching technique with possible general use in entomology. *Ann. Ent. Soc. Amer.*, 56: 407.

HORIKAWA, M., and A. S. FOX, 1964: Culture of embryonic cells of *Drosophila melanogaster in vitro*. *Science*, 145: 1437.

———, and Y. KURODA, 1959: *In vitro* cultivation of blood cells of *Drosophila melanogaster* in a synthetic medium. *Nature*, 184: 2017.

HUMANSON, G., 1962: *Animal Tissue Technique*. Freeman, San Francisco, Calif.

ITO, T., and Y. HORIE, 1962: Nutrition of the silkworm, *Bombyx mori*—VII. An aseptic culture of larvae on semi-synthetic diets. *J. Ins. Physiol.*, 8: 569.

JONES, B. M., 1962: The cultivation of insect cells and tissues. *Biol. Rev.*, 37: 512.

———, and I. CUNNINGHAM, 1961: Growth by cell division in insect tissue culture. *Exptl. Cell Res.*, 23: 386.

KITAMURA, S., 1965: The *in vitro* cultivation of tissues from the mosquito, *Culex pipiens* var. *molstus*. II. An improved culture medium useful for ovarian tissue culture. *Kobe J. Med. Sci.* 11: 23.

KOCH, P., 1964: *In vitro*-Kultur und Entwicklungsphysiologische Ergebnisse an Embryonen der Stabheuschrecke *Carausius morosus* Br. *Arch. Entw.-mech. Org.*, 155: 549.

KRAUSE, G., and J. KRAUSE, 1964: Schichtenbau und Segmentierung junger Keimanlagen von *Bombyx mori* L. (Lepidoptera) *in vitro* ohne Dottersystem. *Arch. Entw.-mech. Org.*, 155: 451.

LANDUREAU, J., 1965: Cultures "primaires" de cellules embryonnaires d'un insecte: *Blabera fusca* Brunner (Dictyoptères). *Compt. Rend. Acad. Sci. (Paris)*, 260: 5379.

LARSEN, W., 1964: Cell proliferation in an insect tissue culture. *Life Sci.*, 3: 103.

LELOUP, A. M., 1964: Cultures organotypiques de gonades d'insecte (*Calliphora erythrocephala*). *Bull. Soc. Zool. France*, 89: 70.

LENDER, T., and J. DUVEAU-HAGEGE, 1963: La survie et la différenciation en culture *in vitro* des gonades de larves de dernier âge de *Galleria mellonella* (Lépidoptère, pyralididae). *Dev. Biol.*, 6: 1.

LESSEPS, R. J., 1965: Culture of dissociated *Drosophila* embryos: aggregated cells differentiate and sort out. *Science*, 148: 502.

MARKS, E. P., and J. P. REINECKE, 1964: Regenerating tissues from the cockroach leg: A system for studying *in vitro*. *Science*, 143: 961.

———, 1965: Regenerating tissue from the cockroach leg: nutrient media for maintenance *in vitro*. *J. Kansas Ent. Soc.*, 38: 179.

MARTIGNONI, M. E., 1963: Insect tissue culture: a tool for the physiologist. In Victor J. Brookes (ed.), *Insect Physiology*, Oregon State University Press, Corvallis, Ore., p. 89.

———, and R. J. SCALLION, 1961: Preparation and uses of insect hemocyte monolayers *in vitro*. *Biol. Bull.*, 121: 507.

MEDVEDEVA, N. B., 1959: The multiplication of polyhedral virus in cultures of insect tissues. *Vopr. Virusol.* (Transl.), 4(4): 64.

MITSUHASHI, J., and K. MARAMOROSCH, 1964: Leafhopper tissue culture: embryonic, nymphal and imaginal tissues from aseptic insects. *Contrib. Boyce Thompson Inst.*, 22(8): 435.

PARKER, R. C., 1961: *Methods of Tissue Culture*, 3rd ed. Paul B. Hoeber, Inc., New York.

PAUL, J., 1960: *Cell and Tissue Culture*, 2nd ed. Williams & Wilkins Co., Baltimore, Md.

PELEG, J., 1965: Growth of mosquito tissues *in vitro*. *Nature*, 206: 427.

———, and W. TRAGER, 1963: Cultivation of insect tissues *in vitro* and their application to the study of arthropod-borne viruses. *Am. J. Trop. Med. Hyg.*, 12: 820.

SANG, J. H., 1956: The quantitative nutritional requirements of *Drosophila melanogaster. J. Exptl. Biol.*, 33: 45.

SCHNEIDER, I., 1964a: Culture *in vitro* of *Drosophila* ovarian tissue. *Genetics*, 50: 284.

———, 1964b: Differentiation of larval *Drosophila* eye-antennal discs *in vitro. J. Exptl. Zool.*, 156: 91.

———, 1965: Inadvisability of using the raft technique for *Drosophila* organ culture. *Dros. Info. Service*, 40: 74.

———, 1966: Histology of larval eye-antennal discs and cephalic ganglia of *Drosophila* cultured *in vitro. J. Embryol. Exptl. Morph.*, 15: 271.

SEN GUPTA, K., 1961: Studies on insect tissue culture. I. Culture of tissues from the wax moth, *Galleria mellonella* L., *in vitro. Folia Biol.*, 7: 400.

TAKAMI, T., 1958: *In vitro* culture of embryos of the silkworm, *Bombyx mori* L. I. Culture in silkworm egg extract, with special reference to some characteristics of the diapausing egg. *J. Exptl. Biol.*, 35: 286.

TING, K. Y., and M. A. BROOKS, 1965: Sodium: potassium ratios in insect cell culture and the growth of cockroach cells (Blattariae: Blattidae). *Ann. Ent. Soc. Am.*, 58: 197.

TRAGER, W., 1935: The culture of mosquito larvae free from living micro-organisms. *Am. J. Hyg.*, 22:18.

———, 1959: Tsetse-fly tissue culture and the development of trypanosomes to the infective stage. *Ann. Trop. Med. Parasitol.*, 53: 473.

VAGO, C., and O. FLANDRE, 1963: Culture prolongée de tissus d'insectes et de vecteurs de maladies en coagulum plasmatique. *Ann. Épiphyties*, 14: 127.

WHITE, P. R., 1963: *The Cultivation of Animal and Plant Cells*, 2nd ed. Ronald Press Co., New York.

WYATT, S. S., 1956: Culture *in vitro* of tissue from the silkworm, *Bombyx mori* L. *J. Gen. Physiol.*, 39: 841.

Plant Cell and Tissue Culture

By Philip R. White

INTRODUCTION

"Tissue culture," or better "cell culture," is a research technique by which cells of complex organisms—animals or plants—are removed from the body and grown in artificial environments, thus isolating them from the various influences which integrate them into an organism without destroying their abilities to function in characteristic fashion. The method depends on the assumption that, within the limits set by genetic content, cells are basically totipotent, and that by so isolating them, the true breadth of this genetic potential can be brought to expression and the means by which it is limited in the organism can be elucidated. This is the major intrinsic objective for which the method was created. The method has found its widest practical use to date, however, in quite a different direction, in providing materials which, possessing selected characteristics of specific organisms needed for special studies, are nevertheless freed of other characteristics which might limit their use. The Salk and Sabin anti-polio vaccines were developed in cell cultures of human origin which provided biologically satisfactory substrata for virus cultivation without the sociological limitations which experiments with intact human beings present. Cultures of plant cells or tissues partake of these same advantages (White, 1943a, 1963).

As applied to plants, the method has depended on the development of suitable nutrients (White, 1943a, b; Heller, 1953; Gautheret, 1959), of effective methods of isolating viable cells or cell aggregates from the plant (White, 1943a, 1963; Gautheret, 1959), and of providing suitable procedures for their maintenance, propagation, and study (White, 1943a, 1963; Gautheret, 1959; White and Risser, 1964). This chapter will deal with some of these questions.

NUTRIENT SOLUTIONS

Nutrients for cultivation of plant tissues are all based, with subsequent modifications, on the solution originally developed by Knop for the cultivation of whole plants. This solution, published in 1865, provided balanced concentrations of the ions: Ca, K, Mg, NO_3, SO_4, and PO_4. The heavy metal, iron, was soon added. Complete nutrients today include manganese, zinc, boron, iodine, copper, molybdenum, and sometimes chloride (White, 1943b; Heller, 1953). Isolated non-chlorophyll-bearing cells must be provided with an energy source; dextrose or sucrose are commonly used, depending on the tissue. All cells studied to date show varying degrees of heterotrophy in regard to other metabolites. This heterotrophy was at first met by supplying complexes such as yeast extract but the effective constituents of such additives have since been identified for most cells. With rare exceptions cells require an external source of thiamine. Few cells will synthesize protein from nitrate without additional help. Tomato roots will utilize nitrate as their sole source of nitrogen if supplied with pyridoxine (White, 1943a, 1963). For many tissues glutamine provides a satisfactory source of organic nitrogen, either in the presence or absence of pyridoxine. Other vitamins, especially niacin, biotin, inositol, and pantothenate, are required by some cells but not by others. In addition to inorganic salts, sugar, vitamins, and organic nitrogen sources, most normal plant cells require an external source of auxins or kinins, and there may be other specific requirements (White, 1943a, b; Gautheret, 1959). Indoleacetic acid (IAA) or naphthaleneacetic acid (NAA) are suitable auxins for most cells. Some cells, however, contain enzymes which inactivate these compounds but leave 2,4-dichlorophenoxyacetic acid (2,4-D) unaffected (see Morré and Key, this volume, pp. 575–593). To obtain satisfactory growth, spruce tumor cells, for example, require 100 times as high a concentration of IAA as they do of 2,4-D (2,4-dichlorophenoxyacetic acid). With further refinements of method still other requirements have come to light.

The two most widely used basic formulas today are those of White (1943a, b), derived from Knop by way of Uspenski, and of Heller (1953), likewise derived from Knop by way of Gautheret. These are prepared as follows:

White's basic nutrient is made up from four stocks:

1. Set out three flasks each containing 1 liter of distilled water. To No. I add 12.0 gm $Ca(NO_3)_2{\cdot}4H_2O$, 3.2 gm KNO_3, 2.6 gm KCl, 0.20 gm $MnSO_4{\cdot}H_2O$, 0.12 gm $ZnSO_4{\cdot}7H_2O$, 0.06 gm H_3BO_3, and 0.03 gm KI. To No. II add 30.0 gm $MgSO_4{\cdot}7H_2O$ and 8.0 gm Na_2SO_4. To No. III add 0.76 gm $NaH_2PO_4{\cdot}H_2O$. When these are quite dissolved, the three are mixed slowly and made up to a total of 4 liters to provide stock 1. This should be stored in the dark or in black or nonactinic bottles.

2. In 100 ml of water dissolve 300 mg glycine, 50 mg niacin, 10 mg thiamine, and 10 mg pyridoxine. Sterilize by filtration, draw off into test tubes, and store in the refrigerator.

3. Dissolve 100 mg chlorophenol red in 25 ml 0.01 *N* NaOH, then add water to make 250 ml. Adjust pH to 6.0, filter, and store in tubes in the refrigerator.

Stocks 1 and 3 will keep indefinitely if not allowed to become contaminated; stock 2 should not be kept longer than 60 days unless frozen (−15°C).

4. One liter of nutrient is prepared by taking 889 ml of water, dissolving therein 20 gm sucrose (or 10 gm dextrose) and 2.5 mg $Fe_2(SO_4)_3$ to constitute stock 4, and adding 100 ml stock 1 (salts), 1 ml stock 2 (vitamins), and 10 ml stock 3 (indicator). The nutrient should have a pH of about 5.5 as indicated by a pink color; if it is too yellow it can be adjusted with 1.0 *N* KOH. When complete it is distributed to culture flasks, bottles, or tubes, autoclaved, and allowed to cool. It is then ready for use.

For tissues requiring a semisolid substratum the same procedure is followed except that only 389 ml of water instead of 889 ml are used in the first step. Five grams of agar (Difco "Noble" agar or its equivalent) are dissolved in 500 ml of hot water. When the agar is thoroughly liquefied the two solutions are combined, to give stock 4, distributed, and autoclaved.

This basic nutrient will be subject to modifications for particular tissues.

Heller's nutrient is prepared in seven stocks:

In seven flasks of 1 liter of water each dissolve:

1. 100 gm KCL.
2. 100 gm $NaNO_3$.
3. 100 gm $MgSO_4 \cdot 7H_2O$.
4. 10 gm $NaH_2PO_4 \cdot H_2O$.
5. 10 gm $CaCl_3 \cdot 2H_2O$.
6. 1 gm $FeCl_3 \cdot 6H_2O$.
7. 1 gm $ZnSO_4 \cdot 7H_2O$; 1 gm H_3BO_3; 10 mg $MnSO_4 \cdot 4H_2O$; 30 mg $CuSO_4 \cdot 5H_2O$; 30 mg $AlCl_3$; 30 mg $NiCl_2 \cdot 6H_2O$; and 10 mg KI.

In preparing nutrients, to 962 ml of water add 20 gm dextrose, 7.5 ml stock 1, 6 ml stock 2, 2.5 ml stock 3, 12.5 ml stock 4, 7.5 ml stock 5, 1 ml stock 6, and 1 ml stock 7. One milligram of thiamine per liter will be added to most nutrients.

To these, supplements of vitamins, organic materials such as glutamine or asparagine, auxins, and special inorganic catalysts will be added for particular cells or to promote particular processes.

Not all cells respond satisfactorily to these fully defined nutrient formulas. In early research it was customary to add a blanket source of unknown additives in the form of yeast extract (White, 1943a). This has today been largely replaced, either by a casein digest or by the liquid endosperm of the coconut (coconut "milk" or coconut "water") (Steward *et al.*, 1952, 1955). The milky endosperm of the coconut is essentially a coenocytic mass of protoplasm containing large numbers of nuclei. It is thus rich in nucleic acids, free amino acids, sugars, vitamins, and inorganic ions. In its native state it is also highly charged with free carbon dioxide. For many cells this has provided an extraordinary stimulus to cell growth and multiplication. For this purpose 10 or 20 percent of filtered or autoclaved coconut milk is added to the nutrient. All efforts, however, to isolate and identify the specific constituents responsible for this stimulus have failed. Since the stimulating quality is not destroyed by boiling or autoclaving these constituents must be highly stable, and since they pass a dialysis membrane, they must be of small molecular dimensions. Moreover, no cells which have been thoroughly studied have failed to grow reasonably well on nutrients devoid of this complex. While the use of coconut milk as an additive may be acceptable where precise definition of the environment is secondary to the use of cells for specific purposes, the experimenter will do well to avoid it except as a last resort.

CHOICE AND ISOLATION OF CELLS

The first step in any culture is to obtain cells capable of growth by cell division (White, 1943a, 1963; Gautheret, 1959). These may come from characteristically "meristematic" cells—embryos, stem or root growing points, procambium, cambium, pericycle, phellogen—or they may come from cells which, being already somewhat "differentiated," would not normally divide but in which dedifferentiation to a meristematic state is still possible. Parenchyma of pith, medullary rays, or cortex, even some collenchymas, epidermal cells, glandular cells, leaf mesophyll, and some storage cells may be caused to divide by treatment with suitable auxins and/or kinins (see this volume, Morré and Key, pp. 575–593, and Miller, pp. 613–622). So long as a cell contains a nucleus and cytoplasm, its suitability as a source of a culture can never be safely excluded and can only be determined by experiment.

The first successful cultures of plant origin (1934) were of the meristematic root apices (White, 1943a). These characteristically lose none of their normal organization; they provide organ cultures rather than tissue cultures.

PRIMARY CALLUS CULTURES

A step beyond the root culture was provided in 1939, by the cultivation of calluses (see White, 1963). Gautheret (1939) and Nobécourt (1939) independently and by slightly different methods established strains of callus from slices of carrot. Sterile slices containing cambium were placed on a suitable nutrient until callus developed from the cambial region. This was cut away and transferred to fresh nutrient. It continued to grow and could thereafter be cut up for further subculturing at suitable intervals. These strains, now more than 25 years old, are still in culture. Their success depended on the inclusion of indoleacetic acid in the nutrient, an ingredient not previously tested with isolated cambial tissue. In the same year White (1939) established cultures from procambial material from a hybrid tobacco (*Nicotiana Langsdorffii* × *N. glauca*) known to be subject to spontaneous tumors. This tumorous tissue, unlike most normal tissues, makes its own auxin and grows satisfactorily without an external source. This strain is also still in culture.

Since 1939 this method has been elaborated and refined and is now applied to a great variety of plants. Three examples will suffice to characterize the methods of isolation in common use.

Herbaceous Plants

The carrot can be taken as an example. A crisp, fresh carrot is washed thoroughly and surface dried. It is then broken across, exposing two aseptic surfaces. No local sterilization is needed. The cambial region is recognizable as the boundary between the orange core and the yellow outer region. With a sharp, sterile 5-mm cork borer a series of cores are removed and transferred to a sterile Petri dish. Here they are cut transversely into disks 1–2 mm thick. The disks are transferred to sterile nutrient agar (White's or Heller's formula). The cultures are then placed at room temperature (22°–25°C) in the dark.

If the cores were removed from the cambial ring so that each disk includes cambial (meristematic) cells, callus will form promptly, that is, within 10 days or 2 weeks, on any reasonably complete nutrient. If, however, they are taken from outside the cambial ring (phloem) (Steward *et al.*, 1952) or from the older central tissues, their mitotic potential may be limited (cells reversibly differentiated) and it may be necessary to add an auxin or other catalyst to the nutrient in order to initiate growth. It was for such cultures that coconut milk was first introduced.

When nodules of callus 2 mm or more thick have formed on the surface of the cultured disks, this callus is cut away and transferred to fresh nutrient. It can then be subcultured for potentially unlimited periods.

This method, with minor modifications, can be used in establishing cultures from any fleshy stem or root. If a clean, sterile surface cannot be exposed by breaking or tearing, the surface of the plant body may be sterilized by washing with alcohol and burning, or by immersion in a mild detergent or other wetting agent followed by treatment with Clorox diluted 1:6 and washing with sterile water. Once the surface has been sterilized it can be cut with sterile instruments to expose suitable areas for more precise dissection. Cores from the Jerusalem artichoke or from kohlrabi require an auxin in the nutrient, those from tobacco stem pith require auxin and kinin, those from potato have been grown successfully only by providing both auxin and coconut milk. Disks cut from the fleshy leaves of cabbage or from surface-sterilized leaves of tobacco can be substituted for carrot root or tobacco-pith disks. Even more coreacious members can serve as primary explants. In these cases satisfactory growth is most likely if the disks contain some vein tissue (cambium), but division can often be evoked from non-vascular tissues by adding suitable auxins or kinins (dedifferentiation of parenchyma). Cultures can be obtained from a wide variety of herbaceous tissues, including leaf mesophyll, by suitable modifications of this method.

Woody Plants

Woody perennials and plants with thin, coreacious, papery, or needlelike leaves do not lend themselves to the removal of fleshy explants. For these a different approach is necessary. The white spruce, *Picea glauca*, will serve as an example (White and Risser, 1964). Select a clean, rapidly growing tree and, with a chisel, remove the rough outer bark over a small area. Two approaches are then equally effective. If a 10-mm increment borer is available, wash the exposed area and the borer with alcohol and remove one or more cores 2–4 cm long, carrying them to the laboratory in sterile containers. Dip the bark ends of the cores in 95 percent alcohol and burn this off twice to ensure sterility of the cut surfaces; then trim off the bark down to 1 mm from the cambium and split the wood 1 mm inside the cambium to provide a disk 2 mm thick. Trim off and discard the crushed and burnt edges; then divide the disk into six equal pieces, soak them for 10 minutes in sterile liquid nutrient so that the surfaces are thoroughly imbibed, and place them on nutrient agar, phloem side down. Incubate in the dark at 20°–25°C. Callus should form from the cambium in about 10 days, from the phloem somewhat later, and eventually from the xylem also. This callus can then be excised and removed to fresh nutrient.

If an increment borer is not available it will be necessary to isolate a larger initial explant. Choose an area without blemishes such as branch traces and with a saw make two transverse cuts about 8–10 cm apart and penetrating 2–3 cm into the wood. With a chisel mark out two vertical cuts, also 8–10 cm apart. Remove a wedge of bark and wood along one side to a depth of 1 cm and then by driving the chisel in at the bottom of this last cut and on the line of a chord to the tree surface, remove the outlined block with cambium intact. These steps require no special sterile precautions. The block is now taken to the laboratory, brushed, and the bark removed to within about 2 mm from the cambium. It is then washed with alcohol which is burned off twice. Then an additional 1 mm of bark is carefully removed, this time with a sterile knife. A series of intersecting cuts about 5 mm apart are made to a depth of 2 mm into the wood. A sharp carton-opening knife with sterilized blade makes an excellent implement for this operation. One series of the rectangular blocks so outlined is removed along one edge and discarded. This is done to eliminate tissue which might have been injured in the earlier operations or which might harbor contaminations driven into the wood from these edges during the field work and might thus have escaped the later sterilizing procedures. The interior blocks are then carefully lifted out one by one, placed in a sterile liquid nutrient for about 10 minutes, and then planted, phloem side down, on agar nutrient. These are now comparable to those prepared from increment borings and can be treated in like fashion.

Cultures have been prepared in this way from a great variety of forest trees. Not all will respond to the same nutrients. Primary callus can usually be obtained on almost any nutrient of suitable sugar content (osmotic value), and the time of year seems to make little difference in their initial viability. When the primary callus is removed and transferred to fresh nutrient, however, it can no longer draw on the original block for special or trace metabolites and becomes completely dependent on the nutrient provided. It is at this stage that most failures occur. The nutrient may have to be tailored to each species and even to each strain. We have rapid-growing permanent strains from raspberry, cactus, Virginia creeper, Boston ivy, *Vinca*, carrot, and *Scorzonera*, all growing on the nutrient developed for hybrid tobacco cells, without auxin, yet spruce tissue dies out within no more than four passages on this nutrient. Normal spruce tissue requires inositol, ascorbic acid, glutamine, and 2,4-D in addition to the other ingredients. Other species will undoubtedly have other specific requirements. The basic methods of isolation, however, are applicable to them all.

Where, as in the case of woody shrubs, it is not possible to obtain disks or blocks of the above types, it is often possible to strip off the outer cortex just back of the growing point, discarding the potentially contaminated surface layers, and then to cut directly across the stem, providing disks which contain all the internal tissues including the cambium or procambium (White, 1963). These will then serve as primary explants. Older medullary ray parenchyma has been used in making cultures, for example, from sycamore, by removing from old trees wood blocks adjacent to the pith. Primary callus has thus been obtained from cells which had been dormant for 50 or more years. Permanent strains have not been established from such callus but should present no special problems different from those involved in finding suitable conditions for any new strain.

Primary Meristems as Sources of Callus

There are many sources of primary callus to which the above methods do not apply. The prothallus cells in pollen are an example. When pollen is germinated on nutrient agar, growth normally consists of the extension of the intine and the cytoplasm to form the pollen tube, followed by migration of the sperm nuclei without proliferation of the vegetative nuclei. These last remain functionally dormant. If, however, the pollen is placed on a nutrient containing an auxin, the vegetative nuclei may be caused to resume the mitotic function, giving rise to a tissue. This has been done especially effectively with pollen of *Ginkgo* (Gautheret, 1959; Tulecke and Nickell, 1960) but enough has been done with other species to suggest that this may represent a general phenomenon. In this case the pollen is removed from surface-sterilized anthers, or is collected by suspending unsterilized microsporophylls in a dry atmosphere above a collecting surface. It is sowed on nutrient agar in a Petri dish. Where tissue is produced it will appear as white nodules which are visible within a week or so. These nodules can be removed to fresh nutrient. The tissue so formed differs in no important way from that formed from cambium, ray parenchyma, phloem parenchyma, or other sources.

Many other plant organs will provide local callus. Anthers, styles, the petioles of leaves taken from buds, petals, excised stem growing points, young flowers and fruits, seed primordia, stipules, in fact any member which contains meristematic, procambial or cambial tissues, or undifferentiated parenchyma, can be caused to produce callus on a suitable auxin-containing nutrient. Any of the members which one tries, by careful adjustment of the nutrient, to maintain in their normal pattern of development as organ cultures, even roots, are likely to give rise to massive callus instead, if placed on nutrients containing auxins.

SECONDARY CULTURES

Once a strain of tissue, such as that of carrot, spruce, ginkgo, aster, etc. has been established, it can be treated in a number of ways, depending on the purpose of the research. These may be roughly divided into three classes: (1) massive cultures, (2) suspension cultures, and (3) single-cell cultures (White, 1963; Gautheret, 1959).

Massive Cultures

Where the objective is to study general problems of physiology, nutrition, or organization, cultures can best be grown on a semisolid substratum, either on agar (White, 1943a; Gautheret, 1959) or on filter paper imbibed with nutrient (Heller, 1949). A nutrient is made up from Heller's (1953) or some other formula to which 0.5–1.0 percent of a highly purified agar is added. This is distributed to tubes (25- × 150-mm Pyrex lipless test tubes have been much used, either placed vertically or sloped), flasks (125-ml Erlenmeyers, for example) or bottles (1-ounce French Squares, 4-ounce flat pharmaceutical bottles). The 1-ounce French Squares are especially useful on account of their small size, low cost, and easy handling (White and Risser, 1964). Such a bottle, if slightly sloped while cooling, will hold 10 ml of nutrient. Screw caps are quite satisfactory. A suitable explant with which to start a culture in such a bottle or tube will consist of about 20–50 mg blotted wet weight of tissue. The size of the explant required will depend on the growth characteristics of the strain under study. If meristematic activity is uniformly distributed through the callus, a small explant, as small as 2 mg, may routinely give good results (Steward *et al.*, 1952). If, on the other hand, meristematic activity is limited to discrete nodules or to surface areas, larger explants will be needed to ensure inclusion of meristem. Cultures of carrot, tobacco, or spruce cells can be maintained from very small inocula while cultures of *Scorzonera* will die out unless the inocula are of at least 50 mg blotted weight. Such explants will usually be prepared by placing a freshly blotted stock culture on sterile filter paper in a Petri dish and cutting it up with a sharp scalpel, the pieces being transferred with forceps, needle, or with the cutting knife.

Cultures so prepared and placed in the dark at 25°C will reach their log phase of growth in about a week. For experimental studies subcultures should be made at about 2-week intervals. Stock cultures may be left for much longer periods, up to 10–12 weeks. This will depend somewhat on the growth characteristics of each particular strain and on the stability and proportional constitution of the nutrient. A suitable measure of growth of such cultures is the increment in blotted weight which, under adequate conditions will be 5- to 10-fold in a 2-week passage (White and Risser, 1964).

Where there is question of possible effects of trace impurities in the agar, or of the adsorptive properties of colloidal substrata, cultures can be supported on tables of ash-free filter paper, resting in tubes in such a way that the paper is constantly saturated with liquid nutrient. Heller in particular has made such tables by folding paper around a mandril, leaving a flat end on the cylinder so formed (Heller, 1953). This can then be slipped into a suitable test tube and pushed down to the level of the nutrient.

Cultures prepared by either of these methods make excellent material not only for physiological studies but also for anatomical and cytological preparations.

Suspension Cultures

In massive cultures there are always environmental gradients and resulting polarizations of development. Where it is desired to minimize this polarization cultures can be grown in suspension in liquid nutrient. This requires some means of providing constant agitation. The mechanical stirring sometimes used for animal cells has not proved satisfactory for plant materials, since the shearing forces involved are much more damaging to the semirigid walls of plant cells than they are to freely deformed animal cells. Successful results have, however, been obtained by three other methods. Steward has employed special flasks, either "T"-shaped tubes which can be rotated around the stem axis so that nutrient is periodically transferred from one end to the other of the cross arm, or multiarmed flasks providing similar circulation (Steward *et al.*, 1952, 1955). These have been very successful but require complex equipment which is costly. Nickell and Tulecke (1956, 1960) have designed large carboy containers in which continuous circulation is maintained by bubbling sterile air through the nutrient (Tulecke and Nickell, 1960). These are also complicated and costly. A more generally useful method is to place standard culture vessels—bottles, flasks, or tubes—on a reciprocating shaker (Bergmann, 1959; Dougall, 1964). If the shaking interval and excursion are properly adjusted to the size and character of the culture vessels used, a high degree of circulation can be maintained without excessive mechanical damage, foaming, or splashing. When grown on such a shaker most cultures will produce suspensions consisting of single cells or small groups of cells which can then be transferred to fresh nutrient by wide-mouthed pipette. Continuous suspension cultures are suitable for studies of chemical exchanges, nutrition, metabolism, production of specific substances such as pharmaceutical products, etc. They can also be used for cytological studies, although for this purpose they are not superior to mass cultures. For studies of morphogenesis or of development in general, true suspension cultures are quite useless. Even in shaken cultures, however, some cells will often be thrown clear of the main mass of nutrient and will become fixed to the glass, within reach of the capillary film of nutrient on the glass yet not subject to being washed free and returned to the general circulation. Such cells are then in a newly polarized environment and will often grow into organized, three-dimensional masses. It is from such masses that embryoids have been found to develop from which complete plants have been derived (Steward *et al.*, 1952; Halperin, 1964). This formation of embryoids depends on many factors which are still only imperfectly understood. It has been observed especially in suspension cultures of members of the Umbelliferae (carrot, parsley, celery) but is known to occur in some other cultures as well (Vasil *et al.*, 1964, 1965).

Single-cell Cultures

For many purposes it is important to work with, or at least to start with, single cells. The question of whether variations in cell potency exist within a particular strain can be answered only in this way. Suspension cultures are a suitable source of such single cells, and are indeed at present the only satisfactory source. Although it should theoretically be possible to isolate cells from organized plant bodies by enzymatic maceration or mechanical dissection, these are at present not practical possibilities.

Single cells can be isolated from a suspension either by mechanical picking or by dilution plating. Cells which have been mechanically picked from a drop of suspension by use of a micropipette have been transferred to bits of filter paper placed on massive agar cultures which then serve as "nurse" cultures (Muir's method) (Muir *et al.*, 1958) or have been transferred to special microculture chambers (method of Mazurier-Jones) (Jones *et al.*, 1960).

The Muir method does not permit following the development of the cell in detail but does identify the resulting colony as being derived from a single cell, and the colony can ultimately be handled like any other massive culture. The Jones method permits day-by-day study of the fate of the selected cell but under conditions where later recovery of the colony, although not impossible, is difficult. Better methods for such studies are urgently needed.

More satisfactory for most studies is the dilution plating method, adapted from bacteriological techniques (Bergmann, 1959). A drop of a suspension is first examined and its concentration determined by hemocytometer count. The suspension is then serially diluted to such a point that, when spread on an agar plate, the cells or intact cell clusters will be isolated and will give rise to discrete colonies. For some strains it may be necessary to use a nutrient which has been "conditioned" by growing therein a massive culture to its log phase and then removing the cells by filtration or centrifugation, leaving only the noncellular metabolites. Such metabolites appear to be necessary for the mitosis of isolated cells of some strains. Once spread on a suitable nutrient the isolated cells or cell clusters will grow to form discrete colonies which can be picked up and transferred either to fresh plates or bottles, or new suspension flasks. This does not guarantee that each colony came from a single cell; this can be ensured only by manual selection under the microscope. It does, however, provide an easily handled method of obtaining large numbers of colonies of discrete origin. Once established such colonies can be handled as can any massive strain.

These are, in brief, the major methods used at present for the study of cultures of plant cells and tissues. Many of these methods are similar to those suitable for study of plant organs, embryos, and seedlings. The nutrients in particular are much alikc, and the methods differ largely because of differences in dimensions of the materials to be studied. Thcse methods are constantly being improved and expanded in scope. I have chosen not to dcal with specialized approaches such as those for radiobiology but to limit this treatment to more general approaches of wide applicability.

REFERENCES

BERGMANN, L., 1959: A new technique for isolating and cloning single cells of higher plants. *Nature*, 184: 648.

DOUGALL, D. K., 1964: A method of plant tissue culture giving high growth rates. *Exp. Cell Res.*, 33: 438.

GAUTHERET, R. J., 1959: *La Culture des Tissus végétaux.* Masson, Paris.

HALPERIN, W., 1964: Morphogenetic studies with partially synchronized cultures of carrot embryos. *Science*, 146: 408.

HELLER, R., 1949: Sur l'emploi de papier filtre sans cendres comme support pour les cultures de tissus végétaux. *Compt. Rend. Soc. Biol. (Paris)*, 143: 335.

———, 1953: Recherches sur la nutrition minérale des tissus végétaux cultivés *in vitro*. *Ann. Sci. Nat., Bot., Biol. Végét.*, 14: 1.

JONES, L. E., A. C. HILDEBRANDT, A. J. RIKER, and J. H. WU, 1960: Growth of somatic tobacco cells in microculture. *Am. J. Bot.*, 47: 468.

MUIR, W. H., A. C. HILDEBRANDT, and A. J. RIKER, 1958: The preparation, isolation and growth in culture of single cells from higher plants. *Am. J. Bot.*, 45: 589.

NICKELL, L. G., 1956: The continuous submerged cultivation of plant tissue as single cells. *Proc. Nat. Acad. Sci. U.S.*, 42: 848.

———, and W. TULECKE, 1960: Submerged growth of cells of higher plants. *J. Biochem. Microbiol. Technol. Eng.*, 2: 287.

NOBÉCOURT, P., 1939: Sur la perennité et l'augmentation de volume des cultures des tissues végétaux. *Compt. Rend. Soc. Biol. (Paris)*, 133: 530.

STEWARD, F. C., S. M. CAPLIN, and F. K. MILLAR, 1952: Investigations on growth and metabolism of plant cells. I. New techniques for the investigation of metabolism, nutrition and growth in undifferentiated cells. *Ann. Bot. (London)* New Ser., 16: 57.

STEWARD, F. C., and E. M. SHANTZ, 1955: The chemical induction of growth in plant tissue cultures. In *The Chemistry and Mode of Action of Plant Growth Substances*, Butterworth, London, p. 165.

TULECKE, W., and L. NICKELL, 1960: Methods, problems and results of growing plant cells under submerged conditions. *Trans. N.Y. Acad. Sci.*, Ser. II, 22: 196.

VASIL, I. K., A. C. HILDEBRANDT, and A. J. RIKER, 1964: Endive plantlets from freely suspended cells and cell groups grown *in vitro*. *Science*, 146: 76.

VASIL, V., and A. C. HILDEBRANDT, 1965: Growth and tissue formation from single, isolated tobacco cells in microculture. *Science*, 147: 1454.

WHITE, P. R., 1943: *A Handbook of Plant Tissue Culture*. Jaques Cattell Press, Lancaster, Pa.

———, 1943: Nutrient deficiency studies and an improved inorganic nutrient for cultivation of excised tomato roots. *Growth*, 7: 53.

———, 1963: *The Cultivation of Animal and Plant Cells*. 2nd (rev.) ed. The Ronald Press, New York.

———, and P. G. RISSER, 1964: Some basic parameters in the cultivation of spruce tissues. *Physiologia Plant.*, 17: 600.

Avian and Mammalian Cell Dissociation

By Malcolm S. Steinberg

INTRODUCTION

The experimental separation of tissues into their component living cells evidently has its earliest historical root in the observation of Schiefferdecker (1886) that incubation in an aqueous extract of pancreas powder will loosen epidermis from the underlying dermis. Other workers, using other tissues and organisms, have employed mechanical and chemical means, or combinations of the two, for separating cells (reviewed in Rinaldini, 1958; Steinberg, 1958; Moscona, 1962a). It is not our present aim to review the literature or to cite all relevant references. Rather, we will be concerned mainly with variations of the principal technique in current use for dissociating tissues of mammals and birds. These techniques are built around incubation of tissues in a solution containing proteolytic enzymes, usually in the form of an extract of crude trypsin powder.

Dissociation techniques have been applied to normal and malignant adult tissues, to embryonic tissues, and to tissue cultures *in vitro*. Enzymatic methods appear to have been least successful with *normal, adult tissues*, which have often been subjected instead to procedures involving mechanical disruption and removal of divalent cations (e.g., Anderson, 1953; Longmuir and ap Rees, 1956). However some adult tissue cells can be separated with proteolytic enzymes (e.g., Herrmann and Hickman, 1948; Buschke, 1949; Hinz and Syverton, 1959; Garvey, 1961). Tryptic dissociation has evidently found greater favor among those working with tumors (e.g., Dabrowska-Piaskowska, 1959; Boyse, 1960; Madden and Burk, 1961).

Cultured cells can be suspended by tryptic digestion of a plasma clot upon which they may be grown (Rous, 1916) or by action of the protease or of chelating agents upon links which may mediate the attachment of the cells to a solid surface (see Scherer *et al.*, 1953; Lieberman and Ove, 1958; Rosenberg, 1960). The enzyme may have an additional action at the mutual abutments of the cells themselves. While trypsin is evidently well tolerated by cells of many kinds, this is not always the case, and care must be taken to avoid unnecessarily harsh treatment (see Rappaport, 1956; Harris, 1955; Puck *et al.*, 1956; Weiss, 1958; Laws and Stickland, 1961; also review by Moscona, 1962a).

The separation of *intact tissue layers*, especially of epithelia from underlying connections, deserves special comment. After Schiefferdecker's initial observation, this was made use of by Medawar (1941). It appears that, at least for some tissues, the epithelium-separating action can be enhanced in comparison with the cell-dispersing action by conducting the digestion at a low temperature (Szabo, 1955; Rawles, 1963). In my own experience with chick embryos, brief trypsinization is useful in isolating intact somites and in separating notochord from spinal cord, the pigmented retina from the choroid coat, and epidermis from dermis.

Proteolytic dissociation of *embryonic tissues and organs* had its origin in the work of Moscona (1952; Moscona and Moscona, 1952) and is now widely practiced for a variety of purposes, prominent among which is the study of the mechanisms by which cells organize themselves into specific histological configurations (see also Cahn, Coon, and Cahn, this volume, pp. 493–530). Owing in part to actual differences in the responses of different tissues and in part to a dearth of thorough comparative studies of dissociation techniques, a great variety of protocols are in current use. In general, embryonic tissues become increasingly resistant to trypsinization with increasing age. There is also an accompanying decrease in the aggregative capacity of the dissociated cells (Grover, 1961, 1962; Moscona, 1961), which I have confirmed for cells from several other tissues. My own experience has been with chick embryonic tissues, but mammalian embryonic tissues of comparable stages usually respond similarly. Because of the variability in existing practices and requirements, no single sample protocol could serve for all applications. Therefore I have tried to present, in the next section, a range of procedures in use for each step. Where it is possible, a discussion of potential problems and ways to avoid or solve them will be presented.

A discussion of cell dissociation technology appears in Paul (1961, Chapter XIV); discussions of both this subject and of cell aggregation and associated phenomena have recently been published by Moscona (in Willmer, 1965, pp. 49–60 and 489–529) and bear with them his personal viewpoints; and a student laboratory exercise on cell aggregation, with a set of step-by-step procedures, appears in Merchant, Kahn, and Murphy (pp. 64–69).

A TISSUE DISSOCIATION PROTOCOL

1. *Store* dissected tissues at a cool temperature (e.g., 13°–18°C) if they are not to be used within about a half hour.

2. *Mince* the tissue (suspended in physiological saline) with fine-pointed scissors or fine scalpels or knives. The knives may be ground down from steel sewing needles or made from tungsten wire (see Hamburger, 1960, for techniques and bibliography, or article by Cutter, this volume, pp. 623–634). Tungsten needles have the advantage of not flaking off bits of rust to which tissues will adhere tenaciously.

3. *Rinse* away blood cells or other debris by decantation.

4. *Soak* the rinsed fragments in CMF (any Ca^{++}- and Mg^{++}-free physiological saline) for 15–30 minutes, perhaps with a change of solution at the halfway point. Some investigators omit this soaking, others carry it out at 37°C, while others conduct it at cooler temperatures. It is convenient to carry out both this step, if it is used, and the subsequent trypsinization step in screw-capped culture or centrifuge tubes about half full of solution. The tubes should be subjected to a constant stirring action, such as that provided by a roller tube rotor revolving at 20–60 rpm with the tubes placed horizontally or at a pronounced slant.

5. *Replace the CMF solution, if used, with "trypsin" solution* prewarmed to

37°C. It is important to use a very large volume of the latter in relation to the volume of tissue (for example, 1,000:1, v/v).

The "trypsin" solution is best prepared freshly, although a 1 percent solution may be stored frozen (preferably at extremely low temperature, such as −70°C) and diluted just before use. The trypsin is typically a crude preparation such as BDH (British Drug House) or trypsin 1:250 or 1:300 from Nutritional Biochemicals Co. or Difco in the United States. Other pancreatic proteases (chymotrypsin, elastase) are present as well, and they may in some instances be the principal active agents. The solution may be made up with 0.05 percent to 3.0 percent "trypsin." The lowest usable concentration for a given application should be determined empirically. The solvent is typically CMF, which is adjusted to pH 7.4 after the insoluble residue of "trypsin" powder is removed. In certain cases, use of saline containing divalent cations as the trypsin solvent is effective (see Konigsberg *et al.*, 1960). In other cases the divalent cations inhibit the cell-dispersing action of the protease, even though they may have little or no influence upon the digestion of a test substrate (Buschke, 1949; Steinberg, unpublished observations). Where this effect of divalent cations is pronounced, and where relatively high enzyme concentrations are used, the alkaline earth ions present in the trypsin powder itself (Steinberg, 1963) must be eliminated by dialysis against CMF, passage through an appropriate Sephadex column, or addition of a chelator such as ethylenediaminetetraacetate (EDTA; Versene).

Enzyme solutions are conveniently sterilized by passage through a 0.45-μ pore size type HA Millipore (or comparable) filter used together with a depth prefilter (such as the Millipore microfiber glass prefilters) if clarification and sterilization need be done together. See Cahn (1967) for caution concerning detergents in filters. In my laboratory trypsin and deoxyribonuclease (DNase) solutions are kept at hand in hypodermic syringes fitted with metal Millipore filter assemblies (Millipore Filter Co., Bedford, Mass.). Sterilization occurs as the solutions are added to the tissue fragments.

6. *Agitate* the preparation constantly, as in step 4, at 37C° for 10–40 minutes. It may be desirable to triturate the softening tissue fragments once or twice during this process either by passing them rapidly to and fro through the tip of a pipette or by means of a "Vortex"-type mixer. In the latter case, the volume of solution should be such that the vortex of air penetrates to the bottom of the tube; all of the liquid should be sheared around the inner surface of the tube. Five to fifteen seconds of such shearing at a time are ordinarily adequate, but the shortest possible time should be used. When only truly minute amounts of tissue are available (i.e., even by the embryologist's standards) the device described by Auerbach and Grobstein (1958) is useful. In our experience, however, soaking in trypsin works much better when conducted in a larger vessel containing a larger volume of trypsin than Auerbach and Grobstein's tubes will hold. Only the actual shearing and related steps should be conducted in the small tubes recommended by them. Trypsinization should not be allowed to proceed too long, since trypsinized cells tend to be fragile. In some laboratories trypsinization is carried out without any trituration at all, and the enzyme solution is replaced with culture medium before strong mechanical stresses are applied. It is likely that this procedure, where it can be applied, is gentler to the cells.

Often a "mucoid" or slimy material appears during trypsinization and entrains the cells (Auerbach and Grobstein, 1958;

Rinaldini, 1958; Weiss, 1958; Moscona, 1960; Boyse, 1960; Easty *et al.*, 1960; Laws and Stickland, 1961; Madden and Burk, 1961; Steinberg, 1963). In general such "mucoid" gels are unresponsive to hyaluronidase (but see St. Amand and Tipton, 1954). Rinaldini (1958) found them to be digested by a pancreatic "mucase," and Auerbach and Grobstein (1958) observed that a component of pancreatin digests them. Boyse (1960), Madden and Burk (1961), Moscona (1962b) and Steinberg (1963) could digest such gels with crystalline DNase, and Steinberg (1963) showed a gel of this type to possess a structural backbone of DNA. The active component of pancreatin which digested the gel was DNase in this case and in several others as well. It may be that the pancreatic "mucase" referred to above was contaminated with pancreatic DNase. If "sliminess" of a trypsinized preparation presents a problem, 1 percent pancreatin (Auerbach and Grobstein, 1958; Steinberg, 1962a, 1963) or crystalline DNase (0.05–0.1 mg per milliliter) (Boyse, 1960; Madden and Burk, 1961; Steinberg, 1963) added to the trypsin solution or used as a posttreatment is often the answer. It must be borne in mind, however, that pancreatic DNase has a Mg^{++}-requirement. In our experience the DNase in trypsin-DNase mixtures loses its activity even in solutions kept frozen in a freezing chest. Thus, the two enzymes must be stored separately.

Enzymes other than trypsin may be used, and some are superior for certain tissues. Chymotrypsin, papain, elastase (Rinaldini, 1959; Levinson and Green, 1965), and pronase have all found use, and purified collagenase may work where trypsin fails (Hinz and Syverton, 1959), and it may yield healthier dissociated cells (Smith and Berndt, 1964).

We have sometimes made up trypsin in Ca^{++}-Mg^{++}-free Eagle's MEM medium (Baltimore Biological Laboratory, P.O. Box 6711, Baltimore, Md., 21204) rather than in ordinary CMF saline. This has been done on the grounds that the nutrient ingredients of Eagle's medium could hardly be harmful, and they might be beneficial at such a time of stress, when cellular permeability and consequent leakage might be expected to be increased. Other serum-free, divalent cation-free nutrient media could equally well be used. The procedure is effective, but I cannot say that it is clearly superior, since even the ordinary trypsinization procedure, applied to the tissues with which we have worked, typically yields at least 95 percent healthy cells as judged by dye exclusion (but see Levinson and Green, 1965).

Often, some portions of a tissue mass are resistant to digestion. It is best to keep trypsinization time short and to decant the free cells, rather than prolong digestion in the hope of bringing it to completion. The yield of live, healthy cells is likely to be greater, too, if this precaution is observed.

7. *Add serum-containing liquid culture medium* (in some laboratories this is chilled) to stop the digestion. Serum contains inhibitors of pancreatic proteases. Undissociated fragments, if they are still present, should be removed at this time by allowing them to settle and decanting or aspirating off the solution containing the free cells.

8. *Pack the cells* by gentle centrifugation for 3–5 minutes in a clinical centrifuge equipped with swing-out tube shields. Packing is much better in the presence of serum than in its absence. Aspirate off the supernatant, which may contain some cell fragments and light debris. Replace the aspirated fluid with fresh liquid culture medium, and gently resuspend the pellet by pipetting or brief shearing. Pelleting and resuspension may be repeated once more if it is deemed desirable, but if an adequate excess of medium has been used, this may not be necessary for many purposes.

9. *Determination of cell concentration* can be performed at this time with a hemocytometer. If a sample is diluted with a 0.5 percent solution of nigrosin, water soluble (Kaltenbach *et al.*, 1958), or some other suitable high molecular weight acid dye, the percentage of cells with impaired permeability can be determined while the cell counts are being made.

10. *The cell suspension is diluted* to give the desired concentration. For aggregation in liquid medium, 10^6 cells per milliliter of medium is usually a convenient concentration. If the suspension is to be kept for more than, perhaps, 15 minutes before use, it should be stored at a lower temperature. The range 13°–18°C works well. This will retard premature aggregation.

REAGGREGATION

If dissociated cells are to be reaggregated, three principal approaches are possible. The cells may be centrifugally pelleted (Trinkaus and Groves, 1955; Trinkaus and Lentz, 1964; Weiss and Taylor, 1960); they may be deposited on a liquid-air (Grover, 1961, 1962; Steinberg, 1962b) or liquid-solid (Moscona and Moscona, 1952; Wolff and Haffen, 1952) interface and allowed to make contact through their own movements (see Stefanelli and Zacchei, 1958); or the cells may be maintained in suspension and brought into contact by means of the motion of the suspending liquid (see Moscona, 1961; Steinberg, 1962a).

Aggregation on a Surface

A suspension of cells in liquid culture medium is introduced into a hollow-ground slide. The volume of solution used and the appropriate cell concentration are functions of the shape, size, and surface area of the concavity and must be determined empirically. Usually "rich" media are used, such as equal parts of serum and embryo extract or of these ingredients diluted to $\frac{2}{3}$ concentration with Tyrode's, Earle's, or some other balanced salt solution. The air space may be gassed with 5 percent CO_2 in air before the culture is sealed with a cover slip, the latter being attached to the slide with Vaseline or a mixture of Vaseline and paraffin. The melted mixture may be applied with a fine brush or is conveniently poured into a syringe equipped with a blunt needle, from which it is later dispensed. After a day or two at 37°–38°C the resulting aggregates may be transferred to the chorioallantoic membrane (see Weiss and Taylor, 1960) or to the surface of an agar gel (Wolff and Haffen, 1952; also Trinkaus and Lentz, 1964) for further culture. The reader is referred to the appropriate chapters of this book for more detailed information concerning culture methods.

Aggregates produced by pelleting suspended cells in a centrifuge may be, if necessary, allowed to tighten up by incubation for an hour or longer in complete culture medium, after which they can be cut into pieces of the desired size and cultured on an appropriate surface or in agitated vessels containing liquid culture medium.

Aggregation in Shaker Flasks

Introduced by Moscona (1961), the technique of aggregation in shaker flasks has been far more satisfactory in our hands than the hanging drop method which we previously used. Aggregate size can be controlled either through control of the stirring rate or by changing, when the aggregates have reached the desired size, from a low stirring rate which promotes aggregation to a high rate which discourages it. Our experience has been with custom-built 10-ml Erlenmeyer flasks containing usually 2 ml of liquid medium and maintained at 37°C on gyrating shakers having ½-inch diameter of gyration (Steinberg, 1962a).[1] Under these conditions, 70–80 rpm is a good range for bringing about limited aggregation with cells from a variety of chick embryonic tissues. Aggregates visible under a dissecting microscope usually begin to appear within less than an hour (at 10^6 cells per milliliter) and with most tissues their continued fusion tapers off within 24–36 hours while the aggregates are still of a convenient size. In our experience an aggregate diameter of 0.2–0.3 mm is optimal. Below 0.1 mm the aggregates become unhealthy, no doubt due to inadequacy of the nutrient medium, and above 0.3 mm the aggregates often become centrally necrotic. The latter effect can be overcome to some extent by substituting oxygen for the air of the air-CO_2 mixture which constitutes the gaseous phase. Initial aggregation is usually considerably faster at 60 rpm, but if this low gyration rate is maintained, all viable cells often become incorporated into a single, huge aggregate. Probably the hydrodynamics are different under these circumstances, producing a centripetal vector which is absent at higher rates of gyration, and resulting in the concentration of the cells centrally within the flasks rather than in their dispersion. In any case, with our apparatus one can start aggregation at a low rate such as 60 rpm and then stop it at any time by speeding up to about 120 rpm. Too rapid gyration can result in frothing of the medium, however, with a resultant destruction of cells at the liquid-air interfaces which are produced.

While gyratory shakers without (Moscona, 1961) or with (Steinberg, 1962a; see also footnote 1) built-in temperature and gas-phase control are very convenient, almost any kind of stirring device could in principle be adapted for use in cell aggregation studies. Similarly, the liquid culture medium employed is not very critical for many applications. The choice of a medium should be dictated by the material used. We often use Eagle's MEM + 10 percent horse serum.

In conclusion, I have presented generalized procedures, together with some idea of their existing variants, which are often effective in separating living tissues and cells from their attachments, and in bringing about the reestablishment of cellular connections. Because of the pragmatic orientation under which such procedures evolve, little has been done to investigate the procedures themselves. Successful application of these general methods to new biological materials will surely, in many cases, require the methods to be further modified.

[1] A new model gyratory shaker, Model G77, is available from New Brunswick Scientific Co., 1130 Somerset Street, New Brunswick, N.J. 08903. It appears better suited than its predecessors for a variety of applications in problems involving cell aggregation in suspension cultures.

REFERENCES

ANDERSON, N. G., 1953: The mass isolation of whole cells from rat liver. *Science*, 117: 627.

AUERBACH, R., and C. GROBSTEIN, 1958: Inductive interaction of embryonic tissues after dissociation and reaggregation. *Exptl. Cell Res.*, 15: 384.

BOYSE, E. A., 1960: A method for the production of viable cell suspensions from solid tumors. *Plastic and Reconstr. Surg. and Transpl. Bull.*, 25: 100.

BUSCHKE, F., 1949: Studies on intercellular cohesion in corneal epithelium. Methods. Effects of proteolytic enzymes, salts hydrogen ion concentration, and polar-nonpolar substances. *J. Cell. Comp. Physiol.*, 33: 145.

CAHN, R. D., 1967: Detergents in membrane filters. *Science*, 155: 195.

DABROWSKA-PIASKOWSKA, K., 1959: Observations on the histoformative capacities of tumor cells dissociated by digestion with trypsin. *Exptl. Cell Res.*, 16: 315.

EASTY, G. C., D. M. EASTY, and E. J. AMBROSE, 1960: Studies of cellular adhesiveness. *Exptl. Cell Res.*, 19: 539.

GARVEY, J. S., 1961: Separation and *in vitro* culture of cells from liver tissue. *Nature*, 191: 972.

GROVER, J. W., 1961: The relation between the embryonic age of dissociated chick lung cells and their capacity for reaggregation and histogenesis *in vitro*. *Exptl. Cell Res.*, 24: 171.

———, 1962: The influence of age and environmental factors on the behavior of reaggregated embryonic lung cells in culture. *Exptl. Cell Res.*, 26: 344.

HAMBURGER, V., 1960: *A Manual of Experimental Embryology*. Rev. ed. University of Chicago Press, Chicago, Ill., p. 9.

HARRIS, H., 1955: Some quantitative studies on the multiplication of connective tissue cells *in vitro*. *Brit. J. Exptl. Pathol.*, 36: 115.

HERRMANN, H., and F. H. HICKMAN, 1948: VII. The adhesion of epithelium to stroma in the cornea. *Bull. Johns Hopkins Hosp.*, 82: 182.

HINZ, R. W., and J. T. SYVERTON, 1959: Mammalian cell cultures for study of influenza virus. I. Preparation of monolayer cultures with collagenase. *Proc. Soc. Exptl. Biol. Med.*, 101: 19.

KALTENBACH, J. P., M. H. KALTENBACH, and W. B. LYONS, 1958: Nigrosin as a dye for differentiating live and dead ascites cells. *Exptl. Cell Res.*, 15: 112.

KONIGSBERG, I., N. MC ELVAIN, M. TOOTLE, and H. HERRMANN, 1960: The dissociability of deoxyribonucleic acid synthesis from the development of multinuclearity of muscle cells in culture. *J. Biophys. Biochem Cytol.*, 8: 333.

LAWS, J. O., and L. H. STICKLAND, 1961: The adhesion of liver cells. *Exptl. Cell Res.*, 24: 240.

LEVINSON, C., and J. W. GREEN, 1965: Cellular injury resulting from tissue disaggregation. *Exptl. Cell Res.*, 39: 309.

LIEBERMAN, I., and P. OVE, 1958: A protein growth factor for mammalian cells in culture. *J. Biol. Chem.*, 233: 637.

LONGMUIR, I. S., and W. AP REES, 1956: Preparation of cell suspensions from rat livers. *Nature*, 117: 997.

MADDEN, R. E., and D. BURK, 1961: Production of viable single cell suspensions from solid tumors. *J. Nat. Cancer Inst.*, 27: 841.

MEDAWAR, B. P., 1941: Sheets of pure epidermal epithelium from human skin. *Nature*, 148: 783.

MERCHANT, D. J., R. H. KAHN, and W. H. MURPHY, 1964: *Handbook of Cell and Organ Culture*. Burgess Publishing Co., Minneapolis, Minn.

MOSCONA, A., 1952: Cell suspensions from organ rudiments of chick embryos. *Exptl. Cell Res.*, 3: 535.

———, 1960: Patterns and mechanisms of tissue reconstruction from dissociated cells. In D. Rudnick (ed.), *Developing Cell Systems and Their Control*, Ronald Press, New York, p. 45.

———, 1961: Rotation-mediated aggregation of dissociated cells. A quantifiable approach to cell interactions *in vitro*. *Exptl. Cell Res.*, 22: 455.

———, 1962a: Cellular interactions in experimental histogenesis. *Int. Rev. Exptl. Pathol.*, 1: 371.

———, 1962b: Analysis of cell recombinations in experimental synthesis of tissues *in vitro*. *J. Cell Comp. Physiol.*, 60 (Suppl. 1): 65.

———, and H. MOSCONA, 1952: Dissociation and aggregation of cells from organ rudiments of the early chick embryo. *J. Anat.*, 86: 287.

PAUL, J., 1961: *Cell and Tissue Culture*. 2nd ed. E. and S. Livingstone Ltd., Edinburgh, Scotland, and London, Eng.

PUCK, T. T., P. I. MARCUS, and S. J. CIECIURA, 1956: Clonal growth of mammalian cells *in vitro*. Growth characteristics of colonies from single HeLa cells with and without a "feeder" layer. *J. Exptl. Med.*, 103: 273.

RAPPAPORT, C., 1956: Trypsinization of monkey-kidney tissue: an automatic method for the preparation of cell suspensions. *Bull. World Health Org.*, 14: 147.

RAWLES, M. E., 1963: Tissue interactions in scale and feather development as studied in dermal-epidermal recombinations. *J. Embryol. Exptl. Morphol.*, 11: 765.

RINALDINI, L. M. J., 1958: The isolation of living cells from animal tissues. *Intern. Rev. Cytol.*, 7: 587.

———, 1959: An improved method for the isolation and quantitative cultivation of embryonic cells. *Exptl. Cell Res.*,16: 477.

ROSENBERG, M. D., 1960: Microexudates from cells grown in tissue culture. *Biophys. J.*, 1: 137.

ROUS, P., 1916: A method for obtaining suspensions of living cells from the fixed tissues, and for the plating out of individual cells. *J. Exptl. Med.*, 23: 549.

SCHERER, W. F., J. T. SYVERTON, and G. O. GEY, 1953: Studies on the propagation *in vitro* of poliomyelitis viruses. IV. Viral multiplication in a stable strain of human malignant epithelial cells (Strain HeLa) derived from an epidermoid carcinoma of the cervix. *J. Exptl. Med.*, 97: 695.

SCHIEFFERDECKER, P., 1886: Methode zur Isolierung von Epithelzellen. *Zeitschr. f. wiss. Mikr.*, 3: 483.

SMITH, T. E., JR., and W. O. BERNDT, 1964: The establishment of beating myocardial cells in long-term culture in fluid medium. *Exptl. Cell Res.*, 36: 179.

ST. AMAND, G. S., and S. R. TIPTON, 1954: The separation of neuroblasts and other cells from grasshopper embryo. *Science*, 119: 93.

STEFANELLI, A., and A. M. ZACCHEI, 1958: Sulle modalità di aggregazione di cellule embrionali di pollo disaggregate con trypsina. *Acta Embryol. Morphol. Exp.*, 2: 1.

STEINBERG, M. S., 1958: On the chemical bonds between animal cells. A mechanism for type-specific association. *Am. Naturalist*, 92: 65.

———, 1962a: The role of temperature in the control of aggregation of dissociated embryonic cells. *Exptl. Cell Res.*, 28: 1.

———, 1962b: On the mechanism of tissue reconstruction by dissociated cells, III. Free energy relations and the reorganization of fused, heteronomic tissue fragments. *Proc. Nat. Acad. Sci., U.S.* 48: 1769.

———, 1963: "ECM": its nature, origin and function in cell aggregation. *Exptl. Cell Res.*, 30: 257.

SZABÓ, G., 1955: A modification of the technique of "skin splitting" with trypsin. *J. Path. Bact.*, 70: 545.

TRINKAUS, J. P., and P. W. GROVES, 1955: Differentiation in culture of mixed aggregates of dissociated tissue cells. *Proc. Nat. Acad. Sci. U.S.*, 41: 787.

———, and J. P. LENTZ, 1964: Direct observation of type-specific aggregation in mixed cell aggregates. *Dev. Biol.*, 9: 115.

WEISS, L., 1958: The effects of trypsin on the size, viability and dry mass of sarcoma 37 cells. *Exptl. Cell Res.*, 14: 80.

WEISS, P., and A. C. TAYLOR, 1960: Reconstitution of complete organs from single-cell suspensions of chick embryos in advanced stages of differentiation. *Proc. Nat. Acad. Sci. U.S.*, 46: 1177.

WILLMER, E. N., (ed.), 1965: *Cells and Tissues in Culture*, Vol. I. Academic Press, New York.

WOLFF, ET., and K. HAFFEN, 1952: Sur une méthode de culture d'organes embryonnaires *in vitro*. *Texas Rep. Biol. Med.*, 10: 463.

Part III

SPECIAL TECHNIQUES

Auxins

By D. James Morré and Joe L. Key

INTRODUCTION

Developmental studies in plants are facilitated by use of excised and cultured cells or tissues chosen to be representative of a particular developmental stage. Transfer of these explants to a defined medium is usually accompanied by a reduced rate of growth, termination of cell division, and a general cessation of development. If auxin is supplied, these processes continue at a rate nearer that of the intact plant. More important, however, is the fact that growth rate of excised plant tissues can be controlled precisely by the level of exogenously supplied growth substance.

The knowledge that minute quantities of auxin have the ability to regulate growth and development of excised plant parts is based on more than three decades of experimental findings. Low concentrations of auxin characteristically stimulate the growth of stem cells, induce curvature in aerial parts, and exert a specific action in loosening cell wall structure. Auxin can affect the duration of cell expansion and induce cell division. In combination with other plant hormones (gibberellin and cytokinin) and nutrients, auxin influences the nature and extent of differentiation of plant parts.

In this chapter, experimental systems are described which employ auxin as a biochemical regulator of plant growth and development. The usefulness of these systems in unraveling the mysteries of gene-based control mechanisms will be influenced by many factors. It must be fully realized that the particular response of a cell or tissue to auxin depends upon the choice of conditions under which the experiment is conducted.

CHOICE OF COMPOUNDS

Auxin

Auxin is a generic term for compounds characterized by their capacity to promote cell elongation in shoot cells of plants. Auxins generally affect other processes besides elongation, but elongation is considered critical.

Indole-3-acetic acid (IAA) is a naturally occurring auxin and is the standard reference compound for growth studies. Other auxins (of which there are many synthetic compounds) resemble IAA in biological activity. Two widely used synthetic auxins are 2,4-dichlorophenoxyacetic acid (2,4-D) and α-naphthaleneacetic acid (NAA). Even though their chemical structures differ from that of

methods and measurements with other tissues indicate that elastic extension also may be increased by auxin treatment (Morré, 1965; Morré and Bonner, 1965). The auxin-induced extensibility component is proportional to the logarithm of auxin concentrations and not dependent upon actual growth of the tissue. Cell wall loosening, like growth, is a true auxin-induced response.

For purposes of measurement, force extension data obtained using standard fiber testing techniques and equipment appear to give the least ambiguous results (Olson *et al.*, 1965). Using these methods, the changed mechanical properties are measured in the absence of turgor stress and influences of a living protoplast. This and other evidence (Bonner, 1961) verify that the auxin-induced changes involve interactions between wall polymers.

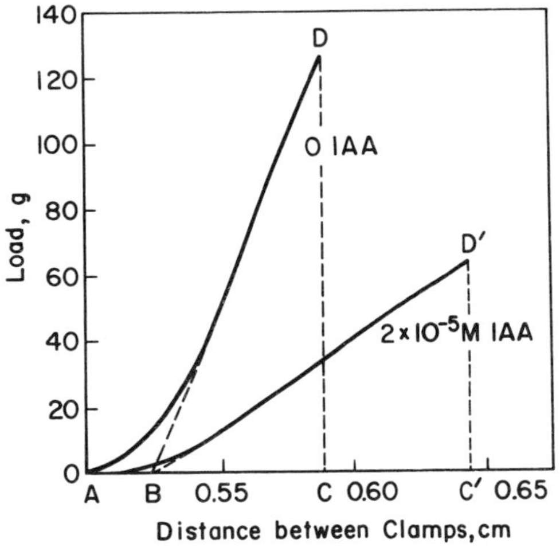

FIG. 3. Force-extension curves of pea epicotyl sections (boiled in methanol for 5 min. and rehydrated in water) obtained using an Instron Universal Testing Instrument. Incubated with and without IAA 6 hours prior to methanol treatment and measurement and restricted from growing during this period with 0.25 M mannitol. Mannitol alone did not appreciably alter extensibility of control sections. SOURCE: Coartney & Morré, unpublished.

Load-extension curves may be obtained using a constant-rate-of-extension instrument (Instron Universal Testing Instrument, Instron Engineering Corp., Canton, Massachusetts). With coleoptiles, sections are fastened vertically between two clamps a preset distance apart. With the upper clamp fixed, the lower clamp is traversed down at a constant rate increasing the load on the coleoptile. Using the above apparatus, load is measured electrically by a resistance strain-gauge connected to the upper clamp. Extension of the coleoptile is controlled by an error-operated servo-system. Probine and Preston (1962) and Lockhart (1965a) have described relatively inexpensive devices for measurement of wall extension rates at constant imposed loads.

Typical force-extension curves for pea epicotyl sections (Fig. 3) illustrate the increased extensibility resulting from prior auxin treatment of the tissue. Coleoptiles, epicotyls, hypocotyls, petioles, and mesocotyls have been successfully analyzed. Break-load (the load at which the tissue separates at a point of maximum weakness) is given by the line CD (Fig. 3). With coleoptiles, the extensibility of turgid or thawed frozen sections is similar to that of sections treated with hot water, hot methanol, or organic solvents. For convenience, sections are killed by boiling in methanol, stored in methanol, and rehydrated in water prior to measurement.

The chemical basis for the auxin-induced deformability is not known (see Wilson, 1964, for possible clues). However, the internal factors affecting wall bonding may be studied by specific chemical and enzymatic modifications of wall structure (Olson *et al.*, 1965). With coleoptiles, cellulase weakens wall structure whereas treatment with acetic anhydride

TABLE 6. EFFECT OF SEQUENTIAL ENZYMATIC AND CHEMICAL TREATMENTS ON THE CELL WALL EXTENSIBILITY OF *Avena* COLEOPTILES PREVIOUSLY INCUBATED IN THE PRESENCE OR ABSENCE OF IAA

TREATMENT	EXTENSIBILITY ($cm \times 10^3/gm$) CONTROL	IAA
None	1.0	2.3
Acetic anhydride	0.5	1.0
Acetic anhydride; cellulase	0.5	1.0
Acetic anhydride; 0.1 *N* NaOH	1.0	2.0
Acetic anhydride; 0.1 *N* NaOH; cellulase	2.5	5.1
Cellulase	2.5	5.1
Cellulase; acetic anhydride	1.3	2.5

SOURCE: Olson, Bonner, and Morré (1965).

results in cell wall stiffening (Table 6). Subsequent acetic anhydride treatment reverses the effect of cellulase. That acetylation essentially stops the action of cellulase is good evidence that the cellulase substrates, cellulose and hemicellulose, are altered by acetylation. Note, however, that the difference in extensibility due to IAA treatment is retained through acetylation and cellulase treatment. This provides yet another demonstration of the permanence of cell wall loosening effects due to auxin treatment. In addition, the magnitudes of the changes brought about by acetylation and deacetylation are similar to those introduced by IAA. Results of other enzymatic and chemical treatments on wall loosening have been given by Olson *et al.* (1965).

The extent of the chemical changes that result in altered properties may be relatively small, and the nature of the changes is not well established. However, controlled alteration of cell wall mechanical properties by auxin treatment, combined with force extension analyses, should continue to be useful in studies of internal wall bonding factors as they affect growth and development.

SEPARATION OF METABOLIC AND GROWTH EFFECTS INDUCED BY AUXIN

It is often desirable to separate responses derived secondarily from auxin-induced growth from those directly attributable to auxin. For example, increases in respiration associated with auxin treatment may occur only as a result of the rapid growth (French and Beevers, 1953). Tissues stimulated to grow by IAA would use ATP and accumulate ADP. Assuming that the level of ADP limits respiratory rate, the net respiratory turnover would be expected to increase with increasihg growth rate induced by auxin and thus represent one kind of secondary effect.

Direct and indirect (growth-induced) effects are often separated by auxin treatment under conditions where growth is blocked by divalent cations (Ca^{++} or Mg^{++}) or isotonic solutions (mannitol, Carbowax, sucrose, raffinose, or lactose). In this way auxin-induced wall loosening has been shown to proceed independently of any actual cell expansion. Divalent ions are considered to inhibit growth by cell wall stiffening through cross-linking of anionic wall polymers. Growth of

Avena coleoptiles is inhibited about 95 percent by 0.01 *M* $CaCl_2$ (Ray, 1962). Transfer of sections to monovalent ion solutions (e.g., K^+ in 10-fold excess) results in a rapid reversal of divalent ion inhibition. A 0.4 *M* mannitol solution is isotonic to *Avena* coleoptiles and is generally considered to inhibit cell elongation osmotically. Mannitol, however, inhibits both growth and cell wall synthesis in *Avena* coleoptiles even at hypotonic concentrations where plasmolysis is not involved (Ray, 1962). Similar results were obtained with Carbowax (polyethylene glycol). Restriction of elongation by divalent ions was accompanied by reduced wall synthesis but to a lesser degree than with mannitol. Isotonic sucrose or lactose solutions can be utilized to block auxin-induced cell expansion temporarily without the apparent drastic effects accompanying exposure to mannitol or Carbowax. Effectiveness is lost as the osmotic pressure of the cell contents increases through uptake of the osmoticum.

CONCEPTS OF AUXIN REGULATION

Simple organic molecules such as auxins might be expected to produce their varied responses through some "master reaction" (Thimann, 1960) to which different cells respond in different ways. In any event, a series of reactions must be involved between the initial locus of auxin interaction (hypothetical receptor) and the final morphogenetic expression. Probably the best understood property of auxin is the ability to increase rate of cell elongation. Here the biochemical changes establishing the new growth rate are accomplished rapidly (less than 15 minutes).

For many years, cell elongation was considered to be a physical yielding of some as yet unspecified bonding forces within the cell wall under tensions exerted by turgor pressure. The existence of an auxin-induced extensibility component, a property widely called plasticity, led to the view that auxin regulates cell expansion through an increase in the yield properties of the wall (Bonner, 1961; Lockhart, 1965a). Despite the attractive simplicity of this relationship (recently analyzed quantitatively by Lockhart, 1965b), the mechanisms involved in cell expansion require active metabolism and are much more complex. For example, both RNA and protein synthesis are required for auxin-induced growth (Noodén and Thimann, 1963; Key, 1964) and for the induction of wall loosening by auxin (Morré, 1965; Coartney and Morré, unpublished). By use of inhibitors of RNA and protein synthesis, auxin-induced growth can be blocked independently of the amount of wall loosening induced by prior auxin treatment of the tissue (Cleland, 1965; Morré, 1965; Coartney and Morré, unpublished) and osmotic pressure of the cell contents (Morré, 1965). However, the metabolic nature of the forces causing cell elongation remains obscure.

Actinomycin D (4 to 8 × 10^{-6} *M*), an inhibitor of DNA-dependent RNA synthesis, inhibits both growth and wall loosening. 5-Fluorouracil (2.5 × 10^{-3} *M*) inhibits ribosomal and soluble RNA synthesis by 75 to 90 percent in plants but does not affect auxin-induced growth or synthesis of DNA-like (messenger) RNA. Thus the requirement for RNA synthesis in auxin regulation of growth seems to be restricted to the synthesis of messenger RNA.

Protein synthesis inhibitors (cycloheximide, 5 × 10^{-6} *M*; puromycin, 5 × 10^{-4} *M*; and chloramphenicol, 5 × 10^{-3} *M*) also inhibit auxin-induced growth. Unlike the induction of α-amylase activity by gibberellin treatment (see Johri and Varner, this volume, pp. 595–611), the kinetics of growth inhibition by inhibitors of RNA and protein synthesis suggest that the system limiting the rate of auxin-induced cell elongation is unstable [both template RNA(s) and protein(s)], i.e., with a mean life of only a few hours.

In concert with current views on hormone action (*Symposium on Hormonal Control of Protein Biosynthesis*, 1965), auxin might be visualized as an effector substance (Bonner, 1965) regulating the transcription of DNA into templates which in turn direct the synthesis of growth-specific enzymes. An alternative explanation is that the auxin-responsive system is itself unstable and must be continually regenerated by active RNA and protein synthesis. At present, it is not possible to choose between these alternatives. For instance, nothing is known of the nature of the proteins whose continued synthesis is required for cell elongation.

It is possible, however, to apply modern biological concepts to our present understanding of auxin regulation. We know that transfer of tissue explants to a defined medium lacking auxin usually results in a diminished growth rate and cessation of normal developmental activities. Although the over-all capacity to synthesize protein and RNA is reduced, excised tissues do appear to synthesize relatively more messenger-like RNA than ribosomal RNA (Loening, 1965; Ingle and Key, 1965; Cherry and van Huystee, 1965). These changes in excised tissues are similar to the "step-down" transition in bacterial cells following transfer from a rich to a minimal medium. Here, ribosome synthesis ceases and synthesis of messenger RNA continues (Hayashi and Spiegelman, 1961). (Bacterial growth, however, is determined by rate of cell division and thus is more comparable to growth of single cell suspensions of higher plant tissues; see above, section on tissue culture and single cell suspensions, p. 585.)

With excised stems, and perhaps other tissue explants as well, auxin accelerates both growth and rate of ribosome synthesis (Key and Shannon, 1964: Ingle and Key, 1965) in much the same manner as transfer of bacteria from a minimal to a rich medium (Neidhardt and Fraenkel, 1961) causes renewed synthesis of ribosomes ("step-up" condition). Thus, auxin-induced growth may be viewed as a "step-up" transition where activation of a vast array of development-specific protein and RNA synthetic activities occurs, the precise spectrum depending upon any one of a number of possible control mechanisms (e.g., balance with other hormones, substrate levels, etc.).

REFERENCES

ADAMSON, D., 1962: Expansion and division in auxin-treated plant cells. *Can. J. Bot.*, 40: 719.

AUDUS, L. J., 1963: *Plant Growth Substances.* 553 pp. Interscience Publishers, Inc., New York.

BONNER, J., 1961: On the mechanics of auxin-induced growth. In R. M. Klein (ed.), *Plant Growth Regulation*, Iowa State University Press, Ames, Iowa, p. 307.

———, 1965: *The Molecular Biology of Development.* The Oxford University Press, New York, p. 117.

———, and R. J. FOSTER, 1955: The growth-time relationships of the auxin-induced growth in *Avena* coleoptile sections. *J. Exptl. Bot.*, 6: 293.

CHERRY, J. H., and R. VAN HUYSTEE, 1965: Effects of 5-fluorouracil on photoperiodic induction and nucleic acid metabolism of

Xanthium. *Plant Physiol.*, 40: 987.

CLELAND, R., 1958: A separation of auxin-induced cell wall loosening into its plastic and elastic components. *Physiol. Plant.*, 11: 599.

———, 1965: Auxin-induced cell wall loosening in the presence of actinomycin D. *Plant Physiol.*, 40: 595.

———, and N. MC COMBS, 1965: Gibberellic acid: Action in barley endosperm does not require endogenous auxin. *Science*, 150: 497.

FILNER, P., 1965: Semi-conservative replication of DNA in a higher plant cell. *Exptl. Cell Res.*, 39: 33.

FRENCH, R. C., and H. BEEVERS, 1953: Respiratory and growth responses induced by growth regulators and allied compounds. *Amer. J. Bot.*, 40: 660.

GALSTON, A. W., and W. K. PURVES, 1960: The mechanism of action of auxin. *Ann. Rev. Plant Physiol.*, 11: 239.

GORTER, C. J., 1961: Morphogenetic effects of synthetic auxins. In W. Ruhland (ed.), *Encyclopedia of Plant Physiology*, Springer, Berlin, Vol. XIV, p. 1084.

HABER, A. H., 1962: Effects of indoleacetic acid on growth without mitosis and on mitotic activity in absence of growth by expansion. *Plant Physiol.*, 37: 18.

HAYASHI, M., and S. SPIEGELMAN, 1961: The selective synthesis of informational RNA in bacteria. *Proc. Nat. Acad. Sci.*, 47: 1564.

HOUSLEY, S., 1961: Kinetics of auxin-induced growth. In W. Ruhland (ed.), *Encyclopedia of Plant Physiology*, Springer, Berlin, Vol. XIV, p. 1007.

INGLE, J., and J. L. KEY, 1965: A comparative evaluation of the synthesis of DNA-like RNA in excised and intact plant tissues. *Plant Physiol.*, 40: 1212.

———, ———, and R. E. HOLM, 1965: Demonstration and characterization of a DNA-like RNA in excised plant tissue. *J. Mol. Biol.*, 11: 730.

JACOBS, W. P., 1952: The role of auxin in differentiation of xylem around a wound. *Amer. J. Bot.*, 39: 301.

KEY, J. L., 1964: Ribonucleic acid and protein synthesis as essential processes for cell elongation. *Plant Physiol.*, 39: 365.

———, and J. INGLE, 1964: Requirement for synthesis of DNA-like RNA for growth of excised plant tissue. *Proc. Natl. Acad. Sci.*, 52: 1382.

———, and J. C. SHANNON, 1964: Enhancement by auxin of ribonucleic acid synthesis in excised soybean hypocotyl tissue. *Plant Physiol.*, 39: 360.

LARSEN, P., 1961: Biological determination of natural auxins. In W. Ruhland (ed.), *Encyclopedia of Plant Physiology*, Springer, Berlin, Vol. XIV, p. 521.

LEOPOLD, A. C., 1964: Plant hormones. In G. Pincus, K. V. Thimann, and E. B. Astwood (eds.), *The Hormones*, Academic Press, New York, Vol. IV, p. 1.

LOCKHART, J. A., 1965a: Cell extension. In J. Bonner and J. E. Varner (eds.), *Plant Biochemistry*, Academic Press, New York, p. 826.

———, 1965b: An analysis of irreversible plant cell elongation. *J. Theor. Biol.*, 8: 264.

LOENING, U. E., 1965: Synthesis of messenger ribonucleic acid in excised pea-seedling root segments. *Biochem. J.*, 97: 125.

LOOMIS, R. S., and J. G. TORREY, 1964: Chemical control of vascular cambium initiation in isolated radish roots. *Proc. Natl. Acad. Sci.*, 52: 3.

MC RAE, D. H., and J. BONNER, 1953: Chemical structure and antiauxin activity. *Physiol. Plant.*, 6: 485.

———, R. J. FOSTER, and J. BONNER, 1953: Kinetics of auxin interaction. *Plant Physiol.*, 28: 343.

MORRÉ, D. J., 1965: Changes in tissue deformability accompanying actinomycin D inhibition of plant growth and ribonucleic acid synthesis. *Plant Physiol.*, 40: 615.

———, and J. BONNER, 1965: A mechanical analysis of root growth. *Physiol. Plant.*, 18: 635.

NEIDHARDT, F. C., and D. G. FRAENKEL, 1961: Metabolic regulation of RNA synthesis in bacteria. *Cold Spring Harbor Symp. Quant. Biol.*, 26: 63.

NITSCH, J. P., and C. NITSCH, 1956: Studies on the growth of coleoptile and first internode sections. A new, sensitive, straight-growth test for auxins. *Plant Physiol.*, 31: 94.

NOODÉN, L. D., and K. V. THIMANN, 1963: Evidence for a requirement for protein synthesis for auxin-induced cell enlargement. *Proc. Natl. Acad. Sci.*, 50: 194.

OLSON, A. C., J. BONNER, and D. J. MORRÉ, 1965: Force extension analysis of *Avena* coleoptile cell walls. *Planta*, 66: 126.

OSBORNE, D. J., 1965: Interactions of hormonal substances in the growth and development of plants. *J. Sci. Food Agric.*, 16: 1.

PROBINE, M. C., and R. D. PRESTON, 1962: Cell growth and the structure and mechanical properties of the cell wall in internodal cells of *Nitella opaca*. II. Mechanical properties of the walls. *J. Exptl. Bot.*, 13: 111.

RAY, P. M., 1962: Cell wall synthesis and cell elongation in oat coleoptile tissue. *Am. J. Bot.*, 49: 928.

———, and A. W. RUESINK, 1962: Kinetic experiments on the nature of the growth mechanism in oat coleoptile cells. *Dev. Biol.*, 4: 377.

SETTERFIELD, G., 1963: Growth regulation in excised slices of Jerusalem artichoke tuber tissue. *Symp. Soc. Exptl. Biol.*, 17: 98.

SKOOG, F., and C. O. MILLER, 1957: Chemical regulation of growth and organ formation in plant tissues cultured *in vitro*. *Symp. Soc. Exptl. Biol.*, 11: 118.

STOWE, B. B., 1960: Growth promotion in pea stem sections. I. Stimulation of auxin and gibberellin action by alkyl lipids. *Plant Physiol.*, 35: 262.

Symposium on Hormonal Control of Protein Biosynthesis, 1965: *J. Cellular Compar. Physiol.*, 66 (Suppl. 1): 1.

THIMANN, K. V., 1960: Plant growth. In W. W. Nowinski (ed.), *Fundamental Aspects of Normal and Malignant Growth*, Elsevier Publishing Co., Amsterdam, Holland, p. 748.

TORREY, J. G., and J. REINERT, 1961: Suspension cultures of higher plant cells in synthetic media. *Plant Physiol.*, 36: 483.

TULECKE, W., R. TAGGERT, and L. COLAVITO, 1965: Continuous cultures of higher plant cells in liquid media. *Contrib. Boyce Thompson Institute*, 23: 33.

VASIL, V., and A. C. HILDEBRANDT, 1965: Differentiation of tobacco plants from single, isolated cells in microcultures. *Science*, 150: 889.

WENT, F. W., and K. V. THIMANN, 1937: *Phytohormones*. 294 pp. Macmillan, New York.

WILSON, K., 1964: The growth of plant cell walls. *Intern. Rev. Cytol.*, 17: 1.

Gibberellins

By M. M. Johri and J. E. Varner

INTRODUCTION

Although gibberellins probably occur in all higher plants and the dramatic effects of applying exogenous gibberellins and inhibitors of gibberellin biosynthesis have been reported for many plants, we shall describe in detail only those systems which seem most amenable to experimentation aimed at defining at the molecular level the role of the gibberellins. Toward this end the literature review is purposely selective and subjective.

Early History

Four major categories of growth regulators—auxins, gibberellins, cytokinins, and abscisins—are known.[1] Our knowledge of gibberellins is a product of fairly recent times, although the *bakanae* (=foolish seedling) disease of rice, now known to be due to gibberellins, was on record in Japan more than a century and a half ago. The disease is characterized by the appearance of excessively long, pale-green seedlings. The causal organism was found to be *Fusarium moniliforme* Sheld. (syn. *Gibberella fujikuroi* [Saw.] Sr.) and it was shown in 1926 (Kurosawa) that the principle responsible for the symptoms was a metabolic product of the fungus. The term gibberellin was coined for this product in 1935 (Yabuta). The gibberellins (really a group of several related compounds) attracted a belated and intense interest beginning in the 1950's and hundreds of articles and many reviews have appeared since then. The diverse responses elicited by gibberellins include stimulation of cell division or cell elongation, or both, induction of flowering, parthenocarpy, seed germination, acceleration or retardation of leaf abscission, retardation of leaf senescence, and formation and secretion of hydrolases by the aleurone layers of the Gramineae.

For a long time the gibberellins were regarded as metabolites unique to the fungus. At present, however, there is overwhelming evidence for the widespread occurrence of gibberellins in the plant kingdom. The first successful isolation of a

[1] Abbreviations: Amo 1618 (4-hydroxyl-5-isopropyl-2-methylphenyl trimethyl ammonium chloride, 1-piperidine carboxylate), CCC [(2-chloroethyl)-trimethylammonium chloride], FUDR (5-fluorodeoxyuridine), IAA (indole-3-acetic acid), GA_1 (gibberellin A_1), GA_2 (gibberellin A_2), GA_3 (gibberellic acid, gibberellin A_3) and other gibberellins, MAK (methylated albumin-kieselguhr), Phosfon D (2,4-dichlorobenzyltributylphosphonium chloride).

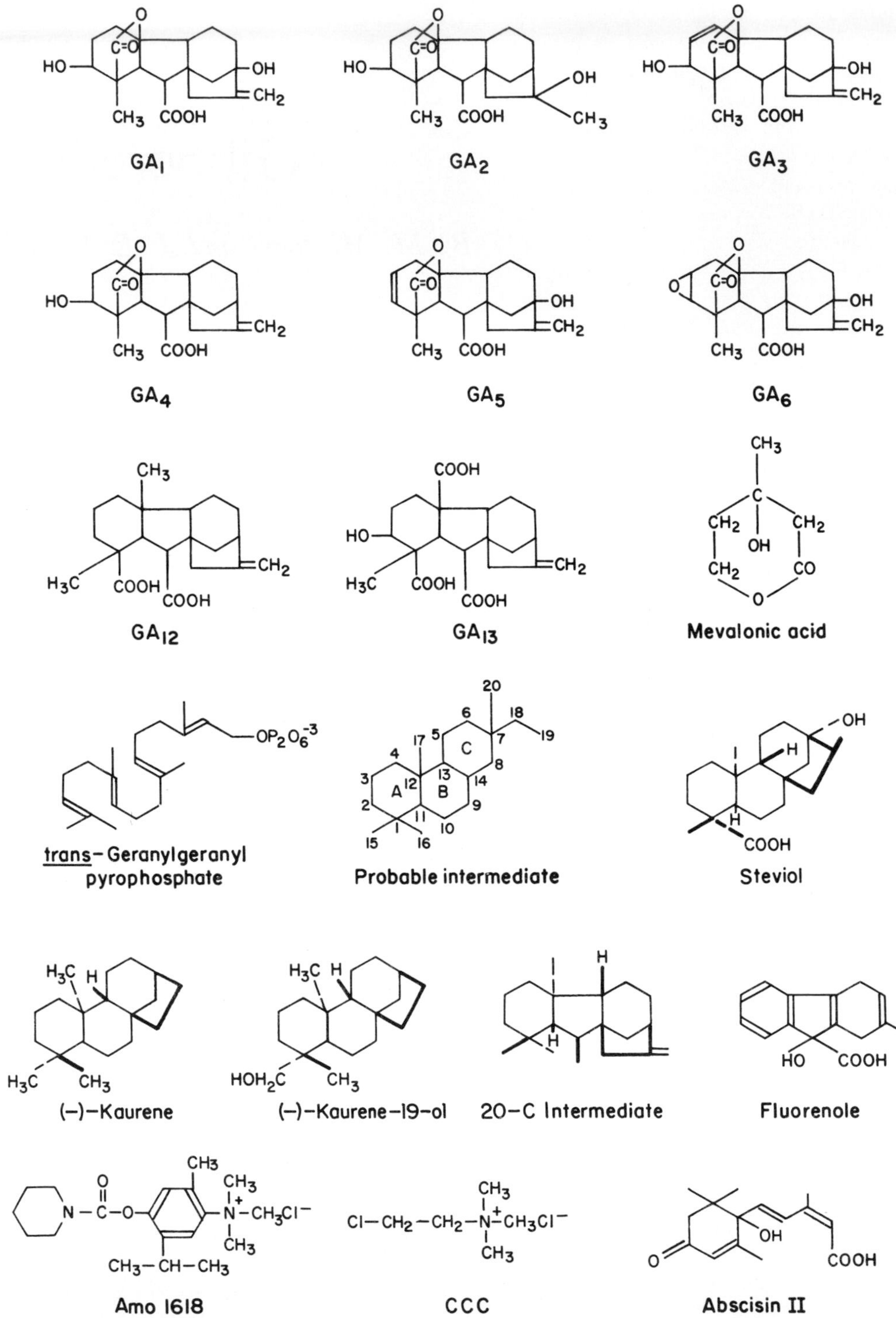

FIG. 1. Chemical structure of some of the gibberellins, intermediates or compounds related to their biosynthesis; growth retardants; and abscisin II.

gibberellin-like substance from a higher plant (bean seed, *Phaseolus vulgaris*) was reported in 1956 (West and Phinney, see also Phinney *et al.*, 1957). Later this substance was identified as GA_1 (MacMillan and Suter, 1958). Gibberellins have since been reported in many higher plants and probably occur in all higher plants. They seem to be present in varying amounts in all parts of the plant including roots, shoots, leaves, young and mature inflorescences, seeds and seed parts including endosperm, and fruit parts. Immature seeds, however, have been found to contain the greatest amount and, as in other plant parts, more than one gibberellin has been found. The seeds of *Echinocystis macrocarpa* contain GA_1, GA_3, GA_4, and GA_7 (Elson *et al.*, 1964) while those of *Phaseolus multiflorus* and *P. coccineus* have GA_1, GA_3, GA_5, GA_6, and GA_8. Gibberellin-like substances have also been reported in gymnosperms, ferns, a moss, fungi, and in green and brown algae.

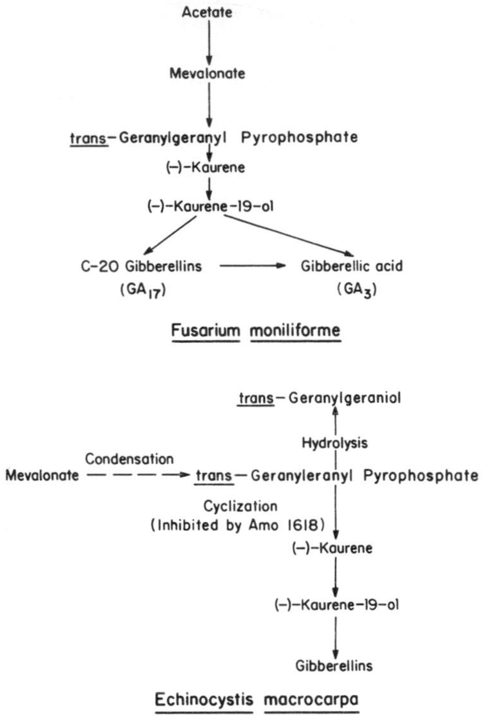

FIG. 2. Possible pathways of gibberellin biosynthesis.

Chemical Structure

The chemical structure of at least 17 different gibberellins is known. All the gibberellins have a gibbane skeleton; GA_1 through GA_{11} possess a lactone ring also, while GA_{12} and GA_{13} do not (Fig. 1). A definite relation between the possession of biological activity and certain substitutions at some places in the gibbane skeleton is wanting but the free carboxyl group at C-10 position seems to be essential for high activity.

Biogenesis

Early information about the biogenesis of gibberellins has been obtained from studies on the fungus *Fusarium moniliforme*. This pathway (Fig. 2), in analogy to the biosynthesis of terpenes, has been visualized to involve the condensation of isoprenoid units derived from mevalonate to form an acyclic diterpene. This C_{20} acyclic precursor would give rise to a tricyclic compound (Fig. 1) by cyclization. Gibberellic acid could be derived from this intermediate by contraction of ring B and removal of the carbon at the C-17 position followed by lactone ring formation. Using labeled acetate and mevalonate this scheme has been confirmed (Birch *et al.*, 1958; Birch and Smith, 1959; Zweig and Cosens, 1959), and it has been shown that GA_3 can arise specifically from (−)-kaurene (Cross *et al.*, 1964a, b). A similar mechanism operates in higher plants (Dennis *et al.*, 1965; Graebe *et al.*, 1965). In particular, enzymatic synthesis of *trans*-geranylgeranyl pyrophosphate, (−)-kaurene and (−)-kaurene-19-ol from mevalonic acid has recently been demonstrated with a crude homogenate of the endosperm of *Echinocystis macrocarpa*.

Trans-geranylgeranyl pyrophosphate is derived by the condensation of four molecules of mevalonic acid and cyclization leads to the formation of kaurene.

At what stage is the biological activity conferred upon the various intermediates? The little work that has been done indicates that intermediates up to the kaurene stage lack activity but substitution at C-15 position of a hydroxyl or carboxyl group results in weak biological activity. Thus, compounds like steviol (Fig. 1) have biological activity (Ruddat *et al.*, 1965), but apparently only after conversion, perhaps to an "unnatural" gibberellin.

Several compounds, which reduce growth of plants (particularly of stems) and have therefore been called growth retardants or dwarfing chemicals, such as Amo 1618, CCC, and Phosfon D (see Cathey, 1964; Harada and Lang, 1965; Kende *et al.*, 1963), block gibberellin biosynthesis. They have been employed successfully in solving problems relating to gibberellins and flowering. Some of these inhibitors block the cyclization reaction and thus inhibit the formation of kaurene (Fig. 2; Dennis *et al.*, 1965). These growth retardants appear to interfere only in the biosynthesis and not in the action of gibberellins. Recently another group of growth regulators—morphactins (chemically, derivatives of fluorene) have been described and these inhibit the elongation of normal peas (Schneider, 1964; Schneider *et al.*, 1965). The mechanism of this inhibition remains to be established.

Isolation

Chemical isolation procedures involve the extraction of gibberellins with an organic solvent, most commonly methanol, from fresh or lyophilized plant material. The methanol is removed *in vacuo* and lipids and other inactive substances are removed from the aqueous phase at alkaline pH (8.5) while acidic gibberellins remain in the aqueous phase.[2] The gibberellins are recovered from the aqueous phase at acidic pH (pH 3 or lower). Further purification involves adsorption and elution from columns of charcoal, kieselguhr, or silica gel (Khalifah *et al.*, 1965). The gibberellins in the eluates can be tentatively identified by thin layer or paper chromatography. For comparatively pure samples, thin layer chromatography (Elson *et al.*, 1964; Kagawa *et al.*, 1963; Sembdner *et al.*, 1962) is especially useful because of the short time required. Following development with the appropriate solvent the chromatograms are sprayed with ethanolic sulfuric acid and heated at 120°C. The various gibberellins appear as fluorescent spots when viewed in ultraviolet light.

Several bioassay systems have been developed to test the gibberellin-like activity of extracts. In most of these assays, the response is the enhanced growth of intact seedling, hypocotyl, internode, leaf sheath, or leaf segment. The barley endosperm test measures the gibberellin-enhanced formation of α-amylase or the release of reducing sugars. Some of these biological assay systems are described in detail in the experimental section. Often these are to be preferred over, or combined with, the chemical procedures because of their greater specificity.

PHYSIOLOGICAL RESPONSES TO GIBBERELLINS

Shoot and Root Growth

Various plants respond differently to the application of gibberellins. In general

[2] There is evidence now for neutral gibberellins which are lost in this procedure (*see* Hayashi *et al.*, 1962; Hayashi and Rappaport, 1962, 1965; Hashimoto and Rappaport, 1966). The conventional fractionation methods generally used ethyl acetate in which the neutral substances are insoluble. In *n*-butanol, these are, however, soluble.

these responses are most dramatic in shoots and less so in roots, excised organs, tissues, and tissue cultures.

A marked increase in the growth of the shoot is the most general response in higher plants. The leaves turn pale green or become etiolated and in extreme cases plants may look like climbers, e.g., lettuce and dwarf beans, and the development of branches may be suppressed, e.g., clover, cereals, and sugar cane.

Single-gene dwarf mutants of peas, maize, rye grass, barley, morning glory, sweet pea (*Lathyrus*), French bean (*Phaseolus vulgaris*), coffee, and wheat respond significantly in terms of growth to gibberellin treatment and become morphologically indistinguishable from the normal tall plants. Phinney (1961) has suggested from his work on dwarf corn mutants that each dwarfing gene may interfere with a particular step in the biosynthesis of gibberellin and thus lead to a decrease of native gibberellin. However, in peas, dwarfing seems to result not from inability to synthesize gibberellins but rather from an insensitivity to GA_5 in light (Kende and Lang, 1964).

The increase in the length of plants due to gibberellin application involves both cell enlargement and cell divisions. Even though the earlier investigators presumed only cell elongation it soon became evident that this alone could not account for all the growth responses observed and that cell division must be involved in at least some tissue. In the shoot meristems of *Hyoscyamus*, *Perilla*, *Rudbeckia*, and *Samolus*, in the meristem of spur shoots of *Prunus armeniaca*, and in the cambium of *Acer*, *Begonia*, *Fraxinus*, *Phaseolus*, *Populus*, and potato, higher frequencies of cell divisions have been found after gibberellin treatment (see Lang, 1965; Paleg, 1965).

The effect of exogenous gibberellins on tissue cultures is not well defined. Whether this is due to an adequate endogenous supply or an inability of undifferentiated cells to respond to gibberellins is not known. Calli originating from stem, root, leaf, or cotyledon of various plants have been demonstrated to produce gibberellin-like substances (Nickell, 1958).

Many plants exhibit a dimorphism of leaves from juvenile to adult stage. In *Eucalyptus* for example the juvenile leaves are broad, ovate, and opposite but change to a linear or lanceolate shape and spiral phyllotaxis. The application of gibberellins can bring about the transition of leaves from juvenile to adult stage or reversal from adult to juvenile in *Eucalyptus*, *Hedera*, and *Ipomoea* (Njoku, 1958; Robbins, 1957). The development of autumn foliage color may also be delayed by GA_3 application (Brian *et al.*, 1959).

The response of excised roots depends on the strain employed and growth may be enhanced or inhibited by gibberellin application (Whaley and Kephart, 1957; Lee, 1959). Growth of main and lateral roots of tomato is promoted at low concentration of GA_3 but inhibited at higher ones (Butcher and Street, 1960); GA_1, GA_2, and GA_4 behave like GA_3.

Formation of Flowers

In 1956, Lang discovered the gibberellin-induced stem elongation followed by flowering in biennial *Hyoscyamus niger* which normally retains the vegetative rosette habit unless cold-treated. Since then, these responses have been reported for many other biennials and perennials which normally require low temperature and long days for elongation (see Lang, 1965). Application of gibberellin will also induce or promote flowering under strictly noninductive photoperiod conditions in many of the long-day plants, e.g., annual varieties of *Crepis*, *Hyoscyamus*, *Lactuca*, and *Lapsana*. The gibberellins do not cause flowering in short-day plants kept on long days. Gibberellin treatment of short-day plants maintained under short days may enhance, reduce, or in some cases even completely inhibit flower formation (see Lang, 1965). The long-short-day plants *Bryophyllum crenatum* and *B. daigremontianum* also do not respond with flowering if gibberellin treatment is done under continuous long days but do if it is done under short-day conditions. Thus, gibberellins replace the long-day but not the short-day requirement. Treatment under long-day conditions, however, enhances the subsequent response to short days.

An increase in the level of endogenous gibberellins has been found in cold-requiring plants during or following cold treatment, and in long-day plants during and following long-day treatment (Harada, 1962; Chailakhyan and Lozhnikova, 1962). In cold-requiring plants the gibberellins seem to be involved in the stages subsequent to vernalization. Further indication of this comes from the observations that maximum response to gibberellin application in Petkus winter rye is obtained when the plants have formed nine or ten leaves (Caso *et al.*, 1960; Purvis, 1960). Earlier application causes little or no promotion of flowering.

Pollen Germination, Fruit and Seed Development

Gibberellins affect pollen germination and the elongation of pollen tubes profoundly. Stimulation of the growth of tubes has been found in *Lilium*, *Lobelia*, *Lonicera*, *Petunia*, *Pisum*, *Pseudotsuga*, *Tradescantia*, and *Verbena* (Bose, 1959; see Brian *et al.*, 1960) and it has been suggested that this effect of gibberellins may be used for overcoming certain types of incompatibilities. Inhibition and abnormalities in pollen tube extension due to gibberellin treatment are also known. In the Black Corinth grapes, GA_3 reduces the germination of pollen to 1–7 percent (Weaver and McCune, 1960).

The development of parthenocarpic fruits due to application of gibberellins was first reported in tomato (Wittwer *et al.*, 1957). Since then such development has been found in many other fruits, e.g., apple, currant, cucumber (*Cucumis sativus*), egg plant (*Solanum melongena*), pepper (*Capsicum frutescens*), pear, *Pereskia*, *Rosa*, and *Zephyranthes* (see Crane, 1964).

In clementine mandarin (*Citrus reticulata*), Washington Navel orange, almond, apricot, and peach (Soost and Burnett, 1961; Hield *et al.*, 1958; Crane *et al.*, 1960, 1961), where the auxins fail to induce parthenocarpy, the gibberellins on the contrary have been shown to enhance fruit set.

Not only are the gibberellins involved in the setting of fruits but also, in conjunction with auxin, in the later stages of fruit growth. In tomato, IAA and GA_3 together produce fruits more than twice as large as those obtainable by the application of either IAA or GA_3 alone. In peaches, the whole process of fruit development (sclarification of endocarp, regulation of cell divisions, and cell enlargement in mesocarp) can be regulated by the application of gibberellin.

Besides the role of gibberellins in fruit development, a positive correlation between the extractable level of gibberellins and seed growth seems to be emerging from recent reports. Evidence for the existence of gibberellin-like substances in the seed has been provided by numerous investigators (see reviews by Phinney and West, 1960; Nitsch, 1965). In all cases the amount per seed is low in the young seeds a short time after fertilization and rises rapidly with the seed growth. When the seeds attain final size or maximum fresh weight, or even before, the amounts decline to a low level, but seeds of *Pharbitis* and other Convolvulaceae retain high gibberellin activity even at maturity.

The dormancy behavior of seeds, buds, and underground organs, due to a specific temperature or light requirement, is overcome in many cases by applied gibberellins. Thus, germination occurs in the light-requiring seeds of lettuce, tobacco, *Arabidopsis thaliana*, *Bidens radiatus*, *Carnegiea gigantea*, *Kalanchoe*, *Lepidium virginicum*, *Parthenium argentatum*, and others (see Vegis, 1964). Grains of wild oats (Fischnich *et al.*, 1957; Simpson, 1965) that normally afterripen during storage show higher percentage of germination after gibberellin treatment. All the known gibberellins enhance the germination of lettuce seeds but GA_4 and GA_7 are especially active (Brian *et al.*, 1962).

The low temperature requirement of *Arabidopsis* (Kribben, 1957), Douglas fir (Richardson, 1958), and sweet cherry seeds (Fogle, 1958) can be wholly or partially replaced by gibberellins, while in the seeds of apple, peach, hazel, and birch (see Vegis, 1964) gibberellins fail to replace the low temperature requirement. The gibberellins seem to substitute for the temperature afterripening requirement in some seeds and an increase in the endogenous gibberellin-like substances following vernalization of dormant seeds or the plants from such seeds has been found (Chailakhyan and Lozhnikova, 1962; Frankland and Wareing, 1962). The observations that a much lower concentration of gibberellin is required to break the bud dormancy in partially chilled plants supports this generalization. Recent Russian work quite strongly suggests that GA_3 mainly promotes the growth of embryos in seeds with underdeveloped embryos, a feature often combined with a cold requirement, but does not overcome the cold requirement as such.

Gibberellic acid treatment in combination with appropriate light or temperature requirements has been shown to remove the physiological dwarfing in the seedlings of plants such as *Malus arnoldiana*, peach, and sweet cherry, normally caused by the germination of non-afterripened seeds or embryos (Barton, 1956; see Vegis, 1964).

Lower Plants

Although most of the studies pertaining to the effect of gibberellins are restricted to the flowering plants, comparable responses have been found in the lower plants. The growth of prothallia of *Dryopteris* and *Camptosorus* (Knobloch, 1957) and the protonema of mosses such as *Splanchnum* (Maltzahn and MacQuarrie, 1958) are greatly improved by gibberellin. In *Pohlia* the number of buds destined to give rise to leafy gametophores is greatly increased by gibberellins (Mitra and Allsopp, 1959). The seta of *Pellia epiphylla* sporophytes elongates on application of IAA and GA_3 under short days (Asprey *et al.*, 1958) whereas normally this elongation occurs during the spring with the onset of increasing day length. The formation of antheridia on comparatively young prothallia of *Anemia* and *Lygodium* is induced by gibberellin application to germinating spores, GA_7 being the most effective (Schraudolf, 1964).

The above account clearly shows the importance of gibberellins in the regulation of various processes of plant growth. Growth is controlled by the interaction of the various endogenous growth substances. The varying amount of any of these due either to intrinsic genetic control mechanisms or to exogenous factors, therefore, modifies the growth. The levels of native gibberellins, as well as of other growth substances, are dependent on external factors such as light and temperature. The elongation of the seta in the excised sporophytes of *Pellia* (Asprey *et al.*, 1958) and of the debladed petioles of *Ipomoea* (Kuse, 1958) is greatly stimulated when both IAA and GA are present.

TABLE 1. HOAGLAND'S MEDIUM

STOCK SOLUTIONS		VOLUME REQUIRED/ LITER
$Ca(NO_3)_2$	(1M)	10 ml
KNO_3	(1M)	10 ml
$MgSO_4$	(1M)	14 ml
KH_2PO_4	(1M)	2 ml
FeEDTA	(3.8 gm/100 ml)	2 ml
Micronutrients*		2 ml

* The micronutrient stock solution contains 2.86 gm H_3BO_3, 1.81 gm $MnCl_2 \cdot 4H_2O$, 0.11 gm $ZnCl_2$, 0.05 gm $CuCl_2 \cdot 2H_2O$, and 0.025 gm $Na_2MoO_4 \cdot 2H_2O$ per liter.

percent Tween 20 or Tween 80) or test solutions and apply a 5-μl aliquot (with the help of a micropipette) to the top portion of the epicotyl hook of each of ten pea plants. The control plants receive 0.05 percent Tween solution only. Measure the length of the shoot after plants have grown in red light for 5 to 6 days following treatment. Plot the response (increase in length over control plants) against log dosage.

Dwarf Corn System

This assay was developed by Neely and Phinney (1957) and at least five different dwarf mutants (d_1, d_2, d_3, d_5, an_1) which respond to gibberellins are known. One great advantage of this test is its low sensitivity to toxic materials.

Soak the corn grains for 12 to 24 hours and plant in vermiculite or perlite (the pointed end of the grains from where the radicle bursts out faces down). The seedlings are grown in light at 27°–30°C for 6 to 7 days. Discard the tall seedlings and use only the dwarf seedlings for the assay after selecting for uniformity of size. Deliver 0.1 ml of test solution containing 0.0001 to 10 μg of gibberellin and 0.05 percent Tween from a syringe into the funnel formed by the first unfolding leaf in each of ten plants. Allow the seedlings to grow for another 7 days till the first and second leaves have grown fully. Measure the length of the first plus the second leaf sheaths and plot the log of the increment in length against log dosage.

Cucumber Hypocotyl System

This test was described by Brian and Hemming (1961) and Brian *et al.* (1962). Germinate the cucumber seeds in the dark for 48 hours, remove the seed coats, and transplant the seedlings into dishes containing 1 percent agar. Apply 2 μl of the aqueous gibberellic acid solution to one of the cotyledons and measure the length of the hypocotyl after the seedlings have grown for 2 to 3 days in light. Gibberellins A_4, A_7, and A_9 are most active in this test. This assay is not specific to gibberellins and responds also to auxins (Katsumi *et al.*, 1965).

Lentil Epicotyl System

As indicated earlier gibberellic acid specifically induces cell elongation during the growth of the epicotyls in lentil (*Lens culinaris*). Because of specificity and lack of complications due to cell divisions, this system is extremely useful in elucidating the problems of cell elongation. Germinate the lentil seeds in the dark at 22°–25°C for 48 hours, remove the seed coats, and cut the radicle below the point of attachment of cotyledons. Transfer ten such seedlings to 30 ml of 10-fold diluted Hoagland's nutrient solution containing 1,000 units per milliliter of penicillin G (potassium salt). Include test chemicals such as gibberellic acid in the nutrient solution. Place the flasks with seedlings in a reciprocating type of horizontal shaker and measure the length of epicotyls after these have grown in dark at 19°–22°C for 48 hours. Maximum response is obtained at a dosage level of 100 μg of GA_3 per milliliter (2.5×10^{-4} *M*) and epicotyls elongate to almost twice the size of controls.

The growth of epicotyls is inhibited by FUDR (10^{-7} to 10^{-5} *M*) and 10^{-4} thymidine can completely reverse the inhibition. The gibberellic acid application causes a substantial increase of DNA and RNA in each seedling and this is prevented by FUDR. The latter not only blocks DNA synthesis by inhibiting thymidylate synthetase activity but also, and at the same time, inhibits cell elongation. DNA synthesis appears to be an important phase if cell elongation is to occur in lentil epicotyls.

Barley Endosperm System

RELEASE OF REDUCING SUGARS

In the grains of cereals, the development of several hydrolytic enzymes during germination has been found to be dependent upon the release of gibberellic acid from the embryo. In half-seeds devoid of embryos there is a linear relationship between amount of gibberellic acid applied and reducing sugars released after a suitable incubation time (Nicholls and Paleg, 1963).

Surface sterilize the grains of a naked variety of barley by treating with Clorox (diluted with 4 volumes of water) for 1 hour and rinse in distilled water repeatedly. Cut the grains transversely (discard the embryonal half), weigh in lots of four half-grains, and transfer to small glass vials containing 1 ml of test solution. Each vial contains 50 μl of streptomycin (10 mg per milliliter), gibberellic acid (5, 50, 500, 5,000, and 50,000 $\mu\mu$g per vial), or a known volume of plant extract[3] and water to a total of 1.0 ml. Prepare three vials for each concentration, stopper them, and place in an incubator at 30°C for 48 hours. Determine the reducing sugars quantitatively in the samples of ambient media following any suitable method. In the original procedure photometric adaptation of Somogyi's method has been employed for the estimation of sugars (Somogyi, 1952; Nelson, 1944).

INCREASE IN α-AMYLASE IN HALF-SEEDS

Cut the barley seeds (almost any naked variety is satisfactory) transversely in half and discard the embryo-half. Sterilize the endosperm-half by soaking for 20 minutes in Clorox (diluted with 4 volumes of water) followed by rinsing three times in sterile water. Transfer about 100 of the sterile, rinsed half-seeds to sterile sand in a 4-inch Petri dish. (To prepare the Petri dish, add 100 gm of clean, dry sand to a 4-inch Petri dish, cover, and autoclave for 15 minutes at 15 pounds pressure. Moisten the sand with 20–21 ml sterile distilled water.) Wrap the covered Petri dishes with aluminum foil and incubate at 20°–22°C for 3 to 4 days. Transfer the sterile half-seeds (ten half-seeds per flask) to sterile 25-ml Erlenmeyer flasks containing 2 μmoles acetate buffer (pH 4.8), 20 μmoles $CaCl_2$, and 0.2 to 2,000 $\mu\mu$moles of GA_3 (final concentrations of GA_3 from 10^{-6} to 10^{-10} *M*) in a final volume of 2.0 ml. Incubate the flasks at 25°C for 48 hours in a metabolic shaker at about 120 oscillations per minute. After the incubation period, pour the medium from around the

[3] Aqueous extracts of ethyl acetate contain an unknown substance(s) which also causes sugar release from barley endosperm (Briggs, 1966).

half-seeds into a plastic centrifuge tube. Rinse the half-seeds once with 3.0 ml distilled water and add the rinse water to the medium. Mix well and centrifuge at about 1,000 *g* for 10 minutes to remove starch grains and cellular debris. Extract the ten half-seeds with 0.2 *M* NaCl by grinding in a porcelain mortar and pestle with a little sand—first with 2.0 ml of 0.2 *M* NaCl until a thick paste is formed, then with an additional 3.0 ml of 0.2 *M* NaCl until a thin slurry is formed. Pour this slurry into a plastic centrifuge tube and centrifuge at 2,000 *g* for 10 minutes. Pipette suitable aliquots (0.01 to 0.2 ml) from the medium and extract supernatant fractions into enough water in a 16- × 150-mm test tube to make 1.0 ml total volume. Start the reaction by adding and mixing 1.0 ml of starch solution. (Prepare the starch as follows: boil for 1 minute a suspension which contains 150 mg of native [not solubilized] potato starch, 600 mg of KH_2PO_4, and 200 μmoles of $CaCl_2$ in a final volume of 100 ml; cool, centrifuge for 10 minutes at 3,000 *g*; decant the clear supernatant fraction for use.) Incubate the reaction mixture for a suitable time (1–10 minutes). Stop the reaction by adding 1.0 ml of iodine reagent solution. (Make the iodine reagent solution by diluting 1.0 ml of the iodine stock solution to 100 ml with 0.05 *N* HCl. The iodine stock solution contains 6 gm of KI and 600 mg of I_2 dissolved in 100 ml H_2O.) Add 5.0 ml distilled water to each tube and mix thoroughly. Read the optical density at 620 mμ. The decrease in optical density at 620 mμ is directly proportional to the quantity of α-amylase present over the range of 20 to 80 percent decrease in optical density. The susceptibility of various starch samples to α-amylase catalyzed hydrolysis varies. Therefore a conversion of the optical density changes to micrograms of α-amylase requires the use of an α-amylase of known purity. As an approximate figure, 3 μg of α-amylase gives an optical density change of 1.0 in a 1.0-minute incubation in this assay.

INCREASE IN α-AMYLASE OF ISOLATED ALEURONE LAYERS

In this system for observing the effect of gibberellins, only the aleurone layers are used. Prepare barley half-seeds, sterilize, and rinse as in the barley endosperm assay on page 605. Some care must be used in selecting the barley because not all varieties are susceptible to easy dissection. Nupana is one easily dissected commercial variety. Use a pair of forceps and a microspatula to remove the aleurone layers from the starch endosperm. (This dissection should be done in a transfer room under aseptic conditions.) Place 10 half-aleurone layers in the final incubation medium in a 25-ml Erlenmeyer flask. The incubation medium contains 2 μmoles of acetate buffer (pH 4.8), 20 μmoles $CaCl_2$, and the gibberellin (0.2 μμmole to 2,000 μμmoles) in a final volume of 2.0 ml. The flask containing the $CaCl_2$ and the buffer is sterilized by autoclaving. The gibberellin solution should be sterilized by filtration and added to the sterile flasks. If microbiological contamination becomes a problem, add 25 μg each of streptomycin, mysteclin, and penicillin and/or 20 μg of chloramphenicol to each flask when adding the aleurone layers.

Incubate the aleurone layers at 25°C for 24 hours. Decant the medium into a plastic centrifuge tube and rinse once with 3.0 ml distilled water. Extract the aleurone layers with 5.0 ml 0.2 *M* NaCl by grinding with a little sand in a porcelain mortar and pestle. Grind first with 1.0 ml to a thick paste then with 5.0 ml to a thin slurry. Pour into a plastic centrifuge tube. Centrifuge the medium and extract at about 2,000 *g* for 10 minutes. Assay suitable aliquots (0.01–0.20 ml) for α-amylase as described in the barley endosperm assay on page 606.

The α-amylase produced is directly proportional to the log of the gibberellic acid concentration over the range 10^{-7} to 10^{-10} *M*, in both barley endosperm assays (Jones and Varner, 1967).

REFERENCES

ADDICOTT, F. T., H. R. CARNS, J. L. LYON, O. E. SMITH, and J. L. MC MEANS, 1964: On the physiology of abscisins. In *Régulateurs Naturels de la Croissance Végétale*, Colloques Internationaux du Centre National de la Recherche Scientifique No. 123, p. 687.

ASPREY, G. F., K. BENSON-EVANS, and A. G. LYON, 1958: Effect of gibberellin and indoleacetic acid on seta elongation in *Pellia epiphylla. Nature* (London), 181: 1351.

BARTON, L. V., 1956: Growth response of physiologic dwarfs of *Malus arnoldiana* Sarg. to gibberellic acid. *Contr. Boyce Thompson Inst.*, 18: 311.

BIRCH, A. J., and H. SMITH, 1959: The biosynthesis of terpenoid compounds in fungi. In G. E. W. Wolstenholme (ed.), *Biosynthesis of Terpenes and Sterols*, Little, Brown & Co., Boston, Mass., p. 253.

———, R. W. RICKARDS, and H. SMITH, 1958: The biosynthesis of gibberellic acid. *Proc. Chem. Soc.*, 1958: 192.

BOSE, N., 1959: Effect of gibberellin on the growth of pollen tubes. *Nature* (London), 184: 1577.

BRIAN, P. W., J. F. GROVE, and J. MAC MILLAN, 1960: The gibberellins. *Fortschr. Chem. org. Naturstoffe*, 18: 350.

———, and H. G. HEMMING, 1961: Promotion of cucumber hypocotyl growth by two new gibberellins. *Nature* (London), 189: 74.

———, ———, and D. LOWE, 1958: Effect of gibberellic acid on rate of extension and maturation of pea internodes. *Ann. Bot.*, New Ser. 22: 539.

———, ———, and ———, 1962: Relative activity of the gibberellins. *Nature* (London), 193: 946.

———, J. H. P. PETTY, and P. T. RICHMOND, 1959: Effects of gibberellic acid on development of autumn colour and leaf fall of deciduous plants. *Nature* (London), 183: 58.

BRIGGS, D. D., 1966: Residues from organic solvents showing gibberellin-like biological activity. *Nature* (London), 210: 419.

BUTCHER, D. N., and H. E. STREET, 1960: The effects of gibberellins on the growth of excised tomato roots. *J. Exp. Bot.*, 11: 206.

CASO, O. H., H. R. HIGHKIN, and D. KOLLER, 1960: Effect of gibberellic acid on flower differentiation in Petkus winter rye. *Nature* (London), 185: 477.

CATHEY, H. M., 1964: Physiology of growth retarding chemicals. *Ann. Rev. Plant Physiol.*, 15: 271.

CHAILAKHYAN, M. KH., and V. N. LOZHNIKOVA, 1962: Gibberellin-like substances and vernalization (Russian with English summary). *Fiziol. Rast.*, 9: 21.

CHRISPEELS, M. J., and J. E. VARNER, 1966: Abscisin II inhibition of gibberellic acid induced formation of α-amylase. *Nature* (London), 212: 1066.

———, and ———, 1967: Gibberellic acid-enhanced synthesis and release of α-amylase and ribonuclease by isolated barley aleurone layers. *Plant Physiol.*, 42: 398.

CORNFORTH, J. W., B. V. MILLBORROW, and G. RYBACK, 1966: Identification and estimation of (+)-abscisin II ("Dormin") in plant extracts by spectropolarimetry. *Nature* (London), 210: 627.

———, ———, ———, and P. F. WAREING, 1965: Chemistry and physiology of dormins and sycamore. *Nature* (London). 205: 1269.

CRANE, J. C., 1964: Growth substances in fruit setting and development. *Ann. Rev. Plant Physiol.* 15: 303.

———, P. E. PRIMER, and R. C. CAMPBELL, 1960: Gibberellin-induced parthenocarpy in *Prunus*. *Proc. Amer. Soc. Hort. Sci.*, 75: 129.

———, C. A. REBEIZ, and R. C. CAMPBELL, 1961: Gibberellin-induced parthenocarpy in the J. H. Hale peach and the probable cause of button production. *Proc. Amer. Soc. Hort. Sci.*, 78: 111.

CROSS, B. E., R. H. B. GALT, and J. R. HANSON, 1964a: The biosynthesis of the gibberellins. Part I. (−)-Kaurene as a precursor of gibberellic acid. *J. Chem. Soc.*, 1964: 295.

———, ———, ———, 1964b: Recent work on the gibberellins. I. The biosynthesis of gibberellins. In *Régulateurs Naturels de la Croissance Végétale*, Colloques Internationaux du Centre National de la Recherche Scientifique No. 123, p. 265.

DENNIS, D. T., C. D. UPPER, and C. A. WEST, 1965: An enzymatic site of inhibition of gibberellin biosynthesis by Amo 1618 and other plant growth retardants. *Plant Physiol.* 40: 948.

DURE, L. S., and W. A. JENSEN, 1957: The influence of gibberellic acid and indoleacetic acid on cotton embryos cultured *in vitro*. *Bot. Gaz.*, 118: 254.

EDELMAN, J., and M. A. HALL, 1964: Effect of growth hormones on the development of invertase associated with cell walls. *Nature* (London), 201: 296.

EL-ANTABLY, H. M. M., and P. F. WAREING, 1966: Stimulation of flowering in certain short-day plants by abscisin. *Nature* (London), 210: 328.

ELSON, G. W., D. F. JONES, J. MAC MILLAN, and P. J. SUTER, 1964: Plant hormones IV. Identification of the gibberellins of *Echinocystis macrocarpa* Greene by thin layer chromatography. *Phytochemistry*, 3: 93.

FILNER, P., and J. E. VARNER, 1967: A simple and unequivocal test for *de novo* synthesis of enzymes: Density labeling with H_2O^{18} of barley α-amylase induced by gibberellic acid. *Proc. Natl. Acad. Sci.*, (Wash.), in press.

FISCHNICH, O., M. THIELEBEIN, and A. GRAHL, 1957: Brechung der Keimruhe bei Gerste durch Gibberellinsäure und Rindite. *Naturwissenschaften*, 44: 642.

FOGLE, H. W., 1958: Effects of duration of after-ripening, gibberellin and other pretreatments on sweet cherry germination and seedling growth. *Proc. Amer. Soc. Hort. Sci.*, 72: 129.

FRANKLAND, B., and P. F. WAREING, 1962: Changes in endogenous gibberellins in relation to chilling of dormant seeds. *Nature* (London), 194: 313.

GORTER, C. J., 1961: Dwarfism of peas and action of gibberellic acid. *Physiol. Plant.*, 14: 332.

GRAEBE, J., D. T. DENNIS, C. D. UPPER, and C. A. WEST, 1965: Biosynthesis of gibberellins. I. The biosynthesis of (−)-kaurene, (−)-kaurene-19-ol and *trans*-geranylgeraniol in endosperm-nucellus of *Echinocystis macrocarpa*. *J. Biol. Chem.*, 240: 1847.

HARADA, H., 1962: Étude des substances naturelles de croissance en relation avec la floraison. Isolement d'une substance de montaison. *Rev. gén. Bot.*, 69: 201.

———, and A. LANG, 1965: Effect of some (2-chloroethyl) trimethylammonium-chloride analogs and other growth retardants on gibberellin biosynthesis in *Fusarium moniliforme*. *Plant Physiol.*, 40: 176.

HASHIMOTO, T., and L. RAPPAPORT, 1966: Variations in endogenous gibberellins in developing bean seeds. I. Occurrence of neutral and acidic substances. *Plant Physiol.*, 41: 623.

HAYASHI, F., S. BLUMENTHAL-GOLDSCHMIDT, and L. RAPPAPORT, 1962: Acid and neutral gibberellin-like substances in potato tubers. *Plant Physiol.*, 37: 774.

———, and L. RAPPAPORT, 1962: Isolation and detection of neutral gibberellin-like substances in potato tubers. 14th Annual Meeting Am. Chem. Soc., Atlantic City, N.J., p. 14-C.

———, and ———, 1965: *In vitro* conversion

of neutral gibberellin-like substances from potato tubers. *Nature* (London), 205: 414.

HIELD, H. Z., C. W. COGGINS, JR., and M. J. GARBER, 1958: Gibberellin tested on *Citrus*. *Calif. Agr.*, 12: 9.

HILLMAN, W. S., and W. K. PURVES, 1961: Does gibberellin act through an auxin-mediated mechanism? In R. M. Klein (ed.), *Plant Growth Regulation*, Iowa State College Press, Ames, Iowa, p. 589.

JONES, R. L., and J. E. VARNER, 1967: The bioassay of gibberellins. *Planta*, 72: 155.

KAGAWA, T., T. FUKINBARA, and Y. SUMIKI, 1963: Thin layer chromatography of gibberellins. *Agr. Biol. Chem.* (Tokyo), 27: 598.

KATSUMI, M., B. O. PHINNEY, and W. K. PURVES, 1965: The role of gibberellin and auxin in cucumber hypocotyl growth. *Physiol. Plant.*, 18: 462.

KENDE, H., and A. LANG, 1964: Gibberellins and light inhibition of stem growth in peas. *Plant Physiol.*, 39: 435.

———, H. NINNEMANN, and A. LANG, 1963: Inhibition of gibberellic acid biosynthesis in *Fusarium moniliforme* by Amo-1618 and CCC. *Naturwissenschaften*, 50: 599.

KHALIFAH, R. H., L. N. LEWIS, and C. W. COGGINS, JR., 1965: Gradient elution column chromatography systems for the separation and identification of gibberellins. *Anal. Biochem.*, 12: 113.

KNOBLOCH, I. W., 1957: Gibberellic acid and ferns. *Amer. Fern J.*, 47: 134.

KRIBBEN, F. J., 1957: Gibberellinsäure und Blattwachstum. *Naturwissenschaften*, 44: 429.

KURAISHI, S., and T. HASHIMOTO, 1957: Promotion of leaf growth and acceleration of stem elongation by gibberellin. *Bot. Mag.*, 70: 86.

KUROSAWA, E., 1926: Experimental studies on the nature of the substance excreted by the bakanae fungus. *Trans. Nat. Hist. Soc. Formosa*, 16: 213.

KUSE, G., 1958: Necessity of auxin for the growth effect of gibberellin. *Bot. Mag.*, 71: 151.

LANG, A., 1956: Induction of flower formation in biennial *Hyoscyamus* by treatment with gibberellin. *Naturwissenschaften*, 43: 284.

———, 1965: Physiology of flower initiation. In W. Ruhland (ed.), *Encyclopedia of Plant Physiology*, Springer-Verlag, Berlin, Heidelberg, and New York. Vol. XV, Part 1, p. 1380.

LEAVER, C. J., and J. EDELMAN, 1965: Nucleic acid synthesis in carrot tissue slices. *Biochem. J.*, 95: 27P.

LEE, A. E., 1959: The effects of various substances on the comparative growth of excised tomato roots of clones carrying dwarf and normal alleles. *Amer. J. Bot.*, 46: 16.

LOCKHART, J. A. 1959: Control of stem growth by light and gibberellin. In R. B. Withrow (ed.), *Photoperiodism and Related Phenomena in Plants and Animals*, Amer. Assoc. Adv. Sci., Washington, D.C., Publ. No. 55, p. 217.

———, 1959: Studies on the mechanism of stem growth inhibition by visible radiation. *Plant Physiol.*, 34: 457.

MAC LEOD, A. M., and G. H. PALMER, 1966: The embryo of barley in relation to modification of the endosperm. *J. Inst. Brew.*, 72: 580.

MAC MILLAN, J., and P. J. SUTER, 1958: The occurrence of gibberellin A_1 in higher plants: Isolation from the seeds of runner bean (*Phaseolus multiflorus*). *Naturwissenschaften*, 45: 46.

MALTZAHN, K. E. VON, and I. G. MAC QUARRIE, 1958: Effect of gibberellic acid on the growth of protonema of *Splanchnum ampullaceum* (L.) Hedw. *Nature* (London), 181: 1139.

MITRA, G. C., and A. ALLSOPP, 1959: Effects of kinetin, gibberellic acid and certain auxins on the protonema of *Pohlia nutans*. *Nature* (London), 183: 974.

NEELY, P. M., and B. O. PHINNEY, 1957: The use of the mutant *dwarf-1* of maize as a quantitative bioassay for gibberellin activity. *Plant Physiol.*, 32: Suppl. p. xxxi.

NELSON, N., 1944: A photometric adaption of the Somogyi method for the determination of glucose. *J. Biol. Chem.*, 153: 375.

NICHOLLS, P. B., and L. G. PALEG, 1963: A barley endosperm bioassay for gibberellins. *Nature* (London), 199: 823.

NICKELL, L. G., 1958: Production of gibberellin-like substances by plant tissue cultures. *Science*, 128: 88.

NITSAN, J., and A. LANG, 1965: Inhibition of cell division and cell elongation in higher plants by inhibitors of DNA synthesis. *Devel. Biol.*, 12: 358.

———, and ———, 1966: DNA synthesis in the elongating non-dividing cells of the lentil epicotyl and its promotion by gibberellin. *Plant Physiol.*, 41: 965.

NITSCH, J. P., 1965: Physiology of flower and fruit development. In W. Ruhland (ed.), *Encyclopedia of Plant Physiology*, Springer-Verlag, Berlin, Heidelberg, and New York, Vol. XV, Part 1, p. 1537.

NJOKU, E., 1958: Effect of gibberellic acid on leaf form. *Nature* (London), 182: 1097.

PALEG, L. G., 1964: Cellular localization of the gibberellin-induced response of barley endosperm. In *Régulateurs Naturels de la Croissance Végétale*, Colloques Internationaux du Centre National de la Recherche Scientifique No. 123, p. 303.

———, 1965: Physiological effects of gibberellins. *Ann. Rev. Plant Physiol.*, 16: 291.

PHINNEY, B. O., 1961: Dwarfing genes in *Zea mays* and their relation to the gibberellins. In R. M. Klein (ed.), *Plant Growth Regulation*, Iowa State College Press, Ames, Iowa, p. 498.

———, and C. A. WEST, 1960: Gibberellins as native plant growth regulators. *Ann. Rev. Plant Physiol.*, 11: 411.

———, ———, M. RITZEL, and P. M. NEELY, 1957: Evidence for gibberellin-like substances from flowering plants. *Proc. Natl. Acad. Sci.* (Wash.), 43: 398.

PURVIS, O. N., 1960: Effect of gibberellin on flower initiation and stem extension in Petkus winter rye. *Nature* (London), 185: 479.

RADLEY, M., 1958: The distribution of substances similar to gibberellic acid in higher plants. *Ann. Bot.*, 22: 297.

RICHARDSON, S. D., 1958: Radicle elongation of *Pseudotsuga menziesii* in relation to light and gibberellic acid. *Nature* (London), 181: 429.

ROBBINS, W. J., 1957: Gibberellic acid and the reversal of adult *Hedera* to a juvenile state. *Amer. J. Bot.*, 44: 743.

RUDDAT, M. E., E. HEFTMANN, and A. LANG, 1965: Biosynthesis of steviol. *Arch. Biochem. Biophys.*, 110: 496.

SCHNEIDER, G., 1964: Eine neue Gruppe von synthetischen Pflanzenwachstumregulatoren. *Naturwissenschaften*, 51: 416.

———, D. ERDMANN, S. LUST, G. MOHR, and K. NIETHAMMER, 1965: Morphactins, a novel group of plant-growth regulators. *Nature* (London), 208: 1013.

SCHRAUDOLF, H., 1964: Relative activity of the gibberellins in the antheridium induction in *Anemia phyllitidis*. *Nature* (London), 201: 98.

SCHROEDER, C. A., and C. SPECTOR, 1957: Effect of gibberellic acid and indoleacetic acid on growth of excised fruit tissue. *Science*, 126: 701.

SEMBDNER, G., R. GROSS, and K. SCHREIBER, 1962: Die dünnschichtchromatographie von Gibberellinen. *Experientia*, 18: 584.

SIMPSON, G. M., 1965: Dormancy studies in seed of *Avena fatua*. 4. The role of gibberellin in embryo dormancy. *Canad. J. Bot.*, 43: 793.

SKINNER, C. G., F. D. TALBERT, and W. SHIVE, 1958: Effect of 6-(substituted)-purines and gibberellin on the rate of seed germination. *Plant Physiol.*, 33: 190.

SOMOGYI, M., 1952: Notes on sugar determination. *J. Biol. Chem.* 195: 19.

SOOST, R. K., and R. H. BURNETT, 1961: Effect of gibberellin on yield and fruit characteristics of Clemantine mandarin. *Proc. Amer. Soc. Hort. Sci.*, 77: 194.

SPECTOR, C., 1958: *Growth Responses of Gibberellic Acid and Indole-3-acetic Acid in Fruit Tissue Cultures of* Citrus media. Unpublished Ph.D. thesis, University of California, Los Angeles, Calif.

THOMAS, T. H., P. F. WAREING, and P. M. ROBINSON, 1965: Action of the sycamore 'dormin' as a gibberellin antagonist. *Nature* (London), 205: 1270.

VARNER, J. E., and G. RAM CHANDRA, 1964: Hormonal control of enzyme synthesis in barley endosperm. *Proc. Natl. Acad. Sci.*, (Wash.), 52: 100.

VASIL, I. K., 1957: Effect of kinetin and gibberellic acid on excised anthers of *Allium cepa*. *Phytomorphology*, 7: 138.

VEGIS, A., 1964: Dormancy in higher plants. *Ann. Rev. Plant Physiol.*, 15: 185.

WAREING, P. F., 1958: Interaction between indoleacetic acid and gibberellic acid in cambial activity. *Nature* (London), 181: 1744.

WEAVER, R. J., and S. B. MC CUNE, 1960: Further studies with gibberellin on *Vitis vinifera* grapes. *Bot. Gaz.*, 121: 155.

WEST, C. A., and B. O. PHINNEY, 1956: Properties of gibberellin-like factors from extracts of higher plants. *Plant Physiol.*, 31: Suppl. xx.

WHALEY, W. G., and J. KEPHART, 1957: Effect of gibberellic acid on growth of maize roots. *Science*, 125: 234.

WITTWER, S. H., M. J. BUKOVAC, H. M. SELL, and I. E. WELLER, 1957: Some effects of gibberellin on flowering and fruit setting. *Plant Physiol.*, 32: 39.

YABUTA, T., 1935: Biochemistry of the *bakanae* fungus of rice. *Agr. and Hort.*, 10: 17.

YOMO, J., and H. IINUMA, 1966: Production of gibberellin-like substances in the embryo of barley during germination. *Planta*, 71: 113.

ZWEIG, G., and G. R. COSENS, 1959: Residue analysis of gibberellic acid in grapes and isotope methods. *J. Agric. Food Chem.*, 7: 717.

Cytokinins

By Carlos O. Miller

INTRODUCTION

The cytokinins (Skoog *et al.*, 1965) are especially characterized by their ability to promote cell division in plant tissue cultures otherwise supplied with sugar, mineral salts, vitamins, and auxin. Activity is not restricted to such promotion, however, and effects on senescence, cell enlargement, seed germination, induction of organs such as roots or stems, apical dominance, mobilization of organic and inorganic nutrients, enzyme activities, and protein, nucleic acid, and chlorophyll contents have been studied quite extensively. Obviously the action of cytokinins in control of plant development is a fruitful area of investigation. The response of tissues to cytokinins is influenced by the presence or absence of other plant growth substances, especially gibberellins and auxins, and some practical aspects of this are mentioned subsequently. (Also, consult the articles in this volume by Morré and Key, pp. 575–593, and Johri and Varner, pp. 595–611.) Kinetin (6-furfurylaminopurine, Fig. 1) serves as the type compound and any substance having kinetin-like biological activities may be classified as a cytokinin.

The most active compounds thus far studied are 6-(substituted)-aminopurines and these are quite similar to kinetin in structure (*cf.* Fig. 1 for some compounds commonly used). One apparent exception to this is 8-aza-kinetin (nitrogen instead of carbon in position 8); this compound, however, might very well act as a purine in at least some phases of metabolism. Another type of compound which gives cytokinin activity includes various substituted ureas and thioureas (Shantz and Steward, 1955; Bruce *et al.*, 1965). Even with the most active of these substituted ureas, the concentrations needed for threshold activity in a tobacco pith assay seem to be considerably higher than is needed for the purine derivatives. The relationship between the two groups of compounds is not understood.

Few cytokinins of known structure have been identified in plants. Kinetin, for example, has not been shown to be a plant product. One purine derivative, however, has been isolated from young plums and from maize kernels and its structure has been established (Letham *et al.*, 1964). This compound is known as zeatin, and is chemically designated as 6-(4-hydroxy-3-methylbut-*trans*-2-enyl) aminopurine (Fig. 1). Zeatin is extremely active and may promote cell division when supplied in media at concentrations as low as 5×10^{-11} *M*. It apparently

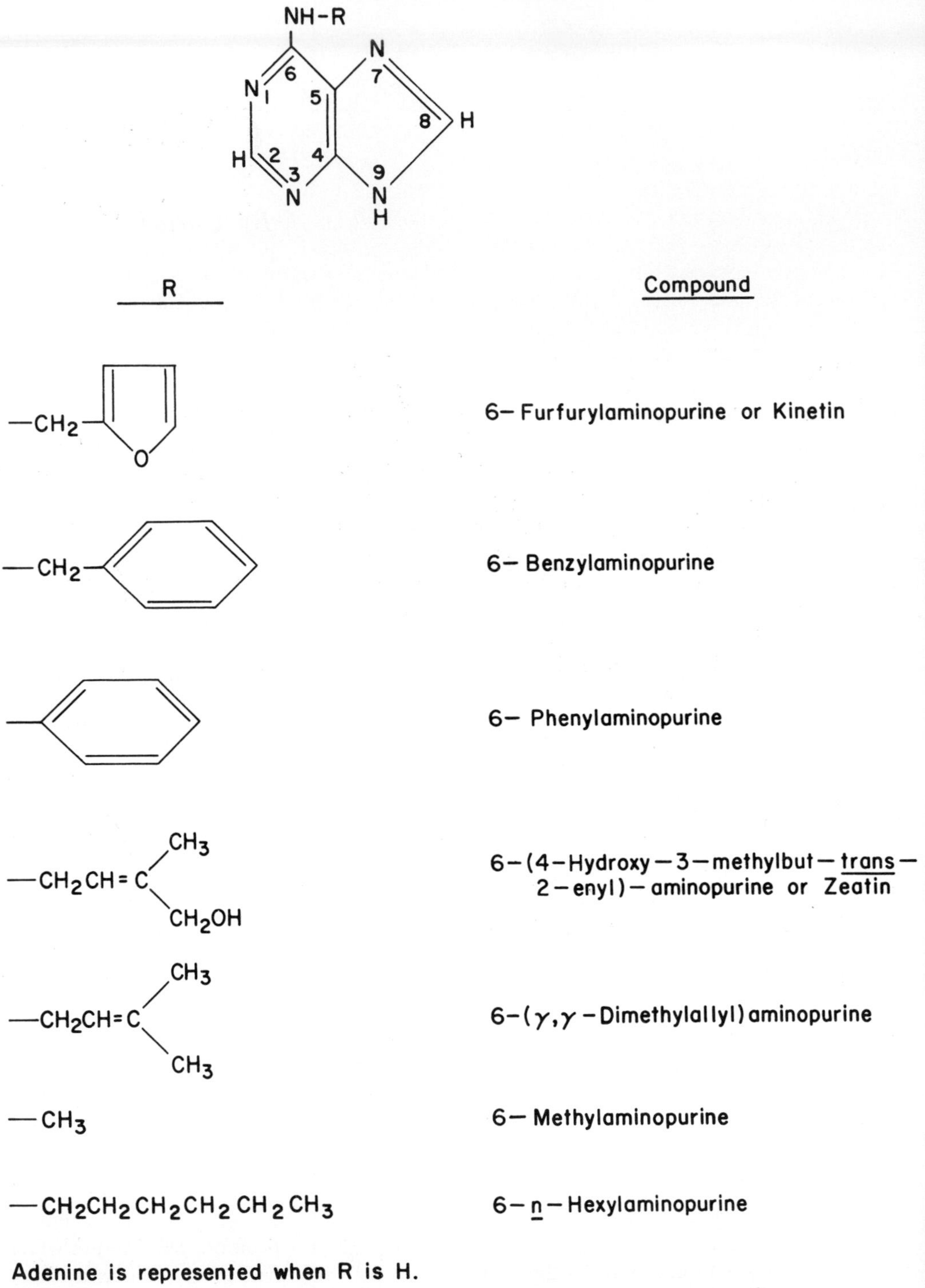

FIG. 1. Some 6-(substituted)-aminopurines which show cytokinin activity.

occurs in the corn grains in several forms including a nucleoside (probably 9-β-D-ribofuranosyl zeatin) and a phosphate derivative, probably a ribotide; other derivatives are likely to be present (Miller, 1965). 6-Methyl-aminopurine has slight cytokinin activity and is known to occur in many biological materials. *Sym*-diphenylurea has been obtained from coconut milk by Shantz and Steward (1955) and shows some activity in various cytokinin assays.

Not all aspects of cytokinin methodology are mentioned here and the reader may consult an earlier treatment (Miller, 1963) and, of course, the original papers.

ASSAY SYSTEMS

Recently, carrot, soybean, and tobacco tissues have been widely used for detecting the naturally occurring cytokinins and evaluating synthetic compounds. These tests have a rather high specificity, detect very low concentrations of active materials, and do not involve the possible complications which must be considered in nonsterile tests. On the other hand, the responses obtained are quantitatively measurable only after a considerable lapse of time, and it is often desirable to use fairly large quantities of media. The tests have, however, been most favored in projects designed to isolate naturally occurring cytokinins. Some media currently employed are indicated in Table 1; all are variations of White's medium. These media may be autoclaved although proper checks should be made when untested or unknown chemicals are involved in the assays.

Tobacco Tissue Tests

Nicotiana tabacum, var. Wisconsin #38, is most frequently utilized although other varieties might do. From healthy, vigorously growing plants, sterile tissues may be obtained quite readily. If the leaves are cut off flush from stems which have formed some wood, the outer layers (the bark) may be carefully pulled off so as to bare a central cylinder which is sterile except for the bases of the leaves. These bases may then be flipped off with a sterile scalpel. Smaller cylinders (perhaps 3 inches or more in length) may next be cut with a sterile razor blade and dropped into a Petri dish. It is convenient to subdivide these sections further into cylinders about 1 cm long using a sterile blade or scalpel. From these short cylinders one may slice either tangential pieces containing some xylem, internal phloem, and pith, or blocks of pith alone. The tangential slices will form some wound callus when cultured on a basal medium (medium "a" or "d" of Table 1 serves well) in the absence of a cytokinin, but the growth of such wound callus slows or stops upon subculture unless a cytokinin is supplied. The pith, on the other hand, must be supplied with a source of cytokinin in the medium from the beginning if cell division is to occur to any extent. Sterile tissues may also be obtained from stem sections by soaking the sections (without peeling) either in 0.1 percent $HgCl_2$ for about 10 minutes or in 0.5 percent sodium hypochlorite (Clorox diluted ten times is adequate) for 10 to 30 minutes and then rinsing several times with sterile distilled water. Pith cylinders may be cut with sterile cork borers and pushed from the borers with sterile glass rods.

The group at the University of Wisconsin (Rogozinska *et al.*, 1964) recently has used callus originally derived from pith and subcultured every 4 weeks on medium "a" (Murashige and Skoog, 1962) with 0.2 mg per liter of kinetin. Before actual use in the assay, however, kinetin carryover was reduced by trans-

TABLE 1. MEDIA RECENTLY USED IN THE TOBACCO (a, b), CARROT (c), AND SOYBEAN (d) TISSUE TESTS

COMPONENT	CONCENTRATION (mg/liter) (a)	(b)	(c)	(d)
NH_4NO_3	1650	1000	160	1000
$(NH_4)_2SO_4$	..	..	400	..
KNO_3	1900	1000	200	1000
$CaCl_2 \cdot 2H_2O$	440	..	..	..
$Ca(NO_3)_2 \cdot 4H_2O$	..	500	470	500
$MgSO_4 \cdot 7H_2O$	370	71.5	500	71.5
KH_2PO_4	170	300	..	300
K_2HPO_4	..	..	175	..
KCl	..	65	..	65
Sodium ferric ethylene-diaminetetraacetate	..	32	20	..
Sodium ethylene-diaminetetraacetate	37.3*	..	..	13.4†
$FeSO_4 \cdot 7H_2O$	27.8*	..	..	9.9†
H_3BO_3	6.2	1.6	2.9	1.6
$MnSO_4 \cdot 4H_2O$	22.3	6.5	2.0	14.0
$ZnSO_4 \cdot 7H_2O$	8.6	2.6	0.2	3.8
KI	0.83	0.8	..	0.8
$Na_2MoO_4 \cdot 2H_2O$	0.25	..	..	..
$(NH_4)_6Mo_7O_{24} \cdot 4H_2O$	..	..	0.04	0.1
$CuSO_4 \cdot 5H_2O$	0.025	..	0.1	..
$Cu(NO_3)_2 \cdot 3H_2O$	..	..	..	0.35
$CoCl_2 \cdot 6H_2O$	0.025	..	..	..
Glycine	2.0	2.0	30	..
myo-Inositol	100	..	50	100
Nicotinic acid	0.5	0.5	5	0.5
Pyridoxine·HCl	0.5	0.1	1	0.1
Calcium pantothenate	..	..	0.2	..
Thiamine·HCl	0.1	0.1	1	0.1
Cysteine·HCl	..	..	10	..
Biotin	..	..	0.2	..
Indoleacetic acid	2	5	2	..
α-Naphthalene acetic acid	..	..	..	2
Sucrose	30,000	30,000	20,000	30,000
Agar	10,000	..	..	10,000
pH‡	5.7–5.8	5.8	6.4	5.8

* 5 ml/liter of a stock solution containing 5.57 gm $FeSO_4 \cdot 7H_2O$ and 7.45 gm Na_2 ethylenediaminetetraacetate·$2H_2O$ per liter, the two salts being heated in water together.

† 5 ml/liter of a stock solution containing 1.98 gm/liter $FeSO_4 \cdot 7H_2O$ and 2.68 gm/liter Na_2 ethylenediaminetetraacetate·$2H_2O$; the iron salt was added to a hot solution of the complexing salt.

‡ Adjusted with NaOH or HCl as needed.

ferring the callus onto the basal medium with only 0.03 mg per liter of kinetin and subcultured once more on this same medium. In the actual assay the Murashige-Skoog medium without kinetin served as the basal solution. Three pieces of tissue weighing about 50 mg each were planted on 50 ml of medium in each 125-ml Erlenmeyer flask, four flasks per treatment being used. After 5 weeks' growth at about 28°C under continuous dim light, fresh and dry weights were obtained.

The group at Canberra, Australia, has employed fresh pith tissue for assays of cytokinins from various plant sources and of synthetic ureas and thioureas (Bruce *et al.*, 1965; Bottomley *et al.*, 1963). Strips (4 × 0.9 cm) of Whatman #1 filter paper were placed in glass tubes (7.5 × 1.2 cm) and 0.5 or 1.0 ml of test medium (medium "b" served as control medium) was added to each tube before sterilization at 18 pounds per square inch for 5 minutes. When the tubes were placed at 20 degrees to the horizontal, a layer of medium was spread along the filter paper. After sterilization of the media, one block of pith (3 × 5 × 10 mm and free of internal phloem) was placed in each tube in a manner to provide for access of the tissue to the medium only through the filter paper. Treatments were run in triplicate and cultures were kept in darkness at a high humidity at 25°C for 22 days. New growth along the surface of the blocks may easily be seen, and simple visual inspection was used to detect threshold concentrations needed for various compounds to give some cell division. At higher concentrations, the number of cells was indicated by fresh and dry weights or by actual cell counts. The latter is preferable with tobacco tissue since the cytokinins may decrease average cell size at concentrations which cause increased cell division. For cell counting, the method of Brown and Rickless (1949) was employed. Pieces of tissue were soaked overnight in 2 percent w/v aqueous chromic oxide solution, stained with orsellein BB in 3 percent acetic acid for 1 hour, washed, drained, and then macerated by drawing through a pipette (Zwar *et al.*, 1963). Counts were made with a cytometer.

Carrot Tissue Test

Carrot roots have been intensively used in the search for substances which stimulate cell division, especially by Professor Steward's group at Cornell University. Although growth of tissues from these roots often seems to have rather complex requirements for exogenous substances, their use has yielded much information of value—perhaps in part because of the complex requirements. Letham (1963) used carrot tissue in assays which led to his isolation of zeatin. Pieces (2 mg) of carrot root phloem were cultured in liquid medium "c" with or without the cytokinin preparations. The methods of Caplin and Steward (1949) were utilized. Cell counts were made 21 days after the start of the experiment. Counts were accomplished after maceration in chromic acid (Brown and Rickless, 1949) or in a 2 percent sodium hexametaphosphate solution (Letham, 1962). The latter solution must be in the pH range of 3.7 to 4.1 (dilute HCl added) and 10 ml must be used for each gram of tissue. After being placed in a vacuum desiccator for 10 minutes, the solution with the tissue was covered with layers of chloroform and toluene and the container stoppered and shaken vigorously. After storage at 23°C for 1 week (much shorter periods sometimes suffice), the material was shaken and blended in distilled water or in 0.25 *N* NH_4OH containing 1.3×10^{-3} *M* sodium ethylenediaminetetraacetate.

Soybean Tissue Test

I have preferred this test (Miller, 1963) because the tissue, once established, can be kept in continuous culture with little alteration in nutritional requirements, because cell size does not seem to depend on the concentration of cytokinin, and because the tissues on the control medium ("d" in Table 1 represents our latest version) show little if any growth. From many thousands of tissue pieces, we have obtained only one which can be continuously subcultured on the basal medium without added cytokinin. We currently are making assays for cytokinins with tissue descended from a cotyledon put into culture in 1959. Seeds of *Glycine max*, var. Acme, were sterilized by soaking in 0.1 percent $HgCl_2$ for 15 minutes and then rinsed four times with sterile distilled water. These seeds were germinated on basal medium without auxin. After germination, slices were cut from the green cotyledons and placed on the basal medium containing both the auxin and 0.5 mg per liter of kinetin. The callus which formed was then transferred to more of the same medium, 50 ml per each 125-ml Erlenmeyer flask being used. Four pieces of tissue each weighing 3 to 4 mg were planted in each flask. The large lumps (up to around 1500 mg) which resulted when cultured at 27°C under fluorescent lighting were subdivided in 5 to 6 weeks. The illumination used was about 40 ft-c, but perhaps this is not too critical if high light intensities are avoided. Medium "d" serves for an assay of control pieces of tissue, and extracts or chemicals are added to it. We set up and grow the test tissues as just described and routinely weigh the pieces individually after 28 days of culture. Fresh weights serve the purpose and dry weights usually are fairly proportional. Perhaps the greatest difficulty for an assay is in choosing the large lump to be subdivided into test pieces. For best results, I believe that fully grown lumps just beginning to show a very slight amount of browning should be used. If obtained from younger lumps, the control pieces may show too much growth. If older pieces are employed, too many of the cells may be dead.

Leaf Chlorophyll Tests

When separated from the plant, leaves of many species quickly begin to show a loss of chlorophyll. Such loss may be slowed or prevented by the application of a cytokinin to the leaf. The level of chlorophyll in a detached leaf may therefore serve as the basis for a cytokinin assay. Several variations currently are practiced. Earlier, Osborne and McCalla (1961) outlined an assay with *Xanthium* leaves. More recently, leaves of cereals such as wheat, oats, and barley have been widely employed. Kende (1964) grew barley at 20°C under continuous illumination for 13 days, and then he cut pieces from the first leaves between the third and fourth centimeters from the tip of the blade. The sections were floated for 24 hours on distilled water in darkness at 25°C. They then were blotted and put in screwcap vials containing 1 ml of test solution, such solution containing 250 units per milliliter of penicillin G. Four sections were put in each vial and replicates were run. The sections were incubated for 48 hours at 25°C in darkness and then extracted with 80 percent ethanol. After adjusting to a standard volume, the optical densities were read at 665 mμ. The response to kinetin in terms of increased chlorophyll was linear between 0.003 and 3.0 μg per milliliter of kinetin when results were plotted on a logarithmic scale. Srivastava and Ware (1965) planted barley (*Hordeum vulgare*, var. Wolfe) in the greenhouse and exposed seedlings to 16 hours of light daily. When the plants were 9 days old, the first seedling leaves were excised and washed with deionized distilled water. The leaves then were floated on test solutions in Petri dishes kept in the dark at 23°C. At intervals of time up to 7 or 8 days, the test leaves were washed, blotted, homogenized, and extracted thoroughly with 80 percent ethanol. The extract was made up to 25 ml per gram of leaf tissue. The optical densities at 660 mμ indicated the amounts of chlorophyll. Another variation of this type of cytokinin assay may be made by using wheat leaves according to the method of Person *et al.* (1957).

The leaf chlorophyll tests have advantages in the time needed for an assay, the amount of test solution necessary, and the ease with which the assay material is obtained and with which the quantitative measurements may be made. One disadvantage is in working with nonsterile solutions, especially when the test material is still in a crude form.

Germination Tests

Lettuce (*Lactuca sativa*) seeds are still being used for some cytokinin assays. Skinner *et al.*, (1957) soaked seeds of the variety Early Curled Simpson in test solutions (distilled water served as control solution) for 8 hours in the dark at 25°C. About 100 seeds were placed in a Petri dish containing filter paper wetted with the test solution and then germinated at 30°C in darkness. Percentage germination was then determined in 24 to 60 hours. In a variation, Miller (1958) placed 100 dry seeds of the variety Grand Rapids on a pad of three sheets of Whatman #1 filter paper (9 cm) in a Petri dish. The filter paper had been wetted with 5 ml of the test solution. After 16 hours of imbibition in the dark at 25°C, all dishes were exposed to dim (98 ergs/sq cm-sec) red light for 4 minutes. The red light was obtained by filtering light from a 15-watt standard daylight fluorescent tube through two layers of DuPont red cellophane. Percentage germination was determined after an additional 32 to 56 hours in darkness at 25°C.

The germination tests for cytokinins require rather high (optimal concentration of kinetin around 5 to 10 mg per liter) concentrations and involve risks from microorganisms. On the other hand, the plant material may be obtained from the store and the test requires little work and little time. Another drawback is that the tests are not specific since germination may be promoted by red light, gibberellins, and thiourea.

Bud Initiation

Promotion of leafy gametophyte formation by cytokinins in the moss *Tortella caespitosa* has been reported by Gorton *et al.* (1957). The cytokinin was added to a basal solution containing: $Ca(NO_3)_2$, 800 mg per liter; KNO_3, 200 mg per liter; KH_2PO_4, 200 mg per liter; $MgSO_4$, 200 mg per liter; and a trace of $FePO_4$. The solution was gelated with 0.3 percent agar. The moss spores were sown on the gel and the resulting protonema cultured under fluorescent light for 15–25 days, after which time the buds were counted with a binocular microscope. An increase in bud formation was detected with as little as 0.0005 mg per liter of kinetin, and greater concentrations gave even better responses.

Bud formation from tobacco tissues also is promoted by cytokinins (Skoog and Miller, 1957). Tissues obtained by the methods described earlier may be used on various media; for example, medium "d" (Table 1) with 5 mg per liter indoleacetic acid instead of the α-naphthalene acetic acid is satisfactory. In some cases, considerably lower concentrations of the auxin will be better since bud formation may be inhibited by the compound. In the laboratory at Indiana University, Mrs. Doerschug recently has obtained very striking results using cotyledons from sterile seedlings of *Lactuca sativa*, var. Grand Rapids. Dry seeds were soaked in 0.1 percent $HgCl_2$ for 10 minutes and then thoroughly rinsed with sterile distilled water. The seeds were planted either on a pad of wet, sterile filter paper in a Petri dish or on sterile agar gel containing medium "d" (Table 1) without an auxin in 125-ml Erlenmeyer flasks. These were placed in continuous, low-intensity light. After several days, the cotyledons from the resulting seedlings were cut off and transferred to the test media, basal medium "d" with 5 mg per liter indoleacetic acid being used instead of the naphthalene acetic acid. The cultures were kept in light or dark at 28°C. Buds quickly appeared (in about 1 week) but only if a cytokinin was present in the medium; otherwise only roots and some callus formed. Mrs. Doerschug obtained good responses with concentrations of kinetin as low as 0.05 mg per liter. The specificity of these tests is high and accentuates their usefulness. One must be cautious, however, in interpreting results, especially with crude extracts, since the budding response may be modified quantitatively by auxins, gibberellins, the ammonium ion, various inorganic salts, and probably many other compounds. One interesting observation we have made is that the concentration of iron sequestrene in the medium may very markedly influence the budding in tobacco and lettuce tissues. No growth of any kind occurred when this salt was omitted; with tobacco the optimal concentration was about 14 mg per liter, and higher concentrations cut out budding without inhibiting over-all growth.

Other Tests

Cytokinins relieve the inhibition of lateral bud growth; an assay modification utilizing this property is given in the paper by Bruce *et al.* (1965). The compounds also promote leaf disk expansion, and tests based on this ability are discussed in the review by Miller (1963).

CHEMICAL AND PHYSICAL PROPERTIES

Being adenine derivatives, the purine cytokinins share many properties in common with that compound. Thus, in simple forms they may be exchanged onto resins such as Dowex 50 or other strong cation exchangers under slightly acid conditions. From such resins they can be eluted with fairly strong acid (2 *N* to 4 *N* HCl has been used) or with alkaline solutions (6 *N* NH_4OH is satisfactory); neutral solutions will not remove the compounds. Such simple forms may also exchange onto anion resins such as Dowex 1 under alkaline conditions (pH about 10.0). The nucleosides may be handled much the same way. The nucleotides may be exchanged onto Dowex 1 at a lower pH (we use a pH of about 8) and eluted with formic acid (Miller, 1965). A compound which we believe to be a zeatin ribose phosphate comes off from such a column right after adenylic acid is eluted.

Like adenine, these purine cytokinins strongly absorb ultraviolet light having absorption peaks in the 260–275 mμ region. Kinetin has a peak at 267.5 mμ in absolute ethanol (ϵ_{max} 18,700), at 267 mμ in aqueous buffer at pH 6.4 (ϵ_{max} 18,800), at 274 mμ in 1 *N* HCl (ϵ_{max} 17,000), and at 273.5 mμ in 1 *N* NaOH (ϵ_{max} 17,600). Zeatin gives absorption peaks at 269 mμ in 95 percent ethanol, at 273 mμ in 0.1 *N* HCl, and at 274 mμ in 0.1 *N* NaOH. Zeatin riboside shows some shifts with peaks at about 268 mμ in 95 percent ethanol, 268 mμ in 0.1 *N* NaOH, and 264 mμ in 0.1 *N* HCl. (Dr. G. Shaw, private communication, gets 270 and 266 mμ for the latter two values.) The extinction coefficients for zeatin and its riboside are very near those values given for kinetin.

If cytokinins from rich natural sources are being investigated, preliminary separations by paper chromatography are possible and may be very revealing. Solvent systems which separate adenine and its common derivatives from each other are useful. Solvents containing various butanols have been especially valuable for such work and can be expected to give higher R_f values for the cytokinins than for their adenine equivalents; this is because all purine cytokinins thus far discovered or synthesized have a greater degree of fat solubility than do the adenine compounds. We routinely employ water-saturated *sec*-butanol for small-scale separations, since this system gives good and reproducible separations; the alcohol evaporates quickly from the paper and we have no trouble with toxicity from the solvent. Zeatin moves to R_f 0.88, its riboside to 0.80, and the zeatin ribose phosphate to about 0.2 on Whatman #1 filter paper when this system is used as an ascending solvent. *n*-Butanol, *tert*-butanol, or *iso*-butanol in various combinations with water, NH_4OH, or acetic acid give at least slightly different migration rates.

REFERENCES

BOTTOMLEY, W., N. P. KEFFORD, J. A. ZWAR, and P. L. GOLDACRE, 1963: Kinin activity from plant extracts. *Austral. J. of Biol. Sci.*, 16: 395.

BROWN, R., and P. RICKLESS, 1949: A method for the study of cell division and cell extension with some preliminary observations on the effect of temperature and of nutrients. *Proc. Roy. Soc. Lond.*, B 136: 110.

BRUCE, M. I., J. A. ZWAR, and N. P. KEFFORD, 1965: Chemical structure and plant kinin activity—the activity of urea and thiourea derivatives. *Life Sci.*, 4: 461.

CAPLIN, S. M., and F. C. STEWARD, 1949: A technique for the controlled growth of excised plant tissue in liquid media under aseptic conditions. *Nature*, 163: 920.

GORTON, B. S., C. G. SKINNER, and R. E. EAKIN, 1957: Activity of some 6-(substituted)-purines on the development of the moss *Tortella caespitosa*. *Arch. Biochem. Biophys.*, 66: 493.

KENDE, H., 1964: Preservation of chlorophyll in leaf sections by substances obtained from root exudate. *Science*, 145: 1066.

LETHAM, D. S., 1962: Separation of plant cells with hexametaphosphate and the nature of intercellular binding. *Exptl. Cell Res.*, 27: 352.

———, 1963: Regulators of cell division in plant tissues. *New Zealand J. Bot.*, 1: 336.

———, J. S. SHANNON, and I. R. MC DONALD, 1964: The structure of zeatin, a factor inducing cell division. *Proc. Chem. Soc. Lond.*, p. 230.

MILLER, C. O., 1963: Kinetin and kinetin-like compounds. In H. F. Linskens and M. V. Tracey (eds.), *Modern Methods of Plant Analysis*, Springer-Verlag, Berlin, Germany, p. 194.

———, 1965: Evidence for the natural occurrence of zeatin and derivatives: compounds from maize which promote cell division. *Proc. Nat. Acad. Sci.*, 54: 1052.

MURASHIGE, T., and F. SKOOG, 1962: A revised medium for the rapid growth and bioassays with tobacco tissue cultures. *Physiol. Plant.*, 15: 473.

OSBORNE, D. J., and D. R. MC CALLA, 1961: Rapid bioassay for kinetin and kinins using senescing leaf tissue. *Plant Physiol.*, 36: 219.

PERSON, C., D. J. SAMBORSKI, and F. R. FORSYTH, 1957: Effect of benzimidazole on detached wheat leaves. *Nature*, 180: 1294.

ROGOZINSKA, J. H., J. P. HELGESON, and F. SKOOG, 1964: Tests for kinetin-like growth promoting activities of triacanthine and its isomer 6-(γ,γ-dimethylallylamino)-purine. *Physiol. Plant.*, 17: 165.

SHANTZ, E. M., and F. C. STEWARD, 1955: The identification of compound A from coconut milk as 1,3-diphenylurea. *J. Amer. Chem. Soc.*, 77: 6351.

SKINNER, C. G., J. R. CLAYBROOK, F. D. TALBERT, and W. SHIVE, 1957: Effect of 6-(substituted) thio- and amino-purines on germination of lettuce seed. *Plant Physiol.*, 32: 117.

———, and W. SHIVE, 1957: Effect of some isomeric purine analogues on germination of lettuce seed. *Plant Physiol.*, 32: 500.

SKOOG, F., and C. O. MILLER, 1957: Chemical regulation of growth and organ formation in plant tissues cultured *in vitro*. *Symposia Soc. Exptl. Biol.*, 11: 118.

———, F. M. STRONG, and C. O. MILLER, 1965: Cytokinins. *Science*, 148: 532.

SRIVASTAVA, B. I. S., and G. WARE, 1965: The effect of kinetin on nucleic acids and nucleases of excised barley leaves. *Plant Physiol.*, 40: 62.

Surgical Techniques in Plants

By Elizabeth G. Cutter

INTRODUCTION

Surgical techniques have been applied to plants at the organ, tissue, and cellular level and for many different purposes. They are particularly useful in establishing the potentialities for growth and development of organs and tissues—potentialities which are often not revealed during the normal development—and in studying the effects of one part of the plant on another. Surgery at the macroscopic level is employed in many everyday horticultural practices, such as pruning, grafting and budding, layering, and propagation from cuttings. This last technique reveals also that isolated organs and tissues have developmental potentialities which they do not exhibit in the intact plant. Since the primary growth and development of the plant may be attributed to the activities of the apical meristems of shoot and root, these meristematic regions have been frequently studied, and some of these investigations have employed microsurgical methods. Most apical meristems are usually much less than 1 mm in diameter, so that instruments of appropriate dimensions often have to be specially devised.

This article will survey briefly some sources of useful material for experiments involving microsurgery, the kinds of instruments employed, and the different techniques used, with a discussion in more detail of some of the materials and methods most familiar to the author. A short summary of the principal results obtained using surgical techniques is also given.

PLANT MATERIAL

Shoot Apices

Ideally, a suitable shoot apex for surgical treatment would be of large size, situated on a solid rhizome or rootstock of small height (which can thus be readily placed under a binocular dissecting microscope), not readily susceptible to attack by fungi or bacteria, not palatable to nematodes, insect larvae, or other animal life, not too susceptible to necrosis resulting from handling or surgical treatment, and surrounded by relatively few simple, exstipulate, nonhairy leaves. Unfortunately, probably no such apex exists. Those which have been used for most surgical experiments usually possess some, but by no means all, of these desirable features. The fern *Dryopteris* has a large shoot apex, approximately 1 mm in diameter, situated on a solid rhizome, but is surrounded by many leaf primordia, covered by scales, and is very susceptible to the touch of any instrument. Shoot apices of the water-lilies *Nuphar* and *Nymphaea*, although large and situated on thick rhizomes, are covered with mucilaginous hairs. The apex of *Lupinus albus*, although of fair size, has compound, stipulate leaves. *Petasites* has very hairy leaves. Plants of *Primula*, *Petunia*, *Dipsacus*, and *Epilobium* have a more or less rosette habit of growth so that apices are situated at most on quite short stalks; they are also relatively hairless, but the shoot apices are fairly small.

Where apices are situated terminally on a rhizome, e.g., *Dryopteris*, *Nuphar*, *Petasites*, pieces of these may be excised and planted in pots or flats; potato apices ("eyes") seated on a plug of tuber tissue may be removed from the tuber with a cork borer and maintained on moist filter paper in covered dishes (Sussex, 1955a); and the other plants mentioned may be grown singly in small pots suitable for bringing under the dissecting microscope. *Lupinus albus* may be used about 30 days after sowing (Ball, 1950), *L. annuus*, *Petunia*, and *Tropaeolum* at 6–8 weeks old (this time estimate is for fairly late in the season).

Root Apices

The tap roots and lateral roots of *Vicia faba* and *Fagus sylvatica* (Clowes, 1953) and of *Phaseolus vulgaris* (Pellegrini, 1957), among others, have been successfully used in surgical experiments. Cut surfaces were smeared with lanolin to reduce desiccation, and the roots maintained in moist sphagnum moss. Surgically treated roots have also been maintained in water culture or in sawdust (Lopriore, 1892).

The hypocotyl of the embryo of *Ginkgo biloba* (Ball, 1956) and the radicle of *Pisum sativum* (Torrey, 1957) have also been used in experiments where the surgically treated embryos or roots were subsequently maintained in sterile culture.

INSTRUMENTS

General

Within the span of the 70 years or so during which surgical techniques have been used on apical meristems and other meristematic tissues the instruments employed have changed relatively little, though there has been a trend toward greater delicacy. Investigators have used razors (Lopriore, 1895), sharp knives or small scalpels (Figdor, 1906; Karzel, 1924; Clowes, 1953), cataract knives or lancets (Snow and Snow, 1931; Camus, 1943), and fragments of razor blades (Ball, 1946; Gulline and Walker, 1957; Kuehnert and Steeves, 1962; and others). The fragments of razor blades are either soldered to sewing needles which are held in a dissecting needle holder (Ball, 1946), or the blades are simply held in a clamp-type holder (Gulline and Walker, 1957). Instruments known as pin slides, obtainable from watchmakers (Fig. 1e, f), are suitable for this purpose. The razor blade fragments may be obtained with the shape of a pointed knife (Fig. 1a) by placing the blade of a chisel in an appropriate position at the edge of a *thin* razor blade, still wrapped in its inner paper covering, and hitting the chisel a sharp blow with a hammer. (The razor blade should be on the floor or a substantial bench when this is done.) Fragments are readily broken off ordinary razor blades by this treatment; with stainless steel blades the final breaking off may have to be done with forceps. Such razor blade fragments may be further ground down on a stone (see Sussex and Clutter, this volume, pp. 435–443).

Thin plates of mica are sometimes

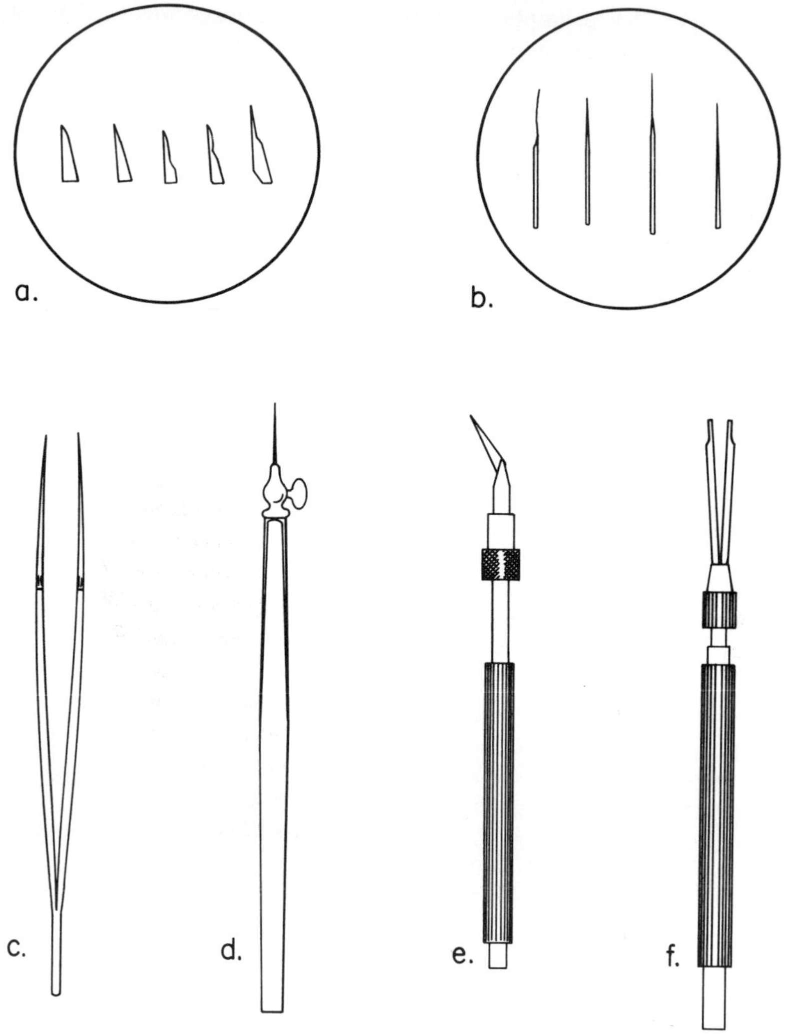

FIG. 1. Instruments used in surgical experiments on plants. (a) knives made from fragments of razor blade; (b) tungsten needles; (c) fine forceps, obtainable from watchmakers; (d) needle holder with sharpened sewing needle; (e) pin slide with razor blade knife; (f) pin slide in the open position. × ½.

inserted into incisions to prevent grafting of the tissues or passage of diffusible substances (e.g., Simon, 1908; Snow and Snow, 1959).

Very fine pointed forceps, e.g., the No. 5 size of those manufactured by Dumont Fils, Switzerland, and used by watchmakers (Fig. 1c), are useful in removing hairs or scales from apical regions.

For dissecting apices or for rough puncturing experiments, fine sewing needles sharpened to a point on a stone and held in a needle holder may be used (Fig. 1d). Finer needles, capable of puncturing the single apical cell of a fern shoot apex, for example, may be manufactured from tungsten wire heated in fused sodium nitrite (Cannon, 1941) or by the electrical method described below. Irradiation of a fern apex with a 25-μ deuteron beam (Kuehnert and Miksche, 1964) produced a wound effect similar to puncturing. Needles and knives fine enough to be used for removing fertilized eggs from fern archegonia have also been made from very fine insect pins sharpened on an oil stone (DeMaggio, 1961). Very finely pointed glass needles can readily be made by pulling out glass rods or tubes as though to make capillary tubes, but although these may be useful for work with thallophytes they usually do not have enough strength to penetrate the apices of higher plants. Tungsten needles possess both the necessary strength and delicacy.

For delicate experiments investigators sometimes find it beneficial to use a micromanipulator (e.g., Jayasekera and Bell, 1959). Various types of instruments are available.

Electrical Method for Making Tungsten Needles

The method described below was devised by Mr. Frank J. Myers of the Philadelphia Academy of Natural Sciences, modified by Dr. John Towne Conover and since used by him, Dr. R. H. Wetmore, Dr. Louis Kornicker, and others. Since this technique for etching needles has never been published it is included here for convenience. I am greatly indebted to Dr. John Towne Conover and Mr. J. H. Wallace for supplying the details of the method.

Cut 1½-inch lengths of thoriated tungsten wire of thickness 0.02 inch or 0.04 inch, type Th-55, and place in a chuck-type needle holder. To make microknives instead of needles, use the thicker wire and blunt cutters, which will split the wire along its length. Each half can then be used to make a knife; if desired, the rounded back can be ground down first on a stone. It is important to make an insulated handle for metal-shafted needle holders. Now use the holder with the needle as one electrode of an AC, 30–60 volt electro-etching circuit. Use an electrolyte such as a 50 percent saturation concentration of sodium hydroxide or potassium hydroxide in water. This concentration is not critical. Drop the 120-vac 60-cycle current from the power mains through a suitable autotransformer and/or through a series of 60-watt bulbs connected in one side of the line (Fig. 2). Use zinc, copper, or iron for one electrode (copper wire is appropriate); the tungsten needle itself serves as the opposite electrode. More than one needle can be etched at a time. This system utilizes considerable voltages, and it is important to be certain that the setup is shockproof. Do not handle the metal shaft of the needle holder while the current is on; always use the insulated handle.

Plunge the needle 1 cm below the surface of the liquid and adjust the holding clamp or battery clip on an uninsulated part of the needle holder to maintain the needle at this depth. Turn on the current and allow the needle to be etched away until a long, very thin point is obtained. The needle is still soft at this point, and can be shaped into loops or hooks or flattened into small spatulas by removing it repeatedly from the solution and bending or shaping it against a flat metallic surface, while observing the process under a dissecting microscope.

The wire must now be tempered to restore its strength. This is done by very carefully raising the tip of the needle to the surface where it will spark and glow red. Plunge it immediately deep into the liquid,

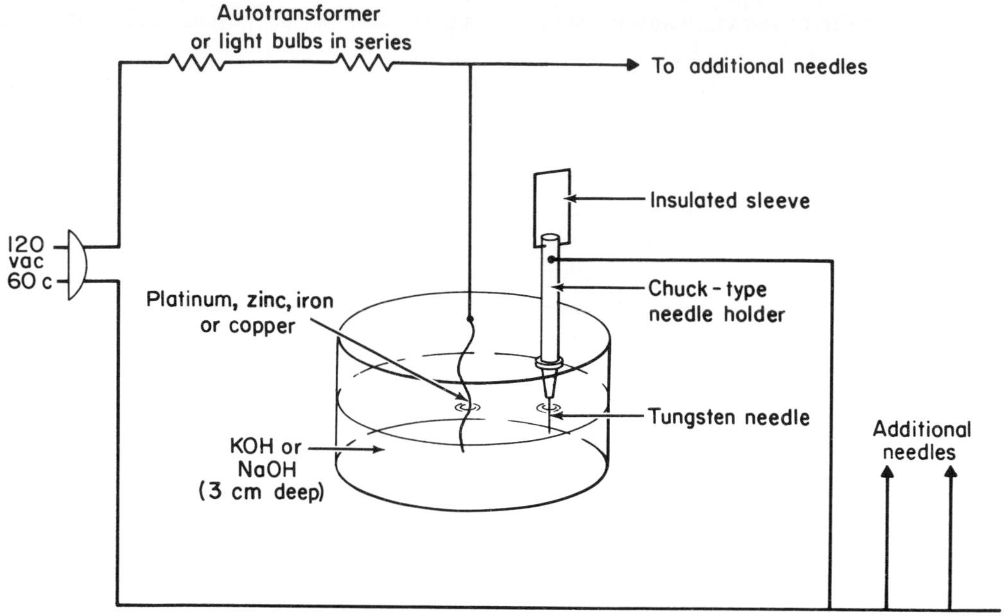

FIG. 2. Diagram of the electrical circuit for etching tungsten needles.

then test it carefully against a metal plate under the microscope to see whether the tempering process is complete. With a little practice tempering can be done quickly without distorting the shape of the tool. Heating over a flame and quenching in an oil bath is also effective.

Microforceps can be made by this method by soldering tungsten needles with silver or tin-lead on to the tips of ordinary forceps.

With practice, needles with tips only 2 or 3 μ in diameter can be made by this method.

SURGICAL TECHNIQUES APPLIED TO *DRYOPTERIS*

The species which has been used in most of the surgical experiments on ferns is *Dryopteris dilatata* (Hoffm.) A. Gray. Other species of *Dryopteris* seem also to be suitable, and it is quite probable that any fern with a crown of numerous leaves would be equally good. *Polypodium vulgare* has also been successfully used in surgical experiments (Dasanayake, 1957).

Dryopteris dilatata possesses numerous leaves and leaf primordia in various stages of development arranged spirally around the apical cone. Only about 12–14 leaves expand each season, and about four years' supply of leaves is present on a mature specimen. The terminal region of the rhizome, with all the unexpanded leaves, can be cut off and brought into the laboratory. The shoot apex is situated in the central hollow into which the circinate leaves curve. The outermost leaves can be removed with a knife or coarse scalpel, and the piece of rhizome can now be cut down to form a cube with sides of about 3–4 cm ($1\frac{1}{2}$ inches); the apical cone should be situated in the center of one of the sides. Younger developing leaves should now be removed with a sharp scalpel;

it is safer to direct the cut away from the apical cone, which is still covered by young leaves or scales, in case the operator's hand slips and the whole of the apical region is inadvertently excised.

Some of the scales may be removed by grasping a tuft with ordinary fine forceps and giving a gentle tug in an upward direction. (Too much force may remove the whole apical region.) Elimination of some of the scales will reveal more leaf primordia surrounding the apex. Some of these can be excised, again in an outward direction, with a finely pointed scalpel. At this stage the edges of the piece of rhizome should be trimmed, smoothing off the bases of excised leaves, and the specimen should be placed under the low power of a binocular dissecting microscope (20–30 × magnification).

More leaf primordia can now be excised, using a fine-pointed scalpel and directing the cuts away from the apex. Scales should be pulled gently upward, using the very fine forceps described earlier. It is very important not to touch the apical cone, or any leaf primordia which are to be left on the specimen, with the forceps. At this stage it should be possible to glimpse the central apical cone, surrounded by a number of leaf primordia and numerous white-brownish scales (developing ramenta). For most experiments it is sufficient to retain about 10–12 leaf primordia, unless the older leaf primordia themselves are to be treated. The more leaf primordia retained the more difficult it is to complete the dissection without damaging the apex.

Removal of incipient scales must now be completed. For this purpose a sharpened sewing needle in a holder is probably the best instrument. The point of the needle must be used to bend the scales outward; it will thus usually detach them at the base. A magnification of about 30 × is usually adequate. The apical region should be turgid but not wet; presence of surface water renders the task more difficult. It is necessary to remove almost all the incipient scales in order to get a clear view of the small flat mounds which constitute the youngest leaf primordia. If the apical cone or the tips of the leaf primordia are touched with the needle they will turn brown and necrotic. Such damage may not be immediately evident, but will appear within a few hours. For many purposes, damage to one or two leaf primordia may be unimportant.

The apical cone of *D. dilatata* is covered with an opaque deposit, which has to be removed in order to see with certainty the positions of the youngest leaf primordia; this is especially necessary if the apices are to be photographed. The deposit can be removed with small triangular pieces of filter paper, moistened with saliva or water. The degree of moistening is important; too much will render the filter paper soggy and useless, too little will leave sharp edges which can cut into the apex. Sometimes it helps to tear the filter paper instead of cutting it; the protruding fibers left by this method may be helpful. The apex should be washed under running water; this will not damage it, but neither will it remove the deposit. The moist filter paper must be drawn repeatedly across the apical cone and young primordia with sufficient force to remove the deposit, gradually, but without enough force to damage the tissues. This requires care and experience: it is at this stage that damage is most frequently incurred. A higher magnification may prove helpful.

When the apex has been laid bare and cleaned, it should be covered with a wad of moist absorbent cotton. The pieces of rhizome can be maintained successfully in pans or flats of damp peat moss covered with sheets of glass (Wardlaw, 1944). After some time (at least a week) the pieces of cotton can be removed if desired.

It is inadvisable to carry out any surgical experiments within the first 24 hours after dissection. If incisions are made immediately a much higher proportion of damaged specimens will be obtained. After this recovery period has elapsed the specimens can be examined and selected for treatment. It is helpful to group together all apices in which the phyllotactic spiral is clockwise, and all those in which it is counterclockwise. The position of the youngest leaf primordium must now be determined; the apices should be rotated under the dissecting microscope so that the light strikes them from different angles. The youngest primordium will be a flat mound of tissue which reflects the light. It is now useful to cut out a horizontal slice of the outer rhizome tissue behind the site of the next leaf primordium which will be formed; this will serve as a marker from which the primordia present at the beginning of the experiment can later be recognized.

Incisions or punctures can conveniently be made with a magnification of 30 or 40 diameters. For puncturing single apical cells of shoot or leaf, which is possible with tungsten needles, higher magnifications may be beneficial. It is convenient to place the razor blade fragments in the holder at an angle (Fig. 1e), so that the point of the knife penetrates the tissue first. Deep incisions, such as are used for isolating leaf primordia from the apex or from other primordia, penetrate several layers of cells. Shallow incisions which penetrate only the superficial layer of cells in the apical cone (Wardlaw and Cutter, 1956) can be made by just touching the apex with the knife blade and drawing it gently across. It is possible also to destroy deeper layers of tissue leaving the superficial layers intact, using a tungsten needle inserted from one side of the apical cone, but it is difficult to control this maneuver precisely because of the curvature of the apical cone.

Using fragments of razor blade, it is possible also to make one or more small incisions in the flanks of older leaf primordia, in order to investigate the effects of the leaf apex on these tissues (Cutter and Wardlaw, 1963). For experiments of this kind, about 20–25 leaf primordia have to be retained around the apex, and dissection is consequently more difficult.

Preparation of the apices of most of the angiosperms which have been used for surgical experiments is relatively simple. Older leaf primordia which obscure the apex can usually be broken off by inserting a needle adaxial to them and bending them backward. The apical region should be fully turgid at the time this is done. Some trimming of the leaf bases may be required; this is particularly necessary in some rosette plants, where the apex occupies a more or less sunken position among the leaf bases. Dissection of apices of *Nuphar* and *Nymphaea* is similar to that of *Dryopteris*, except that hairs are present instead of scales, and the apices do not need to be cleaned with filter paper.

SUMMARY OF MICROSURGICAL TECHNIQUES USED AND RESULTS OBTAINED

Notches have been cut into growing stems in order to study the regeneration of xylem (Simon, 1908; Sinnott and Bloch, 1945; Jacobs, 1952, 1954, 1956; Fosket and Roberts, 1964), phloem (LaMotte and Jacobs, 1963), and vascular cambium (two articles by Warren Wilson and Warren Wilson, 1961). These experiments on older internodes involve relatively coarse surgical methods and do not require the microsurgical techniques necessary with meristematic tissues.

On apical meristems of plants, perhaps

d'Endive sur des fragments de tissus cultivés in vitro. *Compt. Rend. Séanc. Soc. Biol.*, 137: 184.

CANNON, H. G., 1941: A note on fine needles for dissection. *J. Roy. Microscop. Soc.*, 3, 61: 58.

CLOWES, F. A. L., 1953: The cytogenerative centre in roots with broad columellas. *New Phytol.*, 52: 48.

CUSICK, F., 1956: Studies of floral morphogenesis. I. Median bisections of flower primordia in *Primula bulleyana* Forrest. *Trans. Roy. Soc. Edinb.*, 63: 153.

CUTTER, E. G., 1956: Experimental and analytical studies of pteridophytes. XXXIII. The experimental induction of buds from leaf primordia in *Dryopteris aristata* Druce. *Ann. Bot.*, New Ser., 20: 143.

———, 1958: Studies of morphogenesis in the Nymphaeaceae. III. Surgical experiments on leaf and bud formation. *Phytomorphology*, 8: 74.

———, 1965: Recent experimental studies of the shoot apex and shoot morphogenesis. *Bot. Rev.*, 31: 7.

———, and C. W. WARDLAW, 1963: Induction of buds on older leaf primordia in ferns. *Nature* (London), 199: 985.

DASANAYAKE, M. D., 1957: Aspects of morphogenesis in dorsiventral ferns. Unpublished doctoral thesis, University of Manchester, England.

DE MAGGIO, A. E., 1961: Morphogenetic studies on the fern *Todea barbara* (L.) Moore. I. Life history. *Phytomorphology*, 11: 46.

FIGDOR, W., 1906: Über Regeneration der Blattspreite bei *Scolopendrium scolopendrium*. *Ber. Deut. Botan. Ges.*, 24: 13.

FOSKET, D. E., and L. W. ROBERTS, 1964: Induction of wound-vessel differentiation in isolated *Coleus* stem segments *in vitro*. *Am. J. Bot.*, 51: 19.

GULLINE, H. F., and R. WALKER, 1957: The regeneration of severed pea apices. *Aust. J. Bot.*, 5: 129.

JACOBS, W. P., 1952: The role of auxin in differentiation of xylem around a wound. *Am. J. Bot.*, 39: 301.

———, 1954: Acropetal auxin transport and xylem regeneration—a quantitative study. *Am. Nat.*, 88: 327.

———, 1956: Internal factors controlling cell differentiation in the flowering plants. *Am. Nat.*, 90: 163.

JAYASEKERA, R. D. E., and P. R. BELL, 1959: The effect of various experimental treatments on the development of the embryo of the fern *Thelypteris palustris*. *Planta*, 54: 1.

KARZEL, R., 1924: Untersuchungen über die Regeneration von Sprossspitzen. *Jahrb. wiss. Bot.*, 63: 111.

KUEHNERT, C. C., and J. P. MIKSCHE, 1964: Application of the 22.5 Mev deuteron microbeam to the study of morphogenetic problems within the shoot apex of *Osmunda claytoniana*. *Am. J. Bot.*, 51: 743.

———, and T. A. STEEVES, 1962: Capacity of fragments of leaf primordia to produce whole leaves. *Nature* (London), 196: 187.

LA MOTTE, C. E., and W. P. JACOBS, 1963: A role of auxin in phloem regeneration in *Coleus* internodes. *Devel. Biol.*, 8: 80.

LOISEAU, J.-E., 1959: Observations et expérimentation sur la phyllotaxie et le fonctionnement du sommet végétatif chez quelques Balsaminacées. *Ann. Sci. Nat., Botan.*, XI, 20: 1.

———, 1960: Application des techniques de microchirurgie à l'étude expérimentale des méristèmesc aulinaires. *Année biol.*, 36: 249.

LOO, SHIH-WEI, 1945: Cultivation of excised stem tips of asparagus *in vitro*. *Am. J. Bot.*, 32: 13.

———, 1946: Cultivation of excised stem tips of dodder *in vitro*. *Am. J. Bot.*, 33: 295.

LOPRIORE, G., 1892: Ueber die Regeneration gespaltener Wurzeln. *Ber. Deut. Botan. Ges.*, 10: 76.

———, 1895: Vorläufige Mittheilung über die Regeneration gespaltener Stammspitzen. *Ber. Deut. Botan. Ges.*, 13: 410.

PELLEGRINI, O., 1957: Esperimenti chirurgici sul comportamento del meristema radicale di *Phaseolus vulgaris* L. *Delpinoa*, 10: 187.

———, 1959: Esperimenti microchirurgici sul funzionamento del meristema apicale dei germogli di *Phaseolus vulgaris* L. *Delpinoa*, New Ser., 1: 205.

PILKINGTON, M., 1929: The regeneration of the stem apex. *New Phytol.*, 28: 37.

SIMON, S., 1908: Experimentelle Untersuchungen über die Entstehung von Gefässverbindungen. *Ber. Deut. Botan. Ges.*, 26: 364.

SINNOTT, E. W., and R. BLOCH, 1945: The cytoplasmic basis of intercellular patterns in vascular differentiation. *Am. J. Bot.*, 32: 151.

SNOW, M., and R. SNOW, 1931: Experiments on phyllotaxis. I. The effect of isolating a primordium. *Phil. Trans. Roy. Soc. London, Ser. B*, 221: 1.

———, and ———, 1935: Experiments on phyllotaxis. III. Diagonal splits through decussate apices. *Phil. Trans. Roy. Soc. London, Ser. B*, 225: 63.

———, and ———, 1952: Minimum areas and leaf determination. *Proc. Roy. Soc. (London), Ser. B*, 139: 545.

———, and ———, 1955: Regulation of sizes of leaf primordia by growing-point of stem apex. *Proc. Roy. Soc. (London), Ser. B*, 144: 222.

———, and ———, 1959: The dorsiventrality of leaf primordia. *New Phytol.*, 58: 188.

SOMA, K., 1958: Morphogenesis in the shoot apex of *Euphorbia lathyris* L. *J. Fac. Sci., Univ. Tokyo*, III, 7: 199.

STEEVES, T. A., 1961: The developmental potentialities of excised leaf primordia in sterile culture. *Phytomorphology*, 11: 346.

———, H. P. GABRIEL, and M. W. STEEVES, 1957: Growth in sterile culture of excised leaves of flowering plants. *Science*, 126: 350.

———, and I. M. SUSSEX, 1957: Studies on the development of excised leaves in sterile culture. *Am. J. Bot.*, 44: 665.

SUSSEX, I. M., 1951: Experiments on the cause of dorsiventrality in leaves. *Nature* (London), 167: 651.

———, 1952: Regeneration of the potato shoot apex. *Nature* (London), 170: 755.

———, 1954: Experiments on the cause of dorsiventrality in leaves. *Nature* (London), 174: 351.

———, 1955a: Morphogenesis in *Solanum tuberosum* L.: apical structure and developmental pattern of the juvenile shoot. *Phytomorphology*, 5: 253.

———, 1955b: Morphogenesis in *Solanum tuberosum* L.: experimental investigation of leaf dorsiventrality and orientation in the juvenile shoot. *Phytomorphology*, 5: 286.

TORREY, J. G., 1957: Auxin control of vascular pattern formation in regenerating pea root meristems grown *in vitro*. *Am. J. Bot.*, 44: 859.

WARDLAW, C. W., 1944: Experimental and analytical studies of pteridophytes. IV. Stelar morphology: experimental observations on the relation between leaf development and stelar morphology in species of *Dryopteris* and *Onoclea*. *Ann. Bot.*, New Ser., 8: 387.

———, 1945: An experimental treatment of the apical meristem in ferns. *Nature* (London), 156: 39.

———, 1949a: Further experimental observations on the shoot apex of *Dryopteris aristata* Druce. *Phil. Trans. Roy. Soc. London, Ser. B*, 233: 415.

———, 1949b: Experiments on organogenesis in ferns. *Growth* (Suppl.), 13: 93.

———, 1950: The comparative investigation of apices of vascular plants by experimental methods. *Phil. Trans. Roy. Soc. London, Ser. B*, 234: 583.

———, 1952: The effect of isolating the apical meristem in *Echinopsis*, *Nuphar*, *Gunnera* and *Phaseolus*. *Phytomorphology*, 2: 240.

———, 1963: Experimental investigations of floral morphogenesis in *Petasites hybridus*. *Nature* (London), 198: 560.

———, 1965: *Organization and Evolution in Plants*. Longmans, Green & Co., London, England.

———, and E. G. CUTTER, 1955: Experimental and analytical studies of pteridophytes. XXX. Further investigations of the formation of buds and leaves in *Dryopteris aristata* Druce. *Ann. Bot.*, New Ser., 19: 515.

———, and ———, 1956: Experimental and analytical studies of pteridophytes. XXXI. The effect of shallow incisions on organogenesis in *Dryopteris aristata* Druce. *Ann. Bot.*, New Ser., 20: 39.

WARREN WILSON, J., and P. M. WARREN WILSON, 1961: The position of regenerating cambia—a new hypothesis. *New Phytol.*, 60: 63.

WARREN WILSON, P. M., and J. WARREN WILSON, 1961: Cambium formation in wounded Solanaceous stems. *Ann. Bot.*, New Ser., 25: 104.

WETMORE, R. H., 1954: The use of "*in vitro*" cultures in the investigation of growth and differentiation in vascular plants. *Brookhaven Symp. Biol.*, 6: 22.

———, and S. SOROKIN, 1955: On the differentiation of xylem. *J. Arnold Arbor.*, 36: 305.

Control of Illumination for Plant Growth

By R. J. Downs and W. A. Bailey

INTRODUCTION

The primary prerequisite for design and construction of lighting devices is a thorough understanding of the purpose of the system. The biological purpose will then define the energy levels, the spectral energy distribution, and even the physical size of the system. Prior to design of a biological lighting device one should understand the characteristics of the light source, especially the spectral emission and the parameters that control the efficiency of the lamps. The physical characteristics of various light sources can be obtained from a number of excellent texts (Allphin, 1959; Elenbaas, 1959; Staley, 1960). The purpose here is to discuss the design, construction, and availability of lighting devices currently in use. Although our discussion will center around the photosystems of plants, the lighting devices are equally applicable to studies concerning insects or small animals. Manufacturers from whom the equipment mentioned in the text may be procured are referred to in numbered footnotes.

GENERAL LIGHTING

Current studies in developmental biology frequently require plants grown or maintained under more or less controlled conditions, where artificial light sources provide all or part of the necessary illumination. Investigators often find it necessary, or at least desirable, to maintain plant material or tissue cultures in or near the laboratory; and teachers usually prefer to have living plants in the classroom for study and demonstration. Since the process of photosynthesis requires light of rather high intensity, plants grown indoors will obviously need more light than normally used for general building lighting, and additional lamps must therefore be installed.

The most commonly used lamps for plant growth purposes are a combination of fluorescent and incandescent, the incandescent lamps providing about 10 percent of the total illuminance. Because of the etiolating effect of radiation from incandescent lamps they are not always a beneficial addition. Moreover, the incandescent lamps are often used alone to extend the photoperiod or to interrupt the dark period, so they are usually switched separately from the fluorescent system. The light intensity required for different kinds of plants varies considerably but a minimum of three or four 1,500-ma (milliampere) fluorescent lamps will probably be required per foot width of growing space, depending on the design of the luminaire. The 1,500-ma lamp is available in 4-, 6-, or 8-foot lengths, and manufacturers have special trade names for their particular lamps, e.g., Power Groove, Power Twist, SHO (super high output), T-10, and VHO (very high output). Irrespective of name, all 1,500-ma lamps of a given length are interchangeable.

Fluorescent lamps are available in various colors and in different degrees of "whiteness." The standard cool white is the most popular lamp for plant growth, although the warm white seems to give equally satisfactory results. The least satisfactory of the "white" lamps is the daylight type. The daylight lamp does not simulate sunlight, yet the unfortunate nomenclature has frequently induced the uninitiated to use it as a light source for plant growth. Lamps of specific colors such as red, blue, gold, etc., generally produce less satisfactory growth than "white" lamps. Moreover, the spectral emission of many single-color lamps changes with use.

Special lamps such as the Agricultural, Gro-Lux, and Plant-Gro are supposed to be especially designed to meet the requirements of the photosynthetic apparatus. However, the relative merits of the special phosphor lamps are still a matter of considerable debate, and the lack of comprehensive data makes recommendations impossible at this time.

Are some 1,500-ma lamps better than others? The answer is yes but the choice depends upon the application. On a per lamp basis the Power Groove (a T-17 lamp) provides the most light and is least sensitive to transient temperature fluctuations. However, because of their large diameter only about five Power Groove lamps can be used per foot of width whereas seven VHO or SHO (T-12 lamps) and eight T-10 lamps can be used per foot. Obviously, per foot of space, higher intensities can be obtained using a larger number of smaller diameter lamps.

The lamps must be mounted in a fixture and supplied with an appropriate ballasting system. Fluorescent lamps are usually operated in series with a choke coil in order to limit the current in the lamp to the desired value. Industrial luminaires suspended above the plants may supply an adequate amount of light, but the enclosed system of ballasting will generate a considerable amount of heat. Placing the ballasts in hallways or basements some distance from the lamps engenders additional problems due to the nature of the hot cathode, rapid start system (Allphin, 1959; Elenbaas, 1959). The number of wires between lamps and ballasts is relatively large (20–24 for an eight-lamp module), and the wire size must be increased with distance. Unless considerable thought is given to the location and design of the remote-ballast mounting system, premature failure of the ballasts may occur because of overheating. Ballasts should be mounted on metal with the long axis vertical. The ballast rack should be covered with a sheet metal shield open at the bottom with a blower that moves about 300 cubic feet a minute of air through the housing mounted near the top.

Many problems of plant growth lighting equipment can be avoided by using a commercial product expressly designed for the purpose. One such unit, the Vacha system, uses a special ballast design that can be remoted several hundred feet using no more than eight or nine No. 16 wires per eight-lamp module. Ballasts are premounted in a special housing, and both the ballast case and lamp module are prewired and tested.[1] Another special design, the Darco system, uses high voltage, direct current to drive the lamps, and it can be placed several hundred feet from the lamps. This system uses as few as two wires for 24 lamps.[2]

Bench lighting has definite limitations because the photoperiod cannot be controlled, and under many laboratory conditions a period of complete darkness is almost never obtained. A small chamber has been designed (Fig. 1) for laboratory and classroom use in which complete darkness can be obtained when the internal lamps are not in use. The chamber is ventilated with ambient air and, therefore, should be used only in air-conditioned rooms or buildings. Plans for this chamber may be obtained from any state university Agricultural Engineering department as drawing number EX-5980.

Where air-conditioned rooms are not available or when some temperature control is required, one may install controlled-environment chambers, commonly called growth rooms. A number of experienced manufacturers market prefabricated units in several sizes ranging from small plug-in cabinets to walk-in rooms using several kilowatts of power.[3]

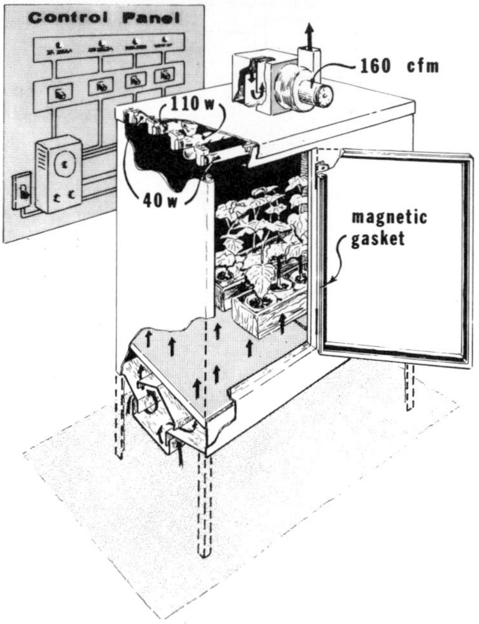

FIG. 1. A plant growth chamber: roomette for biological studies. The roomette acts as an integrating sphere and results in an illuminance many times greater than would be obtained from the same lamps suspended in a large room SOURCE: Downs *et al.,* 1964.

A wide range of general lighting devices are available, both commercially manufactured and owner-designed and -constructed units. Published designs range from simple models that can be built by the average homeowner (Arditti and Arditti, 1964; Hall, 1965) to more elaborate models where environmental conditions are more carefully controlled (Britten and Kinch, 1960; Carpenter and Moulsley, 1960; Van Schilfgaarde and Williams, 1961). Although there are exceptions, as indicated here, owner-designed facilities generally have a rather unsavory history of high cost and poor performance. Clearly on-site design and construction should be attempted only

[1] Norman H. Vacha Lighting Co., 21200 St. Claire Ave., Cleveland, Ohio.

[2] Darco, Inc., 5706 Frederick Ave., Rockville, Md.

[3] Environmental Growth Chambers, P.O. Box 407, Chagrin Falls, Ohio.

Labline Instruments Inc., 15th and Bloomingdale Ave., Melrose Park, Illinois.

Parce Engineering Co., P.O. Box 1807, 900 W. Van Buren, Harlingen, Texas.

Percival Refrigerating and Manufacturing Co., Boone, Iowa.

Sherer-Gillette Co., Marshall, Michigan.

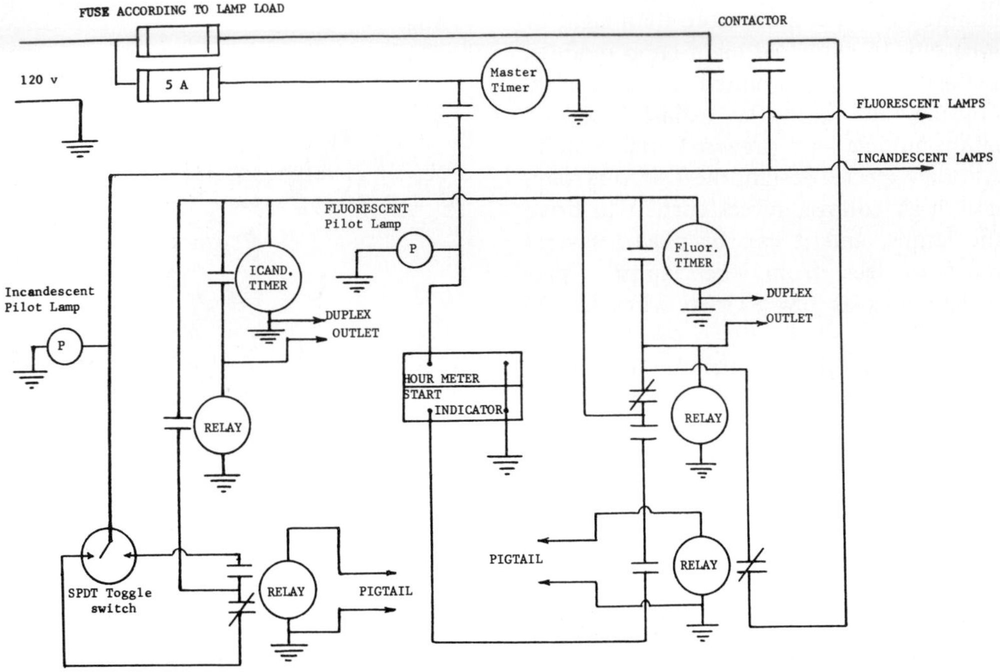

FIG. 2. Schematic of a lighting controller. Lamp load pigtails can be plugged into portable time switches that may be powered from the duplex outlets. The load is then controlled by the inserted time switches for the period set by the 24-hour cycle timers.

with the assistance of a bioengineer experienced in this type of system.

TIMING DEVICES

The duration of the light period is usually controlled by simple, 24-hour time switches with a minimum on-off time of 15 minutes. Light intensity is generally controlled by switching on a few lamps at a time. If a few lamps are connected to each of several time switches operating in sequence, a dimming system is obtained. Dimming controls are available for the Vacha system and are a part of the design of the Darco system mentioned earlier.

Rapid-cycle, repeating timers are often used in conjunction with the 24-hour time switches to provide dark period interruptions and cyclic lighting. Inexpensive, adjustable-cam programmers are especially adaptable to multicircuit control (Cathey *et al.*, 1961).

The 24-hour-cycle time switches are usually wired into the lighting circuit. Insertion of additional timers or a change of time switching quite often necessitates rewiring the system. A multipurpose timing device (Fig. 2) was designed to alleviate this difficulty. The controller uses one 24-hour-cycle time switch to control the incandescent lamps and another one to control the fluorescent lamps. A third time switch controls both kinds of lamps simultaneously. However, any type of cycle timer can easily be inserted into the system. The lamp load is plugged into the selected timer which is powered from the 120-volt duplex outlet. The lamps are then controlled by the inserted cycle timer for the period of time set by the 24-hour time switches. The selector switch in the incandescent lamp circuit makes it possible to control the load exclusively by the inserted timer.

SPECIALIZED LIGHTING

Many of the specialized lighting systems used in developmental biology are not available commercially but must be designed and built by the investigator. Some studies require light from broad but limited spectral regions and others require monochromatic radiation. Moderately broad regions of the spectrum can be isolated with relatively inexpensive filters[4] (Withrow and Price, 1953) and an appropriate light source (Van der Veen and Meijer, 1959). The word "appropriate" should be emphasized because a common misconception about filter systems seems to be that the transmission characteristics of the filter completely define the radiation incident upon the organism. The filter does define the spectral region but the light source limits the energy in that region. Thus the incident energy is a function of filter transmittance, source emittance, and distance from the source. Obviously it would be possible to use a filter with adequate transmittance in a particular spectral region yet have little energy reach the organism because the source does not emit in the region of transmittance. For example, a pink fluorescent lamp emits about twice as much energy at 660 nm (nanometers = 10^{-9} meters, current standard unit for wavelength, identical to the millimicron) as a cool white lamp (Downs and Borthwick, 1958), so that with a given filter and equal distance a pink fluorescent source will produce twice the irradiance at 660 nm as a cool white lamp with the same filter. However, neither pink nor cool white fluorescent lamps emit much radiation at 740 nm, so irradiance at 740 nm would be low regardless of the transmittance of the filter.

The simplest method of using filters is to place the material to be irradiated in a light-tight box which has the filter mounted in the lid or cover. The box is then placed under an appropriate light source and the material irradiated for a predetermined time. Unfortunately the simplest methods cannot always be used and it may be necessary to place the light source in the box, cover it with the filter, and irradiate biological material some distance away. When a lamp, especially an incandescent lamp, is placed in an enclosure some device for ventilation without light leakage must be provided. Moreover, the radiant heat may damage the filter or increase the temperature of the biological material, so some method of removing long-wavelength radiant energy must be devised. Figure 3 shows a far-red module designed for studies of phytochrome physiology. The unit has four 150-watt PAR (parabolic aluminized reflector) lamps as an energy source and uses a filter of FRF-700 plastic[5] or two layers of red and two layers of dark blue cellophane. At a distance of 78 cm the energy at 740 nm is 22 μwatts cm^{-2} (microwatts per square centimeter) with the plastic and 19 μwatts cm^{-2} with the cellophane filter (Downs *et al.*, 1964). The module uses forced-air ventilation to remove conductive and convective heat and a water bath to remove radiant heat. Additional lamp heat is transferred to the water by immersing the face of the lamps.

[4] Corning Glass Works, Corning, New York. Westlakes Plastics, West Lenni Mills, Pa.

[5] Westlakes Plastics, West Lenni Mills, Pa.

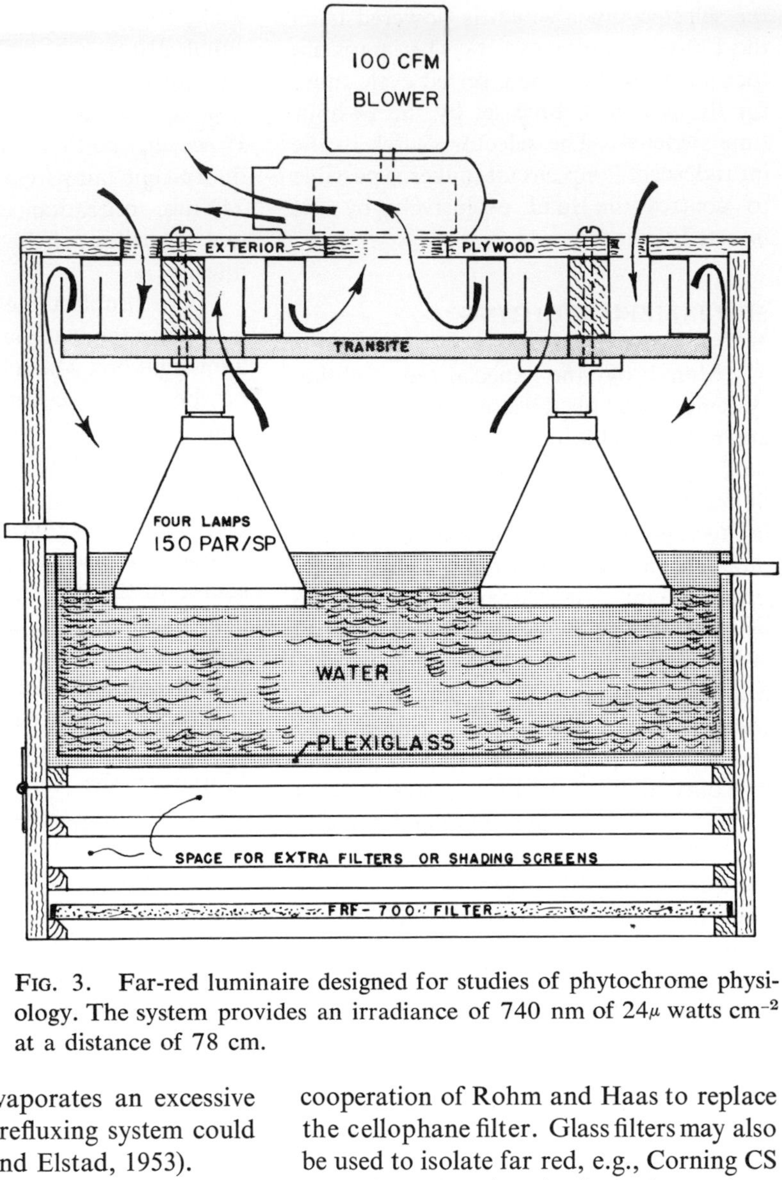

FIG. 3. Far-red luminaire designed for studies of phytochrome physiology. The system provides an irradiance of 740 nm of 24μ watts cm^{-2} at a distance of 78 cm.

If the lamp heat evaporates an excessive amount of water a refluxing system could be used (Withrow and Elstad, 1953).

Cellophanes make excellent broad band filters for many biological irradiations. However, the dark blue portion of the red and dark blue cellophane combination used for a number of years to isolate far-red radiant energy from incandescent lamps (Downs and Borthwick, 1958) is no longer available. The FRF-700 filter[6] was designed with the cooperation of Rohm and Haas to replace the cellophane filter. Glass filters may also be used to isolate far red, e.g., Corning CS 7-84, but the size is limited to about 8 × 8 inches. Other glasses, thin film, and rigid plastics may also be suitable for far-red filters but the transmittance must be carefully checked to ensure no leakage of red and a high transmittance at 740 nm.

Red radiant energy for phytochrome and other studies should be relatively free of far-red and can be obtained inexpensively by using fluorescent lamps filtered by two layers of red cellophane or by sheets

[6] Westlakes Plastics, West Lenni Mills, Pa.

of 2444 red Plexiglas (Downs and Borthwick, 1958). Corning[7] glass filters are also available but the limited size makes irradiation of large areas somewhat difficult. Ventilation of a fluorescent lamp box is not so important as with incandescent lamps, provided the ballasts are mounted externally. Many investigators simply wrap the cellophane around the fluorescent lamp although such methods seem hazardous. A convenient method is to use tubes of 2444 red Plexiglas that are expressly made to fit around a T-12 fluorescent lamp.[8]

Flexiglas tubes for fluorescent lamps can also be obtained in blue. It should be noted, however, that the literature is full of reports about blue responses obtained with sources contaminated with far-red. Many plastics and filter manufacturers fail to extend transmittance data past 700 nm, and the biologist may not realize that most blue filters have some transmittance in the far-red region of the spectrum. For example, if transmittance data of the red and dark blue cellophane combination stopped at 700 nm the observer might assume that no radiation passed the filter. Yet the dark-adapted eye can discern a faint reddish transmission and further data obtained between 700 and 800 nm reveals a high transmittance window in that region.

Fluorescent sources reduce the far-red contamination of most blue filters because of the low emission in the spectral region beyond 700 nm. Yet the complete absence of red will allow the trace amounts of far-red to alter the equilibrium of the phytochrome system and result in a considerable plant response—not to blue but to the low level of far-red (Borthwick, 1964; Withrow, 1959). Studies concerning the blue region of the spectrum should use a source of low far-red emittance plus a liquid filter of $CuSO_4$ (Withrow and Withrow, 1956) to eliminate any chance of far-red contamination of the blue radiant energy.

Narrow regions of the spectrum may be obtained with spectrographs or interference filter monochromators. Prism and grating spectrographs are thoroughly described in a number of texts (Clark, 1960; Seliger and McElroy, 1965; Withrow and Withrow, 1956). Only a few biological spectrographs have been constructed and perhaps the best known are those reported by Koski *et al.* (1951), Parker *et al.* (1946), and Monk and Ehret (1956).

Interference filter monochromators are more numerous than spectrographs and a few have been described in sufficient detail so that similar instruments can be readily constructed by others (Mohr and Schoser, 1959, 1960; Withrow, 1957). Unfortunately, interference filters are sometimes used in such a casual way that the resultant data are almost meaningless. It should be remembered that interference filters are dielectric films where the reinforcement or transmission depends on the length of the path through the reflecting multilayer of films. Light entering the filter at any angle other than normal to the surface will have an increased path length and the filter will no longer be monochromatic. It is absolutely essential to use a collimated source to produce a beam of parallel light that enters the filter normal to the surface. Needless to say, diffusing plates cannot be used between the source and the interference filter.

MEASUREMENT OF RADIANT ENERGY

The best method of measuring the radiant energy used for plant growth is an unresolved problem, not because of a lack of adequate instrumentation but because investigators cannot agree as to what

[7] Corning Glass Works, Corning, New York.
[8] Westlakes Plastics, West Lenni Mills, Pa.

TABLE 1. CONVERSION FACTORS FOR VARIOUS UNITS OF IRRADIANCE AND ILLUMINANCE

IRRADIANCE		ILLUMINANCE	
Ergs cm^{-2} sec^{-1}	1	Foot candles	1
Joule cm^{-2} sec^{-1}	1×10^7	Lux	0.093
Microwatts cm^{-2}	10	Lumens cm^{-2}	929
Gram-calorie cm^{-2} sec^{-1}	4.2×10^7		

constitutes a meaningful measurement.

White light is usually measured as illuminance in foot candles. The foot candle is a unit related to human vision (Seliger and McElroy, 1965; Withrow and Withrow, 1956) but has no absolute relationship to the absorption characteristics of plants. The most common transducer used in foot-candle meters is a selenium cell corrected to match the spectral sensitivity of the average human eye. Peak sensitivity is therefore at 555 nm. Situations readily arise where lamps with different spectral energy distributions and quite different total energies will provide the same foot-candle illuminance. It follows that for biological purposes a given number of foot candles from a fluorescent source is quite different from the same illuminance from an incandescent source, or even from a different type or color of fluorescent system.

Although illumination measurements are generally rather meaningless they do provide a useful relative measure of the energy values produced by similar sources, provided sufficient information is included. For example, a lighting system monitored 3 feet from the source providing 2,000 ft-c from fluorescent and 200 ft-c from incandescent lamps could be duplicated by other investigators within the limits of the respective meters. However, a report that a system of fluorescent and incandescent lamps provided 2,200 ft-c would be practically useless. Even if the type of fluorescent lamp and the distance were included, duplication of the system would be difficult without knowledge of the relative contribution of the two kinds of lamps to the total illuminance.

Some investigators prefer to measure white light in terms of absolute energy rather than by illumination units. Thermal-radiation transducers such as thermopiles and bolometers are frequently used. Generally radiation transducers have a fast response time, a lack of spectral sensitivity (Lion, 1959), and seem to offer a solution to the problems of measurement of radiant energy for plant growth. Unfortunately absolute energy measurements are of little more biological significance than illumination units because the total energy sensor also records very long wavelengths that have no proven photobiological significance. Confusion is further enhanced by a lack of standardization of units which include ergs or kiloergs cm^{-2}, microwatts cm^{-2}, joules cm^{-2}, gram-calories cm^{-2}, and even Langleys cm^{-2}. Although the various units can be equalized by suitable conversion factors (Table 1) less confusion would result if biologists could agree upon one particular unit.

The study of biological responses to light is directly involved with the absorbing substance or pigment system. Photochemical reactions are based on the absorption of quanta by a pigment system and each molecule that takes part in the photoreaction absorbs one quantum of radiation. The quantum yield of the primary photoreaction is the ratio of the number of molecules undergoing chemical change to the number of quanta absorbed. From the quantum yield, certain conclusions can be drawn about the mechanism of the complete reaction. For example, large quantum yields would indicate a chain reaction whereas low quantum yields may be due to deactivation of the pigment molecule before it has time to react or to a recombination of the products of the photochemical reaction.

Neither illuminance nor irradiance measurements can be converted to quanta unless the spectral region is defined. Therefore, the best method of describing a lighting system for biology is to present a spectral energy distribution curve where irradiance in μwatts cm^{-2} is plotted against wavelength. The irradiance in μwatts cm^{-2} at the absorption maxima of the biological pigment system under study can easily be converted to quanta by the conversion factor

$$\frac{\text{Wavelength in angstroms}}{1{,}987} \times 10^{12}$$

Several spectroradiometers are described in the literature (Norris, 1964; Teubner *et al.*, 1963; Bulpit *et al.*, 1965) and similar instruments are now available commercially.[9] Most spectroradiometers read out in terms of μwatts cm^{-2} and cover a 10–20 nm band. Correction factors can be applied to reduce the readings to μwatts cm^{-2} nm^{-1}. The spectroradiometers have a range of 380 to 1,200 nm and a sensitivity selection that will allow readings from full sunlight to as low as 0.1 μwatts cm^{-2}. Moreover, the spectroradiometer is an excellent instrument to measure spectral irradiance from filtered light sources. Recently developed spectroradiometers sufficiently accurate for biological purposes are portable and are simple to operate; the equipment can be calibrated by the owner.

In many cases the design of a lighting system for plant growth or of luminaires for photobiological studies consists simply of the proper choice of commercially available equipment. Where a special design is required previously described equipment can often be modified. In every case, however, a knowledge of the biological purpose of the system is a prerequisite to a successful design.

[9] Agricultural Specialty Co., Inc., P.O. Box 705, Hyattsville, Md.
Instrumentation Specialties Co., 5624 Seward Ave., Lincoln, Nebraska.
Gamma Scientific Inc., 5841 Mission Gorge Road, San Diego, Calif.

REFERENCES

ALLPHIN, W., 1959: *Primer of Lamps and Lighting*. Chilton Co., Philadelphia, Pa.

ARDITTI, J., and M. ARDITTI, 1964: Construction of an inexpensive growth chamber for orchids. *Bull. Am. Orchid Soc.*, 33: 102.

BORTHWICK, H. A., 1964: Phytochrome action and its time displays. *Am. Nat.*, 68: 347.

BRITTEN, E. J., and D. M. KINCH, 1960: A low cost controlled environment cabinet with diurnal temperature fluctuation. *Ecology*, 41: 801.

BULPIT, T. H., M. W. COULTER, and K. C. HAMMER, 1965: A spectroradiometer for the spectral region of biological photosensitivity. *Applied Optics*, 4: 793.

CARPENTER, G. A., and L. J. MOULSLEY, 1960:

The artificial illumination of environmental control chambers for plant growth. *Jour. Agri. Eng. Res.*, 5: 283.

CATHEY, H. M., W. A. BAILEY, and H. A. BORTHWICK, 1961: Cyclic lighting to reduce cost of timing chrysanthemum flowering. *The Florists' Review*, Sept. 21.

CLARK, G. L., 1960: *The Encyclopedia of Spectroscopy*. Reinhold Publishing Corp., New York.

DOWNS, R. J., and H. A. BORTHWICK, 1958: Comparison of incandescent and fluorescent lamps for lengthening photoperiods. *Proc. Am. Soc. Hort. Sci.*, 71: 568.

———, K. H. NORRIS, W. A. BAILEY, and H. H. KLUETER, 1964: Measurement of irradiance for plant growth and development. *Proc. Am. Soc. Hort. Sci.*, 85: 663.

ELENBAAS, W., 1959: *Fluorescent Lamps and Lighting*. Philip's Tech. Library, Macmillan Co., New York.

HALL, F. C., 1965: Geraniums grow in Brooklyn. *Geranium*, 13: 33.

KOSKI, V. M., C. S. FRENCH, and J. H. C. SMITH, 1951: The action spectrum for the transformation of protochlorophyll to chlorophyll a in normal and albino corn seedlings. *Arch. Biochem. Biophys.*, 31: 1.

LION, K. S., 1959: *Instrumentation in Scientific Research. Electrical Input Transducers.* McGraw-Hill Book Co., Inc., New York.

MOHR, H., and G. SCHOSER, 1959: Eine Interferenzfilter—Monochromatoranlage für photobiologische Zwecke. *Planta*, 53: 1.

———, and ———, 1960: Eine mit Xenonbogen ausgerüstete Interferenzfilter—Monochromatoranlage für kurzwellige sichtbare und langwellige ultraviolette Strahlung. *Planta*, 55: 143.

MONK, G. S., and D. F. EHRET, 1956: Design and performance of a biological spectrograph. *Radiation Res.*, 5: 88.

NORRIS, K. H., 1964: Simple spectroradiometer for 0.4 to 1.2 micron region. *Trans. Am. Soc. Agri. Eng.*, 7: 240.

PARKER, M. W., S. B. HENDRICKS, H. A. BORTHWICK, and N. J. SCULLY, 1946: Action spectra for floral initiation in short day plants. *Bot. Gaz.*, 108: 1.

SELIGER, H. H., and W. D. MC ELROY, 1965: *Light: Physical and Biological Action.* Academic Press, New York.

STALEY, K. A., 1960: *Fundamentals of Light and Lighting*. General Electric Bull. LD-2. Nela Park, Cleveland, Ohio.

TEUBNER, F. G., S. H. WITTWER, R. S. LINDSTROM, and H. ARCHER, 1964: Design and calibration of a portable spectroradiometer for the visible range (400–700 mu). *Proc. Am. Soc. Hort. Sci.*, 82: 619.

VAN DER VEEN, R., and G. MEIJER, 1959: *Light and Plant Growth.* Macmillan Co., New York.

VAN SCHILFGAARDE, J., and R. E. WILLIAMS, 1961: Growth chamber for evaluating excess moisture conditions for drainage design. *Trans. Am. Soc. Agri. Eng.*, 4: 108.

WITHROW, R. B., 1957: An interference filter monochromator system for the irradiation of biological material. *Plant Physiol.*, 32: 355.

———, 1959: *Photoperiodism and Related Phenomena in Plants and Animals.* Publ. 55, Assoc. Adv. Sci., Washington, D.C.

———, and VICTOR ELSTAD, 1953: Water cooled lamp systems with refluxing aqueous filters. *Plant Physiol.*, 28: 334.

———, and L. PRICE, 1953: Filters for the isolation of narrow regions in the visible and near ultraviolet spectrum. *Plant Physiol.*, 28: 105.

———, and A. P. WITHROW, 1956: Generation, control and measurement of visible and near visible radiant energy. In A. Holleander, *Radiation Biology*, McGraw-Hill Book Co., Inc., New York, Vol. III, p. 125.

Isolation of Plastids from Higher Plants

By Donald Spencer

INTRODUCTION

A mature chloroplast is a complex saucer-shaped structure, 5–10 μ in length and 1–4 μ in height, which can be envisaged as a stack of approximately 15 to 20 flattened sacs. These sacs comprise the stroma lamellae. Fused to these lamellae and providing continuity in the vertical plane are the smaller stacks of grana lamellae in which the chlorophyll is concentrated. The whole structure is enclosed in an outer limiting membrane which serves to retain the soluble, non-structural components. The whole organelle is relatively large and readily fragmented by physical forces, and the isolation of these organelles, wholly intact and in useful quantities, presents a real challenge to biologists.

Plastids are usually isolated from plants for one or both of two reasons: to study their structure and physical properties, or to measure their biochemical activities. The particular procedures adopted for chloroplast isolation will to some extent depend on the use to which the isolated chloroplasts are to be put. In general the leaf cells must be broken open and the chloroplasts released into the extracting medium. Since chloroplasts are osmotically sensitive organelles with a limiting membrane it is necessary to provide the appropriate osmotic environment for the released chloroplasts. Methods available for breaking open leaf cells are usually such as to cause some fragmentation of the plastids at the same time. The more violent the method of homogenizing the leaf tissue, the greater the degree of fragmentation of the released chloroplasts and nuclei. The more gentle methods for breaking open cells are less efficient and therefore give a lower yield of chloroplasts which, however, are physically better preserved. A great variety of media have been used to provide a favorable osmotic environment for isolated chloroplasts, the most common being either buffered sucrose or sodium chloride. There is no doubt that the latter is far less effective in preserving chloroplast structure than the former, and its use is not recommended for this reason. A number of procedures for chloroplast isolation will be described together with an assessment of the condition of the resultant chloroplasts and some indication will be given of the studies to which such chloroplasts are suited. As a general principle, temperatures should be maintained as close as possible to 0°C throughout all preparative procedures. Not only enzymatic activity but also structural integrity is preserved better at low temperatures.

EXTRACTING MEDIA

Medium A contains 0.4 *M* sucrose, 0.05 *M* tris [tris(hydroxymethyl)aminomethane] pH 7.8, and 0.01 *M* KCl.

Medium B contains 2.5 percent Ficoll, 5 percent Dextran 40, 0.25 *M* sucrose, 0.025 *M* tris (pH 7.8), 0.001 *M* magnesium chloride. Ficoll and Dextran 40 are obtainable from Pharmacia, Sweden. This medium was devised by Dr. Shigeru Honda, University of California. It has the advantage of favoring the preservation of nuclei as well as chloroplasts.

There are many variations of the basic buffered sucrose medium. In general these do not affect the degree of structural preservation, but are included to satisfy some other requirements. Phosphate is commonly substituted for tris buffer, and NaCl for KCl. Many plant extracts commonly undergo rapid "browning" due to the action of polyphenol oxidases. The products of the browning reaction may be inhibitory toward some chloroplast activities. Extracts of older leaves are particularly prone to suffer in this way. Browning can sometimes be prevented by the addition of 2-mercaptoethanol (4 m*M* final concentration). Glutathione (1 m*M*) and sodium diethyldithiocarbamate (1 m*M*) have also been used for this purpose. Mercaptoethanol also helps to preserve the amino acid incorporating activity of chloroplast ribosomes from tobacco and spinach.

Some plants, such as tomato, sun- [illegible]ower, red kidney bean, and cabbage, [illegible] extracted in standard media yield [illegible]ts with low Hill reaction activity. [illegible]hloroplasts can be obtained from these plants if the extracting medium contains 0.01 *M* EDTA (ethylenediaminetetraacetate) and if the pH of the buffer is increased to 8.5 (Jagendorf and Evans, 1957). More recently it has been found that this treatment protects the chloroplast galactolipids from degradation during isolation (McCarty and Jagendorf, 1965). Not all plants are favored by this high pH medium, and some such as spinach and oats yield less active chloroplast preparations under these conditions

Although NaCl (0.35 *M*) has been widely used in the past as a medium for chloroplast isolation, its use is not recommended. It is a far less effective osmotic agent than sucrose and intact chloroplasts are now known to swell and deteriorate rapidly in this medium.

EXTRACTION PROCEDURES

Microhomogenization

The lower epidermis of a fresh turgid leaf is carefully stripped back to expose the underlying mesophyll cells. A drop or two of extracting medium (medium A or B) is placed on the exposed cells which are then lightly stroked with a pointed rod of wood or plastic. The mesophyll cells burst readily and release their contents into the extracting medium. The drop of medium, now containing the cell contents, can be withdrawn with a Pasteur pipette. By repeating this process a small but useful yield of chloroplasts and other cell organelles can be obtained. This procedure has been developed and used extensively by Dr. S. G. Wildman (personal communication) for direct observation of chloroplasts. It is one of the most satisfactory methods known for obtaining intact chloroplasts which retain many of the morphological characteristics of the chloroplasts in the intact leaf cell. This method has the obvious drawback of yielding relatively small numbers of chloroplasts, although quantities sufficient for a limited number of measurements of activities such as the Hill reaction can be readily obtained. Many dicotyledonous species are suited to this procedure.

Chopping Procedure

This method was developed in an effort to scale up the previous procedure so as to yield larger quantities of intact chloroplasts. The rationale was to attempt to release chloroplasts by cutting open the cells with a fine blade and thus reduce to a minimum any fragmentation of the chloroplasts. In this procedure 5 to 10 gm of chilled leaf laminae are placed in a shallow, flat-bottomed plastic dish (about $3 \times 3 \times \frac{1}{2}$ inches high) containing two volumes of extracting medium A or B. The flat dish sits on ice in a hollowed out block of polystyrene foam plastic. Using a new razor blade, the leaves are chopped for 10 minutes by which time they are reduced to a fine slurry. The extract is filtered through four or eight layers of fine organdy cloth, the mesh of which (110 to the inch; or see information on Nitex in Gould, this volume, pp. 163–171) is such that all unbroken cells and clusters of cells are filtered out. The cell-free extract is then centrifuged at 1,000 *g* for 3 minutes. Chloroplasts are the major component of the resultant pellet, which also contains well-preserved nuclei, starch, crystals, and some mitochondria and cytoplasmic ribosomes which are carried down with the bulky chloroplast fraction.

The chloroplasts in this preparation are well preserved. Approximately 80 percent will have retained their outer limiting membrane. The microscopic appearance of these and other types of chloroplast preparations will be discussed later in this chapter.

Chloroplast preparations made in this way have been used extensively for studying amino acid incorporating activity (Spencer and Wildman, 1964; Francki *et al.*, 1965; Spencer, 1965), RNA polymerase activity (Semal *et al.*, 1964), and the ribonucleic acids of isolated chloroplasts (Spencer and Whitfeld, 1966). This procedure is the best method of obtaining structurally well-preserved chloroplasts in a yield sufficient for most biochemical studies. Some fragmentation of chloroplasts does occur, but this is relatively slight. A measure of the degree of intactness of the chloroplasts is indicated by the fact that of the chlorophyll present in the cell-free homogenate about 90 percent is recovered in the pellet after centrifugation at 1,000 *g* for 3 minutes. From 5 gm of spinach leaves, chloroplasts equivalent to 2 mg of chlorophyll are obtained.

A nuclear fraction, free of chloroplasts, can be obtained from the above 1,000 *g* pellet by resuspending in medium A or B, and adding the neutral detergent Triton X-100 (alkylphenoxypolyethoxyethanol—Rohm and Haas, Philadelphia) to a final concentration of 1 to 4 percent. This detergent completely solubilizes the membranes of the chloroplast, but does not affect the nuclear membrane. Intact nuclei can then be centrifuged down at 1,000 *g* for 5 minutes. More drastic methods of homogenization described below will usually fragment leaf nuclei extensively.

Grinding Procedures

One of the most widely used methods for homogenizing leaves is to grind in a mortar with a pestle. Leaves are scissored or sliced into small pieces and then ground in a chilled mortar for about 5 minutes with one to two volumes of medium A or B. The brei is then filtered through four to eight layers of fine cloth to remove whole cell debris, and the chloroplasts are sedimented at 1,000 *g* for 5 to 10 minutes. Providing no abrasive such as sand has been added, this procedure yields from spinach leaves a chloroplast preparation in which about half the chloroplasts have retained their outer limiting membrane. The remainder of the chloroplasts of this preparation are mostly "naked," i.e., the lamellar and grana systems are intact, so that the over-all gross morphology is preserved, but the outer limiting membrane and an appreciable proportion of the soluble components of the chloroplasts have been lost. The lost components include ferredoxin and some essential constituents of the CO_2-fixing system (Spencer and Unt, 1965).

From the cell-free homogenate obtained after grinding in a mortar, it is possible by differential centrifugation to prepare fractions which are enriched with respect to intact chloroplasts. This is achieved by centrifuging the homogenate for 3 minutes at 121 *g*. When spinach is used the resultant pellet contains about 80 percent of intact, whole chloroplasts.

The addition of abrasives such as sand to the grinding medium causes a greater release of chlorophyll into the cell-free extract, but it also greatly increases the degree of fragmentation of the isolated chloroplasts, and is not recommended where intact chloroplasts are required.

Blending Procedures

A typical example of a blending procedure is that of Jagendorf and Evans (1957). Approximately 5 gm of finely scissored leaves are homogenized for 60 to 90 seconds in 60 ml of medium A in an Omni-Mixer (Ivan Sorvall Inc., Conn). or similar blender at 40 percent of line voltage. The homogenate is filtered through four to eight layers of fine cloth and centrifuged at 1,000 *g* for 10 minutes. The pellet is resuspended in 30 ml of medium A and again centrifuged at 1,000 *g* for 10 minutes. The pellet contains 80 to 90 percent of chloroplasts which have lost the outer membrane, but have retained the over-all grana and stroma lamellar systems. Such chloroplasts have lost much of their soluble contents.

Note that all the above procedures depend on filtration of the crude homogenate through fine cloth to remove all fractions as large as, or larger than, whole single cells. The more commonly used filtration through a pad of glass wool in muslin does not achieve this, and it is important to check the efficiency of this step microscopically. If filtration through cloth does not remove cell debris it is necessary to include a preliminary centrifugation of the filtered homogenate at approximately 200 to 500 *g* for 2 to 3 minutes. This step inevitably removes a significant amount of chloroplast material along with the cell debris.

PURIFICATION OF PLASTIDS

For many purposes the 1,000 *g* pellet obtained from the cell-free extract is satisfactory as a source of isolated chloroplasts. This is especially true where photochemical activities are to be studied. However, depending on the prėparative procedure employed, this pellet contains a proportion of nonchloroplast material. These would include starch grains, nuclei, and nuclear fragments, together with some mitochondria and cytoplasmic ribosomes adsorbed or occluded in the bulky chloroplast pellet. Some of the more common methods for removing these other organelles will be described below.

Washing Procedures

Smaller or less dense organelles can be removed by several cycles of resuspension of the 1,000 *g* pellet in isotonic medium followed by centrifugation at

1,000 *g*. Nuclei can be largely removed by several cycles of differential centrifugation. The 1,000 *g* pellet is gently resuspended in isotonic medium and the suspension centrifuged for 2 minutes at 1,000 *g* to produce a stratified pellet with nuclei and starch at the bottom. The green upper layer of the pellet is carefully resuspended in isotonic medium without disturbing the lower layer. The suspension is recentrifuged at 1,000 *g* for 5 minutes and again the green upper layer is resuspended. This process is repeated two or three times to produce a suspension which is virtually free of whole nuclei. However such preparations would still contain some nuclear fragments. The more gentle leaf extraction procedures preserve the nuclei in a more intact form and facilitate the more complete removal of nuclear material.

The disadvantage of washing procedures is that chloroplasts undergo extensive leaching and fragmentation. Each time isolated chloroplasts are pelleted and resuspended in isotonic medium a significant proportion of the chloroplasts lose their outer membrane and become progressively fragmented. However, for the investigation of functions which are closely associated with the lamellar structures of the chloroplast this is an acceptable procedure. Such chloroplast functions include some photochemical activities such as the Hill reaction, and RNA polymerase activity (Semal *et al.*, 1964). Washing procedures should be used with caution where chloroplast ribosomes are to be studied. Ribosomes are readily lost from broken chloroplasts of some species such as tobacco (Boardman *et al.*, 1965) and far less readily from others such as spinach (Spencer, 1965).

Density Gradient Centrifugation

Many investigators have made use of centrifugation through either continuous or discontinuous sucrose gradients to obtain a chloroplast fraction free of other organelles. Actual concentrations of sucrose used need to be determined for each particular plant species, and microscopic inspection of all fractions is essential for gauging the success of the separation. In principle the aim is to arrange the sucrose concentration range in such a way that nuclei, starch, and crystals are sedimented to the bottom of the tube, whole chloroplasts collect in a less dense band above these, and chloroplast fragments, mitochondria, and other smaller organelles are found at still higher positions. It is essential that the chloroplasts undergoing purification should be relatively free of starch, otherwise they will tend to sediment with the starch and nuclei fraction. In some plants such as tobacco, it may be necessary to hold the plants in darkness for 1 or 2 days before harvest in order to de-starch them. In other plants, such as spinach, it is sufficient to harvest them within a few hours of sunrise.

Following a very gentle homogenization procedure, Leech (1964) layered the chloroplast fraction from broad bean (*Vicia faba*) leaves over a discontinuous gradient consisting of 6 ml of 40 percent sucrose ($\rho = 1.20$) on top of 10 ml of 50 percent sucrose ($\rho = 1.299$). All sucrose solutions were made in 0.15 M Na_2HPO_4-KH_2PO_4 buffer at pH 7.3. Tubes were centrifuged in a swing-out rotor for 20 minutes at 1,000 *g*. Intact chloroplasts were found in a discrete green band just above the junction of the two sucrose layers. Naked chloroplasts, chloroplast fragments, and mitochondria were found higher up the gradient. The layer containing intact chloroplasts could be removed with a Pasteur pipette. Electron microscopy revealed this fraction to consist of well preserved chloroplasts with intact limiting membranes.

Kirk (1963) used a slightly modified procedure to purify a broad bean chloroplast fraction obtained by a blending procedure. In this case 1 ml of chloroplast suspension was layered over a discontinuous gradient consisting of 0.5 ml of 35 percent (w/v) sucrose layered on 1.5 ml of 45 percent sucrose, which was in turn layered on 1.0 ml of 60 percent sucrose. All sucrose solutions contained 0.05 *M* tris, pH 7.4, and 1 m*M* EDTA. Tubes were centrifuged at 76,000 *g* for 60 minutes in a swing-out rotor. The purified chloroplasts were found in the 45 percent sucrose layer. Since a blending procedure was used to extract the chloroplasts, it is likely that these would predominantly be lacking the outer membrane.

It should be noted that not all chloroplasts are amenable to purification by sucrose density gradient centrifugation procedures. In the high sucrose concentrations of a density gradient, spinach chloroplasts rather surprisingly lose their outer membrane and, even in a continuous gradient, no fractions are completely free of smaller contaminating particles.

ISOLATION OF PROPLASTIDS

Leaves of dark-grown plants lack both chloroplasts and chlorophyll. Instead one finds their respective precursors, the proplastids containing protochlorophyll. Upon illumination of these etiolated plants the proplastids are transformed into chloroplasts, with many concomitant changes in structure and composition.

Boardman and Wildman (1962) have described a method for the isolation and purification of proplastids from dark-grown bean (*Phaseolus vulgaris* var. Brown Beauty) plants. Plants are grown in total darkness for 12 to 18 days at 25°C, and isolation procedures are carried out in weak green light. Six-gram lots of leaves are ground in 60 ml of 0.4 *M* sucrose containing 0.05 *M* phosphate (pH 7.4), in a Servall Omni-mixer for 30 seconds at 40 percent of line voltage. The chopping procedure described above could be substituted for this blending step. The homogenate is filtered through four layers of fine cloth and then through four layers of Kleenex paper tissue, and centrifuged at 1,000 *g* for 10 minutes. The pellet is resuspended in buffered sucrose, recentrifuged, and resuspended in a small volume of buffered sucrose. This suspension contains whole proplastids together with large quantities of starch and some fragments. Purification is achieved by layering a 2-ml aliquot of this suspension on a sucrose gradient made up of 1.0, 1.2, and 1.0 ml respectively, of solutions containing 240, 500, and 700 gm per liter of sucrose and 0.05 *M* phosphate (pH 7.4). Centrifugation is carried out for 30 minutes at 119,000 *g* in a swinging bucket rotor. Two intensely yellow bands are formed. The lower band contains pure, whole proplastids; the upper band contains proplastids together with fragments. Starch is pelleted at the bottom of the tube. Fractions may be collected by puncturing the tube with a hollow needle about 3 mm above the base. Proplastids are most readily recognized with fluorescence microscopy by virtue of their protochlorophyll which is confined to two or three red fluorescent centers (Boardman and Wildman, 1962).

CHLOROPLAST ISOLATION IN NONAQUEOUS MEDIA

The losses in soluble constituents which occur during the isolation of chloroplasts in aqueous media have prompted a number of investigators to make use of nonaqueous media. The rationale is that since water-soluble constituents of the chloroplast are insoluble in the nonpolar extracting medium there should be no loss of these constituents from the chloroplast during isolation. This method has been used extensively to determine the localization of enzymes (Stocking, 1959; Heber, 1960; Smillie, 1963; and Bird *et al.*, 1965) and metabolites (Santarius and Heber, 1965) in the chloroplast. In particular, the enzymes concerned with the incorporation of CO_2 into hexoses, sucrose, and starch have been closely studied.

Stocking (1959; see also Bird *et al.*, 1965) and Heber (1957; see also Heber and Tyszkiewicz, 1962) have developed somewhat similar procedures for nonaqueous chloroplast isolation using as the nonpolar solvent mixtures of hexane (or petroleum ether) and carbon tetrachloride of specific densities. Leaves are frozen in dry ice or liquid air, thoroughly dried by lyophilization, and stored *in vacuo* over P_2O_5 at $-5°$ to $-20°C$. The freeze-dried material is suspended in ice-cold hexane/CCl_4 mixture and homogenized either by hand in a Ten Broeck homogenizer, or in a Waring Blendor. The appropriate density of the hexane/CCl_4 mixture must be slightly greater than that of the chloroplasts. This is usually in the range 1.3 to 1.4 and needs to be determined for each particular plant material. It is most important that at harvest the leaves be as free of starch as possible since this increases the density of the chloroplasts and prevents their separation from nuclei, crystals, and cell debris. The homogenate is filtered through a pad of glasswool and cheesecloth and centrifuged at 12,000 *g* for 15 minutes to sediment components more dense than chloroplasts. The supernatant containing the chloroplasts is diluted with an equal volume of hexane and the chloroplasts centrifuged down at 1,000 *g* for 5 minutes. The chloroplast fraction may be washed several times in such a density as to permit chloroplasts to sediment readily. Bird *et al.* (1965) have used a density gradient of hexane/CCl_4 ($\rho = 1.29$ to 1.36) to purify the chloroplast fraction from tobacco leaves. The whole chloroplasts were found in the lightest fraction. In all cases the chloroplast-containing fraction was evaporated to dryness *in vacuo* and resuspended in dilute buffer prior to enzyme assay or analysis. It is important that all traces of water should be excluded and cold conditions be maintained during all earlier stages of this procedure.

The nonaqueous isolation procedure yields chloroplasts which are surprisingly well preserved. Electron micrographs (Stocking and Ongun, 1962; and Heber and Tyszkiewicz, 1962) reveal that, although the outer membrane is lost, the grana and stroma lamellae are fairly well preserved. Stocking and Ongun (1962) found that nonaqueous chloroplasts contained 70 percent of the total leaf nitrogen, whereas chloroplasts isolated in aqueous medium by a blending procedure, and washed once, contained only 30 to 35 percent of leaf nitrogen. Extracts of nonaqueous chloroplasts exhibit a wide range of enzyme activities, such as aldolase, ribulose diphosphate carboxylase, and the enzymes of sucrose synthesis. Many of these activities are readily lost from chloroplasts during aqueous isolation although more recent techniques, such as the chopping procedure, which preserve the outer chloroplast membrane go a long way toward overcoming this objection. Nonaqueous chloroplasts are devoid of photochemical activities, presumably due to the loss of essential lipids during isolation.

Although nonaqueous chloroplasts have commonly been used to determine localization of enzymes or metabolites within the chloroplasts, the possibility of contamination of such chloroplasts with cytoplasmic constituents must not be overlooked. This danger is illustrated by the fact that nonaqueous chloroplasts, prepared from spinach leaves by the above procedures, have been found to have associated with them a significant proportion of cytoplasmic ribosomes (D. Spencer, unpublished observations). Cytoplasmic and chloroplast ribosomes can be readily distinguished in the analytical ultracentrifuge by virtue of their differing sedimentation constants, which are 80 *S* and 70 *S* respectively.

MICROSCOPY OF ISOLATED CHLOROPLASTS

A great deal can be learned of the state of preservation of isolated chloroplasts by conventional light microscopy, and it is recommended that such examinations be routinely carried out. For this purpose a good phase-contrast microscope, such as the Zeiss Research Model, is essential, and observations are made at up to 1,250 magnifications. In this way the state of the chloroplasts and the degree of contamination by other organelles can be determined.

Some practice is needed to permit an accurate assessment of the state of isolated chloroplasts. These have been described in detail by Spencer and Wildman (1963). In general, intact chloroplasts, complete with outer membrane, at first sight do not appear to be well preserved. This is because in the isolated state the outer limiting membrane appears to contract slightly and deform the rather regular saucer shape of the chloroplast *in vivo* into a more highly folded cup shape. This object frequently appears as a somewhat irregular, "bright," highly refractive body under phase contrast with the grana rather poorly resolved. If, however, the osmotic strength of the medium is lowered, the folded chloroplast will be seen to unfold and the outer limiting membrane to swell. By using a combination of Honda medium (medium B) and a gentle method of isolation (microhomogenization, or chopping) many intact chloroplasts are preserved in a relaxed open form which resembles more closely the chloroplast *in vivo*. Grana are seen more clearly in such chloroplasts and they frequently retain the mobile protuberances of the stroma phase which are a feature of chloroplasts in the living cell (Spencer and Unt, 1965).

Chloroplasts which have lost the outer limiting membrane during isolation appear, at first sight, to be very well preserved. The over-all original saucer shape of the chloroplast is seen and the grana are very distinct. However, close examination of the outer margin of the organelle reveals a somewhat ragged outline owing to the loss of the outer membrane. If the osmotic strength of the medium is lowered, these chloroplasts swell and become distorted, but no surrounding outer membrane becomes evident during this process.

Small fragments of chloroplasts containing one, two, or three grana can be readily seen under phase contrast, but it is possible to confuse these with other organelles such as mitochondria, spherosomes, or even starch grains. For an unequivocal demonstration that structures are chlorophyll-bearing, it is preferable to use fluorescence microscopy rather than phase contrast. When illuminated with blue light of 400–450 mμ (BG12 Schott filter) chlorophyll and protochlorophyll emit a characteristic red fluorescence, thus enabling grana or prolamellar bodies to be readily identified.

The term "grana preparation" has been rather loosely used in biochemical literature in the past. This expression usually refers to a chloroplast preparation which has been fragmented by some mechanical means such as high-speed blending or sonication. These fragments would contain portions of both grana and stroma lamellae and are not derived solely from the grana. No method has been devised to date for obtaining preparations which contain only true grana material.

Isolated chloroplasts can be studied by the standard procedures of electron microscopy. Leech (1964) found that it is important to reduce the tonicity of the medium gradually throughout the fixation and dehydration procedures in order to avoid distortion and rupture of the outer chloroplast membrane.

SELECTION OF APPROPRIATE EXTRACTION PROCEDURES

The extraction procedure chosen for the isolation of chloroplasts will vary with their intended fate. The principles involved in this choice are fairly obvious. If it is intended to investigate some aspect of chloroplast structure or function which requires the intact chloroplast and its soluble as well as structural components, then procedures such as the microhomogenization method, the chopping method, or the grinding method, followed by differential centrifugation would be chosen. The soluble components of the chloroplast (i.e., the stroma) will be retained only if the outer limiting membrane is preserved. As might be expected, endogenous activities in general are higher in preparations of intact rather than "naked" chloroplasts (Spencer and Unt, 1965). The use of nonaqueous extraction media ensures the retention of the soluble, stroma components, but has the disadvantage of inactivating photochemical functions.

It is important to note that the preservation of the outer limiting membrane under aqueous conditions does not guarantee complete retention of all soluble chloroplast components. The outer membrane of the isolated chloroplast, although apparently intact and osmotically sensitive, is nonetheless "leaky" and even large molecules such as the Fraction 1 protein (mol. weight, 0.5×10^6) can diffuse out. Smaller molecules such as ferredoxin do so very readily. For this reason, where the aim is to retain the maximum of soluble components, one should avoid unnecessary dilution of the isolated chloroplast preparations and minimize the time elapsed between homogenization of the tissue and centrifugation of the chloroplast pellet.

Where the intention is to study chloroplast functions involving the particulate lamellar structures there is no need to preserve the outer membrane and the soluble constituents. For this purpose the less gentle grinding or blending procedures including washing steps are quite suitable. Chloroplast activities such as the Hill reaction and photophosphorylation come into this category. In these cases, the reactions involve the structural elements and any essential soluble components such as Hill oxidants, ferredoxin, adenosine diphosphate, inorganic phosphate, and redox mediators are normally added to the chloroplast preparations in nonlimiting amounts. Indeed the absence of the outer chloroplast membrane is probably an advantage in this situation because it permits a more ready access of exogenous metabolites to the sites of photochemical activity on the grana lamellae. By the same token, fragmented chloroplasts can yield more active preparations than "naked" chloroplasts, presumably because of even more ready access of exogenous reactants to the active sites (Spencer and Unt, 1965).

For some purposes it is advantageous to isolate chloroplasts by a procedure which yields intact organelles even though this is not essential for the chloroplast property to be studied. The advantage arises from the fact that if chloroplasts are kept intact they are far more readily and more completely sedimented out of the cell-free homogenate. Contamination of the chloroplast fraction with smaller organelles, and conversely of higher speed fractions with chloroplasts and their fragments, is thus greatly reduced.

Having obtained a pellet of isolated chloroplasts by centrifugation at 1,000 *g*, the choice of the resuspending medium will also depend on the nature of the intended analysis. It may be an advantage, as is the case for amino acid incorporation (Francki *et al.*, 1965), to suspend the chloroplasts in low ionic solution. This causes rupture of the outer membranes and permits more rapid entry of exogenous reactants. In general it is preferable to maintain chloroplasts in isotonic conditions for maximum photophosphorylating activity. The presence of low concentrations of Mg^{++} (10^{-4} to 10^{-3} *M*) in the low ionic resuspending media offsets to some extent the disruptive effect of osmotic shock on photophosphorylating activity (Jagendorf and Smith, 1962) and on chloroplast structure (Spencer and Unt, 1965).

SELECTION OF PLANT MATERIAL

A few principles can be listed to guide the choice of plant material for chloroplast studies. As a general rule, young expanding leaves yield more active chloroplasts than fully expanded leaves. This is due in part to the fact that with increasing age there is a buildup in the vacuoles of metabolic by-products such as tannins and polyphenols. During leaf homogenization these vacuolar contents are released and can react with the chloroplasts. Where possible leaves should be harvested immediately before use and prolonged storage should be avoided. Although market spinach has been used extensively and successfully in photosynthesis studies, App and Jagendorf (1964) have found that bacterial contamination of such stored leaf material can cause misleading results in the measurement of amino acid incorporation by isolated chloroplasts. The high specific activity (200–300 mc per mmole) of the C^{14}-amino acids now in use can result in a significant incorporation by quite low levels of contaminating bacteria.

It is a considerable advantage during both isolation and purification procedures if chloroplasts are free of starch. Chloroplasts containing large starch grains are far more readily fragmented and less amenable to purification by density gradient centrifugation in either aqueous or nonaqueous media. Starch-free chloroplasts are also more suitable for electron microscope studies.

The choice of plant species for plastid studies is rather wide, although a great deal of work has been concentrated on relatively few species. By far the most commonly used species, especially for photosynthesis studies, is spinach (*Spinacia oleracea*). Other species yielding chloroplasts suitable for photosynthesis studies include various varieties of *Beta vulgaris* (sugar beet, Swiss chard, silver beet), peas (*Pisum sativum*), broad bean and red kidney bean (*Phaseolus vulgaris*), barley (*Hordeum sativum*), and oats (*Avena sativa*). Some species such as tobacco, tomato, and red kidney bean require special extraction media described earlier to prevent chloroplast inactivation during isolation. While all the above species yield chloroplasts with Hill reaction activity (Jagendorf and Evans, 1957) the capacity for active photophosphorylation is more restricted, presumably owing to inactivation during isolation. Spinach, Swiss chard, and sugar beet have been most commonly used for this purpose.

Protein synthesis has been studied in chloroplasts from tobacco, spinach, and radish (*Raphanus sativus*), while broad bean and tobacco chloroplasts have been shown to exhibit RNA polymerase activity.

Most of the above species can be grown readily under standard glasshouse conditions, although the growth of some plants may be restricted to certain seasons. This restriction applies to spinach which, as a long-day plant, tends to terminate leaf production as soon as the critical day length is reached. Avron (1960) advocates the use of Swiss chard which is insensitive to day length, and can be grown under glasshouse conditions throughout the year. Plants may be grown in a variety of media including soil, perlite, vermiculite, and water culture. A suitable nutrient mixture for growth of spinach and tomato in water culture is that of Tsui (1948).

ASSAY OF SOME CHLOROPLAST ACTIVITIES

Chlorophyll Content

Chlorophyll content is determined by the method of Arnon (1949). An aliquot of the isolated chloroplast preparation is diluted to 5 ml with water and to this is added acetone to give a final volume of 25 ml. After standing at least 15 minutes in the dark at room temperature, the suspension is filtered through Whatman No. 42 filter paper and the optical density (O.D.) is measured at 645 and 663 mμ in a 1-cm cuvette against a blank of 80 percent acetone. Total chlorophyll is calculated from the equation:

$$\text{Total chlorophyll (mg/liter)} = (20.2 \times \text{O.D.}_{645}) + (8.02 \times \text{O.D.}_{663})$$

Chlorophyll a and b concentration can be calculated separately from the equations:

$$\text{Chlorophyll a (mg/liter)} = (1.27 \times \text{O.D.}_{663}) - (2.69 \times \text{O.D.}_{645})$$

$$\text{Chlorophyll b (mg/liter)} = (2.29 \times \text{O.D.}_{645}) - (4.68 \times \text{O.D.}_{663})$$

Endogenous CO_2 Fixation

Endogenous CO_2 fixation is readily measured in a reaction mixture consisting of 0.5 ml of chloroplasts (0.1 mg chlorophyll) suspended in 0.4 *M* sucrose, 0.05 *M* tris (pH 7.3), 0.01 *M* NaCl, and 0.001 *M* $MgCl_2$ together with 7 to 10 μl of $NaHC^{14}O_3$ (equivalent to approximately 1 μmole and 10^5 cpm). Reaction mixtures are gassed with N_2 for 3 minutes prior to, as well during, the incubation which is carried out at 15°C for 30 minutes either in the dark or in white light of approximately 4,000 ft-c. The reaction is stopped with 0.25 ml of 1 *N* HCl and the extent of $C^{14}O_2$ fixation determined by plating onto stainless steel planchettes 0.05-ml aliquots of the reaction mixture, which are then dried and counted on a gas flow counter fitted with a thin window. The amount of CO_2 fixed is calculated from the specific activity of the starting material and expressed as μmole CO_2 fixed per milligram chlorophyll per hour. Photochemical CO_2 fixation is given by the difference between the light and dark incubations. For high endogenous activities, chloroplasts should be prepared, with minimum dilution, by either the chopping procedure or the grinding procedure followed by a low speed centrifugation as described earlier.

Indophenol Dye Reduction

One expression of the Hill reaction activity of isolated chloroplasts is the light-dependent reduction of the blue dye, trichlorophenolindophenol, to a colorless form (Jagendorf and Evans, 1957). To a 3-ml cuvette of 1 cm light path are added chloroplasts (2 to 10 μg chlorophyll), 0.07 μmoles of 2,3′,6-trichlorophenolindophenol, and 0.1 *M* tris buffer (pH 7.3), to give a final volume of 3.0 ml. The optical density at 620 mμ is read, the cuvette is illuminated at approximately 2,000 ft-c by a 250-watt Photoflood lamp for 45 seconds, and the change in optical density at 620 mμ is determined. The amount of chlorophyll in the reaction mixture is selected so as to give an optical density change of 0.09 to 0.12 under these conditions. Using a millimolar extinction coefficient of 18 for the oxidized dye, the dye reduction capacity of the chloroplasts is expressed as μmoles of dye reduced per milligram chlorophyll per hour.

The Development of Photochemical Activity During Greening

Illumination of dark-grown plants sets in motion the transformation of proplastids to chloroplasts. The acquisition of Hill reaction activity during this developmental change can be determined by the procedure of Anderson and Boardman (1964).

Bean plants (*Phaseolus vulgaris* var. Brown Beauty) are grown in the dark at 25°C and 80 percent relative humidity in trays of perlite which has been soaked with nutrient solution. After 10 to 14 days the greening transformation is initiated by providing continuous illumination of 400 ft-c from white fluorescent tubes (Boardman and Anderson, 1964). Harvests are made of 5 gm of leaves from the dark-grown plants just prior to illumination, and from the greening plants after 12 hours' illumination. Dark-grown plants should be handled in weak green light during proplastid isolation in order to avoid conversion of protochlorophyll to chlorophyll.

The leaves are ground in a Servall Omni-Mixer at 40 percent of line voltage for 30 seconds in 50 ml of a phosphate buffer (0.05 *M*, pH 7.8) containing 0.4 *M* sucrose and 0.01 *M* KCl. The homogenate is filtered first through four layers of cloth, and if cell debris is still present, then through four layers of Kleenex paper tissue, and the plastids sedimented at 1,000 *g* for 10 minutes. In this way the plastids are packed onto a dense layer of starch and care is taken to leave behind as much starch as possible on resuspension into 40 ml of grinding buffer. The centrifugation is repeated and the pellet, which constitutes a crude plastid preparation, is resuspended in a small volume of grinding buffer.

Hill reaction activity is measured with ferricyanide as artificial oxidant (Jagendorf and Smith, 1962). A reaction mixture containing plastids (equivalent to 0.04 mg chlorophyll), 3.0 μmoles potassium ferricyanide, 140 μmoles NaCl, and 80 μmoles tris (pH 8.2), in a volume of 6 ml is prepared and divided between two glass centrifuge tubes. One tube is kept dark and the other is illuminated at 4,500 ft-c provided by a 250-watt Photoflood lamp for 4 minutes at 20°C. After the illumination period, 0.3 ml of 20 percent trichloroacetic acid is added to both the illuminated and darkened tubes, the precipitates are sedimented by centrifugation, and the optical density of the supernatants is measured at 420 mμ in 1-cm cuvettes. The difference in optical density between the illuminated and darkened mixtures gives a measure of light-dependent ferricyanide reduction catalyzed by the plastids. The amount of ferricyanide reduced is calculated from the optical density change at 420 mμ using a millimolar extinction coefficient of 1.0 for potassium ferricyanide. The plastids from dark-grown leaves, which contain protochlorophyll but no chlorophyll, will show an appreciable dark reduction of ferricyanide but no light-dependent reduction. After 12 hours' illumination chlorophylls a and b will have been formed and the protochlorophyll content is negligible. In the "12-hour" leaves total chlorophyll can be determined from an aliquot of the plastid fraction by the Arnon (1949) method given above. These plastids will show a light-dependent reduction of 300 to 400 μmoles of ferricyanide per milligram chlorophyll per hour. The protochlorophyll content of the "dark-grown" plastids can be determined in the same way from an 80 percent acetone extract of an aliquot of the plastids.

$$\text{Protochlorophyll (mg/ml)} = O.D._{626} \div 34.9$$

If harvests are made after shorter periods of illumination the plastids may contain a mixture of protochlorophyll, and chlorophylls a and b. These can be determined separately in an 80 percent acetone extract as described by Anderson and Boardman (1964).

REFERENCES

ANDERSON, J. M., and N. K. BOARDMAN, 1964: Studies on the greening of dark-grown plants. II. Development of photochemical activity. *Austral. Jour. Biol. Sci.*, 17: 93.

APP, A. A., and A. T. JAGENDORF, 1964: C^{14}-amino acid incorporation by spinach chloroplasts. *Plant Physiology*, 39: 772.

ARNON, D. I., 1949: Copper enzymes in isolated chloroplasts. Polyphenol oxidase in *Beta vulgaris. Plant Physiology*, 24: 1.

AVRON, M., 1960: Photophosphorylation by Swiss-chard chloroplasts. *Biochim. Biophys. Acta*, 40: 257.

BIRD, I. F., H. K. PORTER, and C. R. STOCKING, 1965: Intracellular localization of enzymes associated with sucrose synthesis in leaves. *Biochim. Biophys. Acta*, 100: 366.

BOARDMAN, N. K., and S. G. WILDMAN, 1962: Identification of proplastids by fluorescence microscopy and their isolation and purification. *Biochim. Biophys. Acta*, 59: 222.

———, and J. M. ANDERSON, 1964: Studies on the greening of dark-grown plants I. Formation of chloroplasts from proplastids. *Austral. Jour. Biol. Sci.*, 17: 86.

———, R. I. B. FRANCKI, and S. G. WILDMAN, 1965: Protein synthesis by cell-free extracts from tobacco leaves. II. Association of activity with chloroplast ribosomes. *Biochemistry*, 4: 872.

FRANCKI, R. I. B., N. K. BOARDMAN, and S. G. WILDMAN, 1965: Protein synthesis by cell-free extracts from tobacco leaves. I. Amino acid incorporating activity of chloroplasts in relation to their structure. *Biochemistry*, 4: 865.

HEBER, U., 1957: Über der Lokalisation von löslichen Zuckern in der Pflanzenzelle. *Ber. Deutsch. Botan. Ges.*, 70: 371.

———, 1960: Vergleichende Untersuchungen Chloroplasten, die durch Isolierungs-Operationen in nicht-wassrigem und in wassrigem Milieu erhalten wurden. II. Kritik der Reinheit und Ferment Lokalisation in Chloroplasten. *Z. Naturforsch.*, 15b: 100.

———, and E. TYSZKIEWICZ, 1962: The rate of photosynthesis in isolated chloroplasts. *Jour. Exptl. Bot.*, 13: 185.

JAGENDORF, A. T., and M. EVANS, 1957: The Hill reaction of red kidney bean chloroplasts. *Plant Physiology*, 32: 435.

JAGENDORF, A. T., and M. SMITH, 1962: Uncoupling phosphorylation in spinach chloroplasts by absence of cations. *Plant Physiology*, 37: 135.

KIRK, J. T. O., 1963: The deoxyribonucleic acid of broad bean chloroplasts. *Biochim. Biophys. Acta*, 76: 417.

LEECH, R., 1964: Isolation of structurally intact chloroplasts. *Biochim. Biophys. Acta*, 79: 637.

MC CARTY, R. E., and A. T. JAGENDORF, 1965: Chloroplast damage due to enzymatic hydrolysis of endogenous lipids. *Plant Physiology*, 40: 725.

SANTARIUS, K. A., and U. HEBER, 1965: Changes in the intracellular levels of ATP, ADP, AMP, and P_i and regulatory function of the adenylate system in leaf cells during photosynthesis. *Biochim. Biophys. Acta*, 102: 39.

SEMAL, J., D. SPENCER, Y. T. KIM, and S. G. WILDMAN, 1964: Properties of a ribonucleic acid synthesizing system in cell-free extracts of tobacco leaves. *Biochim. Biophys. Acta*, 91: 205.

SMILLIE, R. M., 1963: Formation and function of soluble proteins in chloroplasts. *Canad. Jour. Botany*, 41: 123.

SPENCER, D., 1965: Protein synthesis by isolated spinach chloroplasts. *Arch. Biochem. Biophys.*, 111: 381.

———, and H. UNT, 1965: Biochemical and structural correlations in isolated spinach chloroplasts under isotonic and hypotonic conditions. *Austral. Jour. Biol. Sci.*, 18: 197.

———, and P. R. WHITFELD, 1966: On the nature of the ribonucleic acid of isolated chloroplasts. *Arch. Biochem. Biophys.*, 117: 337.

———, and S. G. WILDMAN, 1963: Observations on the structure of grana-containing chloroplasts and a proposed model of chloroplast structure. *Austral. Jour. Biol. Sci.*, 15: 599.

———, and ———, 1964: The incorporation of amino acids into protein by cell-free extracts from tobacco leaves. *Biochemistry*, 3: 954.

STOCKING, C. R., 1959: Chloroplast isolation in nonaqueous media. *Plant Physiology*, 34: 56.

———, and A. ONGUN, 1962: The intracellular distribution of some metallic elements in leaves. *Amer. Jour. Bot.*, 49: 284.

TSUI, C., 1948: The role of zinc in auxin synthesis in the tomato plant. *Amer. Jour. Bot.*, 35: 172.

The Isolation of Some Organelles from Embryonic Cells*

By Fred H. Wilt

INTRODUCTION

The student of problems of development has a real need for knowledge of methods for isolation and characterization of various subcellular components, since it is an essential part of efforts to understand the cellular and biochemical basis of development. This applies especially to isolation of organelles containing nucleoprotein because of their central role in the transfer and control of genetic information. It is impossible to present a comprehensive compendium of all the approaches to the isolation of various cell organelles that have been elaborated during the past several decades. However, in a large number of instances distinctive problems do exist when dealing with embryonic materials which require modification of existing methods of cell fractionation.

I will briefly discuss some of the general methodological problems presented by a variety of embryonic systems and state some general considerations. Next, some approaches will be discussed which have been used to isolate successfully some organelles from three different kinds of material: sea urchin, frog, and chick embryos. It is hoped that this will illustrate the types of considerations one might entertain for solving problems of organelle isolation from embryonic material. As mentioned previously, special emphasis will be put on organelles containing nucleoprotein, i.e., the ribosomes and nuclei of embryonic cells. It was realized very early in studies of experimental embryology that the biochemical equipment and architecture of the egg played a large and important role in the ensuing drama of epigenesis. A number of reviews may be consulted for the current stage of the art of the isolation of the several different kinds of organelles (Allfrey, 1959; Brachet, 1957; Peterman, 1964).

GENERAL PROBLEMS

Many eggs and embryos are surrounded by membranes and gelatinous materials which pose a problem for adequate cell disruption. Elsewhere in this volume, Berg (pp. 767–776) has compiled a list of

* Work from the author's laboratory has been supported by grants from the National Science Foundation and the National Institutes of Health. I am grateful to Dr. Dan Mazia for allowing publication in this article of new techniques developed in his laboratory.

a large number of available methods for removing membranes and jelly from a wide variety of marine materials, and Brown (pp. 685–701) has discussed removal of jelly from amphibian eggs. The disruption of the cell by homogenization is the usual first step in isolation of organelles. The tightness of the homogenizer can influence the results of the fractionation considerably, and depending upon the problem at hand, different tolerances should be selected. Minimal shear is obviously essential for isolation of some very delicate structures, such as polysomes.

For the small cells from an avian or mammalian embryo, conventional homogenization in a Potter-Elvejhem homogenizer may be adequate. For the large cells of early amphibian embryos, a looser-fitting homogenizer is required. The Dounce type homogenizer is useful with sea urchin eggs. Pestle clearances in all these cases should be adjusted for the size of the cells. A gentle method of disrupting eggs is by osmotic lysis, and this is practical for sea urchin eggs. It has been little applied to embryonic cells, but should be considered as a very promising approach. Sonication will also disrupt most embryonic cells (see Rutter, this volume, pp. 671–683) and the sonication time and voltage must be determined empirically. Some surface active agents such as Triton X-100 (Rohm and Haas) are very effective in disrupting cells (see Rutter, this volume). Effects of Triton on the integrity of most organelles of embryonic cells have not been extensively investigated.

During the preparation of organelles from embryos and eggs, one is often faced with the necessity of using small amounts of tissues. This has been a very difficult obstacle, but introduction of new techniques (isotopes, micromethods) and new equipment virtually eliminate this problem. There is really nothing objectionable to carrying out all cell isolations in rather dilute solutions, and it may even be preferable. Brown (1962a) found that ribosomes could be isolated from *Rana pipiens* eggs when they were homogenized in very large volumes of solution, but not when the usual range of three to twelve volumes of homogenization medium per volume of eggs was used. If one has a distinctive marker for the various constituents to be isolated or characterized, carrier may be used to reduce denaturation and help visualize the components. A convenient way to do this is to label the cell constituent from the embryonic cell isotopically, and carry out the isolation in the presence of adult unlabeled cells. A variant of this technique has recently been used to analyze ribonucleic acid (RNA) synthesis in very small rudiments of developing mouse pancreas (Wessells and Wilt, 1965). In addition, new microtechniques have become available for the detection of enzymes, coenzymes, and substrates from small numbers of cells (Lowry and Pasonneau, 1963). Microhomogenizers and microcentrifuges are available now from commercial sources (Microchemical Specialties, Berkeley, California; Beckman Instruments, Richmond, California).

A fundamental problem of the isolation of the cell constituents from embryos and eggs is based on the fact that embryos contain large amounts of inclusions not usually found in other cells. The yolk and pigment granules contribute a considerable amount of contamination to certain fractions. Furthermore, inclusions may possess the property of binding or complexing with other normal cell constituents, and thus interfere with routine methods of isolation. A good case in point is the binding of ribosomes by yolk of *Rana pipiens* embryos (Brown and Caston, 1962a). These difficulties can usually be overcome only by a systematic search for conditions which prevent this complexing (or destruction) and leave the desired constituents intact. Obvious variables to be investigated would be the type of homogenizer, the conditions of centrifugation, the concentration of eggs homogenized, the pH, ionic strength, temperature, ionic composition of the medium employed, the use of detergent and surface active agents, and the addition of compounds which might interfere with binding, complexing, and destruction.

The other general comment that should be made is that it is often not possible to devise a convenient scheme for isolation of a number of constituents from the same homogenate. Sometimes different media and techniques must be used for preparation of a given component, and separate isolations are necessary for different organelles. For instance, isolation of ribosomes from embryos of *Rana pipiens* would not result in intact mitochondria. Detergents are necessary to keep the ribosomes from complexing with the yolk, and this destroys the integrity of the mitochondria. Furthermore, methods may have to be varied with different stages of development of a given organism. Changes in yolk concentration, cell size, and the nature of cell association are all considerations which would affect the yield and purity of components; it is necessary to check yields (preferably by cross-mixing experiments) at each stage to ensure realistic comparisons.

ISOLATION OF CONSTITUENTS FROM SEA URCHIN EMBRYOS AND EGGS

Preliminary Considerations

Prior to cell disruption it is usually necessary to remove the jelly and fertilization membranes. This is essential for isolation of nuclei, mitotic apparatus, and relatively undergraded polysomes, but a less important consideration for other organelles. If membranes are not removed special efforts to wash the cells prior to homogenization should be made. Many of the ions in sea water are relatively injurious to the structure and function of different organelles. Subsequently, cells may be broken by homogenization in a conventional homogenizer, but often with a poor yield. Sonication gives complete cell breakage, but may lead to destruction of the desired constituents, and this should be carefully examined. Two better methods are homogenization in a tight-fitting Dounce homogenizer, and lysis in hypotonic medium. Several convenient sizes of Dounce homogenizers are available from Kontes Glass Co. (Vineland, New Jersey) but even their tight-fitting pestle is often too loose and must be reshaped by a glass blower to closer tolerances (e.g., 100 μ). Unfortunately, trial and error is the best procedure to be used in choosing the proper clearance for the homogenizer. If a rather dilute egg or early embryo suspension (one volume of eggs to five to ten volumes of medium) is used, all the embryos can be disrupted in one or two passes of the homogenizer pestle. The other method is to disrupt demembranated eggs osmotically, after they have been thoroughly washed in 1.0 *M* dextrose by centrifugation and resuspension (three or four times). The cells can then be diluted into a hypotonic buffered solution, and they will slowly cytolyze. Dispersal of the cytoplasm can be aided by shaking of the flask of the cytolyzing embryos, or by passage of embryos through a large syringe (No. 20 gauge needle), as described by Hinegardner (1962). Divalent cations, essential for the preservation of most organelles, rather retard the dispersion of cytolyzed cells, as do cold temperatures. Higher tonicities can be restored by addition of concentrated sucrose solutions to the cytolyzing mixture. The late gastrula, prism, and older embryonic stages are much more difficult to disrupt by these techniques; hypotonic lysis is virtually impossible and more vigorous, mechanical methods of cell breakage are employed at these older stages.

Recent attention has been given to the isolation of particles containing nucleoprotein from sea urchin embryos, but there is no barrier to isolation of other constituents. For instance, virtually all of the mitochondria sediment at less than 10,000 *g* in 8–10 minutes, as do various other kinds of material. Further purification of mitochondria from this sediment can probably be easily accomplished by the traditional methods of differential centrifugation (Allfrey, 1959). Sea urchin material is not very favorable for the isolation of nucleoli. Mature sea urchin oocytes have completed meiosis and contain no nucleoli; none reappear until gastrulation is reached. However, the closely related oocytes of the starfish have been used with a great deal of success by Vincent for preparation of very pure fractions of nucleoli (1955). Sea urchin eggs vary a great deal in their yolk content, and little attention has been paid to isolation and characterization of the yolk. We have noticed that during the isolation of the mitotic apparatus by the dithiodipropanol method (Mazia *et al.*, 1961; Sakai, 1966) the yolk granules are dispersed together with the rest of the cytoplasm, and they seem to have retained their integrity when viewed by phase-contrast microscopy. This would seem to be a favorable initial observation for devising methods of purification of yolk.

Nuclei

Excellent methods for preparation of pure nuclei from various stages of *Strongylocentrotus purpuratus* have been devised, and these probably apply to other species without major modification. Hinegardner (1962) gives detailed instructions on preparation of nuclei. The demembranated eggs are washed several times in dextrose solution, cytolyzed in hypotonic salt solution, and the cytoplasm dispersed by mechanical agitation, whereupon the homogenate is centrifuged at low speed. The crude nuclear pellet is purified by centrifuging the resuspended nuclei through a series of layers of sucrose solutions of different densities, ranging from 1.160 to 1.301. The whole intact nuclei sediment to the lowest interface because of their size and density. The use of step density gradients to purify nuclei is probably generally applicable (Hogeboom, 1955). Mazia and Ruby have devised some variants of this original scheme. Embryos can be disrupted by sonication in sucrose solutions, and this is especially important when the method of hypotonic lysis is difficult. The embryos are sonicated for 30 seconds to 2 minutes while suspended in a beaker immersed in ice. It would be best to familiarize oneself with this method using very early gastrula embryos, when the yield of nuclei is rather high. Because of the enormous cytoplasm/nucleus ratio in the younger stages, the yields of nuclei are much lower.

Mazia and Ruby have found the use of the methods just described produces nuclei containing relatively short stretches of intact deoxyribonucleic acid (DNA). The DNA in the chromatin is apparently subject to digestion by a magnesium-dependent DNase and this enzyme has not been separated from chromatin. A method has been devised in which nuclei are at no time exposed to magnesium, and the DNA in nuclei prepared by the new technique is very long (when examined in the electron microscope), comparable to the long stretches of DNA found in sea urchin sperm by Solari (1965). The new method of Mazia and Ruby is carried out as follows. Demembranated embryos are washed in

1.0 *M* dextrose containing 0.15 *M* NaCl and 0.015 *M* Na citrate, and then washed again in saline citrate without dextrose. The embryos are resuspended in 0.15 *M* NaCl, 0.015 *M* sodium citrate. The suspension is squirted through a No. 20 gauge syringe needle to disrupt the cells, and an equal volume of cold 2.0 *M* sucrose is added and mixed. The suspension is then centrifuged at 11,000 rpm in the high speed rotor of an International centrifuge for 30–45 minutes. The pellet, which is difficult to resuspend and must be teased into a homogeneous suspension, may be further purified by washing in 0.15 *M* NaCl, 0.015 *M* sodium citrate, 1.0 *M* sucrose.

Ribonucleoprotein Particles

Ribosomes and microsomes are easily isolated from sea urchins, and the most extensive studies were carried out by Hultin and his collaborators (1960, 1961). Other important contributions were made in Monroy's laboratory (1965). Conventional methods have employed washing the eggs in solutions intermediate in ionic content between sea water and the final homogenization medium. The high sodium and calcium content of sea water is undesirable. The eggs are first washed one to three times in calcium-free sea water (see Hinegardner, this volume, pp. 139–155); then once or twice in 0.24 *M* KCl, 0.24 *M* NaCl, 0.016 *M* $MgCl_2$, 0.15 *M* sucrose, and 0.169 *M* $NaHCO_3$; then once or twice in a solution containing 0.24 *M* KCl, 0.016 *M* $MgCl_2$, 0.35 *M* sucrose, 0.05 *M* tris (pH 7.8); and finally in the homogenization medium, which is usually buffered with tris 0.03 *M* (pH 7.6–7.9), sucrose 0.15–0.25 *M*, magnesium 0.003–0.01 *M*, and 0.25 *M* KCl. The high potassium content (may be replaced by ammonium chloride) is necessary for optimal amino acid incorporation, *in vitro*, by these particles, but it is not necessary for physically intact ribosomes. After preliminary centrifugation at 10,000 *g* for 10 minutes to remove mitochondria, yolk, whole cells, and nuclei, the microsomes and ribosomes may be sedimented by centrifugation for 1 hour at 100,000 *g*. The resultant pellet may be quite contaminated with pigment granules. The particles may be resuspended by homogenizing the pellet in homogenization medium and washed by resedimenting the particles. Or the first sedimentation can be carried out through a layer of homogenization medium containing 0.3 *M* sucrose and the usual salts and buffer. Addition of desoxycholate (1 percent) and Lubrol W (0.5 percent) to the mitochondria-free supernatant will dissolve most of the lipoprotein membranes of the microsomes and result in a collection of ribosomes. Sometimes Hultin (1960) homogenized very early stages in sucrose-free media, and subsequently concentrated sucrose solutions were added to adjust the final sucrose concentration to 0.25 *M*. It should be added that some cytoplasmic DNA, which has not been fully characterized, is present in homogenates of early sea urchin embryos (see article by Brown, this volume, pp. 685–701; Piko and Tyler, 1965).

The cells may also be disrupted by sonication, freezing and thawing, or hypotonic lysis. Older stages with smaller cells are much harder to disrupt, and some vigorous homogenization is usually employed. We have found that the tight-fitting Dounce homogenizer again gives good results with the least amount of shear and heating. Preliminary attempts in this laboratory to employ lysis of early embryos in hypotonic solutions have resulted in much improved yields of polysomes and the isolation of large microsomes not found by other methods. In *Strongylocentrotus purpuratus*, at least, most of the ribosomes are present in the mitochondria-free supernatant, but in early stages of embryogenesis many of the ribosomes active in amino acid incorporation, *in vivo*, are attached to membranes which sediment at less than 10,000 *g* when the cells are broken by gentle methods (Wilt, 1966).

Polysomes can be released from this low speed microsome pellet by addition of desoxycholate. After gastrulation the situation more closely parallels that encountered in cells from mammalian material, and extremely large microsomes are not so prevalent. The activity of ribonuclease can be a considerable difficulty in isolation of intact and active microsomal and ribosomal preparations. Addition of ribonuclease inhibitors, such as bentonite (Wilt, 1964) or polyvinylsulfate (Brown and Littna, 1964), may be advisable sometimes. Control of temperature is also critical. If these precautions are followed, especially on cell breakage, use of low temperature, ribonuclease inhibitors, and media, intact ribonucleoprotein-containing structures can be obtained with relatively undegraded RNA, which may be extracted from them by use of conventional sodium dodecyl sulfate-phenol methods (Brown and Littna, 1964).

AMPHIBIA

Preliminary Considerations

In some ways amphibian embryos represent very difficult material for isolation of cell constituents. The cells are large, contain large amounts of yolk and pigment inclusions, and they are surrounded by a large, relatively insoluble jelly layer. Yet, much of our knowledge of the principles of development is based on results from amphibians. For many years egg extracts have served as the basis for descriptive studies on various proteins and enzymes of amphibian cells. Usually dejellied eggs or embryos were homogenized in hypotonic buffers and centrifuged, the supernatant being subsequently used for studies of so-called soluble enzymes (Wallace, 1961).

The yolk platelets have served as a basis for careful study, and good methods have been devised for isolation of these structures (Gross and Gilbert, 1956). Recently, Wallace and Karasaki (1963) have improved the methods to obtain completely intact yolk platelets, as judged by the electron microscope. They homogenized jelly-free eggs in cold 0.25 *M* sucrose containing 5 percent (weight/volume) polyvinylpyrollidone (PVP), and the homogenate was layered over 1 *M* sucrose containing 5 percent PVP and gently centrifuged. The yolk concentrates at the bottom of the centrifuge tube after centrifugation. Further details of the method can be found in their original paper (Wallace and Karasaki, 1963). Intensive investigations of methods for preparing mitochondria from amphibian embryo cells are not available, but crude fractions of mitochondria are easily prepared by the usual methods of homogenization in sucrose-containing media and differential centrifugation. Lang and Grant (1961) have prepared cell fractions containing active mitochondrial enzymes. Chemical methods for denuding the eggs of their jelly may not be desirable for most purposes (however, see Brown, in this volume, pp. 685–701). Many workers prefer to remove the jelly manually from the eggs, and this is not a difficult procedure. Several hundred eggs can be dejellied in an hour by an experienced investigator. Detailed directions are given in Hamburger (1960). We usually remove the eggs from water and place them on ordinary paper toweling. The jelly can be removed by grasping (with watchmaker's forceps) the jelly on one side of the egg and gently rolling the egg away from the investigator. The egg usually "pops out" from the jelly, and can then be picked up gently by watchmaker's forceps or pipetting, and replaced in the water. Jelly-free eggs can also be obtained by a simple surgical procedure. One simply makes an incision in the abdominal cavity and ligatures the oviducts. After the usual procedure for stimulating production of eggs, the jelly-free eggs accumulate in the body cavity of the female, rather than receiving a jelly layer in the oviducts.

Because of the tough membrane surrounding amphibian eggs it is usually standard practice to homogenize the eggs in a Teflon-in-glass homogenizer. If one uses rather dilute suspensions (one volume of eggs for ten volumes of homogenization medium) three or four passes of a pestle rotated by electric motor at a few hundred rpm will completely disrupt the cells. The efficiency of homogenization may vary from stage to stage, and homogenates should always be examined microscopically when making studies based on comparison of different stages.

Nuclei

Crude preparations of nuclei with degraded DNA can be obtained by any of several procedures (Hogeboom, 1955). But systematic preparation of cytoplasm-free nuclei from embryonic cells has only recently been attempted in *Xenopus laevis* by Mariano (1964). Fifty embryos are freed of their jelly and membranes, washed and suspended in 1.5 ml of 0.25 M sucrose containing 8×10^{-3} M phosphate, pH 6.6, and 1×10^{-3} M magnesium. The eggs or embryos are homogenized in a loose-fitting Teflon-in-glass homogenizer, and the resultant homogenate is layered over a step gradient of sucrose solutions containing phosphate buffer and magnesium. Two milliliters of 2.1 M buffered sucrose and 2 ml of 1.8 M buffered sucrose are placed in the centrifuge tube and the homogenate carefully layered over these sucrose solutions. The centrifuge tube is centrifuged at very high speed (80,000 g for 90 minutes in a swinging bucket rotor), and a very satisfactory preparation of nuclei can be obtained at the bottom of the centrifuge tube. Flickinger (1965) has obtained nuclei from which he was able to prepare chromatin which acted as a primer for bacterial RNA polymerase. The nuclei were obtained by homogenizing the embryos in 0.25 M sucrose containing 2×10^{-3} calcium chloride. The homogenate was filtered through cheesecloth and nuclei were isolated by centrifugation through a sucrose gradient. Contaminating yolk platelets were removed by exposing the nuclear preparation to 20 volumes of 1 percent citric acid. The article by Brown in this volume describes methods of isolation of DNA from early amphibian embryos.

Ribonucleoprotein Particles

Isolation of ribosomes from amphibia illustrates some of the difficulty in preparing intact organelles from these cells. *Xenopus laevis* and *Rana pipiens* have been extensively investigated for isolation of ribonucleoprotein particles and relatively undegraded RNA. Polysomes have not been isolated from either of these materials, but investigations are underway (Brown, 1965). The earlier work by Brown (1962a, b) clearly outlined the difficulties—following homogenization most of the ribosomes were irreversibly bound to material sedimenting at low speed, presumably yolk. Furthermore, other constituents interfered with the quantitative estimation of RNA by the orcinol method; ferritin was present (Brown, 1962c), which contaminated the ribosomes and made their estimation difficult by the usual methods. By using large volumes of homogenization medium and working very rapidly Brown did obtain some ribosomes from early stages, and it became progressively easier to isolate ribosomes as the embryos developed further. When routine methods were applied to *Xenopus*, the same difficulties were not encountered to the same extent, and the methods have been published in detail by Brown and Littna (1964). Undegraded RNA can be obtained from these ribosomes. Some ribosomes are sedimented at low speed from homogenates of *Xenopus* embryos, and they are released if one adds a detergent (1 percent desoxycholate).

I shall concentrate here on methods developed for *Rana pipiens*, since this represents potentially a more difficult problem and should be instructive in the types of methods used to solve the difficulties. Kohne (1965) systematically examined the conditions needed for isolation of intact ribosomes from early embryos and eggs of *Rana pipiens*. The starting material used was always a jelly-free egg preparation. The homogenate had a high buffering capacity. He found it necessary to use rather dilute egg suspensions for homogenization and to increase the strength of the buffer to keep the pH from becoming quite acid. As always, magnesium was necessary; the ribosomes, microsomes, and polysomes are unstable in the absence of magnesium. A high concentration of monovalent cation seemed to be useful. Absolutely essential is the inclusion of a detergent in the homogenization medium. The usual detergent used is desoxycholate (1 percent), but this sometimes precipitates from solution at low temperature. Another commonly used detergent is Lubrol W (Imperial Chemicals Industries) at a level of 0.5 to 0.75 percent. Lubrol W will help retain desoxycholate in solution. The final procedure adopted by Kohne was to homogenize jelly-free eggs in a Teflon-glass homogenizer using three to twelve volumes of medium for a volume of eggs. The medium contains 0.1 *M* KCl, 0.01 *M* magnesium chloride, 0.05 *M* tris buffer (pH 8), and 0.75 percent Lubrol W. The resultant homogenate is centrifuged at 14,000 *g* for 20 minutes to remove large particulate matter, and the ribosomes are isolated from this supernatant by centrifugation at 100,000 *g* for 1 hour. The crude ribosomal preparation can be further purified by washing, magnesium precipitation, or density gradient centrifugation. It is essential to keep the medium, pipettes, tubes, homogenizers, etc., ice cold during the procedure. When this is done relatively intact particles can be isolated, and undegraded RNA can be extracted from the ribosomes by phenol methods (Brown and Littna, 1964). Special care should be taken during the isolation of RNA to maintain the temperature at exactly 0°C, or considerable degradation will occur.

Reference has often been made to the techniques of sucrose density gradient centrifugation, and some may believe that this is a mysterious and difficult technique. Nothing could be further from the truth. One simply establishes a linear density gradient with sucrose solutions of different concentration containing the appropriate buffers and salts in a tube for a swinging bucket type centrifuge rotor. A small amount of material (0.3 ml for SW 39, 1–2 ml for SW 25 rotors) to be analyzed is carefully layered over the sucrose gradients without mixing of the interface and centrifuged at high speeds in a Spinco preparative centrifuge. If the temperature is maintained relatively constant and the tubes are not shaken, the gradients are very stable; it is often appropriate to make the gradients the evening before use. A number of methods have been devised for collection of fractions from the centrifuge tube after completion of the centrifuge run. If someone in your locality is using this technique, it is often very useful to adopt the method he has found best for collection of gradient fractions. Perhaps the easiest method, requiring the least equipment, is simply to puncture a small hole, using a sewing needle, or a hypodermic needle, in the bottom of the centrifuge tube and allow the contents of the tube to drop through the small hole. Some gentle air pressure may be required to start the flow through the puncture. Collect the fractions by hand by counting drops and moving a test tube rack below the centrifuge tube. After the fractions have been collected, the bottom of the centrifuge tube should always be inspected to see if any pellet has collected, which can be removed by scraping. The discontinuous density gradient can easily be established by carefully layering, by pipette, layers of different densities on top of one another. For continuous density gradients two-chamber mixing devices are commonly employed, and perhaps the most effective one is a design originally proposed by Britten and Roberts (1960) which can be manufactured in any shop. The only difficulty which sometimes is encountered with the device is that air bubbles become trapped in a communication line between the chambers, but with some practice these can be eliminated. Reservoirs to establish gradients are also commercially available for modest prices (J. R. Mycock, Box 704, Princeton, New Jersey).

THE CHICK EMBRYO

Preliminary Consideration

The chick embryo more closely parallels the situation found with adult metazoan tissues, and many of the procedures used for rat liver can be used here. Usually the heavily pigmented eyes with the hard sclera are removed from the embryo before homogenization and fractionation. The very young embryo, 0 to 72 hours of incubation, does present some challenges. One of these, of course, is size, and the markings of cell constituents by isotopes can be applied here. Second, the embryo mass is small in comparison to the amount of yolk. Because of the extreme degree of telolecithality, the embryo may be separated from the yolk at all these stages, and extensive directions are given in Rugh (1962), and Hamburger (1960), and by DeHaan (this volume, pp. 401–412). An experienced investigator can remove 80 to 100 blastoderms from the yolk in an hour. This may be done in large finger bowls; 30 eggs just covered with saline are placed in a large finger bowl. If instruments are not stirred, the yolk does not become dispersed by cutting the vitelline membrane, and one can remove many embryos in the same finger bowl. The pH of the saline should be kept between pH 7.4 and 7.8, and one may dissolve tris buffer to a final concentration of 0.02 *M* in the saline (which contains 0.7 percent NaCl, 0.017 percent $CaCl_2$, 0.037 percent KCl) to maintain the pH. Young embryos can withstand this medium for several hours without ill effects, at room temperature or below. Even after the removal of the embryo from the yolk, many of the cells, especially the endoderm, are yolk laden, and this sometimes hinders fractionation. This dispersed yolk often forms a lipid film after a centrifugation, which can be aspirated if one is willing to sacrifice some of the supernatant. Extraction of the supernatant with ether or filtration through several layers of glass wool will also help remove some of the lipid layer.

The embryos can be minced into small pieces with scissors and the cells disrupted by any of the procedures discussed elsewhere. Homogenization in a small homogenizer, with or without the aid of detergent (Triton X-100 or desoxycholate is useful), effectively breaks the cells. Lerner,

Bell, and Darnell (1963) disrupted embryonic cells by squirting minced fragments through stainless steel gauze (80 mesh). Bell has been able to isolate polysomes from embryos of 3½ days and older, and from several tissues of older embryos (feather, lens, proventiculus, etc.) by homogenizing in a tight-fitting Dounce homogenizer (Scott and Bell, 1964). A freeze-thawing procedure combined with maceration also disrupts the cells. Mitochondria can be isolated by the usual differential centrifugation techniques, and large quantities of pure yolk are, of course, easily available.

Nuclei

Extensive cytological studies for preparation of nuclei or nuclear components from young chick embryos have not been carried out. Adaptation of prevailing popular techniques should be possible. For instance, homogenization in a 0.25 *M* sucrose, 0.003 *M* calcium solution followed by centrifugation at 1,000 *g* for 10 minutes concentrates most of the DNA and nuclei in this low speed pellet (Allfrey, 1959). Application of density gradient methods used by Hinegardner (1962), or as discussed by Hogeboom (1955), should result in very clean preparations of nuclei. Of special promise is the method of Fisher and Harris (1962). In this method dispersed tissue culture cells, previously washed in saline containing 10^{-3} *M* calcium, were stirred in a 0.1 percent solution of the surface active agent, Tween 80, and the cytoplasm was gradually dispersed with resultant high yields of very clean nuclei. This has not been tried, to my knowledge, on chick embryos cells.

Ribonucleoprotein Particles

Extensive studies on the isolation and characterizations of ribosomes, polysomes, and microsomes from chick embryo cells of various stages are now in progress in several laboratories. Techniques applied to mammalian systems are being employed, with attention to the smaller amounts of materials used. Polysomes and microsomes were obtained from 3½-day embryos, and from various organ systems, by homogenization in a tight-fitting Dounce homogenizer (Scott and Bell, 1964). The resultant homogenate was centrifuged at 600 *g* for 10 minutes, and the supernatant was treated with desoxycholate and analyzed by sucrose density gradient methods. With proper attention to temperature, shear, and different composition of media, high yields of ribosomes and polysomes can be obtained. The mitochondria-free supernatant can be treated by any of the methods outlined for the isolation of the particle from sea urchin embryos. If especially small amounts of young embryos are to be analyzed or used, one may premark the desired constituents by incubating the embryo, either *in ovo* or *in vitro*, with an appropriate radioactive precursor. Injections can be made into the egg of P^{32}, H^3, and C^{14} compounds, and satisfactory levels of labeling obtained (Lerner, Bell, and Darnell, 1963). However, it is much more economical to explant the embryos by the Spratt technique (see DeHaan, this volume, pp. 401–412) onto medium containing between 1 and 10 μc of isotope per milliliter of medium for a few hours. Embryos can then be mixed with unlabeled older embryos or adult tissues and followed through the isolation by their radioactivity.

CONCLUSION

The purpose of this article was to highlight some of the special considerations one might make for isolation of cell constituents from cells of animal embryos. Emphasis has been placed on the isolation of particles containing nucleoprotein. A cell constituent which has been totally ignored in this article is the cell surface, which is liable to play an equally important role in further studies on the chemical basis of development, and the reader is referred to the excellent articles by Kalckar (1965) and Konigsberg (1965) in this respect. The chemistry and isolation of cell surface from embryonic cells is still in its initial stages, but discussions of this issue may be found, for instance, in recent papers of Moscona (1963a, b), Steinberg (1964), and Wallach and Kamat (1964). Hopefully, general techniques will be developed in this important area in the near future.

REFERENCES

ALLFREY, V., 1959: The isolation of subcellular components. In J. Brachet and A. E. Mirsky (eds.), *The Cell*, Academic Press, New York, Vol. I, p. 193.

BRACHET, J., 1957: *Biochemical Cytology.* Academic Press, New York.

BRITTEN, R. J., and R. B. ROBERTS, 1960: High resolution density gradient sedimentation analysis. *Science*, 131: 32.

BROWN, D. D., 1965: In *Carnegie Institution of Washington Yearbook*, 64: 450.

———, and J. D. CASTON, 1962a: Biochemistry of amphibian development. I. Ribosome and protein synthesis in early development of *Rana pipiens. Develop. Biol.*, 5: 412.

———, and ———, 1962b: Biochemistry of amphibian development. II. High molecular weight RNA. *Develop. Biol.*, 5: 435.

———, and ———, 1962c: Biochemistry of amphibian development. III. Identification of ferritin in the egg and early embryos of *Rana pipiens. Develop. Biol.*, 5: 445.

———, and E. LITTNA, 1964: RNA synthesis during the development of *Xenopus laevis*, the South African clawed toad. *J. Mol. Biol.*, 8: 669.

FLICKINGER, R. A., S. J. COWARD, M. MIYAGI, C. MOSER, and E. ROLLINS, 1965: The ability of DNA and chromatin of developing frog embryos to prime for RNA polymerase-dependent RNA synthesis. *Proc. Nat. Acad. Sci.* (U.S.), 53: 783.

GROSS, P. R., and L. I. GILBERT, 1956: Chemistry and ultrastructure of amphibian yolk platelets. *Trans. New York Acad. Sci.*, 19: 108.

HAMBURGER, V., 1960: *A Manual of Experimental Embryology.* University of Chicago Press, Chicago, Ill.

HINEGARDNER, R. T., 1962: The isolation of nuclei from eggs and embryos of the sea urchin. *J. Cell. Biol.*, 15: 503.

HOGEBOOM, G. H., 1955: Fractionation of cell components of animal tissues. In S. P. Colowick and N. O. Kaplan (eds.), *Methods in Enzymology*, Academic Press, New York, Vol. I, p. 16.

HULTIN, T., 1961: Activation of ribosomes in sea urchin eggs in response to fertilization. *Exper. Cell. Res.*, 25: 405.

———, and A. BERGSTRAND, 1960: Incorporation of C^{14}-L-leucine into protein by cell-free systems from sea urchin embryos at different stages of development. *Develop. Biol.*, 2: 61.

KALCKAR, H. M., 1965: Galactose metabolism and cell "sociology." *Science*, 150: 305.

KONIGSBERG, I. R., and S. D. HAUSCHKA, 1965: Cell and tissue interactions in the reproduction of cell type. In M. Locke (ed.), *Reproduction: Molecular, Subcellular, and Cellular*, Academic Press, New York, p. 243.

KOHNE, D., 1965: The isolation of ribosomes from eggs and embryos of *Rana pipiens. Exper. Cell. Res.*, 38: 211.

LANG, C. A., and P. GRANT, 1961: Respiratory enzyme changes during frog embryo embryogenesis. *Proc. Nat. Acad. Sci.* (U.S.), 47: 1236.

LERNER, A. M., E. BELL, and J. E. DARNELL, JR., 1963: Ribosomal RNA in the developing chick embryo. *Science*, 141: 1188.

LOWRY, O. H., and J. V. PASSONNEAU, 1963:

Measurement of pyridine nucleotides by enzymatic cycling. In S. P. Colowick and N. O. Kaplan (eds.), *Methods in Enzymology*, Academic Press, New York, Vol. VI, p. 792.

MARIANO, E. E., 1964: The isolation of nuclei from *Xenopus laevis* embryonic cells. *Exper. Cell Res.*, 34: 201.

MAZIA, D., J. M. MITCHISON, H. MEDINA, and P. HARRIS, 1961: The direct isolation of the mitotic apparatus. *J. Biochem. Biophys. Cytol.*, 10: 467.

MONROY, A., 1965: *Chemistry and Physiology of Fertilization.* Holt, Rinehart & Winston, New York.

MOSCONA, M. H., and A. A. MOSCONA, 1963a: Inhibition of adhesiveness and aggregation of dissociated cells by inhibitors of protein and RNA synthesis. *Science*, 142: 1070.

MOSCONA, A. A., 1963b: Studies on cell aggregation: Demonstration of materials with the selective cell-binding activity. *Proc. Nat. Acad. Sci.* (U.S.), 49: 742.

NEMER, M., 1963: Regulation of protein synthesis in the embryogenesis of the sea urchin. *National Cancer Institute Monograph*, 13: 141.

———, and A. A. INFANTE, 1965: Messenger RNA in early sea-urchin embryos: Cytoplasmic particles. *Science*, 150: 214.

PETERMANN, M. L., 1964: *The Physical and Chemical Properties of Ribosomes.* Elsevier Publishing Co., New York.

PIKO, L., and A. TYLER, 1965: Deoxyribonucleic acid content of unfertilized sea urchin eggs. *American Zoologist*, 5: 636.

RUGH, R., 1962: *Experimental Embryology.* Burgess Publishing Co., Minneapolis, Minn.

SAKAI, H., 1966: Studies on SH groups during cell division of sea urchin eggs. VIII. Some properties of mitotic apparatus protein. *Biochem. Biophys. Acta*, 112: 132.

SCOTT, R. B., and E. BELL, 1964: Protein synthesis during development: Control through messenger RNA. *Science*, 145: 711.

SOLARI, A. J., 1965: Structure of the chromatin in sea urchin sperm. *Proc. Nat. Acad. Sci.* (U.S.), 53: 503.

STEINBERG, M. S., 1964: The problem of adhesive selectivity in cellular interactions. In M. Locke (ed.), *Cellular Membranes in Development*, Academic Press, New York, p. 321.

VINCENT, W. S., 1955: Structure and chemistry of nucleoli. In G. H. Bourne and J. F. Danielli (eds.), *International Review of Cytology*, Vol. IV, p. 299.

WALLACE, R. A., 1961: Enzymatic patterns in the developing frog embryo. *Develop. Biol.*, 3: 486.

———, and S. KARASAKI, 1963: Studies on amphibian yolk. II. The isolation of yolk platelets from the eggs of *Rana pipiens*. *J. Cell. Biol.*, 18: 153.

WALLACH, D. F. H., and V. B. KAMAT, 1964: Plasma and cytoplasmic membrane fragments, from Ehrlich ascites carcinoma. *Proc. Nat. Acad. Sci.* (U.S.), 52: 721.

WESSELLS, N. K., and F. H. WILT, 1965: Action of Actinomycin D on exocrine pancreas cell differentiation. *J. Mol. Biol.*, 13: 767.

WILT, F. H., 1964: Ribonucleic acid synthesis during sea urchin embryogenesis. *Develop. Biol.*, 9: 299.

———, 1966: The concept of messenger RNA and cytodifferentiation. *American Zoologist*, 6: 67.

Protein Determination in Embryos*

By William J. Rutter

INTRODUCTION

Many of the changes occurring in embryonic cells during development are directly or indirectly the result of changes in the population of proteins within the cells. One major phase of the analysis of embryological development, therefore, is an attempt to define the changes in the protein components which occur in cells during development and the mechanisms by which such changes arise. The DNA complement is sufficiently large to allow a large population of proteins to be synthesized during the lifetime of the cell. The haploid DNA content of mammalian cells, for example, is approximately 3×10^{-12} gm (Vendrely, 1955) which is equivalent to 3×10^{9} nucleotides. Assuming three nucleotides for a single amino acid in a protein, then a maximum of 10^{9} amino acids in peptide sequence (10^{7} peptides of 100 amino acids each) could be specified. Of course, the proportion of the genome which is actually used to determine the structure of proteins during the life of the cells is unknown, but there is enough genetic information so that whole populations of proteins could be changing during the course of development.

Current evidence suggests that both qualitative and quantitative changes in protein species may occur discontinuously (Rutter and Weber, 1965). Some proteins, termed Class I proteins, may be synthesized continuously in all cells during development, while others (Class II proteins) may be synthesized only in several different cells or tissues, and still others (Class III proteins) may be synthesized only by specific cells, perhaps during a restricted period of development, for example after cytodifferentiation.

For a quantitative evaluation of relative changes in protein levels, it is necessary to normalize changes in specific entities against general changes occurring in the entire system. This is usually performed by assaying the specific component as well as determining the cell number (by analysis of deoxyribonucleic acid [DNA]) and the total protein content. This paper considers some of the more useful methods for determination of total protein and briefly discusses some general

* The experimental work from the author's laboratory cited in this paper was supported in part by grants from the United States Public Health Service and the National Science Foundation.

principles for the assay of specific proteins in embryological systems.

DETERMINATION OF TOTAL PROTEIN CONTENT

There are no completely satisfactory methods for the determination of "bulk proteins." Because of the diversity of the composition and properties of the protein molecules, an accurate determination of their proportionate contribution to the total mass of the system is difficult. Perhaps the most reliable values can be obtained by determination of the amino acid composition after removal of free amino acids. An accurate analysis (Stein and Moore, 1954; Moore and Stein, 1963) requires at least milligram quantities of material, however, and is very time consuming and relatively costly. Certain amino acids (tryptophan, threonine, serine, cystine, cysteine, tyrosine) are destroyed to varying degrees during the usual acidic hydrolysis; hence, additional analyses must be performed after varying periods of hydrolysis and after basic hydrolysis, or supplementary chemical determinations of certain amino acids (such as cysteine and tryptophan) are necessary. Furthermore, the values obtained from crude samples (such as embryonic tissues) may not reflect solely the protein content. Complex lipids and some carbohydrates contain covalently bound amino acids. Whereas the proportion of these compounds relative to the total protein content of most cellular systems may be generally low, the possibility that significant concentrations of "bound" amino acids from nonprotein sources do occur in some tissues should not be overlooked. Precise determination of amino acid content is recommended only in special circumstances, certainly not for routine analyses of proteins.

The general methods which have been employed for routine assay of protein content are based on (1) nitrogen content—analysis of ammonia after appropriate digestion of the material; (2) determination of the amino groups with ninhydrin; (3) the biuret reaction or spectrophotometric methods which detect primarily the peptide linkages; (4) estimation of the aromatic amino acid, especially tryptophan and tyrosine content, by spectrophotometric methods or a modified Folin phenol reagent. These methods will be discussed below. The Biuret method and the Lowry-Folin method are recommended for routine analysis of protein.

Determination of Total Nitrogen

Digestion of biological materials with sulfuric acid in the presence of an appropriate catalyst converts the nitrogen-containing compounds to ammonia (ammonium sulfate in the digestion mixture) (Glick, 1963). The ammonium ions can then be assayed directly by the Nessler reaction (Levy, 1936; Ballantine, 1957) or by the more sensitive phenolate-hypochlorite reaction (Glick, 1963; Exley, 1956). Alternatively, the digestion mixture can be treated with alkali to liberate ammonia which can then be quantitatively absorbed in acid and measured titrimetrically (Glick, 1963). The determinations can be made sensitive to approximately 0.5 μg nitrogen (approximately 3 μg protein) using the Nessler reaction, and 0.02 μg nitrogen (approximately 0.1 μg protein) using the phenolate-hypochlorite reaction (Exley, 1956). Determination of such small quantities, however, requires rigorous precautions to avoid contamination with external ammonia either from the atmosphere or from the hands of the analyst. With care, routine assays are possible. This method has the advantage that all of the sample (both soluble and insoluble materials) is analyzed. It has the disadvantage of nonspecificity (all of the nitrogen-containing compounds of the cell contribute to the final value).

Moreover, there is a substantial variation in the contribution of various proteins to assay values because the various amino acids have different proportions of nitrogen in the molecule. Because the method is cumbersome and nonspecific, it is recommended only in instances where measurement of the alkali-soluble proteins is not sufficient for the purposes of the experiment.

Determination of Amino Acid Content with Ninhydrin

Hydrolysis of the proteins with strong acid or base and subsequent determination of liberated α-amino groups with ninhydrin can, in principle, estimate microgram quantities of protein. This method is not commonly employed because it is relatively cumbersome and there is loss of some of the amino acids during hydrolysis. Furthermore, the assay values are subject to considerable error because the extinction coefficients and the absorption maxima of the amino acids vary, and ammonia and various other amines form similar colors with ninhydrin (Stein and Moore, 1954). Kunkel and Ward (1950) have shown that treatment of soluble proteins with ninhydrin under basic conditions produces a color (perhaps primarily due to the release of ammonia from the glutamine and asparagine residues) which can be used for quantitative estimation of proteins (in microgram quantities). This method has the advantage of sensitivity and simplicity, but suffers from variable color yields elicited by different amino acids, and hence, proteins. Other methods (e.g., the Lowry phenol procedure to be described later) are preferable.

Methods Primarily Sensitive to Peptide Bonds

The biuret reaction (Layne, 1957; Gornall, Bardawill, and David, 1949; Robinson and Hogden, 1940) is based on a reaction of substances having two or more peptide bonds with cupric ions in alkaline solution to form a complex with increased absorbance at about 550 mμ. The reaction is not particularly influenced by the amino acid composition of the protein and hence varies less with different proteins than other methods. Moreover, the reaction is relatively specific for proteins; there are few, if any, interfering substances present in tissues in high enough concentrations to provide a serious source of error in the assays. Urea and even ammonium ions interfere, but only at relatively high concentrations. The biuret reaction is simple and reliable, but unfortunately it is considerably less sensitive than other methods. At least 10 μg protein in 50 μl solution (200 μg per milliliter) are required for analysis. Like other methods to be described, it also has the disadvantage that only proteins soluble in the alkaline biuret reagent are suitable for analysis. Waddell (1956) has developed a spectrophotometric method for analysis of proteins that is based on the absorption of the amide (peptide) bonds in the far-ultraviolet region. By measurement of the ratio of absorbances at 225 and 215 mμ, a relatively specific indication of the protein concentration can be obtained. Values obtained by the Waddell method (Groves, 1962) are considerably closer to those obtained by the Biuret and the Lowry methods than 280/260 absorbance measurements (Layne, 1957; Warburg and Christian, 1941). Nevertheless, care should be exercised in utilizing a method employing absorbance in the far-ultraviolet where the extinction coefficients are so high for a number of nonprotein compounds present in biological systems.

Methods Detecting Primarily Aromatic Residues

The simplest method of assay involves measurement of absorbance at 280 mμ.

Protein absorbance in this region of the ultraviolet is primarily due to tyrosine and tryptophan residues. For an accurate measure of protein content, the relative concentrations of these amino acids should be constant in the protein samples to be assayed. In practice there are sizable variations (up to tenfold) in the extinction coefficients of isolated proteins (Lowry, Rosebrough, Farr, and Randall, 1951). There is considerable uncertainty, therefore, in the values obtained with this method on crude mixtures of proteins. Assays of crude extracts of cells are subject to even greater variation because of the absorbance in the 280-mμ region of other cellular components, especially nucleic acids. Some of the interference of nucleic acids can be corrected by measuring the absorbance at both 260 and 280 mμ and then employing the empirical relationship first derived by Warburg and Christian (1941) from artificial mixtures of yeast nucleic acids and yeast enolase. An equation approximating the Warburg and Christian data (Layne, 1957) follows:

$$\text{Protein concentration (mg/ml)} = 1.55\ A_{280} - 0.76\ A_{260}$$

Even with this correction, however, there are serious discrepancies between the values obtained by this method and the Biuret and Lowry methods (Lowry *et al.*, 1951), hence, it is not recommended for measurement of proteins in crude extracts of embryos.

The tyrosine and tryptophan residues in proteins react with the Folin phenol reagent to produce a color which can be used to determine the protein content (Rideal and Roberts, 1951). Lowry *et al.* (1951) have modified this procedure to include treatment of the protein with cupric ions in alkali (the biuret reaction) in addition to the usual Folin reagent. The resultant method is more sensitive and considerably less susceptible to variations in the tyrosine and tryptophan content than the Folin reagent alone. The extinction coefficients of most proteins are within 50 percent of each other, but variations of threefold in the extinction coefficients of gelatin and trypsin are reported by Lowry *et al.* (1951) (differences of only 33 percent in the biuret color were noticed in these proteins). The advantages of the Lowry method for protein determination lie in its simplicity and sensitivity. Besides the lack of specificity mentioned above, it has the disadvantage that the method requires that the unknown proteins be soluble in base. In general, proteins from crude extracts of tissue dissolve fairly readily in alkali and, hence, a large proportion of the total proteins in the system are usually analyzed. This determination is about 100 times more sensitive than the biuret reaction, and 10 times more sensitive than the measurement of absorbance at 280 mμ. It is much more specific for proteins than the latter method and less liable to disturbance by turbidity in the solution. The reaction is relatively free from interference by nonprotein biological substances. Tryptophan, tyrosine, most phenols (except nitrophenol), uric acid, guanidine, and xanthine react with the reagent to produce a color. Not more than a trace of color is produced with adenine, guanosine, hypoxanthine, cytosine, cytidine, uracil, and thymine. Neither color nor interference with color development is obtained with the following substances at the concentrations indicated: acetic acid (0.5 percent, neutralized), acetone (0.5 percent), ethanol (5 percent), ether (5 percent), urea (0.5 percent), guanidine (0.5 percent), barium hydroxide (0.5 percent), perchloric acid (0.5 percent, neutralized), sodium nitrate (1 percent), sodium sulfate (1 percent), sodium tungstate (0.5 percent), zinc sulfate (0.1 percent). Glycine (0.5 percent) reduces the color by 50 percent, and hydrazine over 0.5 mg per 100 ml interferes. Neutralized ammonium sulfate up to 0.25 percent does not interfere significantly, but a greater concentration decreases color development. The procedure is readily adapted to determine 0.2 μg protein. The color obtained, however, is not strictly proportional to protein concentration; hence, the absorbance values for the unknown must be related to a standard curve constructed from a number of determinations obtained with a "standard" protein. The method is well suited to routine measurement of proteins in tissue extracts when absolute values are not demanded or for serial analysis of many similar protein samples. For many embryological studies, the estimation of the total alkali soluble cellular protein obtained from cells is usually an adequate basis for estimating changes in total protein content. The biuret method for determination is perhaps preferable because of its general specificity, but where greater sensitivity is desired the Lowry method is recommended. A detailed description of these methods is presented below.

THE BIURET REACTION

Reagents

Place 1.60 gm of cupric sulfate ($CuSO_4{\cdot}5H_2O$) and 6.40 gm of sodium potassium tartrate ($NaKC_4H_4O_6{\cdot}4H_2O$) in a 1.0-liter volumetric flask and dissolve in about 500 ml water. Add, with constant swirling, 300 ml of 10 percent sodium hydroxide prepared from fresh sodium hydroxide pellets or from a carbonate-free concentrated sodium hydroxide solution. Water is added to 1.0 liter and the solution is mixed and stored in a polyethylene bottle. The reagent should keep indefinitely, but is discarded if it shows signs of depositing a black or reddish precipitate.

Protein Standards

Standard protein solutions prepared with crystalline bovine serum albumin containing 200–4,000 μg protein per milliliter can be prepared conveniently from a stock solution of albumin containing 4,000 μg per milliliter. The concentration of albumin in solution can be determined from its extinction coefficient

$$E_{1\,\text{cm}}^{1\%} = 6.6 \text{ at } 280\ \text{m}\mu$$

Weight measurements are not satisfactory since different crystalline albumin preparations may have varying water and/or salt content.

Procedure

Determinations are carried out, conveniently, in small tubes; e.g., 400-μl polyethylene test tubes which can be obtained from Spinco Division, Beckman Instruments Inc. The optical density of volumes of at least 100 μl is measured in conventional microcuvettes having 1.0 cm light path and 1.5 mm path width, or in the Model 151 microspectrophotometer (Spinco Division, Beckman Instruments Inc., Palo Alto, California).

1. In a micro test tube place 50 μl of a solution containing from 10 to 200 μg unknown protein.
2. In separate micro test tubes place 50-μl aliquots of solutions of serum albumin, containing 10–200 μg in that volume.
3. Water or buffer, 50 μl, is placed in a micro test tube to be used as the reagent blank.
4. To all tubes 150 μl of biuret reagent are added. The solutions are mixed thoroughly (by vibration), centrifuged in the microfuge for 1 second to remove air bubbles, and allowed to stand for 30 minutes at room temperature. The absorbance at 550 mμ of the tubes is then measured.
5. The extinction coefficient of albumin in this system is found to be approximately 0.14 absorbance units per 100 μg

protein in a final volume of 0.2 ml (1 cm light path at 550 mμ), and approximately 0.065 absorbance units per 100 μg protein, 0.2 ml final volume in the Spinco microspectrophotometer.

6. The volumes can be adjusted upward or downward for convenience providing the relative concentrations of biuret reagent and standard and unknown proteins remain constant.

7. In measurements of crude cellular extracts, a cloudy reaction mixture sometimes will be produced. This is usually caused by the presence of large amounts of lipoidal material in the extract. (See section on Elimination of Turbidity in the Sample for directions.)

FOLIN-LOWRY METHOD

Reagents

Reagent A: 20 gm sodium carbonate, 4 gm sodium hydroxide, 0.2 gm sodium potassium tartrate dissolved in 1.0 liter distilled water, stored in a polyethylene container.

Reagent B: 0.5 gm $CuSO_4 \cdot 5H_2O$ dissolved in 100 ml water.

Reagent C: 50 parts reagent A are mixed with 1 part reagent B *immediately before use.* This solution should be discarded after 1 day.

Reagent D: carbonate-copper solution. Mix 50 ml of 2 percent Na_2CO_3 with 1 ml of reagent B. This solution should be discarded after 1 day.

Reagent E: Folin-Ciocalteu reagent (Folin and Ciocalteu, 1927) (obtained commercially from Fisher Scientific Company, Will Corporation, Van Waters and Rogers, Inc., etc.). Dilute the Folin-Ciocalteu reagent to make it 1 *N* in acid *just before use.* (Determine the acid concentration of the reagent by titration with 1 *N* NaOH to a phenolphthalein end point.) Most commercial preparations are 2 *N*, therefore, they must be diluted 1:1. Reflux gently for 10 hours a mixture consisting of 100 gm of sodium tungstate ($Na_2WoO_4 \cdot 2H_2O$), 25 gm of sodium molybdate ($Na_2MoO_4 \cdot 2H_2O$), 700 ml of water, 50 ml of 85 percent phosphoric acid, and 100 ml of concentrated hydrochloric acid in a 1.5 liter flask. Add 150 gm of lithium sulfate, 50 ml of water, and a few drops of bromine water. Boil the mixture for 15 minutes without condenser to remove excess bromine. Cool, dilute to 1 liter, and filter. The reagent should have no greenish tint.

Protein Standards

Standard protein solutions containing 25–500 μg albumin per milliliter can be conveniently prepared from a stock solution of crystalline bovine serum albumin (500 μg protein per milliliter). The exact concentration of albumin in solution can be determined from its extinction coefficient

$$E_{1\,\text{cm}}^{1\%} = 6.6 \text{ at } 280\ \text{m}\mu$$

Weight determinations are not satisfactory since different crystalline albumin preparations may have varying water and/or salt content.

Procedure for 5–100 μg Protein

1. Add up to 0.2 ml of a sample containing 5–100 μg protein and similar volumes of standards, and water or buffer (reagent blanks) to separate 3-ml test tubes.

2. Add 1 ml of reagent C to each tube, mix well, and allow to stand 10 minutes.

3. Add 0.1 ml reagent E rapidly with immediate mixing. Let stand 30 minutes or longer.

4. After 30 minutes or longer, measure absorbance at 750 mμ (the more concentrated protein concentrations can be read at lower wavelengths, e.g., 500 mμ).

5. Calculate protein concentrations by comparison of optical density values with those obtained from protein standards, read at the same wavelength.

Procedure for 0.5–10 μg Protein

1. Add 100 μl of reagent C to a 400-μl polyethylene test tube.
2. Add 20 μl of water or buffer (reagent blank), standard protein solutions (for standard curve), or unknown solution containing 0.5 to 5 μg protein to each tube.
3. Carefully add 10 μl of the diluted Folin-Ciocalteu reagent in a drop to the side of the tube so that the reagent does not mix with the solutions previously added.
4. The sample is then mixed thoroughly by vibrating for 10 seconds with the micromixer and centrifuged immediately for 5 seconds in the microfuge or similar centrifuge.
5. During the centrifugation in 4 above, add another 10 μl of Folin-Ciocalteu reagent to the next tube (step 3). Mix the sample by vibration (step 4) and place it in the microfuge to replace the first tube which is removed and stored in an appropriate holder. The process should be timed so that the tubes are mixed at regular intervals (30 seconds has been found convenient).
6. The color is allowed to develop for 30 minutes.
7. The samples are then read at 30-second intervals at 650 mμ in the spectrocolorimeter, or for increased sensitivity at 750 mμ in microcuvettes (1 cm light path) in a suitable spectrophotometer.
8. The extinction coefficient of albumin in this system is found to be approximately 0.050 absorbance units at 650 mμ for 1 μg protein in the final volume of 130 μl.

The ultramicroanalytical system procured from the Spinco Division, Beckman Instruments, Inc., Palo Alto, California, was employed in the above assays (Model 152 microfuge, Model 154 micromixer, Model 151 spectrocolorimeter, and 400-μl polyethylene test tubes, micro test tube racks, and micropipettes). Similar equipment could be substituted in this procedure.

Elimination of Turbidity in the Sample

The proteins present in many extracts dissolve readily in the alkaline copper reagent (reagent C, above); however, sometimes cellular preparations produce turbidity which obscures the determination. This may usually be eliminated by one of the following procedures:

EXTRACTION WITH LIPID SOLVENTS

When the turbidity is caused by lipoidal materials in the unknown sample, the final colored solutions of unknowns and standards can be extracted with $\frac{1}{4}$ volume petroleum (or diethyl) ether. This extraction must be carried out in a tube which does not dissolve in the organic solvent (polyethylene tubes, for example, are not suitable).

After thorough mixing, the phases separate (centrifugation aids this process). The lower aqueous phase is then removed, and the absorbance is determined as above. With care, this operation can be accomplished with little loss of colored solution.

CENTRIFUGATION OR FILTRATION TO REMOVE TURBIDITY

The final colored solution may be centrifuged at 15,000 rpm for 1–4 minutes, or filtered through a membrane filter (a microsyringe fitted with a Swinny adapter is suitable for this purpose). The optical density of the resulting solution can then be accurately determined, and the protein concentration calculated via standards. This procedure is subject to errors caused by absorption of colored material on the precipitate. With each system, a check should be made by comparing values obtained by filtration after step 2 and after step 7 in the above experimental section. In our experience, centrifugation or filtration has not interfered with the color yield.

DIRECT EXTRACTION WITH HOT ALKALI

To 10 μl protein solution are added 10 μl 1 *N* NaOH and the mixture is allowed to stand for at least ½ hour, or heated to 100°C for 10 minutes or more (treat standards in the same manner); 100 μl reagent D are then added. The analysis is then continued as described above, beginning with step 3.

Determination of Protein and DNA in the Same Sample

1. The cell preparation (containing at least 2 μg protein) is treated with cold 5 percent trichloracetic acid (final concentration) in a glass 0.4-ml microcentrifuge tube. The suspension is centrifuged at 2,000 gm for 10 minutes. The supernate is removed.

2. The precipitate is extracted with 200 μl 0.1 *N* alcoholic potassium acetate for 5–10 minutes, and then twice with 200 μl absolute ethanol (the first extract is heated to 60°C), centrifuging each time and collecting the precipitate. Finally, the precipitate is extracted with 300 μl absolute ether and dried in a vacuum desiccator.

3. Suspend the ether-dried precipitate in 200 μl 0.6 *N* $HClO_4$; mix well, cap tubes, and heat at 80°C for 1 hour. (This step can be carried out in polyethylene tubes.) The suspension is then centrifuged for 2 minutes at 15,000 *g* (microfuge).

4. The supernate is removed with a micropipette and used for DNA assay; for example, by the method of Kissane and Robbins (1958; see Brown, this volume, pp. 685–701).

5. The precipitate is suspended in 10 μl 1 *N* NaOH; after dissolution (½ hour or more), add 10 μl H_2O and 100 μl reagent D. (With some samples it may be necessary to heat for 10 minutes or more at 100°C in 1 *N* NaOH. All standards must be carried through the same procedure.) After about 10 minutes, 10 μl reagent E (Folin-Ciocalteu reagent) are added as described in step 3 of the microprocedure above. Proceed with the determination as described.

DETERMINATION OF SPECIFIC PROTEINS

The quantitative estimation of particular protein species can be based on biological activity (catalytic or hormonal) or on specific molecular characteristics. For embryological studies, specific and sensitive methods are required. A protein present in the adult at relatively high concentrations may be present at some stages of embryonic development at exceedingly low concentrations. In principle, it would be desirable to be able to detect a single molecule of specific protein within a cell containing several hundred different molecular species and as many as 10^8 protein molecules (assuming 30 μμg protein per cell and an average molecular weight of 100,000 per protein molecule).

Preparation of Extracts for Determination of Specific Proteins

For quantitative analysis of specific proteins from small tissue (cellular) samples, special care must be made to effect complete extraction (or a defined proportion) of the protein in a native form into the sample being assayed. The following methods have been found useful for this purpose:

MICROHOMOGENIZATION

Suitable microhomogenizers of the Potter-Elvehjem type are available commercially, and can be employed for effective homogenization of 100 μg or more tissue. This procedure usually does not effect satisfactory breakage of single cells.

USE OF HYPOTONIC MEDIUM AND DETERGENTS

The cells or tissue are placed in appropriate small tubes (e.g., the 400-μl polyethylene tubes described earlier), washed with appropriate isotonic medium, and centrifuged at slow speeds so that the cells sediment, but remain intact. The supernate fluid is discarded leaving only the cellular pellet. A suitable volume (at least 10 times the volume of the cellular pellet) of hypotonic medium containing a low concentration of a nonionic detergent (e.g., 0.002 percent Triton X-100) is added. The contents are subjected to vigorous vibration, usually at 0°C. If necessary, the solution may also be frozen and thawed before centrifugation.

SONIC OSCILLATION

Disruption of cells and tissues in small volumes may be accomplished by sonic vibration. Washed cells or tissues are suspended in a 400-μl polyethylene tube containing an appropriate volume of hypotonic medium (e.g., 0.002 percent Triton X-100). The tube is capped and then taped firmly to the bottom of a beaker and submerged in ice water. The beaker is then moved so that the sonic probe traverses the length of the tube at a close distance. One minute of such treatment usually is sufficient to break most cells. Since the energy transfer from the sonicator is inefficient, considerable power output from the probe is required for this purpose (Branson 1250-volt Sonifier or equivalent). The appropriate conditions for cell disruption must be empirically determined for each experimental system. This can be performed by variation of the conditions, and subsequent assay of the protein or activity in the supernatant extract, as well as in the precipitate. Maximization of the yield of the desired component in the extract is usually desirable.

Assays Based on Enzymatic Activity

Very few, if any, methods have been developed which can detect with rigorous specificity a single or a few enzyme molecules. Rotman (1961) has described a fluorimetric method for determining the activity of a single molecule of β-galactosidase. Less sensitive micromethods have been developed or can be developed for most enzymes or biologically active proteins (see, for example, Glick, 1963; Seligman, 1963). Most of the common methods for enzyme assay employing spectrophotometric or colorimetric analysis can be made 100 to 1,000 times more sensitive by simply reducing the volume of the system and by increasing the incubation period and/or temperature. Cuvettes having 1 cm light path and requiring 0.1 to 0.2 ml total volume can be used as conveniently for spectrophotometric measurements as the larger volumes usually employed. (The only precautions necessary are to use a pinhole light source and to use care in positioning the cuvettes in the sample compartment so that the light source traverses the fluid without impinging on the walls of the cuvette.) In systems where the enzyme is stable, linear reaction kinetics usually can be observed for several hours (even longer periods are possible if sufficient care is used to avoid turbidity or bacterial growth). The temperature of the assay may be increased to the highest level which permits stability of the enzyme (linear reaction kinetics) during the assay period. Raising the temperature from 20° to 50°C, for example, may increase the reaction velocity tenfold.

Assays Based on Molecular Characteristics

There are a number of sensitive analytical methods which have high resolving power and in favorable instances may be capable of resolving single protein species from a complex mixture. Quantitative immunochemical procedures can be employed to determine quantitatively a few tenths of a microgram of a protein (Oudin, 1952; Campbell *et al.*, 1963). Disc gel electrophoresis also exhibits great resolving capacity (Ornstein, 1964; Davis, 1964). The limit of detection is dependent upon the sensitivity of the assay for proteins employed. The usual dye binding is sensitive to microgram levels of protein in the systems commonly described in the literature (Whipple, 1964), but the sensitivity can be increased considerably by decreasing the dilution of the enzyme. This may be accomplished by decreasing the volume of the polyacrylamide gel; millimicrogram quantities of proteins have been readily detected in polyacrylamide threads (Grossbach, 1965; Matioli and Niewisch, 1965). Another immunochemical method which is considerably more sensitive involves an isotope dilution method in which unlabeled protein molecules present in the unknown sample compete with a known quantity of added labeled (for example, with iodine-131) molecules for a constant number of antibody sites in added antiserum. The displacement of label from the antigen-antibody complex by unlabeled antigen can then be quantitated and used for the evaluation of antigen levels in the unknown sample. This method was originally introduced by Yalow and Berson (1964) for the assay of insulin, and the techniques have been modified by a number of investigators for the assay of both insulin and glucagon. In our own laboratory, the assay system has been used to detect as few as 10^5 and as many as 10^{12} molecules of insulin (Clark and Rutter, 1965). The assay system is potentially applicable to many other protein systems. It requires only that a specific antiserum be prepared (which in turn usually requires preparation of the pure protein) and that the labeled and unlabeled molecules are indistinguishable immunochemically (carrier-free iodine-131 can be employed to label the protein at a multiplicity of one or a few molecules of I^{131} per molecule protein).

Immunoelectrophoresis (Garber, 1959) is perhaps the most discriminating of separation procedures because it combines the resolving power of electrophoresis with the specificity of immunochemical reactions. The analysis can be carried out on a single microscope slide with microgram levels of protein. With this procedure, only qualitative or semiquantitative estimation of a particular protein species can be obtained.

METHODS INVOLVING BOTH BIOLOGICAL ACTIVITY AND SPECIFIC MOLECULAR CHARACTERISTICS

All of the above methods have an element of uncertainty in interpretation of the results. In immunochemical methods, it is possible that a number of protein species cross-react with the same antibody population. Fortunately, such cross-reacting species can usually be detected by gel diffusion techniques or by immunoelectrophoresis. With appropriate controls, therefore, immunochemical methods can be remarkably specific. With methods involving the detection of particular species of proteins by their biological activity (catalytic or hormonal) it is frequently presumed that a particular catalytic or hormonal activity is associated with a single molecular species. In many instances, especially at low relative levels of activity, this conclusion is unjustified. The substrate specificity of most enzymes, for example, is not absolute and, hence, a number of *different* enzymes may be capable of catalyzing the same reaction. In addition, there may be a number of closely related but not identical proteins (isozymes) which are associated with a given catalytic activity. For a more rigorous assay of a specific molecular entity, therefore, it is frequently desirable to combine assays of biological activity with determination of some specific molecular characteristics; for example, immunochemical properties or electrophoretic mobility. In the first instance, catalytic activity is frequently abolished by combination of the enzyme with antibodies; it can also be removed from the solution by appropriate precipitation methods. In the second, activity staining methods are most useful. Frequently histological methods can be adapted to give a satisfactory means of detection of enzymatic activity on gels. There are methods for assay of the dehydrogenases which produce DPNH or TPNH (reduced di- or triphosphopyridine nucleotide) during the course of the reaction (Seligman, 1963; Fine and Costello, 1963). For the detection of enzyme activity, the DPNH formed spontaneously reduces an intermediate electron carrier, phenazine methosulfate, which in turn reduces a tetrazolium compound, usually nitro blue tetrazolium (2,2′-di-*p*-nitrophenyl-5,5′-di-phenyl-3-3′ (3,3′-dimethoxy-4-4′-biphenylene) ditetrazolium chloride) to form an insoluble diformazan dye which is readily detected visually and can be quantitatively estimated by a number of optical scanning procedures. A number of other enzymes can be coupled to dehydrogenases and assayed satisfactorily by this procedure. For example, the enzyme aldolase acts on fructose-diphosphate to produce the triosephosphates, dihydroxyacetone phosphate, and glyceraldehyde-3-phosphate. The latter is a substrate for triosephosphate dehydrogenase which, of course, produces DPNH during the oxidation of the glyceraldehyde-3-phosphate. The position of aldolase can thus be detected (Penhoet and Rutter, 1965) after electrophoresis on a gel by appropriately applying to the surface (in another gel) the substrate fructose-diphosphate, triosephosphate dehydrogenase, inorganic arsenate DPN, phenazine methosulfate, and nitro blue tetrazolium. Assays employing radioactive substrates can frequently be convenient, sensitive, and specific.

DISCUSSION

Suitable micromodifications of the number of current procedures provide sensitive means for detection of specific proteins at moderate levels in developing systems. At extremely low levels of activity (approximating one or a few molecules per cell), additional technical and theoretical problems arise. Most assay procedures require many molecules of the specific protein.

When the system employed is composed of a number of cells, the problem of cell heterogeneity and discontinuity in distribution arises. If a given level of enzyme activity corresponding to 10^4 molecules is found in 10^4 cells, the distribution of the activity is not defined. Considerable care must be employed, therefore, in the interpretation of results obtained with such integrating methods. In many instances, it is possible, with appropriate cytological procedures or by microdissection, to obtain relevant information on the degree of homogeneity of the tissue sample. It is apparent that with currently available techniques, many of the basic changes in the composition of proteins during development can be comprehensively defined. Patterns of events reflecting basic processes in development may become discernible. The romance of this prospect need not obscure the fascinating problems which lie in between.

REFERENCES

BALLANTINE, R., 1957: Determination of total nitrogen and ammonia. In S. P. Colowick and N. O. Kaplan (eds.), *Methods in Enzymology*, Academic Press, New York, Vol. III, p. 984.

CAMPBELL, D. H., J. S. GARVEY, N. E. CREMER, and D. H. SUSSDORF, 1963: *Methods in Immunology*, W. A. Benjamin, Inc., New York.

CLARK, W., and W. J. RUTTER, 1965: Unpublished observations.

DAVIS, B. J., 1964: Disc electrophoresis-II. Method and application to human serum proteins. *Ann. N.Y. Acad. Sci.*, 121: in Art. 2, *Gel Electrophoresis*, p. 404.

EXLEY, D., 1956: The determination of 20–100 mμg quantities of organic nitrogen. *Biochem. J.* 63: 496.

FINE, I. H., and L. A. COSTELLO, 1963: The use of starch electrophoresis in dehydrogenase studies. In S. P. Colowick and N. O. Kaplan (eds.), *Methods in Enzymology*, Academic Press, New York, Vol. VI, p. 958.

FOLIN, O., and V. CIOCALTEU, 1927: On tyrosine and tryptophane determinations in proteins. *J. Biol. Chem.*, **73**: 627.

GLICK, D., 1963: *Quantitative Chemical Techniques of Histo- and Cytochemistry*. Vol. II. Interscience Pub., New York.

GORNALL, A. G., C. S. BARDAWILL, and M. M. DAVID, 1949: Determination of serum proteins by means of the biuret reaction. *J. Biol. Chem.*, 177: 751.

GRABAR, P., 1959: Immunoelectrophoretic analysis. In D. Glick (ed.), *Methods of Biochemical Analysis*, Interscience Pub., New York, Vol. VII, p. 3.

GROSSBACH, U., 1965: Acrylamide gel electrophoresis in capillary columns. *Biochim. Biophys. Acta*, 107: 180.

GROVES, W. J., 1962: *Conservation of Molecular Properties of Aldolase in Phylogeny*. Doctoral thesis, University of Illinois, Urbana, Ill.

KISSANE, J. M., and E. ROBBINS, 1958: The fluorometric measurement of deoxyribonucleic acid in animal tissues with special reference to the central nervous system. *J. Biol. Chem.*, 233: 184.

KUNKEL, H. G., and S. M. WARD, 1950: The immunological determinations of human albumin in biological fluids. *J. Biol. Chem.*, 182: 597.

LAYNE, E., 1957: Spectrophotometric and turbidimetric methods for measuring proteins. In S. P. Colowick and N. O. Kaplan (eds.), *Methods in Enzymology*, Academic Press, New York, Vol. III, p. 447.

LEVY, M., 1936: Beiträge zur enzymatischen Histochemie. XVII. Mikromethode zur Bestimmung von Stickstoff. *Z. Physiol. Chem.*, 240: 33.

LOWRY, O. H., N. J. ROSEBROUGH, A. L. FARR, and R. J. RANDALL, 1951: Protein measurement with the folin phenol reagent. *J. Biol. Chem.*, 193: 265.

MATIOLI, G. T., and H. B. NIEWISCH, 1965: Electrophoresis of hemoglobin in single erythrocytes. *Science*, 150: 1824.

MOORE, S., and W. H. STEIN, 1963: Chromatographic determination of amino acids by the use of automatic recording equipment. In S. P. Colowick and N. O. Kaplan (eds.), *Methods in Enzymology*, Academic Press, New York, Vol. VI, p. 819.

ORNSTEIN, L., 1964: Disc electrophoresis-I. Background and theory. *Ann. N.Y. Acad. Sci.*, 121: in Art. 2, *Gel Electrophoresis*, p. 321.

OUDIN, J., 1952: Specific precipitation in gels and its application to immunochemical analysis. In A. C. Corcoran (ed.), *Methods in Medical Research*, Year Book Pub. Co.,

Chicago, Ill., Vol. V, p. 335.

PENHOET, E., and W. J. RUTTER, 1965: Unpublished observations.

RIDEAL, E. K., and R. ROBERTS, 1951: The photochemistry of native proteins. *Proc. Roy. Soc. (London) A*, 205: 391.

ROBINSON, H. W., and C. G. HOGDEN, 1940: The biuret reaction in the determination of serum proteins. *J. Biol. Chem.*, 135: 707.

ROTMAN, B., 1961: Measurement of activity of single molecules of β-D-galactosidase. *Proc. Nat. Acad. Sci. U.S.*, 47: 1981.

RUTTER, W. J., and C. S. WEBER, 1965: Specific proteins in cytodifferentiation. In Darrel N. Ward (ed.), *Developmental and Metabolic Control Mechanisms and Neoplasia*, Williams & Wilkins Company, Baltimore, Md.

SELIGMAN, A. M., 1963: Histochemical methods for dehydrogenases. In S. P. Colowick and N. O. Kaplan (eds.), *Methods in Enzymology*, Academic Press, New York, Vol. VI, p. 889.

STEIN, W. H., and S. MOORE, 1954: The free amino acids of human blood plasma. *J. Biol. Chem.*, 211: 915.

VENDRELY, R., 1955: The deoxyribonucleic acid content of the nucleus. In E. Chargaff and J. N. Davidson (eds.), *The Nucleic Acids*, Academic Press, New York, Vol. II, p. 155.

WADDELL, W. J., 1956: A simple ultroviolet spectrophotometric method for the determination of protein. *J. Lab. Clin. Med.*, 48: 311.

WARBURG, O., and W. CHRISTIAN, 1941: Isolierung und Kristallisation des Gärungsferments Enolase. *Biochem. Z.*, 310: 384.

WHIPPLE, H., (ed.), 1964: *Gel Electrophoresis. Ann. N.Y. Acad. Sci.*, 121: Art. 2, p. 305.

YALOW, R. S., and S. A. BERSON, 1964: Immunoassay of plasma insulin. In D. Glick (ed.), *Methods of Biochemical Analysis*, Interscience Pub., New York, Vol. XII, p. 69.

Nucleic Acid Determination in Embryos

By Donald D. Brown

INTRODUCTION

The problems posed for nucleic acid analysis in eggs and embryos are unique only to the extent that new material always provides new complications even for the measurement and isolation of well-defined molecules. This discussion will emphasize lessons learned from amphibian and sea urchin embryos since the majority of nucleic acid artifacts in the literature of embryology stem from work with these animals. If there is any generality to make, it must be that each new embryonic system will provide its unique obstacles. This article can serve only as a general guide to serious pitfalls which are common to embryonic systems and to basic isolation techniques. Ribonucleic acid (RNA) and deoxyribonucleic acid (DNA) are discussed here with regard to three aspects: measurement, isolation, and characterization.

DEOXYRIBONUCLEIC ACID (DNA)

Quantitative Measurement and Isolation of DNA

Some of the more popular methods which measure DNA are the diphenylamine reaction (Burton, 1956), fluorimetric assay (Kissane and Robbins, 1958), ultraviolet absorption (Beaven *et al.*, 1955), and the microbiological method (Hoff-Jorgensen, 1951). A general discussion of color reactions is given by Dische (1955).

Some methods which have been developed for isolation of microbial and animal DNA are those of Kirby (1957), Marmur (1961), and Berns and Thomas (1965).

DNA Measurement and Isolation from Eggs and Embryos

Measurement of DNA by standard colorimetric or fluorimetric methods, as well as its isolation in pure form, from late embryos does not provide any special problems. By this time the embryo has synthesized enough DNA *de novo* so that it approximates the DNA content of adult tissue per wet weight. However, DNA analysis of eggs and early embryos provides a special case which has confounded investigators for 15 years. This difficulty arises from the fact that the unfertilized egg is a single cell with a full complement of usual and unusual cytoplasmic structures; but it has only one

TABLE 1. NUCLEIC ACID CONTENT OF SOME EGGS

ANIMAL	CONTENT (mμg/egg)* RNA	DNA	DIPLOID DNA VALUE	REFERENCES
Paracentrotus (sea urchin)	6	0.028	0.002	Elson *et al.* (1954); Hinegardner (1961)
Misgurnus (loach)	2,200	30	. .	Ajtkhozin *et al.* (1964)
Ilyanassa (snail)	4.4	0.428	0.0066	Collier (1961, 1962)
X. laevis	4,000	3.1	0.006	Brown *et al.* (1964a); Dawid (1965)
R. pipiens	5,000	3.6	0.015	Brown *et al.* (1962a); Dawid (1965)

* Somatic cells have from 2 to 5 times more RNA than DNA. Eggs have an RNA/DNA ratio which is one or two orders of magnitude greater.

nucleus, which theoretically has a single haploid or, if meiosis has not occurred, a tetraploid complement of DNA. Although eggs contain "cytoplasmic" DNA, leading to a considerable excess of DNA on a per cell basis, the amount of DNA per wet weight is much smaller than in other tissues. This situation requires considerable modification of standard methods even to measure DNA in eggs. Table 1 lists some values for egg DNA. This is compared with the RNA content of these eggs, and the diploid DNA content of the same species, as determined from sperm (haploid) or nucleated erythrocytes (diploid).

METHOD FOR ISOLATING AMPHIBIAN EGG DNA (AFTER DAWID, 1965)

High molecular weight DNA has been isolated from amphibian eggs by Dawid (1965), and from sea-urchin eggs by Bibring *et al.* (1965) and Carden *et al.* (1965).

The following detailed procedure was developed by Dawid for the isolation of DNA from eggs of frogs, *Xenopus laevis* and *Rana pipiens*. It should be reemphasized that different embryos may require extensive modifications of this procedure, or of the Marmur (1961) and Berns and Thomas (1965) techniques from which it is derived.

Eggs are collected immediately after laying and dejellied chemically.[1] They can be frozen for subsequent isolation or processed immediately. They are homogenized gently in 10 volumes of 0.1 *M* tris-HCl pH 8.5 containing sodium lauryl sulfate (SLS) (0.25–1.0 percent) and pronase (0.5 to 2 mg per milliliter).[2] The homogenate is incubated for 7 hours at 37°C and then shaken with an equal volume of redistilled water-saturated phenol. The aqueous phase is separated by centrifugation, and the large precipitate which forms after adding 0.3 *M* NaCl and two volumes of ethanol is collected by centrifugation and redissolved in tris buffer. At this point the small amount of DNA is contaminated by large amounts of particulate glycogen,

[1] Eggs of *X. laevis* and *R. pipiens* can be dejellied in 2 percent cysteine neutralized to pH 7.8 with NaOH and containing 0.2 percent papain (Nutritional Biochemical Corp.).

[2] Pronase (Calbiochem) is dissolved in 10-fold concentrated solution and preincubated for 30 minutes at 37°C. DNase contamination will be destroyed by this treatment.

phosphoprotein of yolk, and huge amounts of RNA. Most glycogen can be removed by high speed centrifugation in a Spinco Model L (37,000 rpm for 1 hour) or by digestion with α-amylase (shown to be free of DNase [deoxyribonuclease] activity). The phosphoprotein contaminant is removed by precipitation with 0.05 *M* $MgCl_2$ in the presence of 0.5 percent SLS.[3] Nucleic acids are precipitated again with ethanol-salt and the precipitate dissolved in 1 *M* $NaClO_4$ buffered with tris. Further removal of protein is accomplished by shaking the aqueous phase alternately with $CHCl_3$-isoamyl alcohol (25:1) and phenol. (Due to the $NaClO_4$, the aqueous phase is now denser than the phenol.) When no interface is present, the nucleic acids can be recovered again from the aqueous layer by ethanol-salt precipitation. The next step in purification is removal of RNA. The DNA can be separated from RNA by equilibrium density gradient centrifugation in CsCl (Meselson, Stahl, and Vinograd, 1957). In this technique it is important not to degrade RNA with RNase prior to centrifugation since low molecular weight oligoribonucleotides will not band but diffuse throughout the CsCl gradient. The contents of the tube are fractionated and fractions containing DNA located by the diphenylamine test. Further purification is achieved by treatment with RNase,[4] chromatography on methylated serum albumin (Mandell and Hershey, 1960), and rerunning in a CsCl gradient.

[3] In the absence of SLS, the Mg^{++} will coprecipitate DNA. The amount of $MgCl_2$ needed is determined by adding more after centrifugation until no precipitate forms. The material which is removed by precipitation with $MgCl_2$ is apparently a phosphoprotein fraction. It distributes into the aqueous phase in water-phenol partition and contaminates nucleic acid preparations from eggs. The material is less reactive in the Lowry reaction than other proteins, and has a low ultraviolet absorption at 280 mμ. Therefore, these methods underestimate the protein content of a preparation. A better estimate may be obtained by hydrolyzing a sample and applying the ninhydrin reaction. The interference of phosphoprotein with analyses of RNA is described in the section on 4S RNA determination.

AN ALTERNATE METHOD FOR QUANTITATIVE ANALYSIS OF EGG DNA (DAWID, 1965)

Because of the special problems of measurement of egg DNA, Dawid used a method which obviates the need for standard color tests. Since purification of egg DNA is necessary before application of any test, losses can occur; this method corrects for such losses. A known amount of purified highly labeled DNA of known specific activity (counts per minute per microgram) is added to the eggs or embryos at the beginning of the purification. After the extraction and purification of the DNA, its specific activity is measured again. By this isotope dilution technique the total amount of DNA present in the eggs can be accurately determined.

Special Complications for the Measurement and Isolation of Egg DNA

All the problems which complicate this isolation are directly or indirectly due to the extremely small concentration of DNA in eggs.

BACTERIAL CONTAMINATION

Even moderate contamination of eggs with bacteria can add substantially to the *amount* of DNA isolated or measured. In initial studies of amphibian egg DNA by Dawid, bacterial DNA was detected as extra peaks in CsCl gradients. He used the following test to monitor bacterial contamination. Bacteria grown in $P^{32}O_4$ were

[4] RNase is freed of DNase activity by treating a stock solution (1 mg per milliliter in 0.01 *M* sodium acetate pH 5) for 15 minutes at 90°C.

added to egg suspensions. When eggs merely were washed, P^{32}-DNA was found in the purified preparations. However, if the eggs were dejellied chemically with great care, the DNA preparation was contaminated to less than 1 percent with P^{32}-bacterial DNA.

CONTAMINATION FROM MATERNAL TISSUE

Depending on the species, this source of DNA can be more or less serious. An analysis of DNA in oocytes or eggs which are enveloped by a layer of maternal follicle cells or nurse cells would be expected to measure the DNA of these cells rather than the oocyte DNA.

INTERFERENCE WITH STANDARD DNA TESTS

In somatic tissues, tests such as the diphenylamine reaction are specific and give an accurate measurement of DNA even in crude extracts. This is not true for egg DNA. The error from slight reaction of diphenylamine with other substances will be magnified in extracts of eggs because of the small content of egg DNA. Whether deoxyribose is the only reacting substance can be tested by measuring the spectrum of the colored product. Pure DNA reacts with diphenylamine to give a purple-blue color which has a broad absorption spectrum with a peak at 600 mμ. Interfering compounds cause an alteration in this spectrum. Some compounds which react with diphenylamine are listed by Lee (1963). Furthermore the amphibian egg has several times the amount of low molecular weight diphenylamine-reacting substances compared to its content of highly polymerized DNA.

The fluorimetric technique, although more sensitive than the diphenylamine reaction, is less specific for DNA. Izawa *et al.* (1963) increased its specificity by measuring the material released from preparations of oocyte nuclei before and after DNase treatment. The difference was considered to be DNA.

INTERFERENCE OF ISOLATION BY OTHER EGG CONSTITUENTS

Some particulate constituent of amphibian eggs binds nucleic acids (RNA and DNA) and precipitates them (Brown and Caston, 1962). The material is associated with the fraction of homogenates which sediments at low speed. Homogenates of *R. pipiens* can complex an amount of added nucleic acid equal to the endogenous content of RNA. This problem has been found to be less serious in *X. laevis* which has a lower yolk content. Furthermore, amphibian eggs also contain material which prevents DNA and RNA from binding to MAK columns (see footnote 3 on p. 687) (Dawid, 1963).

PRESENCE OF NUCLEASES

A previously unstudied embryo should be tested for DNase activity. *Rana pipiens* eggs and early embryos have low DNase activity (Coleman, 1962), but sea urchins have been found to have considerable DNase activity (Mazia *et al.*, 1948). In the event that active nucleases are present, some special precautions may be necessary, although DNase activity would be expected to be inhibited under the conditions of isolation reported above.

CELLULAR LOCATION OF EGG DNA

Cell fractionation of amphibian eggs has been reported. Finamore *et al.* (1960) isolated nuclei from ovarian tissue which would be expected to consist mainly of follicle cell nuclei. Izawa *et al.* (1963) resorted to microanalysis of isolated oocyte nuclei of the newt and arrived at

TABLE 2. CHARACTERIZATION OF DNA

METHOD	REFERENCE
1. Base composition	
a. Chromatography of hydrolyzate	Wyatt (1955); Kirby (1957)
b. Buoyant density in CsCl	Schildkraut *et al.* (1962)
c. Temperature melting profile of transition from double helix to random coil	Marmur and Doty (1962)
d. Composition of methylated bases	Gold and Hurwitz (1964)
2. Molecular weight	
a. Zonal centrifugation	Burgi and Hershey (1963)
b. Band centrifugation	Vinograd *et al.* (1963)
3. DNA-DNA homology	McCarthy and Bolton (1964)
4. Electron microscopy	Kleinschmidt and Zahn (1959)
5. Sequence analysis	
a. Pyrimidine stretches	Shapiro and Chargaff (1963)
b. Column fractionation	Miyazawa and Thomas (1965)

values for the DNA of oocyte lampbrush chromosomes that were four times (8N) the DNA content of somatic diploid cells (2N). They found another 8N complement of DNA in the nucleoplasm of these oocyte nuclei. A method for isolation of nuclei from sea urchin eggs has been devised by Hinegardner (1961; Wilt, this volume, pp. 659–670) who found them to contain about the same DNA content as sperm (the haploid amount). Therefore the bulk of egg DNA does not seem to be located in the nucleus (see Table 1 for egg DNA values). Baltus and Brachet (1962) have suggested that most of the DNA in eggs of pleurodeles is associated with particles that sediment at low speeds (yolk and pigment). However, Dawid (1965) found that most DNA in amphibian eggs is associated with a particle fraction that sediments at 20,000 *g*. He believes this DNA to be mitochondrial DNA.

Characterization of DNA

DNA cannot be characterized until it is purified. Once it is purified the investigator has the upper hand and characterization can proceed normally. Some methods for characterization of DNA are listed in Table 2.

RIBONUCLEIC ACID (RNA)

Quantitative Measurement, Isolation of RNA, and Characterization of RNA

Colorimetric analyses of RNA are discussed by Dische (1955). Table 3 summarizes some parameters of RNA and how they are studied. Application of standard orcinol color test to cell fractions from *Rana pipiens* may require special precautions because of contributions to the color from non-RNA sources (Brown and Caston, 1962a).

RNA Measurement and Isolation from Eggs and Embryos

Eggs have a high content of RNA (see Table 1); in fact, when expressed per weight, the over-all RNA content of eggs is in the same order of magnitude as

TABLE 3. CHARACTERIZATION OF RNA

CHARACTERISTICS	TECHNIQUES	REFERENCES
Size	Zonal centrifugation	Britten and Roberts (1960)
Cellular location	Cell fractionation	..
Site of synthesis	Radioautography	..
Stability	Kinetics of pulse-chase with radioisotope	..
Base composition	Acid hydrolysis for optical density	Wyatt (1955)
	P^{32}-RNA alkaline hydrolysis	
	(a) Paper chromatography	Lane (1963)
	(b) Electrophoresis	Smith (1955)
	(c) Column chromatography	Cohn (1955)
	Methylated bases	Cantoni *et al.* (1962)
Sequence analysis	Separation of oligonucleotides	Rushizky and Sober (1962)
DNA homology	Hybridization with DNA	Gillespie and Spiegelman (1965)
		McCarthy and Bolton (1964)
		Nygaard and Hall (1964)
dRNA function	Assay for messenger activity *in vitro*	Nirenberg and Matthaei (1961)
4S RNA function	Assay for amino acid acceptor activity	Brown (1963)

multicellular tissues (about 4–10 μg per milligram). Thus, a fairly accurate measurement of total RNA in eggs can be obtained simply by measuring the optical density (at 260 mμ) of that fraction of homogenates which is insoluble in cold acid and then solubilized by hot acid. In later embryos, as with mature tissue, DNA increases relative to RNA until about 20–40 percent of the total nucleic acid content is DNA. Under these conditions chemical fractionation will separate DNA from RNA so that they can be measured individually (see Loring, 1955).

The special problems which relate to RNA analysis are different from the ones discussed previously for DNA and can be categorized as follows:

1. separation and quantitation of each of the three general classes of RNA,
2. isolation of undegraded RNA,
3. cellular location of each class of RNA,
4. measurement of RNA synthesis with radioisotopes.

A METHOD FOR THE ISOLATION OF TOTAL RNA IN UNDEGRADED FORM AND SEPARATION OF THE THREE CLASSES OF RNA FROM AMPHIBIAN EGGS AND EMBRYOS (AFTER BROWN AND LITTNA, 1964)

This technique has been devised for isolation of nucleic acids from eggs and embryos of *X. laevis*. We present it with comments designed to point out various problems and how some of them have been solved in this instance. Extraction of different embryos undoubtedly will require modification of this method.

After collection of embryos, they are carefully dejellied by the cysteine-papain method (see footnote 1, p. 686), rinsed with distilled water, and frozen[5] or processed immediately. All purification steps are carried out at 0°C. A useful

[5] Embryos and purified RNA preparations can be stored indefinitely at −70°C without any degradation of high molecular weight RNA.

ratio of medium to egg mass will yield a final aqueous solution containing about 0.1 mg RNA per milliliter (about 20 eggs per milliliter in the case of *X. laevis*). For example 100 eggs are homogenized in 5 ml of 0.1 *M* sodium acetate pH 5 containing 4 μg per milliliter polyvinyl sulfate (PVS).[6] Sodium lauryl sulfate is added to 0.5 percent and an equal volume of redistilled H_2O-saturated phenol is added. The suspension is shaken for 5–10 minutes and centrifuged at 15,000 rpm for 10 minutes. The RNA in the aqueous phase is precipitated with 0.4 *M* NaCl and two volumes of ethanol and placed at −20°C until a flocculent precipitate appears. The precipitate is collected by centrifugation and the pellet dissolved in 5 ml of 0.01 *M* sodium acetate pH 5 containing 1 μg per milliliter PVS. At this point DNase treatment degrades DNA to low molecular weight polymers. The solution is incubated with 10 μg per milliliter DNase I and 2 m*M* $MgCl_2$ for 10 minutes at 20°C, then chilled to 0°C.[7] SLS is added to 0.5 percent, then phenol is added again, and the mixture is shaken vigorously, separated by centrifugation, and the RNA precipitated once more from the aqueous phase with NaCl-ethanol. The pellet is dissolved and precipitated twice more[8] and finally dissolved in about 1.5 ml of the sodium acetate-PVS solution. The amount of RNA can be determined at this point by its optical density (O.D.) at 260 mμ (1 mg per milliliter = 23 O.D. units) and the solution can be kept frozen at −70°C indefinitely without alteration of its sedimentation pattern (see footnote 5, p. 690).

DETERMINATION OF RIBOSOMAL RNA (rRNA). Since rRNA is the predominant form of all nucleic acids in all tissues including eggs and embryos, the total optical density measurement will be an approximate indication of the rRNA content. To separate rRNA from other ultraviolet-absorbing material, purification is required. Two useful methods are sucrose density gradient (zonal or velocity) centrifugation (Britten and Roberts, 1960) and fractionation on a column of methylated serum albumin (MAK) (Mandell and Hershey, 1960).

1. A solution of purified nucleic acids (previously DNase treated) with less than 1 mg RNA in a volume not exceeding 1.5 ml is overlaid on a linear gradient of sucrose (5–20 percent) dissolved in 0.01 *M* sodium acetate pH 5 with 0.1 m*M* ethylenediaminetetraacetate (EDTA).[9] A good separation of the 28S and 18S rRNA molecules is effected in the SW 25.1 rotor of the Spinco preparative centrifuge at

[6] There are two advantages of extracting RNA at pH 5. First, most of the DNA goes to the interphase and is left behind (Scherrer and Darnell, 1962). Second, RNase inhibitors such as polyvinyl sulfate are more effective at pH 5. PVS (available from Fisher Scientific), Bentonite, heparin, and dextran sulfate (Pharmacia) all inhibit alkaline ribonucleases (pancreatic and bacterial RNase) (Philipson and Kaufman, 1964)). Since these inhibitors complex with basic protein, crude extracts will greatly reduce their efficacy. Furthermore, most nucleases in eggs and embryos are probably not of the alkaline type and thus not affected by these inhibitors. The inhibitor is particularly useful in the DNase step since it protects against RNase contamination of commercial DNase I which is prepared from pancreas.

[7] Although the presence of polyvinyl sulfate can inhibit RNase contamination of impure DNase preparations, it is advisable to use electrophoretically purified DNase (Worthington).

[8] About 3 precipitations of RNA are required to remove traces of phenol which has a high extinction coefficient in the ultraviolet (ϵ_{max} = 270 mμ).

[9] The salt and divalent ion contents of gradient solutions change the sedimentation constants of all classes of RNA. Furthermore, it is now clear that heterogeneous dRNA complexes with rRNA at high salt and Mg^{++} concentration (Asano, 1965). The addition of EDTA and low salt content of the gradient solution minimize this artifact.

25,000 rpm for 14–16 hours (~10°C).

2. A solution containing less than 0.5 mg RNA is adsorbed, washed, and eluted from a 3-gm column (1.8 × 2 cm) of MAK at room temperature. A linear gradient of 0.1 *M* to 1.2 *M* NaCl buffered with 0.05 *M* tris or phosphate at pH 7.2 will elute 4S RNA, DNA, and rRNA in separate peaks (Yoshikawa *et al.*, 1964). The 28S and 18S rRNA elute together at about 0.8 *M* NaCl. MAK has been used to study RNA synthesis in amphibian embryos (Brown and Caston, 1962b), sea urchin embryos (Comb *et al.*, 1965), and fish embryos (Spirin *et al.*, 1964).

DETERMINATION OF 4S RNA. In order to measure 4S RNA it is not adequate to measure optical density in the 4S region of a sucrose gradient since most contaminants sediment in this region (including mononucleotides, degraded DNA, etc.). The 4S RNA from a sucrose gradient can be purified by adsorption and elution from a MAK column. Degraded DNA and lower molecular weight ribonucleotides are not held by the column, while 4S RNA is eluted at about 0.4 *M* NaCl.

Two other techniques for separation of 4S RNA from high molecular weight RNA have been successful with amphibian eggs and embryos. Purified RNA can be fractionated on DEAE-cellulose (D. D. Brown, unpublished). From this material 4S RNA is eluted at about 0.5 *M* NaCl while high molecular weight RNA and DNA are retained even at very high salt concentrations (Brunngraber, 1962).

Finally, 4S RNA is separated from high molecular weight RNA by passage through a Sephadex G-100 column at 4°C (35 × 1.8 cm equilibrated with 0.01 *M* sodium acetate pH 5; Brown, 1965). The sample is applied in 1–2 ml and eluted with pH 5 buffer. High molecular weight RNA and DNA are excluded and pass through the column unretarded while low molecular weight RNA is retarded and can be collected in the next 40 ml of effluent after the unretarded fraction. If desired, the solution can be concentrated *in vacuo*[10] and subjected to further fractionation on DEAE or MAK columns.

A serious contaminant of 4S RNA preparations from amphibian embryos is yolk phosphoprotein which has about the same molecular weight (30,000) and phosphate content (8 percent) (Wallace, 1963), and is solubilized by the addition of sodium lauryl sulfate (SLS; see footnote 3, p. 687). Furthermore, it is extracted into the aqueous phase and precipitated with ethanol. It is retarded on Sephadex G-100, retained on MAK columns, and eluted over a wide range of NaCl concentrations. Large amounts of phosphoprotein reduce the capacity of MAK columns and can cause low molecular RNA to pass through without being retained just as in the case of DNA. Removal of most of this contaminant is effected by adding $MgCl_2$ (0.05 *M*) after the addition of SLS to the initial pH 5 homogenate. Under these conditions most of the low molecular weight 4S RNA is recovered in the aqueous phase while the bulk of high molecular weight RNA (rRNA and dRNA) goes into the interphase or the phenol phase.

DETERMINATION OF dRNA. DNA-like RNA is isolated in undegraded form from pH 5 extracts of whole embryos as described above. At this pH the addition of SLS is necessary to release RNA from ribonucleoprotein complexes. However, two techniques have been devised which differentially extract the three classes of RNA in the absence of SLS. These depend on increasing the temperature of extraction at neutral pH (Georgiev *et al.*, 1963) or raising the pH during extraction (Brawerman *et al.*, 1963). Davidson *et al.* (1964)

[10] RNA solutions free of nuclease activity are very stable. They can be concentrated in a rotary flash evaporator at room temperature without degradation.

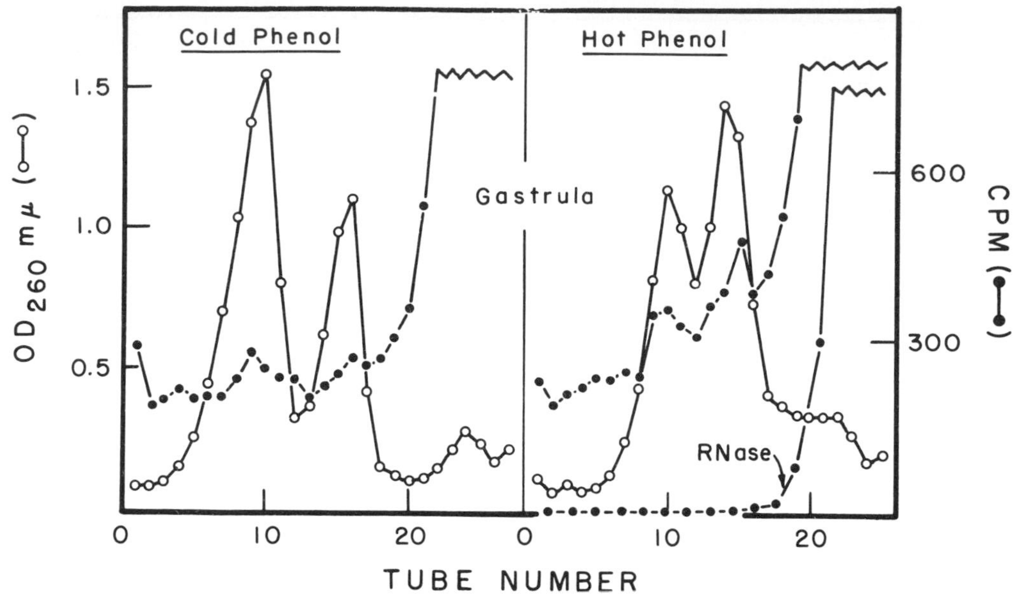

FIG. 1. Sedimentation profiles of RNA from gastrula embryos of *Xenopus laevis* isolated by cold phenol (left) or 60°C phenol extraction (right). Degradation of rRNA (right) occurred after 5 minutes of incubation in a 60°C water bath. Embryos were labeled from the beginning of development with $P^{32}O_4$.

have applied the latter modification to amphibian oocytes. Nemer and Infante (1965) have used Georgiev's method to isolate dRNA from sea urchin embryos.

Due to the low dRNA content in cells, isotopic labeling is used and depends on the rapid labeling of dRNA relative to other classes of RNA in short pulse periods. The ability to distinguish dRNA from 4S and rRNA depends upon the following characteristics of dRNA: (1) Rapid labeling in a pulse period with subsequent rapid degradation of most of this RNA (rapid turnover). (2) DNA-like base composition in contrast to 4S RNA and rRNA. Most animal DNA contains about 42 percent guanylic plus cytidylic (G-C) acid (Sueoka, 1962) while 4S RNA and rRNA contain about 60 percent G-C. (3) Heterogeneity of sedimentation pattern. (4) High efficiency of hybridization with DNA (McCarthy and Bolton, 1964). (5) Association with ribosomes and polysomes (Girard *et al.*, 1965). (6) Ability to stimulate protein synthesis using an *in vitro* amino acid incorporating system (Di Girolamo *et al.*, 1964).

ISOLATION OF UNDEGRADED RNA

Degradation of RNA can be monitored most conveniently by examining changes in the sedimentation profile of rRNA. Figures 1 and 2 compare RNA isolated from *X. laevis* embryos and *R. pipiens* embryos by cold and hot phenol extraction. In extracts of both embryos, rRNA has been partly degraded by hot phenol as shown by a reversal in the relative amounts of 28S to 18S rRNA. Further evidence of degradation comes from the high optical density in the 4S region of sucrose gradi-

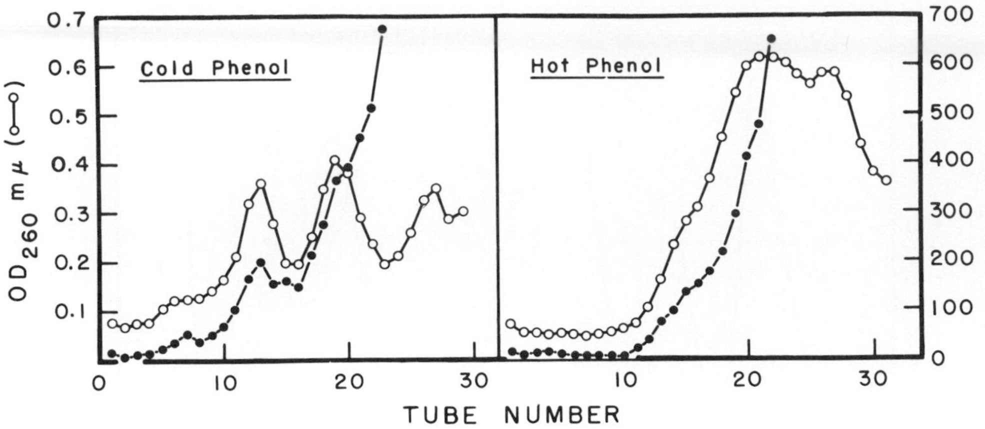

FIG. 2. Sedimentation profiles of (P^{32})-RNA from gastrula embryos of *Rana pipiens* isolated by cold phenol (left) or 60°C phenol extraction (right). Conditions for this extraction were the same as those described in the legend for Fig. 1.

ents. Degradation of RNA is more dramatic in extracts from *R. pipiens*, which have high ribonuclease activity. Degraded high molecular weight RNA can be distinguished from 4S RNA by chromatography on MAK which separates 4S RNA from degraded rRNA or dRNA. Brown and Caston (1962) were unable to isolate undegraded RNA from *R. pipiens* due to RNase activity and to the artifactual binding of RNA to a component of egg homogenate (see section above on determination of 4S RNA). Kohne (1965; see article by Wilt, this volume, pp. 659–670) has succeeded in isolating undegraded RNA from whole extracts and ribosome pellets of *R. pipiens* by taking several precautions. The eggs and embryos must be intact without evidence of cytolysis; the initial homogenization is carried out rapidly with a large volume to egg ratio. Ribosomes were purified successfully from eggs which were homogenized in an alkaline medium with high ionic strength (0.05 *M* tris; 0.01 *M* $MgCl_2$; 0.1 *M* KCl, pH 8) along with addition of desoxycholate or Lubrol. (For further information on precautions against RNA degradation see footnotes 5–10 on pp. 690–692.)

CELLULAR LOCATION OF RNA

Separation of nuclei from cytoplasm of embryos has not advanced to the stage of the techniques developed for thymus (Sibatani *et al.*, 1962), liver (Di Girolamo *et al.*, 1964), or HeLa cell nuclei (Penman *et al.*, 1963). Furthermore, it is likely that special precautions will be necessary due to the large size of nuclei of early embryos. Hinegardner (1962) has reported isolation of nuclei from sea urchins up to the gastrula stage but comments that this technique is not suited for embryos at later stages. Mariano (1964) has described isolation of nuclei from embryos of *X. laevis* (see Wilt, this volume, pp. 659–670). Spirin *et al.* (1964) report experiments on RNA of cytoplasmic fractions of the loach. A common criterion for nuclear integrity is the retention of all of the DNA in the nuclear fraction. However, it remains to be shown that under these conditions the partitioning of RNA fractions between nuclear and cytoplasmic fractions truly represents its *in vivo* distribution. Furthermore, when tissues are homogenized under conditions which permit subcellular fractionation, there is extensive degradation of dRNA and pulse-labeled RNA in general (Brown and Littna, 1964a).

RNA associated with purified ribosome fractions has been studied in amphibia (Brown and Littna, 1964) and sea urchins (Wilt, 1964; Spirin and Nemer, 1965). During development newly synthesized dRNA associates with ribosomes which were present in the unfertilized egg. The same ribosomes which were previously free without attachment to membranes in the unfertilized eggs come to require the addition of desoxycholate for their isolation when purified from extracts of developing embryos (Brown and Littna, 1964; Brown, 1965). Comb and Brown (1964) interpreted this change in the cytoplasmic ribosomes of sea urchin embryo to mean "degradation to the mononucleotide level or . . . conversion of intact cytoplasmic ribosomal RNA to nuclear RNA." The first of these alternatives is clearly wrong since there is no degradation of rRNA during development of the sea urchin (Comb *et al.*, 1965). Despite their contention that cytoplasmic ribosomes come to reside in the nucleus during development, there is no direct evidence to support this idea. At all stages of development electron microscopy shows that ribosomes remain in the cytoplasm (E. Hay, unpublished). The actual change involves aggregation and attachment of ribosomes to membranes; this occurs concomitantly with their association with newly formed dRNA and subsequent participation in protein synthesis (Brown, 1965).

MEASUREMENT OF RNA SYNTHESIS WITH RADIOISOTOPES

Most studies involving synthesis of DNA or RNA require the use of isotopically labeled nucleic acid precursors. The selection and use of radioactive precursors have posed some problems with embryos.

PERMEABILITY OF THE EMBRYO. Intact amphibian and fish embryos are impermeable to organic molecules dissolved in the medium. Even inorganic phosphate does not penetrate amphibian embryos during early development. Isotopes are introduced into amphibian embryos in three ways: (1) Injection of isotopes into the gravid female during ovulation (Kutsky, 1950). The technique was developed for $P^{32}O_4$ but works for nucleosides as well, although incorporation is very inefficient. (2) Isotopes can be injected directly into embryos at any stage with a micromanipulator (Grant, 1958). (3) Intact embryos can be incubated with $C^{14}O_2$ (Cohen, 1954) which labels about everything that is being synthesized, including nucleic acids. Loach embryos (teleost) which have been separated from their yolk will incorporate radioactive nucleosides from a defined medium (Ajtkhozhin *et al.*, 1964). However, once gastrulation begins, this operation cannot be carried out.

Differential permeability of sea urchin eggs and embryos has been reported. Permeability to a number of molecules is greatly increased after fertilization (Piatigorsky and Whitely, 1965); this is of great importance in studies which compare metabolism of the eggs and embryos.

Eggs have been labeled during oogenesis in sea urchins following partial ovulation. Subsequent oogenesis is stimulated, and several weeks later radioactive eggs have matured (Gross *et al.*, 1965). *Xenopus laevis* is particularly suited to studies of this kind since the same female can be induced to ovulate repeatedly (Brown and Littna, 1964b). We have obtained as many as five clutches of eggs from the same radioactive female labeled with a tritiated nucleoside. When H^3-uridine is used, more than 95 percent of the total radioactivity of second or later generation eggs is present as rRNA.

RELATIVE EFFICIENCY OF NUCLEIC ACID PRECURSORS. Although nucleosides are not thought to be precursors on the normal biosynthetic pathways of nucleic acids, they are efficient precursors for both DNA and RNA synthesis in all embryos studied to date. H^3-thymidine has been used successfully in a wide variety of embryos and enters DNA specifically (Nemer, 1962; Collier, 1963; Mintz, 1964). However, attempts to label egg DNA during oogenesis have been unsuccessful. After long periods, radioactivity from H^3-thymidine is present in the egg as protein, which demonstrates that catabolism of thymidine will take place. This is a strong precautionary note for the interpretation of oocyte labeling with H^3-thymidine, particularly the finding of silver grains over cytoplasmic regions of the oocytes (see Favard-Séréno and Durand, 1963; Ficq, 1960).

H^3-uridine has been used in a wide variety of embryos and appears to be a more efficient precursor of nucleic acids than labeled orotic acid, despite the fact that orotic acid is a normal intermediate of the pyrimidine biosynthetic pathway and an excellent precursor of nucleic acids in liver (Hiatt, 1962). Labeling of RNA with any precursor at very early cleavage stages is complicated by the intense rate of DNA synthesis on the one hand, and the very low RNA synthesis on the other hand. Thus H^3-uridine, which normally is incorporated predominantly into RNA by slowly dividing tissues, labels DNA extensively in rapidly cleaving embryos. This has been demonstrated for amphibia (Tencer and Bieliavsky, 1960), mice (Mintz, 1964), fish (Spirin *et al.*, 1964), sea urchins (Ficq *et al.*, 1963), and snails (Collier, 1963) and is an important factor to consider when isolating radioactive RNA from embryos at early developmental stages.

BACTERIAL CONTAMINATION. The most serious cause of artifacts indicated in the literature dealing with synthesis of RNA in embryos is bacterial contamination. The problem arises from the fact mentioned above, that the embryo itself synthesizes very little RNA at early stages. Bacteria could not contaminate an egg or embryo preparation to the extent of contributing significant optical density to the RNA (as with the egg DNA). However, the synthetic capacity of bacteria so exceeds that of embryos that even slight contamination can obscure the metabolism of the embryo. It is usually simple to remove bacteria from the media, but many embryos are surrounded by membranes or jelly layers to which bacteria adhere. Techniques which require direct incubation of egg masses with isotopes are much more likely to accentuate bacterial labeling (for example, $C^{14}O_2$ labeling of amphibia or nucleoside incorporation into marine embryos).

Besides extensive dejellying, two techniques can aid in reducing bacterial contamination. Small amounts of penicillin and streptomycin (0.01 mg per milliliter) can inhibit bacterial growth without harming embryos. Cold-blooded vertebrate embryos and invertebrate embryos often can be reared at temperatures at which bacterial metabolism is exceedingly low (15°C).

A sensitive monitor of bacterial contamination is analysis of the radioactive RNA by sucrose gradient centrifugation. The rRNA of bacteria can be distinguished from animal RNA since both molecular species of bacterial rRNA

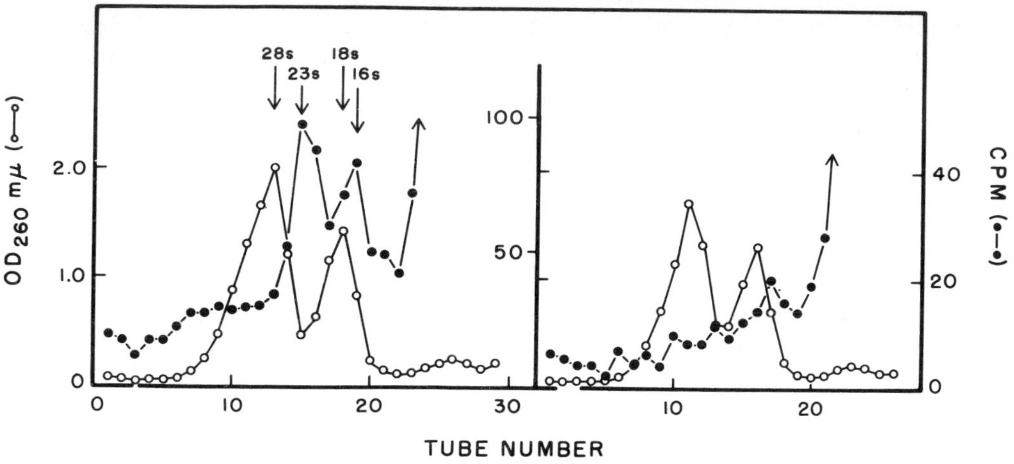

FIG. 3. Sedimentation profile of RNA extraction from cleaving embryos of *Xenopus laevis*. Embryos were incubated with $C^{14}O_2$ for 3 hours during cleavage. Before extraction of RNA, one batch of embryos was chemically dejellied (right) and the other manually dejellied (left).

sediment more slowly than animal 28S and 18S RNA (Hiatt, 1962). Two sucrose gradient profiles of pulse-labeled RNA obtained from cleaving embryos of *X. laevis* are shown in Fig. 3. One batch of embryos was dejellied chemically (right) and the other was dejellied only manually (left). The preparation on the left is contaminated with bacterial 23S and 16S radioactive rRNA superimposed over the newly synthesized heterogeneous dRNA of the cleaving embryos. This heterogeneous labeled RNA is characteristic of RNA synthesized by cleaving embryos (sea urchin, Gross, 1964; amphibia, Brown and Littna, 1964a) and is DNA-like in base composition. Bacterial contamination of RNA synthesized by cleaving sea urchins was the subject of a paper by Glisin and Glisin (1964). Although the rRNA of most animals studied to date sediments with coefficients of approximately 28S and 18S compared to the 23S and 16S RNA of bacteria, it should not be assumed that this will be an invariant rule. According to Sussman, rRNA of the cellular slime mold has sedimentation coefficients resembling bacterial rRNA (personal communication). Recently Applebaum *et al.* (1966) have shown that the two classes of rRNA isolated from the silkworm have sedimentation constants between those of animal and bacterial rRNA.

THE USE OF ISOTOPES TO MEASURE RATES OF SYNTHESIS OF RNA. The amount of radioactivity incorporated into RNA often is regarded as a measure of the *rate* of RNA synthesis. Ideally, rates of RNA synthesis should be expressed as micrograms of RNA synthesized in a given time period per microgram DNA. The translation of radioactivity into quantity of RNA presents a problem which involves many variables such as the specific activity of the precursor pools, separation of classes of RNA, uniformity of cell type, and diversity of synthetic rates in different parts of the embryo. The number of counts in RNA is not meaningful without measurements of the specific activity of the nucleotides in the acid-soluble pool. This technique has been used to quantitate the three classes of RNA synthesized at different stages of amphibian development (Brown, 1965). Recently it has been applied to the quantitation of "messenger" RNA at different stages of amphibian development (Denis, 1965).

REFERENCES

AJTKHOZHIN, M. A., N. V. BELITZINA, and A. SPIRIN, 1964: Nucleic acids during early stages of development in fish embryos of *Misgurnis fossilis*. *Biokhimiya*, 29: 169.

APPLEBAUM, S., R. EBSTEIN, and G. WYATT, 1966: Dissociation of ribosomal ribonucleic acid from silkworm pupae by heat and dimethylsulfoxide: evidence for specific cleavage points. *J. Mol. Biol.*, 21: 29.

ASANO, K., 1965: Size heterogeneity of T2 Messenger RNA. *J. Mol. Biol.*, 14: 71.

BALTUS, E., and J. BRACHET, 1962: Le dosage de l'acide déoxyribonucléique dans les oeufs de batraciens. *Biochim. Biophys. Acta*, 61: 157.

BEAVEN, G. H.,, E. R. HOLIDAY, and E. A. JOHNSON, 1955: Optical properties of nucleic acids and their components. In E. Chargaff and J. N. Davidson (eds.), *The Nucleic Acids*, Academic Press, New York, Vol. I, p. 493.

BERNS, K. I., and C. A. THOMAS, JR., 1965: Isolation of high molecular weight DNA from *Hemophilus influenzae*. *J. Mol. Biol.*, 11: 476.

BIBRING, T., J. BRACHET, F. GAETA, and F. GRAZIOSI, 1965: Some physical properties of cytoplasmic DNA in unfertilized eggs of *Arbacia lixula*. *Biochim. Biophys. Acta*, 108: 644.

BRAWERMAN, G., L. GOLD, and J. EISENSTADT, 1963: A ribonucleic fraction from rat liver with template activity. *Proc. Nat. Acad. Sci.* (*U.S.*), 50: 630.

BRITTEN, R. J., and R. B. ROBERTS, 1960: High-resolution density gradient sedimentation analysis. *Science*, 131: 32.

BROWN, D. D., 1965: RNA synthesis during early development. In D. N. Ward (ed.), *Developmental and Metabolic Control Mechanisms and Neoplasia*, Williams & Wilkins Company, Baltimore, Md., p. 219.

———, and J. D. CASTON, 1962a: Biochemistry of amphibian development. I. Ribosome and protein synthesis in early development of *Rana pipiens*. *Devel. Biol.*, 5: 412.

———, and ———, 1962b: Biochemistry of amphibian development. II. High molecular weight RNA. *Devel. Biol.*, 5: 435.

———, and E. LITTNA, 1964a: RNA synthesis during development of *Xenopus laevis*, the South African clawed toad. *J. Mol. Biol.*, 8: 669.

———, and ———, 1964b: Variations in the synthesis of stable RNA's during oogenesis and development of *Xenopus laevis*. *J. Mol. Biol.*, 8: 688.

BROWN, G. L., 1963: Preparation, fractionation, and properties of sRNA. In J. N. Davidson and W. E. Cohn (eds.), *Progress in Nucleic Acid Research*, Academic Press, New York, Vol. II, p. 259.

BRUNNGRABER, E. F., 1962: A simplified procedure for the preparation of soluble RNA from rat liver. *Biochem. Biophys. Res. Comm.*, 8: 1.

BURGI, E., and A. D. HERSHEY, 1963: Sedimentation rate as a measure of molecular weight. *Biophys. J.*, 3: 309.

BURTON, K., 1956: A study of the conditions and mechanism of diphenylamine reaction for the colorimetric estimation of deoxyribonucleic acid. *Biochem. J.*, 62: 315.

CANTONI, G. L., H. V. GELBOIN, S. W. LUBORSKY, H. H. RICHARDS, and M. F. SINGER, 1962: Studies on soluble ribonucleic acid of rabbit liver. III. Preparations and properties of rabbit-liver soluble RNA. *Biochim. Biophys. Acta*, 61: 354.

CARDEN, G. A., S. ROSENKRANZ, and H. S. ROSENKRANZ, 1965: Deoxyribonucleic acids of sperm, eggs and somatic cells of the sea urchin, *Arbacia punctulata. Nature*, 205: 1338.

COHEN, S., 1954: The metabolism of $C^{14}O_2$ during amphibian development. *J. Biol. Chem.*, 211: 337.

COHN, W. E., 1955: The separation of nucleic acid derivatives by chromatography on ion-exchange columns. In E. Chargaff and J. N. Davidson (eds.), *The Nucleic Acids*, Academic Press, New York, Vol. I, p. 211.

COLEMAN, J. R., 1962: Deoxyribonuclease activities in the development of the leopard frog, *Rana pipiens. Devel. Biol.*, 5: 232.

COLLIER, J. R., 1961: Nucleic acid and protein metabolism of the *Ilyanassa* embryo. *Exptl. Cell Res.*, 24: 320.

———, 1962: The deoxyribonucleic acid content of the egg and sperm of *Ilyanassa obsoleta. Exptl. Cell Res.* 27: 553.

———, 1963: The incorporation of uridine into the deoxyribonucleic acid of the *Ilyannasa* embryo. *Exptl. Cell Res.*, 32: 442.

COMB, D. G., and R. BROWN, 1964: Preliminary studies on the degradation and synthesis of RNA components during sea urchin development. *Exptl. Cell Res.*, 34: 360.

———, S. KATZ, R. BRANDA, and C. J. PINZINO, 1965: Characterization of RNA species synthesized during early development of sea urchins. *J. Mol. Biol.*, 14: 195.

DAVIDSON, E. H., V. G. ALLFREY, and A. E. MIRSKY, 1964: On the RNA synthesized during the lampbrush phase of amphibian oogenesis. *Proc. Nat. Acad. Sci.* (*U.S.*), 52: 501.

DAWID, I. B., 1963: A protein fraction from *Rana pipiens* eggs. In *Carnegie Institution of Washington Year Book 62*, Annual Report of the Director of the Department of Embryology, p. 420.

———, 1965: Deoxyribonucleic acid in amphibian eggs. *J. Mol. Biol.*, 12: 581.

DENIS, H., 1965: Synthesis of messenger RNA studied by the agar-DNA technique. In *Carnegie Institution of Washington Year Book 64*, Annual Report of the Director of the Department of Embryology, p. 452.

DI GIROLAMO, A., E. C. HENSHAW, and H. H. HIATT, 1964: Messenger ribonucleic acid in rat liver nuclei and cytoplasm. *J. Mol. Biol.*, 8: 479.

DISCHE, Z., 1955: Color reactions of nucleic acid components. In E. Chargaff and J. F. Davidson (eds.), *The Nucleic Acids*, Academic Press, New York, Vol. I, p. 285.

ELSON, D., T. GUSTAFSON, and E. CHARGAFF, 1954: The nucleic acids of sea urchins during embryonic development. *J. Biol. Chem.*, 209: 285.

FAVARD-SÉRÉNO, C., and M. DURAND, 1963: L'utilisation de nucléosides dans l'ovaire du grillon et ses variations au cours de l'ovogenèse. II. Incorporation dans l' ADN. *Devel. Biol.*, 6: 206.

FICQ, A., 1960: Métabolisme de l'oogenèse chez les amphibiens. In *Symposium on Germ Cells and Development:* Institut. Intern. d'Embryologie and Fondazione, A. Baselli, p. 121.

———, F. AIELLO, and E. SCARANO, 1963: Métabolisme des acides nucléiques dans l'oeuf d'oursin en développement. *Exptl. Cell Res.*, 29: 128.

FINAMORE, F. J., D. J. THOMAS, G. T. CROUSE, and B. LLOYD, 1960: The biochemistry of amphibian oöcytes. 1. Method of isolation and nucleic acid content of nuclei. *Arch. Biochem. Biophys.*, 88: 10.

GEORGIEV, G. P., P. O. SAMARINA, M. E. LERMAN, M. N. SMIRNOV, and A. N. SEVERTZOV, 1963: Biosynthesis of messenger and ribosomal ribonucleic acids in the nucleochromosomal apparatus of animal cells. *Nature*, 200: 1291.

GILLESPIE, D., and S. SPIEGELMAN, 1965: A quantitative assay for DNA-RNA hybrids with DNA immobilized on a membrane. *J. Mol. Biol.*, 12: 829.

GIRARD, M., H. LATHAM, S. PENMAN, and J. E. DARNELL, 1965: Entrance of newly formed messenger RNA and ribosomes into HeLa cell cytoplasm. *J. Mol. Biol.*, 11: 187.

GLISIN, V. R., and M. V. GLISIN, 1964: Ribonucleic acid metabolism following fertilization in sea urchin eggs. *Proc. Nat. Acad. Sci.* (*U.S.*), 52: 1548.

GOLD, M., and J. HURWITZ, 1964: The enzymatic methylation of ribonucleic acid and deoxyribonucleic acid. VI. Further studies on the properties of the deoxyribonucleic acid methylation reaction. *J. Biol. Chem.*, 239: 3866.

GRANT, P., 1958: The synthesis of deoxyribonucleic acid during early embryonic development of *Rana pipiens. J. Cellular Comp. Physiol.*, 52: 227.

GROSS, P. R., 1964: The immediacy of genomic control during early development. *J. Exptl. Zool.*, 157: 21.

———, L. I. MALKIN, and M. HUBBARD, 1965: Synthesis of RNA during oogenesis in the sea urchin. *J. Mol. Biol.*, 13: 463.

HIATT, H. H., 1962: A rapidly labeled RNA in rat liver nuclei. *J. Mol. Biol.*, 5: 217.

HINEGARDNER, R. T., 1961: The DNA content of isolated sea urchin egg nuclei. *Exptl. Cell Res.*, 25: 341.

———, 1962: The isolation of nuclei from eggs and embryos of the sea urchin. *J. Cell Biol.*, 15: 503.

HOFF-JORGENSEN, E., 1951: A microbiological assay of deoxyribonucleosides and deoxyribonucleic acid. *Biochem. J.*, 50: 400.

IZAWA, M., V. G. ALLFREY, and A. E. MIRSKY, 1963: Composition of the nucleus and chromosomes in the lampbrush stage of the newt oocyte. *Proc. Nat. Acad. Sci. (U.S.)*, 50: 811.

KIRBY, K. S., 1957: A new method for the isolation of deoxyribonucleic acid. *Biochem. J.*, 66: 495.

KISSANE, J. M., and E. ROBBINS, 1958: The fluorimetric measurement of deoxyribonucleic acid in animal tissues with special reference to the central nervous system. *J. Biol. Chem.*, 233: 184.

KLEINSCHMIDT, A. K., and R. K. ZAHN, 1959: Über deoxyribonucleinsäure-molekeln in protein-mischfilmen. *Z. Naturf.*, 14b: 770.

KOHNE, D., 1965: The isolation of ribosomes from eggs and embryos of *Rana pipiens. Exptl. Cell Res.*, 38: 211.

KUTSKY, P., 1950: Phosphate metabolism in the early development of *Rana pipiens. J. Exptl. Zool.*, 115: 429.

LANE, B. G., 1963: The separation of adenosine, guanosine, cytidine and uridine by one-dimensional filter-paper chromatography. *Biochim. Biophys. Acta*, 72: 110.

LEE, J. B., 1963: Compounds interfering in the diphenylamine test for deoxyribonucleic acid. *Nature*, 200: 264.

LORING, H. S., 1955: Hydrolysis of nucleic acids and procedures for the direct estimation of purine and pyrimidine fractions by absorption spectrophotometry. In E. Chargaff and J. N. Davidson (eds.), *The Nucleic Acids*, Academic Press, New York, Vol. I, p. 191.

MANDELL, J. D., and A. D. HERSHEY, 1960: A fractionating column for analysis of nucleic acids. *Anal. Biochem.*, 1: 66.

MARIANO, E. E., 1964: The isolation of nuclei from *Xenopus laevis* embryonic cells. *Exptl. Cell Res.*, 34: 201.

MARMUR, J., 1961: A procedure for the isolation of deoxyribonucleic acid from microorganisms. *J. Mol. Biol.*, 3: 208.

———, and P. DOTY, 1962: Determination of the base composition of deoxyribonucleic acid from its thermal denaturation temperature. *J. Mol. Biol.*, 5: 109.

MAZIA, D., G. BLUMENTHAL, and T. BENSON, 1948: The activity and distribution of deoxyribonuclease and phosphatases in the early development of *Arbacia punctulata. Biol. Bull.*, 95: 250.

MC CARTHY, B. J., and E. T. BOLTON, 1964: Interaction of complementary RNA and DNA. *J. Mol. Biol.*, 8: 184.

MESELSON, M., F. W. STAHL, and J. VINOGRAD, 1957: Equilibrium sedimentation of macromolecules in density gradients. *Proc. Nat. Acad. Sci. (U.S.)*, 43: 581.

MINTZ, B., 1964: Synthetic processes and early development in the mammalian egg. *J. Exptl. Zool.*, 157: 85.

MIYAZAWA, Y., and C. A. THOMAS, JR., 1965: Nucleotide composition of short segments of DNA molecules. *J. Mol. Biol.*, 11: 223.

NEMER, M., 1962: Characteristics of the utilization of nucleosides by embryos of *Paracentrotus lividus. J. Biol. Chem.*, 237: 143.

———, and A. A. INFANTE, 1965: Messenger RNA in early sea urchin embryos: Size classes. *Science*, 150: 217.

NIRENBERG, M. W., and J. H. MATTHEI, 1961: The dependence of cell free protein synthesis in *E. Coli* on naturally occurring or synthetic polyribonucleotides. *Proc. Nat. Acad. Sci.* (*U.S.*), 47: 1588.

NYGAARD, A. P., and B. D. HALL, 1964: Formation and properties of RNA-DNA complexes. *J. Mol. Biol.*, 9: 125.

PENMAN, S., K. SCHERRER, Y. BECKER, and J. E. DARNELL, 1963: Polyribosomes in normal and poliovirus-infected HeLa cells and their relationship to messenger RNA. *Proc. Nat. Acad. Sci.* (*U.S.*), 49: 654.

PHILIPSON, L., and M. KAUFMAN, 1964: The efficiency of ribonuclease inhibitors tested with viral ribonucleic acid as substrate. *Biochim. Biophys. Acta*, 80: 151.

PIATIGORSKY, J., and A. H. WHITELY, 1965: A change in permeability and uptake of ^{14}C uridine in response to fertilization in *Strongylocentrotus purpuratus* eggs. *Biochim. Biophys. Acta*, 108: 404.

RUSHIZKY, G. W., and H. A. SOBER, 1962: Characterization of the major compounds in ribonuclease T_1 digests of ribonucleic acids. *J. Biol. Chem.*, 237: 834.

SCHERRER, K., and J. E. DARNELL, 1962: Sedimentation characteristics of rapidly labeled RNA from HeLa cells. *Biochem. Biophys. Res. Comm.*, 7: 486.

SCHILDKRAUT, C. L., J. MARMUR, and P. DOTY, 1962: Determination of the base composition of deoxyribonucleic acid from its bouyant density in CsCl. *J. Mol. Biol.*, 4: 430.

SHAPIRO, H. S., and E. CHARGAFF, 1963: Studies on the nucleotide arrangement in deoxyribonucleic acids. VII. Direct estimation of pyrimidine nucleotide runs. *Biochim. Biophys. Acta*, 76: 1.

SIBATANI, A., S. R. DE KLOET, V. G. ALLFREY, and A. E. MIRSKY, 1962: Isolation of a nuclear RNA fraction resembling DNA in its base composition. *Proc. Nat. Acad. Sci.* (*U.S.*), 48: 471.

SMITH, J. D., 1955: The electrophoretic separation of nucleic acid components. In E. Chargaff and J. N. Davidson (eds.), *The Nucleic Acids*, Academic Press, New York, Vol. I, p. 267.

SPIRIN, A. S., and M. NEMER, 1965: Messenger RNA in early sea urchin embryos: cytoplasmic particles. *Science*, 150: 214.

———, N. V. BELITSINA, and M. A. AJTKHOZIN, 1964: Messenger RNA in early embryogenesis. *J. General Biology USSR*, 25: 321.

SUEOKA, N., 1962: Variation and heterogeneity of base composition of deoxyribonucleic acids: a compilation of old and new data. *J. Mol. Biol.*, 3: 31.

TENCER, R., and N. BIELIAVSKY, 1960: Étude de l'incorporation de l'uridine tritiée dans les oeufs d'amphibiens. *Exptl. Cell Res.*, 21: 279.

VINOGRAD, J., R. BRUNER, R. KENT, and J. WEIGLE, 1963: Band centrifugation of macromolecules and viruses in self-generating density gradients. *Proc. Nat. Acad. Sci.* (*U.S.*), 49: 902.

WALLACE, R., 1963: Studies on amphibian yolk. IV. An analysis of the main body component of yolk platelets. *Biochim. Biophys. Acta*, 74: 505.

WILT, F. H., 1964: Ribonucleic acid synthesis during sea urchin embryogenesis. *Devel. Biol.*, 9: 299.

WYATT, G. R., 1955: Separation of nucleic acid components by chromatography on filter paper. In E. Chargaff and J. N. Davidson (eds.), *The Nucleic Acids*, Academic Press, New York, Vol. I, p. 243.

YOSHIKAWA, M., T. FUKADA, and Y. KAWADE, 1964: Separation of rapidly labeled RNA of animal cells into DNA-type and ribosomal RNA-type components. *Biochem. Biophys. Res. Comm.* 15: 22.

Fixation Procedures of Embryonal Tissues for Electron Microscopy*

By Daniel Szollosi

INTRODUCTION

Fixation and preparation of various embryonal tissues for electron microscopy have led frequently to disappointing results. With the usual techniques, membrane systems often were disrupted (cell membranes as well as intracellular membrane systems) and coarse precipitation or flocculation artifacts appeared throughout the cell. Embryonal tissues apparently represent a specific problem to electron microscopists. In this article an attempt will be made to discern from reports in the literature the extent to which embryonal tissues differ from adult tissues, and how such differences may actually account for the difficulties in preparing them. After a general discussion, a number of procedures will be outlined in more detail which may, hopefully, lead to successful preservation of certain embryonal tissues for ultrastructural studies.

The different behavior of embryonal tissue to fixatives and to preparatory procedures was noted in one of the first careful studies describing the effects of different solutions on cells and tissues. Thus, Palade and Porter wrote in 1954: "Embryonal tissues, presumably because of their higher water content, proved more difficult to fix and process in this way than did adult specimens and usually showed more precipitation artifacts and extensive extraction effects. It was found that the former could be noticeably reduced by buffering the fixative at a more alkaline pH, e.g., 7.8 to 8.00 instead of 7.3, whereas extraction could be slowed down to an appreciable extent by shortening the time

* The author is indebted to Dr. J. H. Luft, Dr. D. E. Kelly, and Dr. R. A. Cloney for lengthy discussions on fixation problems and for their valuable suggestions and to Dr. N. B. Everett, Dr. J. H. Luft, and Dr. D. E. Kelly for reading the manuscript critically. Many thanks are expressed to Dr. P. C. Baker, Dr. R. A. Cloney, Dr. H. L. Dunlap, Dr. A. C. Enders, Dr. H. M. Jensen, Dr. N. K. Mottet, Dr. D. E. Kelly, and Dr. H. E. Potswald for permitting me to present some of their unpublished electron micrographs as well as for personal communications regarding their most recent preparatory procedures. This study was partially supported by funds provided by the National Institutes of Health Grants HD-01110 and GM-136.

for fixation and dehydration" (Palade and Porter, 1954).

Reference is made to the statement above in most books and review articles on techniques in electron microscopy. In practice, however, apparently the suggested modification has not always significantly improved embryonal tissue preservation judging from continuing complaints of colleagues as well as from examination of results in our own laboratory.

Curiously, Palade and Porter's fleeting comment blaming the "higher water content" was adopted without further ado as one of the chief sources of the problem. In data summarized from a large number of studies by Needham (1931) some measurements of water content in whole embryos have shown that a decreasing water content seems to be a universal accompaniment of growth. However, other measurements show there are inconsistencies in the rule. In certain fish embryos, trout for example, the water content does not seem to change at all, and in some amphibians an increase in water content has been observed until shortly after hatching. These conflicting data and inconsistencies have not been explained satisfactorily but it has been suggested that in many cases the measurement of true protoplasmic water content is difficult. Since the 1930's only very occasional quantitative measurements can be found on water content of cells.

Recently, the dry mass of mouse eggs has been estimated to be in the neighborhood of 15 percent (Loewenstein and Cohen, 1964). This value is in good agreement with values found for the protoplasmic dry mass of mammalian cells from various sources (Giese, 1962; Sponsler and Barth, 1942). In comparison, the dry mass of the sea urchin egg is only slightly higher than the value given above for mammalian cells (Ephrussi, 1933).

Difficulties with such measurements and with their interpretation are compounded when post-blastocyst or blastula stages are studied. In eggs and early cleavage stages it can be assumed that, after taking some precaution, nearly the entire water content measured refers to the cytoplasmic mass. The same cannot be assumed, however, in studies of total water content at later developmental stages. The primitive connective tissue layer, for example, is rich in lymph. Needham (1931) noted that the decreasing water content during development may reflect a change in the proportions of connective tissue elements; in other words, the tissue may shift from a highly mucoid to a more mature connective tissue, with an increasing collagenous fiber content. The former components have a high degree of hydration, estimates ranging between 68 and 520 ml water per gram of hyaluronic acid (Fitton-Jackson, 1964).

Peculiarities of the behavior of eggs and embryonal tissue to fixation may not be due to the "wateriness" or "high degree of hydration" of their protoplasm proper. Considerations of studies concerned with sol-gel transformations already indicate that the ratio of dry mass to water does not change during such transformations. The tendency of bond formation is changed between aggregates (micelles) of rod-shaped particles composed of large molecules when simple changes in physical conditions occur; thixotropic behavior is a good example. Altering the chemical composition of the environment may provide new conditions in which one or the other state is favored. The most striking features of egg cells and of cells of the early cleavage stages are their gigantic size, including, in most cases, giant nuclei and irregular arrangement of clusters of cytoplasmic organelles. With the exception of yolk (wherever this may be apropos), the organelles are generally the same as in adult tissues, although frequently their ultrastructure is highly specialized or modified.

In eggs and protozoans alike, cytoplasmic organelle clusters or islets can be found to consist of one or more representative of each type of organelle embedded in a lake of apparently structureless "hyaloplasm." The fact that nucleated egg fragments, one-fourth the size of mature eggs, can develop after fertilization into a new individual, or that a viable population can be established from nucleated fragments of several protozoans by microsurgical methods may reflect the presence of multiple vital cytoplasmic organelle clusters; these centers suffice until a minimum cytoplasmic-nuclear ratio is reached, below which no recovery is possible. The giant cells mentioned above had to develop different kinds of specializations in some cases to cope with the specialized functions the cells were called upon to perform. Deposition of yolk or the development of excretory vacuoles and gullets may be mentioned as examples.

After establishment of the germ layers, cells of embryonal tissues show even fewer morphological differences from adult tissues. Cell size and distribution of cell organelles are, in these cases, frequently comparable. The difficulties in fixation of these tissues might therefore be suspected to lie in the newly developing supporting or connective tissue elements. Hyaluronic acid, amino sugars, or other polysaccharides, which represent the major fraction of the matrix of this newly developing tissue component, do not react with osmium tetroxide (Bahr *et al.*, 1957). Since, in most cases, tissues are cut prior to fixation to enhance penetration of osmium fixatives, one may deal with a combination of problems: slow penetration of osmium and lack of mechanical resistance to damage during cutting. In fixation of certain types of tissues the quality of tissue preservation showed considerable improvement when alcian blue (Combs, 1966) or ruthenium red (Luft, 1964) was added to the fixative (both compounds react with polyanionic mucoids), or when a new, rapidly penetrating buffering vehicle, *s*-collidine (Bennett and Luft, 1959) was introduced. Fixation quality may directly depend on the penetration rate of fixatives into tissues. An improvement in preservation has been reported when higher concentrations of heavy metal solutions were employed, accelerating their diffusion (Wood and Luft, 1965; Bhowmick and Wohlfarth-Bottermann, 1965).

More recently, a variety of dialdehydes have been employed successfully as fixatives for electron microscopy [acrolein (Luft, 1959), glutaraldehyde, adipic aldehyde, etc. (Sabatini *et al.*, 1963)]. The penetration rate of these fluids into tissues is much faster than that of osmium. Aldehydes are known cross-linking agents and may stabilize delicate, labile fibers of cells. Some of the fixation problems may thus be overcome because either entire embryos or large pieces thereof can be fixed in aldehyde. After initial hardening of the tissues, but prior to the postfixation procedure with osmium, the extirpated tissues can be cut into an appropriate size range with comparatively little damage.

Aldehyde fixation coupled with postfixation in osmium tetroxide brought to attention the fact that most cells, including eggs of several species (invertebrates and vertebrates alike, including mammals) contain a filamentous as well as a microtubular cytoskeleton. Osmium tetroxide, in various buffer systems, fixes such cytoskeletons poorly. Cytoplasmic fixation damage in many cases may be due to the lack of maintenance of an internal cytoplasmic supporting structure. The cross-linking properties of aldehyde may be responsible for the better preservation of these filamentous elements inside and outside cells.

For example, in amebae and certain ciliates, a cytoplasmic fibrous system can be preserved with acrolein which, if followed by osmium fixation, provides a superior preservation of delicate cytoplasmic constituents (Szubinska, 1964).

Comparative studies on fixation of larval tunicates may be mentioned here as a case in point. The caudal epidermal cells of *Distaplia occidentalis* larvae and post-larval stages fix well in osmium tetroxide buffered in bicarbonate. These cells contain many 50- to 70-Å filaments that may contribute to the stability of the cytoplasmic matrix. However, in early larval stages only a few randomly dispersed filaments can be found in the epithelial cells, and fixation with osmium alone is not acceptable (Cloney, personal communication).

An important consideration in fixation response of eggs versus tissues may be the shift in proportions of ectoplasm and endoplasm due to the decrease in cell volume by cleavage and subsequent cell divisions. Until gastrulation, the cytoplasmic mass of the egg is subdivided by newly formed lipoprotein membrane systems into small compartments. During this process and particularly during the ensuing differentiation and morphogenesis, lipoprotein membrane systems also develop to a high degree of organization within the cells. The cytoplasmic organelles by now are distributed more uniformly in the smaller cells and are packed more closely together. This new type of cytoplasmic organization alone may promote more uniform fixation with a greater variety of fixatives. In eggs and early cleavage stages, neighboring clusters of cell organelles might be displaced by unevenly diffusing chemical agents, leaving behind completely empty regions. In later developmental stages, fixation may be more uniform mainly due to the more compact cytoplasmic organization.

Similar lines of thought can be extended to fixation and preparation of other "difficult" tissues. In addition to the uneven distribution of cytoplasmic components of embryonal tissue which exist in a large number of cases, external modifications also can be found and should be taken into account. These may consist of a tunic of greater or lesser complexity, or of some changes in behavior of the plasma membrane proper. In contrast to tissues, amebae, for example, are not readily penetrated by glutaraldehyde, allowing the passage of considerable length of time before cellular activity is stopped (Griffin, 1963), while acrolein penetrates and fixes these protista very rapidly, providing adequate preservation (Szubinska, 1964).

The question can now be posed anew: what might the causes be that make embryonal tissues represent a special problem to the electron microscopists? One finds little that differentiates embryonic protoplasmic material quantitatively from adult tissues: hence, the difference may be qualitative. Some embryonal tissues may represent a fixation problem to the electron microscopist due only perhaps to the distribution of intracellular substances and organelles and/or of the extracellular components. Moreover, fixation of eggs and embryonal tissues may not cause any more difficulties than the fixation of any other tissue which shows a peculiar accumulation and distribution of specialized intracellular and extracellular elements and unusual relationships of their cells to each other.

Our information is fragmentary about the chemical reactions of different fixing agents. Comparative studies disclose significantly different morphological appearance with different primary fixatives. The differences may reflect different chemical composition of certain cellular structures. In evaluating fixation quality of embryonic tissues, the differential reaction of various agents with individual structural elements must be considered. The assumption is probably valid that a structure is preserved better the greater the structural complexity that is evident. It may be desirable to study and to gather information from a variety of fixation experiments, because only under such conditions may we appreciate all the structural complexities of the object in question.

The unpredictable reaction of different chemicals with tissues is reflected in the current literature by the invention of complex fixatives. For certain tissues or cytoplasmic components (e.g., filaments and cytoplasmic microtubules) a mixture of glutaraldehyde and acrolein has been recommended as the primary fixative followed by osmium (Sandborn *et al.*, 1964). In other cases, cold glutaraldehyde and osmium were mixed in *s*-collidine buffer (Trump and Bulger, 1966) and in a variety of buffer systems to give optimal fixation of cellular structures (H. Stanley, unpublished), including the fine fibrillar and tubular cytoskeletal components as well as extracellular fibrous connective tissue elements.

The criteria used primarily for optimal fixation consist of continuity of cellular membrane systems (plasma membrane, intracytoplasmic membranes, particularly of large cytoplasmic vesicles), integrity of mitochondria, homogeneity, and fine dispersion of the background cytoplasm. In embryonic materials the criteria chosen for good fixation must be carefully evaluated because a large number of morphological specializations and transformations occur. One should not expect to find, for example, an image of the "classical" mitochondrion in various embryonal tissues, in which changes in mitochondrial morphology have been reported (André, 1962; Odor, 1965; Adams and Hertig, 1964). In those certain developmental stages mitochondria may be more sensitive or labile to chemical fixatives, due to their morphological reorganization. For each fixation, therefore, a large number of criteria should be established before pronouncement on fixation quality.

With glutaraldehyde fixatives it has been suggested that the fixative should be nearly isoosmotic to the tissue for optimal results (Powell *et al.*, 1964). More recently in a critical study, Fahimi and Drochmans (1965) suggest that a slightly hypertonic fixative, containing 1.7–3 percent aldehyde in 0.1 or 0.05 *M* phosphate buffer respectively, gives better preservation. Osmotic conditions of osmium solutions in a variety of buffer systems may vary greatly (Wood and Luft, 1965). The addition of salts or sucrose has been recommended by different investigators to increase the fixative's osmotic pressure. It can be demonstrated that the addition of calcium, for example, reduces the loss of labeled methionine from the liver of a uniformly labeled rat (Luft and Wood, 1964) and that of hemoglobin from amphibian red blood cells (Tooze, 1964). In other words, it caused reduction of protein extraction during fixation. Calcium, on the other hand, has been excluded from the vehicle for glutaraldehyde fixation of eggs and larval stages of sea urchins, because calcium causes irregular protein precipitation, and clumping occurs in the cytoplasm (G. A. Millonig, personal communication). To counter extraction of the protoplasm, a reduction in fixation time has been suggested by Palade and Porter (1954) and by more recent experimenters (Szubinska, 1964; Bhowmick and Wohlfarth-Bottermann, 1965). Sucrose has been recommended for use for a variety of tissues (Caulfield, 1957) and has recently been used successfully for fixation of chick and mouse limb buds (Jurand, 1965). However, in several cases, marine invertebrate embryos in particular, sucrose addition did not result in improved fixation in this laboratory.

The treatment of tissues to be fixed should also be considered from time of their removal from their natural environment until the time of fixation. Problems with handling or pretreatment may be one of the stumbling blocks to successful preservation. This step is of particular importance in cases in which an intermediate step is unavoidable, e.g., the use of "physiological saline" during the recovery of mammalian eggs and cleavage stages from the reproductive tract, or certain treatments in tissue or organ culture condition. Comments concerning tonicity and pH of the fixatives should consider intracellular environment rather than the extracellular milieu. Conditions well suited for a culture medium may not be found optimal for fixation, and acceptance of values from one to the other should be made cautiously.

Electron microscopists cannot expect to find a simple, unique, or even magic solution for the preservation of a variety of embryonal tissues. One cannot store in the refrigerator a successful fixative for every and all tissues, but every case must be faced as a unique problem in recognition of the intracellular specializations as well as the extracellular components. While certain modifications of cell structures may be preserved successfully with one fixative, other elements may be less well preserved or even leached out. Many complaints about unsuccessful fixation of embryonal tissue for ultrastructural studies could be avoided if the morphological complexities and the chemical specializations of the cells were kept in mind.

SUGGESTIONS AND COMMENTS ON FIXATION IN A FEW SPECIFIC CASES

Fixation of Certain Mammalian Embryonal Tissue

Fixation quality of mammalian ova has been found to be greatly variable. In an experimental series (D. Szollosi, 1963–1964, unpublished experiments) to determine the causes for the variability, it emerged that factors of importance were:

1. the flushing medium of the female reproductive tract,
2. the buffer system employed for the fixation,
3. addition of specific ions to the fixative.

The fixation quality was not uniform when the fixative was employed also as the flushing medium. Results became more uniform when a balanced salt solution was used for removal of ova from the female reproductive tract, but they were best when a complex tissue culture medium, TC 199 (Microbiological Associates), containing 5–10 percent serum, was used. The same solution was also recommended as a successful culture medium for rabbit and hamster ova (Chang, 1959; Yanagimachi and Chang, 1964). Immediately after removal, eggs were rapidly transferred by a small bore pipette with a very small volume of the flushing medium into the osmium fixative.

The fixative found to give most uniform results was:

1 part 0.2 *M* *s*-collidine buffer (pH 7.4)

2 parts 5 percent osmium tetroxide

1 mg $CaCl_2$ (anhydrous powder) per milliliter of fixative

1 ml ice-cold 20 percent formaldehyde (neutralized with 1 *N* NaOH) solution was added to 10 ml of cold osmium-*s*-collidine mixture just before use.

After 30–45 minutes fixation on crushed ice, the ova were pipetted from the fixative directly into 70 percent ethanol solution and washed repeatedly in several changes of the same solution and rapidly dehydrated in an ethanol series. Preimplantation stages of many mammals are small; and it was found desirable to avoid the intermediate propylene oxide step, as recommended originally for Epon 812 embedding (Luft, 1961), because very active convection currents are set up at the time of mixing with absolute alcohol and

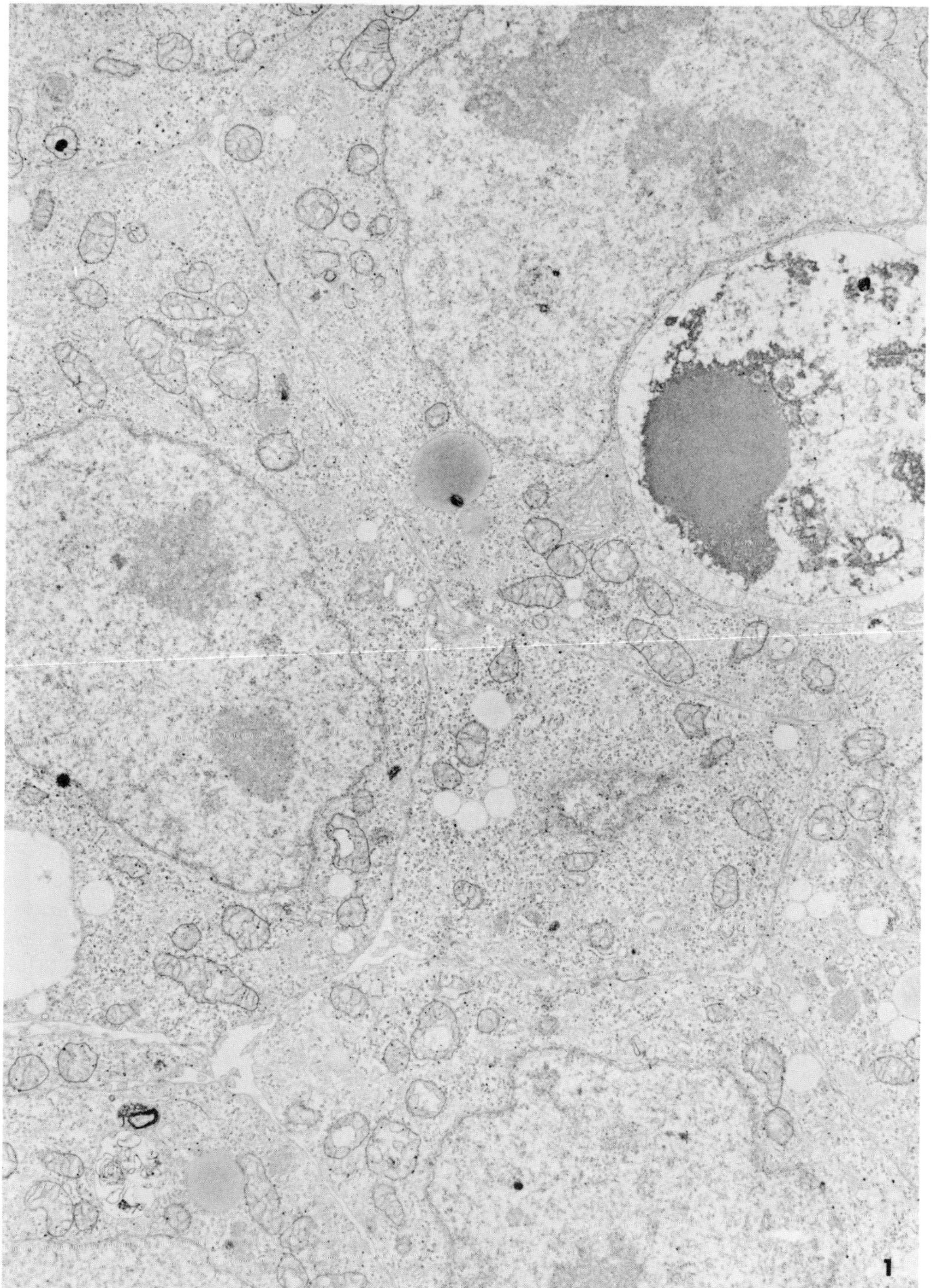

FIG. 1. Embryonal cell mass of a mouse blastocyst recovered and fixed in the afternoon on the fourth day postcoitum. Fixation: osmium tetroxide in *s*-collidine buffer containing calcium chloride and formaldehyde. × 9,200.

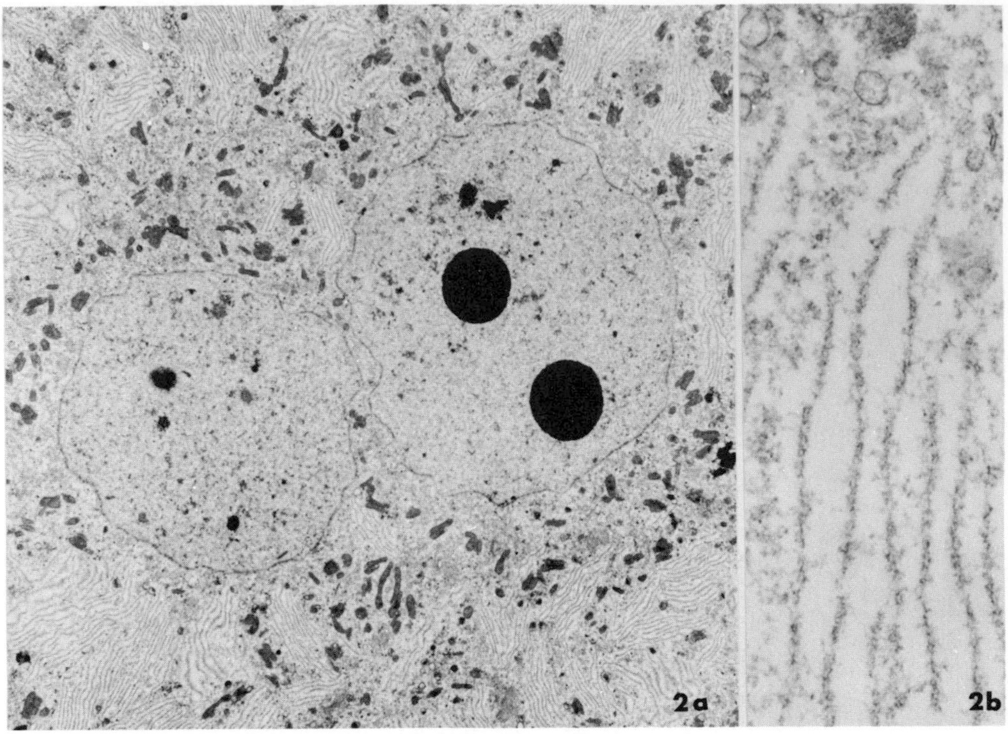

FIG. 2. (a) Hamster egg with two pronuclei. The background cytoplasm is filled with beaded "filamentous" or platelike substance. × 4,200. (b) The structure of the "filamentous" substance is ill-defined with this fixative. Osmium tetroxide, *s*-collidine containing 1 mg calcium chloride per milliliter of fixative. × 39,000.

later because of evaporation of propylene oxide. In most cases a very slow transition from alcohol to Epon embedding medium was found advantageous. Particularly after the appearance of a distinct blastocoel, the dilution steps had to be very gradual to avoid the collapse and distortion of the blastocyst, most probably due to differences in osmotic conditions. In extreme cases it was necessary to mix gradually Epon 812, which is not a very viscous fluid, directly with absolute alcohol, and later to increase gradually the concentration of the Epon embedding medium[1] (Fig. 1).

Originally, an osmium fixative in *s*-collidine buffer containing calcium but lacking formaldehyde was tried and found to be quite successful for eggs completing the first and second cleavage. But in the young morula with 8–16 cells, only a few cells appeared to be preserved well with the same solution. Addition of 2–4 percent formaldehyde apparently solved this problem of general preservation. But the fixative containing calcium ions alone, as

[1] Recently the commercially available Shell Epon 812 delivered had a different epoxy value than earlier batches. It was advantageous to change the proportions of the components in stock solutions A and B to attain blocks with good cutting quality. The proportions used were the following (J. H. Luft, 1966, personal communication.):

Sol. A	Epon 812,	144 ml
	DDSA,	200 ml
Sol. B	Epon 812,	200 ml
	NMA,	153 ml

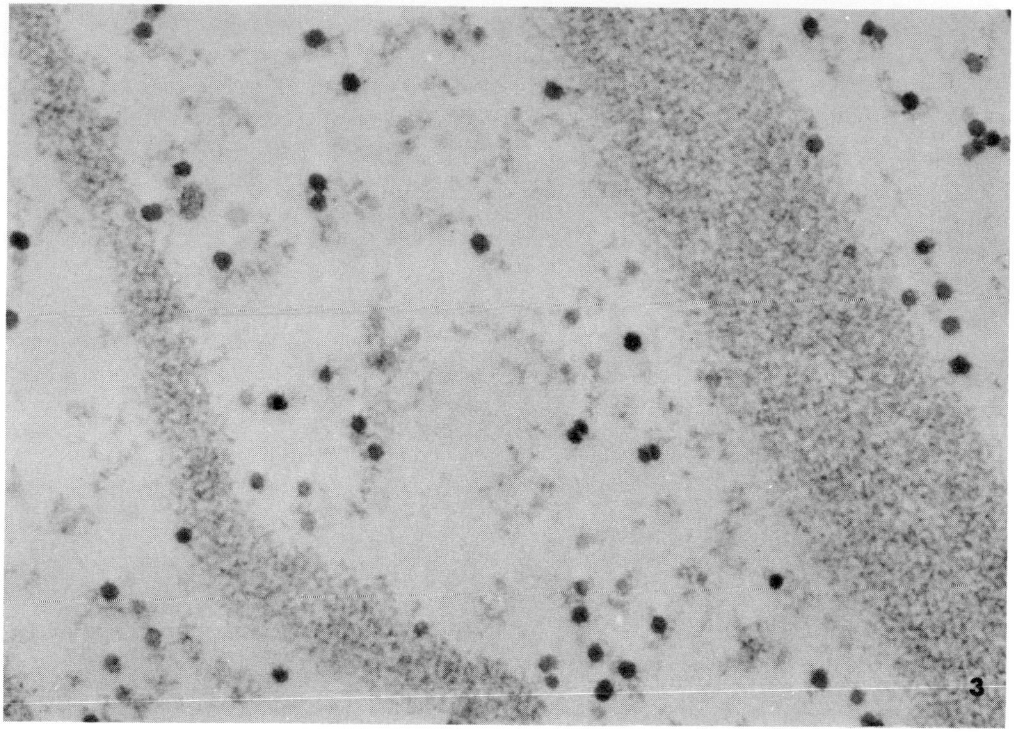

FIG. 3. Hamster egg recovered approximately 4 hours after sperm penetration, fixed in glutaraldehyde, buffered with 0.1 *M* cacodylate and postfixed in osmium tetroxide. The cytoplasmic "filamentous" or platelike material demonstrates great complexity and order. × 75,000.

described at the beginning of this paragraph, preserved long strands with a beaded pattern (Fig. 2, a and b) throughout extensive cytoplasmic regions. These areas were found to be "structureless" or faintly filamentous with osmium fixatives in a variety of buffer systems lacking calcium.

Even greater structural complexity was preserved in the same cytoplasmic regions when 2 percent glutaraldehyde and 1 percent acrolein fixation was used either in 0.1 *M* cacodylate or phosphate buffer, followed by osmium tetroxide treatment in the same buffer. The long strands with a beaded pattern of ill-defined nature noted above, following dialdehyde fixation, appeared as highly organized, paracrystalline platelets (Fig. 3). These were interpreted to be deposits of "yolky" materials (Szollosi, 1965). The preservation of membrane systems in most cell organelles was, however, much less satisfactory.

In contrast to the early cleavage stages, mouse and rat blastocysts can be preserved well in 2 percent glutaraldehyde,[2] 1 percent acrolein in 0.1 *M* cacodylate

[2] The initial supplies of "biological grade" glutaraldehyde have deteriorated on storage. It is necessary for good fixation that the glutaraldehyde solution remain clear after dilution. Glutaraldehyde solution diluted to 25 percent or lower concentration can be stored for long periods of time in the refrigerator (J. H. Luft, personal communication).

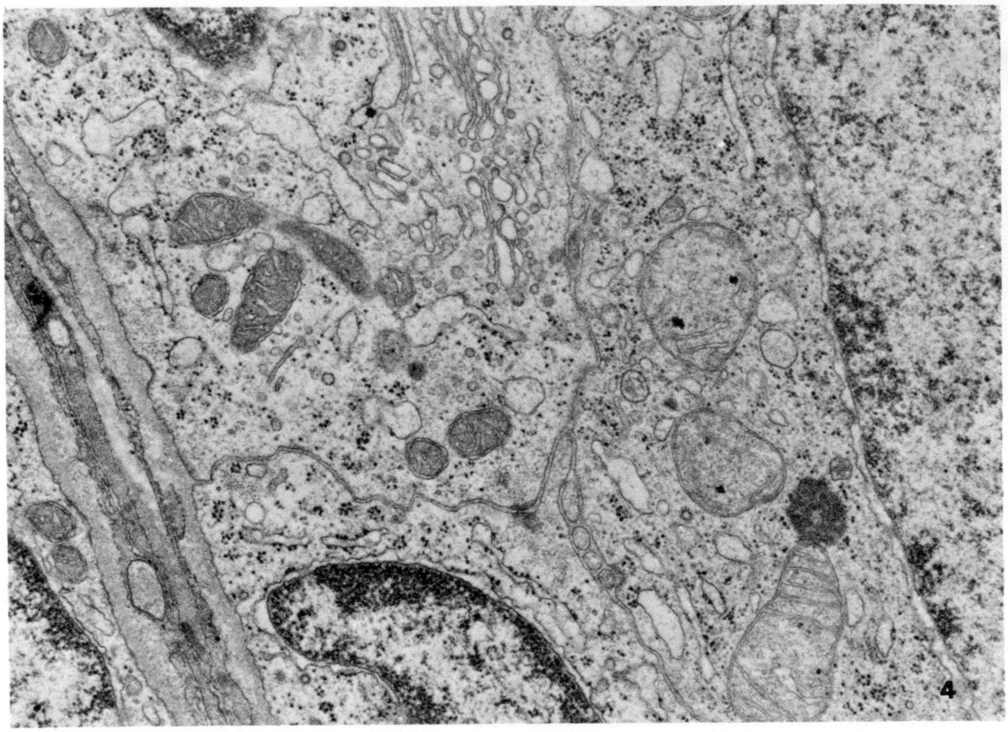

FIG. 4. Ovary of a 27-day-old rat, demonstrating a portion of a small primary follicle. Flattened connective tissue cell processes are outside the basal lamina of the follicle. Two low columnar follicle cells are adjacent to a young oocyte. Primary fixation with glutaraldehyde-acrolein mixture in cacodylate buffer followed with osmium tetroxide. × 25,000.

buffer at pH 7.3. After 60 to 90 minutes fixation, the tissues were washed in several changes of 0.15 *M* cacodylate buffer adjusted to pH 7.3, lasting for 10 to 20 minutes. After washing, the tissues were postfixed in 1 percent osmium tetroxide solution in 0.1 *M* cacodylate buffer at the same pH. Treatment for 30 minutes with osmium tetroxide sufficed, after which the tissues were dehydrated and embedded in Epon.

The glutaraldehyde-acrolein mixture was found to be a satisfactory fixative also for mammalian ovaries (Fig. 4). Fixatives were tested most thoroughly on ovaries of the laboratory white rat, but those of the hamster, human, monkey, rabbit, cat, and gerbil were also prepared. Small oocytes in follicles consisting of a single, flattened cell layer offered no difficulty to a variety of fixation procedures. With the beginning of the oocyte growth phase (which occurs in several species concomitantly with the signs of morphological transformation of some cytoplasmic organelles and further cytoplasmic differentiation), fixation problems became evident with some mixtures. Good fixation was also obtained, in general, with the osmium-formaldehyde-calcium mixture, but in particular nearly mature oocytes in large, tertiary follicles were well fixed.

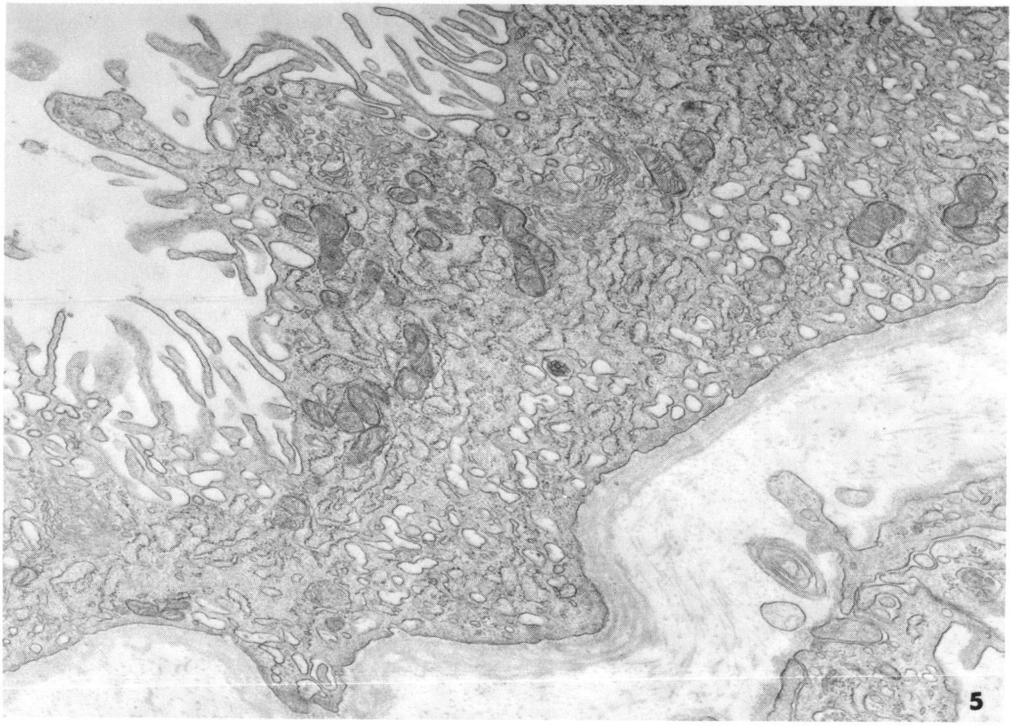

FIG. 5. Armadillo placenta showing the syncytial trophoblast. Fixed in 3 percent glutaraldehyde in 0.1 *M* phosphate buffer. Approximately × 25,000. Original electron micrograph by courtesy of Dr. Allen C. Enders.

Preservation of mammalian eggs emphasizes certain points which were described in the general discussion. It becomes evident that with use of one type of fixation one may not expect optimal preservation of every component in cells containing highly specialized regions. Apparently, the fixation quality of at least one cytoplasmic element has to be sacrificed to gain generally acceptable over-all fixation. This example further demonstrates a case in which a fixative that is satisfactory in an early developmental period fails in later periods.

Generally good fixation of mammalian embryonic tissues was obtained in 3 percent glutaraldehyde in 0.1 *M* phosphate buffer at pH 7.0 by Enders (1965, personal communication) (Fig. 5). The fixative was used for mammalian ova, cleavage stages, implanting blastocysts, placentae, and several tissues of young embryos. A fixation period, lasting 2 hours, was recommended, followed by a buffer wash of about the same duration. Tissues were subsequently postfixed in 2 percent osmium tetroxide, buffered also with 0.1 *M* phosphate buffer. Dehydration in alcohol series of at least 1 hour duration was suggested before passing the tissue block through a 1:1 mixture of propylene oxide and plastic and, finally, it was embedded in Durcupan.

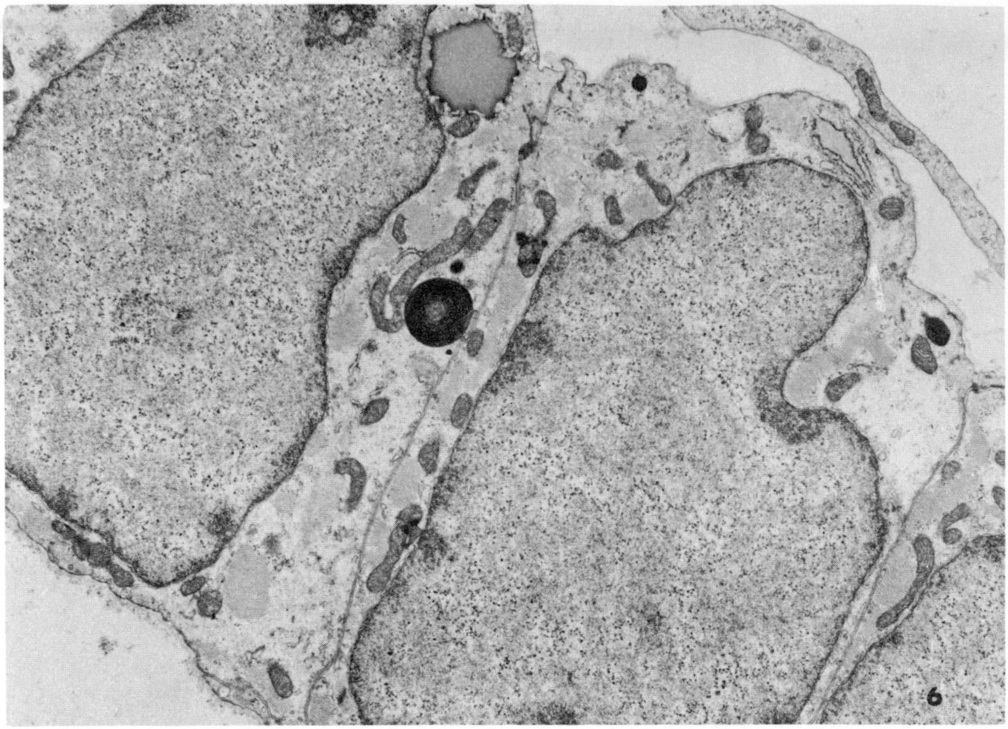

FIG. 6. Myocardial cells of a 2-week-old larva of *Taricha torosa* demonstrating also a thin layer of mesothelium. Fixed in osmium-*s*-collidine. × 6,900. Original electron micrograph by courtesy of Dr. Douglas E. Kelly.

Fixation of Tissues from Developing Amphibians

A recent study on the developing skin obtained from embryonic, larval, and metamorphosed newts, *Taricha torosa*, showed good fixation in that system (Kelly, 1966). Ice-cold 3.75 percent osmium tetroxide in 0.5 *M s*-collidine was utilized frequently for fixation, lasting 1–2 hours. Other blocks were fixed either in 0.5 percent glutaraldehyde solution or 0.25 percent acrolein plus 0.25 percent glutaraldehyde solution in half strength Niu-Twitty solution at pH 7.3–7.5. In the latter cases, the tissue blocks were post-fixed in osmium tetroxide utilizing again the Niu-Twitty solution as a solvent system. The osmotic value of the aldehyde solution was approximately 112–132 milliosmoles (Fig. 6).

For a variety of larval and adult amphibian tissues osmium fixation in *s*-collidine buffer near pH 7.4 provides an excellent fixative (Kelly, 1966, personal communication; J. H. Larson, personal communication). Probably because of the rapid penetration of *s*-collidine, entire embryos or larvae can be fixed *in toto*. Employing this procedure, the dissection of the desired organs, which might result in physical damage, can be avoided. The cell membranes of glial elements of neural components represent, sometimes, the only notable exception to good fixation. Such difficulties could be over-

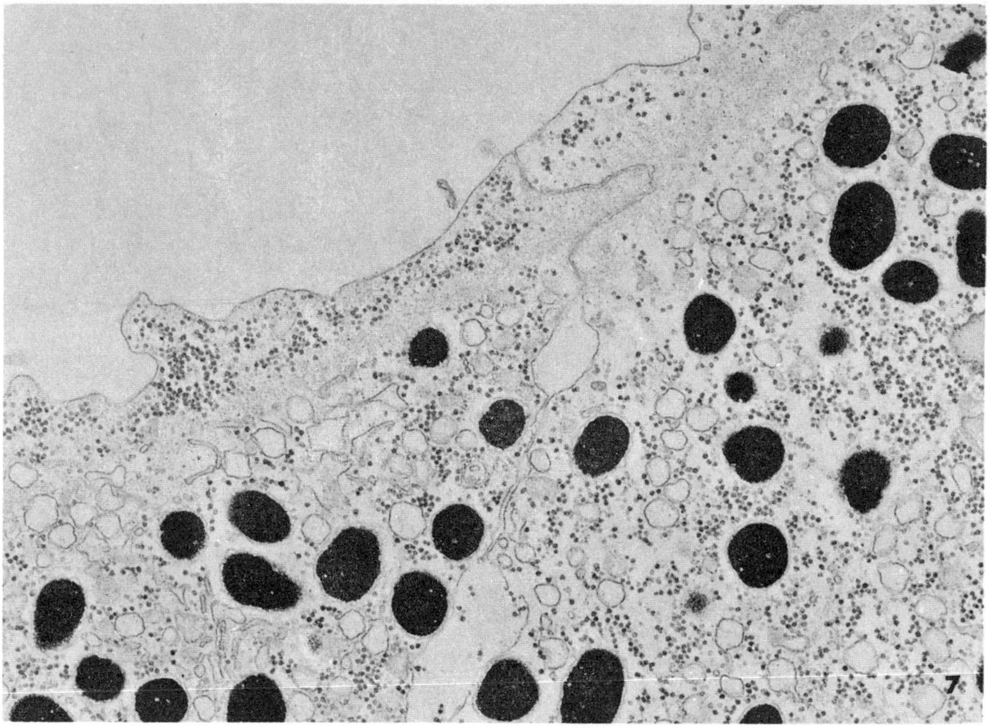

FIG. 7. Neural tube in the head region of Stage 15 neurula of the tree frog *Hyla regilla*. Fixation in osmium tetroxide solution adjusted to pH 7.2 with phosphate buffer. Original electron micrograph by courtesy of Dr. Patricia C. Baker.

come when the deeper lying neural components were rapidly dissected directly in the fixative. Apparently, the good fixation quality depends, in this case, on the immediate availability of the fixative at the tissues concerned and may relate to the rate of penetration of the fixative (W. Flight, personal communication).

Several investigators have reported good fixation of amphibian eggs and early embryonic tissues. The fixation fluids consisted usually of Veronal-acetate buffer in balanced salt solutions (Wartenberg, 1962; Karasaki, 1963). Baker (1964, 1965) used in her studies of early gastrulation in the Pacific tree frog (*Hyla regilla*) 2 percent osmium fixative buffered with Dalton's 4 percent neutralized potassium dichromate solution. This solution gave satisfactory preservation in early to late stages of gastrulation, healing gastrulae and neurulae.

To enhance penetration of the fixative Baker suggested the removal of the tightly adhering vitelline membrane in the preneural stages and the bisection of the embryo (P. C. Baker, personal communication). The operations have been carried out in a Niu-Twitty solution in which the embryos were allowed to heal for 15 minutes before fixation. In this manner embryos could be selected which showed no signs of physical damage. More recent experiments have demonstrated satisfactory preservation of tree frog and *Xenopus* gastrulae and neurulae by 2.5 percent

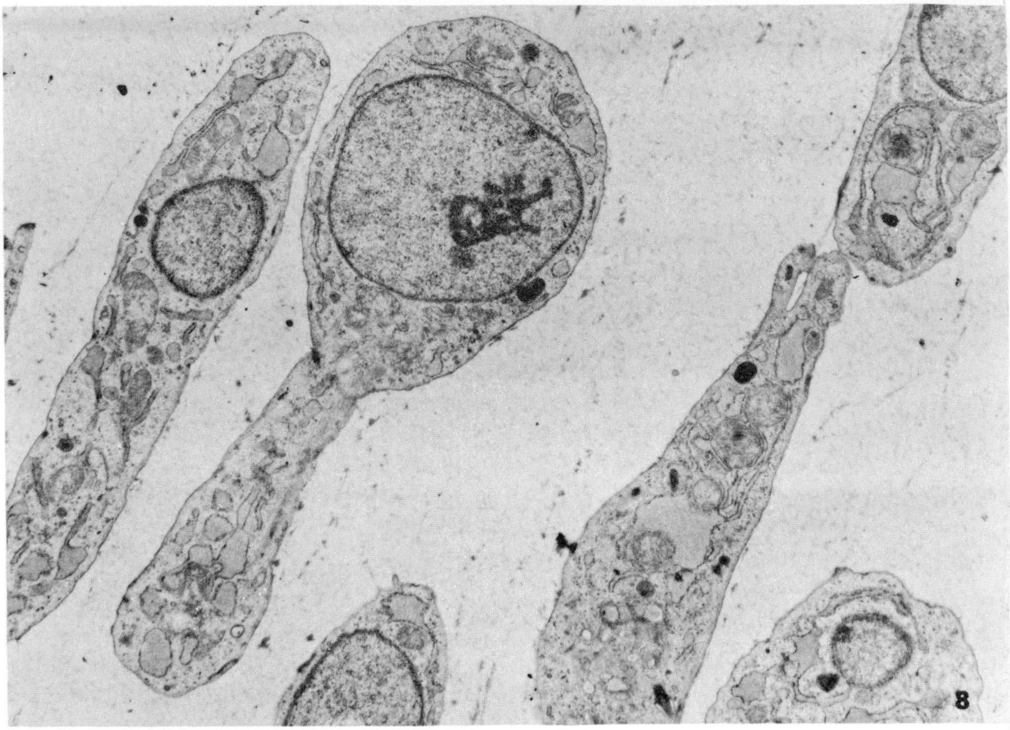

FIG. 8. Mesenchymal cells isolated from the posterior limb bud of a 5-day-old chick embryo and cultured subsequently for 9 days under organ culture conditions. Fixation: glutaraldehyde-osmium in *s*-collidine buffer, Trump and Bulger, 1966). × 6,000. Original electron micrograph by courtesy of Dr. Hanne M. Jensen and Dr. N. Karle Mottet.

glutaraldehyde solution in 0.1 *M* phosphate buffer or 1–2 percent osmium tetroxide solution adjusted to pH 7.4 with 0.1 *M* phosphate buffer (Fig. 7). Cacodylate-buffered glutaraldehyde gave generally poorer fixation. The addition of sucrose to either type of fixation caused extensive cellular damage (P. C. Baker, personal communication).

Fixation of Tissue from Avian Embryos

In contrast to the voluminous literature on experimental embryology of chicken and other birds, only a handful of electron microscopic analyses have been reported on embryos belonging to the class Aves. Recently, several studies were reported on growing and preovulatory follicles of the fowl, examining the relationship between the oocyte and follicle cells. In most of these studies osmium tetroxide was utilized as a fixative, either in Veronal-acetate buffer at pH 7.4 (Press, 1964) or in the same buffer with the addition of salts in an attempt to improve fixation with the increase in osmotic value of the vehicle for osmium (Wyburn *et al.*, 1965). Bellairs (1965) used in her studies a Veronal-acetate or phosphate buffer for

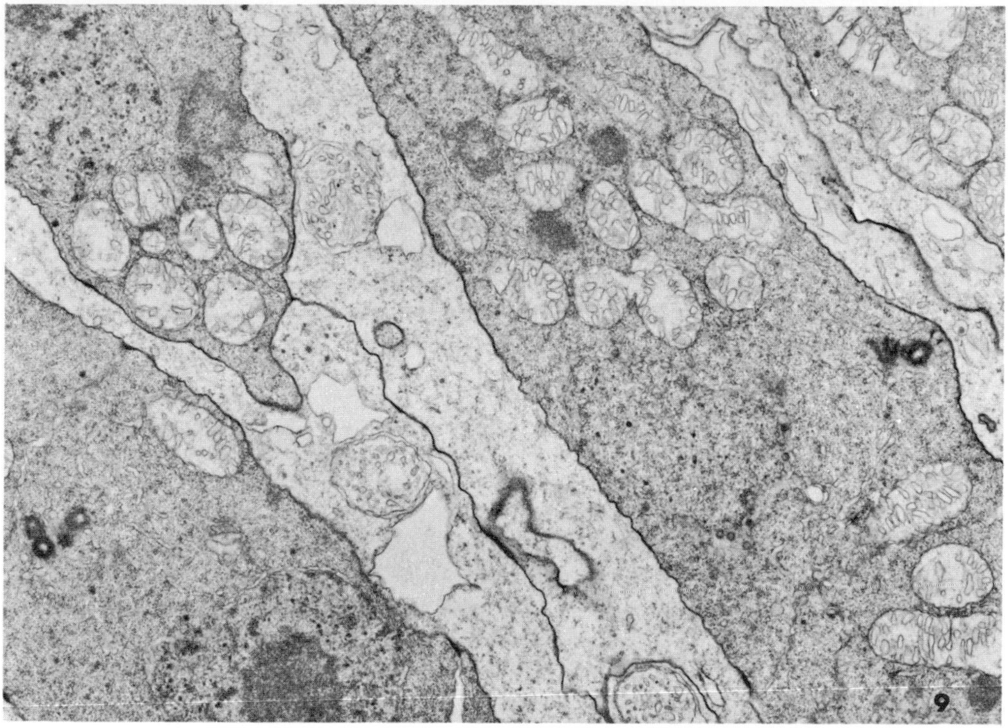

FIG. 9. Testis of *Phialidium gregarium*. Processes of pale supporting cells penetrate between clusters of spermatogonia. Fixed with glutaraldehyde in phosphate buffer containing sodium chloride. × 9,700.

osmium fixation and studied the preservation of ovarian tissues with potassium permanganate and glutaraldehyde.

Overton and Shoup (1964) employed in their studies on the maturing duodenal mucosa osmium buffered with Veronal-acetate at pH 7.9, apparently heeding the suggestion by Palade and Porter (1954) to increase the pH of the fixative for embryonic tissues. These authors showed good preservation of the duodenal mucosa during several days of incubation.

Developing chick wing buds, a favorite subject for experimental embryologists, were prepared for electron microscopy by Jurand (1965). He employed osmium with Veronal-acetate buffer also at a high pH value, 8.15, but added sucrose to increase the osmotic value of this mixture.

More recently, Jensen and Mottet (H. M. Jensen and N. K. Mottet, personal communication) carried out extensive fixation experiments on 5-day-old chick limb buds. They found that fixation for 30 minutes to 1 hour in a mixture of 6.25 percent glutaraldehyde and 1 percent osmium tetroxide in *s*-collidine buffer (Fig. 8) (Trump and Bulger, 1966) or 3 percent osmium tetroxide in *s*-collidine containing calcium chloride and formaldehyde

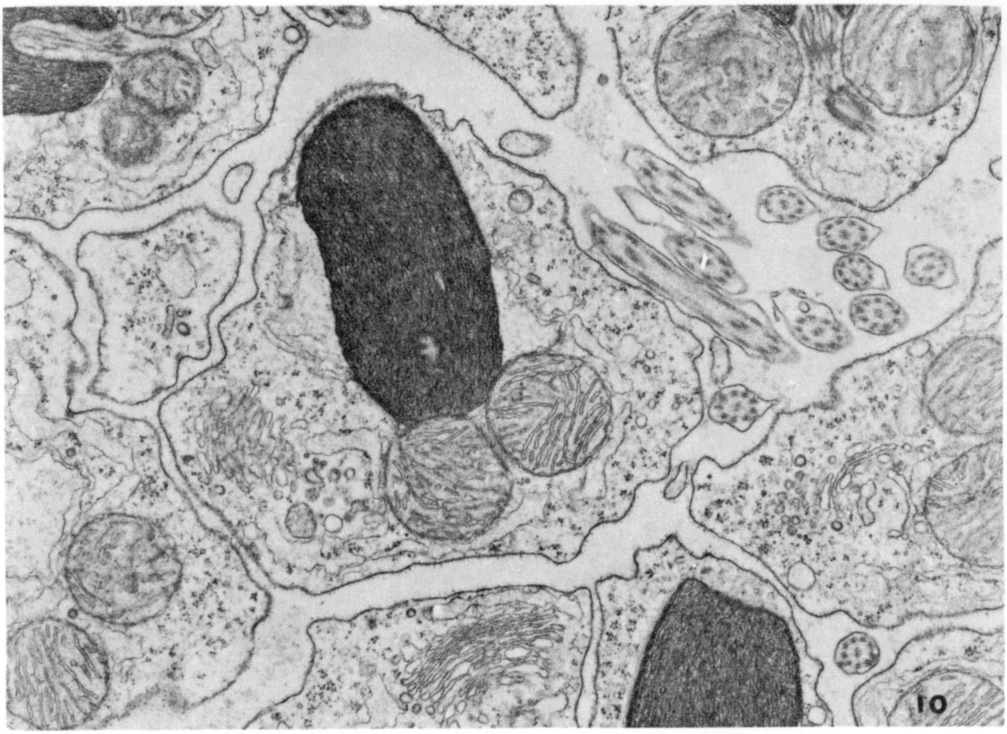

FIG. 10. Spermatids of *Spirorbis (Leospira) mörchi* during their compacting and elongation phase. Fixation: glutaraldehyde-osmium mixture in phosphate buffer. × 22,500. Original electron micrograph by courtesy of Dr. Herbert E. Potswald.

(for details see fixation of mammalian ova) gave generally better preservation than any fixative previously employed and published for chick embryos. Also generally quite acceptable morphological preservation resulted by fixation with 3 percent glutaraldehyde in Eagle's medium adjusted to neutrality with sodium hydroxide.

Fixation of Embryonal Marine Invertebrate Tissues

After successful fixation of a variety of vertebrate tissues with glutaraldehyde, or a mixture of aldehydes, the fixation of marine invertebrate tissues was also attempted with the same agents. Because the fixation of vertebrate tissues in aldehydes was optimal when the fixative was isoosmotic, in some experiments two parts of sea water were mixed with one part neutralized solution of 9 percent glutaraldehyde. Gross observations with the dissecting microscope of sea urchin eggs and eggs of the hydromedusa, *Phyalidium gregarium*, suggested a better preservation with glutaraldehyde than with osmium tetroxide in different buffer systems (phosphate, Dalton's chromate-dichromate, Veronal acetate-sodium acetate, bicarbonate or *s*-collidine; Szollosi, unpublished experiments, 1963–1965). Although this fixation seemed generally satisfactory by electron microscope criteria, the cytoplasm contained coarse precipitates which were thought to be flocculated protein. If a sodium chloride solution was substituted to increase the osmotic value of the fixative, the preservation of cell membranes and cell organelles was equally good, but the floccules were missing. It was postulated that probably the divalent (or multivalent) cations present in sea water act with the fixative to cause flocculation of large cytoplasmic proteins. A fixative prepared after taking some of these considerations into account was quite satisfactory for the preservation of testicular tissue in *Phyalidium* (Roosen-Runge and Szollosi, 1965).

The fixative most frequently used was prepared by mixing:

10 ml 24 percent glutaraldehyde
90 ml 0.22 *M* phosphate buffer
0.82 gm sodium chloride

The sodium chloride renders the solution nearly isoosmotic to sea water. (Calculations were based on the salt content of the sea water near the University of Washington Marine Biological Laboratories at Friday Harbor, San Juan Island. The amount of sodium chloride to be added may have to be adjusted to suit local requirements.) Following a brief rinsing in 0.2 *M* phosphate buffer containing 0.17 gm sodium chloride per 10 ml buffer, the tissues in these studies were postfixed in 1 percent osmium tetroxide in 0.2 *M* phosphate buffer, supplemented with 0.21 gm sodium chloride per 10 ml osmium fixative, dehydrated in ethanol and embedded in Epon 812 (Fig. 9). Millonig (G. A. Millonig, personal communication) and Dunlap and Cloney (H. L. Dunlap, personal communication) have also found that fixation of embryonal tissues of different marine invertebrates with glutaraldehyde was successful when sodium chloride was used to adjust the tonicity of the fixative. They also suggested that calcium salts should be avoided.

Fixation of *Spirorbis* (*Leospira*) *mörchi*, a microserpulid, was very satisfactory in a mixture of 1 ml ice-cold 5 percent glutaraldehyde, 1 ml osmium tetroxide, and 2 ml 0.2 *M* phosphate buffer as suggested by Stanley (H. P. Stanley, personal communication) and others. Cells in different stages of spermatogenesis and oogenesis were well preserved in this mixture as well as different organs of the adult worm (Fig. 10). Fixation was also quite acceptable when 5 percent osmium tetroxide was mixed one to one with 0.2 *M* phosphate or 0.3 *M* bicarbonate buffer at pH 7.4. The usual dehydration and embedding procedure in alcohol and Epon 812, respectively, was carried out after 1 to 2 hours fixation (H. E. Potswald, 1966, unpublished studies).

The intention of this chapter was not to review the extensive literature on fixation of embryonic tissues and to cite all recipes published. Rather, a few selected cases giving good preservation repeatedly were presented in more detail. They may serve as starting points for experiments on other tissues.

REFERENCES

ADAMS, E. C., and A. T. HERTIG, 1964: Studies on guinea pig oocytes. I. Electron microscopic observations on the development of cytoplasmic organelles in oocytes of primordial and primary follicles. *J. Cell Biol.*, 21: 397.

ANDRÉ, J., 1962: Contribution à la connaissance du chondriome. *J. Ultrastruc. Res.*, Suppl. 3.

BAHR, G. F., G. BLOOM, and U. FRIBERG, 1956: Volume changes of tissues in physiological fluids during fixation in osmium tetroxide or formaldehyde and during subsequent treatment. *Exp. Cell Res.*, 12: 342.

BAKER, P. C., 1964: Fine structure of mesodermal and entodermal cells of the blastopore groove in the treefrog, *Hyla regilla. Z. Zellforsch.*, 64: 636.

———, 1965: Fine structure and morphogenetic movements in the gastrula of the treefrog, *Hyla regilla. J. Cell Biol.*, 24: 95.

BELLAIRS, R., 1965: The relationship between oocyte and follicle in the hen's ovary as shown by electron microscopy. *J. Embryol. Exp. Morph.*, 13: 215.

BENNETT, H. S., and J. H. LUFT, 1959: s-Collidine as a basis for buffering fixatives. *J. Biophys. Biochem. Cytol.*, 6: 113.

BHOWMICK, D. K., and K. E. WOHLFARTH-BOTTERMANN, 1965: An improved method for fixing amoebae for electron microscopy. *Exp. Cell Res.*, 40: 252.

CAULFIELD, T. B., 1957: Effects of varying the vehicle for OsO_4 in tissue fixation. *J. Biophys. Biochem. Cytol.*, 3: 827.

CHANG, M. C., 1959: Fertilization of rabbit ova *in vitro*. *Nature*, 193: 466.

COMBS, J. W., 1966: Maturation of rat mast cells. An electron microscope study. *J. Cell Biol.*, 31: 563.

ENDERS, A. C., 1965: A comparative study of the fine structure of the trophoblast in several hemochorial placentas. *Am. J. Anat.*, 116: 29.

EPHRUSSI, B., 1933: Contribution à l'analyse des premiers stades du développement de l'oeuf action de la température. *Arch. Biol. (Paris)*, 44: 1.

FAHIMI, H. D., and P. DROCHMANS, 1965: Essais de standardisation de la fixation au glutaraldehyde. II. Influence des concentrations en aldehyde et de l'osmolalite. *J. Microscopie*, 4: 737.

FITTON-JACKSON, S., 1964: Connective tissue cells. In J. Brachet and A. E. Mirsky (eds.,) *The Cell*, Academic Press, New York, Vol. VI, p. 387.

GIESE, A. C., 1962: *Cell Physiology*. 2nd ed. W. D. Saunders Co., Philadelphia, Pa., and London, Eng.

GRIFFIN, J. L., 1963: Motion picture analysis of fixation for electron microscopy: *Amoeba proteus. J. Cell Biol.*, 19: 77A.

JURAND, A., 1965: Ultrastructural aspects of early development of the forelimb buds in the chick and the mouse. *Proc. Roy. Soc.*, (London), *B*, 162: 387.

KARASAKI, S., 1963: Studies on amphibian yolk. I. The ultrastructure of the yolk platelet. *J. Cell Biol.*, 18: 135.

KELLY, D. E., 1966: Fine structure of desmosomes, hemidesmosomes, and an adepidermal globular layer in developing newt epidermis. *J. Cell Biol.*, 28: 51.

LOEWENSTEIN, J. E., and A. I. COHEN, 1964: Dry mass, lipid content and protein content of the intact and zona-free mouse ovum. *J. Embryol. Exp. Morph.*, 12: 113.

LUFT, J. H., 1959: The use of acrolein as a fixative for light and electron microscopy. *Anat. Rec.*, 133: 305.

———, 1961: Improvements in epoxy resin embedding methods. *J. Biophys. Biochem. Cytol.*, 9: 409.

———, 1964: Electron microscopy of cell extraneous coats as revealed by ruthenium red staining. *J. Cell Biol.*, 23: 54A.

———, and R. L. WOOD, 1964: The extraction of tissue protein during and after fixation with osmium tetroxide in various buffer systems. *J. Cell Biol.*, 19: 46A.

NEEDHAM, T., 1931: *Chemical Embryology*. The Macmillan Company, New York, and University Press, Cambridge, Eng. Vol. II, p. 883.

ODOR, D. L., 1965: The ultrastructure of unilaminar follicles of the hamster ovary. *Am. J. Anat.*, 116: 493.

OVERTON, J., and J. SHOUP, 1964: Fine structure of cell surface specializations in the maturing duodenal mucosa of the chick. *J. Cell Biol.*, 21: 75.

PALADE, G. E., and K. R. PORTER, 1954: Studies on the endoplasmic reticulum. I. Its identification in cells *in situ*. *J. Exp. Med.*, 100: 641.

POWELL, T. E., III, C. W. PHILPOTT, and M. D. MASER, 1964: On the hydrogen ion concentration and osmolarity of fixative components. *J. Cell Biol.*, 23: 110A.

PRESS, N., 1964: An unusual organelle in

avian ovaries. *J. Ultrastruc. Res.*, 10: 528.

ROOSEN-RUNGE, E. C., and D. SZOLLOSI, 1965: On biology and structure of the testis of *Phialidium* Leuckhart (Leptomedusae). *Z. Zellforsch.*, 68: 597.

SABATINI, D. D., K. BENSH, and R. J. BARRNETT, 1963: Cytochemistry and electron microscopy, the preservation of cellular ultrastructure and enzymatic activity by aldehyde fixation. *J. Cell Biol.*, 17: 19.

SANDBORN, E., P. F. KOEN, J. D. MC NABB, and B. MOOSE, 1964: Cytoplasmic microtubule in mammalian cells. *J. Ultrastruc. Res.*, 11: 123.

SPONSLER, O. L., and J. D. BARTH, 1942: Molecular structure in protoplasm. In William Selfriz (ed.), *The Structure of Protoplasm*, The Iowa State University Press, Ames, Iowa, p. 41.

SZOLLOSI, D., 1965: Development of "yolky substance" in some rodent eggs. *Anat. Rec.*, 151: 424.

SZUBINSKA, B., 1964: Electron microscopy of the interaction of ruthenium violet with the cell membrane complex of *Amoeba proteus. J. Cell Biol.*, 23: 92A.

TOOZE, J., 1964: Measurements of some cellular changes during fixation of amphibian erythrocytes with osmium tetroxide solutions. *J. Cell Biol.*, 22: 551.

TRUMP, B. F., and R. E. BULGER, 1966: New ultrastructural characteristics of cells fixed in a glutaraldehyde-osmium tetroxide mixture. *Lab. Invest.*, 15: 368.

WARTENBERG, H., 1962: Elektronenmikroskopische und histochemische Studien über die Oogenese der Amphibieneizelle. *Z. Zellforsch.*, 58: 427.

WOOD, R. L., and J. H. LUFT, 1965: The influence of buffer systems on fixation with osmium tetroxide. *J. Ultrastruc. Res.*, 12: 22.

WYBURN, G. M., H. S. JOHNSTON, and R. N. C. AITKEN, 1965: Specialized plasma membranes in the preovulatory follicle of the fowl. *Z. Zellforsch.*, 68: 70.

YANAGIMACHI, R., and M. C. CHANG, 1964: *In vitro* fertilization of golden hamster ova. *J. Exp. Zool.*, 156: 361.

Cell Marking*

By James A. Weston

INTRODUCTION

It is the purpose of this chapter to describe and evaluate the marking methods which have been used to trace morphogenetic movements. This will be done in terms of (1) the problems requiring markers, (2) the criteria for a suitable marking method, (3) the types of markers which have been used to study cell and tissue movements during embryogenesis, (4) the application of some of these markers, (5) testing the adequacy of marking methods, and (6) a few words on general limitations of all marking methods for studying cell and tissue movements. Since a number of marking methods have been clearly described in a variety of laboratory manuals (e.g., Hamburger, 1960; Rugh, 1962), the purposes of this volume will probably best be served by emphasizing the critical aspects of the various marking techniques and by offering some general guidelines for the design and interpretation of marking experiments.

PROBLEMS REQUIRING MARKERS

Marking studies initially served to determine the origins of organs and tissues in the early embryo—that is, to construct embryonic "fate maps"—and then to follow the morphogenetic tissue movements through which the prospective fates of various regions were realized in embryogenesis (*cf.* Vogt, 1925; Pasteels, 1937, 1942). These problems required that relatively large tissue areas be differentially marked so that their relative movements and interactions could be traced.

To elucidate mechanisms which affect morphogenetic movements at the cellular level, however, more precise analyses of the migratory patterns of individual cells are necessary. Here, methods must be devised to allow a specific cell type to be distinguished from the populations of cells which comprise its environment. This is true *in vivo*, for example, for following the migration of primordial germ cells (*cf.* Blackler and Fischberg, 1961), and neural crest cells (Weston, 1963; Weston and Butler, 1966; Chibon, 1966). In addition, many *in vitro* model systems have been devised to study factors which are thought to affect morphogenetic processes. For example, Moscona (1956, 1960) and Steinberg (1962) have recombined dissociated cells from various tissues and observed the patterns of tissue sorting which occurred. Many opportunities exist for the judicious application of available

* Original work mentioned herein supported by Postdoctoral Fellowship GPD-98728 and U.S. P.H.S. Research Grant GM 13072-01.

marking methods to clarify the fates of individual cells in the process of sorting out (see below, p. 726).

CRITERIA FOR SUITABLE MARKERS

The purpose of marking is to identify unequivocally, and to follow the movements of individual cells or cell groups when they would otherwise be indistinguishable from their surroundings. The demands on methods for accomplishing this task are fourfold: (1) As previously mentioned, the method should mark cells precisely and differentially. That is, the cell types to be studied should be specifically marked while surrounding cells remain unmarked. This means that there should be no transfer or diffusion of the marker from marked cells to their neighbors. (2) The marker should be relatively durable. That is, in addition to not transferring to other cells, the marker should be recognizable in or on the marked cell at least long enough for the processes of interest to go to completion. (3) The marker should be nondeleterious. It should neither harm the cell nor alter its normal pattern of behavior. Finally, (4) the marker should be easily applied and visualized and must be capable of being preserved *in situ* for histological examination. Ideally, the marker should be visible both while the preparation is alive and after the material has been fixed. It will be seen below that few markers fully satisfy these requirements. Even when the first three demands are met, it is seldom that the last requirement can be satisfied adequately.

TYPES OF MARKERS USED TO STUDY CELL AND TISSUE MOVEMENTS

There are two major categories of markers—intrinsic and applied—each of which may be subdivided into several classes.

Intrinsic markers include at least four classes. (1) Cell size and the presence of yolk or pigment granules has often been used to distinguish ectoderm and endoderm cells in amphibia (*cf.* Townes and Holtfreter, 1955). Cell size, as indicated by nuclear size, has also been used to distinguish cells in xenoplastic grafts between amphibian genera (Raven, 1936, 1937). (2) Nuclear staining characteristics may sometimes be used as differential markers. Thus, Moscona (1957) took advantage of the different staining of chick and mouse nuclei with Erlich's hematoxylin to distinguish the cell source in chimeric aggregates of dissociated cells. Similarly, Triplett (1958) used differences in chromatin staining to distinguish the cells of *Rana aurora* and *Hyla regilla* when neural folds of one genus were grafted to the other. (3) Nucleolar number has recently been applied to distinguish donor and host cells in the South African clawed toad, *Xenopus* (Blackler and Fischberg, 1961, see below). Finally, (4) some differentiative traits of cells from advanced embryos have been used as markers *in vitro*. This group of markers includes pigment granules in melanocytes, and a variety of traits made manifest by specific histological, histochemical, or immunohistological procedures. For example, the presence of glycogen in heart myoblasts has been used as a marker in mixed aggregates by Steinberg (1962), and also by Meyer (1964) for identifying primordial germ cells in the young chicken embryo. In another study, tissue-specific antigens were applied as differential markers using fluorescein-conjugated antibodies as specific fluorescent reagents (Okada, 1965a, b). Immunohistological methods have the additional and important potential asset of being cell specific markers in mixed tissues (see below, pp. 726, 731).

Applied markers include three major classes. (1) Vital dyes color cells supravitally and can be observed *in vivo* for some time. This technique has a number of serious limitations, however, and these will be considered in some detail below. (2) Minute particles of carbon, chalk, or carmine have been used to visualize morphogenetic movements in the surface of meroblastic embryos such as the chick (Spratt, 1946, 1947), but uncertainties about the method have led to considerable confusion over the interpretation of some particle marking experiments (*cf.* Spratt and Haas, 1965; and discussion below, p. 733). Recently, microspheres of various ion-exchange resins have been applied as markers on the surface of the alga *Nitella* (Green, 1965), and this technique may prove to be of some use in tracing movements in the surfaces of embryos. (3) Radioisotopes have recently been employed with some success as markers for studying morphogenetic movements. A common and generally useful isotopic marker is tritiated thymidine. This labeled nucleotide is permanently incorporated into nuclear DNA (Friedkin *et al.*, 1956; Hughes, 1958), and because tritium emits a low energy beta particle with a mean free path in photographic emulsion of about 1.0 μ, localization of individual labeled cells by means of radioautography can be precise and accurate (*cf.* Taylor *et al.*, 1957; Falk and King, 1963).

APPLICATION OF MARKERS

Intrinsic Markers

Any naturally occurring, unique cell characteristic that can be visualized might serve as a distinguishing marker to follow cell movements. There are, therefore, many potential markers. The problem, however, is how to distinguish a specific cell or tissue type possessing such markers amidst a homogeneous environment at the time when morphogenetic movements are actually occurring. In fact, most differentiative traits do not appear in early embryos, and therefore are of no use as markers for studying primary morphogenesis. Therefore, a more general class of natural markers must be applied. These include cell size (Raven, 1936; 1937), nuclear staining (Triplett, 1958), and nucleolar number (Blackler and Fischberg, 1961). In each case, differential marking has been obtained by hetero- or xenoplastic grafting *in vivo*.

Raven (1936; 1937), for instance, was able to gain some insight into the neural crest origin of sympathetic ganglia by xenoplastic grafting where reciprocal grafts of neural crest were made between genera of amphibia (*Triturus* and *Ambystoma*) whose cells are of different sizes. Objective criteria of cell size were established by determining the "nuclear value"—that is, the product of the longest nuclear diameter and the diameter at right angles to it. In this case, the frequency distribution of nuclear values of the two genera is bimodal, and donor cells from xenoplastic grafts may be identified in specific regions or tissues of the host as a part of the donor-specific distribution of nuclear values. Clearly, however, the method works only for populations of cells whose nuclear values do not overlap greatly. Individual cells would almost certainly be overlooked. Therefore, such a marker may easily be used only to determine the result of migration but not to observe the process itself.

Another, less equivocal, marking method takes advantage of a mutation in the African clawed toad *Xenopus laevis* (Elsdale, Fischberg, and Smith, 1958). The normal, wild-type *Xenopus* has two nucleoli per nucleus. Mutant animals are anucleolate in the homozygous condition and develop abnormally, while heterozygotes have one nucleolus and develop normally. Blackler and Fischberg (1961) have used the binucleolate nucleus as a cell marker when grafted into uninucleolate host, and *vice versa*. This technique could prove to be one of the more useful devices for studying morphogenetic cell movements in amphibian development. It clearly fulfills the requirements of an adequate marker in that it is cell-specific, permanent, nondeleterious, easily visualized in histological preparations and fairly easy to use.

After differential cellular traits have been expressed, a wide variety of markers become available in various embryonic cell populations. These are, of course, more useful for studies with model systems *in vitro* than they are for studies of the primary organization of the embryo by morphogenetic movements *in vivo*. Two interesting applications of specific cellular traits from the point of view of marking *in vitro* have been made by Trinkaus and Lentz (1964) and Okada (1965a, b).

Following the elegant demonstrations by Moscona (1956, 1960) that dissociated vertebrate tissue cells will re-form tissue-specific structures when reaggregated *in vitro* and by Steinberg (1962) that a hierarchy of externally and internally segregating tissue types existed, considerable interest has centered on the mechanisms of this type of specific segregation. Before hypotheses regarding such mechanisms can be tested, however, the process itself must be observed in some detail. Satisfactory information about the kinetics of this process cannot be obtained solely from histological preparations of different aggregates fixed at intervals. Instead, the continuous process of segregation must be observed within the same aggregate.

For this purpose Trinkaus and Lentz (1964) prepared mixed aggregates of embryonic chick heart cells and retinal pigment cells. Individual retinal pigment cells can be visualized in the living aggregate by virtue of the melanin granules which they contain. The manner by which sorting out of the internally segregating pigment cell component occurred could be observed at closely timed intervals in the three-dimensional tissue system. Naturally, this kind of observation is limited to experimental systems *in vitro* which use pigment cells as the intrinsically marked component. No other vertebrate tissue contains such a readily visible marker. In other heterotypic combinations, moreover, the dissociated organs themselves are complex mixtures of several kinds of tissue. Therefore, until recently, no other method of applying markers labeled one cell type differentially in heterotypic combinations.

Okada (1965a, b) investigated the possibility of using fluorescein-conjugated antibody as an analytical reagent to mark specifically the cells in a tissue which carry the homologous antigen. He prepared antiserum against a chick metanephric microsome fraction (Okada and Sato, 1963) and conjugated the semipurified (precipitated with 45 percent-saturated $(NH_4)_2SO_4$) antibody globulins with fluorescein isothiocyanate (FITC) (for a simple method of conjugating serum and FITC, *cf.* Rinderknecht, 1962). The antiserum was further purified of minor cross-reacting components, and then reacted against intact kidney sections and dissociated embryonic kidney cells. Okada found that antisera thus prepared reacted specifically with the apical cytoplasm of epithelial cells of the proximal secretory tubules. Cells which react with this highly specific reagent may therefore be visualized by fluorescence microscopy (Okada, 1965b), and the pattern of sorting out can be observed.

In summary, intrinsic markers, with the possible exception of nucleolar markers, have rather limited usefulness for studying early morphogenetic cell movements *in vivo*. They can be used to good advantage, however, to determine the *end result* of these movements and may be of considerable value in studying the pattern of sorting out in mixed aggregates *in vitro*. Above all, however, they provide suitable independent markers for controlling applied marking procedures (see below, p. 733), and this should on no account be overlooked.

Applied Markers

There are three main devices by which cells or tissues may be differentially marked from without. These three—vital dyes, particles, and radioisotopes—will be examined with regard to the criteria for markers previously set forth.

VITAL DYES

Nile blue sulfate and neutral red (toluylene red) are the vital stains principally used in marking experiments, although Bismarck brown, methylene blue, Janus green, and several other dyes including an antibiotic (0.05 percent azosulfamide [Winthrop, Neoprontosil]; DeHaan, 1959) have been used.

Vital stains are by definition reasonably nontoxic. This fact has been demonstrated for amphibian embryos reared in 1:750,000 Nile blue sulfate, 1:250,000 neutral red, or 1:100,000 Bismarck brown. At higher concentrations, however, abnormalities begin to appear usually at the time of gastrulation (Zorzoli, 1946). It is generally assumed, *but by no means proven*, that the localized concentration of dyes applied to amphibian embryos with dye-impregnated agar does not greatly exceed these harmful concentrations.

There are two basic methods of using vital dye markers. Donor tissue may be stained overall with a dilute (about 0.05 percent) solution of the dye, and small, stained areas may be grafted into unstained hosts (Detwiler, 1917; Hilber, 1943). Alternatively, localized staining can be effected by essentially the same technique as that used originally by Vogt (1925). Briefly, this technique is as follows (*cf.* Hamburger, 1960):

1. A 1–2 percent agar solution (made with distilled water and heated in a boiling water bath or autoclave to dissolve agar) is poured onto clean microscope slides and allowed to dry completely in a dust-free place.
2. The agar is stained in a 1 percent aqueous solution of stain for about 24 hours. (Gruebler stains obtainable from Roboz Surgical Instrument Co., Washington, D.C., are quite satisfactory.)
3. The stained agar is washed several times in distilled water until most of the excess stain has been removed.
4. The slides are dried, wrapped in foil, and may be stored indefinitely.
5. When staining, small chips of the dye-impregnated agar are removed from the slide with a scalpel blade and placed in a Petri dish containing sterile balanced salt solution (BSS).
6. The size of the moistened chips is adjusted to the needs of the experiment with watchmaker's forceps (No. 5) under a dissecting microscope and applied directly to the embryo at the desired location.

Staining in amphibia must be quite intense (10–20 minutes). Multiple marks may be made simultaneously by arranging agar chips in a depression made in a wax layer on the bottom of an operating dish (*cf.* Hamburger, 1960). The egg is then placed in the depression and held in place with a small glass bridge or a thread anchored in the wax.

Vital stains have been used extensively to study amphibian gastrulation (Vogt, 1925; Pasteels, 1942). Since the movements of relatively large regions of the embryo were involved here, precision of marking on the surface of the egg was not of paramount importance and these methods were adequate. In amphibia, the method was made more reliable by the presence of independent markers in the form of pigment and yolk granules. These could be used to distinguish the initially-stained superficial cells from underlying cells which might have been stained by diffusion of the dye (*cf.* Ballard, 1966, for a discussion of the ambiguities which can result from dye diffusion). When greater resolution was required, however, as with the observations of neural crest cell migration (Detwiler, 1937a, b; Hilber, 1943), vital staining suffered from lack of specificity and permanence and will be criticized further below.

For avian embryos, the technique is essentially the same, but intense staining is undesirable since the early chick blastoderm seems to be more sensitive to the toxic effects of the dyes. In this case, the agar chips are placed on the blastoderm through a small (1 cm^2) window cut in the egg shell with a sharpened hacksaw blade (*cf.* Zwilling [1959] for a useful technique for windowing eggs). A 10- to 30-second application of the dyed agar is usually sufficient time to effect adequate staining. At first, the stain will seem very faint *in ovo* but as it diffuses through the vitelline membrane and is picked up by cells of the blastoderm, staining intensity will appear to increase. After staining, the egg shell window is closed with cellophane tape.

Vital staining is even less satisfactory when applied to avian or fish embryos (Pasteels, 1936, 1937; Spratt, 1947; Ballard, 1966). Results of such studies have been confounded by the lack of specificity and by impermanence of the vital dye. Spratt (1947) and Ballard (1966) have discussed several critical problems with the method. First, staining with vital dyes necessitates staining relatively large areas of the embryo. This is due to physical difficulties in applying the dye to very small areas and, secondarily, to the fact that the dye so finely localized will soon diffuse and become undetectable. Second, diffusing dye may stain underlying tissues in the embryo. Under these circumstances, there is no sure way to determine whether the stained cells in deep regions of the embryo were stained initially by dye diffusing from superficial layers, or whether the cells were carried there by morphogenetic movements (Ballard, 1966). Third, dye marks are almost certainly diminished, and may be translocated during histological treatment, even though Adams (1928) and others (*cf.* Stone, 1932) have devised histological procedures for amphibian material which were thought to preserve the stain *in situ*. Finally, differential reduction and oxidation of the dyes can occur. Neutral red and Nile blue sulfate, like methylene blue and others, are electron acceptors which are colorless when reduced. When chicken blastoderms were stained overall, Spratt (1947) showed that some areas lost the stain completely while the stain concentrated secondarily in its oxidized state in other areas of the blastoderm. As he says (p. 99): "During incubation of the blastoderm, differential reduction of the dye seems to become very pronounced; and, what is worse, cells originally not stained may take up the dye and keep it in the oxidized [colored] state, whereas originally stained cells may have reduced the dye to the colorless form and thus appear unstained." Failure of heavily stained amphibian cells to decolor may indicate that they have been made moribund by high local concentrations of the "vital" dyes, and are no longer able to decolor the dyes by metabolic processes. In any case, it seems clear that the ultimate distribution of stained cells may not truly result from morphogenetic movements undergone by the originally stained cells.

PARTICLES

The technique for marking avian blastoderms *in ovo* with carbon particles is outlined below. Sterile technique should be used to avoid bacterial contamination of the egg.

1. Through a window cut in the egg shell (see above; Zwilling, 1959), a 10- to 30-hour blastoderm (Hamburger-Hamilton [1951], Stages 2–8) should be *lightly* stained overall with neutral red impregnated agar (see previous section). This will improve visibility of the transparent embryo.

2. With a fine tungsten needle (Dossel, 1958),[1] the vitelline membrane is slit over the blastoderm.

3. A small amount of finely powdered blood charcoal (Merck) should be picked up with the moistened tip of the needle. Place on the needle only as much carbon as you wish to leave on the blastoderm.

4. The carbon particles are pushed into the epiblast with the point of the needle. Care should be taken not to push particles *through* the epiblast to underlying tissues.

5. The arrangement of the marks is important if information regarding relative movements of areas of the blastoderm is to be maximized. A line of punctate marks cutting across a suspected migratory pathway and extending into stationary areas of the blastoderm will reveal differential movement. Alternatively, reference marks may be placed in the *area pellucida* lateral to, but at the same level as, marks nearer the primitive streak. The movement of a medial mark may then be compared to the stationary lateral mark.

6. After the blastoderm has been marked and the marks recorded, the egg window is closed with cellophane tape and the egg is returned to the incubator.

Blastoderms may also be marked *in vitro*. This is particularly useful for following the movements of hypoblast cells since the blastoderm may be cultured upside down on its vitelline membrane (*cf.* New, 1955; DeHaan, this volume, pp. 401–412).

Spratt's elaborate critique of vital stains was aided by the simultaneous application of minute carbon particles as independent markers. In contrast to vital stains, these particles can be used to mark very small areas of the blastoderm (but still not individual cells). In addition, they are readily visible *in situ*. Finally, they do not interfere in any way with the processes being studied unless very great quantities of carbon are applied over a small area.

The deficiencies of carbon and other applied particles are, however, also readily apparent. First and foremost, it is very difficult to restrict the particles to one layer of the blastoderm, and this has resulted in considerable confusion about some morphogenetic processes in the avian embryo (*cf.* Spratt and Haas, 1965). Second, when (or if) cells of the epiblast involute through the primitive streak, two things can happen to the carbon marks. Either they may be left behind in the primitive groove as the cells which they marked move through this area, or they may be phagocytized in the area of the primitive streak by cells whose behavior seems to change dramatically at this time (Rudnick, 1944). If this occurs,

[1] 0.010-inch Black Tungsten wire for needles may be obtained from The General Electric Co.-Cleveland Wire Works, Euclid, Ohio. The method for making needles is outlined in Hamburger, 1960. Briefly, the procedure is as follows: (1) With a small oxygen flame, seal 1-inch lengths of wire into drawn out glass rod or tubing. (2) Sharpen the needle by dipping it in and out of fused sodium nitrite in a nickel crucible, or by heating it strongly in an oxygen flame. The temperature of the $NaNO_2$ should be adjusted to give a moderate rate of metal removal and a smooth, unpitted, unoxidized surface on the needle. After sharpening, the needle should be washed thoroughly in boiling water. It may be sterilized during use by passing it through a Bunsen flame.

it is entirely possible for particles to be transferred not only to adjacent cells but also to any cell which might eventually occupy a position in, or pass through, the streak after the marked cell. In addition, the particles remaining outside of cells are highly vulnerable to translocation by histological procedures—especially histological sectioning. Thus, particle marking, too, suffers the same deficiencies as the vital stains—namely a lack of specificity and permanence.

RADIOISOTOPES

The techniques so far considered for marking cells have major deficiencies in terms of the criteria previously established to define a wholly satisfactory marker. Proceeding on the premise that it is better to sacrifice relative convenience of application (which particles and vital stains surely have) than to forfeit precision, the method of labeling with tritiated thymidine seems justified. The major inconvenience with isotope marking arises when prolonged (3- to 12-week) exposures to photographic emulsions are required to visualize the marker. However, the method does seem to fulfill the more important criteria of an adequate marker. That is, it is precise, permanent, operationally nondeleterious, and, with suitable controls, can be made a cell-specific marker. The methods used to test the specificity of this marker are considered later.

The technique of marking with tritiated thymidine may be applied to any system which synthesizes DNA (Taylor *et al.*, 1957; Hughes, 1958). In order to effect differential labeling, donor embryos are usually labeled entirely, and specific cells or tissues are removed from these radioactive donors and transplanted into unlabeled host animals (Weston, 1963; Chibon, 1964; Rosenquist, 1966). However, differential labeling may also be effected by pulse-labeling renewing cell populations, where cells emigrate from regions of localized proliferation (Angevine and Sidman, 1961; Miale and Sidman, 1961).

Clearly almost any combination of labeled and unlabeled tissue is possible *in vitro* and *in vivo*. The procedure outlined below was used to follow neural crest migration *in vivo* in the avian embryo. In this study, segments of neural tube with associated neural crest were transplanted from labeled donor embryos to unlabeled hosts (Weston, 1963; Weston and Butler, 1966. For a similar study in amphibia, *cf.* also Chibon, 1964, 1966).

LABELING. Donor embryos are labeled by introducing 10 μC of tritiated thymidine in balanced salt solution onto the surface of the blastoderm. Dosage depends, in part, on the stage of the embryo.[2] In a stage 13–14 embryo (Hamburger and Hamilton, 1951), for instance, the labeled compound (specific activity about 3 C per millimole) is diluted in BSS to a concentration of 100 μC per milliliter and 0.1 ml of the diluted solution is dropped onto the blastoderm through a small window cut in the egg shell (see above). Incorporation of the radioactive nucleotide into deoxyribonucleic acid (DNA) is very rapid, so that 70 percent of the cells in a 2-day embryo are labeled after 3 hours exposure to the isotope, and almost 100 percent of the cells are labeled after about 8 hours incubation in the presence of the isotope. In every case, it is important to estimate the proportion of donor cells which are labeled so that tissues of mixed donor and host origin can be detected in the host by again estimating the proportion of labeled cells in the tissue of interest.

[2] Younger embryos may be given smaller doses (about 2 μC), while larger, older embryos may require increased doses (e.g., up to 20 μC) administered in fractions over a period of 12–20 hours. In 5- to 7-day embryos, for instance, good labeling has been obtained with a 10-μC dose 24 hours and a 5-μC dose about 4 hours prior to harvesting the labeled tissues.

TOXICITY. Tritiated thymidine is effectively concentrated by the cell in its most radiosensitive structure—nuclear DNA. The question naturally arises, therefore, whether cells labeled with tritiated thymidine suffer any significant radiation damage. Painter *et al.* (1958) concluded from studies on cells which incorporated tritium *in vitro* that the doses normally used for radioautography cause no damage as indicated by inhibition of mitosis. When tritiated thymidine was used at a specific activity of about 2 C per millimole, Sauer and Walker (1961) detected cytological changes in the cells of chick embryos comparable to those encountered in X-irradiated embryos. At no time, however, was there any inhibition of growth in their system, nor were any developmental abnormalities detected which could be attributed to the incorporation of tritium into the sensitive nuclear material. Furthermore, when tritiated thymidine (3.0 C per millimole) was used to label migrating neural crest cells, no evidence of abnormalities was detected either in the neural tube or in the labeled derivatives of the neural crest (Weston, 1963). It is reasonable to conclude, therefore, that at the dosage used for marking, the isotopic label is not harmful to the cells or the morphogenetic processes being studied.

USE OF CARRIER. When labeled donor tissue is transferred to an unlabeled host embryo, spurious labeling of host cells should be avoided. To ensure that the host does not itself incorporate any previously unincorporated tritiated thymidine, carrier may be added along with the donor tissue. Since the probability that a cell will incorporate a labeled thymidine molecule is directly related to the proportion of labeled molecules available in the precursor pool, it follows that if an excess of unlabeled thymidine is added to the system, the incorporation of labeled thymidine molecules will be negligible. Therefore, when the labeled grafts were carried over to host embryos, some BSS containing 4.0 mg per milliliter ($= 1.65 \times 10^{-2}\ M$) of unlabeled thymidine was also added to the host. This represented roughly fifty times the molar quantity of labeled thymidine initially added to the donor embryo, and was certainly in great excess over what might have been introduced into the host with the labeled graft.

HOMOGENEITY. As was previously pointed out, it is very difficult to obtain a uniquely labeled cell type with tritiated thymidine. Most tissues are complex mixtures of various cell types, all of which would probably be isotopically labeled. However, it is often possible to increase the specificity of the marker by selectively removing one or more cell types in control grafts. In the case of the neural crest this was accomplished by selectively removing the neural crest cells themselves from labeled control grafts of neural tube. Any other labeled cells then seen migrating in the host environment could clearly be identified as non-crest cells. In other systems, combinations of markers such as isotopes and immunohistologically identified antigen markers (*cf.* Okada, 1965) may be of use to increase the resolution in complex tissues.

RADIOAUTOGRAPHY. Finally, we must mention the method by which labeled cells are visualized. Radioautography is now a routine laboratory technique and it need not be described in detail. Kopriwa and Leblond (1962) have provided a most useful guide to the techniques of liquid emulsion radioautography including improvements for coating, photographic processing, and minimizing background. The following hints and reminders may be helpful nevertheless:

1. Emulsion type. Kodak[3] NTB-2 (or Ilford K-5 diluted 1:1 with water) is most generally useful. Other types (e.g., NTB, NTB-3, Ilford G-5, L-5) may be

[3] Available from Kodak Special Sensitized Products Division, Rochester, N.Y.

substituted if other sensitivities or grain sizes are required.

2. Storage during exposure. Large numbers of slides may be handled efficiently if they are stored in glass staining racks inside aluminum desiccating cannisters (19 slides per rack; 6 racks per cannister). The cannisters contain silica gel desiccant in the bottom well and are sealed with black plastic electrical tape and stored at 0°–10°C for the duration of the exposure. The slides may be prearranged in the staining racks so that control and experimental slides may be developed together, or groups of slides being exposed the same length of time may be kept together and developed without tedious fumbling in the darkroom.

3. Exposure time depends on the specific activity of the isotope, the amount of dilution of the label as a result of cell division (the label in each cell is halved with each division), the emulsion type (*cf.* Kopriwa and Leblond, 1962), and one's personal requirements for the radioautographs. Embryonic tissues fixed immediately after a 4-hour exposure to 10 μC of tritiated thymidine (3.0 C per millimole) yielded satisfactory radioautographs in about 1 week. Rapidly dividing embryonic tissue fixed about 40 hours after labeling, on the other hand, required about a 1-month exposure with Kodak NTB-2 emulsion for satisfactory radioautographs.

4. Processing. Process for 3 minutes in D-72 (20°C) or in D-19 for 6 minutes in staining dishes. Fix in F-5, rinse, treat with hypo eliminator 1–2 minutes, and wash in running water for 5 minutes.

5. Staining radioautographs. Following photographic processing, radioautographs may be stained 1–5 minutes in Harris' hematoxylin, differentiated in tap water, and the emulsion destained in acid alcohol (1 percent HCl in 70 percent EtOH). The slides are then passed through two baths of ethylene glycol monoethyl ether (2-ethoxyethanol; "Cellosolve"), to xylene, and mounted with Permount.

6. Removing photographic emulsion. If unsatisfactory exposure, accidental fogging, or reticulation of the emulsion due to faulty processing makes valuable preparations useless, one may wish to remove the photographic emulsion from radioautographs. This may also be desirable in order to achieve better histological detail through improved optical conditions. It is difficult, however, to remove the emulsion without also removing sections from the slide or severely damaging the tissue. The following method was devised to salvage valuable preparations when it was found that insensitivity or underexposure of the radioautographic emulsion had rendered these preparations otherwise useless.

The procedure involves the digestion of the emulsion's gelatin matrix with an 0.008 percent solution of Collagenase (Clostridiopeptidase A)[4] in 0.05 *M* phosphate buffer (pH 7.4). The detailed procedure is as follows:

1. Soak slides in xylene to remove cover slips.

2. Run slides to water as usual either through alcohol series or two baths of Cellosolve, 70 percent alcohol, water.

3. Restain the emulsion 1–5 minutes in Harris' hematoxylin until the slide appears quite blue.

4. Rinse thoroughly in water.

5. Place slides in phosphate buffer (pH 7.4) in 37°C bath for 5 minutes.

6. Transfer slides to Collagenase solution for 5–15 minutes at 37°C. Ten minutes is usually sufficient to reach the end point of the digestion which may easily be recognized when the blue-stained slides clear, and the enzyme solution appears light blue.

7. Rinse the slides in two changes of

[4] Available from Worthington Biochemical Corporation, Freehold, N.J., or General Biochemicals, Chagrin Falls, Ohio.

buffer, and then several times in water.

8. Destain tissues in acid alcohol if desired.

9. Rinse thoroughly in water.

10. Recoat slides immediately with new radioautographic emulsion and proceed from this point as with other radioautographic preparations.

This process does not remove tissue sections from the slides, nor does it affect the general staining properties of embryonic material fixed in Bouin's fluid. The quality of subsequent radioautographs is unaffected except, perhaps, for slightly increased levels of background.

TESTING THE ADEQUACY OF MARKING METHODS

No marking method has yet been found which fulfills all the requirements for adequacy which were listed at the beginning of this article. Intrinsic markers are limited in their availability or applicability and often require very laborious searching and statistical scoring of differences between "marked" cells and the cells of the environment. Vital staining techniques and particle marking, on the other hand, suffer in varying degrees from lack of specificity, precision, and permanence. Of the applied markers, only isotopes, and particularly tritiated thymidine, so far appear to meet the requirements as a generally useful, precise, permanent, and nontoxic marker. Here, however, we encounter technical difficulties in effecting differential cell-specific marking in heterogeneous tissues, and considerable inconvenience in visualizing the mark.

This does not imply that meaningful results have not been obtained in marking experiments. It does suggest, however, that before definitive conclusions may be drawn from experiments in which extrinsic markers are applied, the limitations of the marking method should be determined, understood, and controlled. This point cannot be emphasized too strongly. One cannot conclude, for example, that a given extrinsically marked cell moves from one point to another in an embryo or tissue if there is evidence that the mark itself can transfer from the original cell or cell population to some other cell or population. Conversely, one cannot conclude that migration did not occur unless a stationary mark is known to have remained in association with the originally marked cell or region.

The best way to evaluate and control the specificity of a marking method is to use it in conjunction with another, *independent marker* which is known to fulfill at least the first of the four criteria listed above—namely, one which precisely and differentially marks a given cell type. In marking studies with tritiated thymidine, this has been accomplished in two ways. First, it was possible to use the morphological characteristics of a tissue whose developmental origin is known to test the specificity of marking of embryonic precursor cells *in vivo*. Thus, the presence of labeled spinal ganglia surrounded by unlabeled mesenchyme cells of the somite strongly suggested (1) that the embryonic neural crest cells, which are known to give rise to spinal ganglia, could be specifically labeled with tritiated thymidine, and (2) that no transfer of label occurred between the neural crest cells and the surrounding cells of the somite (Weston, 1963).

An independent test of this method of isotopic marking, *in vitro*, relied on the presence of pigment granules as intrinsic cellular markers. Trinkaus and Gross (1961) labeled retinal pigment cells (a homogeneous tissue) with tritiated thymidine and combined them with cells dissociated from mesonephric tissue. Labeled cells which did not also have pigment granules would have been taken as evidence of nonspecific transfer of label from the originally labeled cells to the cells of the environment. Results of such an experiment demonstrated, however, that no significant amount of label was transferred from the marked cells to the other cells in the environment.

Other applied marks such as vital stains and particles have not been adequately tested in this way, and satisfactory conclusions have been reached only when the limitations of these marking methods were recognized (*cf.* Ballard, 1966).

GENERAL LIMITATIONS

A major impediment to satisfactory interpretation of marking experiments, as they have been performed, results from the *multidimensionality* of developing systems. Specifically, the processes we seek to describe and analyze are continuous in time, and occur in a three-dimensional, heterogeneous environment. Until we can observe the continuous process of morphogenetic cell movements in living, morphologically intact systems (e.g., Trinkaus, 1966), we must be content to make kinetic inferences from stroboscopic views of the process. Perhaps the judicious combination of marking and time-lapse cinematography will ultimately confirm our inferences.

REFERENCES

ADAMS, A. E., 1928: Paraffin sections of tissue supravitally stained. *Science*, 68: 303.

ANGEVINE, J. B., and R. L. SIDMAN, 1961: Autoradiographic study of cell migration during histogenesis of cerebral cortex in the mouse. *Nature*, 192: 766.

BALLARD, W. W., 1966: Origin of the hypoblast in *Salmo*. I. Does the blastodisc edge turn inward? *J. Exptl. Zool.*, 161: 201. II. Outward movement of deep central cells. *J. Exptl. Zool.*, 161: 211.

BLACKLER, A. W., and M. FISCHBERG, 1961: Transfer of primordial germ cells in *Xenopus laevis*. *J. Embryol. Exptl. Morph.*, 9: 634.

CHIBON, P., 1964: Analyse par la méthode de marquage nucléaire à la thymidine tritiée des dérivés de la crête neurale céphalique chez l'Urodele *Pleurodeles waltlii* (Michah). *Compt. Rend. Acad. Sci. Paris*, 259: 3624.

———, 1966: Analyse expérimentale de la régionalisation et des capacités morphogénétiques de la crête neurale chez l'amphibian Urodele *Pleurodeles waltlii* (Michah). *Mém. Soc. Zool. France*, 36: 1.

DE HAAN, R. L., 1959: Cardia-bifida and the development of pacemaker function in the early chick heart. *Devel. Biol.*, 1: 586.

DETWILER, S. R., 1917: On the use of Nile-blue sulphate in embryonic tissue transplantation. *Anat. Rec.*, 13: 493.

———, 1937a: Application of vital dyes to the study of sheath cell origin. *Proc. Soc. Exptl. Biol. and Med.*, 37: 380.

———, 1937b: Observations upon the migration of neural crest cells, and upon the development of the spinal ganglia and vertebral arches in *Ambystoma*. *Am. J. Anat.*, 61: 63.

DOSSEL, W. E., 1958: Preparation of tungsten microneedles for use in embryological research. *Lab. Invest.*, 7: 171.

ELSDALE, T. R., M. FISCHBERG, and S. SMITH, 1958: A mutation that reduces nucleolar number in *Xenopus laevis*. *Exptl. Cell Res.*, 14: 642.

FALK, G., and R. C. KING, 1963: Radioautographic efficiency for tritium as a function of section thickness. *Rad. Res.*, 20: 466.

FRIEDKIN, M., D. TILSON, and D. ROBERTS, 1956: Studies of deoxyribonucleic acid biosynthesis in embryonic tissues with thymidine-C^{14}. *J. Biol. Chem.*, 220: 627.

GREEN, P., 1965: Anion-exchange resin

spheres as marking material for wet cell surfaces. *Exptl. Cell Res.*, 40: 195.

HAMBURGER, V., 1960: *A Manual of Experimental Embryology.* University of Chicago Press, Chicago, Ill.

———, and H. HAMILTON, 1951: A series of normal stages in the development of the chick embryo. *J. Morphol.*, 88: 49.

HILBER, H., 1943: Experimentelle Studien zum Schicksal des Rumpfganglienleistenmaterials. *Arch. Entwicklungsmech. Organ.*, 142: 100.

HUGHES, W. L., 1958: Chromosomal replication and the dynamics of cellular proliferation—some autoradiographic observations with tritiated thymidine. In W. D. McElroy and B. Glass (eds.), *The Chemical Basis of Development*, The Johns Hopkins Press, Baltimore, Md.

KOPRIWA, B. M., and C. P. LEBLOND, 1962: Improvements in the coating technique of radioautography. *J. Histochem. Cytochem.*, 10: 269.

MEYER, D. B., 1964: The migration of primordial germ cells in the chick embryo. *Devel. Biol.*, 10: 154.

MIALE, I. L., and R. L. SIDMAN, 1961: An autoradiographic analysis of histogenesis in the mouse cerebellum. *Exptl. Neurol.*, 4: 277.

MOSCONA, A., 1956: Development of heterotypic combinations of dissociated embryonic chick cells. *Proc. Soc. Exptl. Biol. and Med.*, 92: 410.

———, 1957: The development *in vitro* of chimeric aggregates of dissociated embryos in chick and mouse cells. *Proc. Nat. Acad. Sci. U.S.*, 43: 184.

———, 1960: Patterns and mechanisms of tissue reconstruction from dissociated cells. *Sympos. Soc. for Study of Devel. and Growth*, 18: 45.

NEW, D. A. T., 1955: A new technique for the cultivation of the chick embryo *in vitro. J. Embryol. Exptl. Morph.*, 3: 326.

OKADA, T. S., 1965a: Development of kidney-specific antigens; an immunohistological study. *J. Embryol. Exptl. Morph.*, 13: 285.

———, 1965b: Immunohistological studies on the reconstruction of nephric tubules from dissociated cells. *J. Embryol. Exptl. Morph.*, 13: 299.

———, and A. G. SATO, 1963: Soluble antigens in microsomes of adult and embryonic kidneys. *Exptl. Cell Res.*, 31: 251.

PAINTER, R. B., R. M. DREW, and W. L. HUGHES, 1958: Inhibition of HeLa growth by intranuclear tritium. *Science*, 127: 1244.

PASTEELS, J., 1936: Études sur la gastrulation des Vertébrés meroblastiques. I. Teleostéens. *Arch. de Biologie*, 47: 205.

———, 1937: Études sur la gastrulation des Vertébrés meroblastiques. III. Oiseaux. IV. Conclusions générals. *Arch. de Biologie*, 48: 381.

———, 1942: New observations concerning the maps of presumptive areas of the young amphibian gastrula (*Ambystoma* and *Discoglossus*). *J. Exptl. Zool.*, 289: 255.

RAVEN, CHR. P., 1936: Zur Entwicklung der Ganglienleiste. V. Über die Differenzierung des Rumpfganglienleistenmaterials. *Arch. Entwicklungsmech. Organ.*, 134: 122.

———, 1937: Experiments on the origin of the sheath cells and sympathetic neuroblasts in amphibia. *J. Comp. Neurol.*, 67: 221.

RINDERKNECHT, H., 1962: Ultra-rapid fluorescent labeling of proteins. *Nature*, 193: 167.

ROSENQUIST, G. C., 1966: A radioautographic study of labeled grafts in the chick blastoderm. Development from primitive-streak stages to Stage 12. *Carnegie Inst. Wash., Publ. 625, Contrib. to Embryol.*, 38: 71.

RUDNICK, D., 1944: Early history and mechanics of the chick blastoderm. *Quart. Rev. Biol.*, 19: 187.

RUGH, R., 1962: *Experimental Embryology, a Manual of Techniques and Procedures.* Burgess Publishing Co., Minneapolis, Minn.

SAUER, M. E., and B. E. WALKER, 1961: Radiation injury resulting from nuclear labeling with tritiated thymidine in the chick embryo. *Rad. Res.*, 14: 633.

SPRATT, N. T., JR., 1946: Formation of the primitive streak in the explanted chick blastoderm marked with carbon particles. *J. Exptl. Zool.*, 103: 259.

———, 1947: Regression and shortening of the primitive streak in the explanted chick blastoderm. *J. Exptl. Zool.*, 104: 69.

———, and H. HAAS, 1965: Germ layer formation and the role of the primitive streak in the chick. I. Basic architecture and morphogenetic tissue movements. *J. Exptl. Zool.*, 158: 9.

STEINBERG, M. S., 1962: Reconstruction of tissues by dissociated cells. *Science*, 141: 401.

STONE, L. S., 1932: Selective staining of the neural crest and its preservation for microscopic study. *Anat. Rec.*, 51 (abstract).

TAYLOR, J. H., P. S. WOODS, and W. L. HUGHES, 1957: The organization and duplication of chromosomes as revealed by autoradiographic studies using tritium-labeled thymidine. *Proc. Natl. Acad. Sci. U.S.*, 43: 122.

TOWNES, P. L., and J. HOLTFRETER, 1955: Directed movements and selected adhesions of embryonic amphibian cells. *J. Exptl. Zool.*, 128: 53.

TRINKAUS, J. P., 1966: Morphogenetic cell movements. In M. Locke (ed.), *Major Problems in Developmental Biology*, 25th Sympos., Soc. for Devel. Biol, p. 125.

———, and M. GROSS, 1961: The use of tritiated thymidine for marking migratory cells. *Exptl. Cell Res.*, 24: 52.

———, and J. P. LENTZ, 1964: Direct observation of type-specific segregation in mixed cell aggregates. *Devel. Biol.*, 9: 115.

TRIPLETT, E. L., 1958: The development of the sympathetic ganglia, sheath cells, and meninges in amphibians. *J. Exptl. Zool.*, 138: 283.

VOGT, W., 1925: Gestaltungsanalyse am Amphibienkeim mit örlicher Vitalfärbung. Vorwort über Wege und Ziele. I. Teil. Methodik und Wirkungweise der örlicher Vitalfärbung mit Agar als Farbträger. *Arch. Entwicklungsmech. Organ.*, 106: 542.

WESTON, J. A., 1963: A radioautographic analysis of the migration and localization of trunk neural crest cells in the chick. *Devel. Biol.*, 6: 279.

———, and S. L. BUTLER, 1966: Temporal factors affecting localization of neural crest cells in the chicken embryo. *Devel. Biol.*, 14: 246.

ZORZOLI, A., 1946: Effects of vital dyes on the early development of amphibian embryo. *Proc. Soc. Exptl. Biol. and Med.*, 63: 565.

ZWILLING, E., 1959: A modified chorio-allantoic grafting procedure. *Transplantation Bull.*, 6: 115.

Amphibian Nuclear Transplantation*

By Thomas J. King

INTRODUCTION

The first demonstration that living nuclei of embryonic cells could be transplanted into eggs in an undamaged condition was reported by Briggs and King (1952) for the leopard frog *Rana pipiens*. Subsequently, this technique has been used on several other species of frogs (*Rana nigromaculata*, Sambuichi, 1957; *Rana sylvatica*, Moore, 1958, Hennen, 1963; *Rana palustris*, Hennen, 1965; *Rana temporaria* and *Rana arvalis*, Stroeva and Nikitina, 1960, Nikitina, 1964; *Bufo viridis*, Stroeva and Nikitina, 1960; *Bufo bufo*, Nikitina, 1964), and in modified form has been successfully applied to *Xenopus* (Elsdale, Gurdon, and Fischberg, 1960; Gurdon, 1960), *Ambystoma* (Signoret, Briggs, and Humphrey, 1962), *Pleurodeles* (Signoret and Picheral, 1962; Signoret and Fagnier, 1962), and more recently to *Triturus* (Sládeček and Mazáková-Štefanová, 1964, 1965). The differences in the techniques that have been developed for transplanting nuclei in different amphibia and the types of problems to which they have been applied have recently been reviewed by Gurdon (1964) and King (1966).

In this chapter we will limit ourselves to a description of the equipment and operating procedures used in transplanting nuclei from blastula cells of *Rana pipiens* embryos back into an egg of the same species the nucleus of which has been removed. Once the technique of blastula nuclear transplantation has been mastered the transfer of nuclei from other amphibian cell types is mainly a question of patience and practice.

EQUIPMENT

The equipment, as well as a detailed consideration of a number of the aspects of the nuclear transplantation procedure for *Rana pipiens*, has been described before (King, 1966). The reader should consult the King reference for details not covered in the presentation that follows.

* The author wishes to thank Mrs. Audrey L. Harris for her valuable assistance in preparing this manuscript for publication and Mr. Lawrence Anderson for the photography used in the illustrations.

It is also a pleasure to acknowledge Dr. Marie A. DiBerardino and Dr. Robert P. Perry for their critical reading of the manuscript.

The investigations of the author upon which this chapter is based have been supported by research grants from the U.S. Department of Health, Education and Welfare, Public Health Service, National Institutes of Health (CA-05755 and CA-06927).

Micromanipulator

Ever since the invention of the microscope, research workers have attempted to carry out minute dissections on living cells within the microscopic field of view. However, even under the most favorable conditions, microdissection is carried out in a space of very few millimeters, in fact, in many cases, within fractions of millimeters. The transmission of the normal movement of the human hand in such small dimensions is possible only with aids which control these movements accurately and which eliminate vibrations from the operator's hand. These requirements have been met by the development of the micromanipulator.

Of the variety of micromanipulators that are commercially available we have found those manufactured by the J. H. Emerson Co., Cambridge, Massachusetts, and E. Leitz GmbH, Wetzler, Germany, to be particularly well adapted for amphibian nuclear transplantation. Both are sturdy and maneuverable instruments not subject to the variances common to manipulators of pneumatic design. All horizontal motion, with both the Emerson and Leitz manipulators, is controlled by a single control stick which travels about 3 inches and can be moved in an arc of about 1 inch. Vertical, sagittal, and transverse motions, as well as an adjustment for tilting the manipulating mechanism, are under separate control.

Since, as we shall see, the nuclear transplantation operation requires the manipulation of only one micropipette it is sufficient to have but one micromanipulator unit, i.e., either a right- or left-hand operated manipulator unit with accessories.

The description that follows applies specifically to the Leitz micromanipulator. Many of the procedures, however, may be profitably employed with micromanipulators of other designs.

LOCATION

A rigid and vibration-free laboratory bench, such as a 1-inch thick stone (alberine) table, should be chosen for work with the micromanipulator. If such a table is available the manipulator can be attached directly to the table top. If freedom from vibration cannot be assured it is advisable to mount the manipulator on a base plate that is placed on a sheet of $\frac{1}{4}$-inch thick hard rubber to absorb vibrations and ensure a rigid support for the instrument. The Leitz micromanipulator is supplied with a base plate ($50 \times 40 \times 2$ cm) which receives the microscope stand in its center and accommodates a micromanipulator unit and a microinjection syringe on either side of the microscope.

ASSEMBLY

Because its range of operation is limited, the manipulator unit must be properly placed with reference to the microscope. For work with magnifications up to $200\times$ a stereoscopic microscope is positioned in the center of the base plate. If a right-hand operated micromanipulator unit is used it is placed on the dovetail slider to the right of the intermediate plate that supports the microscope (Fig. 1C). In positioning the manipulator on the slider, the scale for the manipulator tilting adjustment should face the operator. The height of the manipulator is adjusted so that the collar in which the micropipette holder rests is set above the stage of the microscope.

Microscope

A stereoscopic microscope which gives good resolution and a wide flat field with considerable depth of focus should be equipped with three objectives with long working distances, a foot-focusing device, and a mechanical stage. The microscope is mounted on an intermediate stand in the center of the base plate (Fig. 1A).

Several models of stereoscopic microscopes may be used for amphibian nuclear transplantation. The AO Spencer stereoscopic microscope (after Greenough) with an inclined binocular body, to minimize the fatigue of working for prolonged periods of time, and a range of magnifications from 6.3 × to 144 × is quite satisfactory. The only disadvantage of this instrument is that, when not in use, the high-power objectives mounted on the revolving nosepiece sometimes hamper the movements of the micropipette. With the Leitz stereoscopic microscope this restriction is obviated by moving the objectives in and out of the operating field in a front-back direction. In addition to affording a convenient means for changing magnification the Leitz nosepiece can accommodate a pair of 12 × objectives which in combination with 18 × eyepieces give a total magnification of 216 ×. However, even the high-power objectives of the Leitz microscope have the disadvantage of limiting the working distance between the objective and object. The Zeiss stereoscope II overcomes this difficulty by allowing the operator, without changing the working distance, to pass from one magnification to another by merely turning the drum of the magnification changer. With low magnification the image in the Zeiss microscope is sharp when the working distance between the objective and object is about 80 mm. When a 2 × attachment is applied in front of the objective the total magnification is doubled, but the working distance is reduced to approximately 28 mm. With a pair of 25 × eyepieces, 4 × objectives, and the 2 × attachment a magnification of 200 × is obtained with the Zeiss stereoscope. At this magnification the field of view is reduced to 1 mm. This, of course, is to be expected since high magnification has the disadvantage of smaller fields of view and limited depth of focus.

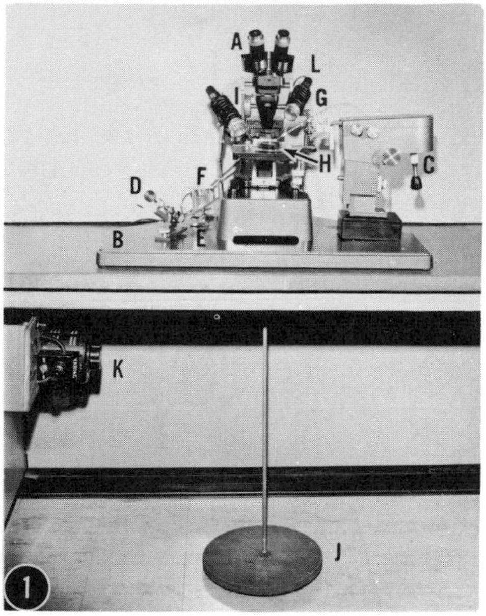

FIG. 1. Photograph of the apparatus for amphibian nuclear transplantation. A Leitz stereoscopic microscope (A), equipped with 1 ×, 4 × and 12 × objectives and 18 × eyepieces, is mounted on an intermediate stand in the center of the base plate (B). A Leitz right-hand operated micromanipulator (C) is attached to the base plate on the right side of the microscope. A 2-ml injection syringe (D), three-way stopcock (E), and 100-ml beaker (F) are fastened to the base plate on the left side of the microscope. The micropipette holder (G) enters the operating dish (H) from the right. The ladder chain (I) on the left focusing knob of the microscope is attached to a foot-focusing apparatus (J) below the operating table. The variable transformer (K), mounted on the left wall of the knee space, controls the intensity of light emitted by the two AO Spencer Universal microscope lamps (L) fastened to the intermediate stand that supports the microscope.

The Leitz stereoscopic microscope shown in Fig. 1A is equipped with 1 ×, 4 ×, and 12 × paired achromatically corrected objectives and 18 × eyepieces. The three pairs of objectives are parfocally adjusted and fitted onto steel slides on the head of the microscope. Two of the three pairs of objectives can be rapidly replaced from the left side of the microscope by means of the slide objective changer, while the third pair (1 ×) is permanently mounted. The low-power objective (1 ×) is needed for the preliminary setting of the microinjection pipette. The next magnification (4 × objective) is useful for locating the donor cells in the operating dish and for centering the micropipette. The high-power objective (12 ×) is used to pick up the donor cell in the orifice of the injection pipette and to transplant its nucleus into the cytoplasm of the recipient egg. The high-power objective must be handled carefully since, as was mentioned above, its working distance and field of view are obviously limited. Accordingly, the fluid level of the medium in the operating dish (see next section on Operating Dishes) must be shallow enough so that the tip of the micropipette will be well within the working distance of the objective.

Since it is frequently necessary to make subtle changes in focus, during the nuclear transplantation operation, it is convenient to have a foot-focusing device attached to the coarse adjustment of the microscope. With the foot-focusing apparatus that we use, the microscope is instantly focused to any desired increment by moving with either foot a wheel that is mounted close to the floor (Fig. 1J and King, 1966). This permits the operator to control the movements of the micropipette with one hand and the plunger that activates the injection syringe with the other.

On occasion, certain measurements of cells in the microscope field need to be made. For this work a removable diaphragm in the bottom of the eyepiece provides for the insertion of a micrometer disc. The eyepiece into which the micrometer disc is inserted is then placed in the fixed eyepiece tube and set into focus by adjusting the eyepiece diaphragm. The micrometer scale is arbitrarily divided into units which can be translated into absolute units by calibrating with a stage micrometer.

Another useful microscope accessory is a mechanical stage for systematically exploring the operating dish. The stage should have a to and fro movement of at least 50 mm and a lateral movement of 25 to 75 mm so that the operating dish can be precisely shifted in two directions from the optical axis of the microscope.

Experience has shown that the nuclear transplantation operation can best be viewed at high magnification when illuminated by the incident light of two AO Spencer Universal Microscope illuminators. The illuminators are mounted on three-link jackknife supports conveniently anchored with reference to the microscope and the operating dish (Fig. 1L). The adaptable jackknife support is useful in quickly adjusting the angle of illumination. The intensity of light can be varied according to requirements by means of a regulating transformer (Fig. 1K).

Operating Dishes

A shallow wax-bottomed Syracuse dish is a satisfactory operating chamber for amphibian nuclear transplantation. The operating dish is prepared by mixing lampblack with melted paraffin and a small amount of beeswax. The melted mixture is poured into a 60-mm Syracuse dish and anchored to the bottom of the dish by means of two glass rods each of which is approximately 3 mm in diameter and 20 mm long. Three or more hemispherical depressions for holding the host eggs are made in the wax by means of a glass rod with a 3-mm ball tip.

A second type of operating chamber that is quite useful, especially when a mechanical stage is employed, is a 75- × 45- × 5-mm Romicron well slide[1] with a 2.5-mm thickness of glass in the bottom of the well. Hemispherical depressions for holding the host eggs can be drilled with a carborundum bit to a depth of 1 mm in the glass floor of the well. The entire surface of the well is then siliconed so that dissociated donor cells can be placed adjacent to the hemispherical depressions of the well without sticking to its surface.

The opening in the center of both types of operating dishes is broad enough to allow for the easy insertion and interchangeability of the injection pipette without hindrance. An added feature of these dishes is that they are shallow enough so that, when filled with the injection medium, the meniscus of the fluid column near the tip of the inclined micropipette, as well as the cells to be operated on, are well within the working distance of the intermediate objective of the microscope.

The operating dish is mounted on the stage of the microscope with the hemispherical depressions for holding the host eggs facing the operator (Fig. 6). If a mechanical stage is employed it should be provided with a clamp in order that the movements of the operating dish can be securely controlled.

Microneedles and Micropipettes

The availability of glass instruments made to precise specifications is an absolute prerequisite for the success of the operative procedures used in amphibian nuclear transplantation.

Glass needles used for activating host eggs must have tips fine enough to penetrate the jelly layers, vitelline membrane, and the surface coat of the egg without appreciably deforming the egg. In addition to this requirement the microneedle used for the enucleation operation must be stiff enough near its tip so that an exovate containing the nucleus of the host egg can be properly formed in the manner described in the section on Activation and Enucleation of Host Eggs. These requirements are satisfied by microneedles drawn from a solid soft-glass rod with an outside diameter of approximately 0.85 mm. Micropipettes used for nuclear transplantation are made from uniformly drawn capillary tubing of similar outside diameter.[2]

Straight microneedles and straight micropipettes can be drawn from 0.85-mm glass stock either by hand in a microburner or on a needle-pulling apparatus.

A microburner can be easily made in the laboratory. The burner tube is removed from a Bunsen burner and the wide end of an 18-gauge steel hypodermic needle, whose beveled end is pinched off, is fastened in a short length of pressurized rubber tubing (about 3 cm long). The free end of the rubber tubing is connected to the gas outlet tube of the burner. The size of the flame may be controlled by a screw clamp on the rubber tubing or directly by the gas jet. A 2-mm blue flame burning from the nozzle of the truncated needle has the correct dimensions for drawing glass microinstruments.

The middle of a 5- to 6-inch piece of glass rod or capillary tubing of uniform diameter is lowered to a distance of a few millimeters above the microflame and rolled constantly between the fingers to avoid onesided melting. When the glass is softened it is removed from the hot air stream above the flame. Holding the length of softened glass in a horizontal position the operator slowly pulls it out

[1] Manufactured by Paul Rosenthal, 300 Northern Boulevard, Great Neck, N.Y.

[2] Precision drawn soft-glass rod and Pyrex capillary tubing with an 0.85-mm outside diameter can be obtained from Drummond Scientific Company, 524 North 61st Street, Philadelphia, Pa.

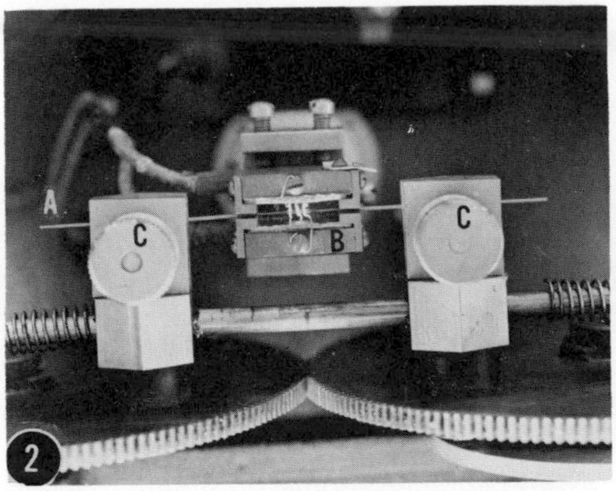

FIG. 2. Photograph of a Livingston needle puller with a 5-cm length of 0.85 mm outside diameter soft-glass rod (A) centered in the 1-mm slot of a platinum-wired heating element (B) and fastened in the needle holders (C).

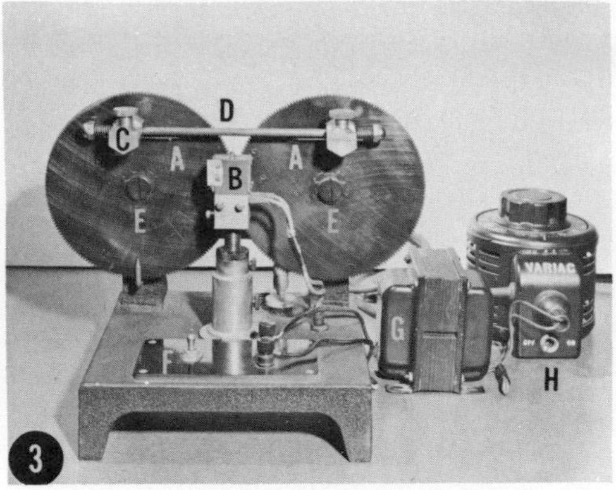

FIG. 3. Over-all view of a Livingston needle puller. Microneedles (A) after their tips have been drawn out in the heating element (B). (C) needle holder; (D) equalizing rod; (E) wheels that pull the needle holders apart after the glass softens; (F) heating element switch; (G) transformer; (H) variac.

until the desired diameter is reached. This work is carried out most effectively with a binocular prism magnifier on a pillar stand or a Beebe binocular magnifying glass which is worn like a pair of spectacles. The closed fine tip of the micropipette drawn out in a microflame may be broken off with a pair of watchmaker's forceps under the low power of a dissecting microscope.

Microneedles and micropipettes are more conveniently and more precisely manufactured by means of a needle-pulling apparatus such as the one designed by L. G. Livingston.[3] A short length of glass rod or capillary tubing of uniform bore (see footnote 2 on p. 741) is aligned in the center of the 1-mm slot of a heating element constructed of platinum wire in the form of a V-shaped grid with parallel sides, three wires wide. The wires are mounted in mica supporting plates which hold them rigidly in place. After the proper temperature for melting the specific type of glass has been determined, the glass is lowered into the heater to an appropriate depth and its ends are firmly fastened in the holders that glide along the equalizing rod attached to the wheels of the machine (Fig. 2). A regulating transformer, connected to the heating element, is set to transmit the desired intensity of heat to the wire filament (Fig. 3H). After these preparations have been made the heating element is switched on. As the glass softens, the pipette holders move apart in an arc so that the final tip of the microneedle or micropipette is pulled just after the glass leaves the top of the heater (Fig. 3A). The tension on the spring that pulls the wheels apart as the glass softens determines the speed at which

[3] Designed by Dr. L. G. Livingston and built by Mr. Otto Habel, Biology Department, Swarthmore College, Swarthmore, Pa.

the glass is pulled. The temperature to which the platinum wire is heated, and the depth to which the glass is held in the heating element, determine the taper of the final tip of the microneedle or micropipette.

To fashion the final tip of a drawn-out glass micropipette it is useful to have a microforge with a stereoscopic microscope and a holding device for positioning the pipette. The most effective micropipette is one that has a sharp final tip, the sides of which are beveled like those of a fine hypodermic needle. The procedure we use for constructing micropipettes of this type with the de Fonbrune microforge has been described elsewhere (King, 1966).

Microinjection Assembly

The microinjection assembly consists of a glass hypodermic syringe of 2-ml capacity, a syringe holder, three-way stopcock, capillary tubing made of flexible synthetic material, such as $\frac{1}{8}$-inch bore clear tygon plastic tubing, and a pipette holder. A micrometer screw may be used to activate the plunger of the syringe, but usually it is easier to activate and stop the injection process by hand.

If the micropipette is carried by a right-hand operated micromanipulator unit the syringe holder and three-way stopcock should be mounted on the base plate to the left of the microscope (Figs. 1D and E respectively). The three-way stopcock is used to facilitate filling the injection system with distilled water. A short length (about 8 cm) of plastic tubing is used to join the syringe to one tap of the three-way stopcock. To prevent leakage, it is advisable to apply a thin film of stopcock grease on the nozzle of the syringe. For the same reason, the plunger of the syringe is carefully and thoroughly lubricated with Vaseline and stopcock grease. A second length of plastic tubing is attached to a second tap of the three-way stopcock. The free end of this length of tubing is anchored in a reservoir of distilled water in a covered container (e.g., a 100-ml beaker, Fig. 1F). The length of tubing connecting the third tap of the three-way valve to the hollow micropipette holder may be chosen as desired, but should be long enough to allow the holder to rest in the instrument collar of the micromanipulator with no appreciable constraint.

To transmit the pressure of the syringe plunger to the micropipette during injection, the syringe and plastic tubing leading to the pipette holder are filled with distilled water through the three-way stopcock. This is done *before* the micropipette is attached to the holder. The distilled water column in the plastic tubing must not be allowed to come in contact with the hollow metal tube that carries the pipette, but rather should end approximately 3 inches before the point of this attachment. In order to make sure that no air bubbles remain in the system it is usually necessary to fill and refill the plastic tubing several times.

The Leitz micropipette holder is a metal tube fitted with a rubber gasket[4] which fits snugly inside the conical end of a metal screw cap. The shaft of a micropipette is introduced into the opening of the screw cap and pushed through a 1-mm hole bored in the center of the rubber gasket. The cap is then securely screwed onto the hollow instrument holder. On tightening the captive nut to the instrument holder the rubber gasket is pushed against the conical end of the inside surface of the cap producing an air-tight seal. After the micropipette has been

[4] A rubber gasket, 3 mm in diameter and 3 mm long, can be bored from a No. 6 rubber stopper with a small cork borer. A 1-mm hole is drilled in the center of the gasket to hold the shaft of the micropipette.

mounted in the instrument holder, the holder is attached to the long length of water-filled plastic tubing leading from the syringe and three-way stopcock. The instrument holder is then clamped into the instrument collar of the micromanipulator (Fig. 1G). The ball-and-socket mechanism which supports the instrument collar permits the operator to rotate the pipette holder in any desired direction.

The arrangement described above leaves a cushion of air between the small column of injection medium in the tip of the pipette and the distilled water column in the plastic tubing leading from the injection syringe. It is this volume of air in the injection system that makes microinjection possible with an apparently crude syringe. If, instead of having an air cushion, the entire system were filled with liquid, then any movement of the syringe plunger would cause a corresponding displacement from the tip of the micropipette. However, with the air gap in the system the downward movement of the plunger compresses the air and thereby builds up an internal pressure. Accordingly, the syringe serves as a controllable compressor and decompressor. In effect, the microinjection procedure requires the development of enough pressure in the air gap to cause the outflow of the injection medium through the microtip into the recipient egg and then, at the right moment, the air gap must be decompressed in order to stop this outflow. Reasonably delicate microinjections can be made with a 2-ml syringe (Fig. 1D). However, many experienced investigators prefer to use a 5-ml syringe, since with a syringe of this capacity pressure can be increased or reduced more quickly (Kopac, 1964).

Upon completing this assembly, the injection system is tested for leaks. The micropipette is removed from the pipette holder and in its place is inserted a piece of solid glass rod. After securing the rod by means of the captive nut, pressure is applied to the plunger of the syringe and the entire system inspected for leaks. If leaks occur at any place in the system, e.g,. between the plunger and barrel of the syringe, at the junction points of the flexible tubing with the syringe, three-way stopcock, and pipette holder or at the juncture of the micropipette holder and the micropipette, they should be corrected immediately.

When the operator is assured that the injection system is leakproof, the entire micromanipulator assembly is adjusted to meet individual working conditions. The height and angle at which the micropipette enters the field of the microscope are regulated by the vertical and tilting adjustments of the manipulator. Using the sagittal and transverse adjustments, the tip of the micropipette is moved to the exact center of the microscope field of view and set approximately 2 cm above the surface of the microscope stage. On completion of these preliminary settings, the microinjection apparatus and micromanipulator are fastened firmly to the base plate. Finally, with the aid of the transverse adjustment of the micromanipulator, the micropipette is removed a great enough distance away from the field of view to permit the operator to place the operating dish in the center of the microscope stage.

OPERATING PROCEDURES

The method of nuclear transplantation devised for the leopard frog, *Rana pipiens* (Briggs and King, 1952), consists of three steps: (1) parthenogenetic activation of host eggs by pricking with a clean glass needle, (2) removal of the egg nucleus with a second glass needle, and (3) transplantation of a donor nucleus into a previously prepared activated and enucleated recipient egg.

Activation and Enucleation of Host Eggs

Eggs from an ovulating female frog[5] are shaken into a clean, flat Syracuse dish containing approximately 10 ml of 10 percent amphibian Ringer's solution (Rugh, 1962). Almost immediately after immersion the swelling of the outer jelly layers attaches most of the eggs to the bottom of the dish with their animal poles uppermost. Parenthetically it should be mentioned that unless the eggs are attached it will be almost impossible to remove their nuclei successfully. Under a dissecting microscope with a magnification of approximately 20 × eggs that remain firmly attached to the bottom of the dish are immediately stimulated parthenogenetically by pricking with a clean glass needle at some point in the animal hemisphere other than the animal pole region (Briggs and King, 1952, 1953). The glass needle is securely mounted in a metal needle holder, fitted with a 1-inch-deep chuck at its open end, that allows the insertion of the shaft of a microneedle. The needle is held firmly in place by means of a screw cap (Arthur H. Thomas Co., No. 4607 or equivalent).

The majority of eggs so treated will be activated, and within 15–20 minutes at 18°C, the cortical granules directly over the second maturation division figure migrate away from the center of the animal pole area permitting the operator to locate the exact position of the egg nucleus which appears as a small but distinct "*black dot*" (Fig. 4). The "black dot" is visible for about 20–25 minutes after activation. Its disappearance signals the completion of the second maturation division. Later on the second polar body emerges at this point.

[5] For a description of the procedure used to induce ovulation in adult *Rana pipiens* and the method of preparing sperm suspensions for artificial insemination, see DiBerardino, this volume, pp. 53–74.

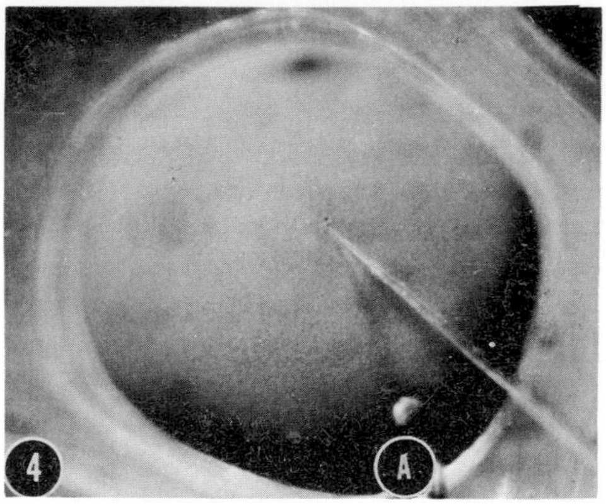

FIG. 4. Photograph showing the animal pole region of a *Rana pipiens* egg 15 minutes after activation with a clean glass needle. The small "black dot," which indicates the position of the egg nucleus, lies immediately in front of the tip of the enucleation needle. The activation exovate (A) lies below the shaft of the needle.

The second part of the procedure for preparing the host egg involves the removal of the egg nucleus. The success of this operation depends on (1) careful observation of the egg after activation under a magnification of 40–60 diameters, for the purpose of detecting the "black dot"; (2) a strong light source, such as that provided by two AO Spencer Universal lamps connected to a variable transformer; and (3) a properly constructed and mounted glass microneedle.

Eggs with distinct "black dots" conveniently located are enucleated by inserting a clean glass needle diagonally through the jelly membranes, vitelline membrane, and surface coat of the egg at a point slightly to one side of and directly beneath the "dot." The needle is moved straight up through the "dot" making a small tear in the surface coat through which an exovate containing the egg nucleus immediately forms (Fig. 5). With

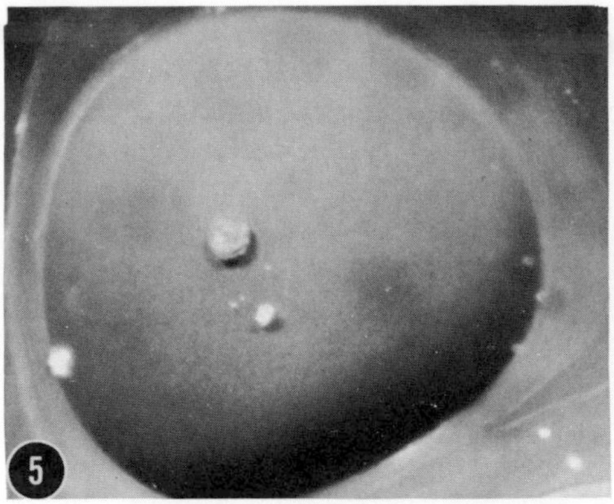

FIG. 5. Photograph of exovate containing the nucleus of the egg which was removed as demonstrated in Fig. 4. The two smaller white specks are air bubbles trapped in the jelly layers.

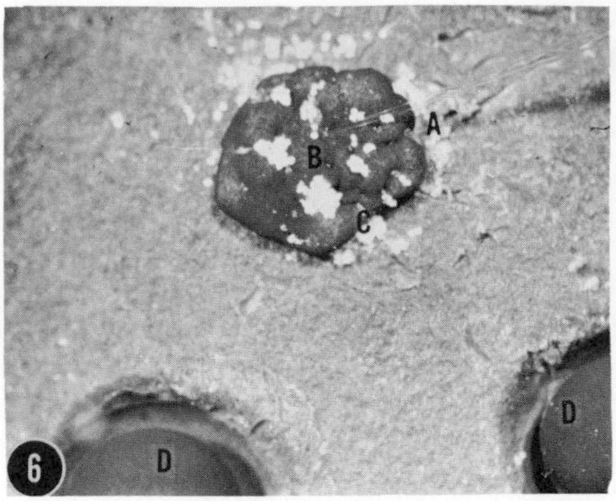

FIG. 6. Photograph of a portion of the operating field. (A) microinjection pipette; (B) isolated blastula cells; (C) blastula operating platform; (D) activated and enucleated host eggs. Magnification 40 ×.

practice it should be possible to enucleate 10 or more eggs in each lot of 30–50 eggs activated. When carefully done, the enucleation exovate, trapped in the inner jelly layer that surrounds the egg, virtually always contains the egg nucleus.

After completing the above operation the enucleated eggs are separated from their unoperated neighbors and their outer jelly layers removed with watchmaker's forceps and a pair of fine-pointed scissors. Enucleated host eggs prepared in this manner are then rinsed in Steinberg's medium (Steinberg, 1957) and transferred, with a wide-mouth pipette, to the hemispherical depressions of an operating dish containing Steinberg's medium (Fig. 6).

Preparation of Donor Cells

Donor cells whose nuclei are to be transplanted are prepared from blastula donors obtained by the artificial insemination of eggs derived from an ovulating female (see footnote 5, p. 745.) A mid- to late-blastula donor (stage 8 to stage 9, Shumway, 1940) is placed in a clean flat Syracuse dish containing Steinberg's medium, and its animal hemisphere is separated from the vegetal hemisphere. The animal pole region of the separated animal hemisphere is removed by means of a glass microneedle bent at an angle of about 45 degrees and a small ball-tipped glass rod in a manner similar to that by which grafts of embryonic anlagen are prepared (Hamburger, 1960). To dissociate the tissue into its component cells, the dissected tissue is then transferred with a wide-mouth pipette to a second Syracuse dish containing Steinberg's medium lacking the divalent ions, calcium, and magnesium (King, 1966). When the tissue is placed into the dissociating medium, its pigmented surface should face down, i.e., in contact with the bottom of the dish.

Within 10–20 minutes after exposure to the calcium- and magnesium-free Steinberg's medium, most of the individual cells of the internal surface of the dissected blastula tissue will have rounded up and become separated from their neighbors. Dissociated cells are picked up in a small-bore glass pipette (1-mm orifice), rinsed in regular Steinberg's medium, and then transferred to the pigmented surface of the animal hemisphere portion of a late blastula, which was previously placed in the center of the operating dish containing regular Steinberg's solution (Fig. 6). The soft surface coat of the ruptured blastula serves admirably as an operating platform. It allows the operator to keep the dissociated donor cells isolated and permits movements of the injection pipette to be carried out freely, without inadvertently damaging the tip of the pipette by an unexpected and abrupt encounter with the hard surface of the operating dish.

Blastula Nuclear Transplantation

The transplantation of nuclei from blastula cells into enucleated eggs should be carried out under a stereoscopic microscope with a magnification of at least 100 diameters.

Before beginning the actual transplantation operation the injection pipette must be installed and properly adjusted in the micropipette holder. A thin-walled glass micropipette, the orifice of which has an internal diameter approximately one-third less than that of the cell whose nucleus is to be transplanted, is inserted into the instrument holder (section on Microinjection Assembly). The diameter of the aperture of micropipettes for blastula cells should range from 25 to 35 μ. Then, in order to overcome the pressure in the syringe, plastic tubing, and instrument holder, the tip of the pipette, while mounted *only* in the cap, is dipped into the Steinberg's medium in the operating dish, and the fluid level is allowed to adjust by capillary adhesion. After the tip of the micropipette has been filled with the injection medium the screw cap is securely fitted onto the hollow instrument holder. At this time the tip of the pipette should be carefully oriented so that its beveled side faces down on the donor cells.

When the tip of the injection pipette is properly positioned in the operating field (Fig. 6), a single blastula cell is gently drawn into the mouth of the pipette. If this is done properly, and the pipette is of the correct size and construction, the cell surface will be broken without dispersing the cytoplasm in the immediate vicinity of the nucleus. This is the most *important* single step in the entire nuclear transplantation procedure. It must be done carefully, so that the nucleus of the broken cell is not exposed to the possible deleterious effects of the injection medium. However, when this part of the procedure is properly done, the small amount of cytoplasm (7×10^{-5} mm^3) that surrounds the translucent nucleus, seen in the center of the broken cell, affords adequate protection to the nucleus until the moment it is liberated into the cytoplasm of the recipient egg.

After the donor cell is carefully broken in the tip of the micropipette, the pipette is moved toward one of the enucleated eggs, previously prepared and placed in one of the hemispherical depressions of the operating dish. Using the control lever of the micromanipulator, the pipette, carrying the broken cell, is inserted into the center of the host egg cytoplasm at a point along the animal-vegetal axis roughly one-third of the distance from the animal pole.

It should be noted that movement of the control lever of the Leitz micromanipulator creates an identical motion of the pipette. Accordingly, under the field of the stereoscopic microscope the motion of the pipette is exactly the same as the motion of the control lever.

The blastula nucleus is liberated into

the host egg cytoplasm by carefully injecting the broken cell with a minimal amount of injection medium. In carrying out this operation it is important to depress the plunger of the syringe *slowly*, otherwise the forces of adhesion in the injection pipette are overcome too quickly, and the injection of the donor nucleus into the recipient egg proceeds too rapidly and cannot be controlled. If, however, the pipette has been thoroughly cleaned,[6] the movements of the column in the lower end of the pipette can be controlled accurately by watching the movement of the meniscus of the fluid column within the shaft of the pipette. The broken cell is kept near the tip of the pipette, while the meniscus of the fluid column is higher in the shaft but still within the field of view of the intermediate objective. If the correct procedure is adopted, the injection process can be stopped immediately and the pipette slowly withdrawn from the recipient egg.

As the pipette is withdrawn it usually pulls the surface coat of the egg up against the vitelline membrane, so that a small canal is formed through which the egg substance may subsequently leak. Leakage can be prevented by severing the stalklike connection between the egg surface and the elevated vitelline membrane with two glass needles, the shafts of which are crossed upon each other to simulate the cutting action of the blades of a pair of scissors.

After receiving a transplanted nucleus each recipient egg is removed from the operating dish and individually placed in a small stender dish with about 5 ml of spring water. The dish is covered with a glass lid and the eggs are left undisturbed except during periods of observation.

Following the successful transplantation of diploid blastula nuclei, cleavage will begin within 2–3 hours after activation, depending on the temperature. The second cleavage occurs 40–60 minutes after the first, and subsequent cleavages occur at similar intervals. During this period the eggs should be examined every hour, at least for the first three cleavage intervals.

One-third or more of the eggs that cleave at the normal interval after activation (approximately 3 hours at 18°C) give rise to diploid blastulae. A delay of one cleavage interval, following the successful transplantation of a diploid nucleus, results in a tetraploid embryo (Briggs and King, 1953). The majority of normally cleaved blastulae, be they on time or delayed, continue to develop normally through gastrulation and subsequent stages (Briggs and King, 1959; King, 1966).

From the blastula stage on, the developing embryos should be observed twice a day and more frequently during gastrulation and neurulation, when the main organ systems of the embryos are being laid down. If one wishes, nuclear-transplant embryos may be maintained throughout the larval stages using the methods described by DiBerardino (this volume, pp. 53–74). Many of these nuclear transplant larvae will metamorphose into young frogs.

Controls for Blastula Nuclear Transplantation

Four types of controls should be carried out for each blastula nuclear transplantation experiment. First, the quality of the recipient eggs and embryos that provide donor nuclei for transplantation should be ascertained. Ninety percent or more of these artificially inseminated diploid controls should develop into normal larvae. Then the reliability of the enucleation procedure should be checked. Three ways are available for doing this. One is to observe the activity of eggs that are simply pricked with a

[6] Instructions for cleaning glass micropipettes are given by King, 1966.

clean glass needle. Eggs treated in this manner form the ephemeral "black dot" and within a few hours at 18°C show puckering of the surface coat or abortive and irregular cleavage furrows. Within 10 hours after activation the abortive furrows fade away and the eggs begin to cytolyze. None of these eggs develop into blastulae. By contrast, eggs which are pricked and then enucleated fail to show any signs of activity whatsoever. When observed at 5–10 hours after activation, these eggs at 18°C show none of the surface activity present in practically all of the pricked eggs at this time. This difference in behavior of the two types of eggs provides a convenient criterion for determining the success of the enucleation operation, but the best means of accomplishing this is to produce androgenetic haploids (Porter, 1939). This is done at the end of each nuclear transplantation experiment.

To produce androgenetic haploids, eggs from an ovulating female are shaken into a clean, dry, flat Syracuse dish and covered with just enough concentrated sperm suspension (2 macerated testes) made up in 10 percent amphibian Ringer's solution to wet the eggs. Within 15–20 minutes after insemination at 18°C the "black dots" will appear. The egg nucleus of the artificially inseminated eggs is then removed in the same manner as that described for enucleating parthenogenetically activated eggs (see section on Activation and Enucleation of Host Eggs). From such eggs one obtains androgenetic haploids when the operation is successful, and diploids when it is not (Porter, 1939). Using separate lots of eggs a total of 20 or more androgenetic haploids should be prepared.

After completing the above operation the successfully enucleated eggs are removed from the Syracuse dish and placed in a large stender dish containing about 20 ml of spring water. A similar number of unoperated eggs from the same lot are placed in another large stender dish. The second group of eggs serve as diploid controls for the first. Records should be made of the over-all form and the rate of development of both groups of eggs. The time of cleavage in both groups of eggs should be observed and recorded at hourly intervals at least through the first three cleavages. Observations also should be made at frequent intervals during the subsequent 2–4 days, particularly during gastrulation and neurulation. Amphibian haploid embryos develop normally to the beginning of gastrulation, but thereafter become retarded and display a combination of abnormalities (microcephaly, edema, stunted external gills and, internally, deficiencies in the gut, central nervous system, sense organs, pronephros, and cardiovascular system). This combination of abnormalities has come to be known as the "haploid syndrome" (Porter, 1939; Subtelny, 1958). In addition to the gross morphological evidences of haploidy, a clear difference in the size of the epidermal cells in haploids and diploids can be seen at the tail-bud stage (stages 17 and 18, Shumway, 1940). When the controls have reached Shumway stage 22 this difference in ploidy can be confirmed by taking tail-tip clippings from representative haploid and diploid embryos. The chromosome numbers of tail-tip squashes, made according to the procedure described by Di-Berardino (1962), are determined by microscopic observation.

The production of androgenetic haploids is the most convenient and most reliable means of determining the validity of the enucleation operation. In our hands it has indicated that at least 99 percent of the attempted enucleations do in fact effectively eliminate the chromosomes of the host eggs (Briggs and King, 1952; 1953).

CONCLUSION

The transplantation of blastula nuclei into the cytoplasm of enucleated frogs' eggs, according to the procedures described in this chapter, was originally used to test the validity of the method. Not only does it show that it is technically feasible to transplant living nuclei in an undamaged condition, and that blastula nuclei, capable of promoting the complete normal development of test eggs, are equivalent to the zygote nucleus at the beginning of development, but it also employs all of the basic techniques necessary for conducting other types of investigations along the same lines. However, before attempts to conduct more complicated manipulations are undertaken, the operative procedures described for blastula nuclear transplantation must be thoroughly mastered. Reasonable skill can be achieved only through practice.

In carrying out the procedures for amphibian nuclear transplantation, it is possible to work as a team with one member preparing the enucleated host eggs and their controls, and the other performing the actual transplantation operation. Under these circumstances an experienced investigator can transplant a blastula nucleus every 3–5 minutes—if everything else is going well. However, the procedures involved are sufficiently exacting so that even under the best circumstances one cannot expect to perform more than 30–50 successful operations in 1 day.

The value of amphibian nuclear transplantation in the analysis of development has been demonstrated on a number of occasions (see King, 1966, for references). The technique has been used principally to investigate the question of whether or not nuclei of somatic cells undergo stabilized genetic changes in the course of embryonic cellular differentiation. In addition to this, in studies on interspecific and intraspecific hybrids, it has permitted certain types of nucleocytoplasmic combinations to be made which cannot be achieved in any other way. Furthermore, since the delay in the initial cleavage interval which follows successful nuclear transplantation results in the complete replication of the chromosome complement of the transplanted nucleus without concomitant cytokinesis, the technique affords a convenient means of obtaining developing embryos with different degrees of ploidy. Successful transplantation of nuclei from single cells of the frog renal adenocarcinoma also have been obtained. Recently, a preliminary insight into the biochemical events of development has been gained by the transplantation of labeled nuclei. Further indications of the usefulness of this technique will be realized when it is applied to the production of inbred strains of frogs and to the development of an optimal medium for studies of nuclear biochemistry.

REFERENCES

BRIGGS, R., and T. J. KING, 1952: Transplantation of living nuclei from blastula cells into enucleated frogs' eggs. *Proc. Natl. Acad. Sci. U.S.*, 38: 455.

———, and ———, 1953: Factors affecting the transplantability of nuclei of frog embryonic cells. *J. Exptl. Zool.*, 122: 485.

———, and ———, 1959: Nucleocytoplasmic interactions in eggs and embryos. In J. Brachet and A. E. Mirsky (eds.), *The Cell*, Academic Press, New York, Vol. I, p. 537.

DI BERARDINO, M., 1962: The karyotype of *Rana pipiens* and investigation of its stability during embryonic differentiation. *Develop. Biol.*, 5: 101.

ELSDALE, T. R., J. B. GURDON, and M. FISCHBERG, 1960: A description of the technique for nuclear transplantation in *Xenopus laevis*. *J. Embryol. Exptl. Morph.*, 8: 437.

GURDON, J. B., 1960: Factors responsible for the abnormal development of embryos obtained by nuclear transplantation in *Xenopus laevis*. *J. Embryol. Exptl. Morph.*, 8: 327.

———, 1964: The transplantation of living nuclei. In M. Abercrombie and J. Brachet (eds.), *Advances in Morphogenesis*, Academic Press, New York, Vol. IV, p. 1.

HAMBURGER, V., 1960: *A Manual of Experimental Embryology*. The University of Chicago Press, Chicago, Ill., p. 87.

HENNEN, S., 1963: Chromosomal and embryological analyses of nuclear changes occurring in embryos derived from transfers of nuclei between *Rana pipiens* and *Rana sylvatica*. *Develop. Biol.*, 6: 133.

———, 1965: Nucleocytoplasmic hybrids between *Rana pipiens* and *Rana palustris*. 1. Analysis of the developmental properties of the nuclei by means of nuclear transplantation. *Develop. Biol.*, 11: 243.

KING, T. J., 1966: Nuclear transplantation in amphibia. In D. M. Prescott (ed.), *Methods in Cell Physiology*, Academic Press, New York, Vol. II, p. 1.

KOPAC, M. J., 1964: Micromanipulators: principles of design, operation, and application. In W. L. Nastuk (ed.), *Physical Techniques in Biological Research*, Academic Press, New York, Vol. V, p. 191.

MOORE, J. A., 1958: Transplantation of nuclei between *Rana pipiens* and *Rana sylvatica*. *Exptl. Cell Res.*, 14: 532.

NIKITINA, L. A., 1964: Transfers of nuclei from the ectoderm and sensory rudiments of developing embryos of *Bufo bufo*, *Rana arvalis*, and *Rana temporaria* into enucleated eggs of the same species. *Dokl. Akad. Nauk., S.S.S.R.*, 156: 1461. (In Russian.)

PORTER, K. R., 1939: Androgenetic development of the egg of *Rana pipiens*. *Biol. Bull.*, 77: 233.

RUGH, R., 1962: *Experimental Embryology—Techniques and Procedures*. 3rd ed. Burgess Publishing Company, Minneapolis, Minn., p. 15.

SAMBUICHI, H., 1957: The roles of the nucleus and the cytoplasm in development. I. An intersubspecific hybrid frog, developed from a combination of *Rana nigromaculata nigromaculata* cytoplasm and a diploid nucleus of *Rana nigromaculata brevipoda*. *J. Sci. Hiroshima Univ.*, B17: 33.

SHUMWAY, W., 1940: Stages in the normal development of *Rana pipiens*. *Anat. Rec.*, 78: 139.

SIGNORET, J., and J. FAGNIER, 1962: Activation expérimentale de l'oeuf de Pleurodele. *Compt. Rend. Acad. Sci.*, 254: 4079.

———, and B. PICHERAL, 1962: Transplantation de noyaux chez *Pleurodeles waltlii* Michah. *Compt. Rend. Acad. Sci.*, 254: 1150.

———, R. BRIGGS, and R. R. HUMPHREY, 1962: Nuclear transplantation in the axolotl. *Develop. Biol.*, 4: 134.

SLÁDEČEK, F., and Z. MAZÁKOVÁ-ŠTEFANOVÁ, 1964: Nuclear transplantation in *Triturus vulgaris* L. *Folio Biol.* (Praha), 10: 152.

———, and ———, 1965: Intraspecific and interspecific nuclear transplantations in *Triturus*. *Folio Biol.* (Praha), 11: 74.

STEINBERG, M., 1957: In *Carnegie Institution of Washington Year Book* 56: 347 (report by J. D. Ebert).

STROEVA, O. G., and L. A. NIKITINA, 1960: Transplantation of nuclei in amphibia and its significance in the study of the problem of differentiation. *Zhur. Obs. Biol. (S.S.S.R.)*, 21: 335. (In Russian.)

SUBTELNY, S., 1958: The development of haploid and homozygous diploid frog embryos obtained from transplantation of haploid nuclei. *J. Exptl. Zool.*, 139: 263.

Insect Surgery

By Howard A. Schneiderman

INTRODUCTION

Many basic developmental problems can be examined in the postembryonic stages of insects. Particular attention has focused on the hormonal control of development (Gilbert, 1964; Schneiderman and Gilbert, 1964; Wigglesworth, 1964) and reproduction (Wigglesworth, 1964), the mechanism of determination (Hadorn, 1964, 1965), morphogenetic fields (Kroeger, 1960), gradients (Locke, 1964), nervous control of muscle development (Nuesch, 1952), regeneration (Pohley, 1961), and cell death in morphogenesis (Lockshin and Williams, 1965), to name a few. A wide variety of biochemical studies have also been undertaken, for example, the mechanism of yolk formation (Telfer, 1961), hormonal effects on RNA synthesis (Sekeris, 1965), and metabolism of giant chromosomes (*cf.* review by Kroeger and Lezzi, 1966). This section is devoted to the surgical techniques which are necessary for both morphological and biochemical studies of postembryonic stages of insects. The methods to be described have been developed particularly for wild silk moths of the family Saturniidae (Cecropia, Polyphemus, Cynthia, Promethea, Luna, etc.) and unless stated to the contrary in the text, the insects referred to in specific surgical procedures are wild silk moths. Methods for exceedingly small insects such as *Drosophila* are considered in a separate section of this book.

Surgical studies on these insects were first carried out extensively by Crampton (1899) who explored the effects of parabiosis between different species. Thereafter, these silk moths attracted little attention until 1946 when C. M. Williams published his classical paper on the role of the brain in the production and termination of pupal diapause in the Cecropia silk moth. Most of the techniques to be described here are based largely upon methods originally developed by Williams. Several of these have worked so well that they have not been modified significantly during the past 20 years. Others have been modified to various extents over the past 13 years in the author's laboratory, notably by S. J. Berry, L. I. Gilbert, A. Krishnakumaran, and H. Oberlander. The adequacy of the description for each operation was tested by Dr. K. Madhavan, who performed each of the operations using the directions provided in the text.

The success of these surgical techniques depends upon the following precautions:

1. Insect blood darkens upon exposure to air as a result of the action of the copper-containing enzyme, phenolase. The

products of this reaction are toxic. To prevent darkening of blood during surgery, it is necessary to work rapidly and to use a phenolase inhibitor such as phenylthiourea.

2. Use clean sharp instruments. Do not leave jagged edges on the incisions.

3. Always operate in a fluid-filled field. When sealing a wound, avoid air bubbles.

4. "Clean" implants of loose tissue debris.

5. In many insects, incisions can merely be pinched together with forceps and punctures can be ignored. This is true of most lepidopterous larvae in which the blood clots readily. Hence, small wounds in larvae can often be left unsealed if the larva is kept anesthetized or cooled until the blood clots. However, the blood of lepidopterous pupae and adults does not clot well and incisions, openings, and even small punctures should be sealed. This is best accomplished with melted wax or with plastic windows sealed to the cuticle with wax. In other insect groups, experience will dictate whether or not sealing wounds is necessary.

ANESTHESIA

Some surgical procedures can be carried out without anesthesia, but to avoid extensive blood loss, to permit fine surgery, and to permit attachment of plastic windows, anesthesia is commonly required. While a variety of anesthetics such as ether, cold, submergence in water, etc., have been employed with insects, a mixture of carbon dioxide and air has proven most effective for many insects including Lepidoptera. Lepidopterous pupae can remain completely immobilized by a mixture of air and carbon dioxide for as long as a day and still recover completely. Larvae and adults can survive exposures of at least an hour without obvious aftereffects.

A convenient anesthesia chamber is a flat-bottom Buchner funnel (porcelain or polyethylene) 14–16 cm in diameter with an internal depth of 3–4 cm (Williams, 1946b). This funnel is mounted flush to the top of an operating bench (Williams, 1959). A rubber tube connects the bottom of the funnel to a commercial carbon dioxide cylinder. An alternative we have used for a number of years is a table-model polyethylene Buchner funnel (diameter 12.5 cm and cut off to an internal depth of 3 cm) whose flat bottom and side-arm hose connection permit the funnel to rest on the bench during use. Carbon dioxide from the cylinder is bubbled through a flask half-filled with water which serves as a flow meter. The stream of carbon dioxide, which is heavier than air, fills the funnel and keeps the insect under continuous anesthesia during surgery. The top of the funnel may be covered to hasten initial anesthesia. Sometimes it is convenient to have two separate funnels, one for initial anesthesia and a second for surgery.

Lepidopterous pupae are anesthetized within 15–30 minutes, adults within 2 minutes, and larvae within 8 minutes. When the insect is fully anesthetized, it is ordinarily flaccid and motionless. However, occasionally, pupae become stiff and distended during anesthesia. This is due to CO_2 absorption and is encountered when CO_2 anesthesia is intermittent. It can be prevented by continuous anesthesia.

EQUIPMENT

Operations are conducted under a dissecting microscope at magnifications between 7 × and 30 ×. Only occasionally are higher magnifications needed. It is convenient if the microscope can be moved freely over the funnel. Two microscope lamps are desirable, one of which can be focused to a bright spot.

They must be furnished with infrared filters to prevent heating. Surface reflections sometimes interfere with observations and surgery, but this can be overcome by placing a Polaroid filter in front of the microscope lamp and positioning a second "cross" filter under the objective lens (Harvey and Williams, 1958). A foot-focusing device which frees both hands for surgery is convenient, but this can be dispensed with.

Dissecting instruments should include several pairs of watchmaker's forceps (No. 3 and No. 5) which must be kept finely ground and should be dressed frequently on an Arkansas stone or fine carborundum paper. Also needed are iridectomy scissors, several pairs of curved and straight iris scissors, a scalpel with detachable blades (e.g., Bard-Parker No. 3 handle with No. 11 detachable blade), some stainless steel razor blades, several straight, bent, and hooked probes made of insect pins of various sizes inserted into wooden handles or into needle holders with adjustable jaws, blunt probes, and a 5- or 10-ml hypodermic syringe filled with insect Ringer's and furnished with a $\frac{1}{2}$-inch needle (22–26 gauge). In some cases smaller gauge needles are necessary and gauges as small as No. 33 can be obtained from the Vita Needle Company, Needham, Massachusetts. Very fine forceps can be made by cementing small insect pins to the tips of a pair of ordinary forceps (Karel Slama, personal communication) and fine scalpels can be made from fragments of razor blade attached to wooden handles with sealing wax.

Various Ringer's solutions can be used to replace blood lost in surgery. We prefer Ephrussi-Beadle Ringer's solution which contains 7.5 gm NaCl, 0.35 gm KCl, and 0.21 gm $CaCl_2$ per liter of distilled water (Ephrussi and Beadle, 1936). This solution should be boiled and kept refrigerated. Boiling once each week to prevent contamination is a wise precaution. Some workers employ the following physiological solution based on the ionic composition of Cecropia blood: 0.06 gm NaCl, 3.0 gm KCl, 5.7 gm $MgCl_2$, 0.6 gm $CaCl_2$, and 0.08 gm $NaHCO_3$ per liter (Michejda and Thiers, 1963; Clark and Harvey, 1965), but we have had no experience with it.

CLEANLINESS

Instruments are rinsed before each operation in 70 percent ethanol. Instruments may be kept upright and tip down in a jar of 70 percent ethanol which has a wad of cotton on the bottom. While rigorous aseptic procedures need not be followed, insect pathogens should be avoided by taking the following precautions: Open all cocoons in a room separate from that in which operations are conducted. Promptly discard all diseased insects. Do not allow diseased insects near healthy insects. If it is necessary to examine a diseased insect, use separate dissecting equipment and do not do this in the same room in which you perform surgery.

The commonest cause of postsurgical death in most insects is darkening of the blood which results from the action of phenolases that function after injury. Mortality from surgery in many insects can be reduced to a low level by employing an effective antiphenolase such as phenylthiourea (PTU). If a few crystals of PTU are placed in all wounds before sealing, the insect's blood will not darken and mortality will be kept low. Commercial PTU can be purified by recrystallizing two or three times from hot (60°C) 95 percent ethanol. It should be stored in a desiccator in the deep freeze until needed. Antibiotics are helpful in preventing infections. For the past 13 years, we have used a 2:1:1 mixture of PTU:streptomycin sulfate:penicillin. The three powders are thoroughly ground together in a mortar and stored in screwcap vials in a desiccator in the deep freeze. A 1-day supply of this mixture is removed at a time. Attention to these simple procedures, which were originally developed by Williams, coupled with general cleanliness and the use of sharp instruments will reduce the mortality in surgical preparations almost to zero.

IMMOBILIZING INSECTS DURING SURGERY

Various techniques have been developed for holding insects during surgery. The simplest one for all but exceedingly small insects is to support them in Plasticine molds of various shapes which can be fitted snugly around the insect. This procedure may be modified by using plastic rings of various sizes which are partially filled with Plasticine, and by using insect pins inserted in the Plasticine and wedged across the insect's body. Another procedure is to immobilize the insect with insect pins on a small dish lined with black wax. In some cases a small clamp can be made from a pair of forceps which will grip the head capsule of the insect and hold it in place for surgery (Karel Slama, personal communication). Another technique is to affix the insect to a glass slide covered with "Scotch tape" (sticky side up). A drop of water will dislodge it from the tape.

SEALING WOUNDS

After surgery is completed a few crystals of phenylthiourea-antibiotic mixture are added to the wound and Ringer's solution is added from the syringe to fill any air space in the wound. If the opening is small (such as a slit to receive an implant), it is merely sealed with molten paraffin wax (melting point 50° to 52°C). A small lump of wax is picked up with a curved dissecting needle, the shaft of the needle is heated until the wax melts and can be used to seal the wound. Since the wax will not stick unless the cuticle is dry, dry the cuticle with a bit of tissue if necessary. Also, care must be taken not to heat the wax too much and so burn the insect. In some cases waxes of lower melting point have been used with success. Lower melting point is obtained by mixing ordinary paraffin wax with petrolatum. A stickier wax may be made from equal parts of rosin and bee's wax, or bee's wax and paraffin wax. Sira wax, a commercial product, can be obtained from British Drug Houses, Ltd. In our experience 50°–52°C paraffin is satisfactory for almost all surgery except on larvae where a stickier wax is useful. For small insects where burning is a problem, wounds may be sealed with wax by heating the head of an insect pin.

To seal wounds larger than a slit in lepidopterous pupae or adults, "plastic windows" are employed. The wound is filled with Ringer's solution from the syringe until the fluid is flush with the surface of the cuticle. A plastic window somewhat larger than the area of the excised cuticle to be covered is cut from a thin sheet of cellulose tetraacetate (0.01 inch or 0.02 inch thick; Williams, 1946a, 1959). (Other forms of acetate are slightly soluble in water or alcohol and warp.) For this purpose we keep a supply of windows of various sizes which have been punched out with a paper punch. The window is rinsed in 70 percent alcohol, wiped dry with tissue, and placed on the open wound. If the cuticle around the window is wet it should be dried with a piece of tissue held in the tips of forceps. The window is sealed in place with melted wax which adheres to the cuticle and to the underside rim of the plastic window, provided that both are dry. One ends up with an insect furnished with a clear window through which one may observe the inside of the living pupa or adult. In larvae, except for the head capsule, large wounds are not easily sealed with windows since the insect's wiggling usually dislodges the window. Larval wounds are best sealed with wax alone.

After surgery is completed the insects are removed to convenient containers for storage. Pupae may be kept in individual shell vials or multicompartment plastic boxes with cotton in the bottom. It is advisable to store pupae with the windows facing upward. In the event that an air bubble has been left in the pupa, it will appear on the surface of the window after some hours. If the bubble is less than a millimeter in diameter, it can be ignored. But if it is much larger, the wound should be opened, the bubble removed, and the window replaced. Adults are best kept in half-pint cardboard containers. The wings may be clipped together with paperclips to prevent them from flapping. After routine surgery, larvae are allowed to recover for about 2 hours at room temperature. After serious surgery, they should be kept at 5°C for 12 to 24 hours before returning them to their food plants or food supply.

Most surgical preparations seem to survive best at 25°C and 60–70 percent relative humidity. This humidity can be maintained by keeping a saturated solution of sodium bromide in the incubator. Certain surgical preparations such as isolated pupal abdomens desiccate and usually die within 2 months, but can be kept alive for much longer by periodically injecting Ringer's solution to compensate for loss of water by evaporation. Plugging vials containing the pupae or pupal fragments with cotton also appears to be helpful.

The surgical insults that pupae and adults can withstand are remarkable. If PTU and antibiotics are used, a pupa that has been cut in half and spread out in a dish of Ringer's solution may continue to wiggle for several days. In general, larvae are less resistant to surgery, but are nevertheless quite hardy.

STORAGE OF ORGANS AND TISSUES FOR TRANSPLANTATION

When organs are excised for implantation they can be conveniently examined in Ringer's solution in small black depression dishes, in Petri dishes lined with black wax or kept on a black background, or in black plastic bottle caps affixed to a slide. Sometimes several organs (e.g., six brains) must be extirpated from several pupae and then implanted into a single pupa. To store such organs, three procedures may be used: (1) They may be stored at room temperature in Ringer's solution. Under such circumstances, the operation should be conducted quickly so that they are in Ringer's no longer than 20 minutes. (2) The organs may be stored in a pupa which has been placed head down in a plastic ring, and had the tip of its abdomen replaced with a loose plastic window. A few crystals of PTU are added. Such a pupa serves as a temporary "bank" for organs to be subsequently implanted. (3) The organs may be stored in Ringer's solution which is kept at 2° to 5°C by immersion in an ice bath. This last procedure is the simplest and we have employed it extensively.

When one first attempts these operations, the location of particular endocrine structures, imaginal discs, and other organs in the living insect may be difficult to ascertain because of the transparency of some of the organs and their nervous connections. Nerves, prothoracic glands, and a number of other organs can be revealed by staining with methylene blue. Although in some cases (e.g., prothoracic glands) the viability of the organ is not impaired (Williams, 1948), methylene blue destroys insect nerve cells (Clever, 1960) and may interfere with subsequent experiments in which the nervous system is critical. Once an organ is located by staining, it is usually simple thereafter to locate it in an unstained preparation. Illustrations of the location of the endocrine organs of saturniid moths are to be found in Williams (1948, 1959) and in Gilbert (1964).

BRAIN EXTIRPATION, IMPLANTATION, AND FACIAL WINDOWS IN DIAPAUSING PUPAE

Debraining is a basic operation and once it is mastered the others are simple. The anesthetized pupa is placed in a Plasticine mold, dorsal side down with its abdomen facing the operator. The facial cuticle and epidermis are removed to expose the brain. This can be done in one of two ways. One method (Williams, 1946b) is to make two scalpel incisions in the integument on each side of the face and a single transverse cut across the top of the face. The flap of the cuticle is grasped with forceps and pulled free of its attachments. An alternative technique which we have used extensively is to hold the pupa in one hand and to slice off the facial cuticle and epidermis with a single cut of a razor blade. It is important in this operation, and in almost all others, to keep the open wound—the operating field—filled with blood (or Ringer's). This is accomplished by maintaining pressure on the abdomen with a piece of Plasticine and adding Ringer's as necessary. If fragments of epidermis or cuticle are still attached to the edges of the wound, they should be trimmed off with scissors and forceps. Similarly, the ends of large tracheae should be removed. The brain should now be clearly visible. By pressing on the pupal abdomen, the brain is floated up toward the operator. To remove the brain, the nerves passing laterally to the site of the future adult eyes are grasped in turn with one forceps and broken with the other. In like fashion, the tracheal supply, nerves passing posteriorly to the corpus cardiacum-corpus allatum complex and the circumesophageal connective are carefully broken loose from each brain hemisphere. The brain can now be lifted free and examined in a drop of Ringer's solution. A few crystals of PTU-antibiotic mixture should be placed in the wound. To close the wound in the pupal integument, the following procedure is employed: A clean circular plastic window slightly larger than the wound is placed over the hole. The tip of the abdomen is pressed until the field is filled with blood and all bubbles have been excluded, but not so far that the window is unseated from the cuticle. Pressure is kept on the tip of the abdomen while the window is sealed in place with melted paraffin. This prevents the paraffin from entering the pupa beneath the window.

Extirpation of the brain will keep a pupa in permanent diapause. Implantation of one or more active brains from a previously chilled pupa into a diapausing pupa or a brainless diapausing pupa leads to the activation of the prothoracic glands of the pupa and the initiation of adult development (Williams, 1948). Active brains may also be obtained from unchilled pupae of various species, e.g., Promethea (S. J. Berry, unpublished observations). Brains may be implanted in almost any location. The tip of the abdomen is a convenient place, but they can be inserted almost anywhere in the body cavity via slits in the integument.

BRAIN EXTIRPATION IN LEPIDOPTEROUS LARVAE

To remove larval brains various maneuvers are possible. Ligation behind the head with surgical thread is the easiest. However, this removes the corpus cardiacum-corpus allatum complex as well.

To remove only the brain the larvae should first be well anesthetized. It is best to keep them on a piece of absorbent tissue during anesthesia, because they commonly defecate and regurgitate when anesthetized. It is often convenient to starve them for 6 to 12 hours before surgery to reduce this. The anesthetized larva should be placed ventral side down with its head pointing away from the operator. The head should be bent forward over a cylinder of Plasticine so that it hangs downward and stretches the "neck." A transverse incision is made through the neck rather than through the head capsule. The brain can easily be removed and the wound sealed with melted paraffin.

EXCISION OF CORPORA CARDIACA AND CORPORA ALLATA

To remove the corpora cardiaca and corpora allata from pupae, the following procedures have been developed (*cf.* Williams, 1959; Gilbert and Schneiderman, 1960). Begin the operation as for brain extirpation. When the brain has been exposed, press it down and gently reflect it toward the posterior of the pupa, to reveal the corpus cardiacum-corpus allatum complex on each side. Each complex lies dorsolateral to the brain and adjacent to the bifurcation of a large trachea. A pair of fine nerves emerges from the posterior face of each brain hemisphere and passes to the corpus cardiacum-corpus allatum complex on that side, but these nerves may not be visible. By means of forceps, connections between the glandular complex and the adjacent tracheae are broken. The complex can then be transferred to a drop of Ringer's solution for examination. Ordinarily, one removes both the corpus cardiacum and corpus allatum, but removal of the corpus allatum (and a small part of the corpus cardiacum) can also be accomplished if desired.

Since the corpora allata of adult male Cecropia and Cynthia produce large amounts of juvenile hormone these glands are often extirpated to provide a source of juvenile hormone. To accomplish this, anesthetize an adult male moth and coat its head and prothorax with melted wax. Allow the wax to cool and peel it away to remove the scales from the head and prothorax. The antennae are excised at their bases and the head and prothorax are cut off with scissors and placed in a black wax dish. The head is split along the dorsal midline with a fine scissors, spread apart with forceps, and pinned open. The pair of corpus cardiacum-corpus allatum complexes is attached to the aorta just behind the brain. The brain is cut in half to fully expose the aorta. A drop of Ringer's is placed in the incision. The glandular complexes float up and can now be detached from the rear of the brain with forceps. The corpus cardiacum and the much larger corpus allatum can be distinguished from one another by their size and by the lobulated character of the corpus allatum.

An alternative procedure, developed by Krishnakumaran (personal communication) is to make a longitudinal slit in the dorsum of the adult "neck." The flaps on each side of the slit are spread outward and the glandular complexes are clearly visible close to the posterior margin of the head capsule.

Excising the corpora allata from larvae is a more difficult procedure. Several techniques have been elaborated, and the reader is referred to the original publications (e.g., Williams, 1961, page 574, and various papers by Fukuda and Bounhiol cited in Wigglesworth, 1954).

TERMINAL WINDOWS

Terminal windows are employed in connection with various kinds of operations, such as castration (see below), removal of abdominal ganglia and implantation of imaginal discs. It is also useful to detect the earliest signs of adult development through a window placed on the tip of the abdomen (Schneiderman and Williams, 1954).

The procedure employed to furnish a pupa with a terminal window is similar to that for facial windows, except that the hole produced is much larger. The pupa is anesthetized and placed head down in a ring of Plasticine. The two terminal segments are cut off with fine scissors or a razor blade and the jagged edges of cuticle removed to aid healing. (Additional segments may be removed.) The cut may be made anywhere in a segment but, in general, cuts through the intersegmental membrane seem to heal the most rapidly. Some fat body is then removed with forceps. It is important in this operation to take special care to remove air bubbles before placing the window over the opening. A simple procedure to ensure removal of air bubbles is to grasp the cut edge of the cuticle with forceps and pull upward to stretch the abdominal segments. This commonly dislodges any bubbles of air trapped in the abdomen. Ringer's solution is added as necessary, and a window of appropriate size is placed over the wound and sealed with melted paraffin.

A timetable for the adult development of Cecropia pupae at 25°C is presented in the article by Telfer, pp. 173–182 in this volume. Similar tables have been developed for other species, e.g., *Antheraea pernyi* (Williams and Adkisson, 1964), *Antheraea polyphemus* (Nuesch, 1965; with good illustrations). Such timetables are simple to prepare and indispensable for developmental studies. It is important to point out that adult development actually begins earlier than when first seen through the window. Thus an increase in pupal respiration and the sudden appearance of DNA (deoxyribonucleic acid) synthesis in several tissues occurs in Cecropia 5 or 6 days before the first visible sign of adult development.

CASTRATION

To castrate a pupa, the following procedure has been devised (Gilbert and Schneiderman, 1961). The tip of the pupal abdomen is cut off as described above for a terminal window. When the opening has been trimmed clean, the cut edge of the cuticle is pulled upward with forceps to stretch the animal and so produce a large air space in the body cavity. This is one of the few instances in which surgery is not conducted in a fluid-filled field. In male pupae, the translucent testes are readily visible dorsolaterally in the region of the fourth abdominal segment, and are removed with forceps. The yellowish-white ovaries, which are only about one-sixteenth the weight of the testes, are more difficult to see since they are usually buried in the fat body of the fourth abdominal segment. However, with practice one can easily excise them with fine forceps. Following castration, sufficient Ringer's solution is added to fill up the body cavity, and the wound is sealed with a plastic window.

ISOLATION OF PUPAL ABDOMENS

Isolated pupal abdomens are convenient preparations for a variety of experiments. They contain none of the principal endocrine organs and are thus excellent test objects for studying hormone action. They are also veritable tissue culture chambers and are excellent "banks" for storing tissues and organs for days or months. When grafted to whole insects, or fragments of insects at other stages of development, they can provide nourishment. Thus, short-lived isolated adult abdomens can be kept alive for weeks or months by grafting them to pupal abdomens (Williams, 1963; Krishnakumaran and Schneiderman, 1964).

To make certain that prothoracic glands are excluded from the isolated abdomen, it is common practice to prepare isolated abdomens that consist only of the terminal six segments.

The principal difficulty is to isolate the terminal abdominal segments without puncturing or rupturing the fluid-filled midgut (Williams, 1947). Tearing the midgut floods the pupa with a dark green fluid filled with particles. This fluid is apparently nontoxic, but its physiological effects are not fully understood. To avoid puncturing the gut, three procedures have been developed. In each of the procedures, the pupae must be well anesthetized.

1. This procedure was developed in our laboratory (Gilbert and Schneiderman, 1960). An incision is made in a pupa with a scalpel or razor blade just posterior to the thorax and completely around the pupa. Iridectomy scissors are used to cut through the wings, legs, and fat body, care being taken not to tear the gut. The pupa is then placed in a Plasticine ring, tail down, so that its anterior half hangs down over the ring, connected to the abdomen only by the gut. The gut is then ligated with surgical thread and cut anterior to the ligature. The section of gut between the incision and the ligature is thoroughly flushed with insect Ringer's to remove any loose gut contents. The open end of the abdomen is sealed with a plastic window in which a central hole has been punched (Williams, 1947, 1959). After the window is sealed in place with melted paraffin, insect Ringer's is added through the hole to displace all the air, and the hole is finally plugged with paraffin.

2. This procedure was devised by Williams (1947). The pupa is placed on its side and is cut through the cuticle and intersegmental membrane just posterior to the tip of wing flaps. The intersegmental muscles, nerve cord, heart, and fat body are also cut through. The hindgut is then transected and the tracheae which attach to the walls of the midgut are gently pushed away. The isolated abdomen can now be separated from the midgut and the anterior fragment, and the opening sealed as described above.

3. When one employs Cynthia pupae, the operation is exceedingly simple (Williams, 1959; Gilbert and Schneiderman, 1960). Since the gut of these pupae contains a solid rodlike mass, it can be cut through without contaminating the animal. The abdomen may be separated from the thorax by simply cutting through the pupa with a razor blade. The rodlike gut fragment in the isolated abdomen may be removed or not, as desired. The abdomen is then placed tip down in a Plasticine ring and the wound sealed as described above.

Isolated pupal abdomens prepared by any of the three methods described above will survive for several months. Transections at levels other than those noted above are easy to accomplish, and isolated anterior ends as well as isolated abdomens can be prepared.

Isolation of larval abdomens and adult abdomens is ordinarily accomplished by ligaturing, cutting off the thorax, and sealing the wound with wax.

PARABIOSIS

Parabiosis is a classical maneuver which permits an investigator to study the effects of the humoral agents of one insect on another. This maneuver lies at the heart of the classical experiments of Wigglesworth and of Williams which outlined the main features of insect endocrinology. Parabiosis between pupae is accomplished in the following way. Pupae are placed in Plasticine molds under deep carbon dioxide anesthesia. The terminal segments of each pupa are cut off to produce openings in each animal of about equal diameter. The animals are then placed tip to tip and pushed gently together until blood begins to ooze at the junction. A small amount of Ringer's is added until the junction is completely fluid-filled. The junction is then sealed with melted wax. It is extremely important in this operation to remove all air bubbles. To test the success of the operation, and to ensure that during the process of healing the connection between the two insects is not occluded, periodically one member of the grafted pair is gently squeezed. If its partner expands, there is probably free circulation between the two. The resulting adults have no anus and cannot void their meconium, but this does not appear to interfere with their longevity (Gilbert and Schneiderman, 1961). Large numbers of insects can be placed in parabiosis with one another. The "tour de force" in this sort of experiment was a chain of eight diapausing Cecropia pupae prepared by Williams (1952).

Pupae can be placed in parabiosis in different positions than those described above (e.g., head-to-head, thoracic dorsum-to-head, etc.).

Parabiosis between adults and pupae or between adult abdomens and pupae can be accomplished as follows (Krishnakumaran and Schneiderman, 1964). The terminal four segments of the abdomen of the adult partner are coated with melted paraffin to stiffen them, and the terminal three segments are excised. The wax on the remaining portion of the abdomen is peeled to remove the scales. Next, a hole equal in size to the open end of the abdomen is cut in the face of the pupal partner and the cut ends are jointed together with melted wax. The animals are now in head-to-tail parabiosis with a free exchange of blood. Other procedures have been described by Williams (1963).

Parabiosis between larvae and pupae has been accomplished, but parabiosis between larvae of Lepidoptera is difficult. However, it has been accomplished successfully with immature stages of many hemimetabolous insects such as *Rhodnius* (*cf.* Wigglesworth, 1954) and *Periplaneta* (Bodenstein, 1953).

A simple procedure for parabiosis with small insects developed by Wigglesworth is to attach a "handle" made of a flexible but sturdy wax (such as Sira wax) to each insect. The handle should be 4 or 5 cm long. Each handle is next attached to a glass slide. When the holes for parabiosis have been made, they may be aligned in proper position for sealing by moving the slides and the wax handles.

PROTHORACIC GLANDS

Because the prothoracic glands are such diffuse organs, it is difficult to extirpate them completely from a pupa. The only way of ensuring that prothoracic glands are removed is to remove the thorax. The remaining portion of the abdomen ordinarily contains no prothoracic glands. Absolute certainty can be assured only by removing the anterior portion of the abdomen as well.

Although complete extirpation of the glands is difficult, it is a fairly simple matter to extirpate parts of them and implant them into other insects as a source of ecdysone. An illustrated description of the glands is to be found in an article by Williams (1948). A simple procedure developed by Oberlander (1965) for extirpating the glands for subsequent implantation is described below.

The thorax of a pupa is cut off with a razor blade and transferred to a black dissecting dish containing Ringer's solution. A dorsal longitudinal incision is made, and the thorax is pinned out. The first tracheal mass on either side is removed under low power (10 ×) by grasping it at the base with a pair of forceps. The tracheal mass is then floated in the Ringer's solution over the black background of the dissecting dish. At a magnification of about 20 × to 30 ×, one can easily locate the almost transparent prothoracic glands against the black background.

BLEEDING A PUPA

A useful procedure in studies of insect development is the collection of blood for replacement after surgery, chemical analysis, or in connection with tissue culture. To bleed a Cecropia pupa exhaustively, one makes an incision about 3 mm long in the forewing, adjacent to the antenna and just posterior to the prothoracic spiracle. The pupa is then squeezed gently, and the blood allowed to drip into a centrifuge tube containing a few crystals of PTU, which is kept in an ice bucket. Care should be taken not to squeeze so hard that the gut breaks. This method provides blood free of fat body. The blood may be centrifuged, if desired, and can then be stored in the deep freeze.

EXTIRPATION OF LARVAL IMAGINAL DISCS

To extirpate imaginal discs from a larva and have the larva survive is necessary for various experiments such as studies of the regenerative capacity of the imaginal discs. Various techniques have been employed but the one developed by Heinrich Kroeger for larvae of the wax moth *Galleria mellonella* is both typical and simple.

Last instar larvae of *Galleria mellonella* are etherized for 3 to 4 minutes and are cleaned by brushing with 70 percent alcohol. Alternatively, they may be cleaned by pushing back and forth in a dish of sterile water. The larvae are placed in a wax-lined dissecting dish filled with insect Ringer's solution. On either side of the dorsal midline of the meso- and metathoracic segments of the larva, there is an opaque white spot which marks the position of the trachea entering the imaginal wing disc. In some species (e. g., *Ephestia kühniella*), the position of the wing disc is marked by bristles. A small longitudinal incision is made in this region with a pair of scissors and the imaginal disc is carefully pulled out and then cut off. The wound is then closed by lightly pressing together the cut edges of the skin with forceps and the larva is dried on filter paper. (It should be pointed out that once the discs are pulled out, they need not be cut off. Instead they can be treated in various ways, e.g., with chemicals, and pushed back inside where they will continue to develop.)

The operated larva is then transferred to a Petri dish whose bottom is covered with filter paper and is kept at 5°C for 24 hours. This procedure facilitates recovery of the larvae from the operation. Later, they are returned to incubators maintained at 30°C and 70 percent relative humidity. A similar procedure for the meal moth *Ephestia kühniella* has been described by Pohley (1961).

By appropriate variations of the basic methods described here, most surgical problems in all but the smallest insects can be met. Techniques for skin grafting (Bodenstein, 1953; Locke, 1959; Marcus, 1962), implantation of imaginal discs (Williams, 1961), implantation of skin fragments (Piepho, 1942), implantation of body parts (Kuske, 1963), etc., have been elaborated. The implantation of labeled tissues and subsequent examination of their fate by autoradiography (Oberlander *et al.*, 1965) can be applied in diverse experiments. Methods have been developed for culturing a few types of insect cells *in vitro* (Grace, 1962; Schneider, this volume, pp. 543–554) and for culturing imaginal discs *in vitro* (Schneider, 1964) and *in vivo* (Hadorn, 1964, 1965). Procedures have also been devised for dissociating imaginal discs of different kinds and mixing the cells so obtained to form new imaginal discs consisting of cells of diverse origins (*cf.* Ursprung, this volume, pp. 485–492). Recent treatises on insect physiology (Rockstein, 1964; Wigglesworth, 1965) and Wigglesworth's (1954) monograph on insect metamorphosis should be consulted. Papers by C. M. Williams are particularly well illustrated and a film strip, "Insect Metamorphosis," depicting Williams' various surgical preparations, is available from Time, Inc.

REFERENCES

BODENSTEIN, D., 1953: Studies on the humoral mechanisms in growth and metamorphosis of the cockroach, *Periplaneta americana*. *J. Exptl. Zool.*, 123: 189.

CLARK, R. M., and W. R. HARVEY, 1965: Cellular membrane formation by plasmatocytes of diapausing Cecropia pupae. *J. Insect Physiol.*, 11: 161.

CLEVER, U., 1960: Selective elimination of single sense cells with methylene blue. *Nature*, 186: 812.

CRAMPTON, H. E., 1899: An experimental-study upon Lepidoptera. *Arch. Entwicklmech. Org.*, 9: 293.

EPHRUSSI, B., and G. W. BEADLE, 1936: A technique of transplantation for *Drosophila*. *Amer. Nat.*, 70: 218.

GILBERT, L. I., 1964: Physiology of growth and development: Endocrine aspects. In M. Rockstein (ed.), *The Physiology of Insecta*, Academic Press, New York, Vol. I, p. 149.

———, and H. A. SCHNEIDERMAN, 1960: The development of a bioassay for the juvenile hormone of insects. *Trans. Amer. Micros. Soc.*, 79: 38.

———, and ———, 1961: The content of juvenile hormone and lipid in Lepidoptera: sexual differences and developmental changes. *Gen. and Comp. Endocrinol.*, 1: 453.

GRACE, T. D. C., 1962: Establishment of four strains of cells from insect tissues grown *in vitro*. *Nature*, 195: 788.

HADORN, E., 1964: Bedeutungseigene und bedeutungsfremde Entwicklungsleistungen proliferiender Primordien von *Drosophila* nach Dauerkultur *in vivo*. *Rev. Suisse de Zool.*, 71: 99.

———, 1965: Problems of determination and transdetermination. In *Genetic Control of Differentiation. Brookhaven Symposia in Biology*, 18: 148.

HARVEY, W. R., and C. M. WILLIAMS, 1958: Physiology of insect diapause. XII. The mechanism of carbon monoxide-sensitivity and insensitivity during the pupal diapause of the Cecropia silkworm. *Biol. Bull.*, 114: 36.

KRISHNAKUMARAN, A., and H. A. SCHNEIDERMAN, 1964: Developmental capacities of the cells of an adult moth. *J. Exptl. Zool.*, 157: 293.

KROEGER, H., 1960: Die Entstehung von Form im morphogenetischen Feld. *Naturwiss.*, 7: 148.

———, and M. LEZZI, 1966: Regulation of gene action in insect development. *Ann. Rev. Entom.*, 11: 1.

KUSKE, G., 1963: Untersuchungen zur metamorphose der Schmetterlingsbeine. *Arch. Entwicklmech. Org.*, 154: 354.

LOCKE, M., 1959: The cuticular pattern in an insect, *Rhodnius prolixus* Stal. *J. Exptl. Biol.*, 36: 459.

———, 1964: The structure and formation of the integument in insects. In M. Rockstein (ed.), *The Physiology of Insecta*, Academic Press, New York, Vol. III, p. 380.

LOCKSHIN, R. A., and C. M. WILLIAMS, 1965: Programmed cell death—III. Neural control of the breakdown of the intersegmental muscles of silkmoths. *J. Insect Physiol.*, 11: 601.

MARCUS, W., 1962: Untersuchungen über die Polarität der Rumpfhaut von Schmetterlingen. *Arch. Entwicklmech. Org.*, 154: 56.

MICHEJDA, J. W., and R. E. THIERS, 1963: Ionic regulation in the development of males of a silkworm: *Hyalophora cecropia. Proc. 16th Int. Congr. Zool.*, 2: 39.

NUESCH, H., 1952: Über den Einfluss der Nerven auf die Muskelentwicklung bei *Telea polyphemus* (Lepid). *Rev. Suisse Zool.*, 59: 293.

———, 1965: Die Imaginal—Entwicklung von *Antheraea polyphemus* Cr. (Lepidoptera). *Zool. Jb. Anat.*, 82: 393.

OBERLANDER, H., 1965: *The Action of Hormones at the Cellular Level during the Post-Embryonic Development of Saturniid Moths.* Doctoral thesis deposited in the library of Western Reserve University, Cleveland, Ohio.

———, S. J. BERRY, A. KRISHNAKUMARAN, and H. A. SCHNEIDERMAN, 1965: RNA and DNA synthesis during activation and secretion of the prothoracic glands of saturniid moths. *J. Exptl. Zool.*, 159: 15.

PIEPHO, H., 1942: Untersuchungen zur Entwicklungsphysiologie der Insektenmetamorphose. Über die Puppenhautung der Wachsmotte *Galleria mellonella* L. *Arch. Entwicklmech Org.*, 141: 500.

POHLEY, H. J., 1961: Interactions between the endocrine system and the developing tissues in *Ephestia kühniella. Arch. Entwicklmech. Org.*, 153: 443.

ROCKSTEIN, M. (ed.), 1964: *The Physiology of Insecta.* Academic Press, New York, Vols. I, II, III.

SCHNEIDER, I., 1964: Differentiation of larval *Drosophila* eye-antennal discs *in vitro. J. Exptl. Zool.*, 156: 91.

SCHNEIDERMAN, H. A., and L. I. GILBERT, 1964: Control of growth and development in insects. *Science*, 143: 325.

———, and C. M. WILLIAMS, 1954: The physiology of insect diapause. IX. The cytochrome oxidase system in relation to the diapause and development of the Cecropia silkworm. *Biol. Bull.*, 106: 238.

SEKERIS, C. E., 1965: Action of ecdysone on RNA and protein metabolism in the blowfly, *Calliphora erythrocephala.* In P. Karlson (ed.), *Mechanisms of Hormone Action*, Academic Press, New York, p. 149.

TELFER, W. H., 1961: The route of entry and localization of blood proteins in the oocytes of saturniid moths. *J. Biophys. and Biochem. Cytol.*, 9: 747.

WIGGLESWORTH, V. B., 1954: *The Physiology of Insect Metamorphosis.* Monographs in Exp. Biol., No. 1. Cambridge University Press, Cambridge, Eng.

———, 1964: The hormonal regulation of growth and reproduction. *Adv. in Insect Physiol.*, 2: 247.

———, 1965: *The Principles of Insect Physiology.* 6th ed. Methuen and Co., Ltd, London, Eng.

WILLIAMS, C. M., 1946a: Physiology of insect diapause: the role of the brain in the production and termination of pupal dormancy in the giant silkworm, *Platysamia cecropia. Biol. Bull.*, 90: 234.

———, 1946b: Continuous anesthesia for insects. *Science*, 103: 57.

———, 1947: Physiology of insect diapause. II. Interaction between the pupal brain and prothoracic glands in the metamorphosis of the giant silkworm, *Platysamia cecropia. Biol. Bull.*, 93: 89.

———, 1948: Physiology of insect diapause. III. The prothoracic glands in the Cecropia silkworm, with special reference to their significance in embryonic and postembryonic development. *Biol. Bull.*, 94: 60.

———, 1952: Physiology of insect diapause. IV. The brain and prothoracic glands as an endocrine system in the Cecropia silkworm. *Biol. Bull.*, 103: 120.

———, 1959: The juvenile hormone. I. Endocrine activity of the *corpora allata* of the adult Cecropia silkworm. *Biol. Bull.*, 116: 323.

———, 1961: The juvenile hormone. II. Its role in the endocrine control of molting, pupation and adult development in the Cecropia silkworm. *Biol. Bull.*, 121: 572.

———, 1963: The juvenile hormone. III. Its accumulation and storage in the abdomens of certain male moths. *Biol. Bull.*, 124: 355.

———, and P. L. ADKISSON, 1964: Physiology of insect diapause. XIV. An endocrine mechanism for the photoperiodic control of pupal diapause in the oak silkworm, *Antheraea pernyi*. *Biol. Bull.*, 127: 511.

Some Experimental Techniques for Eggs and Embryos of Marine Invertebrates

By W. E. Berg

INTRODUCTION

The recent development of closed-circulation marine aquaria and synthetic sea water (*cf.* Clark and Clark, 1964) undoubtedly will lead to increased use of marine invertebrate animals as sources of embryological material, and it is perhaps timely to give some attention to experimental techniques for these forms. The emphasis of the following is on methods for working with relatively small numbers of eggs and embryos. Semimicro- or micromethods are necessary for chemical and physiological studies of parts of embryos; there are at times, however, advantages in using these techniques with whole embryos as well. It may be difficult and time consuming to obtain sufficient eggs for macrochemical analyses. Speed of operation, convenient expression of results per embryo, and in some instances, fewer technical problems are other advantages.

REMOVAL OF EGG MEMBRANES AND COATS

With few exceptions the eggs of marine invertebrates are provided with tough membranes and coats which for some investigations must be removed. This can be accomplished mechanically on a small scale with fine glass needles or forceps; however, it is more convenient and productive to digest or dissolve the coverings by chemical means. A listing, intended more as a guide than a comprehensive review, of effective chemicals is presented in Table 1.

It should be pointed out that these chemicals are listed regardless of their toxicity, and some agents may cause cytolysis of the egg or abnormal development. Toxic reactions may be unexpectedly delayed; thus gastrulation of the ascidian embryo is abnormal if trypsin or protease is used to remove the chorions from unfertilized eggs. Subtle side effects may occur. For example protease removal of sea urchin membranes may lower the subsequent uptake of labeled amino acids although development is normal (Berg, unpublished). Caution must therefore be used in the selection and use of these chemicals for membrane removal. Alkaline solutions, membrane lysins, proteolytic enzymes, and sulfhydryl compounds appear to be the most useful agents.

TABLE 1. CHEMICAL METHODS FOR REMOVING EGG MEMBRANES AND COATS

AGENT	EFFECTS	REFERENCES
Proteolytic enzymes	Trypsin (0.1 %) digests transitional fertilization membrane and hyaline layer of fertilized sand dollar eggs (*Dendraster*). Trypsin (also papain, ficin, and chymotrypsin) treatment of unfertilized sea urchin (*Strongylocentrotus*) eggs prevents formation of fertilization membranes.	Moore (1949, 1952, 1957)
	Trypsin (0.1 %) and chymotrypsin digest jelly layer, fertilization membrane, and hyaline layer on sea urchin eggs (*Paracentrotus*, *Psammechinus*, and *Echinocardium*).	Runnström, Monné, and Broman (1943)
	Papain (0.1 mg per ml) removes hyaline layer of the sea urchin egg (*Arbacia*).	Northrop (1947)
	Trypsin (0.2 %) digests chorions of unfertilized ascidian eggs (*Ciona*).	Berrill (1932); Mansueto (1963)
	Protease (0.1–1.0 %) prevents formation of fertilization membranes and digests transitional fertilization membranes and hyaline layer of sea urchin eggs (*Lytechinus* and *Strongylocentrotus*). Protease (2–3 %, pH 8) digests chorions of ascidian eggs (*Ciona* and *Styela*).	Berg and Cheng (1962); Berg (1957)
	Ficin (0.2–0.4 %, pH 8.2) digests vitelline membrane of the sea urchin egg (*Psammechinus*).	Bohus-Jensen (1950)
	Hatching enzyme (supernatant from concentrated hatching blastulae) digests fertilization membranes of sea urchin eggs (*Strongylocentrotus* and *Arbacia*).	Ishida (1936); Kopac (1941); Sugawara (1943)
	Crustacean stomach enzymes (crab stomach juice diluted 1 to 50) digest chorions of ascidian eggs (*Ciona*, *Styela*, *Phallusia*, *Ascidia*, and *Molgula*).	Berrill (1932); Holter and Zeuthen (1944)
Membrane lysins	Lysins in sea water extracts of frozen-thawed sperm dissolve egg membranes of the keyhole limpet (*Megathura*), abalone (*Haliotis*), mussel (*Mytilus*), and the annelid (*Hydroides*).	Tyler (1939); Berg (1950); Colwin and Colwin (1960)
	Lysin in extract of frozen-thawed sea urchin (*Strongylocentrotus*) sperm dissolves egg membrane of the keyhole limpet (*Megathura*).	Krauss (1950b)
Salts	Ca-free sea water, isosmotic NaCl and KCl disperse the hyaline layer of the sea urchin egg.	Herbst (1900); Kopac (1940)
	NaCl removes jelly coat of the sea urchin egg (*Arbacia*).	Kopac (1940)
	Hypertonic sea water treatment causes subsequent dispersal of the hyaline layer of the sea urchin egg (*Arbacia*).	Harvey (1940)
	KCl and $CaCl_2$ solutions cause dissolution of the membrane of the annelid egg (*Chaetopterus*).	Lillie (1902)
	$CaCl_2$ (pH 6.9, isosmotic with sea water) dissolves vitelline membrane of the fertilized annelid egg (*Nereis*).	Costello (1945)

AGENT	EFFECTS	REFERENCES
Alkaline solutions	NaCl (0.53 *M* NaCl brought to pH 10.5 by addition of 1.0 gm anhydrous Na_2CO_3 per liter) dissolves vitelline membranes of annelid eggs (*Sabellaria*, *Nereis*, *Hydroides*, *Chaetopterus*).	Novikoff (1938); Costello (1945, 1958); Henley (1959)
	Alkaline sea water or the above alkaline NaCl solution dissolves the transitional fertilization membrane of the sea urchin egg (*Lytechinus*) and the membranes of unfertilized eggs of the limpet (*Acmaea*), and the mussel (*Mytilus*).	Berg (unpublished)
	KCN (1 *M*, pH 9.5) dissolves egg membrane of the limpet (*Megathura*).	Krauss (1950a)
Acid solutions	Acidified sea water (pH 3.5–4.5) dissolves jelly coats of a variety of eggs (echinoderms, molluscs, and annelids).	
Sulfhydryl compounds	Cysteine (0.1%, pH 7.8–8.0) and thioglycolic acid (0.5%, pH 7.8–8.0) dissolve transitional fertilization membranes and prevent formation of hyaline layer on sea urchin eggs (*Psammechinus* and *Echinocardium*).	Runnström, Monné, and Broman (1943)
	Thioglycolic acid (0.1 *M*, pH 8), cysteine, and glutathione dissolve egg membranes of the limpet (*Megathura*).	Krauss (1950a)
	Cysteine (0.1 *M*) treatment of unfertilized sea urchin eggs (*Strongylocentrotus*) causes subsequent dissolution of fertilization membranes.	Krauss (1950b)
	Thioglycolic acid (0.01 *N*) softens fertilization membranes of the sea urchin egg (*Psammechinus*) and renders them digestible by proteolytic enzymes.	Monroy and Runnström (1948)
	Mercaptoethylgluconamide (0.1%, pH 7.5–8.5) prevents transitional fertilization membrane of the sea urchin egg (*Strongylocentrotus*) from hardening.	Mazia, Mitchison, Medina, and Harris (1961)
Non-electrolytes	Urea, sucrose, and glycerol (1 *M*, pH 7.0) prevent formation of fertilization membrane and hyaline layer in echinoderm eggs (*Dendraster*, *Strongylocentrotus*, *Paracentrotus*, and *Arbacia*).	Moore (1949); Moser (1940)
	Glycerine and urea (isosmotic with sea water, pH 8) dissolve the membrane of the annelid egg (*Sabellaria*).	Waterman (1936)
Detergents	Duponol (sodium lauryl sulfate) dissolves vitelline membrane of the annelid egg (*Nereis*).	Osterhout (1950)
	Duponols ($<0.005\%$) dissolve vitelline membranes of molluscan eggs (*Toredo* and *Mytilus*).	Fauré-Fremiet and Thaureaux (1949); Berg (unpublished)

DISSOCIATION OF CLEAVAGE STAGES

Separation of cleavage blastomeres, one of the oldest of experimental techniques in embryology, is accomplished with marine forms by removal of egg membranes before or after fertilization followed by treatment, usually with Ca-free sea water, to prevent adhesion of the cells. No attempt will be made to review the many specific procedures although a few notes are presented below on selected forms.

Sea Urchins *Lytechinus* and *Strongylocentrotus*

Transitional fertilization membranes are removed by a brief treatment with 1 percent protease at pH 7.5–8.0. The timing is critical for eggs of *Strongylocentrotus* and must begin 2 or 2.5 minutes after insemination; the *Lytechinus* membrane is less resistant and may be digested over a period of 5–10 minutes. The denuded eggs are washed and kept in an agar-coated dish or in 0.1 percent gelatin in sea water to prevent sticking. There are many alternative methods available for removal of echinoderm egg membranes (see Table 1). A combination chemical and mechanical method is used by Mazia *et al.* (1961) for removing the egg membranes of *Strongylocentrotus*. Transitional fertilization membranes are prevented from hardening by treatment with mercaptoethylgluconamide (0.1 percent, pH 7.5–8.5) and are subsequently stripped off mechanically by several passages through 25-mesh bolting silk (Silk Screen Mfg., Brooklyn, N.Y.). Ca-free sea water with 0.01 *M* Versene prevents the hyaline layer from forming.

Animal and vegetal halves (*Lytechinus*) are obtained by transferring the eggs during the third cleavage to Ca-free sea water with ethylenediaminetetraacetate (EDTA or Versene, 10^{-3} *M*). Animal and vegetal quartets distinguished by a size difference are separated at the 8-cell stage with a fine glass needle (Berg and Cheng, 1962). An experienced operator can obtain several hundred isolated halves per hour. Other forms with an equal third cleavage may be similarly operated on, although less easily, at the 16-cell stage.

Dissociation of micro-, macro-, and mesomeres at the 16-cell stage is accomplished by transference to Ca-free sea water with EDTA as the fourth cleavage begins. After dissolution of the hyaline layer dissociation is facilitated by stirring manually or preferably with a magnetic vibrating stirrer. Low temperature or 5×10^{-3} *M* NaN_3 may be used to slow or reversibly inhibit subsequent cleavages. Complete dissociation of mesomeres and macromeres is relatively easy; dissociation of macro-micromere pairs is more difficult. Low temperature during the Ca-free sea water treatment of *Strongylocentrotus* stages seems to improve the yield of isolated micromeres.

Dissociation of the 16-cell stage of the sand dollar, *Dendraster*, was accomplished with 5 percent protease in Ca-free sea water (Berg, 1958). Lindahl and Kiessling (1950) obtained dissociation of 16-cell stages of the sea urchin, *Paracentrotus*, in Ca-free sea water with 2×10^{-3} *M* colchicine added to prevent further cleavage. Transitional fertilization membranes had been removed mechanically by sucking the eggs through bolting silk.

Later developmental stages of echinoderm embryos are more difficult to dissociate; however, recently Giudice (1962) reports dissociation of blastula, gastrula, and pluteus stages. The embryos were packed by centrifugation and washed with Ca-free sea water. Three volumes of 0.4 *M* sucrose in citrate buffer (0.05 *M*, pH 7.8) containing EDTA (10^{-3} *M*) were then added and dissociation accomplished by gentle agitation in a glass homogenizer. Filtering through gauze and light centrifugation removed the nondissociated fragments of embryos.

Molluscs, Annelids, and Ascidians

The molluscs *Mytilus* and *Ilyanassa* and the annelid *Chaetopterus* are of particular interest because of a unique transport of developmental factors via polar lobes. Dissociation of early cleavage stages is easily accomplished in these forms and furthermore the cells can be readily identified and segregated for quantitative chemical studies (reviewed by Berg, 1954b; Weber, 1961; Collier, 1965).

Methods for procuring and handling the adult animals and obtaining the gametes are reviewed by Just (1939) and Costello *et al.* (1957).

The *Mytilus* egg membrane is rapidly dissolved by a membrane lysin extracted from frozen-thawed sperm (Berg, 1950). Large-scale separation of early cleavage blastomeres is accomplished by allowing cleavage to occur preferably in the sperm extract although Ca-free sea water is also effective. It might be pointed out here that Ca-free sea water usually increases the fragility of cleavage blastomeres and in some forms may prove toxic (Costello, 1945).

Small numbers of isolated polar lobes may be obtained by cutting with a fine glass needle at the trefoil stage. Fortunately in *Mytilus* it was discovered that polar lobes spontaneously constrict from eggs exposed to hypertonic salt solutions (Berg, 1954a). Denuded eggs at the first appearance of the polar lobes are placed in 0.60–0.65 *M* NaCl. Polar lobe formation and cleavage are delayed with a high percentage of polar lobes eventually becoming constricted from the eggs. A hypertonic solution (3.3 gm NaCl in 100 ml 25 percent sea water) was developed to bring about constriction of polar lobes yet maintaining normal adhesion of the cleavage cells, a condition which facilitates large-scale segregation of the polar lobes (Berg, 1954a).

The egg membranes of *Chaetopterus* are soluble in $CaCl_2$. Unfertilized eggs are treated with 0.35 *M* $CaCl_2$ for 1 minute or less and returned to sea water. The timing is critical since $CaCl_2$ is toxic and overexposure causes cytolysis of the egg. First cleavage blastomeres recognizable by the size difference are separated by agitation in Ca-free sea water.

Ilyanassa eggs are deposited in a tough capsule which is easily opened by drawing it across an upright razor blade fragment cemented to the bottom of a dish. The capsular jelly clinging to the eggs may be removed by a brief treatment with acidified sea water. Separation of blastomeres in Ca-free sea water is accomplished by drawing the eggs in and out of a narrow pipette; polar lobes may be removed similarly at the trefoil stage. It is possible to obtain routinely 50–100 segregated polar lobes or blastomeres (Collier, 1957; Berg and Kato, 1959).

The chorion of the ascidian egg (*Ciona* or *Styela*) is digested by 2–3 percent protease (pH 8.0) or diluted crab stomach juice. Depending upon the type of study the latter may be preferred since protease treatment blocks or causes abnormal gastrulation. The digestion of *Ciona* egg membranes may require several hours and accordingly it is advisable to fertilize the eggs after membrane removal. Cleavage is bilateral and it is not until the second cleavage that one can obtain blastomeres with different developmental fates. These are easily separated in Ca-free sea water with the tip of a braking pipette. In *Ciona* the posterior blastomeres are distinguished by transitory clear cytoplasmic caps which after sphering of the cells are visible with oblique lighting as bright crescentic rims of cytoplasm. In *Styela* they are marked by a localization of yellow pigment. Usually 100–200 segregated blastomeres can be obtained routinely for chemical analyses (Berg, 1957).

LARGE-SCALE SEGREGATION OF CELLS

Quantitative microchemical and physiological measurements on specific blastomeres of early cleavage stages are possible providing sufficient numbers of cells can be segregated. Dissociation of early cleavage stages and selection of several hundred of the desired cells with a braking pipette is feasible; however, the total amount of material routinely available by this method is extremely small. Automatic and large-scale segregation of cells of different sizes obviously would permit application of a much greater variety of chemical methods.

A counterstreaming centrifuge for large-scale segregation of cells of different sizes has been described by Lindahl (1948) and Lindahl and Nyberg (1955). In brief, the principle consists of opposing the centrifugal sedimentation of cells with a flow of the suspension medium in the opposite direction. Segregation of cells occurs in different regions of a conical tube according to the equilibrium between sedimentation rates of the cells and streaming rate of the medium. The centrifuge has been used successfully for segregation of micromeres from macro- and mesomeres obtained by dissociation of 16-cell stages of the sea urchin, *Paracentrotus* (Lindahl and Kiessling, 1950).

A recent report describes an electronic particle separator which operates by the electrostatic segregation of water droplets electrically charged according to the particle volume sensed by a Coulter aperture (Fulwyler, 1965). This method as well as the counterstreaming centrifuge requires complex and undoubtedly costly equipment which unfortunately may limit its availability.

A method for segregating cells of different size was proposed by Berg (1954a) based on the elutriation techniques used for sediment analysis. The basic feature of elutriation consists of a rising current of water in which a grading of different particles occurs according to their settling velocities. An elutriator for segregation of cells consists of an upright glass tube in which a carefully controlled ascending flow of water carries the smaller cells upward and out of an outflow whereas the larger ones settle to the bottom. Successful segregation of polar lobes from the eggs of *Mytilus* has been accomplished, although with smaller size differentials it has not proved practical. Slowness of operation and difficulties in obtaining uniform flow limit the usefulness of the elutriator. Simple decantation or differential centrifugation may give partial segregation of cells although these methods, as with elutriation, are limited to cells with considerable size differences.

A method free from some of the above difficulties has recently been used in preliminary tests to segregate polar lobes from the eggs of *Mytilus*. A glass capillary fused array (1-inch disc, 37-μ pore diameter, 61 percent open area; Permeonics Corp., Southbridge, Massachussetts) is placed over a small container immersed in Ca-free sea water and any air trapped in the pores is removed by suction. A glass collar placed on top of the disc serves to confine a dilute suspension of polar lobes and eggs. As the cells settle a percentage of the polar lobes filter through the pores whereas the larger cells are retained. The yield may be increased by repeated "backwashing," i.e., a pulse of water back through the disc unclogs the pores and permits additional polar lobes to filter through. These discs are available in a

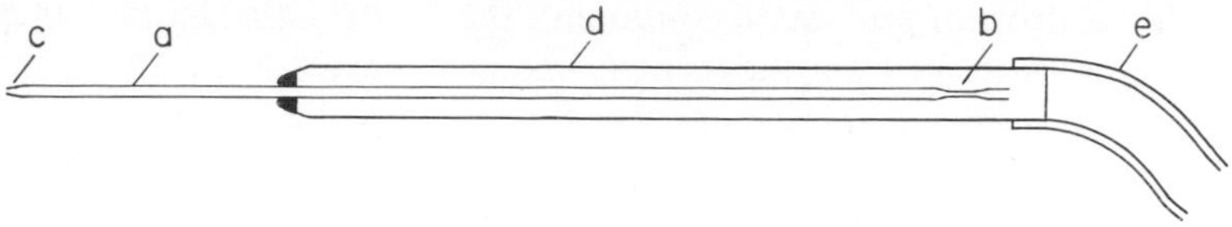

FIG. 1. Braking pipette for handling small numbers of eggs and embryos or for measuring and transferring reagents in the microliter range (modified from Holter, 1943). Capillary glass tubing (a), with constriction (b), to control air flow and tapered tip (c), is cemented into larger glass tube (d). Pipette is operated with mouth tube (e).

wide variety of pore sizes and may prove useful for segregation of some kinds of cells.

HANDLING AND CULTURING SMALL NUMBERS OF EMBRYOS

Pipettes of the braking type (Holter, 1943) are indispensable for handling small numbers of eggs and embryos (Fig. 1). Capillary glass tubing (1-mm bore, 15–20 cm long) is pulled at one end to form a fine constriction. Although "homemade" capillary tubing may be used, commercially available tubing is more convenient. The constriction necessary to provide accurate control is determined largely by experience although the rate of capillary flow when the open end is dipped in water is a useful clue. The capillary tube is sealed with De Khotinsky or "Pyseal" cement into a larger (3–5 mm) tube and the projecting end may be left as is or drawn to the desired tip size and cut with a diamond or carborundum pencil.

An automatic pipette puller used with Pyrex precision capillary tubing (Drummond Scientific Co., Broomall, Pennsylvania) is ideal for mass production of braking pipettes with identical characteristics. These also serve as versatile and inexpensive pipettes for transferring and measuring reagents in the microliter range.

General procedures for handling eggs and embryos of marine invertebrate animals have been reviewed by Just (1939) and Costello *et al.* (1957), and operating procedures by Hörstadius (1937); only a few comments will be made here concerning culture methods.

In addition to the traditional watch glasses, stender dishes, etc., small plastic containers (such as 35-mm Petri dishes) make useful culture chambers. An advantage is that embryos are less likely to stick to plastic as compared to glass, and the water-repellent surface facilitates microdrop cultures. The latter are placed in the center of the bottom dish or prepared as a hanging drop from the cover. Evaporation occurs through the plastic and for long-term cultures the dishes must be kept in a larger moist chamber.

Microdepression culture chambers may be made by pressing the rounded tip of a heated glass needle into Plexiglas blocks (Berg and Cheng, 1962). Depressions of any desired volume can be produced down to nearly the size of a sea urchin embryo. Extreme care must be taken to avoid evaporation from these small volumes.

A useful culture method for repeated or prolonged microscopic examination at high magnifications is as follows. A depression slide (0.8 × 16 mm) is coated with Siliclad (a water-repellent silicone coating; Clay-Adams Inc., New York).

A small drop of sea water containing the embryos is placed in the center of the depression and a plastic cover slip is dropped in place. The water-repellent relatively flat surfaces prevent spreading of the drop and provide excellent optical properties for high magnifications. The slide may be examined for several hours with little evaporation; however for long-term cultures it must be kept in a moist chamber.

Denuded eggs or embryos are generally quite sticky and adhere to solid surfaces. Coating the dish with a thin layer of agar is a traditional method for preventing this. It is advisable to test the agar first since some preparations may be slightly toxic. An alternative method, one which is necessary with very small culture chambers, is the use of 0.1 percent gelatin (Berg and Cheng, 1962) or 5 percent egg albumin (Holter and Zeuthen, 1944) in the sea water to prevent sticking of eggs.

Deleterious effects of bacteria may be reduced by the use of autoclaved or "pasteurized" sea water (Costello, 1945; Clement, 1952) or by filtering the water through a Millipore bacteriological filter. Sulfathiazole (0.005 percent or higher depending upon the sensitivity of the embryos) is particularly effective for inhibiting bacterial growth and may be used in sea water to improve culture conditions.

REFERENCES

BERG, W. E., 1950: Lytic effects of sperm extracts on the eggs of *Mytilus edulis. Biol. Bull.*, 98: 128.

———, 1954a: Large-scale constriction and segregation of polar lobes from the eggs of *Mytilus edulis. Exptl. Cell Res.*, 6: 162.

———, 1954b: Investigations of cytoplasmic determination in mosaic eggs. *Cellular Biology: Proc. 15th Ann. Biol. Colloquium*, Oregon State College, Corvallis, Oreg.

———, 1957: Chemical analyses of anterior and posterior blastomeres of *Ciona intestinalis. Biol. Bull.*, 113: 365.

———, 1958: Distribution of cytochrome oxidase in an early cleavage stage of *Dendraster. Exptl. Cell Res.*, 14: 398.

———, and A. C. CHENG, 1962: Tests for diffusible morphogenic substances in the sea urchin embryo. *Acta Embryol. Morphol. Exptl.*, 5: 167.

———, and Y. KATO, 1959: Localization of polynucleotides in the egg of *Ilyanassa. Acta Embryol. Morphol. Exptl.*, 2: 227.

BERRILL, N. J., 1932: The mosaic development of the ascidian egg. *Biol. Bull.*, 63: 381.

BOHUS-JENSEN, A., 1950: Action of ficin on sea urchin eggs. *Exptl. Cell Res.*, 1: 351.

CLARK, J. R., and R. L. CLARK, 1964: *Sea Water Systems for Experimental Aquariums: A Collection of Papers.* U.S. Dept. of Interior, Fish and Wildlife Research Report No. 63. 190 pp. U.S. Government Printing Office, Washington, D.C.

CLEMENT, A. C., 1952: Experimental studies on germinal localization in *Ilyanassa.* I. The role of the polar lobe in determination of the cleavage pattern and its influence in later development. *J. Exptl. Zool.*, 121: 593.

COLLIER, J. R., 1957: A study of the alanylglycine dipeptidase activity during the development of *Ilyanassa obsoleta. Embryologia*, 3: 243.

———, 1965: Morphogenetic significance of biochemical patterns in mosaic embryos. In R. Weber (ed.), *The Biochemistry of Animal Development*, Academic Press, New York, Vol. I.

COLWIN, A. L., and L. H. COLWIN, 1960: Egg membrane lytic activity of sperm extract and its significance in relation to sperm entry in *Hydroides hexagonus*. *J. Biophys. Biochem. Cyt.*, 7: 321.

COSTELLO, D. P., 1945: Experimental studies of germinal localization in *Nereis*. I. The development of isolated blastomeres. *J. Exptl. Zool.*, 100: 19.

———, 1958: Membrane removal from the egg of the annelid *Hydroides*. *Biol. Bull.*, 115: 349.

———, M. E. DAVIDSON, A. EGGERS, M. H. FOX, and C. HENLEY, 1957: *Methods for Obtaining and Handling Marine Eggs and Embryos*. Marine Biol. Lab., Woods Hole, Mass.

FAURÉ-FREMIET, E., and J. THAUREAUX, 1949: Effet de quelques détergents sur l'oeuf de *Teredo norvegica*. *Biochim. Biophys. Acta*, 3: 536.

FULWYLER, M. J., 1965: Electronic separation of biological cells by volume. *Science*, 150: 910.

GIUDICE, G., 1962: Restitution of whole larvae from disaggregated cells of sea urchin embryos. *Dev. Biol.*, 5: 402.

HAGSTRÖM, B., and BRITT HAGSTRÖM, 1954: The action of trypsin and chymotrypsin on the sea urchin egg. *Exptl. Cell Res.*, 6: 532.

HARVEY, E. B., 1940: A new method for producing twins, triplets and quadruplets in *Arbacia punctulata* and their development. *Biol. Bull.*, 78: 202.

———, 1956: *The American Arbacia and Other Sea Urchins*. Princeton University Press, Princeton, N.J.

HENLEY, C., 1959: Exaggerated elevation of the fertilization membrane of *Chaetopterus* eggs resulting from cold-treatment. *Biol. Bull.*, 117: 284.

HERBST, C., 1900: Über das Auseinandergehen von Fürchungs- und Gewebezellen in kalkfreiem Medium. *Arch. f. Entwick.*, 9: 424.

HOLTER, H., 1943: Technique of the Cartesian diver. *Compt. rend. Lab. Carlsberg, Sér. chim.*, 24: 399.

———, and E. ZEUTHEN, 1944: The respiration of the egg and embryo of the ascidian *Ciona intestinalis*. *Compt. rend. Lab. Carlsberg, Sér. chim.*, 25: 33.

HÖRSTADIUS, S., 1937: Freehand manipulations. In C. E. McClung (ed.), *Handbook of Microscopical Technique*, Hoeber Inc., New York.

ISHIDA, J., 1936: An enzyme dissolving the fertilization membrane of sea urchin eggs. *Annot. Zool. Japan., Tokyo Univ.*, 15: 453.

JUST, E. E., 1939: *Basic Methods for Experiments on Eggs of Marine Animals*. Blakiston's Son and Co., Philadelphia, Pa.

KOPAC, M. J., 1940: Properties of extraneous coats of cells. In *Cold Spring Harbor Symp. Quant. Biol.*, 8: 154.

———, 1941: Disintegration of the fertilization membrane of *Arbacia* by the action of an "enzyme." *J. Cell. Comp. Physiol.*, 18: 215.

KRAUSS, M., 1950a: Lytic agents of the sperm of some marine animals. I. The egg membrane lysin from sperm of the giant keyhole limpet *Megathura crenulata*. *J. Exptl. Zool.*, 114: 239.

———, 1950b: Lytic agents of the sperm of some marine animals. II. Extraction of a hetero-egg membrane lysin from sea urchin sperm. *J. Exptl. Zool.*, 114: 279.

LILLIE, F. R., 1902: Differentiation without cleavage in the egg of the annelid *Chaetopterus pergamentaceus*. *Arch. f. Entw.*, 14: 477.

LINDAHL, P. E., 1948: Principle of a counter-streaming centrifuge for the separation of particles of different sizes. *Nature*, 161: 648.

———, and K. H. KIESSLING, 1950: Separation of micromeres of the 16-cell stage of the sea urchin *Paracentrotus lividus*. *Experientia*, 6: 425.

———, and E. NYBERG, 1955: Counter-streaming centrifuge for the separation of cell fragments of different sizes. *I.V.A.*, 309.

MANSUETO, C., 1963: Amino acid uptake in dark and hyaline fragments of the ascidian egg. *Acta Embryol. Morphol. Exptl.*, 6: 131.

MAZIA, D., J. M. MITCHISON, H. MEDINA, and P. HARRIS, 1961: The direct isolation of the mitotic apparatus. *J. Biophys. Biochem. Cyt.*, 10: 467.

MONROY, A., and J. RUNNSTRÖM, 1948: Some

experiments pertaining to the chemical changes occurring at the formation of the fertilization membrane of sea urchin eggs. *Arkiv Zool.*, 40A: No. 18, 1.

MOORE, A. R., 1949: On the precursors of the fertilization and the hyaline membranes in the egg of the sea urchin *Strongylocentrotus purpuratus. Biodynamica*, 6: 197.

———, 1952: The process of gastrulation in trypsin embryos of *Dendraster excentricus. J. Exptl. Zool.*, 119: 37.

———, 1957: Morphogenetic modifications in the sea urchin by means of trypsin. *Pubbl. Staz. Zool. Napoli*, XXIX: 71.

MOSER, F., 1940: Studies on a cortical layer response to stimulating agents in the *Arbacia* egg. *Biol. Bull.*, 78: 68.

NORTHRUP, J. H., 1947: Action of papain and ficin on tadpoles and *Arbacia* eggs. *J. Gen. Physiol.*, 30: 375.

NOVIKOFF, A. B., 1938: Embryonic determination in the annelid *Sabellaria vulgaris.* I. The differentiation of ectoderm and endoderm when separated through induced exogastrulation. *Biol. Bull.*, 74: 198.

OSTERHOUT, W. J. V., 1950: Relative solubility of the components of the *Nereis* egg. *Biol. Bull.*, 99: 362.

RUNNSTRÖM, J., L. MONNÉ, and L. BROMAN, 1943: On some properties of the surface layers in the sea urchin egg and their changes upon activation. *Arkiv Zool.*, 35A: No. 3, 1.

SUGAWARA, H., 1943: Hatching enzyme of the sea urchin, *Strongylocentrotus pulcherrimus. J. Fac. Sci., Univ. of Tokyo*, Section IV, 6: 109.

TYLER, A., 1939: Extraction of an egg membrane lysin from sperm of the giant keyhole limpet (*Megathura crenulata*). *Proc. Nat. Acad. Sci. U.S.*, 25: 317.

WATERMAN, A. J., 1936: The membranes and germinal vesicle of the egg of *Sabellaria vulgaris. Biol. Bull.*, 71: 46.

WEBER, R., 1961: Submicroscopical and biochemical characteristics of morphodynamic units in spirally cleaving eggs. *Symp. on Germ Cells and Develop.*, Istituto Lombardo, Milano, Italy, p. 225.

INDEX

Index